Colin B. Campbell

HISTOLOGY

HISTOLOGY

ARTHUR W. HAM
M.B., F.R.S.C.

*Professor and Head of Department of Medical Biophysics,
University of Toronto,
Professor of Anatomy, in Charge of Histology,
in the Faculties of Medicine and Dentistry, University of Toronto;
Head of the Division of Biological Research, Ontario Cancer Institute,
Toronto, Ontario, Canada*

AND

THOMAS SYDNEY LEESON
M.A., M.D., B.Ch. (Cantab.)

*Associate Professor of Anatomy, Faculty of Medicine,
University of Toronto, Toronto, Ontario, Canada.*

589 Figure Numbers, Including 8 Plates in Color

FOURTH EDITION

J. B. LIPPINCOTT COMPANY

Philadelphia   Montreal

Preface to the Fourth Edition

In this, the fourth edition, it may be appropriate to begin by recapitulating briefly the two major aims described for this book in the Preface to the first edition, published in 1950.

The first major aim was not only to explain the subject matter of histology as simply, clearly and as interestingly as possible but also, to help the student to become a good histologist. As anyone who has worked with students in the laboratory knows, there is much more to teaching histology than presenting its subject matter clearly. The student beginning microscopic work encounters many difficulties, for example, artifacts and problems associated with learning 3-dimensional structure from studying thin slices which have only 2 dimensions. These and countless other little problems must be overcome successively as the student progresses. Hence, in the first edition of this book many words and illustrations were used to assist the student over obstacles which might otherwise hamper or halt his progress, and this practice continues in this edition.

The second major aim was to explain the significance of histology. This required that the relation of histology to other subjects be explained, and that its subject matter be correlated, so far as possible, with that of other disciplines. When the first edition was written it was possible to do much toward bridging the gap between the subject matter of histology and that of gross anatomy, physiology and histopathology. A considerable amount of effort was directed toward achieving this aim so that histology would not be learned as an isolated entity to be forgotten but as an important and integrated part of a foundation on which an edifice of further biologic and/or medical knowledge could subsequently be added. Continuing to adhere to this second aim has affected the present edition as will now be explained.

In the decade that has passed since the first edition of this book, there has been a tremendous impact on histology from two further disciplines—physics and biochemistry.

Methods and tools evolving from physics, most notably electron microscopy, interference, phase and fluorescence microscopy, microspectrophotometry, differential centrifugation and radio-autography have all been used in histology with increasing productivity; indeed, electron microscopy has literally revolutionized the subject. Moreover, these methods have variously made it possible to apply to histology much of the newer knowledge that has come from biochemistry relating to the structure, the function and the synthesis of the nucleic acids, and their role in protein synthesis, with the result that the correlation between structure and function, which in the past could be visualized at the tissue level and sometimes at the cell level, can now be achieved to an appreciable extent at the intracellular level. For the student who studies the cell, this means that much of what in the past was vague, both as to structure and function, is now clearly demonstrable, and that it is now possible to visualize a division of labor among the various components of the cell much in the way that Virchow originally visualized a division of labor among the cells of the body.

All this means that modern histology has moved a long way from classic microscopic anatomy. Modern histology is so integrated with other biologic sciences that it can no longer be taught effectively by a scientific isolationist. Although the primary function of a histologist will continue to be that of teaching minute structure at all levels, a secondary function will be that of introducing the student to enough of the subject matter of related disciplines to integrate, so far as possible, structure at all microscopic levels with physiological and biochemical activities. This edition has been written with this in mind, and it is hoped that it will not only serve its primary purpose as a histology textbook but also be an introduction to the broad field of biologic science of which structure is an integral part.

The foregoing suggests the major changes that have been made in this edition. The third chapter, which deals with special methods, and even in the previous edition dealt extensively with electron, phase and interference microscopy, has been expanded with regard to histochemistry and radio-autography, and a new section has been added on fluorescence microscopy. The fourth chapter, which deals with the cell, has been mostly rewritten and shortened wherever possible so that the many recent findings relating to the molecular structure, sites, synthesis, movement and functions of the nucleic acids within the cell, and new information about protein synthesis could be included. In keeping with recent developments, the section on cell culture has been almost completely rewritten, and the section on cell differentiation modified. New work on the cell membrane is also included here; this topic is expanded later in Chapter 20 in connection with the formation of myelin sheaths. New findings regarding terminal bars, desmosomes, attachments between cells, and the cell web have been included in Chapter 11, which deals with epithelial tissue.

Since one of the consequences of the general advance in biologic knowledge is that histology and immunology have approached each other in several areas, such relationships as have been established between these two disciplines are described in appropriate sections of this edition. For example, immunofluorescence technics are described in Chapter 3, for they are having increasing application in solving both immunologic and histologic problems. The induction of the differentiation of antibody-forming cells to produce antibody to a specific antigen provides one example of how differentiation can be effected, and this is described in Chapter 4. The discussion of eosinophils in Chapter 8 brings up the problem of allergy. In Chapter 10, which introduces the study of tissues and in which tissue transplantation is discussed, the topic of immunogenetics and histo-incompatability is introduced, and the most important fundamental phenomenon of inherited and acquired immunologic tolerance is described as well as the effects of total body radiation on immunologic responses. Much of Chapter 18, which deals with lymphatic tissue was rewritten so that the cellular reactions that occur in this tissue in primary and secondary responses to anti-

gens could be described. Finally, in connection with the discussion of the thyroid gland, in Chapter 18, the subject of auto-immunity, which is emerging as one of increasing importance, receives consideration, particularly with regard to the possibility of the thyroid gland serving as an example of how a secluded antigen can initiate the condition.

The section in Chapter 19 dealing with striated muscle and the mechanism of contraction has been revised in the light of Huxley's studies, and his electron micrographs are used to illustrate the text. In Chapter 20 further work on the formation and the nature of myelin sheaths is described and illustrated, as is new work relating to the histogenetic relations between cells of the neuroglia series.

In the last part of the book, which deals with the systems of the body, the changes that have been made are with one exception not very extensive, being limited chiefly to adding further electron micrographs and descriptions of the fine structure of such parts of the body as have been investigated extensively in this way and about which information should be provided. The one exception is that in response to many requests a section on the placenta has been added to the chapter on the Female Reproductive System.

Finally, the book in this edition bears the name of a co-author, Dr. T. S. Leeson, a colleague in the Department of Anatomy, University of Toronto. Dr. Leeson has worked with me closely in writing this edition and, although he has been of help throughout, he is almost entirely responsible for the new section on the placenta. Since books may last longer than individuals, it seemed advisable to have a younger co-author who could work with me during this, and I hope further editions, so that our views and methods of presentation will become sufficiently similar for the book to be written in the same style throughout. It has been a great pleasure to have Dr. Leeson work with me, and it is inevitable that his knowledge, close contact with students in the laboratory, interest and enthusiasm will increasingly add to the book in the future.

ARTHUR W. HAM

Toronto, Ontario
February 10, 1961

Acknowledgments

As was mentioned in the Preface, histology has been caught in the general upsurge of knowledge in the physical and biologic sciences that is characterizing our time, and as a result it is now a formidable task for anyone to attempt to keep a textbook of the subject up to date. One solution to the problem would be that of making a full-time occupation out of writing a textbook, but that solution, even though it were possible, might also be associated with disadvantages. In trying to fit the writing of a textbook in with other duties I have been fortunate in having many friends who are interested in the book and have willingly provided me with much information and advice. By such consultations I have saved an enormous amount of time and so been enabled to deal with many more topics than would otherwise have been possible.

I cannot think of anyone whose outlook, knowledge and research epitomizes more the nature of modern histology than those of my good friend Dr. C. P. Leblond of McGill University, Montreal. Likewise, I cannot think of anyone who could be more helpful with regard to the amount of useful information he could provide for a revision such as this and in the way in which it has been provided, and I am most grateful to him. Next, I should like to mention that my work in preparing this edition was facilitated greatly because of my close association with colleagues in a Department of Medical Biophysics, for among these are representatives of many different biologic disciplines as well as of the physical sciences. In particular, I wish to thank Dr. Arthur Axelrad for special help and advice in connection with discussions of chromosomes, cell division, effects of colchicine, genetics of tissue transplantation and many other matters; Dr. Bernhard Cinader for much advice and help in such sections that deal with any aspect of immunology, and because of his influence and help there are several in this edition; Dr. Chris. Helleiner for consultation and help in sections involving some introduction to biochemistry; Dr. Allan Howatson for several electron micrographs and for much help in connection with the discussion of the fine structure of many parts of the body; Dr. E. A. McCulloch for reviewing those chapters of the book that relate to hematology; Dr. Louis Siminovitch for most of the recent education I have received in microbiology, which has resulted in my being able to write with more confidence about many matters relating to nucleic acids, genes, viruses and cell culture; Dr. James Till for advice and help in sections dealing with radiation and, in particular, the one which describes the use of labeled thymidine for determining the various stages in the interphase of the cell cycle; Dr. Murray Williams for help in preparing material on fluorescence microscopy; and Drs. Gordon Whitmore and Robert Bruce for special help on many occasions.

Although the source of each new illustration that has been used in this edition is given in its caption, I should like to thank especially Dr. George Palade and Dr. Keith Porter for the ones that they have supplied over the years in such a manner as to make me feel that they had an interest in this book's serving as a means of stimulating interest in, and disseminating knowledge about, electron microscopy and its application to histology. I should also like to thank Dr. Don Fawcett for several beautiful electron micrographs arising from work in his laboratory; Dr. H. E. Huxley for his illustrations of the fine structure of striated muscle; Dr. Johannes A. G. Rhodin for electron micrographs illustrating certain aspects of kidney structure; and Dr. Henry Movat for various electron micrographs which he made available on short notice when they were particularly required.

Dr. Guy Sainte-Marie was most helpful in supplying information and one illustration for the section that deals with plasma cells and the formation of antibodies. We are most grateful to Dr. J. David Roberston for giving us special help with regard to cell membranes and the formation of myelin sheath. We are greatly indebted to Dr. W. J. Hamilton and to Dr. J. D. Boyd for the many beautiful photomicrographs relating to the placenta, and to Miss Elizabeth Blackstock of Toronto for the plate of drawings that also illustrate this new section.

Since this edition retains, from former editions, much material that was written with the special help of others, I feel that this help should again be acknowledged. In particular I again thank Dr. Y. Clermont for his most valuable assistance in revising the chapter on the Male Reproductive System, Dr. J. A. Duckworth for his help in writing and illustrating the section on the impulse conducting system, Dr. Phyllis Hartroft for aiding in preparing manuscript regarding J.G. cells, Dr. D. C. Pease for illustrations relating to the fine structure of the kidney, Dr. Keith MacDonald for his original and continuing assistance with the section on the Eye, and my colleague, Dr. Sylvia Bensley, for her help, interest and constructive criticism about all four editions. And although she did not participate in this present edition, I should like once again to acknowledge my gratitude to Louise Gordon for the many beautiful illustrations she prepared for the previous editions, which, of course, still stand in this.

It is a pleasure to acknowledge the very considerable assistance provided by Mr. F. Athron and, in particular, by Mr. R. S. Gilder of the Photographic Department of The Ontario Cancer Institute for several drawings, and for making and labeling many prints that appear in this edition. I wish also to thank Mr. J. Wilkinson for several new photomicrographs.

Once again I have had the inestimable help of Miss Mary McConnell who has cheerfully typed all the manuscript, often through many rewrites, arranged all the new inserts in their proper places and, in general, managed the many matters involved in preparing a revision for the publishers and then reading and correcting all the proof. Miss Margaret Murphy also deserves our thanks for typing manuscript for Dr. Leeson. And, once more, our publishers have been as patient, helpful, considerate and kindly as it is possible for a publisher to be.

ARTHUR W. HAM

Contents

PART THREE

THE FOUR PRIMARY TISSUES AND THEIR SUBDIVISIONS

PART FOUR

THE HISTOLOGY OF THE SYSTEMS

PART ONE

What Histology Is and How It Is Studied

Chapter 1

A Description of Histology and Simple Histologic Technics

Definition of Histology and Microscopic Anatomy. The word histology is fairly new. It is derived from two Greek words, *histos* and *logia,* which mean "tissue" and "the study of," respectively. This definition does not mean much unless the word tissue is also defined. This was taken from the French *tissu,* which means "weave" or "texture." Almost anything that is woven together can be called a tissue; indeed, a connected series of false-hoods, woven together so as to form a plausible story, can properly be termed a "tissue of lies."

The word tissue came into anatomic use chiefly because of the work of Bichat, a brilliant young French anatomist (1771-1802). As he dissected human bodies he became very much impressed with the fact that the various layers and structures he saw on gross dissection were of different weaves or textures. So he made a classification of these according to their various textures. This was the first classification of the tissues, and since histology means the study of the tissues, Bichat, even though he made his studies with the naked eye, should perhaps be regarded as the first histologist.

Even in Bichat's time the microscope was coming into use in anatomy, but Bichat would have little to do with it, and so it was left to others to use it for elucidating the minute structure of various parts of the body. Anatomic studies with the microscope led to the term *microscopic anatomy* coming into use. Thereafter, anatomy had two main branches —gross anatomy, which embraces the realm of structure visible to the naked eye, and microscopic anatomy, the realm of structure which can be seen only with the microscope.

Why has the term "histology" been retained? With the advent of the microscope and the subject named microscopic anatomy, it might be thought that the term "histology" would be dropped. The reason it has not is that the study of the body with the microscope substantiated Bichat's concept that the body is composed of certain basic tissues. It is most important for the student to realize that all the different parts of the body are assembled from these. Fortunately for the student, the microscope has shown that there are far fewer than Bichat thought from his gross observations; indeed, most histologists now believe that there are only 4 primary tissues (but there are, of course, subtypes in each primary group).

It is hoped that the foregoing discussion will prepare the student for the order which is generally followed in a course of study in this area. The student will find that his first task is to become thoroughly familiar with the microscopic structure and function of the 4 primary tissues and their various subdivisions, for these are the things out of which all the body's more complex structures are made. Once the student knows the basic materials out of which all parts of the body are assembled, his further study is greatly simplified. Indeed, the key to understanding readily the microscopic anatomy of any organ is a knowledge of the structure and the function of the basic tissues of which it is composed.

In the past a textbook covering the same field of knowledge as this book does would probably be termed "A Textbook of Histology and Microscopic Anatomy," thus emphasizing that these two terms do not mean precisely the same thing, and that the study of histology is the proper prelude to the study of the microscopic structure of the organs of the body. However, in our present-day search for brevity, one term or the other is generally dropped from the title of a book in this field, and if a choice is required it seems to us that histology is the better term because it emphasizes the concept of all parts of the body being composed of tissues, and the principle that the nature of these must be learned first if the ways in which they are arranged and combined to form organs and other structures is to be meaningful.

Does the study of histology involve learning the function as well as the microscopic structure of tissues? The answer is yes. Histology is the study of the tissues, and since the tissues have functions as well as structures, histology involves the study of both. Indeed, as will become apparent, the reason for histology's being such an intriguing, understandable and easily remembered subject is that the microscopic structure of each tissue is adapted to its particular functions. Accordingly, the imaginative histology student will soon find that if he knows the function of an organ he can anticipate much of its microscopic structure; conversely, if he examines any unknown structure he can anticipate much about its function.

The Relation of Histology to Other Biologic Sciences. From the foregoing it should be obvious that the study of histology not only complements the study of gross anatomy but increases its significance by making the student aware of the nature and the functions of the tissues that he dissects. Moreover, histology, because it relates to the minute structure of the body, provides the structural basis for the study of physiology—the subject that deals with the functions of the body and its parts. The role of histology in this respect is steadily increasing as the fine structure of different parts of the body is being explored and determined with the electron microscope; information from this field is providing a basis for understanding function at the subcellular level. Since histology deals with the function of tissues as well as their structure, a considerable amount of physiology is introduced in the modern histology course; this brings the two subjects so close together that the transition from one to the other is not abrupt but almost imperceptible for the student. Pathology is the subject that deals with the alterations in the structure and the function of the body and its parts that are caused by disease.

The nature of these alterations, of course, has become understood only since the microscope became available. It is obvious that a knowledge of the normal is a necessary prelude to the study of the abnormal; hence, the study of histology provides an indispensable background for the study of histopathology.

In view of the foregoing, the importance of a sound background in histology as a preliminary to the study of other subjects in the medical and dental curriculum can scarcely be overemphasized. However, what may not be so obvious is the great value of histology as a background subject for biology students who are not proceeding to professional degrees. It would be unfortunate if the obvious application of histology in the study of medicine and dentistry, and the fact that it is so commonly taught in medical and dental schools, led to the thought that histology is a "medical" subject only, because this would detract from an appreciation of the extent to which its study can provide, with an economy of time, a rich background of valuable knowledge for students who propose to proceed to undergraduate and graduate degrees in some special field of biologic science.

HOW HISTOLOGY IS STUDIED

ORDINARY HISTOLOGIC METHODS

The easiest and most efficient way for the beginner to study the tissues of the body with the microscope is to use *sections*. In histology, the term *section* is used to designate a very thin slice cut from a small piece of tissue, stained, mounted in a medium of proper refractive index on a glass slide, and finally covered with a cover slip, so as to provide a more or less permanent preparation. In a histology course it is usual for the student to be provided with, or have access to, a *set* of sections; the set contains thin stained slices (sections) cut from all representative tissues and organs of the body. The student should understand that the preparation of a good section entails considerable work by a skilled individual; hence, a box of sections is a valuable property and must be looked after carefully.

The various ways by which sections can be prepared for general and special purposes constitutes the subject matter of *histologic technic*. This is a subject in itself, and many books have been written about it; several of these are listed at the end of this chapter for any reader who wishes detailed information. However, detailed information is generally not required for the usual histology student; yet he should know enough about the preparation of sections to be able to study them intelligently. Accordingly, we shall describe here, and in a very general way, some of the usual ways in which sections are prepared for student use, so that the student can use them intelligently. Most are prepared by the *paraffin technic* which will now be described.

1. **Obtaining the Tissue.** Tissue for microscopic sections should be obtained as soon as possible after death or, if obtained at operation, as soon as possible after the tissue is removed so that the tissue can be *fixed* (next step to be described). The reason for haste is that between the time that cells die and the time that they are fixed, they undergo chemical changes that progressively alter their appearance and lead eventually to their decomposition. These changes that occur after death and before fixation are the result of what is termed *postmortem degeneration* to distinguish them from degenerative changes that occur in cells as a result of disease while the cells are still part of a living body.

Any piece of tissue obtained for sectioning should be removed from the body with a very sharp knife. A dull knife or scissors squeezes tissue and distorts the arrangement of cells in the piece taken (Fig. 20). Furthermore, the piece should not be a "chunk," of tissue but rather a slice not more than a few millimeters thick; otherwise, the next procedure to be described will not work satisfactorily.

2. **Fixation.** This has at least 3 functions: (1) to "set" the constituents of tissue so that no further postmortem changes can occur in it, (2) to harden the tissue so that it can be cut more easily into thin slices, and (3) to kill any bacteria or disease organisms present. Fixation can also helpfully accentuate the differences between the refractive indices of different tissue ingredients. Moreover, some fixatives increase the affinity of certain tissue constituents for certain dyes.

Tissues are most commonly fixed by immersing them in certain chemical solutions that penetrate them and coagulate their constituents. Probably the commonest solution used is a 4 per cent solution of formaldehyde. However, a great variety of other chemicals is used, among them mercury bichloride, potassium dichromate, acetic acid, picric acid, osmic acid and ethyl alcohol. Many of the better fixatives are mixtures. These are often named after the people who devised them—for example, Bouin's fluid. There is no perfect fixative, and the choice of one is usually determined by the particular tissue ingredient that is to be studied and by the stain that is to be used.

3. **Dehydration.** Tissue contains much water. In making a paraffin section a piece of tissue must be thoroughly and completely infiltrated with paraffin wax. Paraffin, of course, is not soluble in water, and a piece of tissue with its normal water content could lie in melted paraffin wax for days without becoming infiltrated with wax. This difficulty is overcome by placing the piece of tissue, fresh from the fixative, in a weak solution of alcohol (to put it immediately into a strong solution would cause too much distortion), then into stronger and stronger solutions until finally it is passed through absolute alcohol. During this process the water in the tissue is replaced by alcohols of increasing strengths and, after being treated with absolute alcohol, *all* the water which was formerly in the tissue is replaced. This step is known as dehydration.

4. **Clearing.** At first thought, it might seem that we were no further along in our attempt to infiltrate this piece of tissue with paraffin wax because alcohol, like water, is not soluble in paraffin. But, happily, certain chemicals are soluble both in alcohol and in melted paraffin wax; these are known as *clearing agents*. Xylol, toluol, chloroform, benzene and cedar oil are examples. So the piece of tissue is taken from the absolute alcohol and placed in a clearing agent and, just as the alcohol replaced the water, the clearing agent replaces the alcohol in the tissue. Clearing agents are so called because some of them tend to make tissue translucent.

5. **Embedding.** The piece of tissue is now put into melted paraffin wax in an oven warm enough to keep the wax liquid. Following this,

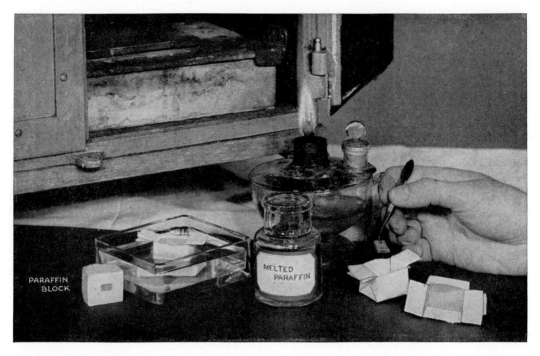

Fig. 1. A block of tissue that has been infiltrated with paraffin being placed in a paper boat filled with melted paraffin. Toward the left, a paraffin block prepared in this fashion may be seen.

while still in the oven, the original wax is twice replaced by fresh wax at 2-hour intervals. By this time the wax has permeated the tissue and replaced all the clearing agent. A little paper "boat" is now filled with melted paraffin, and the piece of tissue is placed deep down in the boat (Fig. 1) with the surface from which slices are to be cut resting on the bottom of the boat. Next, the boat is "launched" in a dish of water (Fig. 1) and held upright long enough for a scum of solid paraffin to form on its surface, after which it is completely immersed. This procedure hardens the paraffin so that the paper can be peeled off it, and the solid *paraffin block* containing the piece of tissue, which is now infiltrated with solid paraffin, is ready for sectioning (Fig. 1).

For very special studies tissue can be embedded in paraffin without subjecting it to any preliminary treatment with fixatives, dehydrating solutions or clearing agents. This is known as the freezing-drying method. In using this method, fresh tissue is frozen in liquid

air, or in isopentane chilled in liquid nitrogen.

Dehydration is accomplished by storing the frozen tissue in a chilled chamber which is kept exhausted of air and vapor by means of a vacuum pump (certain chemicals are used to help remove the vapor). When all the water of the tissue has turned to vapor and has been removed, the temperature can be raised to that of melted paraffin, into which the tissue is placed (or it can be placed in paraffin oil at a lower temperature), where it becomes infiltrated with the melted wax (or the oil), provided that this step also is carried out under a vacuum.

6. **Sectioning.** The ease with which thin shavings can be cut from a candle suggests the reason for embedding tissues in paraffin. Tissue embedded in, and so impregnated with, paraffin may be sliced very thinly. For most kinds of microscopic work the slices must be extremely thin, usually between 3 and 10 *microns* (a micron is $\frac{1}{1,000}$ mm.). To cut such thin slices necessitates special equipment, a slicing machine, sturdy yet capable of deli-

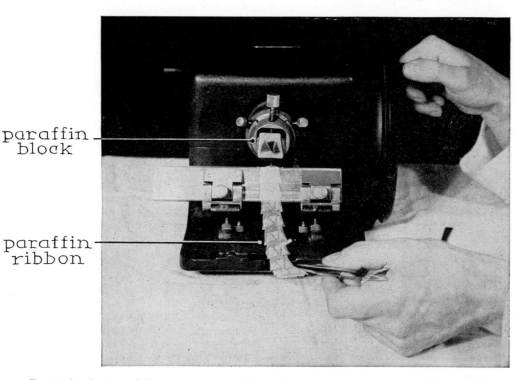

paraffin block

paraffin ribbon

Fig. 2. A microtome being used to cut a ribbon of paraffin sections. Notice that the paraffin block has 3 pieces of tissue embedded in it, and the outline of these may be seen in each of the sections whose edges are adhering to one another to form the ribbon.

cate movements, called a *microtome,* and an extremely sharp, heavy knife, *a microtome knife* (Fig. 2).

A microtome has an arrangement whereby a paraffin block can be firmly attached to it, and it operates so that when the crank is turned, the paraffin block is swept past the edge of the knife and then back again. Between each full stroke the paraffin block is moved a few microns farther toward the knife edge. Hence, each sweep of the block past the knife results in a thin slice being cut from the face of the block. Each slice, after it is cut, tends to adhere to the knife edge until it is displaced by the next slice, and then it adheres to the free edge of the slice that displaces it. In this fashion a *paraffin ribbon,* consisting of individual slices adhering to one another, comes away from the machine (Fig. 2). Each slice, of course, passes through the tissue embedded in the block, hence each slice of paraffin contains a slice of tissue. On close

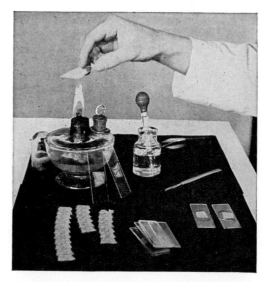

Fig. 3. One method of straightening the wrinkles in a paraffin section. Glass slides with sections adherent to them may be seen leaning against the lamp.

FIG. 4. A glass slide with a section adherent to it being passed through hematoxylin and eosin.

inspection of Figure 2, the three pieces of tissue in each paraffin slice may be seen.

7. **Attaching Sections to Slides.** A ribbon of paraffin sections is gently laid down, and the individual sections are carefully separated from one another by a scalpel. One surface of a glass slide is now made a little sticky by rubbing it with a weak solution of egg albumen or by some other adhesive medium. Then a little water is floated over the slide, and a single paraffin section is floated on the water. The slide is warmed very gently so as to straighten out any wrinkles that may have formed (Fig. 3), for they form easily; then the water is drained off, and the paraffin section adheres to the slide. To make sure that it adheres, the slide is dried in an incubator for a few hours.

8. **Staining.** A paraffin section, prepared as described above, is very much like a photographic negative that has been exposed but not yet developed. What might be termed the "development" of a section is obtained by exposing it to the action of dyes having more or less of a selective action on different tissue ingredients, so that these different tissue ingredients take on different colors and with different intensities.

The ways that dyes affect tissue in staining procedures are not exactly known. There are two general theories about their action: the physical and the chemical. When any minute structure within tissue becomes colored with a dye, the physical theory explains it by postulating that the dye becomes adsorbed by this particular minute structure; however, the chemical theory explains the same phenomenon by postulating the formation of a new chemical compound of tissue and dye. Certainly, the action of dyes is a very complex problem, and it is difficult to understand very much about it unless one first has a considerable knowledge of organic, physiologic and physical chemistry. Only a few elementary matters will be discussed here.

Most stains are said to be *acid* or *basic*. (What are termed *neutral* stains will be discussed in a later chapter.) Furthermore, tissue constituents are commonly referred to as *acidophilic* or *basophilic* (*phileo* = I love), depending on whether they "love," and hence are colored by, acid or basic stains.

Two false inferences may be drawn from the foregoing: (1) that acid stains are acids, and basic stains bases; and (2) that acidophilic substances, because they love acid, must, in themselves, be basic and that, correspondingly, basophilic substances must be acidic.

Actually, acid and basic stains are not acids or bases but neutral salts. Neutral salts have both an acid radical (the anion) and a basic radical (the cation). If the ability of a neutral salt to color anything resides in the acid radical (the anion), it is called an acid stain, and if it resides in the basic radical (the cation), it is called a basic stain. Hence, acid and basic stains are not acids and bases, but neutral salts and they are called acid or basic stains according to whether their ability to color lies in their acid or basic radicals.

Even so, because acidophilic substances attract the acid radicals of acid stains, it might be thought that they themselves might be basic, and by the same reasoning basophilic substances acid. But the nature of the attraction possessed by tissue for the anions and the cations of dyes of the neutral-salt class is not always so simple, and it is unsafe to assume that acidophilic substances are necessarily basic, or that basophilic substances are acid.

Most histologic sections are stained with both a basic stain and an acid stain, one after the other. The two commonest stains used are *hematoxylin* and *eosin* (Fig. 4), and a section

FIG. 5. A coverslip being placed over a stained section.

FIG. 6. A section being cut by means of the freezing method. The slices of frozen tissue obtained by this method usually are removed from the microtome knife by a soft brush.

stained with these is often referred to as an *H and E section*. Hematoxylin acts as a basic stain and colors basophilic materials in an H and E section blue or purple. Eosin acts as an acid stain and colors acidophilic substances in an H and E section pink or red. Eosin is so commonly used for an acid stain that it has become customary to use the terms *acidophilic* and *eosinophilic* synonymously.

Perhaps it should be explained that although hematoxylin acts as an excellent basic stain, it does not do so directly but only because a substance called hematein forms in a solution of it. Hematein is the substance that accounts for the basic training demonstrated by solutions of hematoxylin. However, even hematein does not act very efficiently by itself; it must be associated with a *mordant*. Mordants are substances that act something like catalysts to affect certain staining reactions in one or both of two ways—to make the staining reaction proceed more quickly and to make the coloration permanent.

Most stains are employed in aqueous solutions; therefore, to stain a paraffin section, it is necessary to remove the paraffin which permeates the thin slice of tissue by placing the section in a paraffin solvent (a clearing agent). The clearing agent must be removed by absolute alcohol and the section placed in successively weaker solutions of alcohol and finally in water (the reverse of the order employed in embedding the tissue) before it can be stained in aqueous solutions first of hematoxylin and then of eosin (Fig. 4). The details of the staining procedure are not essential here, and if further information is desired, one of the books listed at the end of the chapter should be consulted.

9. **Mounting.** After the section is stained, it must be treated in some way to convert it into a permanent preparation, and this must be done with materials that have suitable optical properties.

The first step is to remove the water from the section by passing it through solutions of alcohol of increasing strengths. After absolute alcohol, the section is transferred to a solution of clearing agent. The slide is wiped dry except for the area containing the thin slice of tissue (which is now permeated with clearing agent). A drop of mounting medium (for paraffin sections—Canada Balsam) is put on the section or on a coverslip, and the coverslip is dropped gently on the section (Fig. 5) so that the mounting medium covers and permeates the slice of tissue. Then, as the coverslip is pressed

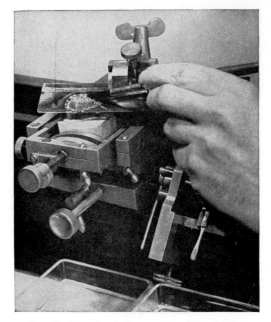

FIG. 7. A section being cut by the celloidin method.

firmly onto the section, the mounting medium spreads out to form a thin film (which contains the slice of tissue) between the coverslip and the slide. The subsequent "setting" of the mounting medium firmly attaches the coverslip to the slide. Satisfactory mounting media must be capable of displacing the clearing agent in the slice of tissue and of "setting" into an inert solid possessing a proper refractive index.

OTHER WAYS OF PREPARING SECTIONS

Two other methods are employed fairly extensively for special purposes—the *freezing* method and the *celloidin* method.

The Freezing Method. In employing this method, a piece of tissue is placed on the stage of a freezing microtome (Fig. 6). Beneath the stage is an outlet through which carbon dioxide gas can be released to cool the stage sufficiently for the piece of tissue to become frozen. It is then firm enough to allow fairly thin slices to be cut from its surface by the microtome knife, which, in this type of microtome, is arranged so that it sweeps over the surface of the frozen block of tissue horizontally. The slices are gathered from the knife with a brush and, after allowing them

to become flattened out on water, they are gently placed on slides to which they adhere, and so can be stained. They may be mounted in a water-soluble mounting medium.

Certain of the solutions, particularly the clearing agents, through which the tissue is passed in preparing the paraffin section, dissolve out the fat that the tissue contains. Frozen sections can be prepared without exposing the tissue to these fat solvents. Hence, frozen sections can be stained profitably with specific fat stains. Another advantage of frozen sections is that they can be prepared very quickly; that is why the pathologist uses this technic at the operating room for his "quick section" diagnoses. But, in general, frozen sections are thicker than paraffin sections and not as satisfactory for general work.

The Celloidin Method. Celloidin is a celloidinlike material in which tissue can be embedded after suitable preliminary treatment. The procedures employed require no heat; they are all carried out at room temperature; hence, celloidin embedding does not tend to cause as much shrinkage of tissue as do the steps employed in paraffin embedding. Furthermore, relatively large objects, such as teeth, can be sectioned to best advantage by the celloidin method because the celloidin holds all their different parts firmly in place. Possessing these advantages, celloidin sections obviously have great usefulness. But preparing them takes longer, and they are usually thicker than paraffin sections. They are cut on a heavy microtome which has a knife mounted so that its edge may be drawn across the face of the block at an angle (Fig. 7).

REFERENCES

GENERAL

Baker, John R.: Cytological Technique, ed. 3, London, Methuen, 1950.

Bensley, R. R., and Bensley, S. H.: Handbook of Histological and Cytological Technique, Chicago, Univ. Chicago Press, 1938.

Carleton, H. M.: Histological Technique, ed. 3 (Oxford Medical Publications), London, Oxford, 1957.

Clayden, E. C.: Practical Section Cutting and Staining, ed. 3, London, Churchill, 1955.

Cowdry, E. V.: Laboratory Technique in Biology and Medicine, ed. 3, Baltimore, Williams & Wilkins, 1952.

Gray, Peter: The Microtomist's Formulary and Guide, New York, Blakiston Division of McGraw-Hill, 1954.

Guyer, M. F.: Animal Micrology, ed. 5, Chicago, Univ. Chicago Press, 1953.

Krajian, Aram A.: Histological Technique, ed. 2, St. Louis, Mosby, 1951.

Lee, Arthur Bolles: The Microtomist's Vade-Mecum, ed. 11, New York, Blakiston Division of McGraw-Hill, 1950.

Lillie, R. D.: Histopathologic Technic and Practical Histochemistry, ed. 2, New York, Blakiston Division of McGraw-Hill, 1954.

McClung, C. E.: Handbook of Microscopical Technique, ed. 3, New York, Hoeber, 1950.

Mallory, Frank Burr: Pathological Technique, Philadelphia, Saunders, 1938.

Peacock, H. A.: Elementary Microtechnique, ed. 2, London, Arnold, 1940.

Romeis, B.: Mikroskopische Technik, Munich, Leibniz, 1948.

Freeze-Dry Method

Bell, L. G. E.: The application of freezing and drying techniques in cytology, Internat. Rev. Cytology 1:35, 1952.

Bensley, R. R., and Gersh, I.: Studies on cell structure by the freezing-drying method, Anat. Rec. 57:205, 1933.

Freezing and Drying: A Report of a Symposium, London, Institute of Biology, 1951.

Gersh, Isidore: The Altmann technique for fixation by drying while freezing, Anat. Rec. 53: 309, 1932.

Harris, R. J. C.: Biological Applications of Freezing and Drying, New York, Acad. Press, 1954.

Hoerr, N. L.: Cytological studies by the Altmann-Gersh freezing-drying method; I. Recent advances in the technique, Anat. Rec. 65:293, 1936.

Hoerr, N. L., and Scott, G. H.: in Medical Physics, Otto Glasser (editor), Chicago, Year Book Pub., 1944.

Moberger, G., Lindström, B., and Andersson, L.: Freeze-drying with a modified Glick-Malmström apparatus, Exper. Cell Res. 6:228, 1954.

Packer, D. M., and Scott, G. H.: Cryostat of new design for low temperature tissue dehydration, J. Tech. Methods 22:85, 1942.

Simpson, William L.: An experimental analysis of the Altmann technic of freezing-drying, Anat. Rec. 80:173, 1941.

Stains and Staining

Conn, H. J.: Biological Stains, ed. 6, Geneva, N. Y., Biotech. Publications, 1953.

————: The Development of Histological Staining, Ciba Symposia 7, 1946.

————: The History of Staining, ed. 2, Geneva, N. Y., Biological Stain Commission, 1948.

Conn, H. J., and Darrow, M. A. (compilers and editors): Staining Procedures Used by the Biological Stain Commission, ed. 2, Geneva, N. Y., Biotech. Publications, 1960.

Chapter 2

How Histology is Studied:
Study and Interpretation of Sections

There is a poem by Saxe, entitled "The Blind Men and the Elephant," that is of significance to beginners in histology. The first 3 verses follow:

> It was six men of Indostan,
> To learning much inclined,
> Who went to see the elephant
> (Though all of them were blind),
> That each through observation
> Might satisfy his mind.
>
> The first approached the elephant
> And, happening to fall
> Against his broad and sturdy side,
> At once began to bawl,
> "Why bless me! but the elephant
> Is very like a wall!"
>
> The second, feeling of the tusk,
> Cried: "Ho! What have we here
> So very round and smooth and sharp?
> To me, 'tis very clear,
> This wonder of an elephant
> Is very like a spear!"

In the remaining verses the experiences of the other 4 blind men are recounted, and as each touched a different part of the elephant each derived a concept of an elephant very different from that of his fellows. A knowledge of this poem, and some experience in helping students in the histology laboratory, inspired the following:

> They were like young microscopists
> Who study single sections
> And picture "wholes" from single parts
> With many misconceptions—
> Especially if they never learn
> To think in three dimensions.

Without being aware of it, many medical students suffer from a curious form of "blindness" that is a great handicap not only in interpreting histologic sections but also in many matters that arise in gross anatomy,

surgery, obstetrics and internal medicine. The little verse above suggests the nature of this condition: it is an inability to visualize structures in 3 dimensions. Some psychologists view the ability to do this as a special aptitude which is distributed very unevenly among people. Certainly every medical student has reason to practice the art of thinking in 3 dimensions, and those who have little natural aptitude for doing so must practice diligently if they are to compete on anything like equal terms with students who possess this ability. The following shows how essential this ability is in interpreting histologic sections and gives some idea as to how this art may be developed.

WHY 3-DIMENSIONAL VISUALIZATION IS NECESSARY IN HISTOLOGY

In the study of gross anatomy, the student may both see and make dissections. By this method he can find out where an artery or a nerve comes from and where it goes; he can lift up muscles and look underneath them and can inspect organs from many different aspects. Dissections, then, allow the various structures in the body to be studied in their 3 dimensions. However, there is another method of studying anatomy that is useful for supplementing the information gained from dissections: that of studying cross sections of the human body. Cross sections are essentially slices cut across a whole frozen body at different levels. These provide certain information that is not easy to gain from dissections alone. For example, if a person were shot and the bullet entered the body traveling at right angles to the body surface, it might be difficult to decide exactly what parts of what organs and structures would be pierced by the bullet on its journey if only dissections had been studied. However, the memory of a cross section cut at the level at which the

12

bullet traveled would quickly tell what organs and structures would be pierced. But learning anatomy by studying cross sections alone would be unsatisfactory because the cut surface of a cross section, which is all that may be seen when it is examined, presents only 2 dimensions. Without other knowledge, one could not tell from a single cross section how far any organ, blood vessel or nerve extended up or down the body, or whether it were larger or smaller above or below the section being studied. To tell this it would be necessary to examine consecutive cross sections, but it is easier to gain this knowledge from dissections, in which the structures of the body may be seen in 3 dimensions.

This is why histology is peculiarly difficult. It is not practical to try to learn microscopic structure by making dissections that allow things to be seen in 3 dimensions under the microscope. Most microscopic anatomy must be learned from the study of thin slices cut through the various tissues and organs of the body. This, then, presents much the same problem as would occur if the student were forced to learn gross anatomy from only the study of cross sections. Of course, in microscopic anatomy, longitudinal and oblique sections may be used as well as cross sections; nevertheless, it is a great handicap to have to learn 3-dimensional structure from thin slices which, for all practical purposes, have no depth. For example, a single thin slice cut from an organ may give a false impression of its architecture. This can be easily illustrated by cutting slices through such a simple thing as a hard-boiled egg. As is shown in Figure 8, no single one of the 4 slices illustrated would give a person who never had seen an egg a correct idea of its structure. For this reason, in the study of an organ it is usual to use several sections, taken from different sites and in different planes. Even so, the structure of some organs is so complicated that it has been necessary to make what are called *reconstructions* in order to learn the details of their microscopic structure.

HOW RECONSTRUCTIONS ARE MADE

To make a reconstruction, say, of a small but typical part of an organ, the whole part

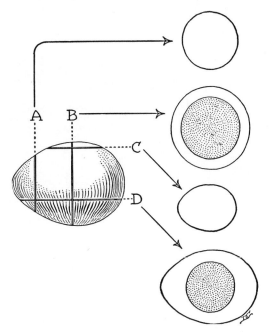

Fig. 8. Diagram showing how sections cut through an object in different planes or at different levels may give different impressions about its structure. A hard-boiled egg is shown at the left side of this illustration. Notice how cross sections cut at A and B would be different from one another and in turn different from longitudinal sections cut at C and D.

is embedded and cut into serial sections. Each section is mounted and numbered in the order in which it was cut. Then the first one cut is put into a microprojector, an instrument which projects a greatly enlarged image of a section on a screen. However, the screen is first covered with a thin, transparent material such as cellophane so that the image of the section thrown on the screen may be carefully traced out of the cellophane, both with regard to its outline and its important internal detail. Then the cellophane sheet is removed from the screen and placed on a wax plate, the thickness of which is decided by multiplying the thickness of the section by the number of diameters it was magnified on the screen. The drawing on the cellophane is retraced over the wax plate so as to make an impression on it. Next, the wax plate is cut with a knife or a

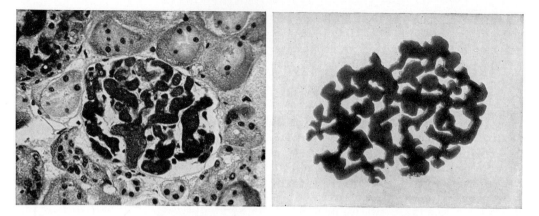

FIG. 9. (*Left*) A medium-power photomicrograph cut through the glomerulus of a kidney whose blood vessels were injected with a material that shows black in the photomicrograph. (*Right*) A photograph of a wax reconstruction of a similarly prepared glomerulus (but not the same one).

fine saw so as to conform to the tracing in outline and also in all important detail in the interior of the section. The finished wax plate thus becomes a greatly enlarged replica of the tiny thin piece of tissue that was mounted on the slide (Fig. 9). The same procedure is employed for each successive serial section until finally a greatly enlarged replica of every section cut from the original part of the organ is obtained. The wax plates are now put together in the right order, and when this is accomplished, one has a huge replica of the whole part of the organ, one large enough to study with the naked eye. Cuts may be made in to this in such a way that different segments can be removed at will, and this allows one to see and understand its various internal structural features.

SOME AIDS TO MAKING MENTAL RECONSTRUCTIONS

Enough time is not available for the student to make any reconstructions himself—except mental ones—and these must be made almost every time that the microscope is used. When the student looks at any section, he always should try to visualize the series of sections that would lie above and below the one under view. This helps one to appreciate the structure of the organ in 3 dimensions, and this appreciation helps, in turn, to explain why certain

things appear as they do in the single slice being studied.

The art of making mental reconstructions, of visualizing in 3 dimensions when only 2 are seen, may be learned by a difficult method or an easy one. The difficult way is to plunge immediately into the study of histologic sections; the easy way is to practice first on some common and familiar objects. Now it so happens that some common and familiar objects are very much like certain things in the body. For example, most organs of the body contain a complicated assortment of tubes, partitions and cords, and these extend throughout their substance in almost every conceivable direction and in different sites follow straight and curved paths. Some organs, indeed, consist of little more than these 3 things. The lung, for example, contains tubes that carry air, tubes that carry blood, tubes that carry lymph, and tubes that carry the secretions of glands. It is riddled by partitions, and it contains some nerves that are in the form of cords. Therefore, sections cut through the lung will pass through tubes and partitions, and some of them through cords; and as all these run in many different directions, a section cuts them at many different angles. So if the student has a knowledge of how straight tubes, curved tubes, partitions and bundles of cords appear in slices cut through them at different

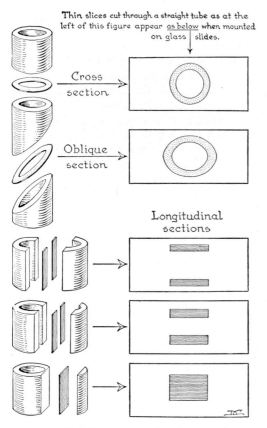

Thin slices cut through a straight tube as at the left of this figure appear as below when mounted on glass slides.

Cross section

Oblique section

Longitudinal sections

FIG. 10. Diagram showing how sections cut through straight tubes in different planes have different appearances when mounted on slides and viewed through the microscope. Notice that it is possible to cut a longitudinal section of a tube without having a lumen in the section.

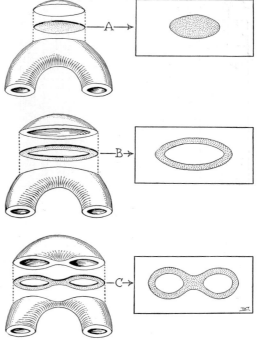

FIG. 11. Diagram showing the different appearances of sections cut through a curved tube at different levels.

angles (Figs. 10-13), he will be able not only to recognize these various structures for what they are when he sees them in a section, no matter at what angle they are cut, but also, by deducing the various phases in which they must have been disposed to present the particular appearance they present in the section, he will be able to build up a mental 3-dimensional reconstruction of the piece of organ or tissue from which the single slice under observation was cut.

Therefore, it is of the greatest importance, in learning to interpret sections, to become

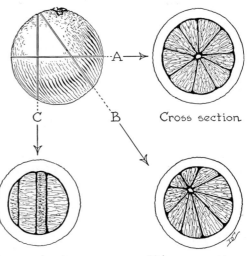

Cross section

Longitudinal section   Oblique section

FIG. 12. Diagram showing the different appearances presented by sections cut in different planes through an object which contains partitions (an orange).

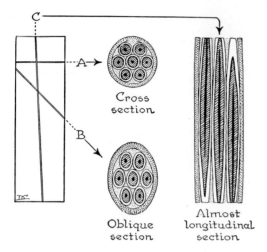

Cross section.

Oblique section

Almost longitudinal section

FIG. 13. Diagram showing how the appearance of sections cut through a cable containing   any insulated wires differs according to the plane in which the section is cut.

familiar with the appearances presented by slices cut through straight tubes, curved tubes, partitions and bundles of cords in different planes. Figures 10-13 are provided to assist in this matter. The student is advised to study them carefully, and then, as he proceeds to the study of histologic sections, to be prepared to refer back to these 4 figures frequently. Those students who are relatively deficient in their aptitude for visualizing 3 dimensions from seeing only 2 are strongly advised to purchase some plasticine of different colors and construct models, and then to slice up the models with a knife so that they may have direct experience in associating the 2-dimensional appearances presented by cut surfaces with the 3-dimensional models from which the slices are cut. For some students, *15 minutes spent with plasticine and a knife may be of more help in this subject than hours of microscopic study.*

HOW TO STUDY A SECTION

INSPECTION WITH THE NAKED EYE

Both for examinations and for ordinary laboratory work, the student, before examining a section with the microscope, should hold the section to the light and examine it with the naked eye. Some reasons for this are:

1. There may be more than one slice of tissue mounted on the slide, or one slice may have broken into two or more parts. Unless this is noted with the naked eye it may be missed with the microscope. Using a microscope is like using a telescope. If a person looks out to sea with the naked eye and sees 3 ships, he can focus a telescope on each in turn with little difficulty. However, if he does not look out to sea with the naked eye, but only with the telescope, he would not know that there were 3 ships to examine or where they were; and so, after much effort, if he were lucky enough to see one he would spend all his time examining it.

2. The *color* of the stained slice of tissue may give a clue about the particular tissue that has been sectioned. For example, lymphatic tissue (described later in this book) has a great affinity for hematoxylin; hence, blue patches seen with the naked eye suggest its presence. Another example is provided by fat tissue, for, in paraffin sections, it absorbs almost no color; hence, irregular, seemingly empty spaces seen with the naked eye suggest the presence of fat.

3. The outer and, if present, the inner *profile* of the slice of tissue may give clues about the particular structure or organ that has been sectioned. For example, from an inspection by the naked eye some sections appear as rings; this suggests that they are cross sections cut through tubular structures, and this narrows the number of possibilities that must be considered in their identification. Generally, it is easy to recognize sections of joints, the eye, the fingernails or the toenails, and so on, from their profiles. Furthermore, many blocks of tissue that are obtained for sectioning are cut from organs, so that the capsule of the organ is left on one side of the block. The capsular surface is generally smooth, whereas the other surfaces that have been cut with a knife are generally ragged. This can be noted from an inspection by the naked eye, and this gives the orientation necessary to examine the section intelligently.

INSPECTION WITH THE MICROSCOPE

In the following text, a description of some of the parts of the microscope will be more or less combined with an account of how the instrument should be used to study a section to best advantage.

The Mirror and Illumination. The mirror (Fig. 14) has two surfaces: one flat and the other concave. For low-magnification work the concave surface may be used instead of the condenser (to be described presently) to focus the beam of light on the object. However, for high-power work a condenser (Fig. 14) is essential. Under these circumstances, the function of the mirror is to direct the beam of light through the condenser, and for this purpose the plane surface of the mirror is used. Under ideal conditions, daylight provides excellent illumination, but conditions are seldom ideal, so it is best to become accustomed to some standard type of artificial illumination. Many types of microscope lamps are available; some are designed to direct a beam of light to the mirror, and some are mounted below the condenser in place of the mirror. For studying stained sections, artificial light should be passed through a *ground glass* and a *blue filter*, or if a blue filter has a ground surface it may be used alone.

The Condenser. The condenser (Fig. 14), as its name implies, converges the roughly parallel beam of light that comes from the mirror below so that a cone of light emerges from its upper surface (Fig. 14). This converging cone of light passes through the aperture of the stage of the microscope and is directed at the section that is mounted on the stage (Fig. 14).

In using the high-power and the oil-immersion objectives it is of great importance to adjust the condenser to obtain optimum illumination of the section. This may be done as follows. The condenser, which can be moved up and down by a rack-and-pinion movement (Fig. 14), is adjusted so that an image of the light source, or, if the lamp has a lens and an aperture, the aperture itself, is focused in the plane of the object. A slight adjustment of the mirror or the lamp aperture may be necessary to ensure that the field is illuminated completely and uniformly. With student microscopes it is not unsual for the condenser to slip down the sleeve into which it is fitted (Fig. 14). Under these conditions good illumination cannot be obtained, as the condenser cannot be raised high enough. This should

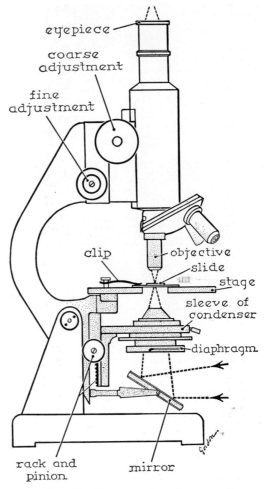

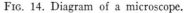

Fig. 14. Diagram of a microscope.

always be suspected when illumination is poor. The simple and obvious remedy is to push the condenser up its sleeve as far as it will go and then to tighten the little screw that fastens it in position.

An iris diaphragm, called the substage diaphragm, generally is built into the condenser just below the lenses. Its purpose is to provide a means for controlling the width of the beam of light entering the objective lens. Too wide a beam may cause glare, so the aperture should be reduced in size only to the point where glare is eliminated.

Further closure of the diaphragm, or lowering the condenser, sometimes is resorted to in order to improve contrast, but it should be

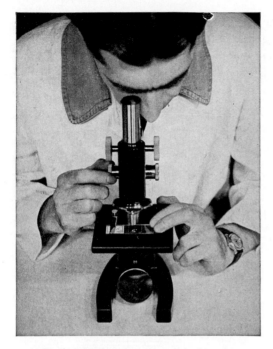

FIG. 15. The proper way to use the microscope. Notice that the section is held by only 1 clip so that it can be moved by 2 fingers placed on its other end. This method leaves 1 hand free to manipulate the fine adjustment as the section is moved about.

realized that the increased contrast obtained this way is gained at the expense of a loss in resolution. If lack of contrast is a problem it is best to use a special type of microscope called a phase-contrast microscope which will be described in a later section.

The Stage. Today it is the fashion for students to buy microscopes with mechanical stages. Mechanical stages are probably more important for research work than for the routine study of sections in histology or histopathology; for the latter they are by no means necessary. If the student who is using a fixed stage is right-handed, he should use only one clip to hold the slide in place, the clip that he would naturally put in position with his right hand. *This clip should be pushed down firmly.* With this arrangement, 2 fingers of the left hand may be used to move the slide about (if both clips are used the slide cannot be moved readily) as is illustrated in Figure 15,

and the right hand may be used to manipulate the fine adjustment of the microscope as the slide is moved about. Each time a slide is moved the microscope must be refocused; so, if the slide is moved either with a mechanical stage or with one hand, the other hand must be free to manipulate the fine adjustment. For this reason mechanical stages should have the knobs that control their 2 movements close enough together for them to be adjusted by one hand.

The Objectives. The usual student microscope has 3 objectives. Commonly, these consist of a low-power objective, which magnifies around 10 times, a high-power objective, which magnifies around 40 times, and an oil-immersion objective, which magnifies around 90 times.

The 3 objectives are mounted on a revolving nosepiece; this has the form of a turntable and allows any objective to be swung into place below the microscope. The standard objectives supplied on new microscopes are commonly parfocal, which means that when the microscope is adjusted with any objective so that the image is in focus, the image will still be approximately in focus when any other objective is swung into place. However, if objectives that have been purchased independently are used, it cannot be expected that they will be parfocal; hence, each one that is used must be focused separately.

The images obtained with the 3 objectives, in which the object is magnified 10, 40 and 90 times respectively, are magnified further by the lenses of the eyepiece. The different total magnifications obtainable by different combinations of the objectives and the eyepieces will be given later in this section.

Use of the Low-Power Objective. Beginners are too inclined to assume that the value of an objective varies directly with its ability to magnify. As a consequence, beginners tend to use the higher-power objectives too much and the low-power objective too little. It is said that a famous pathologist, to combat this tendency, used to remove all the high-power objectives from the microscopes of those who came to study with him when they first arrived, and he would release them only when the students had learned the enormous value of the low-power objective.

The first rule in studying a section is to

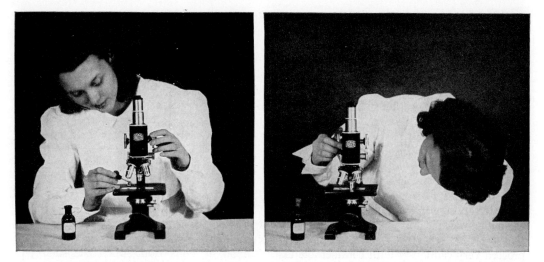

FIG. 16. The proper way to use the oil-immersion objective. (*Left*) The tube of the microscope is raised, and a drop of oil is being put over the center of the slide under view. (*Right*) The microscope tube is being lowered and watched from the side so that the time when the objective reaches the oil can be ascertained.

examine it with the naked eye. The second rule is to examine all of the section with the low-power objective before using the higher powers. As the student gains experience he will rely more and more on the thorough study of a section with the low-power objective for identifying sections in ordinary laboratory work and at examinations.

Use of the High-Power Objective. In examining a section with the low-power objective a certain area may be seen which warrants a more detailed examination. Before switching to the high-power objective the section should be maneuvered under the low-power objective so that the area to be examined further is in the center of the field of vision. It should be realized that the high-power objective encompasses a much smaller field than the low-power objective; hence, if the area warranting further investigation is at one side of the low-power field it may be excluded from view when the high-power objective is used. So, areas to be examined with the high-power objective always should be centered first with the low-power objective. Likewise, areas to be examined with the oil-immersion objective should be centered first with the high-power objective.

Use of the Oil-Immersion Objective. The use of the oil-immersion objective is associated with a special difficulty: the objective must approach the coverslip of the section very closely. Hence, in bringing a section into focus with the oil-immersion objective there is a danger of making a direct contact between the coverslip of the slide and the objective, and this may cause injury to either or both.

Probably the best way to bring the oil-immersion objective into focus safely is this: after centering the particular area to be examined with the high-power objective raise the tube of the microscope with the coarse adjustment and switch on the oil-immersion objective. Place a drop of oil on the part of the slide that lies directly over the center of the condenser (Fig. 16, *left*). Then lower the tube of the microscope, watching it from the side, as shown in Figure 16, *right*, until the objective is seen just entering the drop of oil. At this point the oil-immersion lens is still above the point at which the section would be in focus. So, one can now look through the microscope and lower the tube slowly with the fine adjustment until the field comes into focus. If it does not come into focus with a turn or two of the fine adjustment it is best to stop and question whether or not something has gone wrong. Two possibilities should be considered: (1) there may be no stained part of the section under the oil-immersion objective, either because the slide was moved or because there is an open space of some sort in the section near its central part; or (2) the objective is *below* the level at which it is in focus. If color can be seen on looking down the microscope the first possibility has become neglected, and if the color has become better defined with focusing downward the chances are that the objective is still above the point of focus and can be safely lowered somewhat farther. But if there is reason to doubt, the tube should be raised, the oil wiped off the objective and the slide, the area centered with the high-power objective again and the rest of the procedure repeated. It is always best to proceed very cautiously until considerable experience has been gained.

Always wipe dry the oil-immersion objective after use; this may be done with lens paper or soft paper such as Kleenex. Oil that has dried on the objective may be removed with soft paper that has been wetted with xylol.

The Eyepiece. Most microscopes have 3 interchangeable eyepieces which magnify 5, 10 and 15 times, respectively. For general work the 10× eyepiece is used. Sometimes the 5× eyepiece is used for the low-power inspection of large areas. In discussing the use of the 15× eyepiece it is relevant to point out that, as will be explained in the next chapter, the resolution of the microscope is limited by the wave length of light. Since the resolution of the microscope is limited, it is probable that almost anything that can be resolved by the oil-immersion objective of the microscope can be seen with a 10× eyepiece. Sometimes, however, the 15× eyepiece is used because even if it does not reveal *more* detail it makes the detail somewhat easier to examine because of the magnification.

Very commonly eyepieces become dirty or misty. To know whether specks or hazy areas are due to dirt or smears on the eyepiece the student should rotate the eyepiece while looking down the microscope. All spots and hazy areas that turn with the eyepiece are on the eyepiece. To clean them a common procedure is to breathe on the lenses and then rub them with lens paper until they are clear and bright. However, loose specks generally remain after this procedure, and they must be blown off, not with the breath, but with a blast of air

from a rubber syringe that is kept for this purpose. Any small syringe, such as an ear syringe, that can be purchased very cheaply from any medical supply house serves this purpose well, and every student should have one.

Beginners should mount pointers in their eyepieces so that they can indicate to their teachers appearances that puzzle them. A pointer is mounted as follows: Remove the eyepiece from the microscope and unscrew and remove the top lens. Look down the eyepiece and see a circular shelf with a central aperture that is about halfway down the eyepiece tube. Cut a little piece of straight hair just long enough for it to project from the side to the center of the tube. Place a tiny drop of Canada Balsam or immersion oil on the shelf and then, with a pair of tweezers, lower the hair onto the shelf so that the part of the hair that rests on the shelf is in the drop of oil. Adjust the hair with the tweezers so that it lies flat on the shelf and so that its free end reaches just short of the center of the tube. Then the top lens is screwed back into place.

ESTIMATING SIZE WITH THE MICROSCOPE

Only a small part of a section can be viewed at any one time with the microscope. The area of the section that can be seen at any one time is circular. The width of this circular area of the section varies with the magnification being employed; the greater the magnification the smaller the area of the section that can be seen. For example, with the low-power objective and the 10× eyepiece the diameter of the part of a section that can be viewed at any one time is around 1.5 mm. or 1,500 μ. However, with the oil-immersion objective and a 15× eyepiece the diameter of the area is about 0.1 mm. or 100 μ. It is helpful to know the approximate diameters of the parts of sections that occupy the field under conditions of different combinations of objectives and eyepieces. If this is known, the size of objects seen in the field can be measured roughly by comparing them with the width of the field, which is a known quantity. For example, if the diameter of the area seen with an oil-immersion objective and a 15× eyepiece is only about 100 μ, objects one tenth as wide as the field are roughly 10 μ wide. For the convenience of the student, the following table gives in round numbers (for microscopes

Eye- piece	Objective	Magnifi- cation	Width of Circular Area of Section Seen
5 ×	Low-power 10 ×	50	About 3 milli-meters or 3,000 microns
10 ×	Low-power 10 ×	100	About 1.5 milli-meters or 1,500 microns
10 ×	High-power 40 ×	400	Nearly 0.4 mil-limeters or 400 microns
10 ×	Oil-immersion 90 ×	900	About 0.15 mil-limeters or 150 microns
15 ×	Oil-immersion 90 ×	1,350	Slightly less than 100 mi-crons

vary somewhat) the approximate widths of the areas of sections that can be seen under different magnifications.

For the electron microscope the unit of measurement commonly used is the *milli-micron,* which is one 1/1,000th of a micron, or the Ångstrom unit, which is one tenth of a millimicron. The Greek letter μ is commonly used for micron, the symbol mμ for milli-micron, and the symbol Å for Ångstrom unit.

Photomicrography

So much medical literature is illustrated by photomicrographs that the student should know something about the taking of pictures with a microscope. The many students who are amateur photographers may wish to take photomicrographs themselves. All that is needed is a good microscope and some inexpensive or even homemade equipment.

No other lenses besides those of the microscope are required. The camera need be no more than a light proof box with a hole in one end and a slot for taking a film pack, a plate holder, or a ground glass at the other. An old plate camera from which the lenses have been removed is better than a homemade box because the bellows allows the magnification to be varied.

In taking photomicrographs, the microscope is used as a projector. A strong light source should be used, and the light from it should be directed so that it strikes the substage con-denser squarely. The end of the microscope tube containing the eyepiece is pushed through the hole at one end of the camera, and the ground glass is put in the other. Then a sec-tion can be put on the stage. When the micro-scope is focused, a sharp image of the part of the section under view appears on the ground glass. A picture may be taken by turning off the light, replacing the ground glass with film or a plate, and turning on the light for the period of time required. The expert will use a light meter to determine the time of expo-sure, but it can be determined easily by trial and error. Once the exposure time for low-power pictures has been learned, those for the higher powers can be calculated roughly by multiplying the low-power exposure time by the number of times the magnification is in-creased with the objective being used.

Histologic sections usually contain an assortment of blues and reds, and it is desir-able to obtain contrast between these two colors in black-and-white prints. This entails the use of filters and films with suitable color sensitivity. Books on photomicrography should be consulted for detailed information about the various combinations of filters and films that can be employed. Generally, however, in photographing H and E sections, good results may be obtained if a green filter is used with film that is sensitive to all colors. Most of the photomicrographs that illustrate this book were taken by using a green filter and pan-chromatic plates. Thin, flat, well-stained sec-tions are essential if good high-power pictures are to be obtained. The student will find that a partly closed condenser diaphragm sharpens the focus of most sections, but the diaphragm must not be closed too far or undesirable effects will be obtained.

Artefacts

The first few minutes a student looks down a microscope at a stained section are not likely to be encouraging ones. A kaleidoscopic assort-ment of colors will meet his eye, and literally hundreds of different tissue ingredients will seem to be present. He can derive comfort from realizing that there are only 3 categories of materials in the human body: (1) cells, (2) intercellular substances and (3) fluids; hence, these 3 things are all that are contained

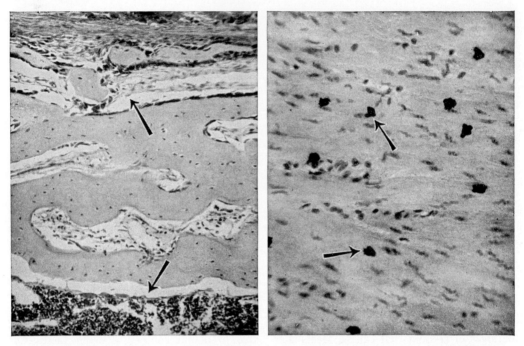

FIG. 17. (*Left*) A medium-power photomicrograph of a section of bone. The 2 arrows indicate sites where shrinkage has caused the adjacent tissue to draw away from the bone itself. (*Right*) A photomicrograph of smooth muscle. Imperfectly removed fixative in the form of crystalline material is indicated by the arrows.

FIG. 18. Photomicrographs of very thin sections of pancreas showing many folds.

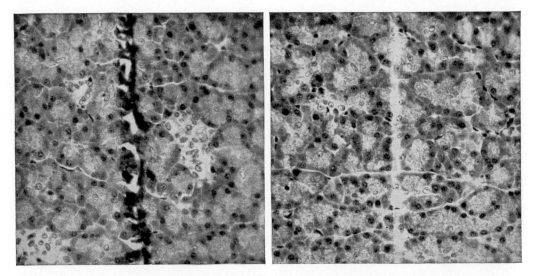

Fig. 19. Medium-power photomicrographs of pancreas showing the type of artefact produced by a nick in the microtome knife. (*Left*) The broad vertical streak through the middle of the section is due to a fairly large nick. (*Right*) The finer vertical streak in the middle of the section is due to a smaller nick.

in any perfect section of normal tissue. Furthermore, these 3 things have distinctly different appearances under the microscope. Hence, to make definite progress toward becoming a good practical histologist, one has to learn not hundreds of different appearances but only 3.

However, all sections are not perfect. Even the most careful preparation of a section alters the arrangement of the tissue elements to some extent, and errors in technic alter it considerably. Sections, then, may exhibit flaws, and these are called *artefacts* because they are artificial appearances caused by technical procedures.

Artefacts may confuse a student who is commencing to classify the things he sees into cells, intercellular substances and fluids. Therefore, it is best to have some idea of their appearance when first beginning the study of sections, so that an undue amount of time will not be wasted upon them. The common artefacts and their causes will now be discussed.

The different chemicals with which tissue is treated in making a section may cause considerable *shrinkage* in its substance. This may result in portions of tissue which were adjacent

in life being pulled away from one another, as has occurred at the sites indicated by arrows in Figure 17, *left*.

Sometimes the fixative is imperfectly removed from tissue, and crystals of it remain behind. The appearance these present is indicated by arrows in Figure 17, *right*. The appearance of any other foreign material added during the preparation of the section is somewhat similar, but it depends, of course, on the nature of the material.

Paraffin sections are so thin that it is not unusual for them to become somewhat crinkled or folded as they are cut, and sometimes these little crinkles or *folds* cannot be entirely smoothed out when the section is being mounted on a slide. These appear in a section as shown in Figure 18.

Microscopic nicks in the microtome knife cause a characteristic defect. As the knife sweeps across the paraffin block in a straight plane, any nick in it creates a defect in the section that appears as a straight line across it. Figure 19 shows 2 examples of defects caused in this way. The picture on the left shows one caused by a large nick, and the one on the right by a small nick. Any curious appearance in a section that is seen as a straight

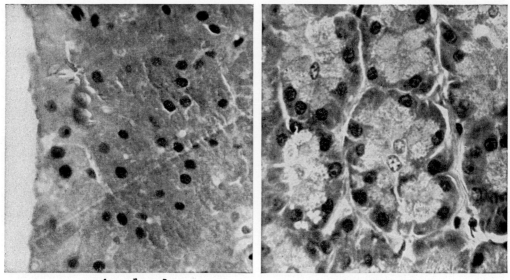

pinched   normal

FIG. 20. High-power photomicrographs of a section of pancreas. (*Left*) Picture taken from an area where the tissue had been pinched as it was obtained. (*Right*) This picture illustrates the normal appearance.

line that passes from one of its sides to the other is most likely to be an artefact of this type.

Another type of appearance that is often seen in sections which may lead to the incorrect surmise that the tissue under view has been the seat of pathologic change is the artefact produced by the rough handling of tissue as it is being cut from the animal body. Commonly, in obtaining tissue, forceps are used to hold a piece that is being cut away; sometimes the cutting is done with scissors (instead of a very sharp knife) and dull ones at that. The pinching caused by holding living tissue with forceps and cutting it with dull scissors profoundly affects the appearance it presents in stained sections. This appearance is illustrated on the left side of Figure 20. The right side of the same figure shows how the tissue would have appeared had it not been mistreated. Since this type of artefact presents an appearance somewhat similar to that of tissue that has died while it still was present in a living body (Fig. 57), the stu-

dent, when he studies pathology, should keep this kind of artefact in mind.

REFERENCES

American Society for Testing Materials: Symposium on Light Microscopy, Philadelphia, The Society, 1953.

Barer, R.: Lecture Notes on the Use of the Microscope, ed. 2, Springfield, Ill., Thomas, 1956.

Hall, C. A.: How to Use the Microscope, ed. 4, Toronto, Macmillan, 1955.

Needham, G. H.: The Practical Use of the Microscope, Springfield, Ill., Thomas, 1958.

Olliver, C. W.: Intelligent Use of the Microscope, New York, Chemical Pub. Co., 1953.

Photomicrography, an Introduction to Photography with the Microscope, ed. 14, Rochester, Eastman Kodak Co., 1945.

Shillaber, C. P.: Photomicrography in Theory and Practice, New York, Wiley, 1944.

Tobias, J. C.: The Student's Manual of Microscopic Technique with Instructions for Photomicrography, Boston, Am. Photographic Pub. Co., 1936.

Chapter 3

Electron Microscopy, Histochemistry and Other Special Methods

Limitations of the Ordinary Light Microscope. A coarse probe cannot be used to search out a fine crevice. Light is the probe that is employed with the microscope, and the coarseness of this probe is unalterably set by the wave length of visible light (0.4 to 0.7 μ). No matter what lens system is employed, light cannot be used to distinguish clearly the structure of objects that are smaller and no farther apart than about half its wave length (say 0.2 μ). Since the unaided eye can distinguish fine lines that are about 0.2 mm. apart (when the object is held at the distance of most distinct vision), there is not much point in using a magnification of more than 1,000 times in the light microscope because the human eye at that magnification can distinguish anything that is revealed by light of that wave length (0.2 $\mu \times 1,000 = 0.2$ mm.). Greater magnifications than 1,000 times yield a larger picture but reveal no further detail.

The wave length of ultraviolet light is only about half that of visible light; hence, if a microscope is equipped with quartz, or some other type of lenses that transmit ultraviolet light, smaller objects can be resolved than is possible with ordinary light. The images of these objects cannot be seen with the eye because it does not discern ultraviolet light. However, as will be explained in detail under "Fluorescence Microscopy" later in this chapter, there are certain materials that, when they are exposed to ultraviolet light or certain other invisible rays, such as x-rays, *fluoresce;* that is, they give off light of a wave length that can be seen by the eye. Accordingly, if the image from an ultraviolet microscope is focused on a screen coated with fluorescent materials, the screen will glow in such a way as to reveal the image. After the image has been focused by this means it can be photographed, because photographic emulsion is sensitive to ultraviolet light.

THE ELECTRON MICROSCOPE (E/M)

The revolutionary development in the microscope, which increased its resolving power 100 or more times, came only after physicists, frustrated by the limitations imposed on them by the wave length of light, turned to electrons. The wave length of these is very short, so short that this factor so far has not limited the resolving power of the new instrument.

In obtaining a magnified image with the light microscope, advantage is taken of the fact that rays of light bend as they pass from a medium of one refractive index into one of another. By using glass with curved surfaces (lenses), light from a small object can be bent so that it produces a large image (Fig. 21, *left*). In the E/M advantage is taken of the fact that the paths of electrons can be influenced similarly by magnetic fields. Accordingly, the lenses of the E/M are magnetic fields, and the strength of these fields can be varied by the amount of current that is passed through the coils of wire (stippled in Fig. 21, *right*) which excite the fields.

In describing an E/M it is convenient to compare its lens systems with those of the light microscope. The optics of both are shown in Figure 21, but in using this figure the student should keep in mind that the light microscope shown at the left is upside down.

In the ordinary microscope, light from a suitable source is focused with a condenser lens (Fig. 21, *upper left*). The condenser lens directs a strong beam of light through the aperture of the microscope stage and *through* the specimen, for example, a stained section that is on the stage (Fig. 21); the specimen is termed the *object* (Fig. 21). The light that passes through the specimen is then focused by the objective lens (Fig. 21). The objective lens brings an *image* of the object into focus somewhere between the objective and the pro-

25

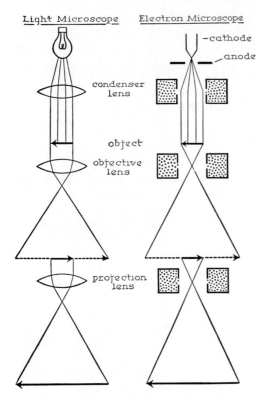

FIG. 21. Diagram showing optical paths in light and electron microscopes.

poses, is generally an unbelievably thin slice of tissue prepared as will be described presently. As the electrons pass through the section more are scattered out of the beam by some parts of the section than by others. The stream of electrons that emerges from the object is first focused by the objective lens, and an enlarged image of the object is obtained thereby (Fig. 21, *right*). This image is enlarged further by the projection lens and focused by it at the site indicated by the bottom arrow of the illustration.

Like ultraviolet light and x-rays, electrons do not register as light in the eye. However, like ultraviolet light and x-rays, they make certain substances fluoresce and they also affect photographic film. So, as with the ultraviolet microscope, a fluorescent screen must be used for focusing the image obtained with the E/M, and then the image can be photographed. Those parts of the final image that correspond to parts of the section that scattered electrons strongly will be faint on the fluorescent screen, light in a photographic negative and dark on a print made from the negative. Conversely, those parts of the image of the section that correspond to parts of the section that do not scatter electrons strongly will be bright on the fluorescent screen, black on the photographic negative and light on a print made from the negative.

There is not much point in greatly enlarging an ordinary photomicrograph because the amount of detail in the photographic image is limited by the wave length of light. However, there is every reason for making great enlargements of negatives exposed in the E/M because these negatives contain a vast amount of detail that can be detected by the unaided eye only in greatly enlarged prints.

It is important for the student to realize that he can learn far more about the fine structure that is revealed by the E/M by studying enlarged prints of negatives exposed in the E/M than he can by using the instrument himself. This is in contrast with the light microscope, for with the latter instrument the student can learn more by studying sections than he can from photomicrographs. Enlargements of photomicrographs do not reveal any more or even as much detail as can be seen by the eye that is applied to the light microscope eyepiece. So, to learn what can be dis-

jection lenses. The projection lens, which is the one in the eyepiece of the ordinary microscope, can further magnify the image up to 10 or 15 times and can be used to bring the enlarged image into focus either on a screen or a photographic plate placed at the site indicated by the bottom arrow (Fig. 21).

The optics of an E/M are illustrated at the right of Figure 21. The whole instrument is, in essence, a demountable cathode-ray tube in which a vacuum must be maintained by continuous pumping. From the cathode, which is a V-shaped tungsten filament (Fig. 21, *top right*) that can be heated electrically, electrons are emitted and attracted toward the anode (by a potential difference of 50,000 to 100,000 volts). The anode has an aperture in it so that a diverging stream of electrons passes through it (Fig. 21, *right*). The diverging stream is focused by the condenser lens (a magnetic field) and directed at the object (Fig. 21, *right*), which, for our pur-

closed by the light microscope the student should use the instrument himself, but to learn what is disclosed further by the E/M the student should study enlarged electron micrographs.

THE USE OF THE E/M
IN HISTOLOGY

Although the E/M is a relatively recent invention, its widespread application to the study of histology is more recent still, having occurred only in the last few years. The reason for this is that although instruments of high performance have been available commercially for well over a decade, satisfactory technics for preparing intact tissue for examinations in the E/M have been evolved relatively recently. These improvements that have permitted the E/M to be used effectively in histology will now be described.

The preceding chapter shows that the study of histology depends a great deal on the study of sections, which are thin slices cut through the different body tissues. A major obstacle to the use of the E/M in histology was the seeming impossibility of ever being able to cut sufficiently thin sections. Electrons penetrate matter so poorly that they will not pass through even the thinnest sections used in light microscopy. For electron microscopy sections must be less than $\frac{1}{10}$ of a micron in thickness, preferably about $\frac{1}{40}$ of a micron (almost exactly 1 millionth of an inch) for the best results. It was impossible to cut sections at anything even approximating this thinness with the microtomes and embedding media commonly used to prepare sections for light microscopy. To achieve the thin sections required several improvements had to be made. First, microtomes with special advance mechanisms capable of operating in the range required for electron microscopy, that is from $1/10$ to $1/40\ \mu$, had to be designed (Fig. 22). The advance mechanisms on the so-called "ultra" microtomes may be either mechanical or thermal. Furthermore, it was found important to avoid having the block pass back over the knife edge on the return stroke after the cutting stroke was completed. Accordingly, "ultra" microtomes are usually designed so

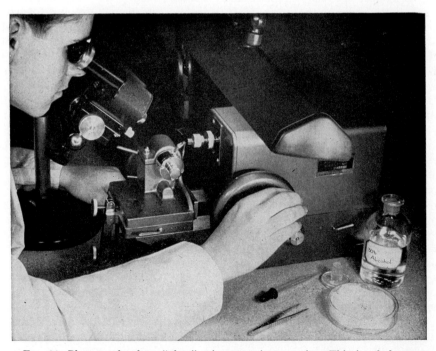

FIG. 22. Photograph of an "ultra" microtome in operation. This is of the type designed by Porter and Blum. Observe that the operator requires a binocular microscope to see the thin sections that are being cut by the instrument.

FIG. 23. Close-up photograph of the block of tissue (seen at the apex of the pyramid) approaching the edge of the glass knife. Observe that there is a little reservoir on the upper surface of the knife; as the sections are cut they float onto the fluid in this reservoir.

that the block takes a circuitous course and bypasses the cutting edge on the return stroke. Another advance was the introduction by Latta and Hartman of the fracture edge of a piece of plate glass as a cutting edge for this type of work (Fig. 23). Glass knives are prepared easily, and selected edges have cutting properties at least as good as the most carefully polished steel knives (which are still used by some electron microscopists). More recently, specially ground diamond knives have become available, and their use is increasing. The cutting edge of a diamond knife is no sharper than that of a glass knife but it is so very hard that it can be used for a long time, whereas a glass knife can be used for only a very limited period before it becomes dull. Moreover, the hardness of a diamond knife makes it particularly useful for cutting sections of very hard tissues, e.g., enamel, dentin and bone.

Improvements in the medium in which tissue is embedded were also necessary before satisfactory thin sections could be secured. In 1949, Newman, Borysko and Swerdlow introduced the use of a plastic material, n-butyl methacrylate, which proved to be very suc-cessful and is now used almost universally in this type of work. After fixation and dehydration the tissue is infiltrated with n-butyl methacrylate monomer, which is a clear liquid with a pungent odor. On heating for several hours in an oven maintained at about 50° C., the liquid, in the presence of an added catalyst, polymerizes to a clear solid resin with excellent cutting properties. For harder blocks a mixture of methyl and n-butyl methacrylate is used. Methacrylate has some disadvantages, the main one is that it shrinks during polymerization and so distorts the tissue embedded in it.

Other plastic materials for embedding are becoming available, e.g., "Araldite," "Vestopal" and "Epon"; these may prove to be preferable to methacrylate for at least some tissues in that they cause less distortion.

Since the E/M resolves such minute detail, it is of the greatest importance that the tissue from which sections are cut be fixed as perfectly as possible. It was shown some time ago by Strangeways and Canti that most fixatives produce gross precipitation of protein in cells and cause varying degrees of distortion of cell components. Of all the fixatives tested they found that osmium tetroxide produced the least alteration in cells. These results were fully confirmed in early E/M studies, and since then solutions of osmium tetroxide have been generally employed as the fixatives of choice.

In 1952, Palade introduced a further improvement in technic. He noted that as the OsO_4 solution penetrated the tissue it was preceded by a wave of acidification which had a deleterious effect on the preservation of the tissue. To avoid the reduction in pH, Palade introduced the use of a buffered solution of osmium tetroxide. The use of this solution, or slight modifications of it, results in the most faithful preservation of tissue structures that has been achieved so far.

Although the electron microscopist is denied the benefits available to the light microscopist, which evolve from the use of stains which color different tissue components selectively, it is possible to enhance contrast between different tissue components seen under the electron microscope by chemicals that are "electron dense" and attach themselves to different extents to different tissue components. Osmium tetroxide itself acts this way because osmium, which scatters electrons strongly, is taken up to different extents by different tissue components. Other salts of heavy metals act in a similar manner and are used to increase contrast. Such solutions are referred to as "electron stains." One which has come into common use is *lead hydroxide;* some of the electron micrographs in this book were taken from sections stained in this way.

Another new development is that of "negative staining." This technic involves the use of a solution of an electron-dense chemical (phosphotungstic acid is commonly used for this purpose) in which the tissue is immersed and this, instead of combining specifically with any particular organic ingredients of the material, fills all the interstices in and between different parts of the material and leaves the material itself relatively untouched. Hence, in an electron micrograph of material prepared in this way a negative rather than a positive image of the sectioned material is obtained. This method has particular value in demonstrating the surface contour of bodies of a delicate nature for these, in themselves, would not take up enough electron stain to be outlined sharply, but if the spaces between them are made electron dense by negative staining their limits are outlined clearly.

These four advances—the development of microtomes capable of routinely cutting sections of 1/40th of a micron or less, the introduction of glass knives, the discovery of an embedding medium with satisfactory cutting properties, and the improvements in the fixative solution—all of which were made between 1949 and 1952—were necessary to make the study of the fine structure of cells and tissues a practical procedure for histology laboratories.

SOME DETAILS OF THE TECHNICS USED IN PREPARING SECTIONS FOR, AND USING THEM IN, THE E/M

There are some important points of difference between preparing and using sections for light and electron microscopy.

1. Much smaller tissue blocks are used, because OsO_4 penetrates tissue very slowly so that only very small pieces of tissue can be fixed satisfactorily. Indeed, even with tissue blocks of the size commonly used (about 1 cu. mm.), fixation in the central region is distinctly inferior to that of the periphery.

2. The tissue has to be very fresh. Post-mortem changes are more obvious at the high resolution employed in the E/M.

3. The procedures of fixing, dehydrating and embedding, though essentially similar to those employed in ordinary histologic work, can be carried out more rapidly because the pieces of tissue employed are much smaller.

4. The sections are not stained, since there is no color differentiation in electron micrographs. However, the incorporation of osmium or other heavy metals into the tissue has an effect similar to that of a single stain, because osmium, which scatters electrons strongly, is taken up to different extents by different tissue components. Hence, the use of osmium tetroxide fixation improves the contrast in electron micrographs in much the same way that a single stain that has different affinities for different tissue components improves contrast for light microscopy.

5. The sections cut from the final trimmed block are minute, usually about 1/4 mm. square, and since they are only about 1 millionth of an inch thick they are almost invisible to the naked eye. Therefore, their manipulation must be carried on under a light microscope of the type commonly used for making delicate dissections (Fig. 22). Since the extremely thin sections are very fragile, they can be handled only by floating them, as they are cut, onto the surface of a liquid. A small cuplike reservoir containing a mixture of alcohol, or acetone, and water is attached to the back of the cutting edge of the knife for this purpose (Fig. 23). As the sections are cut they float on this mixture in the form of a ribbon. Relatively thick sections appear to be colored by reflected light, but sections sufficiently thin for study appear colorless or silvery.

6. The thin sections, floating on the surface of the fluid, cannot be mounted on glass slides as are sections for light microscopy, because electrons, of course, would not penetrate the glass. The problem of obtaining proper support for these very thin sections and yet permitting the passage of electrons through them is solved by mounting the sections on little copper grids each of which is coated with a very thin supporting film of

FIG. 24. A late model electron microscope. (RCA)

formvar (a plastic) or carbon. The copper grid supports the film, and the film supports the section. Electrons can pass through the holes in the grid, and penetrate through the supporting film and the parts of the section that overlie the holes in the grid.

7. Thin sections, so mounted, are placed on the specimen holder of the microscope and inserted into the instrument. A high vacuum must be produced in the instrument before the electron beam can be switched on and the specimen examined. Controls are provided for moving the specimen around, changing the magnification and the brightness of the image, and so on (Fig. 24). The magnification can be changed very easily by turning a knob which controls the current passing through the intermediate or projector lens. Focusing of the image is accomplished not by moving the object up and down as in the light microscope but by altering very slightly the ob-

jective lens current. The focal length of the objective lens is altered thereby, and the image may be brought into sharp focus on the fluorescent screen. The focusing must be done very accurately, and as an aid to sharp focusing it is customary to observe the screen through a low-power binocular microscope. The photographic plate lies immediately below the screen. To take a micrograph the screen is tilted out of the way, and the electron beam is allowed to hit the photographic emulsion for a few seconds. The exposed plate is developed and fixed in the usual way. The detail in the developed negative is much greater than that which can be observed on the fluorescent screen.

8. The depth of an ordinary paraffin section is much greater than the depth of focus obtainable with high-power objectives of the light microscope, so that in scanning a section completely with the light microscope it is necessary not only to traverse the whole area of the specimen but also to focus up and down. This is not so with the E/M. Owing to the narrow aperture of the electron beam the depth of focus at the object is relatively great (approximately 1 μ), and this distance is much greater than the thickness of the sections used (about 1/40th of a micron). Hence, objects at all depths in the section are in focus at one time, and it is possible for the overlapping of structures to occur. Although this point should be remembered in examining micrographs, overlapping rarely causes any difficulty in interpretation because the sections now used are so thin that the picture obtained is almost a true 2-dimensional one.

The Terms "Fine Structure" and "Ultrastructure." The E/M permits the discernment of cell and tissue structure beyond that seen with the light microscope. To designate this particular realm of structure requires the use of some term, and the one most commonly used is that of *fine structure*. In describing the *fine structure* of the cell or any other tissue component, one, therefore, refers to those elements of structure that can be elucidated only with the E/M. The term *ultrastructure* is also used for this purpose but this term is not so desirable, because it actually means *beyond* structure.

HISTOCHEMISTRY

The development of methods for staining

sections so that different components of cells and tissue take on different colors had many consequences. For example, it inspired a search for chemotherapeutic drugs, for Ehrlich, after finding that he could color the bacillus that causes tuberculosis differently from the cells that it infects, dreamed of finding a substance that would have a selective affinity for, and so destroy, disease agents in the body while leaving the body cells unharmed. After years of searching he did find a very effective one, compound 606, which, for many years, played the dominant role in the treatment of syphilis.

Origin. The fact that different cell and tissue components could be stained differently also inspired the development of the special science of histochemistry. It was only natural that the imaginative histologist would understand that the different affinities that different tissue and cell components had for stains were due to chemical differences between them and that he would begin to use known chemical reagents on tissue sections in an attempt to produce color reactions that would give specific information about the chemical nature of various cell and tissue components.

Many marriages have occurred between the basic scientific disciplines which have given rise to interdisciplinary subjects. Some of these new subjects through the years have gained the stature of basic subjects in their own right, for example, biochemistry arose from the application of chemistry to biologic phenomena and is now regarded as a separate discipline. More recently, biophysics, which arose from attempting to explain biologic phenomena by the laws of physics, and the study of biologic phenomena with the tools and the methods of physics, has also gained the stature of a discipline in its own right. Histochemistry also arose as an interdisciplinary subject, the disciplines in this instance being histology and biochemistry. Since it developed in such a large measure from histology, much of its subject matter is still regarded as being part of histology and so some histochemistry is generally taught in a course of histology. At the moment there is no rule as to how much histochemistry should be included in a histology course. This is generally decided by the particular interest of the instructors concerned and also by the extent to which students have studied biochemistry before taking histology. In this book an attempt will be made to give the student some concept of the nature and the scope of the subject and a general account of the more important methods used in its study; this will be done here. In later sections of the book histochemical methods that apply to the elucidation of the particular aspect of histology under consideration will be described in more detail. References are given to books, monographs and articles where more comprehensive and detailed treatment of the subject may be found.

Inorganic Substances. Since tests for inorganic materials were in general developed in the general field of chemistry before tests for organic materials, some of the first histochemical methods used on sections were tests for inorganic substances. An example of an early one was an adaptation of the familiar Prussian blue reaction used in the chemical laboratory for the detection of ferric iron; this was introduced into histochemistry nearly a century ago by M. Perle, in 1867. In sections treated with the potassium ferrocyanide reagent, iron deposits are colored blue and hence are easily identified under the microscope. However, iron can be present in tissue in certain combinations in which it does not react with the reagent, and in order to be demonstrated such iron must first be unmasked, and there are histochemical procedures for this. Other histochemical tests for iron have also become available as have histochemical tests for many other inorganic materials, including zinc, nickel, lead, copper, mercury, silver, gold, platinum, magnesium, calcium, potassium, bismuth, arsenic and others.

Organic Substances. Certain organic substances can be identified by histochemical methods; only a few examples will be considered here. As might be expected, it became apparent through the years that certain staining procedures would more or less specifically identify certain organic materials in cells and tissues. At first the chemistry of many of these reactions was not understood, and even yet many methods are still used empirically. Examples of the latter are Best's carmine method for staining glycogen and the mucicarmine technic for demonstrating mucin. However, as histochemistry continued to develop less dependence was placed on ill-understood empiric technics and more on tests in which the chemical reactions that occurred were understood. Many histochemical tests are not specific for the actual substances as they exist in tissues but require that some chemistry be done on the section so that the substance sought for either liberates or produces some substance for which a specific test exists. The Feulgen reaction, which is widely used to identify sites of deoxyribonucleic acid (Fig. 34) and is described in detail in its proper context on page 72, is a test of this kind. The P.A.S. technic, another widely used histochemical test, is described in detail on page 142; it is also in this category. Moreover, this latter test illustrates a histochemical test that identifies not a single substance but the members of a group of substances which have chemical components in common. After some chemistry is done on the section, it yields compounds of a specific category which are readily identified by a color reaction (Fig. 464).

Some reactions used in histology and histochemistry depend on physical rather than chemical affinities. For example, fat is commonly detected in sections (which have not been exposed to fat solvents) by stains such as Sudan III, because these stains have a physical affinity for oil and so are absorbed by the fat which thus becomes colored.

Enzymes. Histochemistry is concerned not only with identifying and localizing different inorganic and organic materials in cells and tissues; it is concerned also with the reactions that proceed in cells and hence with the demonstration and the localization of the enzymes that catalyze these reactions. An early histochemical test for an enzyme that was developed was the one that is commonly used to detect and localize the enzyme alkaline phosphatase in tissue sections. This test provides an example of a reaction that detects the enzyme by exposing the section to a substrate of the enzyme. In the instance of alkaline phosphatase the substrate used is glycerophosphate. The enzyme at the sites where it is present catalyzes the breakdown of glycerophosphate with the release of phosphate ions. If sufficient calcium ions are present, the liberated phosphate ions immediately react with the calcium ions to form a precipitate. The calcium phosphate precipitate can be blackened by various methods, and

by this means the sites of the enzyme are indicated in the sections by black deposits (Figs. 141 and 189). Histochemical methods are now available for identifying many enzymes, in addition to phosphatases, for example, dehydrogenases, peptidases and phosphorylases.

Relation to Biochemistry. As might be inferred from the above paragraph, the development of modern histochemistry has been closely linked to and dependent on the development of modern biochemistry. Indeed, the subjects may seem to embrace so much common territory that it may be difficult for the student to understand the fundamental difference between them. Perhaps the easiest way to explain this is to point out that the biochemist, working with the whole body, or body fluids, or ground-up tissue in test tubes and flasks, elucidates in detail the chemical reactions on which life depends, while the histochemist, working generally with tissue preparations that can be observed under some kind of microscope, seeks to localize these reactions in cells or extracellular sites and to interpret the significance of their being disposed in these particular sites. However, there is one area where the biochemist and the histochemist occupy common ground, for with the development of methods of differential centrifugation, it is now possible to separate broken-up cells into various fractions. The content of each fraction can be determined by sectioning the materials gathered in each fraction and examining the sectioned material under the electron microscope (Figs. 63 and 68). By this method the biochemist who works with different cell fractions has knowledge of the localization in cells of the material with which he works; hence, in this area it is very difficult to draw any distinction between biochemistry and histochemistry. While attempting to give some concept of the similarities and the differences between histochemistry and biochemistry, another term which may be encountered, namely, cytochemistry, should be mentioned. Histochemistry deals with tissues and so includes studies on all their components—cells, intercellular substances and fluids. Cytochemistry deals only with cells; hence, it is not as broad a subject as histochemistry, being more or less a special subdivision of it.

Radioautography. The chemical substances that are absorbed into the body almost continuously from the intestine meet with one or more of three fates. First, in the growing animal some of these substances are incorporated into tissue where they will remain for a very long time, in some instances all through life. One example of incorporation for the long-term is provided by the nucleosides that enter into the composition of the DNA of the chromosomes (see p. 78 for details) of newly forming cells that will have a long life-span, for the DNA will last as long as the cells last provided that they do not divide. Another example is provided by calcium that is deposited in bones and in general remains as long as does the particular piece of bone in which it is deposited. (This may not be as long as might be thought at first, for as we shall see in Chapter 15, there is much remodeling of bone during the growing period which requires the dissolving of previously formed bone.) Secondly, in both the growing and the mature animal, there are many tissues in which cells have a short life span; they wear out and die and so must be replaced by cell division occurring fairly steadily in such cells as still remain alive in that part. This is generally described by saying that there is a considerable turnover of cells in many parts of the body, and in these parts of the body there must be a considerable incorporation of materials for the production of these cells which, in due course, wear out and die. Thirdly, in all cells, whether they are short-lived or long-lived, there is a continuous turnover of many materials to provide these cells with the energy required for their continued life; in other words, even in tissues in which there is little or no turnover of cells, there is a turnover of materials in the nondividing cells.

From the foregoing it is obvious that if different substances that are used by cells could be labeled in some way and fed, or otherwise given, to an animal, the labeled substance would soon appear in cells or tissues. If the labeled substance that was used were used merely as fuel for energy, the label would last only for the short time before the substance was metabolized. If the substance were of a kind that was built into some lasting part of the cell, such as the DNA of the chromo-

somes, it would last as long as the cell; in parts of the body where there is a rapid turnover of cells, this would be a short time, but if the labeled material were given while cells which were to last all through life were forming, the label would remain all through life, provided of course that the label would last this long. This brings up another problem, for the labels commonly used are radioactive isotopes, and the different ones have very different half-lives. Some last a long time; for example, C^{14} has a half-life of 5,100 years; while others last only a short time; for example, I^{131} has a half-life of only 8 days.

Radioactive isotopes of many of the elements that are normally incorporated into body tissues are now available. Furthermore, many organic materials that are ordinarily incorporated into body tissues can be labeled in one way or another with one of the radioactive isotopes of one of the elements. There are, therefore, many labeled substances that can be fed or otherwise given to animals, and in the minute amounts in which they are given they are absorbed and utilized in the same manner as if they were unlabeled. The histochemical technic by which the labeled substances are located in tissues is known as *radioautography*.

Coated Radioautographs. In using this method, tissue from animals given a labeled substance is fixed and sectioned. The sections may be stained if certain precautions are observed. In employing the method devised by Belanger and Leblond, and improved by Messier and Leblond, the stained sections are coated with celloidin and then, in the dark room, they are coated with photographic emulsion and dried. The coated sections are then left in a lightproof box for a suitable length of time during which each minute amount of isotope in the section of tissue acts as a point source of radiation. The isotopes used for radioautography are beta emitters; therefore, from each site in the section where there is isotope, electrons are given off. The emitted electrons travel in reasonably straight tracks, and in the instance of the weak beta emitters that are generally used for radioautography the tracks are short. The electrons in the tracks that extend into the photographic emulsion have sufficient energy to bring about the ionization of occasional atoms; and wherever an atom is ionized in the emulsion, the latter, at that site, may be affected as if it had been exposed to light, and so when the preparation is developed a black dot called a "grain" will mark this spot (Fig. 48). After the preparation is developed (using an ordinary photographic developer), the section with its overlying emulsion is fixed and washed similarly to a photographic negative. Then the preparation can be examined under the microscope, and the position of the grains can be related to the cell or tissue components over which they lie (Fig. 48). One very common beta emitter used in radioautography is tritium-labeled thymidine; this, as will be explained in the next chapter, is incorporated into the DNA of newly forming chromosomes. The electrons emitted by tritium have very short tracks, and so the electrons that travel from each site on a chromosome where there is labeled thymidine cause grains to appear in the emulsion very close to their point of origin (Fig. 48). This makes it relatively easy to localize the site of the labeled thymidine in the chromosome. When more energetic radioactive labels are used, as for example P^{32}, the electrons have longer tracks, and so grains may be formed in the emulsion at con-siderable distances from the site of the label. This, of course, renders the localization of the labeled isotope in the section less precise.

The Stripping Film Method. This method employs the use of a special kind of film which readily permits the emulsion to be stripped from its backing. Of course, this step is carried out in the darkroom, and the stripped emulsion is placed on the surface of water in a dish. A glass slide with a section mounted on it, but with no cover slip, is then slipped under the floating stripped emulsion and brought up under it so that the layer of emulsion rests flat on the section. Subsequent steps are much the same as in the previous technic. The stripping method has the advantage, for the inexperienced worker with a minimum of equipment, of giving some assurance that the emulsion is of fairly constant thickness, and this is important in quantitative work, which involves the counting of numbers of grains.

Micro-incineration. The minerals in different parts can be studied by the technic of micro-incineration. This was evolved by Policard and brought to a high state of development on this continent by Scott and in Great Britain by Horning. In the usual employment

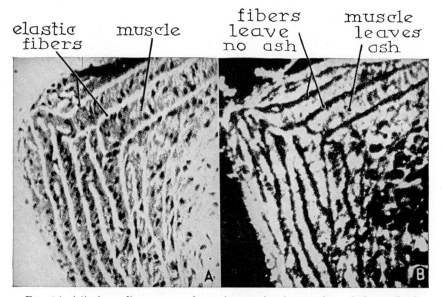

Fig. 25. (*A*) A medium-power photomicrograph of a section of the wall of a rat's aorta stained with H and E. (*B*) A photomicrograph of a similarly cut section which was incinerated. With darkfield illumination the ash shows up as white and an absence of ash shows up as black. (Ham, A.: Arch. Path. *14*:613)

of this technic paraffin sections of tissue fixed in a solution of alcohol and formalin are mounted on slides and placed in an electric furnace. The temperature of the furnace is raised slowly to a point where all the organic matter of the section is burned off and only the mineral skeleton of the tissue is left on the slide. This may be studied conveniently with darkfield illumination with which it appears white (Fig. 25).

THE USE OF THE INTERFERENCE AND THE PHASE MICROSCOPE FOR THE STUDY OF LIVING UNSTAINED TISSUE

The study of living unstained cells is difficult with the ordinary light microscope because there is so little contrast between their different parts. Two developments, the *interference* and the *phase microscopes*, have made studies of living cells much easier and more profitable. The principles on which they operate will now be described briefly.

Light waves can differ from one another in their (1) amplitude, (2) wave length and (3) phase, as will now be described.

1. The amplitude of a light wave is responsible for its intensity; the greater its amplitude, the greater its intensity. If light is passed through a neutral filter its intensity is diminished (Fig. 26) because the filter diminishes the amplitude of the wave that passes through it (Fig. 26).

It might be thought that the various tissue components in an unstained section or in a living fresh preparation of tissue would each act like a neutral filter of a different degree of opacity and so reduce the amplitude of the waves that pass through them to different extents. If they did, it would be easy, in examining a fresh preparation of tissue, to recognize different tissue components because they would be of different degrees of brightness. Unfortunately, however, although most tissue components do indeed act like neutral filters, they all transmit about the same amount of light, and so, with the ordinary microscope, they all appear to be of about the same degree of brightness. Hence, they cannot be distinguished readily from one another (Fig. 29, *left*). Accordingly, histologists were driven to the use of stained sections, which take advantage of the attribute of light waves next to be described.

2. The wave length of light—the distance between two successive crests (Fig. 27)—determines its color. The wave length of red light is greater than that of green, and that of green is greater than that of blue (Fig. 27). Filters that absorb light of different wave lengths can be constructed; for example, a green filter transmits only light that has the wave length of green light; it absorbs red and blue light.

When sections are stained, say with H and E, the different tissue components in them

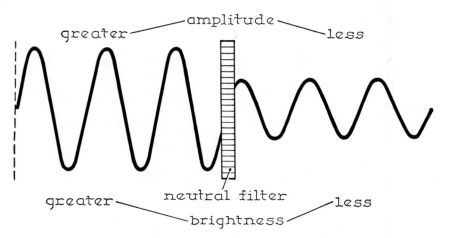

FIG. 26. Diagram showing how the amplitude of light waves is decreased by the waves passing through a neutral filter.

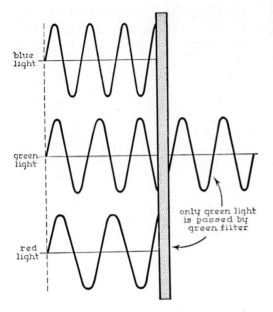

blue
light

green
light

only green light
is passed by
green filter

red
light

FIG. 27. Diagram showing how waves of blue and red light are held back by a green filter while waves of green light can pass through the filter.

take up one or the other of the two dyes to become colored blue and red to different extents. When such sections are examined with the microscope the various red-and-blue tissue components in them act as blue-and-red filters (of different degrees of color selectivity and opacity), and so each tissue component can be

recognized because it transmits light of a different color and amplitude to the eye.

3. In the foregoing it has been shown that the various components in a preparation of unstained tissue do not change the amplitude of the light waves that pass through them to very different extents and they do not absorb light waves of different wave lengths to different extents. Hence, on the grounds of amplitude and wave length, light waves that pass through an unstained specimen cannot be readily distinguished from one another (Fig. 29, *left*). However, the different components in unstained tissue do alter the phase of light waves that pass through them to different extents. This fact is not easily taken advantage of, because phase differences as such are not discernible to the eye. If somehow phase differences could be converted into differences of amplitude, different tissue components in unstained preparations could be made to appear of different degrees of brightness and so be distinguished easily from one another (Fig. 29, *center and right*). The phase and the interference microscopes are designed to accomplish this aim, as will now be described.

Anyone who has seen the waves on a lake sweeping around both sides of an anchored boat and then reuniting has seen an illustration of the principle that is employed. When the waves that come around one side of the boat join with those coming around the other side of the boat, one of two things may happen: the combining of the waves may result

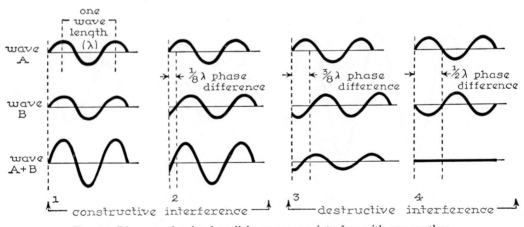

FIG. 28. Diagrams showing how light waves can interfere with one another to increase or decrease the amplitude of the resultant waves.

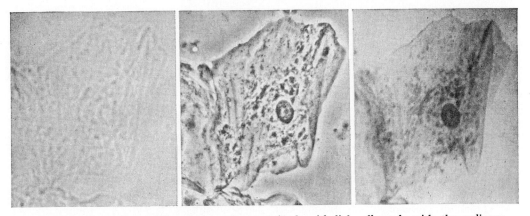

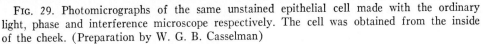

Fig. 29. Photomicrographs of the same unstained epithelial cell made with the ordinary light, phase and interference microscope respectively. The cell was obtained from the inside of the cheek. (Preparation by W. G. B. Casselman)

in the formation of waves that have either (1) a greater or (2) a smaller amplitude than the individual waves that join one another. To illustrate, in Part 1 of Figure 28, *left,* two waves, A and B, of the same amplitude and length are shown as being in phase with one another, that is, the peaks and the troughs of each are directly above one another. If two such waves are combined, as is shown in the lower left corner of this figure, the resulting wave has a greater amplitude than each of the original two. Even if the waves are slightly out of phase with one another, as is illustrated in Part 2 of Figure 28, the amplitude of the resulting wave is still greater than that of each of the waves that combined (but less than that of the wave that results from the combining of two similar waves that are perfectly in phase with one another). When waves interfere with one another to form waves of greater amplitude the interference is said to be constructive. However, if waves of a given amplitude are considerably out of phase with one another, as is illustrated in Part 3 of Figure 28, their combining results in waves that are smaller than the original ones, and, indeed, if they are completely out of phase with one another they can obliterate each other completely, as is shown in Part 4 of this illustration. It can be seen readily from Figure 28 that by variously combining light waves that are out of phase with one another it is possible to produce combined waves of greater or lesser amplitude and hence of greater or lesser brightness. This is the principle used in the phase and the interference microscopes to provide contrast between tissue components that are of approximately the same relative opacities. However, to do this, two sets of waves must be used.

Although two sets of waves are obtained and reunited in both the interference and the phase microscopes, the way in which this is accomplished differs. In both instances the two sets of waves must be derived from the same source; thus they are said to be *coherent.*

In the interference microscope two sets of waves are obtained before light reaches the object; this is done by placing a beam-splitter in the condenser. The beam-splitter allows one beam to pass directly through it to the object; this is called the *object beam.* A second beam passes out from the beam-splitter parallel with, but a short distance off from, the object beam. This is called the *reference beam* and it passes up, not through, the object but at one side of it, ideally through some clear area close to the cell or whatever object is being examined. On reaching the objective lens, the reference and the objective beams are recombined by another beam-splitter, used, as it were, in reverse.

So far we have discussed two beams. However, it should be understood that the object beam contains a multitude of light waves that pass through all the different parts of the object. For example, if a nucleus is being examined some light waves would pass through chromatin granules and others through nuclear sap. These two objects would alter the phase of the waves that pass through them to a different extent. When the multitude of waves in the object beam are reunited with the corresponding multitude of waves in the reference beam, the light waves that passed through chromatin granules will interfere with the reference beam (the waves of which are all in the same phase) differently from the light waves that passed through nuclear sap; hence, there will be differences in amplitude between the two resultant sets of waves. This will permit chromatin granules to be distinguished from nuclear sap by their different degrees of brightness.

Since the phase of the light waves in the reference beam is practically unaltered it provides a standard for measurement. By seeing how much interference is caused by waves that pass through different objects such as chromatin granules or nucleoli, it is possible to measure quantitatively the extent to which these objects alter the phase of the waves that pass through them. Hence, the interference microscope can be used as an interferometer to provide quantitative data.

In the phase microscope two beams from the same light source are obtained in a different way from that employed in the interference microscope. No beam-splitters are used. Instead, an annular diaphragm is placed in the condenser so that all the light that strikes the object is in the form of a hollow cone. On striking the transparent object, light acts as it does when it strikes a diffraction grating, by giving rise to two types of waves. One type passes through the object in a straight line; these form the *undiffracted* waves. However, other waves are diffracted by the object, and their course is changed somewhat. These constitute the *diffracted* waves.

The different components in the object diffract to different extents the light waves that strike them. Consequently, the relative intensity (amplitude) of the diffracted and the undiffracted waves that arise as light strikes these components of the object varies. With some components the undiffracted light would be of much greater amplitude than the diffracted, but with others not so great. Of course, if the diffracted and the undiffracted

waves from any given component in the object were combined they would not necessarily differ greatly in amplitude from the combined waves from any other component. But advantage is taken of the fact that the relative amplitudes of the diffracted and the undiffracted beams from different components differ. This is done by inserting a phase retarder in the objective. Phase retarders, depending on the type used, act by retarding primarily either the diffracted or the undiffracted waves from the different components of the object. Different components of the object diffract light to different extents. Accordingly, the percentage of diffracted and undiffracted light that emerges from each component in the object is different. When a phase retarder (that affects *either* the diffracted light *or* the undiffracted light) is inserted in the objective it will, depending on the kind used, retard the phase of *either* the diffracted or the undiffracted light from every component in the object equally. But, since the percentage of diffracted and undiffracted light from every component in the object is different it is obvious that a recombination of the diffracted and the undiffracted light from each component in the object, after the phase of one or the other kind has been altered by the phase retarder, will result in different amounts of interference between the recombined waves from each component in the object and this, of course, affects the amplitude of these waves, and this in turn results in different components of the object exhibiting contrast with one another in terms of brightness or darkness. The extent to which any component in the object diffracts light is, of course, dependent on the surrounding medium of that component of the object. Therefore, it is possible to alter the ability of any component of the object to diffract light by the use of different mounting media which have different refractive indices. Different components can be made lighter or darker than certain others by using phase retarders that act primarily on the diffracted or the undiffracted rays; hence, it is possible to have either "dark" or "bright" contrast objectives. Figure 29 shows how the same unstained cell, removed fresh from the inner lining of the cheek, appears when viewed with the ordinary light microscope (*left*), the phase microscope (*center*) and the interference microscope (*right*).

Fluorescence Microscopy. This histochemical technic has yielded and is yielding so much information of value to the medical sciences that the student should be conversant with it. The technic has many applications in localizing substances that cannot be localized by other methods, as will now be described in the following brief account.

Fluorescence is the property, exhibited by certain substances, of being able to absorb radiant energy of one wave length and to emit radiant energy at another and longer wave length. Therefore, fluorescent substances can be used to advantage to detect invisible ultraviolet light and x-rays because suitable fluorescent substances exposed to the relatively short waves of ultraviolet light or the still shorter ones of x-rays absorb these and re-emit the longer waves of visible light. Since fluorescence is a very curious phenomenon, it may be of interest to attempt to explain the mechanism involved in its production.

A photon of ultraviolet light or x-rays, on encountering a peripheral electron in an atom in a substance, can impart its energy to that electron. The extra energy now possessed by this electron causes it to be excited. In the instance of nonfluorescing substances, the excited electron loses the extra energy it has gained by emitting a photon of the same kind that caused its excitation, and, as a result of this, the electron returns to its former unexcited state. However, in the instances of fluorescent materials, a peripheral electron in an atom, after being excited by a photon of ultraviolet light or x-rays, may not return to its unexcited state by emitting a photon of the same kind that excited it; instead, because of the particular chemical and physical environment provided by the fluorescent material in which it has become excited, it may lose a small part of its extra energy in some way other than by the emission of radiant energy and, as a consequence, it does not have enough extra energy left to emit a photon of the same wave length as that which excited it in the first place. Since photons of longer wave lengths have less energy than those of shorter wave lengths, the excited electron in the fluorescent material, although it has lost part of its extra energy, still has enough to emit a

photon of a longer wave length in the range of visible light, and it is by doing this that it returns to its unexcited state. Practically, this means that the existence of ultraviolet light in any beam can be demonstrated by the ability of fluorescent materials to absorb the invisible light of short wave length and re-emit visible light of a longer wave length. This is being applied increasingly in microscopy as will now be explained. We shall give a few details.

1. There are several naturally occurring fluorescent materials in the body; of these groups, one of the most interesting is the porphyrins. These all have a particular chemical configuration in common, and many contain a metal. Porphyrins are important components of many of the enzymes that are concerned in oxidation-reduction reactions, for example, the cytochromes and the catalases. Some of the vitamins are fluorescent—vitamin A and vitamin B_2 (riboflavin). Still other substances in the body are fluorescent to some extent; for example, natural teeth can be distinguished from artificial teeth by the fact that the natural ones fluoresce.

2. There are several dyes that fluoresce and can be used to stain ordinarily nonfluorescing cell and tissue components, so that these cell and tissue components can then be demonstrated. For example, acridine orange combines with both the DNA and the RNA of the cell (described in the next chapter). When cells stained with this fluorescent dye are examined, the DNA fluoresces with a green to yellow color, and the RNA with an orange to red color. Other fluorescent dyes used for certain purposes are thioflavine S, thioflavine T, rhodamine B, and primulin.

3. As has been done so successfully by Coons and his associates, antibodies can be conjugated with fluorescent dyes to locate antigens in the tissues of the body.

We all remember having had an infectious disease and having recovered from it. One way in which the body reacts to infectious agents —for example, pathogenic bacteria or viruses —and so aids our recovery, is by producing antibodies to the infectious agent or to some part or product of it. Antibodies are chemical substances that have special chemical configurations which combine with the substance that led to their formation, much as two gear wheels intermesh with one another, and by this union the noxious effect of the agent or its product is nullified.

Substances that induce the formation of antibodies in the animal body are termed *antigens*. An important feature of an antigen is that it is a substance foreign to the body. The most important antigens that gain entrance to the body are disease agents, and it is easy to understand that these could have a chemical constitution different from that of any normal component of the body. However, an antigen need not be a disease agent; any macromolecule that is foreign to the body, provided that it has a molecular weight greater than 10,000, can act as an antigen and induce the formation of antibodies that will react specifically with it. Macromolecules from other species act as antigens in man; for example, when a person is injected with horse serum, as occurs when an individual is given tetanus antitoxin, which is made by injecting tetanus toxin into horses, he reacts to the macromolecules that are in it by producing antibodies against them. Indeed, macromolecules from one human being may act as an antigen if they are injected into the body of another, for, except in the instance of identical twins, many of the macromolecules of one person are sufficiently different from those of another to act as antigens in them. For this reason, the living tissues of one person cannot be transplanted successfully into another; some of the macromolecules of the transplanted tissue act as antigens and induce antibodies that eventually cause the death of the transplanted cells and the rejection of the transplanted tissue.

Antibody formation will be described in more detail when the cells that produce antibodies are considered in Chapter 18; here we shall discuss only the technic that is employed in using antibodies labeled with fluorescent dyes to locate antigens in tissue preparation.

The easiest way to describe a technic is to give an example of its use. For our example we shall choose a virus that is a good antigen. Viruses are generally very specific with regard to the kind of body cells that they infect and in which they multiply, so we shall see how the fluorescent technic could be used to locate the particular cells which would be-

come infected when a particular virus is given an animal. A few days after the animal is infected with the virus we obtain the organ that we wish to study and immediately freeze a representative piece of this in liquid nitrogen and store the piece at $-20°$ C. until it is sectioned. The latter step is performed with a microtome that is housed in a freezing cabinet called a cryostat; the material is kept frozen from the time it is taken until it is sectioned so that no shift in the virus can occur. The sections are then dried in air at room temperature and are fixed, the particular fixative to be used depending on the type of antigen being investigated. The sites of the virus (the antigen) in the section then can be located by either of two means: the direct or the indirect method.

In the direct method, an animal that is not very susceptible to the virus is injected with enough virus to produce antibodies to it. The serum from the animal (containing antibodies to the virus) is then collected, and the fraction containing the antibodies is purified as much as possible and then conjugated with a fluorescent dye. Then a drop of the fluorescent antibody solution is placed over the section and left in a covered dish for $\frac{1}{2}$ hour or more; during this time the antibody combines with any antigen (virus) in the section. The section is then washed to remove all antibody that has not become fixed by combining with antigen. Next, the section is mounted in 10 per cent glycerol in buffered saline, covered with a coverslip and examined under the microscope for fluorescence. The sites of fluorescence indicate where the antibody has attached itself to the antigen; hence, the sites that are indicated are the cells in which there are substantial concentrations of virus.

The indirect method is perhaps more sensitive than the direct one outlined above. The indirect method involves an additional step. First, if we were attempting to locate sites of virus in, say, the kidney of the hamster, a species susceptible to the virus, we would first inject an animal of some other species, for example, a rabbit, with the virus; the serum of the latter would then come to contain antibodies to the virus. Next, we would take some serum from the rabbit and inject this into an animal of still another species, for example, a sheep. The sheep would make

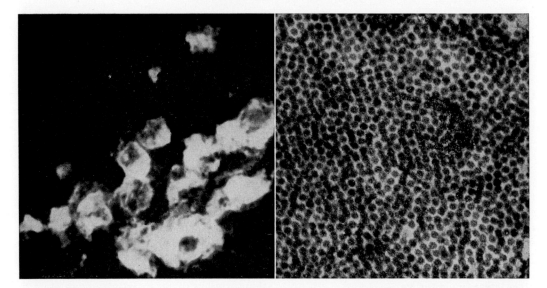

FIG. 30. (*Left*) High-power photomicrograph taken with a darkfield condenser of section of kidney of hamster that was infected at birth with polyoma virus. The cells that contain virus fluoresce under ultraviolet light and appear white against a dark background of cells that do not contain virus and hence do not attach fluorescent dye. (*Right*) Electron micrograph (× 60,000) of a cell of the type demonstrated by fluorescent technic in picture on left. Here with the great resolution of the electron microscope the virus particles that serve as the antigen can be seen in closely packed arrays.

antibodies against certain macromolecules of rabbit serum, and this antirabbit antibody would be conjugated with a fluorescent dye. The section containing virus would first be exposed to the antivirus antibody made in the rabbit, and as a result rabbit antibody to the virus would combine with virus wherever it was present in the section. All the unattached antibody would then be washed off the section. However, the rabbit antibody to the virus is not fluorescent; to make these sites fluoresce, the section must be exposed to the antirabbit antibody that was made in the sheep and then made fluorescent. The fluorescent antirabbit antibody from the sheep will then mark all the spots in the section where rabbit antibody to the virus has combined with virus, so that by this indirect method the fluorescent antibody marks the sites of virus, not because it is virus but because it has certain rabbit macromolecules attached to it; this is why it is called the indirect method. The sections are washed and mounted as in the direct method.

To locate sites of fluorescence under the microscope does not require special quartz or other types of objectives and eyepieces that transmit ultraviolet light, for the observer of fluorescence looks for visible light emitted from sites in the section, and, of course, this visible light is transmitted by ordinary objectives and eyepieces. (This is not true of the ultraviolet microscope.) Nevertheless, if these sites in the section are to be made fluorescent, they must be illuminated from below by light of a shorter wave length than that which they emit. Accordingly, the light source that is employed must be one that emits light in the ultraviolet range. Any light it emits in longer wave lengths must be filtered out; indeed, by means of special filters, light in various ranges of the shorter wave lengths can be selected. The wave lengths in the ultraviolet spectrum that are used in fluorescence microscopy are generally long enough to pass in appreciable amounts through an ordinary condenser and one of the darkfield type generally is employed so that fluorescent sites can be seen easily against a dark background (Fig. 30). Since light of relatively long wave lengths in the ultraviolet spectrum is employed, some of it, after passing through the nonfluorescing parts of the section, may continue on through the objectives and the eyepieces. Accordingly, to prevent injury to the eyes from this invisible light, filters which exclude ultraviolet rays but permit the passage of light in the visible spectrum, should be inserted in the eyepiece for inspecting sections. A filter which excludes ultraviolet but permits the passage of visible light must also be used in the eyepiece for photographing sections; otherwise, ultraviolet light passing through the nonfluorescing parts of the section may fog the photographic film. Figure 30 (*left*) is a photograph of fluorescing virus-containing cells in the hamster kidney, labeled by the indirect method. Figure 30 (*right*) is an electron micrograph of similar cells showing their great content of virus.

WAYS IN WHICH LIVING OR FRESH TISSUE CAN BE PREPARED FOR MICROSCOPIC STUDY OUTSIDE THE BODY

Tiny pieces of tissue removed from a living animal body can be mounted on slides in salt or other types of solution and examined with the microscope as they are or after being teased apart. For phase microscopy the preparations should be very thin. If the ordinary light microscope is used the study may be facilitated by the use of *supravital stains* (for example, Janus Green B). Supravital stains depend for their staining qualities on cells' being alive; that is, these stains do not color dead cells effectively. However, supravital stains are generally toxic, and although cells must be alive to be stained properly by them they subsequently kill the cells that they stain.

The Differential Centrifugation of Tissue Components. The separation of the components of homogenized tissue by the use of the modern high-speed centrifuge has yielded a vast amount of useful information. Since this method has its greatest use in separating the different components of cells, a discussion of centrifugation will be left to the next chapter where it can be related to the structures within cells that can be separated (see pp. 89 and 100).

Tissue Culture. It is possible to remove bits of tissue from a living body and to cultivate the cells they contain in glass vessels containing suitable nutritive solutions called *media*. The study of cells in tissue culture, or, as it is often termed, *in vitro* (*vitrum* = glass), has yielded many interesting facts about cells. These facts can be explained more readily after we have considered cells; hence, a further discussion of the method of tissue culture will be postponed until cells have been considered (see p. 114).

METHODS FOR EXAMINING TISSUES IN THE LIVING BODY

It is possible to examine certain parts of an animal body under the microscope without separating the part from its blood supply. Perhaps the easiest tissue to examine in this way is the web of a frog's foot. This is sufficiently thin to allow light to pass through it. The mesentery of the frog can also be similarly studied while alive; it is pulled out through a small incision and spread over a slide on the stage of a microscope and covered to keep it from drying. Both these procedures nicely demonstrate the circulation of blood.

The Quartz-Rod Illuminator. Knisely has studied less accessible organs and structures by utilizing an ingenious method for conducting light to them by means of rods of fused quartz. These convey light even around corners, because the refractive index of quartz is such that all light is reflected within the rod; hence, light can be delivered to deeply situated organs which otherwise would be almost impossible to illuminate sufficiently well for microscopic examination. By the use of the quartz-rod illuminator, Knisely has made very impressive contributions toward elucidating the circulation of the blood through certain organs and toward what is known as the "sludging of blood." The method is also employed to great advantage in the transillumination of the eye.

Transparent Chambers. Very clear observations can be made through certain types of glass windows (or windows made of other transparent materials) that can be inserted by surgical procedures into some parts of the body. Sandison devised this method in 1924; he cut holes in rabbits' ears and, using the borders of these as window frames, he sewed in double windows that fitted the window frames closely. The two panes were separated from each other slightly by transparent spacers, and the space between them was filled with a suitable salt solution. From the living "window frame" cells and blood vessels grew into the space between the two panes of the double window, and by placing the rabbit ear on the stage of a microscope, with the window directly under the objective, he was able to observe the growth and the movement of the living cells that grew in between the two panes of the window. This work was begun and carried out under the direction of E. R. Clark who, with E. L. Clark, has since devised the further improvements and refinements of the method by which they have been able to perform their many illuminating studies, particularly on the smaller blood vessels of the body.

Micrurgy. The dissections that can be performed on fresh living tissue under a microscope by means of instruments held with the hands are limited, because it is not possible to make freehand movements of the delicacy required. However, movements of the greatest delicacy can be made because of the development of what is known as micromanipulative technic (micrurgy, which means "small work"). Mechanical devices have been constructed which are affixed to a microscope and allow the turn of a screw or some other easily controlled movement to act through reduction gears or similarly functioning mechanisms so that gross movements of the hand cause movements of only the most minute latitude in the instruments under the microscope. The instruments which can be used are of different sorts, but all are minute. With the use of such equipment, fine dissections can be accomplished, injections can be introduced with great accuracy, and many other actions can be performed which otherwise would be impossible.

REFERENCES

GENERAL

Engström, A., and Finean, J. B.: Biological Ultrastructure, New York, Acad. Press, 1958.
Glasser, O.: Medical Physics, vols. 1, 2 and 3, Chicago, Year Book Pub., 1944 and 1950.

ELECTRON MICROSCOPY—GENERAL

Bretschneider, L. H.: The electron microscopic investigation of tissue sections, Internat. Rev. Cytol. *1*:305, 1952.

Burton, E. F., and Kohl, W. H.: The Electron Microscope, ed. 2, New York, Reinhold, 1946.
Claude, A.: Fine Structure of Cells, Groningen, Noordhoff, 1955.
Fischer, R. B.: Applied Electron Microscopy, Bloomington, Indiana Univ. Press, 1953.
Hall, C. E.: Introduction to Electron Microscopy, (International Series in Pure and Applied Physics), ed. by G. P. Harnwell, New York, McGraw-Hill, 1953.
Oberling, C.: The structure of cytoplasm, Internat. Rev. Cytol. *8*:1, 1959.
Pease, D. C.: Histological Techniques for Electron Microscopy, New York, Acad. Press, 1960.
Wyckoff, R. W.: The electron microscope in biology, Nature, London *173*:419, 1954.

ELECTRON MICROSCOPY—SPECIAL

Bargmann, W., Peters, D., and Wolpers, C.: Biologischmedizinischer teil, IV Internat. Conference on E/M., II. Berlin, 1960.
Barrnett, R. J., and Palade, G. E.: Applications of histochemistry to electron microscopy, J. Histochem. Cytochem. *6*:1, 1958.
Dalton, A. J.: A chrome-osmium fixative for electron microscopy, Anat. Rec. *121*:281, 1955.
Farquhar, M. L.: Preparation of ultra-thin tissue sections for electron microscopy, Lab. Invest. *5*:317, 1956.
Fernández-Morán, H.: A diamond knife for ultra-thin sectioning, Exper. Cell Res. *5*:255, 1953.
Latta, H., and Hartmann, F. J.: Use of glass edge in thin sectioning for electron microscopy, Proc. Soc. Exper. Biol. & Med. *74*:436, 1950.
Möllenstedt, G., Niehrs, H., and Ruska, E.: Physikalisch-technischer teil, IV Internat. Conference on E/M., I. Berlin, 1960.
Palade, G. E.: A study of fixation for electron microscopy, J. Exper. Med. *95*:285, 1952.
Porter, K. R., and Blum, J.: A study in microtomy for electron microscopy, Anat. Rec. *117*: 685, 1953.
Rhodin, J.: Correlation of Ultrastructural Organisation and Function in Normal and Experimentally Changed Proximal Convoluted Tubule Cells of the Mouse Kidney, Karolinska Institutet, Stockholm, Aktiebolaget Godvil, 1954.
Sjöstrand, F. S.: A new microtome for ultra-thin sectioning for high resolution electron microscopy, Experientia *9*:114, 1953.
Watson, M. L.: The use of carbon films to support tissue sections for electron microscopy, J. Biophys. & Biochem. Cytol. *1*:183, 1955.

HISTOCHEMISTRY AND CYTOCHEMISTRY

Bensley, S. H.: The scope and limitations of histochemistry, Am. J. Med. Technol. #1, *25*:15, 1959.

Caspersson, T. O.: Cell Growth and Cell Function; A Cytochemical Study, New York, Norton, 1950.

———: Quantitative cytochemical methods for the study of cell metabolism, Experientia *11*:45, 1955.

Casselman, W. G. B.: Histochemical Technique, New York, Wiley, 1959.

Danielli, J. F.: Cytochemistry, New York, Wiley, 1953.

Dempsey, E. W., and Wislocki, B. B.: Histochemical contributions to physiology, Physiol. Rev. *26*:1, 1946.

Gierlach, Z. S.: Fluorescence microscopy and photomicrography, M. Radiog. & Photog. *31*: 110, 1955.

Glegg, R. E., Clermont, Y., and Leblond, C. P.: The use of lead tetraacetate, benzidine, o-dianisidine and a "film test" in investigating the periodic-acid-Schiff technic, Stain Technol. *27*: 277, 1954.

Glick, D.: Techniques of Histo- and Cyto-Chemistry, New York, Interscience, 1949.

———: Use of microchemical methods for quantitative localization in histochemistry, J. Histochem. *5*:539, 1957.

Gomori, G.: Microscopic Histochemistry: Principles and Practice, Chicago, Univ. Chicago Press, 1952.

———: Pitfalls in histochemistry, Ann. New York Acad. Sc. *50*:968, 1949-50.

Hooghwinkel, G. J. M., and Smits, G.: The specificity of the periodic-acid-Schiff technique studied by a quantitative test-tube method, J. Histochem. *5*:120, 1957.

Lillie, R. D.: Histopathologic Technique and Practical Histochemistry, ed. 2, New York, Blakiston, 1954.

Lison, L.: Histochimie et cytochimie animales, ed. 2, Paris, Gauthier-Villars, 1953.

Mellors, R. C.: Analytical Cytology, New York, Blakiston, 1955.

Nachlas, M. M., Young, A. C., and Seligman, A. M.: Problems of enzymatic localization by chemical reactions applied to tissue sections, J. Histochem. *5*:565, 1957.

Novikoff, A. B., and Podber, E.: The contributions of differentiated centrifugation to the intracellular localization of enzymes, J. Histochem. *5*:552, 1957.

Oster, G., and Pollister, A. W.: Physical Techniques in Biological Research, vol. 1: Optical Techniques, New York, Acad. Press, 1955.

Pearse, A. G. E.: Histochemistry: Theoretical and Applied, London, Churchill, 1953.

(*See also* general references on Histologic Technic, Chapt. 1)

RADIOAUTOGRAPHY

Belanger, L. F., and Leblond, C. P.: A method for locating radioactive elements in tissues by covering histological sections with a photographic emulsion, Endocrinology, *39*:8, 1946.

Boyd, G. A.: Autoradiography in Biology and Medicine, New York, Acad. Press, 1955.

Gross, J., Bogoroch, R., Nadler, N. J., and Leblond, C. P.: The theory and methods of the radioautographic localization of radioelements in tissue, Am. J. Roentgenol. *65*:420, 1951.

Mazia, D., Plaut, W. S., and Ellis, G. W.: A method for the quantitative assessment of autoradiographs, Exper. Cell Res. *9*:305, 1955.

Messier, B., and Leblond, C. P.: Preparation of coated radioautographs by dipping sections in fluid emulsion, Proc. Soc. Exper. Biol. & Med. *96*:7, 1957.

MICRO-INCINERATION

Horning, E. S.: Micro-incineration and the inorganic constituents of cells *in* Cytology and Cell Physiology, Chap. 6, edited by Geoffrey Bourne, London, Oxford, 1942.

Policard, A.: Twenty years of microincineration; cytological results, J. Roy. Micro. Soc. *62*:25, 1942.

Policard, A., and Okkels, H.: Localizing inorganic substances in microscopic sections, Anat. Rec. *44*:349, 1930.

Scott, G. H.: Critical study and review of method of micro-incineration, Protoplasma *20*:133, 1933.

PHASE AND INTERFERENCE MICROSCOPY

Barer, R.: Phase contrast microscopy, Research *8*:341, 1955.

Bennett, A. H., Jupnik, H., Osterberg, H., and Richards, O. W.: Phase Microscopy: Principles and Applications, New York, Wiley, 1951.

Davies, H. G., Wilkins, M. H. F., Chayen, J., and Lacour, L. F.: The use of the interference microscope to determine dry mass in living cells and as a quantitative cytochemical method, Quart. J. Micr. Sc. *95*:271, 1954.

Linfoot, E. H.: Phase difference microscopy, Nature *155*:76, 1945.

Mellors, R. C.: Quantitative analysis of the cell by interference and ultra-violet microscopy, Texas Rep. Biol. & Med. *11*:693, 1953.

Zernike, F.: How I discovered phase contrast, Science *121*:345, 1955.

———: Phase contrast, a new method for the microscopic observation of transparent objects, Physica *9*:686, 1942.

FLUORESCENCE MICROSCOPY

Coons, A. H.: Fluorescent antibody methods *in* Danielli, J. F. (ed.): General Cytochemical Methods, pp. 399-422, New York, Acad. Press, 1958.

Loofbourow, J. R.: Fluorescence: Methods *in* Glasser, O. (ed.): Medical Physics, vol. 1, pp. 446-451, Chicago, Year Book Pub., 1944.

TRANSPARENT CHAMBERS AND OTHER TECHNICS FOR VIEWING LIVING CELLS IN VIVO

Algire, G. H., and Legallais, F. Y.: Recent developments in the transparent chamber technique as adapted to the mouse, J. Nat. Cancer Inst. *10*:225, 1949.

Bensley, S. H.: Microscopic studies of the living iris, Anat. Rec. *138*:39, 1960.

Bloch, E. H.: The bulbar conjunctiva of man as a site for the microscopic study of the circulation, Anat. Rec. *120*:349, 1954.

Clark, E. R.: The transparent chamber technique for the microscopic study of living blood vessels, Anat. Rec. *120*:241, 1954.

Clark, E. R., and Clark, E. L.: Changes in blood vascular endothelium in the living animal, Am. J. Anat. *57*:385, 1935.

Forbes, H. S.: The fused quartz rod technique for transilluminating living internal organs *in situ* for microscopic study, Anat. Rec. *120*:265, 1954.

———: Study of blood vessels on cortex of living mammalian brain—description of technique, Anat. Rec. *120*:309, 1954.

Knisely, M. H.: An improved fused quartz living tissue illuminator, Anat. Rec. *71*:503, 1938.

———: A method of illuminating living structures for microscopic study, Anat. Rec. *64*:499, 1936.

———: Microscopic observations on the circulatory systems of living transilluminated mammalian spleens, Proc. Soc. Exper. Biol. & Med. *32*:212, 1934.

———: Spleen studies, Anat. Rec. *65*:23, 131, 1936.

Leitz, B. R., and Fulton, G. P.: The use of the hamster cheek pouch for the study of vascular changes at the microscopic level, Anat. Rec. *120*:293, 1954.

Moore, R. L.: Adaptation of the transparent chamber technique to the ear of the dog, Anat. Rec. *64*:387, 1935-1936.

Sanders, A. G., Ebert, R. H., and Florey, H. W.: The mechanism of capillary contraction, Quart. J. Exper. Physiol. *30*:281, 1940.

Sandison, J. C.: A new method for the microscopic study of living growing tissues by the introduction of a transparent chamber in the rabbit's ear, Anat. Rec. *28*:281, 1924.

———: The transparent chamber of the rabbit's ear, Am. J. Anat. *41*:447, 1928.

Zweifach, B. W.: Direct observation of the mesenteric circulation in experimental animals, Anat. Rec. *120*:277, 1954.

SUPRAVITAL STAINING

Bensley, R. R.: Studies on the pancreas of the guinea pig, Am. J. Anat. *12*:297, 1911.

Cunningham, R. S., and Tompkins, E. H.: The supravital method of studying blood cells *in* Handbook of Hematology, vol. 1, sec. IX, edited by H. Downey, New York, Hoeber, 1938.

Hall, Byron E.: Evaluation of the supravital staining method *in* Handbook of Hematology, vol. 1, sec. XI, edited by H. Downey, New York, Hoeber, 1938.

MICRURGY

Chambers, Robert: New apparatus and methods for the dissection and injection of living cells, J. Roy. Micro. Soc. *42*:373, 1922.

———: Recent developments of the micromanipulative technique and its application, J. Roy. Micro. Soc. *60*:113, 1940.

Chambers, Robert, and Kopac, M. J.: Micrurgical technique for the study of cellular phenomena *in* Microscopical Technique, edited by C. E. McClung, New York, Hoeber, 1937.

Reyniers, James A. (ed.): Micrurgical and Germ Free Technique, Springfield, Ill., Thomas, 1943.

———: Studies in micrurgical technique, V and VI, Anat. Rec. *56*:295, 307, 1933.

PART TWO

Cells,
Intercellular Substances
and Fluids

Chapter 4

The Three Basic Components of the Human Body

The human body is composed of 3 main components:

1. *Cells:* these are individual living entities, minute in size and jellylike in consistency.

2. *Intercellular substances:* these are non-living substances that are made by certain cells and, as their name implies (*inter* = between), they often lie between cells. Some are soft, but many are firm.

3. *Fluids of several kinds:* two important ones, *blood* and *lymph,* are confined to vessels in which they circulate. Another important one, *tissue fluid,* bathes the cells of the body; this requires that it occupy any frank spaces that exist in intercellular substances and that it penetrate any permeable substances.

Intercellular substances are responsible for the body having form; hence, the human body is an edifice of intercellular substance in which billions of jellylike cells of many different kinds and families live from short to long periods as residents, exchanging their products with one another, chiefly by means of the fluids of the body and over distances by the great fluid transportation system which is provided by blood circulating through vessels in almost all parts of the body.

Advice to the Student. The study of histology is simplified enormously by the fact that there are only 3 basic components of tissue. It is true that there are different kinds of cells, and that cells present different appearances under different conditions. Moreover, there are several different kinds of inter-cellular substances, as well as different kinds of fluids. Nevertheless, it is a simple matter to learn to distinguish between these 3 categories of materials under the microscope. The wise student will remember this and later, whenever he sees something that he does not readily recognize, will ask himself, "Am I looking at cells, intercellular substances or a congealed fluid or a space which was occupied by fluid which completely or partly dissolved away in preparing the section?" Anything that is seen in normal tissue must be one of these 3 materials unless an artefact is present, as for example, a fold in a section (see Fig. 18).

Since the first step in histology is to learn well the appearances presented by these 3 categories of materials under the microscope, the next several chapters of this book will deal with these 3 basic components of tissue.

CELLS

Some General Features. Cells are the smallest units of living matter that can lead an independent existence and reproduce their own kind; many of the simplest animals consist of only one cell. Amebae, for example, are single-cell animals. Bacteria are very small single-cell animals, and a single one dropped onto a plate of nutritive media can soon become a whole colony. Viruses, which are smaller still, cannot lead an independent existence; for example, they cannot grow when they are placed on or in nutritive media; they can multiply only when they are inside living cells of some kind. Hence, viruses are not cells; they do not have the power of life themselves. They take advantage of and are reproduced with the help of the chemical processes on which depend the life of the cells that they parasitize.

The human body develops from a single cell, the fertilized ovum. As a result of continued cell division, this single cell eventually gives rise to the billions of cells that live in the adult body. These cells, of course, are not all the same, because the human body is composed of many different families or types of cells that are specialized to do different kinds of work. The cells of some families are round, those of others elongated, and so on; in general, the shape of a cell is adapted to the kind of work that it has to do. Most body cells measure from around 10 to 25 μ in diameter.

Before dealing with the appearances presented by cells under the microscope, we must describe certain matters that will make our subsequent microscopic study of cells more meaningful.

SOME ESSENTIAL INFORMATION REGARDING THE COMPOSITION OF CELLS

Protoplasm. The material of which a cell is composed is called *protoplasm*. Huxley has defined protoplasm as the physical basis of life, and indeed it provides the physical medium in which life occurs. It should be understood clearly that life is not a static property of matter; it is a property that arises out of, and is dependent on, the continuous chemical activity that takes place in protoplasm. Therefore, a cell is something more than an inert biologic test tube in which the chemical processes of life proceed, because its substance—the protoplasm of which it consists—is a dynamic participant in these processes.

Composition of Protoplasm. Almost everyone knows that the 3 basic foodstuffs (in addition to water) that we need in our diet and from which we build our bodies are *protein* (nitrogenous substances of high molecular weight), *carbohydrates* and *fats*. In addition, certain salts and small amounts of special organic substances, for example, vitamins, are essential. Protoplasm consists of the same kinds of substances. Its most abundant component is water. Part of this is free but much of it is bound to certain of the other components of protoplasm, as will be explained later. Of the other constituents of protoplasm, proteins are the most abundant and important. Carbohydrates and lipids (the term lipid includes both fats and fatlike substances) also enter into the composition of protoplasm in a substantial way.

Although protein constitutes a much greater percentage of protoplasm than carbohydrates or lipids, it is not necessary for a person to eat proteins in the same proportion as that in which they are present in cells. The reason for this is that carbohydrates and fats can be used for fuel to provide energy and, if this is done, dietary proteins are not required for fuel but only for the synthesis of such new protoplasm as is required to maintain the substance of cells and as is formed in growth processes; for this purpose good proteins are absolutely necessary.

The Colloidal State of Protoplasm. Both the living protoplasm of cells and the nonliving intercellular substances to be considered in the next chapter are examples of materials that exist in the colloidal state. Students not familiar with colloids should read the following section.

A discussion of colloids would be as apt in a cook book as it is in a histology text because thickening a gravy or making a cream sauce, a cream soup, oil mayonnaise or a gelatin desert all involve the preparation of a colloidal solution and all can be done better or more consistently by someone who knows something about the colloidal state. Accordingly, this section may enable the reader to gain prestige in the kitchen as well as in the laboratory.

Many years ago it was observed that watery solutions of crystalline materials, such as sodium chloride, would readily diffuse through a membrane such as parchment, but that similar solutions of noncrystalline materials, such as glue, would not. This led at first to the erroneous conclusion that all substances could be classified as *crystalloids* or *colloids* (*kolla*-glue) by testing them in this fashion. Later it was found that there were many substances which, if they were dissolved in one medium, would yield a crystalloid solution, but in another medium, a colloidal solution.

The basic feature of a colloidal solution is that the particles of the substance that are in solution are not smaller than 5 millimicrons in diameter or larger than 200 millimicrons. It is obvious that the particles in such a solution could not pass through a membrane that had pores of less than 5 millimicrons in diameter.

It might be thought that particles in this size range might be inclined to settle out of the solution and gather at the bottom. Therefore, we shall discuss briefly why colloidal particles stay in solution. First, we shall consider a colloidal solution of a metal, for example, gold.

Gold can be prepared in particles small

enough to stay in solution. The reason for this is that they all bear the same surface charges and so repel each other and do not cluster together to form a precipitate. It is obvious that if the particles were large enough, the force of gravity would exceed the force of their surface charges and they would sink and aggregate. But, with small enough particles, the surface charges can keep the particles apart and in solution.

In discussing colloidal solutions, the material that is dissolved is said to constitute the *dispersed phase* of the colloidal system, and the substance (generally fluid) in which the material is dissolved, the *dispersion medium* of the system. Two other terms are also commonly employed with regard to *colloidal solutions—lyophobic* and *lyophilic*. The former (phobic) indicates that the particles *hate* the state of solution and are prone to settle, while the second (philic) means that the particles *like* the state of solution and so are prone to remain in that state.

Gold provides an example of a lyophobic colloidal solution, one that is difficult to maintain. For example, if any electrolyte gains entrance to the solution it will tend to neutralize the surface charges on the particles so that they no longer repel one another; hence, they clump and settle.

Lyophilic Colloids. These solutions are not precipitated so easily. Examples include the white of an egg or any of the colloids of the cells of the body. Their particles (generally protein) are large molecules or aggregates of molecules, and each particle has a peripheral layer which is hydrated with the dispersion medium. In order to precipitate these particles some agent or agents must be used which will both neutralize the surface charges of the particles and dehydrate them. This is what is done when a saturated solution of ammonium sulfate is used to "salt out" proteins in the biochemistry laboratory. Or colloidal solutions of proteins may be precipitated by a combination of alcohol and weaker electrolytes; the alcohol dehydrates the particles, and the electrolytes neutralize their surface charges. The fact that there are two factors operating to keep the particles in solution makes lyophilic colloidal solutions much more stable than solutions of lyophobic ones.

Lyophilic colloids may be used to help keep lyophobic colloids in solution; in this role they are termed *protective colloids*. Their value in this field is easily apparent to anyone who tries to make mayonnaise which is essentially a lyophobic colloidal solution of small oil droplets in water (vinegar). The easiest way to make such a solution is to start with an egg, providing a protective lyophilic colloid which coats each oil droplet as it forms. While this protective colloid is being beaten, oil can be added until a thick colloidal solution is obtained. Then vinegar can be mixed with this without causing a disaster.

It should be emphasized that the protein content of protoplasm is responsible for its colloidal state. Protoplasm is termed not only a *lyophilic solution* but also a *hydrophilic colloidal solution,* because the dispersion medium of it is water.

As has been noted already, the particles of colloidal solutions are too large to pass through the pores of certain types of membranes. The fact that colloids exert some degree of osmotic pressure and yet are held behind membranes in the body is of the greatest biologic importance, as we shall see in later chapters.

Fluid solutions of colloids are described as *sols.* Characteristically, these are *viscous* to a variable degree. A solution of gelatin in warm water is an example of a sol. However, if a gelatin sol is placed in the refrigerator it undergoes a change; it is said to "set." In this semifirm state it is called a *gel.* Many sols can undergo sol-gel transformations. If the set gelatin is warmed once more it becomes a sol; it is then said to have undergone a gel-sol transformation. Obviously, in this instance temperature is the factor that controls the *state* of the solution, as to whether it is a sol or a gel. Many different factors, such as pH and the presence or the absence of certain electrolytes, operate in the body to bring about sol-gel transformation and the reverse in protoplasm. Sol-gel transformations may account for the movements exhibited by some cells because the attainment of the gel state is associated with a change in the molecular pattern of the solution. In the sol state the particles (molecules or aggregates of molecules) are individual and not arranged into any structure. But when gels form, the molecules become arranged into a structure—generally into a 3-dimensional network that is often described as resembling a brush-heap. The dispersion medium of the gel is held in the interstices between the molecules and is described as the bound water of the gel. If solutions of certain dyes are placed on gels they are seen to diffuse fairly readily into its substance. The dispersion medium, present in the interstices of the molecular arrangement of many gels, permits these gels to function well as vehicles for diffusion phenomena. Therefore, nutritive substances can diffuse into cells, even though the parts of protoplasm are gelled.

The foregoing section, it is hoped, will give some intimation of the enormous importance of the fact that protoplasm (and intercellular substances) are colloidal solutions.

Metabolism. The term *metabolism* (*metabole* = change) refers to the sum total of the chemical reactions that proceed in cells and by which the nutrition of cells is effected. Metabolic processes are of 2 general sorts: (1) *catabolic,* which depend on the breakdown of substances taken into the cell and of protoplasm itself, and they generally produce energy (and waste products); and (2) *anabolic,* which utilize energy, and by which new substances, including new protoplasm, are produced.

The Role of Enzymes in Metabolism. Only in the past few decades has the enormous importance in metabolism of the biologic catalysts known as enzymes become apparent. Probably all enzymes are proteins. Many enzymes have been isolated in pure form and crystallized. More and more of the protein in cells is being found to have enzymatic activity. A vast number of enzymes is present in every cell. Each is extraordinarily specific and acts on its particular substrate by combining with it. The complex so formed becomes reactive and then enters into reactions which the substrate otherwise would not have entered into under the physical conditions existing in the cell. Enzymes bring about reactions in cells that would require drastic procedures to effect in test tubes; for example, many of the reactions, catalyzed in cells by enzymes, could only be effected without them by the use of great heat and strong chemicals.

From what has already been learned about protoplasm and enzymes it would seem that protoplasm is constituted, to a considerable degree, of enzymes. These bring about, step by step, the reactions included under the term metabolism. As enzymes are depleted in cells they must be replenished. Therefore, part of the anabolic activity in cells is concerned with the synthesis of enzymes. Interwoven with this activity is the enzyme-governed catabolism of the food substances that are brought to cells by the blood stream. The reactions they catalyze yield energy, and some of this energy is utilized for the resynthesis of the enzymes concerned.

Cell Death and Postmortem Degeneration. Enzyme reactions are generally sensitive to temperature, pH, electrolyte concentration and certain other factors. Of even greater importance is the fact that their replenishment is dependent on the continuance of metabolism in cells. If metabolism ceases many of the enzymes soon change. If cells are shut off from their sources of nutrition, or if some poison or some such substance prevents the working of some important enzyme system in them, the delicately balanced enzyme pattern of life changes, and death of the cell results. A new set of reactions then appears; these are concerned with the breakdown of the substance of the cell. The results of these reactions account for the appearance seen in sections that is termed *postmortem degeneration;* these appearances wil be described and illustrated (Fig. 57) later in this chapter. It is obvious that life cannot be restored in cells that have died because the proper physical (enzyme) basis for life is lost. However, life can be held in abeyance in some types of cells by the use of very low temperatures; the enzymes of at least some cells withstand this treatment. For example, if little bits of certain tissues are fast-frozen, stored in a deep freeze and then, after months, taken out again and planted in a tissue culture, often the cells of the tissue will grow.

THE CLASSIC PHYSIOLOGIC
PROPERTIES OF PROTOPLASM,
A KNOWLEDGE OF WHICH IS BASIC
TO THE STUDY OF HISTOLOGY

There is a time-honored list of physiologic properties of protoplasm that the student should learn well. Speaking generally, this is a list of the things that cells can do because the various things that cells can do *must* represent expressions of one or more of the physiologic properties of protoplasm. Since there is a specialization of labor among the cells of the body, some kinds of cells can do some things better than other kinds of cells. It follows, then, that in some kinds of cells one of the properties of protoplasm is brought to a higher state of development than it is in other kinds of cells. The bringing of any of the properties of protoplasm to a high state of development generally is reflected in the structure of a cell, so that cells specialized to express different properties of protoplasm to different extents (to do different kinds of work) have different appearances; as we shall see, this enables the histologist to tell them apart.

The physiologic properties of protoplasm are: (1) irritability, (2) conductivity, (3) contractility, (4) absorption and assimilation, (5) excretion and secretion, (6) respiration and (7) growth and reproduction.

Irritability is the basic property of protoplasm that enables it to react to stimuli. Irritability in itself is not a response. It is the prerequisite property that protoplasm has which is necessary if it is to be able to respond. However, the only way an observer can demonstrate that any cell is irritable is by detecting a response in the cell when it is stimulated. Accordingly, the only way this particular property of protoplasm can be demonstrated is by finding whether a cell can manifest one of the other properties of protoplasm, for example contractility. Irritability is appropriately discussed in more detail in Chapter 20, which deals with nervous tissue; for, although all living cells are irritable, it is in nerve cells that this property reaches its greatest development.

Conductivity refers to the ability of the protoplasm of a cell to transmit a "wave of excitation" from the point where a stimulus is received to more distant parts of the cell. That protoplasm has this property is demonstrated by the fact that responses can occur in a part of a cell other than that to which a stimulus is applied, or even in other cells that are in contact with the one stimulated. The degree to which different kinds of cells exhibit conductivity varies; like irritability, as we shall see, it is brought to its greatest state of development in nerve cells which, through

their long cytoplasmic extensions called *nerve fibers,* conduct impulses rapidly between cells in different parts of the body. Conductivity is also well developed in muscle cells.

Contractility refers to the ability of the protoplasm of a cell to alter in such a way that the cell, or part of the cell, becomes shortened in one direction. This property is highly developed in muscle cells. These, to make best use of this property, are long and narrow and, on stimulation, shorten in their long axes with great effect. The phenomenon of contraction is discussed at some length in Chapter 19.

Absorption, Pinocytosis, Phagocytosis and Assimilation. Absorption refers to the ability of cells to take certain dissolved substances into their protoplasm. Fluids, or substances dissolved in fluids, may directly diffuse through the cell membrane, or fluids may be taken up by a process known as *pinocytosis* (*pinein* = to drink); the latter process will be described later in this chapter.

Cells commonly exhibit discrimination in performing absorption. The capacity for absorption is highly developed in certain of the cells that line the intestine; the modifications of the cell membrane that account for this will be described in Chapter 11. Absorption in many instances depends on enzyme activity in the absorptive cells.

If cells take up particulate matter, the phenomenon is termed *phagocytosis,* and cells that manifest this ability are termed *phagocytes* (*phago* = I eat; *kytos* = cell). In a sense, phagocytosis is a variation of absorption and will be described in detail in connection with macrophages in Chapter 13.

Assimilation refers to the ability of the cell to effect the breakdown and the disappearance of material taken into it; generally, assimilation is effected by utilization of the material by the cell.

Excretion and Secretion. Excretion refers to the ability of a cell to extrude waste products (excreta) from within it. If the extruded material is not a waste product but, instead, a useful substance—for example, digestive juice, or a hormone—the extruded material is termed a secretion and the phenomenon itself is also called *secretion.* We shall see that the cells of glands manifest this property of protoplasm to a great degree.

Respiration refers to the process whereby

food substances and oxygen taken into cells interact to form carbon dioxide and water with energy being obtained from the process. Respiration involves a great many different steps that are catalyzed by enzymes, and it will be described in more detail when the mitochondria of the cytoplasm are discussed later in this chapter.

Growth and Reproduction. The term "growth" is used with different meanings for various purposes. With regard to protoplasm, growth refers to the phenomenon of protoplasm's becoming increased in amount. Since protoplasm is always undergoing catabolism, its growth requires that the rate of its synthesis be greater than the rate of its breakdown.

Although the amount of protoplasm can become increased in any part of the body by the cells of the part becoming larger, it is more usual for growth to occur by means of cells becoming more numerous while remaining about the same size. Cells cannot enlarge indefinitely; their size is limited by at least two important factors. (1) Since a cell both absorbs and excretes from its surface, it is important for it to have a high *surface area/total mass* ratio, and this objective is attained by small, rather than by large, objects. (2) The transfer of food and other substances into cells, and the passage of waste products out of cells, depend a great deal on diffusion gradients. If cells were larger than they are, the distance between the central part of one and its surface would be greater; therefore, there would have to be a greater concentration of usable substances at its surface and a greater concentration of waste products in its central part to provide a proper "head" for an effective rate of diffusion. Such concentrations at either site probably would not be compatible with life. Accordingly, most of the increase in protoplasm that occurs as a human body develops and grows is brought about by cells becoming more numerous; this requires that they undergo cell division, which will be described shortly.

SOME FEATURES OF BODY CELLS

There Are Different Kinds of Cells in the Body. The cells of the body, like the people of a country, are organized into an economic community in which there is a divison of labor. This phenomenon in the body is reflected in there being many different families of cells, with different families being specialized to perform different tasks. In general, the members of one family are similar, but they may not be identical because the members of any one family may not all be in the same stage of maturity. Furthermore, some cell-families are so large that they show some specialization within themselves so that their members are not precisely alike but develop along somewhat different sublines. But, fortunately, the members of any one family, whether it be large or small, are generally sufficiently different from the members of other cell-families to permit them to be told apart under the microscope.

Potentiality and Differentiation of Body Cells. For all these different families of cells to arise from a single cell—the fertilized ovum—requires that the fertilized ovum be endowed with great *potentiality*. This term is used with regard to cells to denote latent capacities *to form cells of many different kinds*. Since the fertilized ovum gives rise to all the different families of cells in the body, it is said to be a *toti-potent cell*. Also, it is said to be an *undifferentiated* cell because it has not yet expressed any of its latent capacities (potentialities) for forming other types of cells. When, because of continued cell division, the fertilized ovum has turned into a mass of cells, the cells in different parts of this mass begin to develop different family traits; in other words, the cells become different from both the original fertilized ovum and those of other families that are forming in other parts of the mass. The phenomenon of undifferentiated cells turning into cells of some special family that exhibits special features and abilities is termed *differentiation;* this will be discussed in detail later in this chapter.

Relation of Differentiation to Potentiality. When cells become differentiated into various families the cells of any one family thereafter lack the ability to produce all the different kinds of cells that the fertilized ovum could produce; hence, the differentiation of cells is associated with their losing some degree of potentiality. In general, undifferentiated cells have more potentiality than differentiated cells; in fact, fully differentiated cells have little potentiality. Moreover, the cells of any particular family are genetically different from those of other families and so, in general, they can produce by division only cells of their own particular family type.

General Arrangement of Families of Cells in the Body. Just as some families of people all live together, some cell families do also. On the other hand, some families of people become distributed throughout a whole country; likewise, some families of cells in the body have members distributed throughout most of its different parts. The former are, of course, easier for the beginner to study, so it may be helpful for the student to start his study of body cells by examining a section of some organ that is populated chiefly by one family of cells. The liver is a good example of such an organ, for most of its cells are of the same family type and they are not found elsewhere in the body. Therefore, to begin our study of cells we shall describe what can be seen when an H and E section of liver is inspected under the microscope.

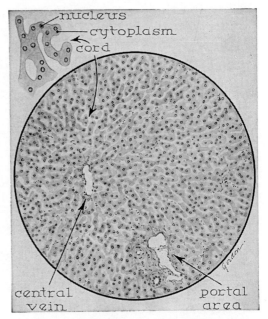

Fig. 31. Drawing of the field that is seen with the microscope when an H and E section of a human liver is examined with the low-pore (10 ×) objective with a 10 × eyepiece. (*Upper, left*) A small area of the field is reproduced at a somewhat greater magnification so that liver cords, nuclei and cytoplasm can be identified.

THE MICROSCOPIC STUDY OF CELLS IN SECTIONS

Before examining a section of liver with the low-power objective, the beginner should recall that every cell has 2 main parts and that these stain differently. The more central part of each cell is occupied by a round, oval or ovoid body that is basophilic and hence is colored blue-purple in an H and E section. This body is termed the nucleus (nut) of the cell (Fig. 31, *upper left*). The remainder of the cell, the part that surrounds the nucleus, is termed *cytoplasm,* and this generally is colored pink in an H and E section.

Since the beginner often has in his mind a picture of cells as discrete rounded bodies he is apt, when he first studies a section of tissue, to look for discrete rounded bodies. Since the nuclei of cells *do* appear as discrete rounded bodies (as in Fig. 32), therefore, the beginner is prone to think of them as whole cells, and the smaller rounded bodies that can be seen within them, which are the nucleoli, as their nuclei. In the study of sections of tissue most cells do not appear as discrete rounded bodies; indeed—as for example in sections of liver prepared by ordinary technics—the cell boundaries between individual cells may not be very distinct (Fig. 32, cell boundary not apparent here). Accordingly, the student must

remain on guard lest he fall into the common error of thinking that the nuclei that he sees so distinctly are *whole cells.*

With the low-power objective any field that is examined in a section of liver will reveal hundreds of small rounded blue-purple bodies that often seem somewhat lighter in their central parts than around their rims (Fig. 31). These tiny blue-purple bodies are the nuclei of the cells. On examining the section further with the low-power objective, it will be noticed that most nuclei seem to be embedded in cords of pink material (Fig. 31). This is the cytoplasm of the cells, and from a low-power inspection it would seem to be continuous from one cell to another.

At this point it may be helpful to recall that with the low-power objective and a 10× eyepiece the field seen is around 1,500 μ wide, and so, if liver cells are around 20 μ in diameter, it would take about 70 of them to extend

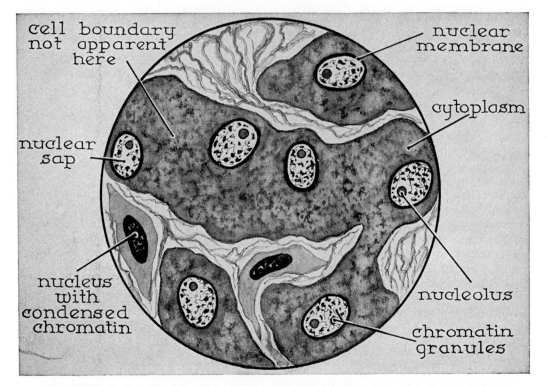

FIG. 32. Drawing of cords of liver cells from an H and E section as seen with the oil-immersion objective and a 15 × eyepiece. The circular area of the section that can be seen with this magnification is less than 100 μ wide, and it takes only about 4 large liver cells to bridge the area from side to side. Notice the open-face type of nuclei and the condensed chromatin type.

across the field (Fig. 31). If the high-power objective is used it would take about 20 cells to extend across the field, and with the oil-immersion it would take only about 7 cells, or with the oil-immersion objective and a 15× eyepiece, only about 4 or 5 cells, as is illustrated in Figure 32. We shall now describe some features that are to be seen under magnification as high as this; the student should check these points with his oil-immersion lens.

NUCLEI

With the oil-immersion objective the nuclei of cells are seen as rounded-to-ovoid blue-purple bodies. In a section of liver most of the nuclei that are seen are of what are termed the *open-face type* because some detail can be seen in their interiors (Fig. 32). Another type, less commonly seen, is smaller and almost evenly dark-staining; these are termed "nuclei with condensed chromatin" (Fig. 32), for reasons to be described presently. Before

describing the structure of open-face nuclei, we must explain what is meant by the term *interphase* nuclei.

INTERPHASE NUCLEI

The appearance of nuclei becomes greatly altered when a cell is in the process of dividing into 2 cells, and a few pages on this matter will be considered in detail. Here we shall limit ourselves to a description of nuclei in cells that are not in the process of division; such nuclei commonly are termed *interphase nuclei* because they are between 2 successive phases of division. Almost all the nuclei in a section of normal liver are of the interphase type. Most show the following features:

The Open-face Type of Interphase Nucleus.

1. Each open-face nucleus is limited by a reasonably well-defined dark-staining membrane, the *nuclear membrane* (Fig. 34).

2. Within each nucleus there may be one or

more rounded blue- or pink-staining bodies; this is, or these are, the largest and roundest of the bodies within the nucleus. These two facts distinguish this body, or these bodies, as a *nucleolus* (Fig. 34) or *nucleoli*.

3. Within each nucleus there are numerous bits of blue-staining material. These are *chromatin granules* (*chrome* = color; these granules are readily colored by basic stains). Chromatin granules (Fig. 34) are smaller than nucleoli and of various sizes and of irregular shapes. The larger ones sometimes are referred to as *flakes*.

4. The space in the nucleus not occupied by chromatin granules and nucleoli is said to be filled with a fluid material called *nuclear sap*. In stained sections this material is represented by very pale-staining or almost clear areas (Fig. 34).

More details about the interphase nucleus will be given later.

The Condensed Chromatin Type of Interphase Nucleus. As noted previously, some of the nuclei seen in a section of liver are smaller, more solid and darker than those of the open-face type; these are termed nuclei with con-

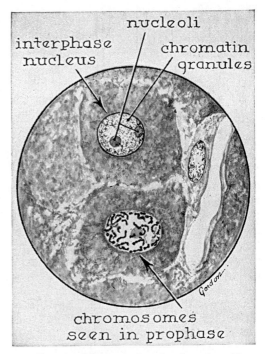

FIG. 33. Oil-immersion drawing of an H and E section of regenerating rat liver, illustrating the prophase of mitosis.

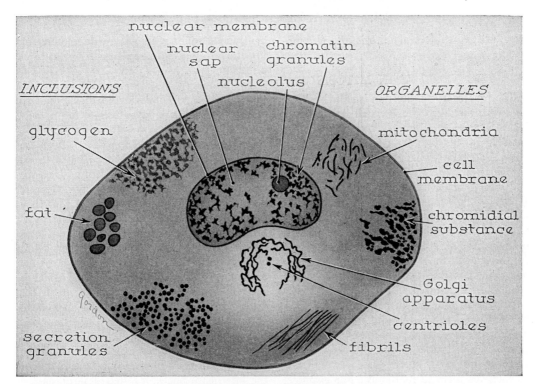

FIG. 34. Diagrammatic drawing of a composite cell designed to show in one cell all the various important components of nucleus and cytoplasm that can be demonstrated by different technics in various cells by light microscopy. Cytoplasmic inclusions are shown on the left and cytoplasmic organelles on the right.

densed chromatin (Fig. 32). Most of these are the nuclei of a different family of cells from those that have open-face nuclei. Such nuclei have the same components as interphase nuclei of the open-face type but, because all these components are packed so tightly together, they cannot be distinguished very readily, if at all, in ordinary sections.

Most of the nuclei in the body are round to ovoid in shape and are of the open-face or condensed chromatin type. Accordingly, the nuclei seen in a section of liver are representative of nuclei in general. However, as we shall see later, there are some families of cells in the body that are characterized by nuclei of different shapes from the common round to ovoid type.

We shall now consider in some detail the 4 components of the nucleus that have been listed: (1) the nuclear membrane, (2) the nucleolus, (3) the chromatin granules, and (4) the nuclear sap. However, it will be easier for the student if we do not follow this order but, instead, begin with the chromatin granules. The nature of these will become clear if we describe what happens to them when cells divide. Accordingly, we shall now introduce the subject of mitosis and chromosomes.

THE NUCLEUS IN MITOSIS

The process of cell division is called *mitosis* (*mitos* = thread; *osis* = a condition) because in the condition of mitosis threadlike bodies are seen in the nucleus instead of chromatin granules. These threadlike bodies are called *chromosomes* (*chroma* = color; *soma* = body), for they stain avidly with basic dyes (compare the two large nuclei in Fig. 33).

A nucleus in the process of mitosis is commonly referred to by histologists and pathologists as a *mitotic figure*. It is very important for the student to be able to recognize mitotic figures in stained sections, so their appearances should be learned well.

In sections taken from many of the organs and tissues of a healthy adult mitotic figures are almost never seen; in these organs and tissues the cells are very long-lived, and so there is no need, under ordinary circumstances, for them to reproduce. For example, mitosis is seldom seen in normal adult liver, brain or muscle. However, in some parts of the body mitotic figures are of a normal occur-

rence; in these parts the cells have a short life and must be continuously replaced by others dividing.

As might be expected, mitotic figures are very common in most of the organs and tissues of a growing embryo. They are also common in and about areas of tissue that have been damaged and are being repaired. To provide new tissue for repair cells must divide.

Material for studying mitosis in the classroom can be obtained easily by removing about two thirds of the liver of a rat. When this is done the cells in the remaining third proliferate by mitosis and restore the liver to almost full size in a few days. Sections obtained from the regenerating liver, from 2 to 3 days after the operation, reveal an abundance of mitotic figures which illustrate all stages of the process. Figure 33 was drawn from regenerating liver. Of course, sections of other tissues can also be used for studying mitosis—for example, intestinal epithelium (Fig. 407 B) or the lining of the uterus (Fig. 39).

Mitosis has 4 stages with not very meaningful names: the *prophase*, the *metaphase*, the *anaphase* and the *telophase*. The process is a continuous one with each stage merging imperceptibly into the next (Fig. 39 illustrates all the phases).

The Prophase. As has been already mentioned, when a cell begins to divide and so enters the *prophase* of mitosis, little discrete threadlike or rodlike bodies become visible in the nucleus (Fig. 33). These little bodies are called *chromosomes* (*chroma* = color, *soma* = body) because they stain deeply. When the chromosomes appear, chromatin granules are no longer seen as granules (Fig. 33) for they become incorporated into the chromosomes, as will now be explained.

Structure of Chromosomes. In the past it was believed that chromosomes only existed as such during mitosis and that when mitosis was completed and a cell again entered the interphase, the chromosomes broke up to form chromatin granules, and that when mitosis began again, the chromatin granules were reassembled into chromosomes. It is now known that chromosomes remain intact throughout the interphase but in a different form. In the interphase, chromosomes assume the form of long thin threads. However, along the course of each thread there are many sites where the

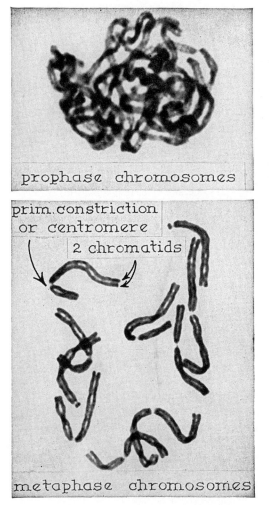

prophase chromosomes

prim. constriction
or centromere

2 chromatids

metaphase chromosomes

Fig. 35. Oil-immersion photomicrographs of squash preparations of chromosomes from root tips of Trillium. Feulgen stain. These illustrations show that both prophase and metaphase chromosomes each contain 2 chromatids. A careful inspection of the lower picture will enable the student to match the 10 chromosomes shown into 5 pairs. (Preparation by Dr. K. H. Rothfels)

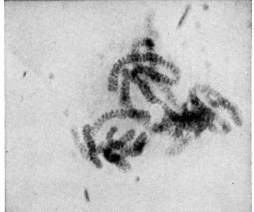

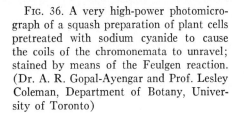

Fig. 36. A very high-power photomicrograph of a squash preparation of plant cells pretreated with sodium cyanide to cause the coils of the chromonemata to unravel; stained by means of the Feulgen reaction. (Dr. A. R. Gopal-Ayengar and Prof. Lesley Coleman, Department of Botany, University of Toronto)

thread is wound into a coil just as a segment of a wire can be wound into a coil spring. At these sites the material of the thread is packed densely enough to be visible in stained preparations. It is probably these tightly coiled segments along the threadlike chromosomes that appear as chromatin granules in the interphase nucleus, such as those illustrated in Figure 34. In sites where the delicate threads are not tightly coiled, they have not enough substance to be seen in stained sections with the ordinary light microscope.

Functions of Chromosomes. The genes of the cell are contained in the chromosomal threads, distributed along all, or most, of their lengths. The genes are the ultimate units that direct the nature and the activities of the cell. When a cell divides into 2 daughter cells, each of the daughter cells is an exact duplicate of the other and of the mother cell that divided. For the daughter cells to be identical requires that each must have exactly the same complement of genes in their chromosomes. Therefore, before cell division can occur, there must be a duplication of the genes so that there will be a set for each of the 2 daughter cells that form. Actually, the genes are duplicated in the interphase. Accordingly, the chromosomes of a cell that enters the prophase of mitosis have a double set of genes. However, the 2 sets of genes do not lie in the same thread, for by this time, the chromosome has split longitudinally into 2 threads called chromatids, each of which has one full set of genes (Figs. 35 and 41). The 2 chromatids of each chromosome remain close to each other and remain firmly attached to each other at one point, the centromere (Figs. 35 and 41) until certain further steps in mitosis occur, as will be described presently.

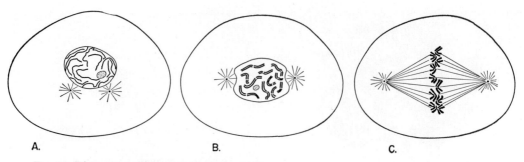

A.   B.   C.

FIG. 37. Diagrams to illustrate spindle formation.

(A) Represents an early prophase. The 2 centrioles have separated from one another, and astral rays extend out from each. The chromosomes are still somewhat elongated and at this stage it would be difficult to see that each consisted of 2 chromatids.

(B) Represents a late prophase. The 2 centrioles have now moved to the opposite ends of the nucleus. The chromosomes are shorter than before, and it can be seen that each consists of 2 chromatids.

(C) Represents a metaphase. The nuclear membrane has disappeared, and the rays from the centriole at each pole extend in to the mid-line of the cell where they are attached to the centromeres of the chromosomes. Since the rays diverge from each centriole toward the mid-line of the cell the appearance given is that of a spindle. The chromosomes have shortened further and the 2 chromatids of each will soon separate completely from one another.

In the late interphase, only some segments of the threadlike chromatids are wound into coils, and these, like the coiled segments of the original chromosomal thread, appear as chromatin granules. However, as the cell enters the prophase, the 2 long threadlike chromatids of each chromosome each become

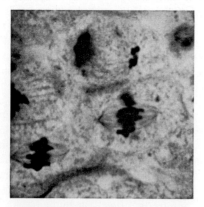

FIG. 38. Oil-immersion photomicrograph of cells in the first mitotic metaphase in the rat testis. Spindles appear to advantage because the tissue was fixed in Flemming's solution and stained with iron hematoxylin. (From Y. Clermont and C. P. Leblond)

wound into a tight coil along their whole course. This, of course, shortens the chromatids, and hence the chromosomes, so much so that the latter now appear as short rods, as in Figure 33. Nevertheless, in excellent preparations each rod can be seen to consist of 2 chromatids (Figs. 35 & 41). The tight coiling of the threads concentrates so much stainable substance in a small volume that the chromatids in their tightly wound state appear as deeply stained bodies.

It should be explained here that whereas we have described the chromatid as consisting of a thread, which indeed it is, it is a thread that is made up of 2 (or multiples of 2) still finer threads which are termed *chromonemata*. The coiling of the bundled chromonemata that make up a chromatid can be demonstrated beautifully by treating squash preparations of certain mitotic chromatids with reagents that cause the individual coils to separate enough so that they can be seen (Fig. 36).

The last part of the prophase is marked by the disintegration of both the nucleolus and the nuclear membrane (Fig. 39, B & C). The metaphase is characterized by the formation of what is termed a *spindle;* this arises as follows.

The Metaphase. Those cells of the body that are capable of division have in their cyto-

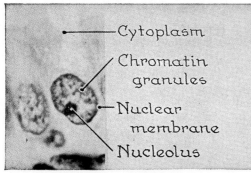

- Cytoplasm
- Chromatin granules
- Nuclear membrane
- Nucleolus

A. Resting Cell

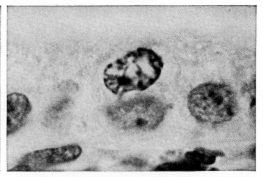

B. Prophase

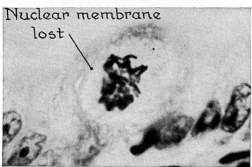

Nuclear membrane lost

C. Metaphase

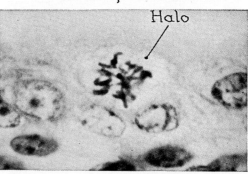

Halo

D. Metaphase-Anaphase

E. Anaphase

F. Telophase

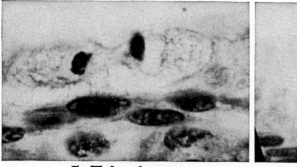

G. Telophase

H. Two new cells

FIG. 39. Oil-immersion photomicrographs taken from sections of the lining of the uterus of a rat that was injected 48 hours previously with a large dose of female sex hormone. The illustrations show the different stages of mitosis.

plasm a little body called the *centrosome* (central body) (see centrioles, Fig. 34). Since the nucleus usually occupies the central part of a cell, the centrosome, since it lies in the cytoplasm, cannot occupy the exact center of the cell. However, it is generally as close to it as is possible; for example, if the nucleus has an eccentric position and an indentation on its more central side, the centrosome generally lies in the indentation. When mitosis begins, the centrosome either contains or produces two smaller bodies called *centrioles* (Fig. 34), and during the prophase these begin to move away from each other, around the edge of the nucleus, toward the opposite poles of the cell (Fig. 37). As they begin their journey, they produce or induce the formation of delicate fibrils that extend from them in all directions like rays. This makes each centriole look like a shining star, and for this reason the delicate fibrils that extend from them are termed *astral* (*astron* = star) *rays* (Fig. 37). By the time the nuclear membrane has disappeared, the centrioles are at opposite poles of the cell, and, since the nuclear membrane no longer acts as an obstacle, the fibrils that extend from each centriole can now extend into the substance of the nucleus and, indeed, they become very prominent in this region. Since fibrils diverge from each centriole toward the mid-plane of the cell where they connect with the centromeres of the chromosomes, the appearance given by this arrangement is that of a *spindle* (Figs. 37 & 38). The fibrils of the spindle cause the chromosomes to gather in what is termed the *equatorial plate*. This is merely the plane that bisects the long axis of the cell (a line drawn between the two centrioles) at right angles (Figs. 37 & 38).

The Anaphase. The fibrils of the spindle extend from the 2 centrioles to the *centromeres* of the chromosomes. As can be seen in Figure 35, the centromere or primary constriction is the point along a chromosome where its 2 chromatids are closely attached. The centromere of each chromosome then divides, and the 2 halves of the centromere repel one another. It seems also that the spindle fibrils contract and that the centrioles move farther apart and, as a result of all of these effects, the 2 chromatids of each chromosome separate and move away from one another (Fig.

39, D & E), toward opposite ends of the cell. Once the chromatids become independent entities, thereafter they are considered as chromosomes in their own right. The stage of mitosis in which the chromatids of chromosomes separate and move toward opposite ends of the cell is termed the *anaphase,* and it is obvious that in this stage the cell comes to have 2 sets of identical chromosomes.

The Telophase. The next stage of mitosis is termed the *telophase*. In this, the final stage of mitosis, a nuclear membrane forms around each of the 2 groups of chromosomes that are now in the cell (Fig. 39, F). In each of the 2 nuclei that are formed, the chromosomes once again become drawn out into long threads with only some segments of them retaining a tightly coiled state to appear as chromatin granules. A nucleolus or nucleoli form in each; this happens in connection with special chromosomes that organize the formation of these bodies. The cell membrane becomes constricted between the 2 nuclei (Fig. 39 F, G & H), and a double-cell membrane appears in this area so that the original cell can divide, each of the 2 cells having a complete surrounding membrane.

Summary. Genes direct the nature and the functions of cells. Mitosis is a process which permits cells to perpetuate their own kind by ensuring that both of the daughter cells that result from the division of any given cell have identical sets of genes and that these are identical with the genes of the cell that divided.

Effect of Colchicine on Mitosis. An alkaloid that can be extracted from the corm or seed of a fairly common plant, *colchicum autumnale,* that flowers in the autumn, is called *colchicine* and has 2 very remarkable biologic properties. One of these properties is of interest to clinical medicine, for colchicine exerts a remarkably specific curative action on joints affected by gouty arthritis. Another is of particular interest to biologists, histologists, cytologists and geneticists because interphase cells under the influence of colchicine will enter the process of mitosis almost as usual, but the process will proceed no further than the metaphase, where it becomes arrested. Consequently, if colchicine is given to an animal over a certain period of time, all the cells that enter into mitosis during that time reach only the metaphase stage (Fig. 40). If sections are then prepared, a count of the mitotic figures arrested at metaphase will tell how many cells entered division in the tissue under study during the time the drug was acting. By this means it is possible to determine the rate at which cells divide in any given tissue or organ. This method has been used for many informative studies in Leblond's laboratory. Colchicine can be added to cultures of cells growing outside the body in glass receptacles to determine similarly how often cells in the culture divide.

Colchicine seems to effect mitosis in two ways. First, it delays the division of the centromeres of the chromosomes. Prior to the division of the centromere, the threadlike chromatids have been coiling and, as a consequence, shortening. The delay of the division of centromeres occasioned by colchicine gives more time for the chromatids to coil and shorten; hence, chromosomes, under the influence of colchicine, become shorter than usual in the metaphase. Secondly, colchicine seems to inhibit the formation of the spindle and the spindle fibers; therefore, after the centromeres of the chromosomes divide and the chromosomes separate into chromatids, the chromatids are not drawn toward opposite ends of the cell as they are normally but remain huddled in the region of the equatorial plate.

In sections, mitotic figures arrested in the metaphase by colchicine are cut in all or every plane; hence, they generally appear as irregular masses of huddled chromosomes (Fig. 40). These mitotic figures can be recognized readily and counted, even though the individual chromosomes in them are not distinct. In stained squash preparations made from cultured cells, or from dissociated cells of certain organs in which mitosis has been arrested by colchicine, much detail can be seen in the chromosomes, and studies made with this type of material have made it possible to make accurate counts and illuminating studies of the chromosomes of the body cells of many species, including man (Fig. 41).

Times Taken for Different Stages of Mitosis. The times ascribed to different phases of mitosis in different kinds of cells and in cells in

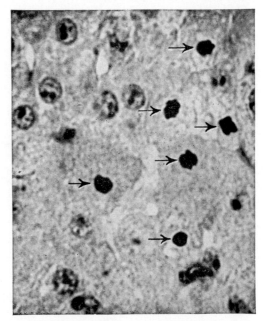

FIG. 40. High-power photomicrograph of an H and E section of a chick embryo obtained about 15 hours after a suitable dose of colchicine was administered (through the shell). At least 6 dividing cells have been arrested at the metaphase stage; these are indicated by arrows.

different kinds of environments by different investigators are somewhat different. Two problems in this work are determining (1) when the prophase begins, and (2) when the telophase ends. Consequently, different figures given by different investigators vary more in regard to the length of these phases than for the others. Catherine Stevens Hooper has recently made an extensive study of mitosis in the intestinal epithelium, using colchicine, and has come to the conclusion that the prophase takes about 70 minutes, the metaphase 20 minutes, the anaphase 2 minutes and the telophase 50 minutes. Those who have studied mitosis in rapidly growing cell cultures generally give a shorter time for the complete process.

Chromosome Numbers, Polyploidy and Aneuploidy. The germ cells of both men and women each contain 23 chromosomes. When a male germ cell fertilizes a female germ cell,

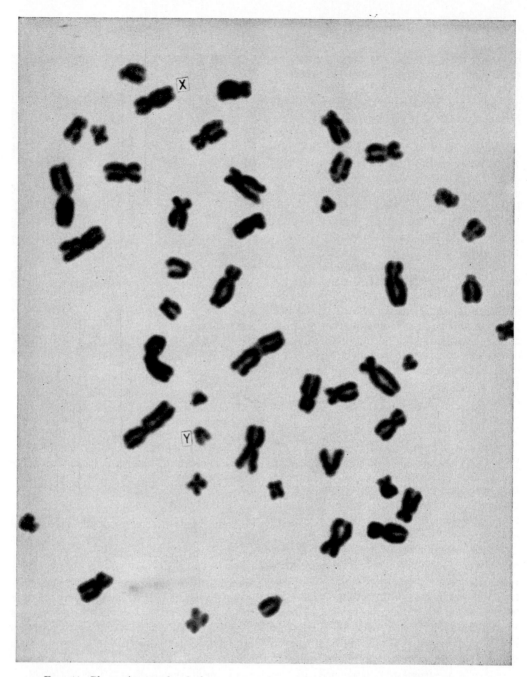

Fig. 41. Photomicrograph of chromosomes in a somatic cell from a human male. The chromosomes, in metaphase and contracted under the influence of colchicine, have been spread so that their number and structure could be studied. Forty-six chromosomes, the normal diploid number in a human somatic cell, can be easily counted. Each chromosome consists of 2 chromatids joined only at the centromere, which can be seen as a constricted region. If this cell had been allowed to proceed into anaphase, the chromatids would have separated at the divided centromere, and they would have gone to the opposite poles of the spindle, so that each daughter cell would have received 46 chromosomes. The spindle is not present in the picture because colchicine has prevented its formation, and the centromere is single because colchicine has delayed its division.

(*Continued on facing page*)

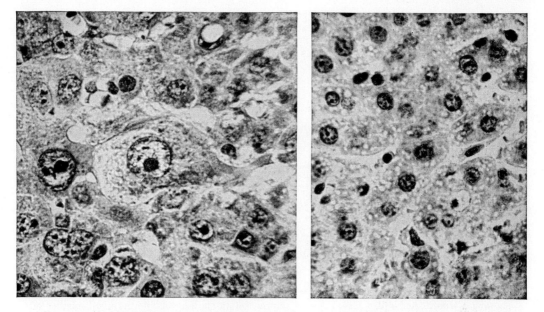

FIG. 42. (*Left*) A high-power photomicrograph of a section of regenerating liver obtained from a rat which previously had sustained liver injury. Notice the huge liver cells with large nuclei and hypertrophied dark-staining nucleoli; these result from polypoidy. (*Right*) A photomicrograph of normal rat liver at the same magnification.

the fertilized ovum obtained comes to have 46 chromosomes consisting of 23 pairs with one member of each pair derived from the father and the other from the mother. Thus, since it has 2 sets of chromosomes, it is said to have a *diploid* (*diplos* = double) number. By continued cell division, the fertilized ovum gives rise to the human body; therefore, the body cells, ordinarily called *somatic* (*soma* = body) cells, generally have the diploid number of chromosomes, which is 46 (Fig. 41). Other mammals have different numbers; for example, the mouse has 40, and the monkey 42. Since germ cells have only a single set of chromosomes (in man, 23) they are referred to as having a *haploid* (*haplos* = single) number.

Somatic cells, for reasons which will be explained presently, may sometimes have more or fewer chromosomes than the diploid number, and special terms are used to describe these altered numbers. The first of these that we shall consider is polyploidy. This word is derived from *polys* = many, *ploos* = fold and *eidos* = form. The key to its meaning is to understand that fold is used here with the meaning it has in 2-fold; in other words, it refers to multiplication. So, just as a diploid

FIG. 41. (*Continued*)

The chromosomes can be classified morphologically according to their length and the position of their centromeres. Twenty-two of them (autosomes) are then seen to have identical mates; one of each such pair came from the individual's father, the other from the mother. The 2 remaining chromosomes (the sex chromosomes) are different from each other in the male. The X is much longer than the Y and has its centromere near one of its ends; the Y has its centromere practically at the end. Both are labeled in the picture. If the cell had come from a female there would have been in addition to the 22 pairs of autosomes—one pair of identical X chromosomes instead of an X and a Y chromosome.

(Tjio, J. H., and Puck, T. T.: Proc. Nat. Acad. Sc. *44*:229)

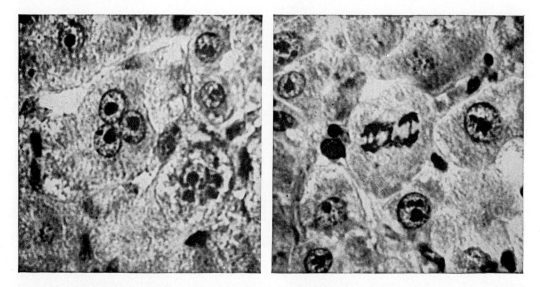

FIG. 43. (*Left*) High-power photomicrograph of an H and E section of regenerating rat liver, showing a trinucleated cell. (*Right*) A similar preparation showing double the usual number of anaphase chromosomes arranged in a common spindle which is just visible above them.

cell has 2-fold or 2 times the number of chromosomes of the haploid cell, a cell is said to manifest polyploidy if it has a *further multiple* of the chromosome number of haploid cells. For example, a *tetraploid* (*tetra* = 4) cell has 4 times the haploid number of chromosomes—this is twice the diploid number. A chromosome number in a somatic cell that is greater than the diploid number but not a multiple of it, or a chromosome number that is less than the diploid number, is said to have an *aneuploid* (*a* = not, *eu* = well, *ploos* = folded, *eidos* = form) number, that is *a not well* folded number or in other words a not-well-multiplied number.

Polyploidy is not uncommon in certain cell families under normal conditions; indeed, some cells manifest it regularly and others only occasionally, and such cells are characterized by large nuclei (Fig. 42, L). The first and probably the most common way that it occurs is for a cell to pass through the prophase and the metaphase of mitosis but then, after the chromosomes have each separated into their 2 chromatids, which thereupon become chromosomes, the 2 sets do not pull apart to opposite ends of the cell but remain in the region of the equatorial plate until a new nuclear membrane forms to enclose them all in the same nucleus.

Another way polyploidy can occur is by the chromosomes of a nucleus all splitting into chromatids without the nuclear membrane dissolving, and as a consequence the nucleus comes to contain a double number of chromosomes. Still another way is more indirect and takes place in 2 stages. First, mitosis occurs and results in 2 nuclei. But the cytoplasm does not divide and, as a result, a binucleated cell is formed. Then it may happen that both nuclei in the binucleate cell enter mitosis at the same time, and that when the nuclear membranes disintegrate the chromosomes of both cells become caught in the same spindle and pulled together again. Therefore, when division is complete there would be only 2 cells, but each would have a tetraploid content of chromosomes because the original nucleus has divided twice. An example of 2 sets of chromosomes caught in a single spindle is illustrated in Figure 43.

Aneuploidy. Under normal conditions the cell population in the various parts of the body is regulated very precisely with the death rate of cells being evenly matched by the birth rate. Hence, except for a falling off in old age, the cell population remains fairly constant in most parts of the body. In the disease known as cancer, some cell or group of cells become altered in some way so that their growth is not restrained by the mechanisms which ordinarily regulate cell growth in the body. Accordingly, the growth of such cells, which is generally rapid, is said to be *autonomous,* that is, controlled only by factors within themselves and not by environmental factors. The change in nature in these cells is a hereditable one; therefore, all their progeny also grow in an unrestrained way. Cancer, then, seems to be the result of a mutation occurring in some body cell or cells, with the mutant cell type manifesting the quality of unrestrained growth (see Fig. 75). It is obvious that unless foci of mutant cells of this type are removed by surgery or destroyed by radiation or some other means, the cancer cells would eventually overrun the body and destroy it. The chromosomes of cancer cells have been much studied recently with the newer technics that are now available, and it has been shown by Stich that the cells of many kinds of cancer have an aneuploid number of chromosomes.

Recently, it has been found that there are certain hitherto not understood disease conditions in which all the cells of the body exhibit aneuploidy. The most striking example is children who are born as mongoloid imbeciles. This is a congenital defect, given this unfortunate name because children born with this defect tend to have obliquely set eyes and certain other features that resemble superficially those of the Mongol race. It has been shown recently that the cells of mongoloid imbeciles all have one extra chromosome; this is not an extra sex chromosome as occurs in some other conditions to be described later, but a duplicate of one of the autosomes.

Amitosis and Unusual Nuclear Appearances. In lower animals there is evidence for cells' being able to divide by another method, namely, *amitosis.* In this method of division the nucleus seemingly undergoes little alteration except that a constriction develops in its mid-region, and this finally separates the nucleus into 2 parts. It is doubtful if this manner of cell division occurs to any extent in the higher animals. Appearances such as that illustrated in Figure 44 have often been regarded in the past as indicative of the operation of the amitotic process. Recently, however, Wilson and Leduc have provided an

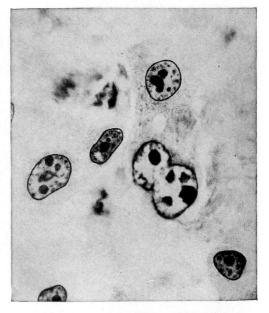

FIG. 44. An oil-immersion photomicrograph of a section of liver obtained from a rat whose liver had been injured and in which active regeneration was occurring. The nucleus that is featured could be interpreted as an example of amitosis but more probably it represents a failure of separation after mitosis.

alternative explanation for nuclei of this appearance, suggesting that they are formed because the spindle becomes suppressed in a mitotic division before the anaphase is completed and that the 2 daughter nuclei become fused as a result.

Effect of Radiation on Chromosomes and Mitosis. The biological effect of x- or gamma rays is exerted by means of the high energy photons of the rays which knock electrons out of some of the atoms of the cell. Atoms which lose an electron by this means are intensely reactive and instantaneously enter into some new chemical combination in their immediate environment. Of course, this alters the chemical composition of the material with which they react. A minor chemical change resulting from this cause in any part of an interphase cell except a gene is probably of no more than temporary significance, because the cell either has many duplicates of the altered component or, if it has none, it still has the proper gene

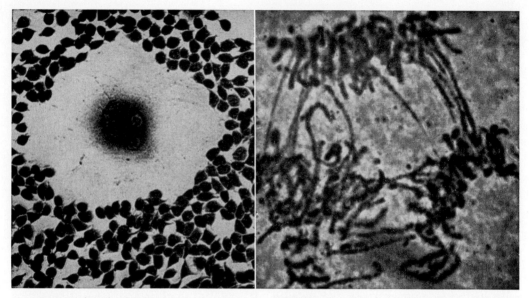

FIG. 45. (*Left*) Photomicrograph of stained preparation of a clone of L cells (clones and L cells are described later in this Chapter under "Cell Culture") growing in culture medium on the bottom of a glass receptacle. The cells were given 5,000 r of x-rays. This interferes with proper mitotic division of the cells, and one effect sometimes observed is that nuclei do not divide, although DNA continues to be duplicated, and chromatids continue to separate into chromosomes. As a result, huge nuclei with abnormally large numbers of chromosomes may form. Since the cytoplasm also increases in amount such cells become *giant cells*. One such cell occupies the center of the picture, and it is surrounded by L cells of normal size.

(*Right*) Oil-immersion photomicrograph of a squash preparation of an L cell in mitosis following 5,000 r of x-rays that was given to the culture in which this cell was growing. The radiation has interfered with the normal process of cell division in that (1) the spindle in this cell has 3 poles instead of 2; (2) many of the chromosomes are lagging and, as a result, they form *chromosomal bridges;* and (3) many are of an abnormal form.

(Till, J. E., and Whitmore, G. F.: Effects of x-rays on mammalian cells in tissue culture *in* Proc. 3rd Canadian Cancer Res. Conf., New York, Acad. Press)

or genes to direct the replacement of the injured cell component.

However, if atoms of or in genetic material are ionized, the results can be more serious, for, in the process by which genes are duplicated in the interphase, each gene serves as a model for each new gene that is synthesized. Accordingly, if the material of a few genes is altered, they will, when the genes are duplicated, model the formation of similarly altered genes. If the alteration in the genetic material as a whole is not too great, the cell may still be able to perpetuate its kind by mitosis, but all the descendants of this cell will lack not only the normal genes of the type that were altered but also the normal qualities imparted

to the cell by normal genes of this type. Moreover, altered genes may impart some new qualities to the cells. This is the way that radiation, in doses that are not lethal to a cell, may induce a cell mutation.

Interphase cells subjected to more severe radiation may (with the light microscope) seem to be unaffected as long as they remain in the interphase, but when the cell attempts to pass through a cycle of mitosis, it will become apparent that serious damage has been done to its mitotic apparatus. Indeed, the cell may not be able to complete a single division, but if it manages this, it will fail and die on attempting some subsequent one. This is the chief basis for using radiation in the treatment of cancer; it acts to prevent the cancer cells from continuing their mitotic cycles and hence their growth. The damage to the mitotic apparatus of the radiated cell—which becomes apparent when the cell attempts division—is manifested in several different ways. (1) The chromosomes may be seen to be altered in form, or broken-up or joined together in abnormal ways. (2) The spindle may show abnormalities; for example, it may have 3 poles instead of 2, with the result that chromosomes are drawn to 3 points instead of 2 (Fig. 45, *right*). (3) The chromosomes act as if they were sticky, and, in the anaphase, the chromatids do not pull apart from one another evenly. Some may lag and form bridges between the 2 groups of chromosomes (Fig. 45, *right*). (4) The chromosomes may divide without the nucleus dividing; this gives rise to large nuclei with more than the normal number of chromosomes (Fig. 45, *left*), or the nuclei may divide without the cytoplasm dividing. In both these latter instances, the cells that are affected become much larger than normal and are called *giant cells*.

As we shall describe later, the turnover of the cell population varies greatly from one part of the body to another. From the foregoing section it can be understood easily that if a whole animal body is radiated, the effects of the radiation will be much more prominent in those parts of the body where there is a great deal of mitosis than it is in those parts where there is little or no cell turnover. Since the rate of cell turnover is great in the blood-forming organs and in the lining of the intestinal tract, these 2 tissues are therefore said to be very *sensitive* to radiation. On the other hand, there is no turnover of nerve cells; hence, they are said to be relatively *insensitive* to radiation.

THE SEX CHROMATIN OF THE INTERPHASE NUCLEUS

The Sex Chromatin, Heteropycnosis and Heterochromatin. In 1949, Barr and Bertram made the surprising discovery that the interphase nuclei of the nerve cells of *female* cats contain a little stainable body (Fig. 288, *left*) that is not noticeable in the interphase nuclei of the nerve cells of *male* cats (Fig. 288, *right*). Barr and his associates quickly extended their studies to other species and to other kinds of

cells and showed that in many species, including man, it is possible to decide on the chromosomal sex of any individual from a microscopic examination of sections or smears prepared from somatic cells of that individual. The availability of a method for determining the chromosomal sex of people by this means has been of inestimable practical importance in medicine as will be explained both here and in Chapter 27. In order to explain the method and the basis on which it rests, we must first introduce some new terms.

Neither interphase nor mitotic chromosomes stain with the same intensities along their lengths, some parts being darker than others. Therefore, chromosomes are said to demonstrate *heteropycnosis* (*hetero* = one or the other of two, *pyknosis* = dense); that is, they demonstrate one or the other of two densities along their lengths. The parts that stain darkly are said to demonstrate positive heteropycnosis, and those that stain lightly, negative heteropycnosis. Furthermore, the sites along interphase chromosomes that demonstrate positive heteropycnosis are said to be *heterochromatic* (*hetero* = other, *chroma* = color); that is, they are colored in another way from the remainder of the chromosomes. It has been explained previously that the parts of the threadlike chromosomes that stain in interphase nuclei to give the appearance of chromatin granules are segments where the thread is more tightly coiled than it is along other parts of its course. Hence, in interphase nuclei, those parts of chromosomes that demonstrate positive heteropycnosis, and thus are heterochromatic, are the parts that appear as chromatin granules and are probably due to the chromosomal threads being more tightly coiled here than elsewhere. Moreover, there is some reason for thinking that heterochromatic parts of the chromosomes have somewhat different functions from the more drawn-out parts; they are probably not primarily concerned with genetic functions as are the more extended parts which are known to contain genes. Because of this the heterochromatic parts of chromosomes are sometimes said to consist of *heterochromatin* as if this were a different kind of chromatin from that in the less densely stained parts of the chromosomes.

Next, chromosomes are of 2 general types—

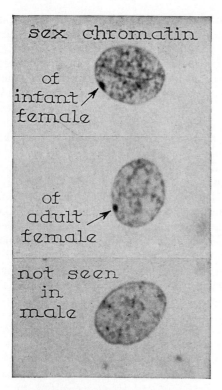

FIG. 46. Photomicrographs of epithelial cells from the oral mucosa stained with cresyl-echt violet (× 2,000). (Moore, K. L., and Barr, M. L.: Lancet 269:57)

the usual kind, called *autosomes,* and the *sex chromosomes.* The germ cells of women contain 22 autosomes and 1 sex chromosome, the latter being called an X chromosome. The germ cells of men contain 22 autosomes and 1 sex chromosome; this may be either an X or a Y chromosome. If a female germ cell is fertilized by a male germ cell that has an X chromosome, the fertilized ovum will have 22 autosomes and 1 X chromosome from each germ cell, making a total of 44 autosomes and 2 X chromosomes. Such a fertilized ovum will normally develop into a female body, the somatic cells of which will all have 44 autosomes and 2 X chromosomes. However, if a female germ cell is fertilized by a male germ cell which has a Y chromosome, the fertilized ovum and the somatic cells of the male body which it forms, will all have 44 autosomes, 1 X and 1 Y chromosome (Fig. 41). Accordingly, the somatic cells of females and males

differ in their chromosome complement in that females have 2 X chromosomes, while males have 1 X and 1 Y chromosome.

The little body that can be seen in the interphase nuclei of the cells of females (Fig. 46, *top*) and is not visible in the nuclei of the cells of males (Fig. 46, *bottom*) is called the sex chromatin. The sex chromosomes are probably paired and so are very close together in an interphase nucleus. The X chromosome is much larger than the Y chromosome (Fig. 41). Therefore, a body consisting of a pair of X chromosomes would be larger than a body consisting of an X and a Y chromosome. Since a good deal of an X chromosome is positively heteropycnotic (heterochromatic), it is conceivable that 2 X chromosomes, situated close together, could constitute a body that would be visible when stained, while a body consisting of 1 X and 1 Y chromosome, when stained, would be scarcely visible. This has been the general explanation for the sex chromatin's being visible in the somatic cells of females and not in males. However, recently this view has been questioned, for there is evidence suggesting that in the interphase nuclei of females, only 1 of the 2 X chromosomes is heterochromatic to any great extent and that it is this one alone that forms the body that can be seen. The X chromosome that is present in the somatic cells of males is not believed to be heterochromatic to any great degree; therefore, it cannot be seen. Furthermore, there seems to be some reason for thinking that if there are 2 X chromosomes, one may exercise some effect on the other to make it heterochromatic; whereas if there is only 1 X chromosome, as there is in male cells, the X chromosome by itself is not heterochromatic. In any event, the body known as the sex chromatin, seen in the interphase nuclei of somatic cells of females, is due somehow to these cells having 2 X chromosomes instead of an X and a Y chromosome.

How the Test Is Performed on Living Subjects. For the first few years after Barr's discovery, the test was commonly performed by excising a tiny piece of skin from a living subject (this is called taking a skin biopsy) and then cutting and staining sections of it (Fig. 47). More recently, Moore and Barr have shown that it is possible to perform the

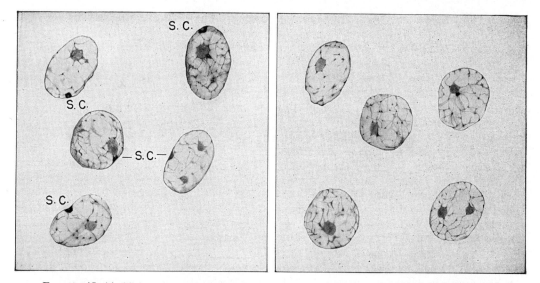

Fig. 47. (*Left*) Oil-immersion drawing of nuclei in the stratum spinosum of the epidermis of a female obtained by biopsy as they appear in a section stained with Harris' hematoxylin and eosin. The sex chromatin (s. c.) lies against the inner surface of the nuclear membrane as it does in most tissues. (*Right*) A preparation in all respects similar except that the epidermis was obtained from the skin of a male. There is no sex chromatin visible. (Preparations by Margaret A. Graham and Murray Barr)

test with even less trouble by simply making a smear of the cells that come off the inside of the cheek when it is rubbed with a flat rounded piece of wood. The cells are smeared onto a glass slide that has been coated with a thin layer of egg albumin and are fixed by immersing the slide in equal parts of 95 per cent ethyl alcohol and ether. The slides are then passed through graded alcohols to distilled water and stained with cresyl violet (Fig. 46).

Form and Disposition. The sex chromatin of the cells of females is seen to best advantage in open-face nuclei, particularly those that are relatively large and pale—the so-called *vesicular* (*vesicule* = a little bladder) type. It is seen easily in smears of cells obtained from the inside of the cheek (Fig. 46). It can also be seen relatively easily in thin well-stained sections of the epidermis of the skin (Fig. 47). It appears as a little dark mass, often planoconvex in form, that is pressed against the inner side of the nuclear membrane (Figs. 46 and 47). Generally, it has a diameter of about 1 μ so that it is clearly visible *if the plane of the section passes*

through it. But it should not be expected that it will be seen in every open-face female nucleus that is examined because the section may not cross the nucleus in the right plane. Even in smears, every female nucleus need not show sex chromatin, because it may be on the upper or the lower part of the flattened nucleus and not at its periphery where it shows up best.

The nuclei of male cells often show bits of chromatin close to the nuclear membrane, which in the occasional instance might be interpreted as sex chromatin; the probable explanation for this is that some chromatin flakes (not sex chromatin) accidentally have been shifted to a position close to the nuclear membrane.

Since the sex chromatin cannot be seen in every female nucleus, and since chromatin masses approximating the appearance and the position of sex chromatin can sometimes be seen in male nuclei, chromosomal sex cannot be determined by a hasty examination of a section or a smear but only by examining, say, 100 consecutive nuclei and then calculating the percentage of cells in which the appearance was noted. In general, what appears to be sex chromatin is often apparent in the nuclei of female cells and relatively seldom apparent in the nuclei of male cells. It is unfortunate that sex chromatin cannot be distinguished in the nuclei of the cells of rodents, because mice, rats and rabbits are the most commonly used experimental animals.

The sex chromatin is particularly clear and easy to see in the large vesicular nerve cells of females (Fig. 288, *left*). However, in the nerve cells of the cat, it occupies a somewhat different position from its place in most cells, being located, more often than not, beside the nucleolus (in the nerve cells of man it is more often beside the nuclear membrane). Since sex differences in somatic cells were first observed by Barr and Bertram in nerve cells of cats, the common position of the sex chromatin beside the nucleolus in these cells led to their first describing it as the *nucleolar satellite*, and this terminology was used in the first (1950) edition of this book.

Aneuploidy Involving the Sex Chromosomes. There are occasional disorders of development due to the number of sex chromosomes in somatic cells being more or less than usual. In some of these conditions the test for sex chromatin may not indicate the true chromosomal sex of the affected individual. Two examples will be given.

There is a condition, termed *Klinefelter's syndrome,* in which the somatic cells of the affected individual each contain 2 X and 1 Y chromosomes. Such an individual, because his cells each possess a Y chromosome, is a chromosomal male. However, the fact that his cells each contain 2 X chromosomes causes them to give a positive test for the sex chromatin; thus, by this test, he would seem to be a female. Such individuals, although they have the general physical form and genitalia of a male, are infertile and appear less masculine than normal males in certain respects.

Another condition, which in its extreme form is termed *Turner's syndrome,* results from the somatic cells of an individual having only 1 X chromosome. Since such individuals have no Y chromosomes, they are chromosomal females, but, since they do not have 2 X chromosomes in their somatic cells, their cells do not give a positive sex chromatin test. Hence, by this test they might be falsely considered to be males. Individuals afflicted with this condition are female in form, short in stature, sexually immature and infertile. Furthermore, they may have congenital defects in organs not related to the reproductive system as, for example, the heart.

CHEMISTRY AND HISTOCHEMISTRY OF CHROMATIN AND CHROMOSOMES

The chromatin granules and the nucleoli of the interphase nucleus and the chromosomes of the mitotic nucleus have a great affinity for basic dyes. The basophilia of the chromatin granules, the chromosomes and the nucleoli is due to their containing *nucleoproteins*. Nucleoproteins are conjugated proteins in which the prosthetic group is nucleic acid. On hydrolysis, the latter yields phosphoric acid. It is probably this latter component of nucleoproteins that is responsible for their basophilic properties.

Two Types of Nucleic Acid in Nuclei, DNA and RNA. The chief nucleic acid present in chromosomes (and hence in the chromatin granules of interphase nuclei) yields, on hydrolysis, a particular sugar, D-2-deoxyribose; thus, this type of nucleic acid is called deoxyribose nucleic acid. The term is commonly abbreviated to DNA.

A second nucleic acid; this is found in nucleoli and also in cytoplasm (as will be described when cytoplasm is considered) on hydrolysis yields the sugar D-ribose. This type of nucleic acid is called ribonucleic acid, commonly abbreviated to RNA or to RNP.

The Feulgen Reaction for DNA. At as distant a time as 1924, Feulgen and Rossenbeck described a method for staining nuclear material, particularly chromosomes. This method is now regarded as a histochemical test for DNA.

The Feulgen reaction is based on an old established test for aldehydes which is generally known as the Schiff reaction. This will be described first.

There is a dye, basic fuchsin, which is of a magenta (red-blue) color. If hydrochloric acid and sodium bisulfite are added to a suitable solution of it in the order named, sulfurous acid is liberated, bleaching the dye so that it becomes colorless. In this form it is termed *leuko* (*leukos* = white) basic fuchsin. Aldehydes restore the magenta color to the bleached dye, and this is how the Schiff reaction tests for them.

The Feulgen reaction is a test for DNA. To perform it, sections are subjected to a mild hydrolysis with first a warm and then a cold normal solution of hydrochloric acid. This procedure liberates aldehydes from the D-2-deoxyribose of the DNA. The mild hydrolysis employed does not liberate aldehyde from the sugar of RNA. Consequently, if slides are subjected to this mild hydrolysis with hydrochloric acid and then quickly washed and immersed in leuko basic fuchsin, the aldehydes liberated from the sugar of DNA react with the dye to restore its color. Since this occurs only where there is DNA, the DNA is colored magenta. Since both DNA and RNA are basophilic, the Feulgen reaction makes it possible to decide which basophilic material in a cell is DNA. Since DNA is confined to chromatin, the Feulgen reaction is an excellent specific stain for chromatin granules or chromosomes (see Figs. 35 and 36).

The nucleic acids strongly absorb ultraviolet light in the 260 millimicron band. Therefore, by photographing slides with ultraviolet light, the sites of nucleic acid in cells can be determined. However, this procedure does not permit the separate localization of DNA or RNA but only of nucleic acids in general. On the other hand, the method can be made specific for DNA or RNA by combining it with another procedure, as will now be described. The enzyme *deoxyribonuclease,* which can be extracted from certain tissues, specifically digests DNA; another, *ribonuclease,* specifically digests RNA. Accordingly, if sections are treated with deoxyribonuclease, the DNA is dissolved away. Then, if an ultraviolet photomicrograph is taken of the section and compared with one taken before the enzyme treatment, and if further but similar sections are correspondingly photographed before and after ribonuclease treatment, when all are compared, it will be shown that DNA is confined to the chromatin granules or chromosomes of the nucleus and that RNA is present in the nucleolus and in the cytoplasm. A little RNA is also present with much DNA in the chromosomes. Ultraviolet absorption methods for studying nucleic acid in cells have been very highly developed by Caspersson and his associates who have used these methods

to determine the amounts as well as the disposition of these 2 nucleic acids in cells.

The DNA content of cells can be determined by chemical means provided that the number of cells in the sample that is assayed is known. Furthermore, the DNA content of individual cells can be determined by microspectrophotometry. This method, though complex, depends essentially on staining sections by the Feulgen technic so that the DNA is specifically colored magenta, and then using a photoelectric cell to measure the amount of light of the magenta wave-length that is absorbed when light is passed through several different and representative interphase nuclei in the section. From the amount of light absorbed, the DNA concentration in the nucleus can be calculated.

By all these various methods it has been possible to determine the DNA content of cells of different types. In general, it has been found that the amount of DNA in normal diploid somatic cells is identical and double that of the haploid germ cells. Of course, there are some exceptions in that some cells of the body normally demonstrate polyploidy; here the amount of DNA is some multiple of the normal content. Aneuploidy, which often occurs in cancer cells, can also be detected by this means, as has been shown by Stich.

HOW INFORMATION IS STORED IN DNA

The nature and the activities of any cell are determined by its genetic constitution. Since the cells of animals of different species are different from one another, the genes of cells of animals of one species must be different from those of another. Therefore, since the cells in any given individual of any species are of many different types which reproduce only their own kind, the genetic constitutions of cells in the same individual must be different. Since the chemical basis for the genetic constitution of any cell is DNA, there must be some chemical explanation for the way that DNA can give different information in different kinds of cells (even though they have the same amount of DNA), and there must also be some way for the particular chemical constitution of DNA of any cell to be duplicated so that the progeny of the cell are identical with it and with each other.

The DNA molecule, which will be described in more detail presently, is a long linear one. Although it stores and conveys a vast amount of information, the molecule is assembled out of only 4 units or building blocks; these are nucleotides. Nucleotides consist of a nitrogenous base, a sugar and phosphoric acid. The 4 that enter into the composition of DNA differ only in their bases which are adenine, thymine, guanine and cytosine, respectively. The reason for DNA's being able to store and provide so many different kinds of information when it is assembed out of only 4 units is that the 4 nucleotides of DNA serve, as it were, as an alphabet of 4 letters which are arranged together in many different sequences along the long DNA molecule to spell out one word here, another word there, and still other words further along. And just as letters arranged into different words convey different information to us when we read them, the sequences in which the 4 nucleotides are arranged along the DNA molecule provides the various kinds of information which will determine the composition of the cells. The modern concept of the gene is that it is a segment of a DNA molecule containing a particular nucleotide sequence.

We shall presently discuss how information stored in DNA could affect such protein synthesis as occurs in a cell, but first we must describe how the particular nucleotide sequences in the DNA molecules of any given cell are duplicated in the interphase so that the genes of the 2 daughter cells that result from a subsequent mitosis will store exactly the same information as the DNA of the original cell. Much of the recent advance in knowledge in this field can be attributed to the attempts that have been made to visualize the form of the DNA molecule. The model of the DNA molecule proposed by Watson and Crick has met with very general acceptance and has served as a basis from which many recent advances have been made.

The Form and the Duplication of the DNA Molecule. According to Watson and Crick, the DNA molecule has the form of a double-stranded helix. In order to visualize how 2 strands can exist in the same helix, perhaps the following will help. Suppose we took 2 identical pieces of wire, each of which has one end that we shall call A and another which we shall call B. We then take the 2 pieces and hold them side by side but with the A end of one beside the B end of the other and vice versa. We could then, holding the 2 pieces of wire side by side but not tightly together, wind them, as if we were winding a single wire, into a loose spiral of the same diameter throughout its length. Then there would be 2 wires (strands) in the same helix, but the A end of one would be next to the B end of the other and vice versa. The 2 strands in the DNA molecule are arranged similarly to the 2 wires described above but, unlike the wires, the 2 strands in the DNA molecule are intimately connected to each other at many sites along their course; indeed, they are more or less fitted together in a way that will now be described in very general terms.

To explain how the 2 strands are fitted together it is necessary to note that the chemical configuration of adenine is such that it could form a hydrogen-bonded structure with thymine, while that of guanine could similarly bond cytosine. This fact is related to the way that the 2 strands in a DNA molecule are probably fitted together because adenine on one strand always fits, by means of a hydrogen bond, with thymine on the opposite strand. Likewise, guanine on one strand always fits with cytosine on the other. Therefore, the 2 strands of the DNA molecule are complementary replicas of one another. In order for mitosis to provide each future daughter cell with a complete and identical set of genes, there must, of course, be an exact duplication of all the DNA in the chromosomes; this occurs in the interphase of mitosis. The first step in the process is probably that of the 2 strands of DNA in each molecule unwinding and separating from each other. Following this, each strand of DNA serves as a template or model for a new strand that is synthesized along its course. In the new strand a thymine base would be synthesized wherever there was an adenine base on the original strand, and so on; as a result, each of the 2 new strands of the new DNA molecule has a nucleotide sequence that is identical, not with its model, but with the mate of its model. The synthesis results in two double-stranded molecules, with one strand of each coming from the original molecule, and the other strand being newly synthesized. The two double-stranded molecules are exact duplicates of one another; hence, each of the two chromatids that separate at the next anaphase can have identical DNA molecules.

The mechanisms by which the information stored in the DNA of the chromosomes of any cell directs the nature and the functions of the cell are under intensive investigation. In considering this matter it should be understood that the nature and the function of any cell depend on the particular array of proteins that enter into its composition and on the enzymatic functions that many of these perform. Molecules of protein are large, long and complex. They are composed of amino acids that are arranged in them in a linear fashion. Only about 20 amino acids enter into the composition of a mammalian protein molecule. The kind and the function of any protein molecule depend not only on the *number* and the *kind* of amino acids that are strung along its course (there may be as many as 100 amino acid molecules in one) but also on the *sequences* in which these amino acids are arranged. Here, then, as in the DNA molecule, the importance of sequence is very impressive, and this leads to the thought that the sequences in the DNA molecule must somehow control sequences in the protein molecules of the cell. However, it is not yet certain as to how this is accomplished for, as we shall see when we discuss nucleus and cytoplasm later in this chapter, the other nucleic acid, RNA, is profoundly involved in protein synthesis. An attractive theory would be that the nucleotide sequences in DNA determine the nucleotide sequences in RNA and that these in turn determine the particular proteins that will be synthesized in any cell. But, as will become apparent when RNA is discussed, all the various relationships between DNA, RNA and protein synthesis have not as yet been definitely established.

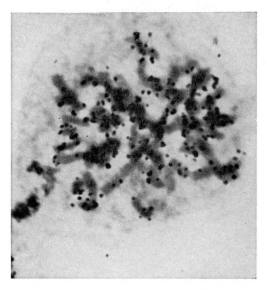

Fig. 48. Radioautograph of an air-dried preparation of an L cell from a culture that was given a 16-hour exposure to tritium-labeled thymidine. The labeled thymidine was taken up as the DNA was being duplicated, and enough time elapsed for the cell to enter mitosis; this cell was obtained when it was in the metaphase. The dark grains that are seen over the chromosomes are due to the short tracks of beta particles from the tritium causing ionization in the overlying photographic emulsion. (Stanners, C. P., and Till, J. E.: DNA synthesis in individual L-strain mouse cells, Biochim. et biophys. acta *37*:406)

THE STUDY OF DNA SYNTHESIS WITH TRITIUM-LABELED THYMIDINE

Thymidine is an essential building block of DNA and is not used in the synthesis of any other material in the body. Accordingly, if it is labeled with the radioactive isotope tritium, which is a soft beta emitter with a long half-life, and given to animals or plants or made available to cells growing in tissue culture, the labeled thymidine will be incorporated only into such new DNA as is synthesized during the time the labeled thymidine is available. If histologic preparations are then made and studied by the radioautographic method, dark "grains" will be seen in the emulsion over sites where labeled thymidine has been incorporated into new DNA. The ability to localize sites of DNA synthesis by this means and to follow labeled cells for various periods of time afterward has been of importance in histology in several ways which will now be described.

Determination of Duration of the 3 Stages in the Interphase. In a rapidly growing cell culture or in a part of the body in which the cell population is constantly being renewed,

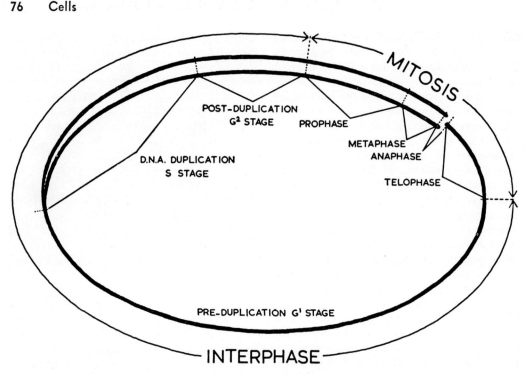

Fig. 49. Diagram to illustrate a complete cell cycle including the 4 stages of mitosis and the 3 stages of the interphase. The relative lengths of the 3 stages of interphase that are indicated on the diagram roughly represent the relative durations of these 3 stages under optimal growing conditions. The relative amounts of time taken by the different stages of mitosis are roughly in accord with the data that is available. However, in this diagram the duration of mitosis in relation to the duration of the interphase is indicated as being greater than it actually is, the reason for this liberty being taken with the diagram was that it permitted the stages of mitosis to be indicated and labeled.

The heavy dark line becomes split into two at the left side of the diagram to indicate the beginning of the DNA duplication stage. At the beginning of the postduplication stage the two previously diverging heavy lines become parallel, indicating that the cell at this time has a doubled DNA content. This persists until the anaphase when the chromatids separate to form nuclei in the telophase, each of which has a normal diploid DNA content.

individual cells exist at any given time in various stages of the cell cycle (refer to Fig. 49); that is, some are in some stage of mitosis, and some are in different stages of the interphase. If labeled thymidine is made available for only a very short time to all the cells in a culture or in some part of the body, only some of the cells take up any label—those cells that are in the particular stage of the interphase during which DNA is synthesized. This stage is termed the *DNA* duplication or the S (synthesis) stage of the interphase (Fig. 49).

The relative amount of label that any cell takes up can be estimated by counting the number of grains that appear over it, and if this procedure is used when labeled thymidine

is available for even the length of time taken for a full cell cycle, it will be found that there is a maximum amount of label that any cell will accumulate at a given concentration of labeled thymidine. A maximum label can be accumulated by a cell only if labeled thymidine is available for the full length of the DNA duplication stage. Hence, if labeled thymidine is made available to a heterogeneous population of cells and samples are taken regularly thereafter and studied, sooner or later a sample will be found to contain a few fully labeled cells. The period of time that elapses between the time that the label is made available and the time when a few fully labeled cells first appear in a sample is the time taken for the DNA duplication stage, for it can be assumed that the few cells that become fully labeled in this time were the few cells that were just beginning their synthesis as the labeled thymidine became available and that they just had time to finish the synthesis when the same was removed.

The method described above for estimating the length of the DNA duplication stage, while easy to understand, is difficult to use in practice because it involves counting accurately a great many grains over each labeled interphase nucleus. To overcome this technical difficulty the time of the DNA duplication period is generally calculated another way. The cells being studied—assumed to be in all different phases of the cell cycle—are exposed to a very short pulse of labeled thymidine. All those that are in the DNA duplication stage, whether they are near one or the other end of the stage, will all take up a small, identical amount of label during the very brief time it is available, and no cells other than those that are in the DNA duplication stage will take up any label. If samples are then taken regularly, label eventually will be seen over metaphase chromosomes (Fig. 48). The first cells in which label is seen over metaphase chromosomes will be those cells that were in the last part of the DNA duplication stage when they were labeled; these will be the first labeled cells to reach the metaphase of mitosis. Along with the first labeled metaphase cells that appear there will be some metaphase cells that are not labeled; these would be cells that had passed through the DNA duplication stage before label became available and had not yet passed through the metaphase into the anaphase. However, these cells proceed through mitosis, so that very shortly a time arrives when all of the metaphase cells that are seen will be labeled, for all the cells reaching metaphase at this time would have been in the DNA duplication stage when label was available. This state of affairs will continue for some time until the cells that were in the preduplication stage when the pulse of label was given begin to reach the metaphase, and then, of course, unlabeled metaphase cells will begin to appear. Very shortly thereafter, since the labeled metaphase cells proceed through the anaphase, all the metaphase cells that are seen will be unlabeled. Therefore, the period between the time when label is first seen over metaphase chromosomes, and the time when unlabeled metaphase cells are again seen, or what is easier to determine, the period between the time when 50 per cent of the metaphase cells first have label and the time when 50 per cent of the metaphase cells last have label, would be the period of time taken for cells to double their DNA.

Following the completion of the duplication stage, the cells enter what is termed the *postduplication* or *G2 stage* (Fig. 49); this lasts until mitosis begins.

The time for the postduplication stage can be estimated as follows.

If samples are taken at successive intervals after cells have been exposed briefly to labeled thymidine, the label, which soon after exposure is seen only over interphase nuclei, will, as has already been explained, begin to be seen over chromosomes in mitotic cells, as is shown in Figure 48. The period between the time when cells are labeled in the interphase and the time when label can first be demonstrated over *prophase* chromosomes gives an estimate of the time taken for the postduplication stage.

Once the time taken for the DNA duplication stage and the postduplication stage is known for any particular type of cell, the time taken for the preduplication stage can be calculated by subtraction provided that the time taken for a full cell cycle, and the time taken during mitosis, is known.

Stanners and Till have determined these various times for L cells growing in tissue culture and have found that the preduplication stage lasts about 9 to 11 hours, the duplication stage 6 to 7 hours, and the postduplication stage 3 to 4 hours (or less because it is very difficult to detect the beginning of prophase). Warburton, Leblond and Messier have used labeled thymidine to determine the length of time for various stages of the cell cycle in the esophagus and the small intestine of the rat and have found the preduplication stage to last 11 hours, the duplication stage 3 hours and the postduplication stage about 1 hour. The time taken for the various stages of mitosis in the intestinal epithelium is given on page 63.

Fate of Labeled DNA in Chromosomes. Taylor has shown that when cells are labeled in the interphase and subsequently pass through mitosis, label can be detected in *all* of the daughter chromosomes that separate at the anaphase. The reason for label's being present in *all* of the daughter chromosomes is to be found in the way that the DNA molecule is duplicated. Label would be found in only one half of the daughter chromosomes if the DNA molecule as a whole served as a model for a new DNA molecule for, under these circumstances, the molecules that served as models would have no label and those that were newly formed would be labeled. The old molecules would remain in their original chromatid, and the new ones would take up a position in the new one and, since chromatids become daughter chromosomes, only half of the daughter chromosomes would be labeled after the first mitosis under these conditions. But this is not the way the DNA molecule is doubled. As has been explained previously, when DNA is duplicated, the double-stranded DNA molecule unwinds and *each strand* serves as a model for a new strand. The 2 double-stranded molecules that are thus formed consist of one old unlabeled strand and one new labeled strand. Hence, all of the doubled number of molecules have label in one of their strands. Accordingly, there is nothing except labeled DNA molecules available for the new chromatids that will become daughter chromosomes.

When the DNA is next doubled in each of the 2 daughter cells (in the absence of label) and the cells enter and pass through mitosis, label, as Taylor has shown, will then be detected in only half of the daughter chromosomes that separate at the anaphase. The reason for this is that when the DNA molecules become doubled in number this time, and each strand of each again serves as a model for a new mate, one strand of the existing molecules is labeled and gains an unlabeled mate, while the other strand, which is unlabeled, also gains an unlabeled mate. Therefore, the first molecule retains a label, but the second has none. Next, it should be understood that the unlabeled molecules, after this second doubling, are the oldest; they are the ones that still retain the original strands of DNA that existed before label became available. True, each has a new strand, but each still retains one original strand. The labeled

molecules are composed entirely of new strands that have been synthesized since the time the label was temporarily made available. For reasons not understood at the present time, the oldest molecules, those with the original strands, all remain in the same chromatid, so that one chromatid has all the molecules with the original strands and the other chromatid has new molecules, one strand in each molecule being a first generation labeled strand, and the other a second generation unlabeled strand.

If the labeled cells continue to divide, only some cells have label, and such cells as still retain label after any division have less than cells had preceding that division. The reason for this is that although label still stays at full concentration in any chromatid (except when crossing over occurs) the labeled chromatids do not all pass to the same daughter cell at division; some labeled chromatids go to one daughter cell and others to the other. Hence, at every division the number of labeled chromatids in daughter cells is reduced on the average by half, and, as a result of this, label is so diluted that it becomes indistinguishable in cells that continue to divide.

If cells are labeled at a time in their lives when they are only going to divide once, or a very few times more, their label can be followed almost indefinitely. If the labeled cell differentiates, the label will, of course, be found subsequently in a different-appearing cell from that which was originally labeled; therefore, this method can be used to study the family trees of cells. For example, if osteoblasts, the cells that make bone, are labeled, label will later be found in osteocytes, the mature cells that are buried in bone, because osteoblasts differentiate into osteocytes. Smart and Leblond, using this technic, have recently obtained some very interesting and unexpected results with regard to the differentiation of the supporting cells of nervous tissue. These will be described in Chapter 20.

THE FINE STRUCTURE OF CHROMOSOMES AND CHROMATIN GRANULES

Sections used for light microscopy are thick enough to contain whole chromosomes, but those used for electron microscopy are not;

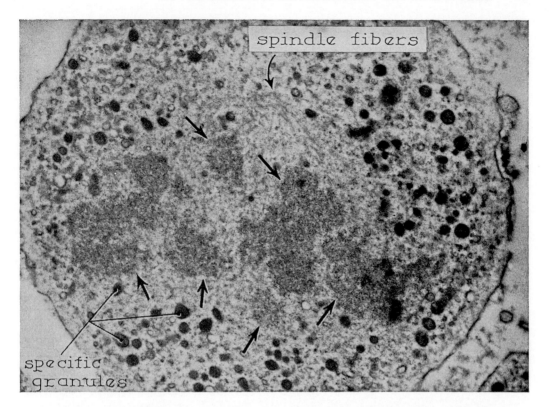

FIG. 50. Electron micrograph ($\times$ 17,500) of a section of a myelocyte in mitosis obtained from the bone marrow of a person with leukemia. Material fixed in tetroxide. (Preparation by A. F. Howatson)

hence, in thin sections of mitotic chromosomes all that can be seen are thin slices of chromosomes.

Thin sections of dividing cells studied with the electron microscope reveal no nuclear membrane. The region ordinarily occupied by the nucleus contains irregular granular dark patches (Fig. 50); there are several of these in the inset in Figure 51. Each patch probably represents a slice cut through a chromatid. Each patch has a relatively homogeneous appearance, and there is no suggestion that the chromatids of somatic cells of mammals have central cores that are different from their peripheral regions, or that they have a limiting membrane.

On superficial examination the dark patches seem to be composed of dark granules that measure between 5 and 20 millimicrons in width but vary in length and lie on a lighter background (Fig. 51). Any granule that demonstrates much length is generally curved. Granules measuring up to one micron in length can sometimes be observed. The picture seen in a single slice cut through a chromatid is what might be expected if the chromatid consisted of threads of material that had a diameter of 5 to 20 millimicrons and pursued curving courses along the chromatid and were separated from one another by a lighter amorphous material.

It has been difficult to determine whether the DNA in the chromosomes is represented by the dark threads that appear as granules or by the amorphous-appearing material that is disposed between the granules. Doubt has been expressed as to whether osmium tetroxide, the usual fixative used for preparing tissues for electron microscopy, is suitable for studying DNA; it has been suggested that it

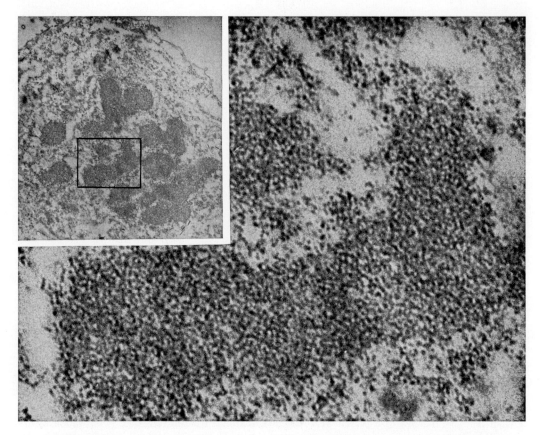

FIG. 51. Electron micrograph of section of a dividing L cell fixed in formalin. The magnification of the inset is 8,000, and that of the main picture 53,000 times. As seen in the latter, the sectioned chromatid has a granular appearance which is probably due to curving microfibrils 5 to 20 millimicrons in diameter, being cut generally in cross and oblique section but occasionally, for short distances, in longitudinal section. (Preparation by Dr. Samuel Dales)

may make the protein of the chromosomes electron-dense instead of the DNA. However, dark granular material can be seen in sections of material fixed in formalin (which does not act as an electron stain), as is shown in Figure 51, and the granules appear much the same as in osmium-fixed material (Fig. 50). Furthermore, Dales has shown that sections from material fixed in acetic-alcohol and then treated with deoxyribonuclease and examined under the electron microscope do not show the dark granules seen in Figures 50 and 51. Hence, there appears to be reason to believe that the dark granular material seen in sectioned chromatids represents cross, oblique and sometimes short longitudinal sections through threads that contain DNA. The DNA molecule is probably around 2 millimicrons in diameter. Therefore, the 5 to 20 millimicron threads cannot be single DNA molecules cut in section; the threads must contain either several molecules or a very considerable amount of some other material, probably protein. For details about the fine structure of chromosomes the student should consult the papers of Ris.

Spindle Fibers. Some fine delicate dark strands may be seen at the upper part of the nuclear material in Figure 50; these probably represent the way that spindle fibers appear in electron micrographs. The fine structure of spindle fibers has received considerable attention by Bernhard and by Porter, who describes at least some as being composed of paired filaments embedded in a fibrous matrix. The writings of both should be consulted for further information.

The Fine Structure of Chromatin Granules. The substance of an interphase nucleus examined under the electron microscope is granular, but, generally, the granules are not distributed evenly, for there are irregular areas in which they are more densely packed than elsewhere (Fig. 53). It will be recalled that in the interphase nucleus, the chromosomal threads are extended, and in this condition they would be long and forced to pursue devious courses for their full lengths to be accommodated in a nucleus. In addition, it will be recalled that there are segments of these threads in which tight coiling persists through the interphase, and that these tightly coiled segments appear as chromatin granules in the interphase nucleus. Therefore, it seems most probable that the irregular areas of *heavier* granulation seen with the electron microscope in the interphase nucleus represent sections cut through the coiled sections of chromosomes, and that the areas of lighter granulation represent sections cut through sites where the chromosomal threads are not tightly coiled. In both instances the granules that are seen are similar to the granules seen in sections cut through chromatids of the mitotic nucleus and, like them, probably represent cross, oblique and short longitudinal sections of DNA-containing fibrils with a diameter of from 5 to 20 millimicrons.

THE NUCLEOLUS

In the preceding portion of this chapter we have been dealing with the first of the 4 components of the nucleus that we listed, chromatin granules and chromosomes. We shall now consider the second component of the nucleus, the nucleolus.

Some General Features. The nuclei of most body cells contain one or more nucleoli (Figs. 33 and 34). Nucleoli are dense bodies, larger than chromatin granules. They either lie suspended in the nuclear sap or are seemingly adherent to the inner surface of the nuclear membrane. Nucleoli are generally rounded in shape; however, some, particularly large ones, may have a somewhat angular appearance.

Nucleoli may be acidophilic or basophilic. The reasons for their behaving two ways are not entirely clear but are probably related to their staining reactions being determined by both the nucleic acid and the protein that they contain. The nucleic acid is basophilic. On the other hand, the protein probably varies in the extent to which it is acid or basic protein. The nucleic acid, together with enough acid protein, would make a nucleolus basophilic, but enough basic protein would make the nucleolus acidophilic despite its nucleic acid content. The staining reaction of the protein also could be affected by the fixative that is used and the pH of the staining solutions.

Even when nucleoli are acidophilic, they may appear as basophilic bodies in sections. The reason for this is that in fixed tissue preparations the chromatin granules tend to adhere to the nucelolus to form a basophilic envelope around it. Since the diameter of a nucleolus is less than the thickness of a section, it is the basophilic envelope (when it exists) that is seen when a section is examined under the microscope.

Nucleoli are most easily seen in open-faced nuclei. They are particularly prominent in the large vesicular nuclei of nerve cells (Fig. 288) where the beginner may mistake them for complete nuclei. They are difficult to see in nuclei of the condensed chromatin type, but they can often be demonstrated in these if especially thin sections are prepared; for example, in extremely thin sections, nucleoli can be seen in the nuclei of lymphocytes.

Nucleoli are relatively heavy. Therefore, they can be forced against the nuclear membrane by centrifugation or may even be pushed out through the cell where they may be collected.

Behavior in Mitosis. Nucleoli persist through part of the prophase (Fig 33, *bottom*), but as this merges into the metaphase they melt away. They are not visible in either the metaphase or the anaphase, but in the telophase they begin to reappear and, by the time 2 daughter cells have formed, nucleoli can be seen in both. Following their disappearance in mitosis they re-form at special sites along the particular chromosome (or chomosomes) that possess the particular ability to organize their formation.

Internal Structure. In the usual preparation

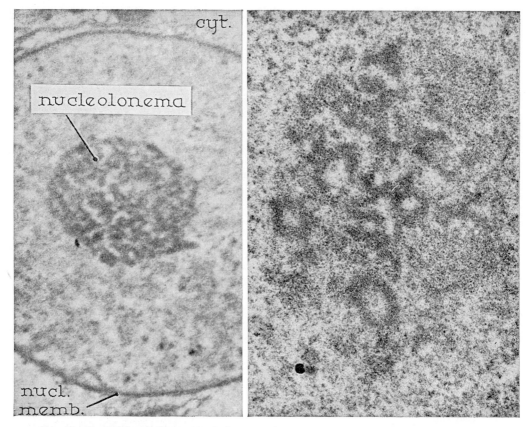

Fig. 52. (*Left*) Electron micrograph (× 16,000) of a section of embryonic liver showing part of a liver cell. Most of the field is occupied by nuclear material, and in the center a prominent nucleolus is present (Preparation by A. F. Howatson). (*Right*) Electron micrograph (× 22,000) of a section of a liver tumor of a rat. The greater part of the illustration is taken up by the nucleolus of a tumor cell. (Howatson, A. F., and Ham, A. W.: Cancer Res. *15*:62)

nucleoli appear to be homogeneous but, by using special technics and the light microscope, Estable and Sotelo showed that they possess a definite internal structure. Each nucleolus consists primarily of a thick filament, the *nucleolonema,* which, during the interphase, is commonly wound loosely into a ball (Fig. 52). The nucleolonema is embedded in an *amorphous component.*

Fine Structure. The E/M gives no evidence that the nucleolus is enclosed by a limiting membrane; hence, the nucleolus lies "bare" in the nucleus (Fig. 52, *left & right*). The E/M does reveal the nucleolonema of Estable and Sotela; however, this is seen in only some nucleoli (Fig. 52). It is composed of fine osmiophilic granules 10 to 20 millimicrons in diameter and of fine filaments 8 to 10 millimicrons in diameter; together these are assembled into a filamentous network that generally appears as a tortuous cord wound loosely into a ball. This cordlike structure is embedded in a less well-organized material; this is probably the amorphous component of the nucleolus described by Estable and Sotelo. Commonly, this amorphous part of the nucleolus completely masks the nucleolonema and, as a result, the nucleolus—even under the E/M—generally appears as a dense opaque body with no internal structural organization. The reason for the nucleolonema sometimes being apparent and sometimes being masked is not clear; this may be related to fixation or to some stage in the cell cycle, but this has not yet been establshed.

Histochemistry. When the Feulgen technic

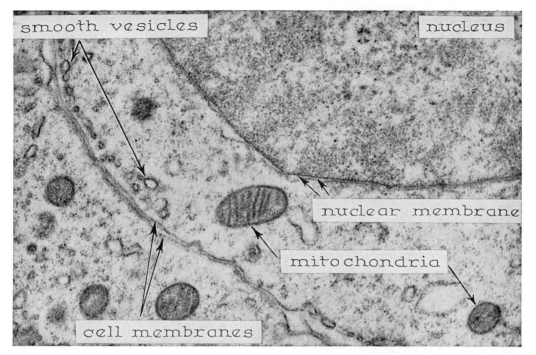

Fig. 53. Electron micrograph (× 30,000) of a section of a liver tumor of a rat showing parts of 2 cells. (Howatson, A. F., and Ham, A. W.: Cancer Res. *15*:62)

became available, it was observed that nucleoli were Feulgen-negative, thus indicating that their composition is different from that of chromatin. However, following this, Caspersson and his associates showed that nucleoli absorb ultraviolet light in the same band as chromatin; this indicated that nucleoli, like chromatin and chromosomes, contain nucleic acid. With the advent of the 2 enzymes, deoxyribonuclease and ribonuclease, it was demonstrated that the nucleic acid in the nucleolus was RNA.

There are now certain staining methods that take advantage of the difference in the staining properties of the 2 nucleic acids and are of use in distinguishing between RNA and DNA in tissue preparations. For example, the methyl-green pyronin method colors DNA green and RNA red. Another method that is helpful is staining tissue with acridine orange and then studying the tissue with the fluorescence microscope. When this is done, the RNA of the nucleolus emits red light, and the DNA of the chromosomes yellow or green light.

Function. For many years it was noticed that there was some association between the size of the nucleolus of a cell and the extent to which that cell was synthesizing protein, either for its own growth or for protein secretions that it was elaborating. Indeed, one of the few fairly consistent differences between the cells of malignant tumors (which are growing rapidly and so synthesizing much protein) and normal cells of the kind from which the tumor developed is that the nucleoli of the tumor cells are larger than those of the normal cells. Likewise, the nucleoli of secretory cells in the pancreas, which synthesize a great deal of protein for secretion, as will be described later, also are prominent.

As will be described in greater detail when cytoplasm is considered, the RNA of the cytoplasm is responsible for most of the protein synthesis that occurs in cells. It now appears that the RNA of the cytoplasm is not formed in the cytoplasm but in the nucleus. For example, it has been shown that if precursors of RNA are labeled, no label is taken up by enucleated cells. It has also been shown that if precursors of RNA are labeled and then made available to cells, radioactivity appears first in the nucleus and only later in the

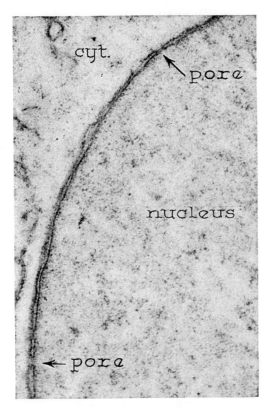

cyt.

pore

nucleus

← pore

FIG. 54. Electron micrograph (× 30,000) of a section of a liver tumor of a rat showing part of 1 cell. (Preparation by A. F. Howatson)

cytoplasm. Furthermore, Amano and Leblond, using labeled precursors of RNA, have provided evidence, by means of determining the specific activity of the RNA in different sites at different time periods, indicating that the RNA of the cytoplasm is best explained as originating in the nucleolus. Hence, the role of the nucleolus would seem to be that of being the site where at least most of the RNA that will subsequently pass to the cytoplasm, is formed.

The function of the RNA of the cytoplasm will be discussed further under "Cytoplasm."

THE NUCLEAR MEMBRANE

The E/M has revealed that the nuclear membrane is a double-layered structure (Figs. 53 and 54). The membrane as a whole is from 250 to 400 Å thick. Its inner layer commonly appears thicker than its outer. The space between the two layers is fairly con-

stant, but in some sites the outer layer bulges away from the inner to make the space wider (Figs. 53 and 54).

The outer nuclear membrane has a rough outer surface because of fine RNA granules adhering to its outer surface (Fig. 54). Moreover, the outer membrane is sometimes seen to be continuous with membranes similar to itself which extend off into the cytoplasm and will be described later, as will the RNA granules.

The nuclei of some kinds of cells are of irregular shape and exhibit depressions and invaginations of the nuclear membrane which are obvious with the light microscope. The E/M has shown that in some cells the nuclear membrane may extend deeply into the substance of the nucleus to form narrow crypts which may be in the form of tubes or crevices too small to be seen with the light microscope (Fig. 80). The cytoplasm extends into these to fill them. Hence, there may be tiny areas of cytoplasm disposed in what would seem with the light microscope to be the substance of the nucleus; if such an area became expanded, for example with fat, it might suggest on inspection with the light microscope that the fat was actually in the substance of the nucleus.

Nuclear Pores. There are little holes about 50 millimicrons wide in the nuclear membrane. These are called *pores*. Where the plane of section is approximately at right angles to the membrane, pores appear as gaps in the membrane (Fig. 54). At each side of the gap the inner and the outer nuclear membranes are seen to be continuous (Fig. 54). Pores are believed to provide a route for the passage of materials between nucleus and cytoplasm; for example, a route by which RNA formed in the nucleus can reach the cytoplasm.

Behavior on Mitosis. The nuclear membrane melts away in the prophase and is re-formed in the telophase (Fig. 39).

NUCLEAR SAP

So far, we have considered 3 of the 4 components of the nucleus, the chromatin granules and the chromosomes, the nucleolus and the nuclear membrane. We shall now consider briefly the fourth component of the nucleus, the nuclear sap.

Nuclear sap is the relatively clear fluid that

fills up all the spaces in the nucleus not occupied by the chromosomes and the nucleolus (Fig. 34). It provides a medium in which these formed structures are suspended and supported. It contains certain proteins, demonstrates a little enzymatic activity and is in the form of a colloidal solution. Whether or not it is a sol or a gel, or shifts from one state to the other at different phases of the cell cycle, has not been established. It seems reasonable to think that it must be a sol during those phases of the cell cycle when changes in the form and the distribution of the chromosomes occur. It has been reported that it contains no RNA, but this has been questioned. With both the light microscope and the E/M the sites it occupies exhibit no structure and appear as if such fluid as they contained had not been preserved and retained during the preparation of the section.

NUCLEAR CHANGES INDICATIVE OF CELL DEATH

It is obvious that all the cells in a section cut from fixed materials are dead. When histologists or pathologists speak of seeing "dead cells" in a section they do not refer to these but to cells which had died while the body in which they were contained was still alive.

Dead cells are encountered in a living body for two main reasons. First, in some tissues it is normal for cells to die and be replaced by others; this occurs, for example, in the outer layer of the skin. Likewise, the white cells of the blood have only a short life span and die within the body. Accordingly, in tissue removed from a healthy body, it is normal to see nuclear changes that are indicative of cell death in sites where it is normal for cells to die. Secondly, dead cells may be present as a result of disease. For example, an artery supplying some limited area of tissue may, as a result of disease, become plugged and, as a consequence, the cells in the area supplied by the artery die from a lack of oxygen and food. In such areas, the nuclei of the cells at some time variously demonstrate the various changes described below. Rapidly growing tumors are prone to contain areas of dead tissue, probably because the blood supply to the rapidly growing cells is inadequate (Fig. 55).

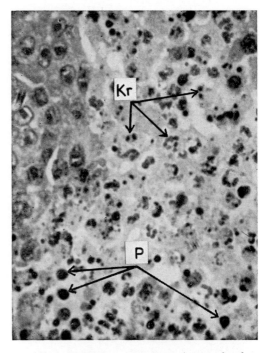

FIG. 55. High-power photomicrograph of a section of a malignant tumor. The cells at the left side were still alive and growing when the specimen was taken, but those on the right side had died previously, and, as a consequence, their nuclei had undergone changes which are indicative of these cells having died. Some nuclei have shrunken into rounded dark-staining bodies (P); this is termed *pycnosis*. Other nuclei have become broken up into fragments (Kr); this is termed *karyorrhexis*. Areas of tissue in which the cells die during life are described as constituting areas of necrosis (*nekros* = corpse). See also karyolysis (Fig. 56).

Although the cytoplasm changes greatly in dead cells, the most positive indication that cells are dead is given by their nuclei. The changes here that indicate cell death are of 3 kinds. The commonest change is called *pycnosis* (dense mass). This consists of a shrinkage of the nuclear material into a homogeneous hyperchromatic mass (Fig. 55, P). The student must take care not to confuse a pycnotic nucleus with a normal nucleus of the condensed chromatin type or with a poorly fixed mitotic figure. If difficulty is encoutered in any instance, it is advisable to examine the cytoplasm of the cell, for if the nucleus is

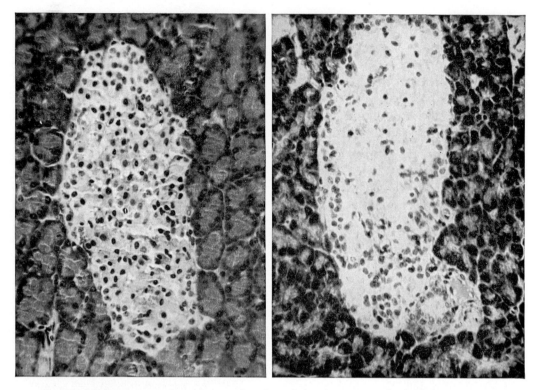

Fig 56. Medium-power photomicrographs of sections of pancreas obtained from rats some hours after they had been given alloxan, a material which destroys many of the cells of the islets of Langerhans. (*Left*) The nuclei of the cells in the oval islet may be seen; there are some examples of pycnosis. (*Right*) The nuclei have mostly dissolved away; this picture illustrates karyolysis.

dead, the cytoplasm will have become altered also in some way so that it no longer has a normal appearance, as may be seen in Figure 55. However, in other instances, death is indicated by the nucleus breaking up into fragments. This is termed *karyorrhexis*. When many nuclei break up in this fashion, nuclear "dust" may be formed (Fig. 55, Kr). In still other instances, cell death is indicated by dissolving of the nucleus. This is termed *karyolysis* (Fig. 56).

Postmortem Degeneration. When cells die, their enzyme complement soon changes, and such activity as thereafter occurs leads to the deterioration and the disintegration of the cells. When a whole body dies, these retrograde changes begin in all its cells, but they proceed in the cells of some parts faster than in the cells of others. If tissue is taken from a dead body at successive intervals, the cells will show increasing signs of deterioration. The cytoplasm loses its normal texture and staining reaction, and the nuclei demonstrate the pycnotic and the other types of changes described above (Fig. 57, *right*). The chief difference between what is seen in postmortem degeneration and in areas of tissue that die in a living body is that in postmortem degeneration all body tissue is affected to a greater or lesser extent, and there is no reaction around the dead tissue as there is around dead tissue in a living body. The student should become familiar with the appearances resulting from postmortem degeneration, because it is often seen in the sections he studies in histology; this is because it is very difficult to obtain some kinds of human tissue soon enough after death to prevent the occurrence of some postmortem degeneration. It is even more common in sections cut from tissues obtained

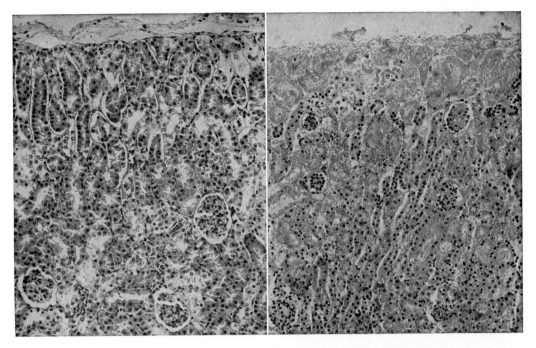

Fɪɢ. 57. (*Left*) Low-power photomicrograph of section of the cortex of the kidney of a mouse. The tissue was fixed immediately after the death of the animal. (*Right*) Similar photomicrograph of a section of similar tissue which was not fixed until the animal had been dead for many hours. Notice that no cellular detail can be seen near the surface where postmortem change has been greatest. Below the surface pycnotic nuclei and degenerating cytoplasm indicates that extensive postmortem degeneration has taken place.

from routine autopsies, for autopsies commonly are not performed immediately after death but many hours afterward.

THE CYTOPLASM

The nucleus directs the work of the cell, but the cytoplasm does most of this work. Since cells are specialized to perform different kinds of work, and since the work is done by the cytoplasm, the cytoplasm of different kinds of cells differs greatly, being specialized to express the different properties of protoplasm to very different extents. Since some kinds of cells are specialized for one kind of work and other kinds for other kinds of work, it is to be expected that those cells that are specialized for contractility would have a different-appearing cytoplasm from those specialized for secretion and that this would enable the histologist to tell them apart. Hence, although some kinds of cells can be identified by their nuclei, most kinds of cells are identified by the appearance and the amount of their cytoplasm.

There is a division of labor in the cytoplasm as well as in the cell as a whole. Cytoplasm is not a homogeneous substance of uniform composition; instead, it has a complex organization and contains structures and bodies of various shapes and sizes and of different compositions and many of these must be segregated from each other. The state of affairs in cytoplasm in this respect is not unlike that at a zoo where, for example, man-eating tigers are kept behind bars. The bars are close enough together to prevent the tigers from escaping, yet they are far enough apart for attendants to toss food between them and so feed the tigers. If there were no bars to confine the tigers they would escape and in all probability destroy some of the attendants and then, in turn, be destroyed themselves by other attendants. Similarly, the segregation of materials of different composition into various

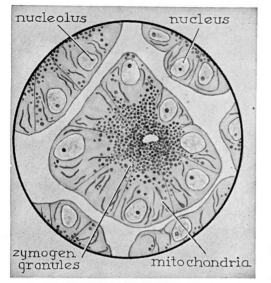

nucleolus   nucleus

zymogen
granules   mitochondria

FIG. 58. Drawing of a section of the pancreas (high-power). The tissue was fixed in an acetic-osmic-bichromate mixture and stained with aniline acid fuchsin and methyl green. A cross section of a secretory unit fills most of the field. Mitochondria are present in the outer parts of the cells of the secretory unit, and zymogen granules are numerous in the parts that approach the lumen of the unit. (Preparation by S. H. Bensley)

bodies and structures within the cytoplasm, but with arrangements at the interfaces or membranes where they come into contact with their surrounding medium, so that substances can pass back and forth between them and the surrounding medium, prevents all the constituents of cytoplasm from becoming thoroughly mixed; this would be as impractical an arrangement for carrying on life as that of permitting the tigers and the attendants in zoos to mix freely.

Organelles and Inclusions. The structures and the bodies in cytoplasm are of 2 main varieties: (1) organelles, which are specialized structural parts of the cytoplasm, and so consist of the *living material* of the cell (Fig. 34, *right*), and (2) inclusions, which are accumulations of *nonliving material* that may be present in cells for one reason or another (Fig. 34, *left*). The organelles will now be considered.

CYTOPLASMIC ORGANELLES

The following will be considered:
1. Mitochondria
2. The ergastoplasm (also called chromidial substance, chromophile substance, the basophilic component of cytoplasm, the cytoplasmic RNA, Palade granules and RNA granules).
3. The system of cytoplasmic membranes
   A. The cell membrane
   B. The smooth-surfaced and the rough-surfaced tubules and vesicles of the endoplasmic reticulum
   C. The Golgi apparatus
4. The centrosome
5. Cytoplasmic fibrils and filaments. Desmosomes, terminal bars and the cell web.

In considering the organelles, and then later the inclusions, in cytoplasm the student may find it convenient to refer to Figure 34 as each new one is considered. This figure is a drawing, not of a typical cell, but of a composite of many cells, stained, as it were, by a composite of technics. It shows the different organelles and inclusions that can be demonstrated by a variety of technics in different cells with the light microscope; in this illustration they are all put together for ready reference, but it should be understood that all will not be seen in any one kind of cell that the student will examine later.

Mitochondria

Mitochondria (*mitos* = thread, *chondrion* = granules) are delicate rods, filaments or granules that are present in the cytoplasm of all animal cells (Figs. 34 & 58). In some cells they are unbelievably numerous; for instance, Allard and his associates found that the normal rat liver cell contains an average of 2,500.

For classroom study, mitochondria can be demonstrated in fresh unstained tissue with darkfield illumination or with the phase microscope. In fresh unfixed tissue they can be stained by the supravital technic with Janus green B and other stains. Pinching or other mishandling of tissue easily results in breakdown of the mitochondria into granules. After ordinary fixation, they are not readily stained, but osmic acid, chromic acid and potassium dichromate prepare them well for staining. However, only certain stains color them to advantage; iron hematoxylin demon-

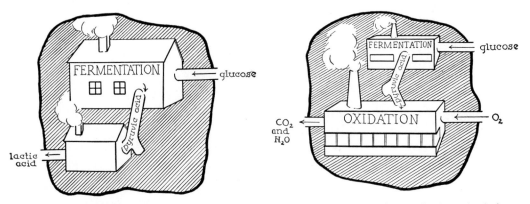

Fig. 59. (A, *Left*) A drawing to help the visualization of the fermentation mechanism of primitive cells. Observe that oxygen is not necessary for the functioning of the fermentation "factory" and that it can produce energy by changing glucose into pyruvic and then into lactic acid, which is excreted. (B, *Right*) A diagram to help the visualization of the operation of the fermentative and oxidative mechanisms that operate in differentiated cells. Observe how the products of fermentation, with the aid of oxygen, are broken down further, with great production of energy and the excretion of carbon dioxide and water.

strates them fairly well and so does acid fuchsin (Fig. 58). They are not visible in H and E sections.

A little more than a decade ago their function was a mystery. Two developments were responsible for determining their function: (1) the vast development of knowledge in the field of enzyme chemistry and (2) the development of differential centrifugation technics whereby whole cells can be broken down in a homogenizer and their different parts centrifuged from the homogenate. Relatively pure preparations of nearly undamaged mitochondria were obtained after sucrose solutions came into use as a medium for suspensing homogenates. That such preparations consist of mitochrondria can be established by sectioning the pellet of material obtained and examining it by means of an electron micrograph (Fig. 63).

From biochemical studies made on mitochondria isolated by this method, it became apparent that they are agents of the greatest importance in cell respiration. Respiration, it will be recalled, is a basic property of protoplasm and is the process whereby food and oxygen taken into the cells react to produce energy, with the formation of carbon dioxide and water. The student will learn more of this when biochemistry is studied, but it may be helpful here to present some elementary data

about cell respiration to serve as a basis for understanding of the fine structure of mitochondria which will be described presently.

Cell Respiration. Although respiration implies oxidation, it should be pointed out that oxygen is not always necessary for the life of cells. Many years ago, Pasteur showed that yeast could live and flourish in sugar solutions in the total absence of oxygen. Under such conditions, yeast cells must obtain energy for life and growth from the chemical process whereby sugar is changed to alcohol, a process we call *fermentation*. Cells of a human body also obtain energy by this primitive and basic mechanism, but the product of the reaction is not alcohol as it is with yeast but pyruvic acid and, in the absence of oxygen, lactic acid (Fig. 59, A). Although fermentation occurs in all body cells, the fermentative mechanism by itself is used only to support the life of very unspecialized embryonic cells and perhaps some others, for example, cartilage cells. Curiously enough, cancer cells (Figs. 55 & 75) utilize fermentation as a source of energy more than their normal counterpart. The fermentative anaerobic mechnism is relatively inefficient for obtaining energy, and, as we shall see, most cells have improved on it.

Pasteur also showed that when oxygen was admitted to cells obtaining their energy from anaerobic fermentative reactions these latter

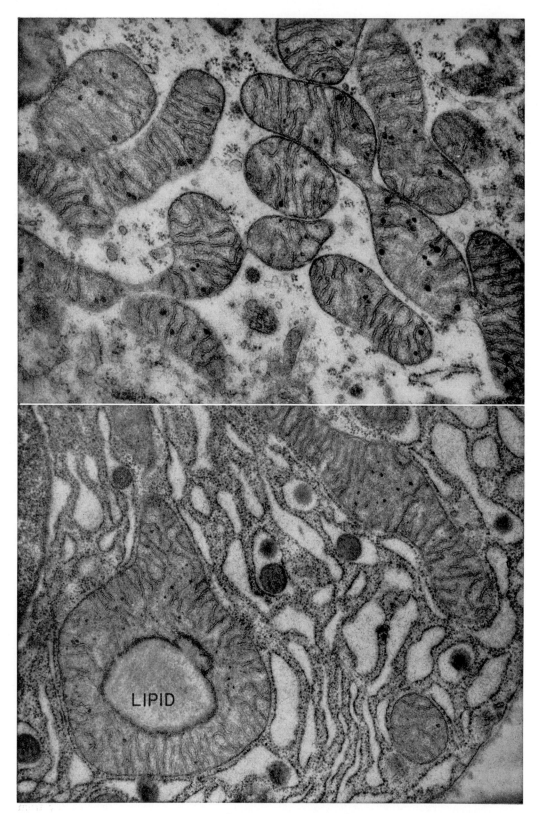

Fig. 60. (*Caption on facing page*).

reactions were suppressed. This phenomenon is now called the *Pasteur effect*. Muscle cells illustrate this effect. If they are forced to work hard without sufficient oxygen, they excrete much lactic acid into the blood, thus showing that in the relative absence of oxygen they obtain more of their energy from fermentation. If supplied with ample oxygen, they excrete more carbon dioxide and less lactic acid: this, then, is an example in man of the Pasteur effect of oxidation suppressing fermentation.

When the Pasteur effect was first investigated in animal cells, fermentation and oxidation probably were thought to be two distinctly different mechanisms for obtaining energy. We now know that they represent two different stages in normal cell respiration. In fermentation, which is now usually termed *glycolysis,* glucose in the absence of oxygen is broken down to lactic acid, and a certain amount of energy is released. If oxygen is available, fermentation produces not lactic acid but pyruvic acid; this subsequently is oxidized with the production of much more energy (Fig. 59, B). Briefly, then, glycolysis is only the first step in cell respiration and is followed by oxidation. Most cells cannot live by glycolysis alone and are dependent for their existence on oxidation occurring in them. This explains why cyanide is such a deadly poison; it arrests oxidation in cells.

Oxidation is a complex process, and the meaning of the term has changed over the years. Originally, it referred to the addition of oxygen to a substance and later it came to include the removal of hydrogen atoms. Now it

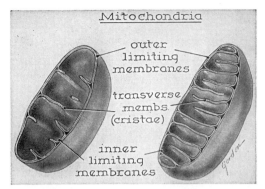

FIG. 61. Diagrammatic drawings to illustrate the structure of mitochondria in 3 dimensions.

refers to any process in which electrons are lost, any substance that oxidases another, being, of course, itself reduced (it gains electrons).

Oxidation of pyruvate is a step-by-step process. The reactions involved are catalyzed by the enzymes of the Krebs citric acid cycle. These enzymes are confined almost entirely to mitochrondria, and, furthermore, the evidence indicates that in mitochondria the enzymes are in a spatial arrangement that permits rapid transfer of the products of one enzyme to the site of action of the next.

Enzymes concerned in glycolysis or fermentation are distributed in other parts of the cytoplasm. It can be deduced that cells depending primarily on fermentation for energy do not contain many mitochrondria; indeed,

---

(Illustration on facing page).

FIG. 60. (*Top*) Electron micrograph ($\times$ 37,000 as reproduced here) of section of acinar cell of pancreas of guinea pig. The section has passed through many mitochondria. Each shows a double limiting membrane. Cristae extend inwardly from the inner limiting membrane as shelves of double membrane. The spaces between cristae are filled with *mitochondrial matrix* which reveals little structure except occasional small spherical dark bodies that are sometimes called *mitochondrial bodies.*

(*Bottom*) Electron micrograph ($\times$ 30,000 as reproduced here) of a section of an acinar cell of the pancreas of a guinea pig that was starved for 48 hours, fed, and killed 1 hour afterward. Lipid droplets appear in the cytoplasm in starvation, and the lipid is oxidized by the enzymes of the mitochondria to provide energy for the cell; this is manifested by the mitochondria coming into close contact with lipid droplets. On the left side a mitochondrion has wrapped itself around a lipid droplet, which is labeled lipid. This illustration also shows zymogen granules being synthesized in rough-surfaced vesicles of the endoplasmic reticulum.

(Both preparations by Dr. G. E. Palade)

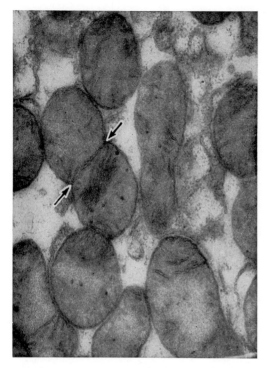

FIG. 62. Electron micrograph (× 30,000) of a section of a liver cell of a rat that was fed an azo dye that causes a great increase in the number of mitochondria in liver cells. The arrows indicate where a mitochondrion may be dividing. (Preparation by Dr. J.-G. Lafontaine)

they do not, and cancer cells generally contain fewer mitochondria than do normal cells.

Fine Structure of Mitochondria. As has been mentioned already, much of histologic structure relates to materials of different composition being separated from one another by membranes. Mitochondria, under the E/M reveal a double-layered limiting membrane (Figs. 60 & 61). Folds of the inner membrane project like shelves into the interior of the mitochondria (Figs. 60 & 61); these are termed *cristae mitochondriales* (Fig. 60 & 61). Obviously, in thin sections, the mitochondria will be cut only infrequently in longitudinal section throughout their whole lengths. Most will be cut in cross and oblique section; hence, deciding on their size, shape and structure from thin sections provides an exercise in 3-dimensional visualization.

Typical mitochondria are of cylindrical form, but some may branch, and usually they vary in size in any one cell type. For example, Palade found they varied from 0.35 μ to 0.74 μ in diameter in liver cells. In different cell types the extent of development of the cristae (internal shelves) varies, the cristae being short and extending only about halfway across the mitochondria of liver cells, but in some cell types, the cristae extend completely across the mitochondria. If a section passes longitudinally through a mitochondrion close to the periphery, relatively short cristae may *appear* to extend all the way across the mitochondrion.

The interior of each mitochondrion is filled with matrix which usually is denser than the surrounding cytoplasm and structureless in appearance. Occasional spherical or ovoid dark granules are sometimes seen in it (Fig. 60, *top*).

Mitochondria in living cells, as viewed with the phase microscope or darkfield illumination, appear to divide and even to re-form. With the E/M appearances sometimes suggest that they divide by simple transverse fission. To study this, Lafontaine utilized the liver cells of animals that had been given a certain azo dye which, over a short time, increases tremendously the number of mitochondria in the liver cells. During this time, many mitochondria similar to the one indicated by the arrow in Figure 62 were seen. This illustration suggests that the mitochondria divide as the result of 2 membranes in a transverse cristae separating from one another with the outer membrane simultaneously dipping in to restore a double membrane over the 2 ends at the site of separation.

Mitochondria change in form under different physiologic conditions. For example, the mitochondria of liver cells swell under conditions of starvation. Sometimes degenerating mitochondria are seen, as, for example, in tumor cells and in embryonic tissue.

The association of mitochondria with lipid inclusions in fasting animals has been described recently by Palade. Under normal conditions, the exocrine cells of the pancreas contain no, or very few, lipid inclusions. After fasting for 2 days, lipid inclusions (Fig. 60, *bottom*, lipid) commonly are found enclosed in a mitochondrial ring (Fig. 60, *bottom*) either incompletely or completely. Such a close association of lipid inclusions and mitochon-

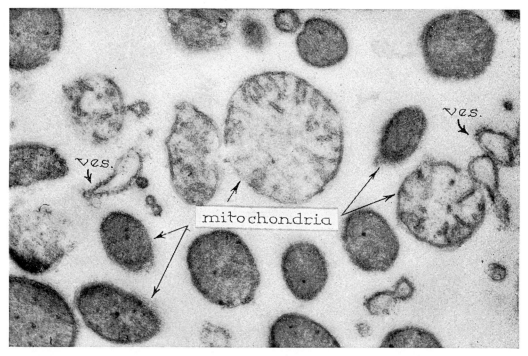

FIG. 63. Electron micrograph ($\times$ 35,000) of a section of a pellet of a mitochondrial fraction separated from homogenized liver cells by differential centrifugation. Although the fraction consists chiefly of mitochondria, a few membranous vesicles (labeled *ves.*) are also present in it. (Separation by C. Allard and G. deLamirande, electron micrograph by A. F. Howatson)

dria probably is an expression of the fact that the fasting animal is obliged to oxidize its reserve fat for energy, and that the enzymes involved in fatty acid oxidation are contained in the mitochondria. Similar morphologic associations of lipid inclusions and mitochondria are found in other tissues, e.g., heart muscle, diaphragm, liver and kidney tubules.

As has been mentioned already, mitochondria for biochemical studies can be separated from homogenized cells by differential centrifugation in sucrose solutions. Pellets so obtained can be sectioned and examined under the E/M to ensure that the fraction that is being studied actually consists of relatively whole, uninjured mitochondria. A section of such a fraction is illustrated in Figure 63.

Ergastoplasm (Chromidial Substance, Chromophile Substance, Basophilic Component of Cytoplasm, Cytoplasmic RNA, Palade or RNA (RNP) Granules)

Early Studies. The name chromatin was coined by Fleming in 1879 for the material in the nucleus that is colored deeply by stains. At different times afterward different observers in different parts of the world noticed that the cytoplasm of at least some cells of the body contained appreciable aggregations of a material that had the same affinity for stains as had nuclear chromatin (Fig. 34). These various observers, who were not always familiar with each other's observations, gave this material different names. Since most of these names are stilled employed, and since further names for the same material have subsequently been added, it is helpful for the student to know why so many names for the same material came into existence.

It was natural, since this material in the cytoplasm stained similarly to nuclear chromatin, that it should be named *chromidial* (chromatinlike) *substance*. Also, since it demonstrated a love for stains, it was logical that it should be called *chromophile substance*. When dyes became better understood, and it

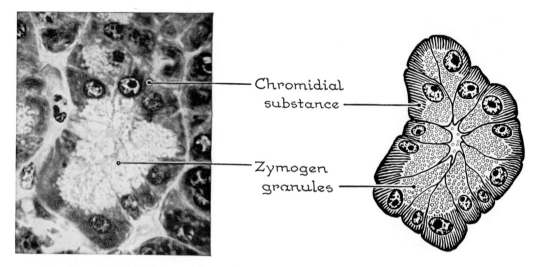

Chromidial
substance

Zymogen
granules

FIG. 64. (*Left*) A high-power photomicrograph of a section of a dog's pancreas. The central and larger part of the picture shows a single secretory unit. Ergastoplasm (chromidial substance) shows in the picture as dark-staining material situated near the bases of the cells comprising the secretory unit. (*Right*) As is indicated in this drawing, zymogen granules are present in the apices of the cells. The chromidial substance tends to have a striated appearance because of the parallel mitochondria in it.

was learned that some were acid and some basic, it was noticed that this material had an affinity only for basic dyes, and since the remainder of the cytoplasm had an affinity for acid dyes, it came to be referred to as the *basophilic component of cytoplasm*. Garnier, whose findings have recently been described in some detail in English by Haguenau, made a remarkable study of this material in 1900. He noticed that its amount and distribution in cells were related to the amount and the kind of work performed by the cell; hence, he termed it *ergastoplasm* (*ergon* = work).

Histochemistry. Although chromidial substance reacts similarily to chromatin with most basic stains, it was shown (after the Feulgen reaction came into use) that it was not identical with nuclear chromatin because it proved to be Feulgen-negative. However, when ultraviolet absorption methods were evolved, it was found to absorb light to the same wave length as nuclear chromatin, which indicated that it contained nucleic acid. When ribonuclease and deoxyribonuclease became available, it was found that it was dissolved by the former and not by the latter. From all this

work, it became apparent that the substance contains nucleic acid, but that the nucleic acid it contains is RNA. As a result of this, it gained still another name—*the cytoplasmic RNA*.

Fine Structure. With the E/M as well as with the light microscope, development of knowledge of this substance was associated with changing concepts and a changing terminology. When thin sectioning technics first became available, it was observed with the E/M that those parts of cells that with the light microscope were seen to contain aggregations of ergastoplasm (as may be seen in Fig. 64, *left*) revealed aggregations of curving dark lines that were often packed closely together. These were at first referred to as filaments, fibrils or lamellae. Then, as technics improved and better resolution was obtained, it became apparent that the dark lines were double, and that they represented sections cut through flattened membranous vesicles and narrow membranous tubules that were packed together in these parts of the cytoplasm. Therefore it was believed that these membranous structures were responsible for the basophilia

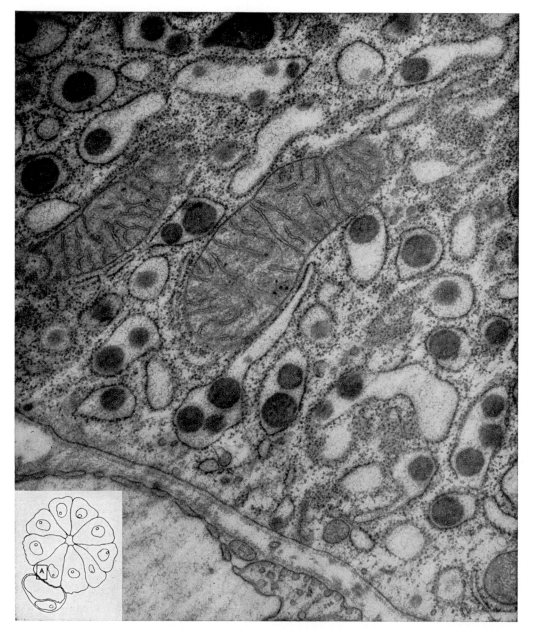

FIG. 65. Electron micrograph (× 35,000 as reproduced here) of section of acinar cell of the pancreas of a guinea pig previously starved and recently fed. A capillary may be seen at the lower left, and the area marked A in the inset at this site indicates roughly the part of the cell illustrated in the micrograph. Note the abundance of RNA granules, which are both free and attached to the outer surfaces of distended vesicles (cisternae) of the endoplasmic reticulum, which is, therefore, of the rough-surfaced type. Within the distended vesicles rounded dark bodies are seen; these are zymogen granules in the process of formation. To follow the further history of the granules see Figure 73. (Preparation by Dr. G. E. Palade)

that the cytoplasm exhibited in these areas—that is, that membranous material constituted the ergastoplasm. As a result of this, the flattened membranous vesicles in these regions came to be referred to very commonly as *ergastoplasmic vesicles*. However, as the resolution obtained with the E/M continued to improve, Palade was able to show that fine osmiophilic granules of a diameter of about 15 millimicrons were distributed along the outer surface of these membranous vesicles as well as in the cytoplasm between them (Fig. 65), and it was soon shown that the basophilia seen with the light microscope in these areas was due not to the membranous vesicles themselves but to the granules that studded their exteriors and were distributed between them. These granules were found to dissolve with ribonuclease treatment and so they came to be called RNA (RNP) granules. They are also called Palade granules after their discoverer. The ergastoplasm therefore turned out to be not the membranous material but the granules that are often associated with the membranous material.

Summary. The basophilic material in the cytoplasm, which (from studies with the light microscope) was named chromidial substance, chromophile substance, the basophilic component of the cytoplasm, ergastoplasm and cytoplasmic RNA, has been shown by combined E/M and histochemical studies to consist of granules of RNA. These are called either Palade granules in honor of their discoverer or RNA granules because of their chemical nature.

Origin of the Cytoplasmic RNA. Many observations in the past suggested that the ergastoplasm might be formed in the nucleus. Recent work in which labeled precursors of RNA have been followed by radioautographic methods support this concept. Studies of this nature have shown, first, that no cytoplasmic RNA is synthesized by cytoplasm if nuclei are removed from cells, and, secondly, that in cells that have their nuclei, the label always appears in the nucleus before it appears in the cytoplasm. In the nucleus, the label appears both along the chromosome and in the nucleolus. A recent study by Amano and Leblond provides evidence indicating that all or at least most of the RNA that ends up in the cytoplasm is synthesized in the nucleolus.

From the nucleolus it probably gains entrance to the cytoplasm through the nuclear pores (Fig. 54).

Function of the Cytoplasmic RNA. The cytoplasmic RNA controls such protein synthesis as occurs in the cytoplasm, and the amount of it in the cytoplasm is related to the extent to which protein synthesis is occurring. Some cells synthesize only enough protein to replace that which is catabolized in their normal metabolism, and cells such as these do not contain large amounts of cytoplasmic RNA. Cells synthesize more protein than is required for replacing that which is catabolized under two conditions that will now be described. In these, RNA is relatively abundant.

1. Cells which are proliferating, as in the normal growth and replacement or in the repair of damaged tissue, or in abnormal growth as occurs in cancer, must synthesize new protein for the new cells that are being formed (in addition to the protein that is required to replace that which is being catabolized); hence, growing cells contain increased amounts of cytoplasmic RNA. Howatson and the author, from E/M studies, have suggested that under these conditions the cytoplasmic RNA has a diffuse distribution, with granules being sprinkled more or less evenly throughout the cytoplasm, and that this accounts for the fact that cells of this type exhibit a diffuse cytoplasmic basophilia when they are studied with the light microscope.

2. Cells may synthesize protein materials that are subsequently secreted by the cell. This occurs, for example, in the cells of glands such as the pancreas, which produces a protein secretion that is delivered by a duct system to the intestine to help in digestion. It also occurs in cells that are synthesizing the precursor materials of the protein intercellular substances such as fibroblasts and osteoblasts. This will be described in a later chapter. Another example is to be found in the cells that synthesize and elaborate antibodies, because these too are protein materials. This also will be described in a later chapter. Here, the point that we wish to elaborate is that protein which is to be secreted or otherwise delivered from the cytoplasm, is synthesized in association with membranous vesicles or tubules within the cytoplasm (Fig. 64) and

probably is segregated from the remainder of the cytoplasm by the membranous containers in which it is formed. However, in order to discuss this matter in more detail, we must first consider the system of cytoplasmic membranes, because they are involved in this process.

The System of Cytoplasmic Membranes

This system includes
1. The cell membrane
2. The endoplasmic reticulum: rough surfaced and smooth surfaced
3. The Golgi apparatus

The Cell Membrane. Many physiologic studies in the past established that the contents of a cell are separated from its fluid environment by a membrane that discriminates with regard to what shall pass through it. Microdissection studies also have indicated the existence of a membrane because substantial tears made through the surface of suitably large cells result in some of the contents of the cell running out through the wound. It might be thought that such proof of the existence of the cell membrane would not be necessary, because its presence could be established readily by light microscopy. But, as will become apparent presently, the cell membrane is too thin to be resolved with the light microscope. This presents a problem, for something that certainly seems to be a cell membrane can be seen around many kinds of cells studied in stained sections with the light microscope. It seems probable that this appearance is due to many factors, for example, fixation artefact, condensation of stain, diffraction, and the fact that sections studied with the light microscope are commonly several microns thick—therefore, the curving sides of cells cut by the microtome knife are seen, even at a given focus over an appreciable distance, and, over this distance, a thin curved line seen from one end would appear thick enough to suggest that it was a membrane.

There are 3 important facts relating to the passage of particles through cell membranes— their size, electrostatic charge and relative solubility in lipids. The last factor, of course, suggests that lipid is an important constituent of cell membranes; hence, lipid enters largely into the models of membranes that have been suggested over the years and, indeed, there is general agreement that cell membranes consist of lipid-protein complexes.

Fine Structures. When osmium-fixed material is examined under the E/M, a single dark line, about 60 to 70 A thick (Fig. 53), can be seen surrounding most cells. Since osmium could be expected to have some affinity for both lipid and protein, it could be assumed that these two components of the membrane would not be distinguished from each other as readily by this method as by the use of other fixatives. Robertson has used $KMnO_4$ as a fixative for his extensive studies and, by this method, he has been able to show that the membrane that surrounds the usual cell appears under the E/M as 2 dark lines, each about 20 to 25 A thick, the lines being separated from each other by a lighter zone of about the same thickness (Fig. 90). It seems probable that the middle lighter portion of the membrane is representative of lipid, and this concept is in agreement with hypothetical models of the cell membrane that have been visualized.

The fine structure of the cell membrane will be considered further in connection with the formation of the myelin sheaths of nerve fibers in Chapter 20 (see Fig. 316 B).

Special arrangements of the cell membrane, such as those that increase the absorptive area of free surfaces, and those that assist in holding adjacent cells together, are dealt with on pages 219 and 221.

Intracytoplasmic Membranes. Before it became possible to cut sections thinly enough for effective study with the E/M, Porter, Claude and Fullam, in 1945, studied the fine structure of cytoplasm in another way. They took advantage of the fact that the cytoplasm of cells growing in tissue culture will spread out very thinly, so thinly that after being fixed and mounted, it can be studied with the E/M. In such preparations they observed that cytoplasm contained a lacelike network of strands and vesicles. They named this the *endoplasmic reticulum*—endoplasmic, because it did not extend out into the peripheral part of the cytoplasm (the so-called ectoplasm), and *reticulum,* because it formed a network. When good thin sectioning methods became available, it was found that what they had described as endoplasmic reticulum consisted of a system of tubules and vesicles, and that the membrane of which these intracytoplasmic

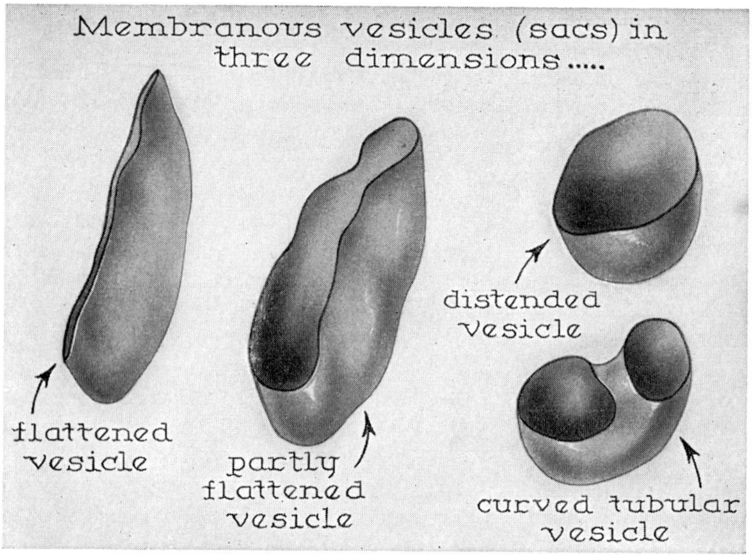

Membranous vesicles (sacs) in three dimensions.....

flattened vesicle

partly flattened vesicle

distended vesicle

curved tubular vesicle

FIG. 66. Diagrammatic drawings illustrating in 3 dimensions various forms assumed by cytoplasmic membranous vesicles. The cut surface of each vesicle shows how it would appear in a section.

structures was composed was similar to the cell membrane. Although the study of thin sections revealed that the endoplasmic reticulum was not confined to the endoplasm but, instead, extended to the periphery of the cytoplasm into the so-called ectoplasm, the term "endoplasmic reticulum" is still widely used for this system of intracytoplasmic tubules and vesicles. This system of narrow tubules and wider flattened or dilated vesicles (the latter are termed cisternae) must be visualized in 3 dimensions. The appearance of the tubular and the vesicular elements in a thin section is illustrated in Figure 66.

Studies of thin sections, in addition to confirming the existence of the endoplasmic reticulum described originally by Porter *et al.*, also provided details about another cytoplasmic structure that had been much studied with the light microscope; namely, the Golgi apparatus. This also was found to consist of membranous tubules and vesicles. Therefore, there is in the cell a vast system of interconnecting cytoplasmic membranes composed of the cell membrane, the tubules and the vesicles of the endoplasmic reticulum, the Golgi apparatus and the outer nuclear membrane.

The Endoplasmic Reticulum

The Smooth-Surfaced Components of the Endoplasmic Reticulum: Agranular Reticulum. Under the E/M, strings of little membranous vesicles often are seen close to the cell membrane (Fig. 53). These vesicles are not studded with RNA granules. Furthermore, little invaginations of the cell membrane, which look as if they might become pinched off to become such smooth-surfaced vesicles, also are often seen. It seems probable that the smooth-surfaced vesicles in this location are formed in this way, and that one function they perform is pinocytosis.

This phenomenon has been mentioned already, and there is much evidence indicating that one method by which a cell can take up fluid is by the formation of fluid-filled vesicles at the cell surface. Such vesicles may pass across the cell to the other surface where the fluid is released; this will be described and illustrated in Chapter 21. It seems also that the mechanism may operate in another way in that adsorption of certain substances may occur on a segment of the cell membrane, with this segment of the cell membrane then becoming infolded and pinched off to become an intracytoplasmic vesicle. The bounding membrane of the vesicle then may disappear, thus delivering the adsorbed material to some appropriate region in the cytoplasm.

In addition to the smooth-surfaced components described above there are in some types of cells large numbers of membranous structures which are closely packed and unassociated with RNA granules. Such appearances are seen, for example, in liver cells after fasting; here it may be one stage in the restoration of granular reticulum which is depleted by starvation. However, agranular reticulum is found in liver without fasting, and Porter has suggested that it plays a role in the synthesis and the segregation of glycogen. Agranular reticulum is also found in large amounts in the interstitial cells of the testis where it may be related to the formation of steroid hormones (Fig. 552). It is also seen in skeletal muscle where it is thought to play some part in impulse conduction (Fig. 258), and in the parietal cells of the gastric mucosa where it may be associated with the secretion of hydrochloric acid (Fig. 401 A). Thus agranular reticulum is found in cells of very different nature and function.

The Rough-Surfaced Components of the Endoplasmic Reticulum. In a previous section, which deals with ergastoplasm, it was pointed out that the basophilia that is imparted to cytoplasm by its RNA granules can either be diffuse, as it generally is in rapidly growing cells, or localized to some part of the cell, and that the latter state of affairs often exists if the protein that is being synthesized is to be delivered from the cell as a secretion. Moreover, it was pointed out that protein that is synthesized within the cell under the influence of the RNA granules and is to be secreted can be, for example, the precursor of potent digestive enzymes. Therefore, if it were permitted to mix freely with the cytoplasm, it might institute chemical reactions which would destroy the cytoplasm. Accordingly, protein destined for secretion is generally kept segregated by means of membranes as it is synthesized. This is accomplished by the rough-surfaced tubules and vesicles of the endoplasmic reticulum (Fig. 64). The RNA granules which stud these tubules and vesicles control the synthesis of the protein, determining the amino acid sequences that it will have. The membrane component of the arrangement permits the protein to be segregated as it is formed. Hence, the rough-surfaced tubules and vesicles of the endoplasmic reticulum are agencies whereby protein destined for secretion can be synthesized and at the same time kept segregated from the remainder of the cytoplasm.

The appearances presented both under the light microscope and the E/M by cells which have rough-surfaced tubules and vesicles of endoplasmic reticulum (and hence aggregations of ergastoplasm) localized to some part of them, can be studied to great advantage in the pancreas, as will become apparent from the following.

The pancreas (this organ will be described in detail in later chapters, and at this time, it is necessary for the student to learn only enough of its microscopic structure to study intelligently the cells that synthesize protein that is destined for secretion) is a gland which makes a secretion that contains several enzymes important in the digestion of food. These enzymes are delivered into the intestine by means of a duct. The cells that synthesize the protein enzymes are arranged in little clusters in the gland; each cluster is called an *acinus* because it resembles a grape. In each acinus the cells are arranged so as to encircle a tiny central lumen (Fig. 64), and they deliver their secretion into this central lumen which drains into the duct system. A cross section cut through an acinus resembles a pie that has been cut into pieces but has not yet been served (Fig. 64). The individual cells of the acinus appear as individual pieces of pie. Each has a broad base and a narrow apex. The secretion is delivered through the apex of each cell, as is indicated on the right side of Figure 64, into the central lumen of the acinus.

Each cell in an acinus manufactures a protein (enzyme-containing) secretion. This is visible in the cells because it appears in the form of rounded bodies termed *zymogen granules* (Fig. 64); these are seen to best advantage toward the apices of the cells.

The cytoplasm close to the base of each cell of an acinus is dark blue (Fig. 64, *left*). This is due to a very substantial amount of cytoplasmic RNA that is concentrated in the basal part of each cell.

With the E/M, these heavily stained basal parts of the secretory cells of the pancreas are seen to contain almost countless flattened and semiflattened membranous vesicles that are often arranged in parallel array (Fig 65). Their exteriors are heavily studded with RNA granules, and many RNA granules are also distributed in the cytoplasm between them (Fig. 65). Mitochondria, which may be oriented in the same general direction as flattened vesicles, are also apparent in this region, distributed between groups of vesicles (Fig. 60,

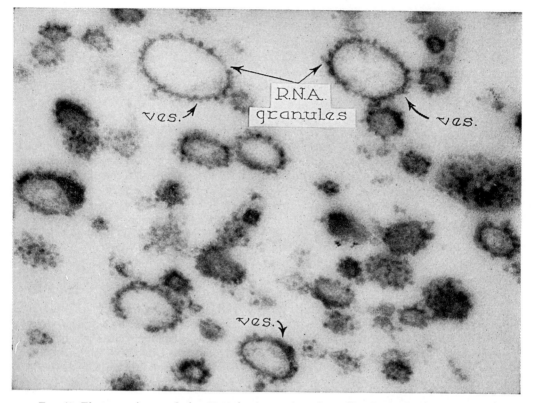

Fig. 67. Electron micrograph ($\times$ 80,000) of a section of a pellet obtained from a microsome fraction obtained by the differential centrifugation of homogenized cells of the pancreas. The illustration shows that the microsome fraction consists chiefly of small vesicles, some of which form from larger vesicles. Most of the vesicles in this fraction have RNA granules attached to their outer surfaces. (Palade, G., and Siekevitz, P.: J. Biophysic. & Biochem. Cytol. *2*:671, labeling added)

bottom). It is the great concentration of RNA granules, both adherent to the vesicles and free in the cytoplasm between them, that accounts for the basophilia seen with the light microscope in this part of the cytoplasm.

With the light microscope, zymogen granules are not seen in the basal parts of these cells but, instead, toward their apices (Fig. 64, *right*). With the E/M, more detail is obtainable, and dark rounded bodies, smaller than mature granules, can be seen deeper in the cell in the rough-surfaced tubules and vesicles of the endoplasmic reticulum of the basal area (Fig. 65), thus indicating that synthesis of protein that is destined for secretion occurs in the basal part of the cell.

The zymogen granules formed in this part of the cell are eventually discharged through the apex of the cell into the central lumen of the acinus (Fig. 64, *right*). Curiously enough, the zymogen granules that are first seen in the rough-surfaced vesicles in which they are synthesized, are seen, when they pass toward the apex of the cell, in smooth-surfaced vesicles, and it is by means of the latter that they are delivered through the cell surface. To follow their transport through the cell requires that we consider the Golgi apparatus, because this, the third part of the membrane system of the cell, is concerned in the transport and the delivery of the granules formed by the rough-surfaced component of the endoplasmic reticulum. However, this is the appropriate place to discuss microsomes, so that before considering the Golgi apparatus we must deal with them.

Microsomes and Submicroscopic Particulates. The late and revered R. R. Bensley, in following the dictates of his view that separable things should be separated before analysis is attempted, and Hoerr, working together, were the first investigators to separate an important cytoplasmic component by means of the differential centrifugation of homogenized cells. In 1934 they reported the successful separation of mitochondria (the mitochondria were identified with the light microscope), and they were able to make a chemical anlysis of them.

Claude followed the lead of Bensley and Hoerr and succeeded in separating certain fractions from homogenized cells that contained particles too small to be seen with the light microscope. The extremely small particles in these fractions came to be called *microsomes* or *submicroscopic particulates,* and the fractions that contained them were called the *microsome fractions.* When these particles were first separated it was not possible to cut sections that were thin enough for electron microscopy, so it could not be determined whether or not the microsomes or submicroscopic particulates, present in certain fractions of homogenized cells, had existed as such in living cells. When it became possible to concentrate microsome fractions prepared by differential centrifugation into a pellet, to cut thin sections of the pellet and to study the sections with the E/M, the true nature of microsomes became apparent. Microsome fractions were found to consist chiefly of the rough-surfaced membranous vesicles of the cytoplasm (Fig. 67). The larger vesicles, of course, become broken up into smaller ones as a result of the technics employed, but many smaller ones seem to remain intact. It is of interest that the RNA granules tend to remain adherent to the rough-surfaced vesicles throughout the whole procedure (Fig. 67); this is the chief or only reason for what were at first thought of as microsome fractions containing RNA. Some vesicles in the pellet, of course, would be of the smooth-surfaced type. So, the so-called microsome fraction was shown by the E/M to consist chiefly of the broken-up membranous vesicles of the cytoplasm with or without attached RNA granules, and no evidence was found to indicate that microsomes are discrete bodies that exist in cytoplasm as independent structures.

As is shown in Figure 68, it is now possible to obtain fractions which consist almost ex-

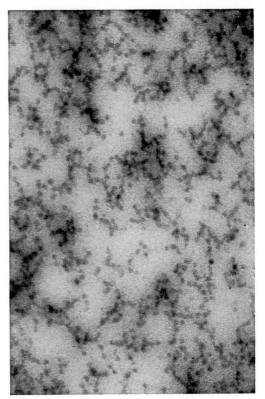

FIG. 68. Electron micrograph ($\times$ 80,000) of a section of a pellet of a fraction obtained by differential centrifugation from a homogenate of pancreas cells. The micrograph shows this fraction to be a very pure preparation of RNA (Palade) granules. (Palade, G., and Siekevitz, P.: J. Biophysic. & Biochem. Cytol. 2:671)

clusively of free RNA granules (see Palade and Siekevitz). However, the fraction obtained by differential centrifugation which contains only these is not the fraction commonly described in the past as the microsome fraction, the nature of which has been described in the preceding paragraph. However, a fraction of more or less pure RNA granules is now sometimes called a microsome fraction. It is obvious that at this time anyone who discusses a microsome fraction must define his meaning lest confusion arise.

It should be noted that it is impossible to obtain as pure fractions of broken-up cytoplasmic membranes as it is of mitochondria. Microsome fractions are generally contaminated with small or ruptured mitochondria,

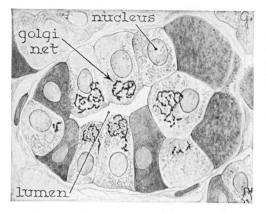

FIG. 69. High-power drawing of a section of pancreas prepared by the ferric chloride-osmic acid technic which blackens the Golgi apparatus. (Preparation by S. H. Bensley)

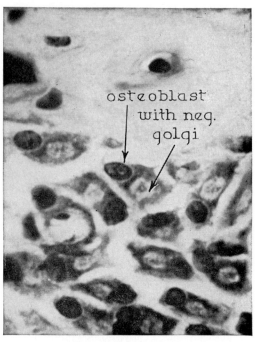

FIG. 70. Medium-power photomicrograph of a section of decalcified bone stained with azure-eosin-hematoxylin. It shows osteoblasts beginning to lay down bone near the site of a fracture. The osteoblasts show pale areas (negative Golgis) in their basophilic cytoplasm.

other cellular debris and parts of the Golgi apparatus, the next organelle to be described.

The Golgi Apparatus

In 1898, Camillo Golgi, of whom we shall hear more when nervous tissue is considered, treated some brain tissue with a silver salt by a somewhat different from usual method. When he examined sections of this tissue he noticed that each of the nerve cells had a little dark network in its cytoplasm; he named this the *internal reticular apparatus* of the cell (Fig. 291). Later it became customary to term it the *Golgi apparatus* in honor of its discoverer. However, some investigators hesitate to designate it as an apparatus and refer to it as the *Golgi region*, or the *Golgi substance* or *Golgi complex* of the cell. Soon after it was noticed in nerve cells, Golgi and others showed that a similar structure could be demonstrated in many kinds of cells by the same technic (chrome-silver impregnation). In 1902, Kopsch showed that the same type of structure could be demonstrated in the cells of tissue that had been subjected to prolonged immersion in 2 per cent osmium tetroxide.

By both technics described above the Golgi apparatus commonly appears as a dark net in some part of the cytoplasm (Figs. 34 and 69). In some cells it appears as a dark granular mass of irregular shape. In cells that secrete through one of their surfaces the Golgi net commonly is seen between that surface and the nucleus (Fig. 69). In some kinds of cells it may have the form of a tortuous, sometimes discontinuous cord that encircles the nucleus (Fig. 291). In still other kinds of cells it has a more diffuse distribution, with bits of it appearing here and there.

Since osmium tetroxide commonly is used for demonstrating fat in cells, the idea arose that the Golgi apparatus was at least partly fatty in nature. It has been suggested, moreover, that the two types of impregnation commonly used to demonstrate the apparatus could act to liberate fat from other parts of the cytoplasm. This gave rise to the suspicion in the minds of some observers that the Golgi apparatus might not be a true organelle but instead an aggregation of fatty droplets liberated from other parts of the cell by the fixatives used. However, recent work with the phase and electron microscope, soon to be described, proves that the Golgi apparatus actually exists as a true organelle.

In ordinary H and E sections, of material that has been fixed in fixatives other than osmium tetroxide, sometimes a pale area can be seen in cells in the site where a Golgi apparatus might be expected. These pale areas generally are referred to as *negative Golgi images* (Fig. 70). Their paleness is explained in two ways. (1) Ordinary histologic technics result in fatty materials mostly dissolving from tissue, so if the Golgi apparatus were of a fatty nature it might be expected that it would mostly dissolve away to leave a relatively clear area. (2) There is a reason to believe that the Golgi apparatus may consist at least in part of a system of clear canals or vacuoles, as will now be described.

Almost immediately after Golgi first described the apparatus that bears his name,

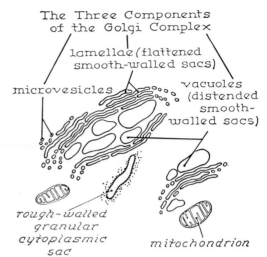

The Three Components of the Golgi Complex

lamellae (flattened smooth-walled sacs)

microvesicles

vacuoles (distended smooth-walled sacs)

rough-walled granular cytoplasmic sac

mitochondrion

FIG. 71. Diagram to illustrate the three components of the Golgi apparatus.

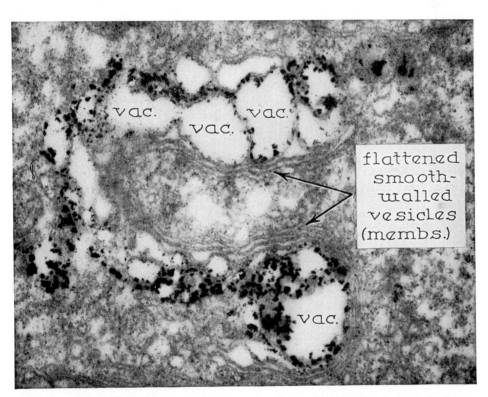

vac.   vac.   vac.

flattened smooth-walled vesicles (membs.)

vac.

FIG. 72. Electron micrograph ($\times$ 34,000) of a section of an epithelial cell of the duodenum. The material was postosmicated so osmium tetroxide was deposited in particulate form in and around the vacuoles. The illustration, in addition to demonstrating the vacuoles of the Golgi region, also shows the flattened smooth-surfaced membranous sacs that are associated with the vacuoles. (Dalton, A. J., and Felix, M. D.: J. Biophysic. & Biochem. Cytol. (Supp.) 2:79, labeling added)

Holmgren observed that many cells exhibited within their cytoplasm a system of tiny canals which appeared to be filled with a clear material; he termed these *juice canals*. Since his time many observers have verified the existence of canals or aggregations of vacuoles in cells and have shown that their position corresponds to the sites of the Golgi apparatus demonstrated by the usual impregnation technics. Therefore, it has been suggested that the negative Golgi images seen in ordinarily prepared sections may be due in part to the presence of these clear canals or aggregations of vacuoles, as well as to fatty material dissolving from the region. Therefore, it has been suggested that the canals or vacuoles are, in effect, the Golgi apparatus (or part of it) and that they or their contents are responsible for reducing the metallic salts that demarcate the apparatus when impregnation technics are used.

There has been much confusion about whether or not any part of the Golgi apparatus stains with certain supravital stains, for example neutral red or methylene blue. The general opinion now is that any staining reaction obtained with these dyes is not due to any part of the Golgi apparatus. However, the P.A.S. technic (to be described in the next chapter) imparts color to one component of the Golgi apparatus, but the precise identity of this has not yet been established.

In recent years the Golgi apparatus has been demonstrated clearly in fresh preparations of certain tissues with the phase microscope. It is particularly easy to see in the cells of the epididymis, and Dalton and Felix have published excellent illustrations of it as it appears in this site. Dalton and Felix point out that it appears to best advantage in cells of the epididymis that are examined immediately after removal from the body. In these it is a rounded or ovoid body, darker than the adjacent cytoplasm, and about two thirds of the size of the nucleus.

Dalton, who has made extensive studies of the Golgi apparatus with the E/M, describes it as consisting of 3 components; these are shown diagrammatically in Figure 71.

1. *Vacuoles* that may be as large as mitochondria and are arranged in groups (Figs. 71 & 72); sometimes the groups are in a horseshoe-shaped arrangement. In the usual thin section fixed in buffered osmium tetroxide, vacuoles appear as distended, smooth-surfaced membranous vesicles that seem to contain only a clear material, but Dalton has shown that if material, prepared in the usual way for the E/M, is subjected to further treatment with osmium tetroxide (it should be remembered that it takes prolonged treatment with osmium tetroxide to demonstrate the Golgi apparatus for light microscopy) dense granular material is then apparent in and beside the vacuoles in electron micrographs (Fig. 72). This finding suggests that the vacuoles actually contain some material that reduces metallic salts, and hence that the vacuoles and their contents may be the important agent in permitting the Golgi apparatus to be demonstrated by the classic impregnation methods for light microscopy. Moreover, the vacuoles may be responsible for the *appearance* of clear canals seen originally by Holmgren.

2. *Aggregations of smooth-surfaced double-layered membranes* (*lamellae*), arranged parallel with one another, on each side of groups of vacuoles (Figs. 71 & 73). It is very probable that these membranes represent sections cut through flattened vesicles, and it is to be emphasized that their outer surfaces are not studded with RNA granules as are similar flattened vesicles in most other parts of the cytoplasm. Furthermore, the flattened vesicles of the Golgi apparatus are more closely packed than rough-surfaced flattened vesicles.

3. *Microvesicles* or *Granules*. These are about 400 Å in diameter and are of low electron-scattering power; hence, they appear relatively light in electron micrographs (Figs. 71 & 73) in contrast with the darker and smaller RNA granules seen elsewhere in the cytoplasm. The microvesicles tail off, as it were, from the ends of the flattened smooth-walled vesicles described under (2); hence, it is probable that they arise as a result of the ends of the flattened vesicles becoming pinched off; this suggests that they are actually very small vesicles and not of a uniform composition throughout, as is generally true of granules.

The system of smooth-surfaced membranous vesicles that comprises the Golgi apparatus is not isolated from the other parts of the system of intracytoplasmic membranes; instead, it is

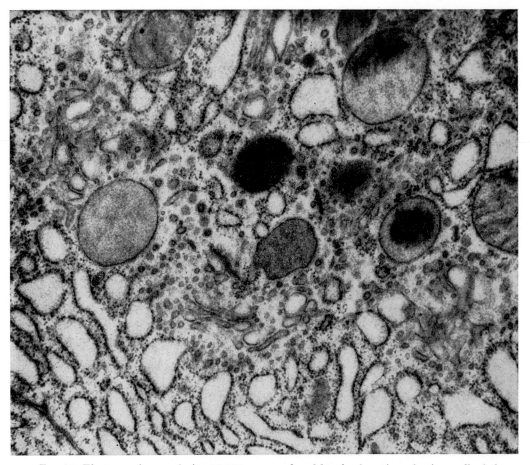

FIG. 73. Electron micrograph ($\times$ 36,000 as reproduced here) of section of acinar cell of the pancreas of a guinea pig. Across the bottom the cytoplasm reveals an abundance of rough-surfaced vesicles of the endoplasmic reticulum; this is characteristic of the more basal part of the cell. In the middle of the illustration and immediately above the middle, many small rounded (smooth-surfaced) microvesicles of the Golgi apparatus may be seen. Just below the center of the picture a few elongated flattened smooth-surfaced vesicles of the Golgi apparatus are obvious. A few that are distended may also be seen here and toward the upper left. The upper half of the picture reveals many large zymogen granules enclosed in smooth-surfaced vesicles of the Golgi apparatus. It is in the region encompassed by this illustration that the zymogen granules that are primarily synthesized in the rough-surfaced vesicles of the endoplasmic reticulum become consolidated and segregated in smooth-surfaced vesicles of the Golgi apparatus, and it is from the latter vesicles that they are delivered into the lumens of acini. (Preparation by Dr. G. E. Palade)

generally believed that it connects with them, being more or less continuous with the rough-surfaced tubules and vesicles of the endoplasmic reticulum (Fig. 73).

Functions. For many years there was general agreement with the concept that the Golgi apparatus was somehow concerned in secretion. When the E/M became available, it was observed that the zymogen granules that are secreted by the cells in the pancreas come to be enclosed in smooth-surfaced vesicles of the Golgi apparatus. To many, this at first seemed to confirm an idea that has been expressed before, having evolved from light microscope studies—that secretion granules are synthesized in the Golgi apparatus. However, this view did not fit with the emerging concept of the cytoplasmic RNA of the cell controlling protein synthesis, because there are no RNA granules associated with the vesicles of the Golgi apparatus. The problem has been resolved, as will now be described.

Production and Secretion of Zymogen Granules. Palade studied the cells of the pancreas of animals that were starved and found that under these conditions the rough-surfaced vesicles of the endoplasmic reticulum in the basal parts of pancreatic cells are closely packed together and exhibit little content. About an hour after a starved animal is fed, the previously flattened vesicles begin to distend, with large dense granules (but smaller than typical zymogen granules) making their appearance within them. Sometimes several are seen in the same vesicle (Fig. 65). After homogenizing cells at this stage and separating the different cell fractions with the centrifuge, Palade was able to show that these granules that developed in the rough-surfaced vesicles in the basal part of the cell contained the enzymes and the precursors of enzymes that characterize zymogen granules. Therefore, this study showed that the actual synthesis of the material of zymogen granules occurs in the rough-surfaced tubules and vesicles of the endoplasmic reticulum in the basal part of the pancreatic cell, and that this synthesis is controlled by cytoplasmic RNA.

Subsequently, zymogen granules make their appearance in the Golgi region and here they are found in smooth-surfaced membranous vesicles (Fig. 73). The fact that the granules later appear in smooth-surfaced vesicles could be explained in either of two ways: (1) that the vesicles in which the granules were formed moved to the Golgi region, losing their RNA granules on the way; or (2) as Palade believes, that the rough-surfaced tubules and vesicles of the endoplasmic reticulum connect with the smooth-surfaced vesicles of the Golgi region, thus permitting the granules to move from vesicles in which they were formed into new ones in which they are stored. Since the granules that appear in the vesicles of the Golgi apparatus are larger than those that are seen in the rough-surfaced vesicles in the basal part of the cell, it would seem that the larger granules represent consolidations of the smaller ones.

As long ago as 1939, Hirsch, from studies made with the light microscope, came to the conclusion that the Golgi apparatus functions as a site of segregation and condensation of secretory products formed elsewhere in the cell. The recent studies with the E/M made by Palade and others support the concept that the material of the zymogen granules is synthesized in the rough-surfaced tubules and vesicles of the endoplasmic reticulum, a concept suggested in an early E/M study by Weiss. Therefore, it would seem that the Golgi apparatus is not a site of synthesis, but, as Hirsch suggested, a site for segregation and condensation.

From his E/M studies, Palade has shown that the zymogen granules are segregated from the cytoplasm by smooth-surfaced membranes not only up to, but also *during*, the time that they are secreted. When a granule, enclosed by a membrane, reaches the free surface of the cell, its surrounding membrane becomes continuous with the cell membrane that covers the free surface of the cell. The granule then breaks through the fused membrane and thereby gains entrance to the lumen of the acinus. However, this does not incur a break in the continuity of the cell membrane at the free surface, for the membrane around the deeper part of the granule remains intact, and since it becomes fused with the cell membrane around the edges of the departing granule, the contents of the cell are always enclosed by a continuous membrane.

The Centrosome

The centrosome, cytocentrum or cell center is a tiny cytoplasmic organelle that, as its name implies, lies as close to the center of the cell as possible. If cells have indented nuclei, this cytoplasmic organelle can closely approach the center of the cell, as is shown in Figure 34, but in most cells the center of the cell is occupied by nuclear material. Hence, in the majority of cells the centrosome lies close to the more central side of the nucleus.

It so happens that the site that is occupied by the centrosome in most cells is the same site in which the Golgi apparatus is contained. Accordingly, what is sometimes termed the *centrosome area* is approximately the same area as that described as the Golgi region. However, the centrosome is not considered as a part of the Golgi apparatus but as a separate organelle.

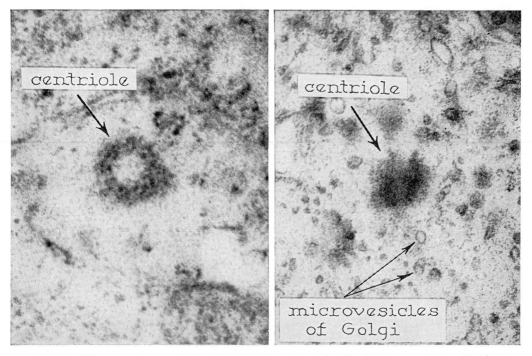

Fig. 74. Electron micrograph (× 65,000) of sections of cells showing centrioles. (*Left*) A centriole has been cut in cross section; this shows that its form is tubular and it has longitudinally disposed fibrils in its wall. (*Right*) A section passing obliquely through the end of a tubular centriole is illustrated; in this the fibrils can be seen in longitudinal section. (Preparation by A. Howatson)

A centrosome, although present in most animal cells, cannot be seen in H and E sections. However, if sections are stained with iron hematoxylin the site of the centrosome is indicated by one or two dark dots (Fig. 34); these are centrioles and they, together with the area of cytoplasm that immediately surrounds them, constitute the centrosome.

Functions. The centrioles seem to have a function in organizing fibrillar material. To give one example: they seem to play a part in the formation of little hairlike processes, termed *cilia* or *flagellae*, which extend from some kinds of cells. The fine structure of cilia will be considered later in connection with epithelial tissue, but it is of interest here to mention that the fine structure of cilia has certain resemblances to the fine structure of centrioles which will be described here. Another example of centrioles organizing fibrillar material about them is to be seen in mitosis, for, as has already been described, the two centrioles separate in mitosis, and astral rays of fibrillar material appear about them (Fig.

37). They continue to separate until each reaches a pole of the cell, and the astral rays between them become highly developed to constitute the spindle (Fig. 38).

Fine Structure. It is obvious that such tiny structures as centrioles would seldom be seen in the thin sections used in the E/M. Since centrioles are better developed and easier to see in dividing cells, Bernhard used colchicine to arrest mitosis, and this made it easier for him to find examples of centrioles in thin sections. He describes them as being from 0.3 to 0.6 μ in length and about 0.1 μ in width and as having the form of an open-ended cylinder. The wall of the cylinder is composed of a number (probably 9) of longitudinally arranged fibrils which are grouped around a central lumen. Between and around the fibrils there is some dark granular material. With good resolution the fibrils appear double and hollow. As will be noted later, cilia have a somewhat similar kind of structure.

Figure 74 illustrates two examples of centrioles encountered in sections by Dr. Allan

Howatson. The one on the left is a cross section; this shows the cylindrical form of the centriole. The one on the right is an oblique section cut through one end of a cylindrical centriole; hence, it appears as a dark horseshoe-shaped structure.

Fibrils, Microfibrils and Fibrillar Structures Within the Cytoplasm

Unfortunately, there are no set rules about how wide a threadlike body must be to be called a fiber or about how fine it should be to be called a fibril, a microfibril or a filament. In general, fibers can be seen clearly with the low power of the light microscope, while fibrils can be seen only with the high-power or the oil-immersion objective, but there are some exceptions to this rule. Microfibrils, filaments and protofibrils can be seen only with the E/M.

If cells have a threadlike shape, as do muscle cells, the cells themselves are called fibers, or if long threadlike strands of cytoplasm extend off from cells, as occurs in nerve cells, these processes are termed fibers. Threadlike structures *within* the cytoplasm of cells and visible with the light microscope are termed fibrils. It should be pointed out here, however, and this will be elaborated on in the following chapter, that nonliving fibers and fibrils also exist; these are present outside of cells in the intercellular substance that lies between cells. So, fibrils will be seen both inside and outside of cells. When examined with the E/M, both kinds may be found to contain microfibrils, filaments or protofibrils, but not all kinds of fibers and fibrils do.

Here we are concerned only with the fibrils that are contained in living cells and form parts of the cytoplasm and hence are organelles of the cell. The best example of this kind is to be found in muscle cells, and these will be described in detail in Chapter 19.

Fibrils are present in a few other kinds of cells, for example, some epithelial cells contain little protein fibrils; these will be discussed in Chapter 11, which deals with Epithelial Tissue, for they are described most appropriately in connection with *Terminal Bars, Desmosomes* and the *Cell Web,* and all of these structures are described to best advantage in Chapter 11.

Having finished our consideration of the nucleus and the organelles of the cytoplasm,

except for a further description and discussion of fibrils, filaments and fibrillar structures within the cell, which will be given in Chapters 11 and 19, we now can consider in somewhat more detail the phenomenon of cell differentiation.

CELL DIFFERENTIATION

By means of *cell proliferation* a multicellular body develops from a single cell, the fertilized ovum. During this process the cells of the developing body begin to become different from one another. The process by which this takes place is termed *cell differentiation,* and it results in the cells of the body eventually becoming divided up into families, the members of each being different from the members of the others, not only in their appearance but also in their ability to perform particular kinds of work. Moreover, differentiation does not end with the establishment of different cell families, for it continues to operate within many of them. Just as families of people consist of adults (who work) and of children who have the potentiality to grow up and become (differentiate into) working adults, many cell families have members which exist in different states of maturity, with the less mature cells more or less constantly differentiating into more mature types.

The problems that are involved in trying to understand how a single cell evolves into the body of a man or a woman, consisting of billions of cells which are organized into different family units to perform different functions for the body as a whole, are so numerous, so difficult and so incompletely solved that the student might question why they should be brought to his notice. Certainly, this is an area where the teacher cannot present a well-organized sequence of facts, which can be remembered easily and can explain matters to the student's satisfaction. However, it is an intriguing area of biology that will fascinate the imaginative student. Moreover, it is an area where at least a few general principles have been established; these must be learned in order to anticipate what will happen in certain disease processes and after certain surgical procedures. Finally, it should be appreciated that only by further exploration of the problems in this field may we hope someday to understand one of the most important diseases of mankind, cancer, for this disease is inherently an expression of some defect in the constellation of those factors that are responsible for maintaining an organized state of affairs in the body in postnatal life. Therefore, we shall now discuss some of the problems in this field and some of the available facts and the theories which relate to these problems in one way or another.

As has been noted previously, the nature and the function of any cell is determined by the proteins that enter into its structure and by the enzymatic activities in which many of these proteins engage. The proteins differ with regard to the number of amino acids that enter into the composition of their molecules and the sequences in which these amino acids are arranged. The number and the sequences of amino acids in any particular protein are probably determined directly by the nucleotide sequences of either the DNA or the RNA of the cell (although some protein appears to be formed in close association with DNA, most, and perhaps all, is synthesized in direct association with RNA). The whole problem would be much simpler if we could assume that all of the nucleotide sequences in the RNA of the cell were determined and controlled by the DNA. If the RNA were the perfect servant of the DNA, with no independence whatsoever, in looking for factors that affect differentiation we would only have to look for factors that affect DNA, for all functions of the cell would be dependent on it alone. But, this has not yet been established; hence, it is possible that there could be factors that affect the RNA of a cell, making it different from before without these factors first or even ever affecting the DNA of the cell. In any event, as we begin to examine some of the factors that have been shown to be concerned in differentiation, we can try to visualize whether they could directly or indirectly affect the DNA or the RNA of the cell, for these are the materials that determine the protein constitution of the cell.

Perhaps the first concept to consider is that genes can be present in a cell without expressing themselves and so disclosing their presence. For example, the fertilized ovum must possess all the genetic potentiality that is subsequently expressed by all the many different kinds of cells that evolve from it. Yet it does not exhibit, for instance, the highly developed contractile properties of the muscle cells, or the highly specialized secretory properties of the cells of the pancreas that develop from it. Therefore, there must be some mechanism whereby genetic potentiality can exist in a cell without its being expressed. This could be due to agencies that supress gene function or to an absence of agencies through which genes act. We shall consider the latter possibility.

If it could be shown that as the fertilized ovum continues to divide, agencies through which genes express themselves are not equally divided between all the progeny of the ovum, there would be some reason for thinking that one way in which cells become different from one another is by their being allotted different amounts of the chemical materials present in the ovum through which genes act. There are examples which suggest that a mechanism such as this may explain the early differentiation in some embryos. For instance, along the axis of the egg of an amphibian there are regional differences in the appearance of the cytoplasm, its various parts containing different amounts of pigment and yolk. The pigments and the fat serve as markers and permit the fate of these different areas of cytoplasm to be followed through subsequent cell divisions. Where the different regions of cytoplasm of the fertilized egg are distributed unequally among the cells of the embryo it becomes obvious that the cells receiving cytoplasm from one region become one kind of structure, and those that receive another cytoplasmic region become another structure, and so on. Supporting this view that differentiation can be influenced by the distribution of substances through which genes may act is the finding that if eggs are caused to divide along an abnormal plane of cleavage, so that the cytoplasm of different areas of the egg is not distributed properly to certain groups of daughter cells, development is faulty.

In experiments of the kind described above, the unequal distribution of different cytoplasmic constituents among daughter cells is followed by tracing the fate of, say, the yolk or the pigment present in the egg to the cytoplasm of the daughter cells. However, it should not be concluded that different amounts of yolk or pigment are necessarily involved in the expression of different genetic functions in the daughter cells; these substances serve only as "markers" that can be followed by the observer. Once the fact of unequal distribution of cytoplasm is established, it could be reasoned that the RNA of the ovum also is distributed unequally, and this could explain why the different daughter cells become different from one another, for if they received different kinds and different amounts of RNA, their protein-synthesizing functions would be different.

It has been mentioned already that genetic potentiality can exist in a cell without its being expressed. Indeed, one school of thought adheres to the view that all the cells of the body retain the same full genetic potentiality as was possessed by the ovum from which they originated. Yet, as we shall see, the evidence that is presently available suggests very strongly that cells which differentiate in one direction lose their potentiality for differentiating in another. Hence, if full genetic potentiality is retained by all differentiated somatic cells, there must be some very effective mechanism which acts to suppress, seemingly on a permanent basis, certain genetic potentialities when others are fully expressed; furthermore, this mechanism must operate so effectively that the differentiated cell, for all practical purposes, can be considered to have lost some of its potentiality. In fact, the evidence for cells, once differentiated, being able to express genetic potentiality in only that one direction is so strong that a second school of thought about this matter subscribes to the view that certain genes of differentiated cells are not merely suppressed—they are lost. Which school of thought is correct probably will be settled in due course. But, at the moment, a great deal of our thinking about the behavior of cells in disease is predicated on the assumption that specialized cells actually lack the genes that would permit them to perform all different kinds of specialized functions, so that in the following, while keeping in mind that the first view possibly may be correct, we shall lean heavily toward the second view.

The concept that differentiation in the embryo is associated with a loss of genetic potentiality on the part of the differentiating cells is strongly supported (but not completely proved) by the experiments of Briggs and King and their associates. These investigators developed a method whereby they can remove the nuclei of cells of different parts of developing frog embryos. They then transplant the nuclei from the embryonic cells into enucleated eggs to develop into complete embryos. They have found that after a certain amount of differentiation has occurred in the embryo, nuclei that are transplanted to eggs will still often permit a complete embryo to form. But, as differentiation proceeds further in the embryo, the nuclei of the more differentiated cells, on transplantation into eggs, do not permit a complete embryo to form. Therefore, it seems justified to assume that cells that have differentiated into some special family of cells in the body have nuclei which have lost some of the genetic potentiality that they formerly possessed.

In the preceding paragraph, evidence indicating that differentiation is associated with a loss of genetic potentiality has been given. As differentiation continues, it results in different families of cells making their appearance in the body. The cells of these exhibit something more than a loss of full potentiality; they reveal that the cells of different family types have evolved different genetic constitutions. Thereafter, the cells of each family can reproduce only their own family type of cell.

As will be explained shortly, environmental factors can play an important part in inducing cells to differentiate into different family types. However, environmental factors can act this way only if the cells are sufficiently undifferentiated to respond to them. Once the cells have been affected by the environmental influence and have differentiated into some family type, they are said to be *determined* or to have developed *cell specificity*. From this point on they will reproduce only their own kind.

That the specificity, demonstrated by the cells of each of the cell families in the body, is due to their particular genetic constitution and not to their being in some particular environment can be proved many ways. For example, cells of a particular family can be transplanted to some other environment in the body, and in this new environment they produce cells, not similar to those that ordinarily live in this environment, but of their own family type; this fact is depended upon in certain surgical procedures. Furthermore, if cells that have developed specificity are removed from the body and grown in tissue culture, where they are apart from many of the environmental influences they would be subject to in the body, they will, in this new medium, continue to reproduce their own kind; indeed, they can subsequently be transplanted back into the body from which they were derived and therein still continue to reproduce their own kind. Finally, when one or more cells of some particular cell family, such as those that produce bone, undergo a malignant transformation and grow into a tumor, the cells of that tumor—even though they have undergone a genetic change because of their undergoing a malignant transformation—still indicate their original specificity, because they continue to attempt to produce bone. Indeed, the fact that cells of malignant tumors, even though they spread to distant parts of the body from their site of origin, continue to manifest in some degree their original characteristics enables the pathologist to classify tumors as to whether they arose from this or that type of cell. Therefore, the evidence is very strong to the effect that the differentiation of cells is associated with some loss of their genetic potentiality and, furthermore, with their eventually coming to have one of many different kinds of special genetic constitutions that characterize the cell families of the body.

The next point to mention is that although environment does not change the genetic nature of cells *after* they have differentiated into some family type (cells whose nature has been *determined*), environmental factors do play a very important part beforehand, for they are often responsible for *inducing* cells whose nature has not yet been determined to differentiate into some family type. Much of the differentiation that occurs in the embryo, resulting in the establishment of different kinds of cells, seems to be due to the ability of tissue developing along one path to induce differentiation in adjacent cells whose nature has not yet been determined. There are many examples of the induction of differentiation by this means; one is illustrated in Figure 568. This is seen in connection with the develop-

ment of the eye. The developing brain sends out a protrusion, called the optic vesicle (the rudimentary retina of the eye), toward the ectoderm covering that region. This exerts a profound effect on the ectoderm in this region, causing its cells to differentiate into lens cells (Fig. 568). There are many other examples of one tissue inducing differentiation in another during development, and the phenomenon has lent itself to much experimental investigation by embryologists. The evidence suggests that the phenomenon involves the passage of some chemical from the inducing tissue into that in which differentiation is triggered. Unfortunately, the chemical basis for induction is not yet clear.

However, there are a few examples of the induction of differentiation by chemical agents which might be mentioned, because descriptions of them will be encountered later in this book. As is described in Chapter 27, every fertilized ovum has the potentiality to develop the organs and the structures of either the male or the female reproductive system. Whether it develops into one or the other depends on whether the steroid hormones that are present in the circulation of the embryo and the fetus are of the male or the female type. Normally, the genetic mechanism in a male embryo causes it to develop sex glands that make male hormones in embryonic life. But, if a genetically determined male embryo, because of some accident in development, does not form sex glands that produce male sex hormone, it will not develop the usual reproductive organs of the male but, instead, those of the female; the reason for this is that every embryo is exposed to female sex hormone produced by the placenta, and a male embryo which does not produce male sex hormone to counteract this, will not only develop male organs but will develop female organs. This state of affairs has no effect on the chromosomal structure of the individual who will retain through life a Y chromosome in all his somatic cells.

Another example of the chemical induction of differentiation, a description of which will be encountered later in this book, provides an example of how a foreign protein can induce specific cell differentiation in postnatal life. We each possess a particular family of cells that are concerned with providing us with antibodies which can act against disease-causing organisms and the toxins that they produce. Most of those who read this were injected with diphtheria toxoid when they were young to provide them with immunity against diphtheria; therefore, we shall use diphtheria toxin for our example. Diphtheria toxoid (modified diphtheria toxin) is a protein; on being injected into the body, it causes certain cells to become highly specialized for producing antibodies which react against diphtheria toxin and nullify its effects. The mechanism is probably as follows. The family of cells that make antibodies have members in various stages of differentiation. The first time diphtheria toxoid is injected into the body, it reaches and affects some of the least differentiated members of this family. Present-day evidence suggests that these unspecialized cells have the capacity to produce, and actually do produce, in very small quantities, an almost infinite variety of antibody proteins. Among these are proteins that have the particular molecular configuration that fits with that of the protein of diphtheria toxoid or toxin. The toxoid unites with this particular antibody protein and so, in effect, removes it from the cell. The cell responds to this removal of one of its products by immediately producing more of this product and this, in turn, is removed by the same mechanism, whereupon the cell makes still more and more until finally it is highly specialized to make this particular antibody protein.

Cells specialized to make a particular antibody persist. Therefore, if at a later time the body is exposed once more to diphtheria toxin, the cells specialized to make diphtheria antitoxin respond immediately by dividing and giving rise to a colony of cells, all of which are specialized to make antibody to this particular antigen. Thus, the mechanism by which antibodies are produced provides an example of how a foreign protein can induce the differentiation of a cell so that thereafter it will transmit its special differentiated qualities to its daughter cells. The way that this seemingly genetic change is brought about is not clear, but it would seem probable that the exploitation of the capacity of the RNA to synthesize antibody protein of a particular type must act somehow to diminish the ability of the RNA to synthesize antibody protein of

other types, and that this characteristic is passed on to daughter cells.

The examples of differentiation that have been described so far could all be explained by a hypothesis which postulates that the increasing expression of some particular genetic potentialities of cells is associated with a reciprocal loss of their genetic potentialities for other special functions, and, as a consequence, differentiation involves a change in the genetic nature of cells. It is probably a question of semantics as to whether or not changes in the genetic potentiality of cells that occur in development should be classified as somatic mutations. If so, the development of the body could be said to be dependent on an orderly sequence of mutations occurring in its proliferating cells, with many of these mutations being induced by environmental influences.

In view of the concept given above and the evidence that supports it, it is very difficult to conceive of there being such a phenomenon as *dedifferentiation,* for this would require that a cell could regain lost genetic potentiality. Yet, dedifferentiation has its advocates. Dedifferentiation has often been called upon to explain, for example, why, in an adult body, bone sometimes develops in an area in which only ordinary fibrous tissue normally is found. Superficially, it might seem that in this area the differentiated fibroblasts, which make the ordinary fibrous tissue, had undergone dedifferentiation and then had redifferentiated into osteoblasts, which make bone. However, it seems much more probable that this is not what occurs, but instead that there are among the fibroblasts in the area some mesenchymal cells that have never differentiated, and that under some new and appropriate stimuli they differentiate into osteoblasts and make bone. Whereas it seems unlikely that dedifferentiation occurs in the higher animals, there is evidence suggesting that it can occur in lower animals. If this is accepted, it would have to be explained by certain cells of these animals being able to develop differentiated qualities without simultaneously losing genetic potentiality.

Another term that should be mentioned here is *anaplasia,* for this is sometimes confused with dedifferentiation. Anaplasia occurs in cells that undergo a malignant transformation and so constitute a cancer. Such cells tend to lose the differentiated qualities ordinarily associated with the cells from which the differentiated cells developed; this is what is meant by anaplasia. However, this does not mean that the malignant cells have regained any potentiality; their changed appearance is due only to their having lost their ability to express differentiated qualities. Therefore, the development of a malignant tumor does not provide an example of dedifferentiation (which infers regaining genetic potentiality) but, instead, of anaplasia (which means only loss of differential features).

All the examples of differentiation, and even the malignant transformation of cells that is the basis for cancer, could be explained by cells losing genetic potentiality and exploiting such as remains. However, it is possible that some of the induction of differentiation that occurs in the developing embryo, and the malignant transformation of cells that occurs in cancer, could be due not entirely to loss of genetic potentiality but to cells acquiring extra genetic material from each other or from other sources. It is very difficult to obtain evidence about this from the study of mammalian cells, but certainly there is evidence from the studies that have been made on bacteria that this phenomenon is possible. These studies will now be described briefly.

Some years ago it was shown that if the DNA from one special strain of bacteria was added to cultures of bacteria of a somewhat different type, the latter would take on some of the characteristics of the strain from which the DNA was obtained and pass these characteristics on to their descendants. This phenomenon is known as *transformation,* and it shows that DNA with genetic potency from one source can be incorporated into the genetic material of another strain of bacteria and thereafter is transmitted to subsequent generations.

Another way in which the genetic constitution of bacterial cells can be changed is by infection with certain viruses. The essential component of virus particles is either DNA or RNA. Ordinarily, when a susceptible cell is infected with a virus, the metabolic machinery of the cell co-operates in multiplying the virus so that the cell is overwhelmed by it and dies. But there are certain viruses that infect certain kinds of bacterial cells and sometimes produce a very different effect. In these instances, the DNA of the virus, after the virus gains entrance to the bacterial cell, is not multiplied as an entity. Instead, it becomes incorporated into the DNA of the genetic material of the cell and in this site loses its identity as a virus and acts as additional genetic material, thus endowing the bacterial cell with new inheritable properties, and is duplicated at the same rate as all the other DNA of the cell. Therefore, there are examples from the study of bacterial cells of both nuclear DNA from other cells and viral DNA becoming incorporated into, and thereby altering, the genetic material of a cell.

It has also been shown that genetic information can be transmitted to cells by RNA viruses. All these observations relating to genetic information being sent to cells from outside encourages speculation as to whether or not a transference of RNA or perhaps even DNA from one cell to another is not one factor involved in normal differentiation. Granted that an environmental influence on cells in a given area induces their differentiation, what is responsible for the differentiation of many cells of the same general type that are not so close to the inducing agent? It is an intriguing thought that once a few cells have differentiated, they could effect the differentiation of adjacent undetermined cells by transferring genetic material to them.

Whether or not the incorporation of genetic material from outside sources is a factor in effecting any of the normal differentiation that occurs in the embryo is problematical at the moment. However, a good case can be made for this being the cause of the malignant transformations that occur in many animal species. It has now been shown that there are several viruses that, if they are injected into newborn animals, will bring about a malignant transformation in certain of the cells of the animal. The way in which these tumor viruses induce a genetic change in the cells that they infect is not yet clear, and it is possible that different mechanisms are involved, for some of the tumor viruses are RNA viruses, and others are DNA viruses. One fact of interest that is emerging from these studies is that relatively undifferentiated rather than differentiated cells are the ones that are susceptible to genetic

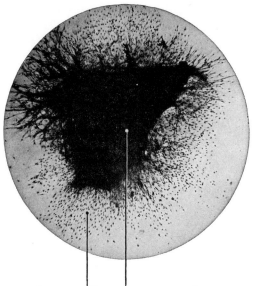

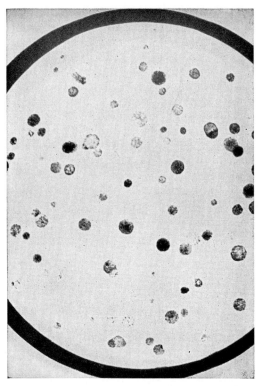

outgrowth   fragment

Fig. 75. (A, *Left*) Low-power photomicrograph of a stained tissue culture. The dark central mass represents the tissue that was transplanted; new cells constituting an outgrowth may be seen radiating out from it. (B, *Right*) Photograph of colonies of L cells growing on glass in fluid medium. Each colony formed from a single cell. (Preparation by Dr. G. F. Whitmore)

nature changes by a tumor virus. This may suggest that virus nucleic acid somehow interferes with the normal genetic change that would have occurred in the cell in its normal differentiation.

Probably enough has been said to suggest that the mechanisms involved in differentiation involve complex relationships between genetic and environmental factors. We have some clues to these factors, but they are not yet satisfactorily understood, and further insight into them will become possible only with further developments in our knowledge of the chemistry of genetic material and its interactions with other parts of cells and their environment in different stages of prenatal and postnatal development and life.

CELL AND TISSUE CULTURE

This is a method whereby cells or even small portions of organized structures that are removed from the body can be kept alive or, in many instances, grown in glass receptacles that contain nutritive media kept at body temperature. The method is commonly termed the *in vitro* (*vitrum* = glass) technic. Some of the reasons for attempting to isolate and grow particular kinds of cells by this procedure will now be described briefly.

There are profound difficulties associated with investigating the factors that affect any particular kind of body cell while these cells are in the body, living with innumerable cells of other kinds. For example, suppose that an investigator wished to determine whether some chemical substance affected some particular kind of cell directly. If he administers the substance to a whole animal and observes some effect on the kind of cell he is investigating, he does not know whether the effect he observes is a direct one on that kind of cell or only an indirect one resulting from the substance first having affected some other kind of cell, which thereupon made something that *did* affect the cell that he is investigating, or whether the substance he administered was changed into something else which affected the cells he was studying, or whether it had some effect on other cells which resulted in their inhibiting an effect on the cells in question which the substance otherwise would have exerted. Such difficulties are avoided by investigating cells grown in pure cultures. Furthermore, it is much easier to obtain quantitative data on cells grown in vitro; for example, they can be counted at intervals, and, therefore, accurate data can be obtained on the way different substances affect their rate of proliferation. And, since it is possible to grow cells in glass containers which permit the cells to be under almost continuous observation with the ordinary light, or even the phase microscope, they can be studied most effectively, and their behavior can even be recorded by time-lapse photography with the motion picture camera.

Methods. One very simple way of obtaining a culture of cells is to remove a tiny piece of tissue from a body (using sterile technic) and to plant it in a suitable medium in a suitable glass receptacle. In the earlier days of cell culture, the explant of tissue was commonly placed in a drop of blood plasma, together with some embryonic juice and a balanced salt solution. The blood plasma formed a clot, and this served as a framework along which cells would grow out from the explant (Fig. 75, A). However, more modern methods involve the transplantation of free cells, rather than of pieces of tissue, to glass containers. This is commonly done as follows. An organ or a portion of an organ is removed from a body under aseptic conditions and is minced finely. Then the enzyme trypsin is added to the minced tissue; this dissolves the attachments by which the cells are held together and, as a result, the individual cells of the tissue become free. Next, the suspension of dissociated cells is placed in suitable media in glass vessels; here the cells stick to the glass and commence to mutiply. Since the cells consume food from and excrete waste products into the medium, and since they may greatly increase in number, it is necessary, if their further in vitro culture is to be carried on, either to scrape them from the glass container at intervals, or to disperse them again by trypsin and then add a suitable sample of the cells to fresh medium in a fresh culture vessel. Cells from many, but not all, parts of the body can be grown in this way.

It is usually very difficult to propagate freshly explanted cells for many generations. However, a few lines of cells are available which are sufficiently adapted to cell culture conditions to grow indefinitely. These are termed "stable" cell lines. They include two famous ones, both of which are cells that have undergone a malignant transformation. One strain, the HeLa cells, was derived from a cancer in a woman; the other, L cells, were obtained from a normal mouse but underwent a malignant transformation while in cell culture.

Methods for Studying Cells in Culture. Cells will spread and multiply on glass surfaces so that cell cultures can be grown in flat-bottomed glass bottles, petri dishes or test tubes. For histologic or cytologic work, the cells are propagated in flat-bottomed glass vessels containing either coverslips or slides. The cells grow on the coverslips or the slides, and then these can be removed, fixed and stained for examination. For biochemical or physiologic work, the cells can be studied either during their growth on glass, or, with some cell lines, the cells can be grown in suspension; with the latter, sampling is more uniform.

The number of cells in cultures can be assayed quantitatively by various methods. Probably the simplest is to suspend the cells with trypsin and then count an aliquot in a hemocytometer (the way this is done is described in Chapters 7 and 8). A more rigid method is to determine the number of cells in the suspension that are capable of growing into a colony. This is done by placing a suitable aliquot of the suspended cells in a flat glass vessel in a medium known to support their growth. Each viable cell sticks to the glass, commences to divide, and over a period of between 1 and 2 weeks gives rise to a colony (Fig. 75, B). From the number of colonies one can calculate the number of cells that could form colonies in the original cell population. In a healthy culture, this number will be nearly equal to the count obtained in a hemocytometer.

FIELDS OF RESEARCH IN WHICH CELL CULTURES ARE USED

Viruses. Probably the most striking example of a discipline benefiting from the in vitro technic is that of virology. As has been explained already, viruses, in order to propagate, must parasitize living cells. All or nearly all known viruses can be propagated in cells grown in vitro and, in almost every instance, the growth of these viruses can be assayed very accurately in such cells. Indeed, this is now the chief way that fundamental investigations on viruses are pursued. The virus used to make polio vaccine is grown in cells cultivated in vitro.

Nutritional Requirements of Cells. A second area of research that has profited greatly by cell culture is cell nutrition. Since the in vitro technic allows for *controlled* variation of the constituents of the media in which the cells are propagated, it has been possible to measure the exact nutritional requirements of cells by this means. Interestingly enough, different types of cells have almost the same nutritional requirements. However, there are certain differences. For example, Puck has shown that if an explant containing more than one type of cell is made and grown in two different types of media, two different types of cells grow out from it (Fig. 76). The two types of cells that emerge from the explant under these two conditions are different genetically, and the differences are maintained through subsequent subcultures. A nongenetic morphologic change can be "induced" in cells by changing the serum in the medium in which they are growing. To some extent cells assume characteristic morphologies which are dependent on the serum in the medium. This is not a genetic change, for, if the cells are grown with the original type of serum, they change back again.

Genetics. The use of cell cultures has provided the possibility of a new way to study the genetics of somatic cells. The major reason for this is the ability to obtain colonies from single cells. Colonies of many different types of mammalian cells can now be obtained fairly easily in vitro, and new cultures can be initiated from these colonies. Any genetic changes

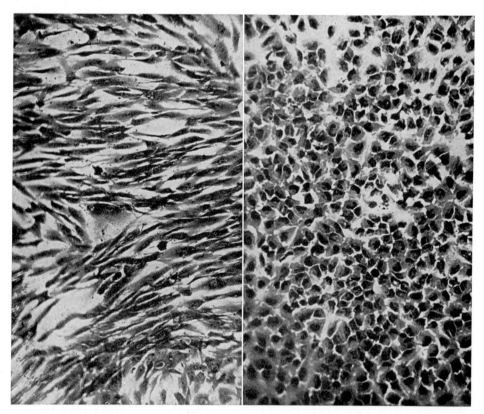

Fig. 76. Photomicrograph showing 2 different types of cells that grew out from the same explant under different nutritional conditions. (Preparation by Dr. T. T. Puck)

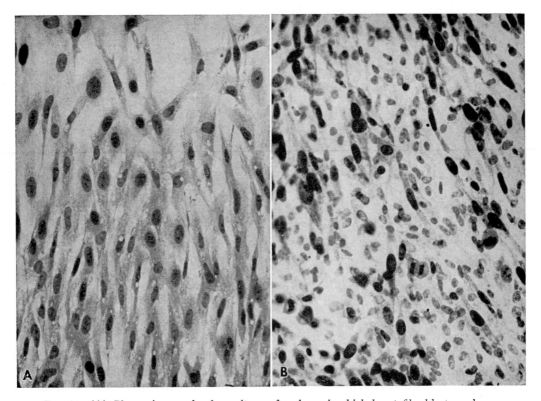

FIG. 77. (A) Photomicrograph of a culture of embryonic chick heart fibroblasts and mouse embryo fibroblasts growing on glass. The mouse cells were planted above the top, and the chick cells below the bottom of the picture. In the area illustrated the mouse cells have grown from above to meet the chick cells that have grown up from below. The mouse cells have darker nuclei than the chick cells and better defined cytoplasmic processes. Notice that these 2 types of cells remain in general toward their respective ends of the culture and, in particular, they both stay in the form of a monolayer; neither type grows up over the other type. (B) Photomicrograph of a culture of chick embryo fibroblasts and mouse sarcoma cells growing on glass; the latter have large dark nuclei. The sarcoma cells have grown down from the top of the picture and the chick cells up from below the bottom of the picture. Notice that the normal cells and the sarcoma do not inhibit each other's growth, for they are freely intermingled; furthermore, they have not continued to grow in the form of a monolayer; instead, they are piled up on one another.
(Preparation by Dr. M. Abercrombie)

that occur can then be picked up easily. Thus the ability to form colonies with animal cells in vitro has aided in determining mutation rates in somatic cells and has made possible the selection and the observation of different cell genotypes.

Radiation. It has been extremely difficult to measure with any precision the radiation sensitivity of different kinds of mammalian cells while they are still in the body. The in vitro technic has made this possible. The ease of making quantitative studies in vitro, and

the ability of mammalian cells to form colonies in vitro, has allowed numerous investigators to measure accurately the radiation sensitivity of different kinds of mammalian cells. This is done by growing a culture of cells in vitro, irradiating the culture and then measuring the number of cells in this culture that are then able to form colonies. Of course, as the dose increases, the percentage of cells in the original culture able to form colonies decreases, and, by this means, a dose-survival curve can be obtained. Curiously enough, it has been found

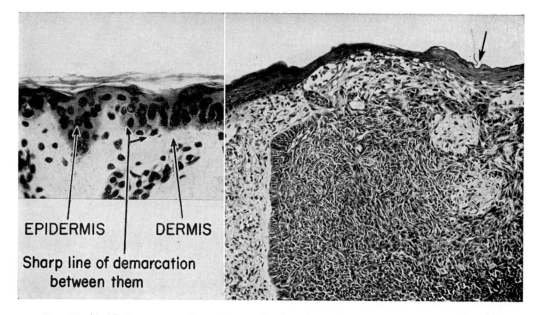

EPIDERMIS | DERMIS

Sharp line of demarcation
between them

Fig. 78. (*Left*). Low-power photomicrograph of section of thin skin of man. Note the sharp line of demarcation between the epidermis and the dermis that is characteristic of normal skin. (*Right*) Low-power photomicrograph of cancer of the skin. The epidermal cells as a result of some change in their nature have, at the point indicated by the arrow, invaded the underlying dermis and therein proliferated to form a mass of cells that constitutes a cancer.

that all the different types of cells so far examined in this way have nearly the same radiation sensitivity. The same technic can be used to measure the effects of other agents that affect the capacity of cells to divide.

Cell Cycles. The measurement of the duration of different periods of the cell cycle by using cell cultures has already been mentioned. Cells grown in vitro offer very suitable material for this type of work because: (1) the addition of the labeled thymidine can be controlled accurately in time and in concentration; and (2) the cells can be prepared readily for radioautography.

Biochemistry. It can be readily understood that the ability to have large numbers of cells of one kind growing in a controlled environment is of immense value to those interested in the biochemistry of the mammalian cell. Indeed, cells grown in vitro have served as material for numerous profitable studies on the transport of materials into cells, enzymology, and so on.

Cell Interactions. The ability to grow cells in vitro has enabled investigators to examine the effect of cells on one another. One extensive investigation of this kind has been made by Abercrombie. He has shown that under normal conditions fibroblasts migrate across the surface of a glass vessel by amoebalike movements. However, if such fibroblasts are confronted with another culture of fibroblasts moving in the opposite direction, the movement of both groups is severely inhibited (Fig. 77, A). Abercrombie has called this *contact inhibition*. However, if the *fibroblasts* are confronted with sarcoma cells (fibroblasts that have undergone a malignant transformation), contact inhibition *does not occur* (Fig. 77, B). Although the sarcoma cells originate from fibroblast cells, the transformation to malignancy dramatically alters their properties in respect to their relationship to other cells. It is tempting to think that this lack of contact inhibition may be related to the invasiveness of tumors (Fig. 78, *right*, shows tumor invasiveness).

Another very interesting study of cell interactions that can be investigated in cell cultures has been made by Moscona. He found that if cells that are differentiating into some particular structure in the embryo—for example, the cells in a limb bud that are forming cartilage, or the cells that are forming into liver cords—are removed from the embryo, dissociated with trypsin and then put in cell cultures, they will reassemble to form the kind of structure that they composed before they were dissociated; for example, dissociated chrondroblasts reassemble to form a mass of developing cartilage. Furthermore, he found that if developing cartilage from both chick and mouse is dissociated and the dissociated cells placed in the same culture, the chick cells and the mouse cells all assemble together to form cartilage that contains both chick and mouse cells. His studies indicate that the affinity that dissociated cells from developing tissues demonstrate in cell cultures relates to the kind of developing tissues from which they are derived rather than to the species from which they were obtained; for example, chick chondroblasts associate with mouse chondroblasts in preference to associating with chick cells that are destined to form some tissue other than cartilage.

Perhaps related to the same phenomenon that Moscona has studied is another curious affinity exhibited by cells in the whole animal. If an animal is given enough whole-body radiation, its hemopoietic tissues are unable to keep producing blood cells, and the animal will die. But, if an animal, given what would otherwise be a lethal dose of radiation, is then injected intravenously with cells from the hemopoietic organs of an animal of the same strain, the injected cells take up a position in the hemopoietic tissues of the radiated animal and reproduce and provide the animal with blood cells so that it does not die. The curious aspect of this is that the injected hemopoietic cells do not grow just anywhere in the animal; they settle out and proliferate in the sites where it is normal for hemopoietic tissue to exist.

TISSUE AND ORGAN CULTURE

One of the difficulties associated with cell cultures is that dissociated cells from many parts of the body will not grow as independent entities in cell cultures. However, if pieces of tissue or organs, or even whole small organs, are placed in nutritive media, many cells that cannot be propagated independently in cell cultures will survive and grow to some extent, as long as their association with the other components of the tissue or organ in which they normally reside are maintained. The possibility of cultivating tissues and organs in vitro has one advantage over cell culture in that it permits observations to be made on the process of differentiation, for this process, as has been explained, depends in part on the ability of differentiating cells of one type to influence the differentiation of others.

CYTOPLASMIC INCLUSIONS

The term *cytoplasmic inclusion* is used for any structure that can be seen in the cytoplasm and is not part of the special living system of protoplasm (Fig. 34, *left*). Inclusions differ from organelles fundamentally in that they are not parts of living systems; they are nonliving materials that somehow come to be *included* in cytoplasm. There are 3 main types:

1. Stored foods
2. Secretion granules and globules
3. Pigments

STORED FOODS

A healthy man may withstand starvation for weeks. During the time he takes no food, his metabolism, though somewhat altered, continues. This requires a constant supply of fuel. Since he obtains no food from outside sources, he must draw on his internal stores. These consist mostly of foods that have been stored in the cytoplasm of certain of his cells as inclusions.

There are 3 basically different types of foods that can be used by the body for energy; carbohydrates, fats and proteins, and all 3 types, under ordinary circumstances, are stored to some extent by cells to provide for a time of need. These food materials are not stored to the same degree by all types of cells; as might be expected, some cells have become specialized to serve as food stores for the body. Carbohydrates are stored chiefly in the cells of the liver and in the cells of muscle. Fat is stored chiefly by special cells called fat cells that are distributed widely throughout the body but particularly in the fat depots (for example, over the belly). Protein is not stored in the

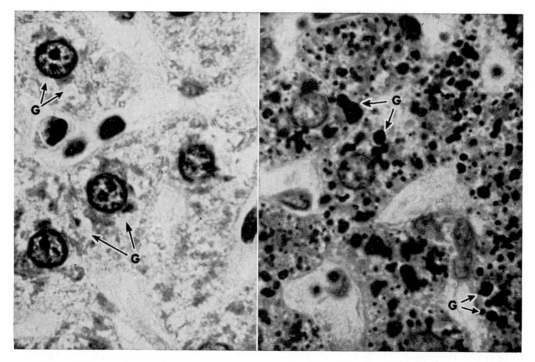

Fig. 79. Photomicrographs of sections of liver of well-fed rat. (*Left*) An H and E section, and the sites of glycogen in the cytoplasm are indicated by irregular ragged clear areas (G). (*Right*) A similar section stained by the P.A.S. technic which colors the glycogen magenta and this appears black in the photograph (G).

form of a specific inclusion, for cytoplasm itself is composed chiefly of protein, and in times of need cells may catabolize their own, or other cells', protoplasm. In a sense, a degree of protein storage is achieved by having large healthy cells.

Since the cells of the liver normally store carbohydrate, and since they sometimes accumulate fat, they may be studied to advantage to learn the appearances conferred on cells by their storing carbohydrate or fat as inclusions.

Carbohydrate is absorbed from the intestine in the form of glucose, and this is brought to the liver by the blood stream. To store it, the cells of the liver convert it into animal starch. This is called *glycogen*. Glycogen is not stained in H and E sections. However, a fairly good idea of the glycogen content of liver cells can be obtained from an H and E section because ordinary aqueous fixatives harden the cytoplasm of cells more quickly than they dissolve out its glycogen; hence, the glycogen

content of a cell acts more or less as a "mold" around which the cytoplasm "sets" on fixation. Then, as the glycogen dissolves away, open spaces are left in the hardened cytoplasm which indicate the site it formerly occupied. The pattern of open spaces left in the cytoplasm of liver cells by the dissolving away of glycogen is fairly characteristic: the open areas are irregular in shape and have ragged borders (Fig. 79, *left*). A cell that contained almost no glycogen when it was fixed has cytoplasm of a more even texture than one that had even moderate amounts of it. A considerable amount of glycogen in a cell (Fig. 79, *left*) does not tend to displace the nucleus to one side of the cell and flatten it to the same extent as does a great deal of fat in a cell (Fig. 81).

Glycogen in cells can be demonstrated beautifully by the histochemical method known as the P.A.S. technic, which will be described in the next chapter. This technic colors the glycogen red (Fig. 79, *right*).

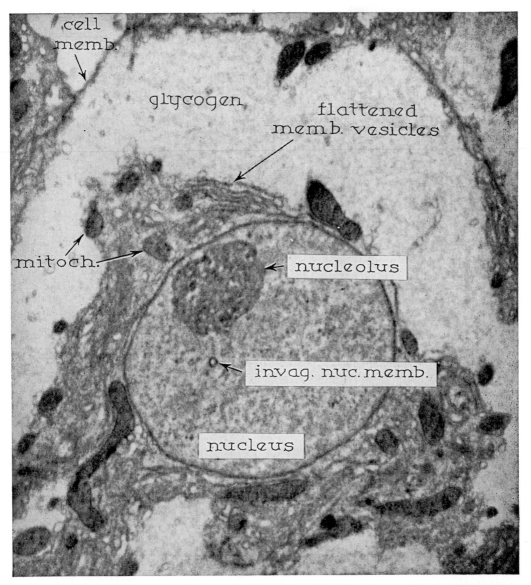

Fig. 80. Electron micrograph (× 11,000) of a section of the liver of a rat fetus in a late stage of development. The membranous vesicles and the mitochondria are closely associated, and areas of cytoplasm containing each are separated by structureless appearing material, most of which is probably glycogen. The nucleus shows a large nucleolus as well as an invagination of the nuclear membrane that has been cut in cross section. (Preparation by A. Howatson)

Fine Structure. Accumulations of glycogen in cytoplasm appear in electron micrographs as pale amorphous areas, as is illustrated in Figure 80. It is of interest that mitochondria and membranous vesicles retain their close association to one another as glycogen accumulates in liver cells; hence, areas of cytoplasm, containing both mitochondria and membranous vesicles, may become widely separated from one another by extensive areas of amorphous material (Fig. 80). That the material labeled glycogen in Figure 80 was actually glycogen was indicated by the fact that other sections obtained from the same liver and stained by

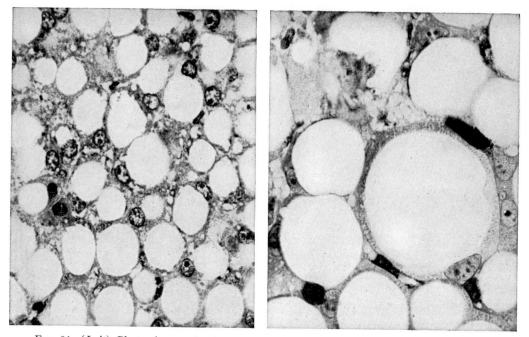

FIG. 81. (*Left*) Photomicrograph of a section of liver from a rat which had experienced a choline deficiency for 12 days. McGregor stain, × 600. The liver cells that are distended with fat are almost twice as wide as normal cells. (*Right*) A similar preparation from a rat that experienced the same kind of deficiency for 45 days. Observe that individual cells have liberated their fat into a cyst which is surrounded by several cells. The black structures seen are capillaries that have been injected with India ink. (Hartroft, W. S.: Anat. Rec. *106*:61)

the P.A.S. technic revealed similar areas of P.A.S.-positive material in the cytoplasm.

Fat is mostly stored in fat cells but it may also accumulate in liver cells, particularly under conditions of dietary deficiency.

How is stored fat in cytoplasm recognized? Fat dissolves away in the preparation of the usual section, in the clearing agents, in which it is very soluble. It can be fixed by a special fixative, osmic acid, so that it does not dissolve out of a section so readily with clearing agents; hence, osmic-acid fixation permits fat to be demonstrated (Fig. 286). It can also be demonstrated by cutting frozen sections and, without subjecting them to either dehydrating or clearing agents, staining them with special fat stains (for example, Scharlach R., which colors the fat droplets a bright red).

In most instances, however, a useful appreciation of the amount of fat that has been present in cells can be obtained by studying the pattern of the cytoplasm that is left behind after the fat has dissolved away. Like glycogen, fat in cytoplasm forms a mold around which cytoplasm sets on fixation. Fat first accumulates in cells in the form of small droplets (Fig. 154), which tend to fuse to form larger droplets. If a droplet is very large, the cell becomes little more than a thin shell around the fat droplet (Fig. 81, *left*); when this is sectioned, it gives the cell a "signet-ring" appearance, the nucleus forming the bulge or "signet" (Fig. 154, *right*). Hartroft has shown that under certain conditions liver cells take up more fat than they can contain subsequently in their cytoplasm. As adjacent cells continue to take up fat their thin walls, at the sites where they touch one another, first fuse and then, as the process continues, they rupture. The fat globules formerly contained in single cells then coalesce into a single pool, and the large globule so formed is surrounded by the crescentic segments of the original cells that still persist about the periphery of the large globule (Fig. 81, *right*). The surrounding cells, although they form a continuous membrane around the large globule, do not actually fuse; so as a result the fat of the large globule is actually extracellular, being contained, as it were, in the cavity of an epithelial cyst. Such structures that form in the liver or in other fat-containing tissues are termed *fatty cysts* (Fig. 81, *right*).

The pattern of open spaces left in liver cells by the dissolving out of fat droplets is different from that left by the dissolving out of glycogen. The spaces left by dissolved fat are spherical and have smooth outlines (Fig. 81). These differ from the jagged outlines of the spaces left by dissolved glycogen (Fig. 80, *left*). Furthermore, as already noted, fat tends to displace the nucleus of the cell to one side and flattens it more than glycogen does.

Proteins are not stored as inclusions. Cytoplasm itself is chiefly protein, and in starvation, cells may, up to a point, consume their own cytoplasm. In this sense, there is a normal reserve of cytoplasm which can serve as stored protein.

Secretion Granules and Globules

Cells that are specialized to secrete the various digestive juices and other special potent fluids needed by the body must synthesize these products in their cytoplasm from raw materials brought to them by the blood and tissue fluid. Commonly, on being synthesized, the material to be secreted is dispersed in the cytoplasm in the form of tiny globules. These are not part of the cytoplasm but constitute new, nonliving material that has been made in the cytoplasm and will be extruded from the cell; hence, secretory granules are inclusions rather than organelles. On fixation, the globules of secretion contained in the cytoplasm usually become coagulated to form granules. Since globules of secretion are commonly studied in fixed tissue, therefore they are commonly called *secretion granules*.

The synthesis, the transport, the delivery and the fine structure of secretion granules already has been described and illustrated (Figs. 65 and 73).

Pigments

The need for the medical student to become interested in the color of tissues cannot be emphasized too strongly. A most important factor and sometimes the chief one in the clinical diagnosis of some diseases is the changed color of some part of the body. Color is of even greater importance to the pathologist than to the clinician. A good part of the description of the gross appearance of diseased organs at operation or at autopsy relates to their changed color. Therefore, the student is advised to learn the causes of the different normal and abnormal colors of the various parts of the body.

Color in any tissue is due chiefly to its content of pigment. Moreover, pigments are usually present in tissues as cytoplasmic inclusions in cells. Fortunately, there are only a few broad groups of pigments with which the student should become familiar. Much is known about some of these but relatively little about others.

It is important to realize what constitutes a pigment. There are many ingredients of cells that, while colorless in life, take on brilliant colors after they are treated with stains. These are *not* pigments. To qualify as a pigment a material must possess color in life; hence, a pigment, to be seen, does not need to be treated with stains. However, pigments are sometimes colored further or differently by stains.

Classification of Pigments. Pigments are usually divided into two groups, *exogenous* and *endogenous*. Exogenous pigments are those that have been *generated* as such *outside* the body and subsequently taken into it by one route or another. Endogenous pigments are *generated inside* the body from nonpigmented ingredients.

Exogenous Pigments. There are several kinds of these and they may be taken into the body in various ways. An important group consists of various vegetable pigments, particularly those of the *carotenoid* group. *Carotin*, the pigment of carrots but contained also in other vegetables, is a very important one. Under normal conditions, enough vegetable pigment is absorbed to color only certain cells of the body, but when carrots or certain other vegetables are eaten to excess, enough carotin may be absorbed and retained to color a great deal of the body; indeed, even the skin and the body fluids may become tinged with it (carotinemia), and a patient demonstrating this condition may, until suitable tests are made, be thought to have jaundice.

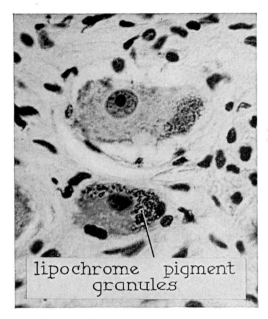

lipochrome pigment granules

FIG. 82. High-power photomicrograph of a human nerve ganglion. Two ganglion cells may be seen in the picture; their cytoplasm contains numerous granules of lipochrome pigment.

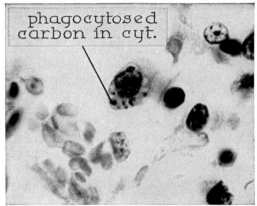

phagocytosed carbon in cyt.

FIG. 83. High-power photomicrograph of a section of a rat's lung. A large alveolar phagocyte may be seen in the center of the picture; its cytoplasm contains granules of phagocytosed carbon derived from smoke.

LIPOCHROMES. Yellow pigments may be found in many kinds of body cells under normal conditions (Fig. 82). Before the extent to which vegetable pigments could be absorbed and retained by the body was known, it was customary to designate many of the yellow pigments found in certain cells as *lipochromes* because it was believed that they were colored fatty materials and probably endogenous in nature. It now seems likely that many of the pigments formerly called lipochromes are of vegetable origin and hence exogenous.

DUSTS. A second important group of exogenous pigments is provided by the various kinds of dusts that gain entrance to the respiratory system through inspired air. Pigmentation of parts of this system by this means is of course pathologic. But there is so much particulate matter in the air in towns and cities where coal is used that it is a usual, if not normal, condition. Coal dust in the tissues of the lungs is termed anthracosis (*anthrax =* coal; *osis =* increase, invasion) and it is of very common occurrence (Fig. 83).

Coal dust is not as harmful to the lungs as certain other particles that may be inhaled by unprotected workers in certain trades. Silica particles, for example, when present in lung tissue in sufficient amounts (silicosis), may lead to serious complications, as will be explained in the study of pathology.

MINERALS. Certain minerals taken by mouth or absorbed through the surface of the body may lead to pigmentation. For example, too much silver applied to body surfaces in the treatment of certain diseases may lead to an accumulation of silver and hence a gray pigmentation of the body. Lead can be absorbed to give a blue line on the gums.

Tattoo marks are due to pigments being driven deeply into the skin by needles.

Endogenous Pigments. The most important one is *hemoglobin,* the iron-containing coloring matter of red blood cells. This serves as the great oxygen carrier of the body. It will be discussed in detail in Chapter 7, so further comment on it will be omitted here. Certain altered forms of hemoglobin, of a different color from the normal, will also be discussed in the same chapter. Here we shall content ourselves with a brief discussion of a group of pigments that result from the normal destruction of hemoglobin in the body.

Pigments from the Destruction of Hemoglobin. Under normal conditions, red blood cells do not survive for more than a few months in the circulatory system. As they wear out, they are phagocytosed by certain large cells in the spleen, the liver and the bone marrow. In the cytoplasm of these, the iron-containing hemoglobin is broken down into an iron-containing pigment called *hemosiderin* and a noniron-containing one called *hematoidin* or *bilirubin*.

Hemosiderin is golden brown and is disposed in the cytoplasm of phagocytes in the form of granules or small irregular masses. By suitable chemical tests hemosiderin can be shown to contain iron; this permits it to be distinguished from the other golden and brown pigments of the body.

The normal human body is very economical of iron, and that of the hemoglobin of old red blood corpuscles is mostly used over again in the synthesis of hemoglobin for new ones. It is not known if all the iron liberated from the breakdown of hemoglobin is converted to hemosiderin before being used over again. Furthermore, little is known about how the iron from hemosiderin goes back into solution to allow its subsequent use in building new hemoglobin.

Whereas hemosiderin is normally present to some extent in the phagocytes of the spleen, the liver and the bone marrow, it becomes greatly increased in these sites in diseases in which red blood corpuscles are broken down much more rapidly than usual. It may even appear in large quantities in certain other cells under certain pathologic conditions.

Hematoidin and Bilirubin. Bile is a yellow-to-brown fluid secreted by the liver, stored and concentrated in a bag termed the gall-bladder, and eventually passed into the intestine where it plays an important role in absorption and digestion. Its coloring matter is *bilirubin*, a yellow-to-brown pigment which is easily oxidized to *biliverdin*, a green pigment. In some animals (birds), a considerable amount of biliverdin is present normally in their bile, hence their bile tends to be green, but in man only a little biliverdin is normally present, so human bile is yellow to brown.

For many years it was believed that bilirubin was manufactured by the liver cells that secrete it. But with further studies it became apparent that bilirubin, like hemosiderin, is a breakdown product of hemoglobin

and hence formed in the sites where old, worn-out red blood corpuscles are destroyed. Unlike hemosiderin, however, bilirubin contains no iron and is very soluble; hence it does not tend to remain in the cytoplasm of the phagocytes that destroy red blood cells but instead dissolves into the blood, from which it is continuously removed by the cells of the liver to be transferred into the bile.

It took a great many observations and experiments to prove that bilirubin originated from hemoglobin. The first tangible lead was given by Virchow, the originator of the cell-state concept, about 100 years ago. He observed that crystals of pigment tended to form in tissues of the body that were the sites of former internal hemorrhages. He named the pigment that crystallized out among the old breaking-down red blood corpuscles in such areas *hematoidin* and concluded that it was derived from hemoglobin. Not content with microscopic examinations alone, he subjected deposits of this pigment to chemical tests and made the remarkable discovery that hematoidin, so far as these tests would demonstrate, was the same thing as the pigment that colors bile (bilirubin), and said "this was of especial interest from its being supposed that the colored constituents of bile are products of the decomposition of the coloring matter of the blood."

However, for many years afterward, hemoglobin was not accepted as the origin of bile pigment and it is only in the last few decades that the idea has gained general acceptance. For further reading the student is advised to consult Rich's most admirable review.

Melanin is usually a brown-to-black pigment found chiefly in the skin and its appendages and in the eye. In white races it appears in skin in appreciable amounts after exposure to sunlight (suntan). Melanin accounts for the dark color of the Negro; here too, however, the degree of pigmentation is increased by sunlight. The color of eyes is due to melanin. Deep in the eye melanin is used as a light-proofing material much in the same way as photographers use black paper, black curtains and black paint (Fig. 574). Melanin appears in the body in the form of granules or clumps of granules in the cytoplasm of cells as inclusions (Fig. 365).

Melanin is a nitrogenous substance **that in**

pure form contains no sulphur or iron. For a time it was suspected that melanin, like hemosiderin and bilirubin, originated from breaking-down hemoglobin, but this theory has long been discredited. The modern theory owes much to studies made on plants. These were found to contain enzymes that, given the opportunity, oxidize certain colorless chromogens (substances that can generate color) of the plant into pigment. The phenomenon can easily be studied by slicing a raw potato. When the fresh-cut surface is exposed to air (oxygen), the enzymes of the potato oxidize certain colorless chromogens of the potato into a brown-to-black pigment. Cooks who peel potatoes in advance of a meal keep them in water away from oxygen to prevent them from darkening.

The problem of melanin formation will be considered in detail in connection with skin in Chapter 22; for the present, it is enough to say that melanin probably forms inside certain body cells by a mechanism somewhat similar to that described for plants. Cells that make melanin are termed *melanoblasts*. They contain an enzyme capable of acting on a colorless chromogen brought to the cell by the blood and tissue fluid, and converting it into melanin.

REFERENCES

For the convenience of the reader the references are arranged as far as possible according to the order in which different aspects of the cell are considered in this chapter and will be found under the following different headings:
General References on the Cell
Morphology of Chromosomes and Chromatin Granules (including Fine Structure)
Polyploidy and Aneuploidy
Use of Colchicine in the Study of Mitosis
The Sex Chromatin
The Chemistry and Histochemistry of Chromosomes and Chromatin (including Studies with Labelled Thymidine)
The Nucleolus, RNA and Protein Synthesis
Nuclear Membrane
Nuclear Sap
Mitochondria
Ergastoplasm (Cytoplasmic RNA)
The Cell Membrane
The Endoplasmic Reticulum
The Golgi Apparatus
The Centrosome
Cell Differentiation

Cell and Tissue Culture
Stored Food in Cells
Pigment in Cells

GENERAL REFERENCES ON THE CELL

Bernhard, W.: Ultrastructural aspects of nucleo-cytoplasmic relationship, Exp. Cell Res. (Supp. 6), *17*:50, 1958.
Bourne, G. (ed.): Cytology and Cell Physiology, ed. 2, London, Oxford, 1952.
Brachet, J., and Mirsky, A. E. (eds.): The Cell, New York, Acad. Press, 1959.
DeRobertis, E. D. P., Nowinski, W. W., and Saez, F. A.: General Cytology, ed. 3, Philadelphia, Saunders, 1960.
Engström, A., and Finean, J. B.: Biological Ultrastructure, New York, Acad. Press, 1958.
Hayashi, T. (ed.): Subcellular Particles, New York, Ronald Press, 1959.
Howatson, A. F., and Ham, A. W.: The fine structure of cells, Canad. J. Biochem. & Physiol. *35*:549, 1957.
McElroy, W. D., and Glass, B. (eds.): The Chemical Basis of Development, Symposium, Baltimore, Johns Hopkins Press, 1958.
Palay, S. L. (ed.): Frontiers in Cytology, New Haven, Conn., Yale University Press, 1958.
Waddington, C. H. (ed.): Biological Organization: Cellular and Sub-cellular, New York, Pergamon Press, 1959.

MORPHOLOGY OF CHROMOSOMES AND CHROMATIN GRANULES INCLUDING FINE STRUCTURE

Dales, S.: A study of the fine structure of mammalian somatic chromosomes, Exper. Cell Res. *19*:577, 1960.
Darlington, C. D.: Evolution of Genetic Systems, ed. 2, Edinburgh, Oliver, 1958.
Fawcett, D. W.: The structure of the mammalian spermatozoon, Internat. Rev. Cytol. *7*:195, 1958.
Hall, C. E., and Litt, M.: Morphological features of DNA macromolecules as seen with the electron microscope, J. Biophys. & Biochem. Cytol. *4*:1, 1958.
Kaufmann, B. P., and De, D. N.: Fine structure of chromosomes, J. Biophys. & Biochem. Cytol. (Supp.) *2*:419, 1956.
Mazia, D., and Katsama, D.: The isolation and biochemical characterization of the mitotic apparatus of dividing cells, Proc. Nat. Acad. Sc. *38*:826, 1952.
Porter, K.: Changes in cell fine structure accompanying mitosis *in* Fine Structure of Cells, p. 236, New York, Interscience, 1955.
Porter, K. R.: Problems in the study of nuclear fine structure *in* Bargmann, W., Peters, D., and Wolpers, C. (eds.): Fourth Internat. Confer-

ence on Electron Microscopy, vol. 2, pp. 186-9, Berlin, Springer-Verlag, 1960.

Ris, H.: A study of chromosomes with the electron microscope, J. Biophys. & Biochem. Cytol. (Supp.) 2:385, 1956.

———: The submicroscopic structure of chromosomes in Fine Structure of Cells, p. 121, New York, Interscience, 1955.

———: Chromosome structure in McElroy, W. D., and Glass, B. (eds.): Chemical Basis of Heredity, p. 23, Baltimore, Johns Hopkins Press, 1957.

———: Fine structure of the nucleus during spermiogenesis in Proc. X Internat. Congress of Genetics, vol. II (Abstracts), p. 235, 1958.

Rothfels, K. H., and Siminovitch, L.: The chromosome complement of the Rhesus monkey (Macaca mulatta) determined in kidney cells cultivated in vitro, Chromosoma 9:163, 1958.

Schrader, F.: Mitosis: The Movements of Chromosomes in Cell Division, New York, Columbia Univ. Press, 1944.

Schultz, J., and Lawrence, P.: A cytological basis for a map of the nucleolar chromosome in man, J. Hered. 40:31, 1949.

Swanson, C. P.: Cytology and Cytogenetics, Englewood Cliffs, N. J., Prentice-Hall, 1957.

Taylor, J. H., and Woods, P. S.: In situ studies of polynucleotide synthesis in nucleolus and chromosomes in Hayashi, T. (ed.): Subcellular Particles, New York, Ronald Press, 1959.

Tjio, J. H., and Levan, A.: Some experiences with acetic orcein in animal chromosomes, An. Estacion Exper. da Aula Dei 3:225, 1954.

———: Quadruple structure of the centromere, Nature 165:368, 1950.

Tjio, J. H., and Puck, T. T.: The somatic chromosomes of man, Proc. Nat. Acad. Sc. 44:1229, 1958.

POLYPLOIDY AND ANEUPLOIDY

Alfert, M.: Quantitative cytochemical studies on patterns of nuclear growth in Fine Structure of Cells, p. 157, New York, Interscience, 1955.

Beams, H. W., and King, R. L.: The origin of binucleate and large mononucleate cells in the liver of the rat, Anat. Rec. 82:281, 1942.

Levan, A., and Hauschka, T. S.: Endomitotic reduplication mechanisms in ascites tumors of the mouse, J. Nat. Cancer Inst. 14:1, 1953.

Sachs, L., and Shelesnyak, M. C.: The development and suppression of polyploidy in the developing and suppressed deciduoma in the rat, J. Endocrinol. 12:146, 1951.

Stich, H. F.: The DNA content of tumor cells. II. Alterations during the formation of hepatomas in rats, J. Nat. Cancer Inst. 24:1283, 1960.

Wilson, J. W., and Leduc, E. H.: Abnormal mitosis in mouse liver, Am. J. Anat. 86:51, 1950.

———: The occurrence and formation of binucleate and multinucleate cells and polyploid nuclei in the mouse liver, Am. J. Anat. 82:353, 1948.

USE OF COLCHICINE IN STUDIES OF MITOSIS

Eigsti, O. J., and Dustin, P.: Colchicine in Agriculture, Medicine, Biology, and Chemistry, Ames, Iowa State College Press, 1955.

Hooper, C. S.: Timing of mitotic phase. Use of colchicine for the measurement of the mitotic rate in the intestinal epithelium, Exper. Cell Res. (in press), 1960.

Leblond, C. P., and Walker, B. E.: Renewal of cell populations, Physiol. Rev. 36:255, 1956.

Price, D. (ed.): Dynamics of Proliferating Tissue, Chicago, Univ. Chicago Press, 1958.

SEX CHROMATIN

Barr, M. L.: The sex chromatin and its application to errors in sex development in Modern Trends in Obstetrics and Gynaecology, London, Butterworth, 1960.

———: Sex chromatin and phenotype in man, Science 130:679, 1959.

———: Sexual dimorphism in interphase nuclei, Am. J. Human Genet. 12:118, 1960.

———: Nuclear sex, Science 126:1187, 1957.

Barr, M. L., and Bertram, E. G.: A morphological distinction between neurons of the male and female, and the behaviour of the nucleolar satellite during accelerated nucleoprotein synthesis, Nature 163: 676, 1949.

Barr, M. L., Bertram, L. F., and Lindsay, H. A.: The morphology of the nerve cell nucleus, according to sex, Anat. Rec. 107:283, 1950.

Davidson, W. M., and Smith, D. R.: A morphological sex difference in the polymorphonuclear neutrophil leucocytes, Brit. M. J. 1:6, 1954.

Graham, M. A.: Sex chromatin in cell nuclei of the cat from the early embryo to maturity, Anat. Rec. 119:469, 1954.

Grumbach, M. M., and Barr, M. L.: Cytologic tests of chromosomal sex in relation to sexual anomalies in man in Hormone Research, vol. 14, p. 255, New York, Acad. Press, 1958.

James, J.: Observations on the so-called sex chromatin, Ztschr. Zellforsch. u. mikr. Anat. 51:597, 1960.

Klinger, H. P.: The fine structure of the sex chromatin body, Exper. Cell Res. 14:207, 1958.

Moore, K. L.: Sex reversal in newborn babies, Lancet 1:217, 1959.

Moore, K. L., and Barr, M. L.: Nuclear morphology, according to sex, in human tissues, Acta anat. *21*:197, 1954.

————: The sex chromatin in benign tumours and related conditions in Man, Brit. J. Cancer *9*:246, 1955.

————: Smears from the oral mucosa in the detection of chromosomal sex, Lancet *2*:57, 1955.

Moore, K. L., Graham, M. L., and Barr, M. L.: The detection of chromosomal sex in hermaphrodites from a skin biopsy, Surg., Gynec. & Obst. *96*:641, 1953.

Prince, R. H., Graham, M. A., and Barr, M. L.: Nuclear morphology according to sex, in Macacus rhesus, Anat. Rec. *122*:153, 1955.

CHEMISTRY AND HISTOCHEMISTRY OF CHROMATIN AND CHROMOSOMES INCUDING STUDIES WITH LABELED THYMIDINE

Bloch, D. P., and Godman, G. C.: A microphotometric study of the syntheses of desoxyribonucleic acid and nuclear histone, J. Biophys. & Biochem. Cytol. *1*:17, 1955.

Caspersson, T., and Schultz, J.: Nucleic acid metabolism of the chromosomes in relation to gene production, Nature *142*:294, 1938.

Chargaff, E., and Davidson, J. N.: The Nucleic Acids, New York, Acad. Press, 1955.

Chayen, J.: The quantitative cytochemistry of DNA and its significance in cell physiology and heredity, Exper. Cell Res. (Supp.) *6*:115, 1958.

Crick, F. H. C.: The structure of DNA *in* McElroy, W. D., and Glass, B. (eds.): The Chemical Basis of Heredity, p. 532, Baltimore, Johns Hopkins Press, 1957.

Daoust, R., Leblond, C. P., Nadler, N. J., and Enesco, M.: Rates of deoxyribonucleic acid formation and cell production in regenerating rat liver, J. Biol. Chem. *221*:727, 1956.

Davidson, J. N.: The Biochemistry of Nucleic Acids, London, Methuen, 1953.

Hoagland, M. B.: Nucleic acids and proteins, Scient. Am. *201*:55, 1959.

Kornberg, A.: Pathways of enzymatic synthesis of nucleotides and polynucleotides *in* McElroy, W. D., and Glass, G. (eds.): p. 579, Baltimore, Johns Hopkins Press, 1957.

Kurnick, N. B.: Histochemistry of nucleic acids, Internat. Rev. Cytol. *4*:221, 1955.

Leblond, C. P., Messier, B., and Kopriwa, B.: Thymidine-H^3 as a tool for the investigation of the renewal of cell populations, Lab. Invest. *8*:296, 1959.

Lessler, M. A.: The nature and specificity of the Feulgen nuclear reaction, Internat. Rev. Cytol. *2*:231, 1953.

Mazia, D.: Some problems in the chemistry of mitosis *in* McElroy, W. D. and Glass, B. (eds.):

Chemical Basis of Heredity, p. 169, Baltimore, Johns Hopkins Press, 1957.

Mellors, R. C.: Quantitative cytology and cytopathology: Nucleic acids and proteins in the mitotic cycle of normal and neoplastic cells, Ann. New York Acad. Sc. *63*:1177, 1956.

Ochoa, S., and Heppel, L. A.: Polynucleotides synthesis *in* McElroy, W. D., and Glass, B. (eds.): The Chemical Basis of Heredity, p. 615, Baltimore, Johns Hopkins Press, 1957.

Palade, G. E.: Functional changes in structure of cell components *in* Hayashi, T. (ed.): Subcellular Particles, New York, Ronald Press, 1959.

Plaut, W.: The nucleus and ribonucleic acid synthesis in Amoeba Proteus, Exper. Cell Res. (Supp.) *6*:69, 1958.

Schultze, B., and Oehlert, W.: Autoradiographic investigation of incorporation of H^3-thymidine into cells of the rat and mouse, Science *131*:737, 1960.

Sherman, F. G., and Quastler, H.: DNA synthesis in irradiated intestinal epithelium, Exper. Cell Res. *19*:343, 1960.

Stanners, C. P., and Till, J. E.: DNA synthesis in individual L-strain mouse cells, Biochem. et biophys. acta *37*:406, 1960.

Swift, H. H.: Quantitative aspects of nuclear nucleoproteins, Internat. Rev. Cytol. *2*:1, 1953.

Taylor, J. H., and Taylor, S. H.: The autoradiograph—a tool for cytogeneticists, J. Hered. *44*:129, 1953.

Taylor, J. H., and Woods, P. S.: *In situ* studies of polynucleotide synthesis in nucleolus and chromosomes *in* Hayashi, T. (ed.): Subcellular Particles, New York, Ronald Press, 1959.

Thomson, R. Y., and Frazer, S. C.: The desoxyribonucleic acid content of individual rat cell nuclei, Exper. Cell Res. *7*:367, 1954.

Walker, B. E., and Leblond, C. P.: Sites of nucleic acid synthesis in the mouse visualized by radioautography after administration of C^{14}-labelled adenine and thymidine, Exper. Cell Res. *14*:510, 1958.

Warburton, F. E., Leblond, C. P., and Messier, B.: Timing of DNA duplication in the epithelia of esophagus and small intestine of the rat by radioautography after thymidine H^3 injection, Exper. Cell Res. (in press), 1960.

Watson, J. D., and Crick, F. H. C.: Genetical implications of the structure of deoxyribonucleic acid, Nature *171*:737, 1953.

THE NUCLEOLUS, RNA AND PROTEIN SYNTHESIS

Amano, M., and Leblond, C. P.: Comparison of the specific activity time curves of ribonucleic acid in chromatin, nucleolus and cytoplasm, Exper. Cell Res. *20*:250, 1960.

Bernhard, W., Bauer, A., Gropp, A., Hagenau, F., and Oberling, C.: L'ultrastructure du nucleole de cellules normales et cancéreuses: étude au microscope électronique, Exper. Cell Res. *9*:88, 1955.

Carneiro, J., and Leblond, C. P.: Continuous protein synthesis in nuclei, shown by radioautography with H³-labelled amino-acids, Science *129*:391, 1959.

Caspersson, T., and Schultz, J.: Pentosenucleotides in cytoplasm of growing tissues, Nature *143*:602, 1939.

———: Ribonucleic acids in both nucleus and cytoplasm and the function of the nucleolus, Proc. Nat. Acad. Sc. *26*:507, 1940.

Estable, C., and Sotelo, J. B.: The behavior of the nucleolonema during mitosis *in* Fine Structure of Cells, p. 170, New York, Interscience, 1955.

Leblond, C. P., Everett, N. B., and Simmons, B.: Sites of protein synthesis as shown by radioautography after administration of S³⁵-labelled methionine, Am. J. Anat. *101*:225, 1957.

Monty, K. J., Litt, M., Kay, E. R. M., and Dounce, R. L.: Isolation and properties of liver cell nucleoli, J. Biophys. & Biochem. Cytol. *2*:127, 1956.

Ochoa, S., and Heppel, L. A.: Polynucleotides synthesis *in* McElroy, W. D., and Glass, B. (eds.): The Chemical Basis of Heredity, p. 615, Baltimore, Johns Hopkins Press, 1957.

Ohno, S., and Kinosita, R.: On the nucleolus-associated chromatin, Exper. Cell Res. *10*:66, 1956.

Stenram, U.: Nucleolar size in the liver of rats fed on high and nonprotein diets after starvation, Acta anat. *26*:352, 1956.

Vincent, W. S.: Structure and chemistry of nuceloli, Internat. Rev. Cytol. *4*:269, 1955.

See also references under Ergastoplasm

NUCLEAR MEMBRANE

Anderson, E., and Beams, H. W.: Evidence from electron micrographs for the passage of material through pores of the nuclear membrane, J. Biophys. & Biochem. Cytol. (Supp.) *2*:439, 1956.

Barnes, B. J., and Davis, J. M.: The structure of nuclear pores in mammalian tissue, J. Ultrastructure Res. *3*:131, 1959.

De, D. N.: Ultrastructure of nuclear membrane of plant cells, Exper. Cell Res. *12*:181, 1957.

Haguenau, F., and Bernhard, W.: Particularités structurales de la membrane nucléaire: étude au microscope électronique de cellules normales et cancéreuses, Bull. cancer *42*:537, 1955.

Kautz, J., and DeMarsh, Q. B.: Fine structure of the nuclear membrane in chick embryo cells: nature of the so-called "pores" in the nuclear membrane, Exper. Cell Res. *8*:394, 1955.

Lehmann, F. E.: Functional aspects of submicroscopic nuclear structures in amoeba proteins, and of the mitotic apparatus of tubifex embryos, Exper. Cell Res. (Supp.) *6*:1, 1958.

Pappas, G. D.: Helical structures in the nucleus of amoeba proteins, J. Biophys. & Biochem. Cytol. (Supp.) *2*:431, 1956.

Watson, M. L.: Pores in the mammalian nuclear membrane, Biochem. et biophys. acta *15*:475, 1954.

———: The nuclear envelope; its structure and relation to cytoplasmic membranes, J. Biophys. & Biochem. Cytol. *1*:257, 1955.

———: Further observations on the nuclear envelope of the animal cell, J. Biophys. & Biochem. *6*:147, 1959.

NUCLEAR SAP

Brown, G. L., Cullan, H. G., and Leaf, G.: Chemical nature of nuclear sap, Nature *156*:600, 1950.

MITOCHONDRIA

Allard, C., Mathieu, R., de Lamirande, G., and Cantero, A.: Mitochondrial population in mammalian cells, Cancer Res. *12*:407, 1952.

Bensley, R. R.: On the nature of the pigment of mitochondria and of submicroscopic particles in the hepatic cell of the guinea pig, Anat. Rec. *98*:609, 1947.

———: Studies on the pancreas of the guinea pig, Am. J. Anat. *12*:297, 1911.

Bensley, R. R., and Gersh, I.: Studies on cell structure by the freezing-drying method. II. The nature of mitochondria in the hepatic cell of Amblystoma, Anat. Rec. *57*:217, 1933.

Bensley, R. R., and Hoerr, N.: The preparation and properties of mitochondria, Anat. Rec. *60*:449, 1934.

———: Studies on cell structure by the freezing-drying method. VI. The preparation and properties of mitochondria, Anat. Rec. *60*:449, 1934.

Bourne, G. (ed.): Mitochondria and Golgi apparatus *in* Cytology and Cell Physiology, p. 99, London, Oxford, 1942.

Claude, A., and Fullam, E. F.: Electron microscope study of isolated mitochondria, J. Exper. Med. *81*:51, 1945.

Cowdry, E. G.: The mitochondrial constituents of protoplasm, Contrib. Embryol. *271*:39, 1918.

Dempsey, E. W.: Variations in the structure of mitochondria, J. Biophys. & Biochem. Cytol. (Supp.) *2*:305, 1956.

Green, D. E.: Mitochondrial structure and function, J. Lab. Invest. *8*:443, 1959.

Hoffman, H., and Grigg, G. W.: An electron microscopic study of mitochondria formation, Exper. Cell Res. *15*:118, 1958.

Hogeboom, G. E., Schneider, W. C., and Palade, G. E.: Cytochemical studies of mammalian tissues: (1) Isolation of intact mitochondria from rat liver—some biochemical properties of mitochondria and submicroscopic particulate material, J. Bio. Chem. *172*:619, 1948.

Low, F. N.: Mitochondrial structure, J. Biophys. & Biochem. Cytol. (Supp.) *2*:337, 1956.

Palade, G. E.: An electron microscope study of the mitochondrial structure, J. Histochem. *1*: 188, 1953.

——: The fine structure of mitochondria, Anat. Rec. *114*:427, 1952.

——: Functional changes in the structure of cell components *in* Hayashi, T. (ed.): Subcellular Particles, p. 64, New York, Ronald Press, 1959.

Pappas, G. D., and Brandt, P. W.: Nuclear-mitochondrial relationship in Pelomyxa, J. Biophys. & Biochem. Cytol. *6*:91, 1959.

Scarpelli, D. G., and Pearse, A. G. E.: Cytochemical localization of succinic dehydrogenase in mitochondria, Anat. Rec. *132*:133, 1958.

Schneider, W. C.: The biochemical composition of mammalian mitochondria, J. Histochem. *1*: 212, 1953.

ERGASTOPLASM (CYTOPLASMIC RNA)

Bernhard, W., Haguenau, F., and Oberling, C.: La structure submicroscopique des éléments basophiles cytoplasmiques dans le foie, le pancréas, et les glands salivaires, Ztschr. Zellforsch. u. mikr. Anat. *27*:281, 1952.

Bernhard, W., and Rouiler, C.: Close topographical relationship between mitochondria and ergastoplasm of liver cells in a definite phase of cellular activity, J. Biophys. & Biochem. Cytol. (Supp.) *2*:73, 1956.

Dalton, A. J., and Striebich, M. J.: Electron microscopic studies of cytoplasmic components of some of the cells of the liver, pancreas, stomach and kidney following treatment with ribonuclease, J. Nat. Cancer Inst. *12*:244, 1951.

Fawcett, D. W.: Changes in the fine structure of the cytoplasmic organelles during differentiation *in* Radmik, D. (ed.): Development Cytology, p. 161, New York, Ronald Press, 1959.

Garnier, C.: Du role de l'ergastoplasme dans la sécrétion, J. Anat. et physiol. *26*:22, 1900.

Haguenau, F.: The ergastoplasm: its history, ultrastructure and biochemistry, Internat. Rev. Cytol. *7*:425, 1958.

Howatson, A. F., and Ham, A. W.: Electron microscope study of sections of two rat liver tumors, Cancer Res. *15*:62, 1955.

Palade, G. E.: A small particulate component of the cytoplasm, J. Appl. Physics *24*:1419, 1953.

——: A small particulate component of the cytoplasm, J. Biophys. & Biochem. Cytol. *1*: 59, 1955.

Porter, K. R.: Electron microscopy of basophilic components of cytoplasm, J. Histochem. *2*: 346, 1954.

Weiss, J. M.: The ergastoplasm: its fine structure and relation to protein synthesis as studied with the electron microscope in the pancreas of the Swiss albino mouse, J. Exper. Med. *98*:607, 1953.

See also Endoplasmic reticulum

THE CELL MEMBRANE

Robertson, J. D.: The ultrastructure of cell membranes and their derivatives, Biochem. Soc. Symposia, No. 16, 1959.

THE ENDOPLASMIC RETICULUM

Munger, B. L.: A phase and electron microscopic study of cellular differentiation in pancreatic acinar cells of the mouse, Am. J. Anat. *103*:1, 1958.

Palade, G. E.: Studies on the endoplasmic reticulum. II. Simple disposition in cells *in situ*, J. Biophys. & Biochem. Cytol. *1*:567, 1955.

——: The endoplasmic reticulum, J. Biophys. & Biochem. Cytol. (Supp.) *2*:85, 1956.

——: Functional changes in the structure of cell components *in* Hayashi, T. (ed.): Subcellular Particles, p. 64, New York, Ronald Press, 1959.

Palade, G. E., and Porter, K. R.: The endoplasmic reticulum of cells *in situ*, Anat. Rec. *112*:68, 1952.

——: Studies on the endoplasmic reticulum. I. Its identification in cells *in situ*, J. Exper. Med. *100*:641, 1954.

Palade, G. E., and Siekevitz, P.: Liver microsomes; an integrated morphological and biochemical study, J. Biophys. & Biochem. Cytol. *2*:171, 1956.

Palay, S. L.: The morphology of secretion *in* Frontiers in Cytology, p. 305, New Haven, Conn., Yale Univ. Press, 1958.

Porter, K. R., Claude A., and Fullam, E. F.: A study of tissue culture cells by electron microscopy, J. Exper. Med. *81*:233, 1945.

THE GOLGI APPARATUS

Adamstone, F. B.: Response of the Golgi apparatus of absorptive cells of the intestinal epithelium of the rat to the ingestion of protein, Am. J. Anat. *103*:437, 1958.

Baker, J. R.: The structure and the chemical composition of the Golgi element, Quart. J. Micro. Sc. *85*:1, 1944.

Bensley, R. R.: The nature of the canalicular apparatus of animal cells, Biol. Bull. *19*:179, 1910.

———: Facts versus artefacts in cytology: the Golgi apparatus, Exper. Cell Res. *11*:1, 1951.

Chu, C. H. U., and Swinyard, C. A.: Morphological and cytochemical identification of the Golgi apparatus, J. Biophys. & Biochem. Cytol. *2*:263, 1956.

Dalton, A. J., and Felix, M. D.: Cytologic and cytochemical characteristics of the Golgi substance of epithelial cells of the epididymis—*in situ,* in homogenates and after isolation, Am. J. Anat. *94*:171, 1954.

———: Studies on the Golgi substance of the epithelial cells of the epididymis and duodenum of the mouse, Am. J. Anat. *92*:277, 1953.

———: A study of the Golgi substances and ergastoplasm in a series of mammalian cell types *in* Fine Structure Cells, p. 170, New York, Interscience, 1954.

———: A comparative study of the Golgi complex, J. Biophys. & Biochem. Cytol. *2*:79, 1956.

Farquhar, M. G., and Wellings, S. R.: Electron microscopic evidence suggesting secretory granule formation within the Golgi apparatus, J. Biophys. & Biochem. Cytol. *3*:319, 1957.

Gatenby, J. B.: A comparative study of the Golgi complex, J. Biophys. & Biochem. Cytol. (Supp.) *2*:79, 1956.

Haguenau, F., and Bernhard, W.: L'appareil de Golgi dans les cellules normales et cancéreuses de vertèbres; rappel historique et étude au microscope électronique, Arch. Anat. Microscope Morphol. Exper. *44*:27, 1955.

Hibbard, H.: Current status of our knowledge of the Golgi apparatus in the animal cell, Quart. Rev. Biol. *20*:1, 1945.

Hirsch, G. C.: Form und Stoffwechsel der Golgi-korpen, Berlin, Protoplasma Monographs, 1939.

Kirkman, H., and Severinghaus, A. E.: A review of the Golgi apparatus, Anat. Rec. *70*:413, 557, 1938; *71*:79, 1938.

Kuff, E. L. and Dalton, A. J.: Biochemical studies of isolated Golgi membranes *in* Hayashi, T. (ed.): Subcellular Particles, p. 114, New York, Ronald Press, 1959.

Owens, H. B., and Bensley, R. R.: On osmic acid as a microchemical reagent with special reference to the reticular apparatus of Golgi, Am. J. Anat. *44*:79, 1929.

Sjöstrand, F. S., and Hanzon, V.: Ultrastructure of Golgi apparatus of exocrine cells of mouse pancreas, Exper. Cell Res. *7*:415, 1954.

CENTROSOME, CENTRIOLES AND SPINDLE

Bernhard, W., and de Harven, E.: Sur la présence dans certaines cellules de mammifères d'un organite de nature probablement centriolaire; étude au microscope électronique, Compt. rend. Acad. sc. *242*:288, 1956.

Darlington, C. D.: Evolution of Genetic Systems, ed. 2, Edinburgh, Oliver, 1958.

Schultz-Larsen, J.: On the structure of the nuclear spindle; an electron microscopic study, Acta path. et microbiol. scandinav. *32*:567, 1953.

(*See* references under Nuclear Structure in the Interphase and in Mitosis.)

CELL DIFFERENTIATION

Brachet, J.: Chemical Embryology, translated from the French by Lester G. Barth, New York, Interscience, 1950.

———: The Biochemistry of Development, New York, Pergamon Press, 1960.

Briggs, R., Green, E. U., and King, T. J.: An investigation of the capacity for cleavage and differentiation in Rana pipiens eggs lacking "functional" chromosomes, J. Exper. Zool. *116*: 455, 1951.

Briggs, R., and King, T. J.: Factors affecting the transplantability of nuclei of frog embryonic cells, J. Exper. Zool. *122*:485, 1953.

———: Transplantation of living nuclei from blastula cells into enucleated frogs' eggs, Proc. Nat. Acad. Sc. *38*:455, 1952.

Caspersson, T. O.: Cell Growth and Cell Function—A Cytochemical Study, New York, Norton, 1950.

Cold Spring Harbor Symposia: Exchange of genetic material. Mechanisms and Consequences. Symposium on Quantitative Biology, *23*, 1958.

Darlington, C. D.: Chromosome chemistry and gene action, Nature *149*:66, 1942.

———: Heredity, development and infection, Nature *154*:164, 1944.

Frankhauser, G.: Nucleo-cytoplasmic relations in amphibian development, Internat. Rev. Cytol. *1*:165, 1952.

Hämmerling, J.: Nucleo-cytoplasmic relationships in the development of acetabularia, Internat. Rev. Cytol. *2*:475, 1953.

Hartman, P. E.: Transduction: A comparative review *in* McElroy, W. D., and Glass, B. (eds.): The Chemical Basis of Heredity, p. 408, Baltimore, Johns Hopkins Press, 1957.

Hotchkiss, R. D.: The genetic chemistry of the pneumococcal transformations, Harvey Lect. Ser. 49, p. 124, 1955.

———: Criteria for quantitative genetic transformation of bacteria *in* McElroy, W. D., and Glass, B. (eds.): The Chemical Basis of Heredity, p. 321, Baltimore, John Hopkins Press, 1957.

King, T. J., and Briggs, R.: Changes in the nuclei of differentiating gastrula cells, as demonstrated by nuclear transplantation, Proc. Nat. Acad. Sc. *41*:321, 1955.

King, T. J., and Briggs, R.: The transplantability of nuclei of arrested hybrid blastulae (*R. pipiens* ♀ X. *R. Catesbiana* ♂), J. Exper. Zool. *123*:61, 1953.

———: Transplantation of living nuclei of late gastrulae into enucleated eggs of *Rana pipiens*, J. Embryol. & Exper. Morph. *2*:73, 1954.

McElroy, W. D., and Glass, B. (eds.): The Chemical Basis of Development, Baltimore, Johns Hopkins Press, 1958.

Needham, J.: Biochemistry and Morphogenesis, London, Cambridge Univ. Press, 1942.

Sonneborn, T. M.: Beyond the gene, Am. Scientist *37*:33, 1949.

Waddington, C. H.: Organizers and Genes, London, Cambridge Univ. Press, 1940.

Waddington, C. H. (ed.): Biological Organization, Cellular and Sub-cellular, New York, Pergamon Press, 1959.

Weiss, P.: The so-called organizer and the problem of organization in amphibian development, Physiol. Rev. *15*:639, 1935.

———: Principles of Development, New York, Holt, 1939.

Willier, B. H., Weiss, P. A., and Hamburger, V.: Analysis of Development, Philadelphia, Saunders, 1955.

CELL AND TISSUE CULTURE

Abercrombie, M., Heaysman, J. E. M., and Karthauser, H. M.: Social behaviour of cells in tissue culture. III. Mutual influence of sarcoma cells and fibroblasts, Exper. Cell Res. *13*:276, 1957.

Dulbecco, R.: Interaction of viruses and animal cells. A study of facts and interpretations, Physiol. Rev. *35*:301, 1955.

Dulbecco, R., and Vogt, M.: Plaque formation and isolation of pure lines with poliomyelitis viruses, J. Exper. Med. *99*:167, 1954.

Eagle, H.: Amino acid metabolism in mammalian cell cultures, Science *130*:432, 1959.

———: Animal cells and microbiology, Bact. Rev. *22*:217, 1958.

Eagle, H., Oyama, V. I., and Levy, M.: Amino acid requirements of normal and malignant human cells in tissue culture, Arch. Biochem. & Biophys. *67*:432, 1957.

Earle, W. R., Schilling, E. L., and Shannon, J. E.: Growth of animal tissue cells on three-dimensional substrates, J. Nat. Cancer Inst. *12*:179, 1951.

Enders, J. F., Weller, T. H., and Robbins, F. C.: Cultivation of Lansing strain of poliomyelitis virus in cultures in various human embryonic tissues, Science *109*:85, 1949.

Fell, H. B.: Histogenesis in tissue culture *in* Cytology and Cell Physiology, London, Oxford, 1951.

———: Recent advances in organ culture, Sc. Prog. *162*:212, 1953.

Frisch, A. W.: A glass wool matrix for roller tube tissue cultures, Proc. Soc. Exper. Biol. & Med. *81*:545, 1952.

Gwatkin, R. B. L., Till, J. E., Whitmore, G. F., Siminovitch, L., and Graham, A. F.: Multiplication of animal cells in suspension measured by colony counts, Proc. Nat. Acad. Sc. *43*:451, 1957.

Leighton, J.: A sponge matrix method for tissue culture. Formation of organized aggregates of cells *in vitro*, J. Nat. Cancer Inst. *12*:545, 1951.

Parker, R. C.: Methods of Tissue Culture, ed. 3, New York, Hoeber, 1961.

Paul, J. C.: Cell and Tissue Culture, Edinburgh, Livingstone, 1959.

Puck, T. T.: Quantitative studies on mammalian cells *in vitro*, Rev. Modern Physics *31*:433, 1959.

Puck, T. T., Cieciura, S. J., and Fisher, H. W.: Clonal growth *in vitro* of human cells with fibroblastic morphology, J. Exper. Med. *106*: 145, 1957.

Puck, T. T., and Marcus, P. I.: A rapid method for viable cell titration and clone production with HeLa cells in tissue culture: the use of X-irradiated cells to supply conditioning factors, Proc. Nat. Acad. Sc. *41*:432, 1955.

Puck, T. T., Marcus, P. I., and Cieciura, S. J.: Clonal growth of mammalian cells *in vitro*. Growth characteristics of colonies from single HeLa cells with and without a "feeder" layer, J. Exper. Med. *103*:273, 1956.

STORED FOOD IN CELLS

Bondareff, W.: Morphology of particulate glycogen in guinea pig liver revealed by electron microscopy after freezing and drying and selective staining en bloc, Anat. Rec. *129*:97, 1957.

Hartroft, W. S.: Accumulation of fat in liver cells and in lipodiastemata preceding experimental dietary cirrhosis, Anat. Rec. *106*:61, 1950.

Millonig, G., and Porter, K. R.: Structural elements of rat liver cells involved in glycogen storage. (Abstract) European Regional Conference on Electron Microscopy, Delft, 1960.

Porter, K. R.: Fine structural changes in rat liver

cells associated with glycogenesis and glycogenolysis (Abstract) X Internat. Congress Cellular Biology, Paris, 1960.

SECRETION GRANULES

See references for ergastoplasm and endoplasmic reticulum and references for Chapter 12.

PIGMENTS IN CELLS, HEMOGLOBIN AND RELATED PIGMENTS

Dobriner, K., and Rhoads, C. P.: The porphyrins in health and disease, Physiol. Rev. *20*:416, 1940.

Rich, A. R.: The formation of bile pigment, Physiol. Rev. *5*:182, 1925.

Watson, C. J.: The pyrrhol pigments with particular reference to normal and pathological hemoglobin metabolism *in* Downey's Handbook of Hematology, vol. 4, p. 2445, New York, Hoeber, 1937.

PIGMENTS IN CELLS, LIPOCHROME PIGMENTS

Connor, C. L.: Studies on lipochromes, Am. J. Path. *4:227, 235, 293,* 1928.

Goodwin, T. W.: Carotenoids: Their Comparative Chemistry, New York, Tudor Press, 1954.

Karrer, P., and Jucker, E.: Carotenoids, Princeton, N. J., Van Nostrand, (Elsevier), 1950.

Palmer, L. S.: Carotenoids and Related Pigments, New York, Chem. Catalog Co., 1922.

PIGMENTS IN CELLS, MELANIN

See references for Chapter 20.

PIGMENTS IN CELLS, PATHOLOGIC PIGMENTATION

See textbooks of pathology.

Chapter 5

Intercellular Substances

GENERAL CONSIDERATIONS

To reiterate: the tissues of the human body are all composed of 3 categories of materials: (1) cells, (2) intercellular substances, and (3) fluids. Having considered cells, we shall now deal with the second of these great components of tissue, intercellular substances.

Nature. Intercellular substances are as different from cells as death is from life. They constitute the nonliving materials that are found between cells. Fundamentally, they are of the nature of building materials. Just as people use bricks, stone, cement, wood and steel to construct the houses in which they live, cells use intercellular substances to form the edifice in which they live. *The human body, then, can be spoken of as an edifice of intercellular substances in which the cells live as residents.* Cells are jellylike; the intercellular substance content of tissues gives form to the human body as a whole and to its various parts.

Relation of Intercellular Substances to Connective Tissue. We shall learn, in the third part of this book, that the human body is made up of 4 primary tissues. One of these is termed connective tissue because it connects the other 3 together. Connective tissue is strong and able to perform this function because it generally has a high content of intercellular substances. Since the intercellular substances of connective tissue connect the other tissues together and support them, there is very little need for the other 3 tissues to produce intercellular substance. Accordingly, the production of intercellular substances is a fairly exclusive property of the cells of connective tissue. It should be noted that intercellular substance is not the same thing as connective tissue. Intercellular substance is only a nonliving material, while connective tissue is a weave of living cells and nonliving intercellular substances. Later in this book we shall consider connective tissue in detail and discuss the relation of its cells to its intercellular

substances. In the present chapter we shall consider intercellular substances as one of the 3 important materials of the body but with the realization that they, unlike cells which are distributed in all 4 body tissues, are limited chiefly to one of the 4 tissues.

Distribution and Types. Connective tissue extends all through the body to hold it together. Accordingly, sections taken from almost any part of the body will reveal the presence of intercellular substance. Moreover, such sections reveal that there are two general kinds of intercellular substance. One kind exists in tissues in the form of fibers. The other kind appears structureless because it exists in the form of jellies of different degrees of viscosity. We shall classify the intercellular substances of the body morphologically as follows:

Intercellular substances ⎡Fibrous
⎣Amorphous (jellies)

The intercellular substances in most parts of the body exist as a mixture, or perhaps a compound, of the formed and amorphous types. Their proportions vary; in some tissues the intercellular substance is predominantly fibrous, while in others the amorphous type dominates and even obscures the fibrous kinds present.

FUNCTIONS

Providing Strength and Support. Intercellular substances perform two general functions. The first is that of providing strength and support for the tissues that contain them. This function is performed chiefly by the fibrous kinds. Those amorphous kinds that are in the form of very stiff gels also help in this matter.

Providing a Medium for Tissue Fluid and Material Through Which Nutrients and Waste Products Can Diffuse Between Cells and Capillaries. To understand the second function of intercellular substances it must be remembered that they are commonly interposed between capillaries and the cells that

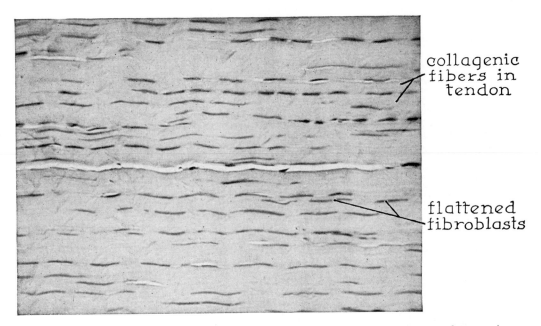

collagenic
fibers in
tendon

flattened
fibroblasts

Fig. 84. Low-power photomicrograph of a longitudinal section of a tendon. Tendons consist chiefly of collagenic fibers and bundles of collagenic fibers which run in one direction, with rows of flattened fibroblasts between them. Notice that this tissue is chiefly intercellular substance.

are nourished by the capillaries (Fig. 91). For food substances to pass from capillaries to cells requires that they diffuse or somehow pass through the intercellular substance of the part. The waste products of cells likewise must pass through intercellular substances to reach capillaries. This problem of the means of interchange between cells and capillaries will be considered in more detail in the next chapter; for the present it is enough to know that an important function of intercellular substances in at least some parts of the body is to provide a medium through which substances can diffuse from capillaries to cells and vice versa. This function of intercellular substance is performed chiefly by the amorphous types which, as sols or gels, allow for circulation or diffusion much more readily than do the fibrous kinds.

Subtypes. There are 3 kinds of formed intercellular substance, that is, 3 kinds of fibers: *collagenic, reticular* and *elastic*. Chemically, they have much in common, being proteins of the order of albuminoids. The members of this group of proteins are characterized by their insolubility in neutral solvents. Hence,

these 3 kinds of fibers are able to exist as such in the more or less fluid internal environment of the body.

The amorphous intercellular substances, in which the fibrous elements are so often embedded, constitute what histologists in the past have termed *ground* and *cement substances*. If the amorphous material is soft it is generally said to be ground substance, but if it is firm it is generally said to be a cement substance.

In contrast with the fibers, which are proteins, two important widespread types of the amorphous kind are more in the nature of carbohydrates than proteins, and for this reason they have been termed *mucopolysaccharides*. One of these is hyaluronic acid, and the other is chondroitin sulfuric acid; they will be discussed in more detail later. The former is the softer and is more prevalent in ground substance; the latter, which is the firmer, is more prevalent in cement substances. It is not unlikely, as will be described in more detail when basement membranes are discussed near the end of this chapter, that there are other and as yet unidentified carbohydrate-containing amorphous materials in at least

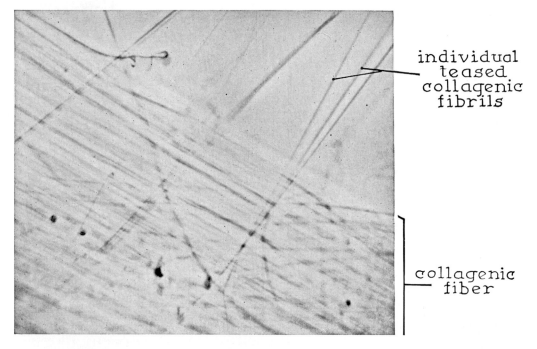

individual
teased
collagenic
fibrils

collagenic
fiber

FIG. 85. Oil-immersion photomicrograph, taken with the phase microscope, of collagenic fibers which had been treated with a mild alkali and then teased apart. Individual collagenic fibrils may be seen (*upper right*), and in the lower part of the photograph a collagenic fiber, having a longitudinally striated appearance due to its fibrils, is present.

some of the intercellular substances; and it is possible that protein materials that are not yet polymerized into visible fibrils may, at least at times, also contribute to the composition of amorphous substances. Hence, it is hazardous, at this time, to be too specific about the composition of the ground and the cement substances, and also about the physiochemical relations of the fibrous and the amorphous types to each other.

In the light of the foregoing, we shall classify the intercellular substance of the body as follows:

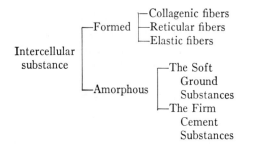

We shall now consider the different varieties of the two general types of intercellular substance in some detail.

FORMED INTERCELLULAR SUBSTANCES

COLLAGENIC FIBERS

Collagenic fibers consist of the protein collagen and they have great tensile strength. Tendons (Fig. 84) and such structures are made chiefly of collagenic fibers. Since these structures are white in their fresh state, collagenic fibers are often called "white fibers." They are very tough. Indeed, the toughness of meat is due largely to its content of collagen. However, if collagen is boiled with water, it becomes hydrated and hydrated collagen is known as *gelatin*. This, of course, is much softer. Meat that contains much collagen is commonly cooked for prolonged periods of time. This converts its collagen into gelatin and makes the meat tender. Most glues are made from collagen. It is also made into leather. The hides of animals, and these consist chiefly of collagen, are treated with tanning agents which react with the collagen to form a material that is even more resistant to chemical change than collagen itself.

Morphology. Collagenic fibers vary from a few to more than 100 microns in width. They also vary greatly in length. In tissues of loose texture, collagenic fibers may be present singly, with individual fibers being loosely woven together (Fig. 147). In tissues of denser weaves, for example in tendon, collagenic fibers are aggregated together to form bundles of fibers (Fig. 84), and this arrangement of course, has great tensile strength.

If fresh collagenic fibers are examined under the higher power of the microscope, particularly after being treated with alkali, they are seen to be made up of fibrils; these are from 0.3 to 0.5 μ in diameter (Fig. 85) although some fibrils seen with the E/M are still narrower. In collagenic fibers the fibrils are probably cemented together by an amorphous intercellular substance; this can be dissolved with alkali. Acids act differently, they make the fibrils swell so that the fibers appear to be homogeneous.

In H and E sections collagenic fibers are colored pink to red. If their identification in any tissue is a problem, special stains may be used which color them more or less selectively. For example, they are colored red with Van Gieson's picro-fuchsin stain, and they take up the acid aniline dyes in Mallory's connective tissue stain and in Masson's trichrome stain. Another aid to their identification is the fact that they are birefringent when examined under polarized light.

Collagenic fibers can be digested by an enzyme, termed collagenase, that is made by certain bacteria.

Fine Structure. As has already been noted (page 108), there is no unanimity about what is meant by the terms "fiber," "fibril" and "microfibril." We consider a collagenic fiber to be a cohesive bundle of collagenic fibrils such as exists *between* rows of cells in a tendon (Fig. 84), which is readily seen under the low power with the light microscope. If such a fiber or a similar one from some other region is teased, the individual fibrils of which it is composed can be seen with the high power

of the light microscope (Fig. 85). Fibrils can exist by themselves or in aggregations of various sizes (if the aggregations are large, they are called fiber). With the E/M, fibrils (as defined above) are seen to be constituted of smaller units called *microfibrils* or *unit fibers* of collagen (Fig. 86). In thin sections these are about 425 to 600 A in diameter and show cross-banding with a periodicity which has been estimated from 534 A to 640 A (Fig. 86). Still finer banding within each period has been described by Gross and Schmitt and by Wassermann, Roth and Minick. The latter authors, in each period describe 6 intraperiodic bands with spaces between. Adjacent microfibrils are always in phase with one another with regard to their intraperiodic bands (Fig. 86, *top*). The microfibrils are further subdivided into filaments of diameter about 30 Å, which probably consist of a single or at most 2 or 3 polypeptide chains; this is shown particularly well by negative staining (Fig. 86, *bottom*).

RETICULAR FIBERS

This name is given to certain very delicate fibers that are commonly arranged into networks (*rete* = a net).

Distribution and Arrangement. Delicate reticular nets are generally connected to, and supported by, stouter collagenic fibers in much the same way that the latticework of a fence is connected to fence posts. And, like the latticework of a fence that can offer intimate support for vines and flowers, reticular nets offer intimate support for individual cells, capillaries, nerve fibers, the secretory units of glands and many other of the more delicate structures in the body. Jacobson has emphasized how reticular networks are found at the boundaries between connective and other kinds of tissue. Under epithelial membranes, which will be considered in Chapter 11, reticular fibers form dense networks, constituting parts of what are termed *basement membranes,* which will be considered in more detail later in that chapter.

Histologic Appearance. Reticular fibers do not take up either hematoxylin or eosin to any extent and so they can be seen only with the greatest difficulty in H and E sections. For a

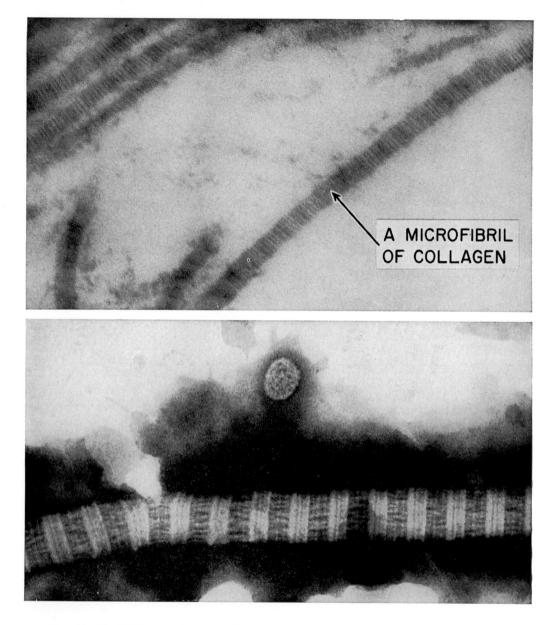

FIG. 86. (*Top*) Electron micrograph (× 150,000 as reproduced here) of a section of umbilical cord in which several microfibrils of collagen are seen in longitudinal section. Notice that the periodicity of the collagen is manifested by an appearance of cross bands. (Preparation courtesy of Dr. H. Movat.) (*Bottom*) Electron micrograph (× 175,000) of material deposited from a homogenate of a wart of man. The preparation was treated by the negative staining technic using phosphotungstic acid. By this technic the spaces not occupied by protein structure are dark and hence the protein structural elements appear light. The periodicity in the collagen microfibril is evident and, in addition it is seen to consist of still finer filaments which are single, or perhaps double or triple polypeptide chains. The spherical structure seen above the center is a single particle of the virus that has been implicated in the etiology of human warts. (Preparation by A. F. Howatson and J. D. Almeida.)

proper understanding of their distribution in any tissue it is absolutely necessary to use special technics. A time-honored method involves their impregnation with silver (Fig. 87); this technic makes them visible as narrow black lines. The collagenic fibers to which they often connect are generally colored a light brown by this method. The P.A.S. technic, to be described later in this chapter, colors them red, while coloring collagenic fibers only a faint pink. Reticular fibers differ from collagenic fibers in still other ways. They are not birefringent when viewed under polarized light, and they are not colored red by Van Gieson's stain. Although roughly in the same size range as collagenic fibrils (which do not branch), reticular fibers do branch.

With the E/M reticular fibers seem to be composed of microfibrils; these show the same axial periodicity as that of collagenic fibrils.

It has been debated for 50 years as to whether reticular fibers are fundamentally different from either collagenic fibrils or small bundles of collagenic fibrils. The investigation of reticular and collagenic fibrils with the E/M would seem to indicate that the fibrillar material present in both is of the same nature. Why then should collagenic and reticular fibers stain differently? Collagenic fibers are, of course, much thicker than reticular fibers, and this physical fact may explain in part why collagenic fibers and reticular fibers stain differently. But why should reticular fibers stain differently from collagenic fibrils which are roughly of the same thickness as themselves? Since the E/M indicates that the fibrillar material in both has the same periodicity, it seems unlikely that the fibrillar material of collagenic and reticular fibers is different. However, there is reason to believe that reticular fibers, to a far greater extent than collagenic fibrils or fibers, have associated with them an as yet imperfectly understood amorphous material which is responsible for at least some of their staining reactions. Since this amorphous material seems to be different from the usual and more abundant amorphous intercellular substances, which will be described in the next few pages, we shall postpone further discussion of it until the usual kinds of amorphous intercellular substances have been considered.

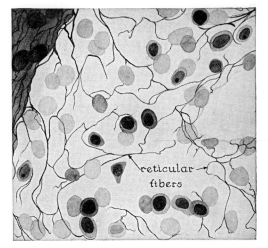

Fig. 87. Drawing of a section of spleen stained by the Bielschowsky technic for reticular fibers (high-power). By this method, silver is precipitated on the reticular fibers, which makes them stand out as fine black lines.

Elastic Fibers

These consist of the protein *elastin*. This albuminoid is probably the most resistant of all the body proteins to chemical change. Even in mummies thousands of years old the elastic fibers of arteries are often sufficiently well preserved to allow some conclusion to be drawn about the arterial diseases suffered by the Egyptians of that era.

Histologic Structure of Fibers. Fresh elastin is said to be yellow, but Lansing says this is not true of fibers from the young. They are highly refractile in contrast with collagenic and reticular fibers (Fig. 145 A). They are long and narrow, ranging from less than a micron to a few microns in thickness. They are not composed of fibrils as are collagenic fibers but instead are homogeneous (Fig. 88).

Histologic Structure of Membranes. Elastin is not uncommonly disposed as membranes or plates in the body, particularly in the walls of blood vessels (Figs. 330 and 332). Elastic membranes are commonly fenestrated, probably because elastin is not very permeable and fenestra are required to permit the passage of nutrients and waste products through them. If sections containing elastic fibers are incin-

Fig. 88. Electron micrograph ($\times$ 37,000) of an elastic fiber from the aorta of a rabbit, showing the essentially amorphous nature of elastic fibers which is in sharp contrast with the highly ordered structure of collagenic fibrils illustrated in Figure 86. (Gross, J.: J. Exper. Med. *89*:699)

erated, the fibers are seen to contain no mineral elements (Fig. 25). They are mildly acidophilic, but their staining with eosin is erratic. They are stained more or less selectively by certain dyes—for example, dark brown by orcein and dark blue by resorcin fuchsin.

As their name implies, elastic fibers, on being stretched and then released, tend to snap back, like rubber bands, to their original state. To help impart a diffuse elasticity to tissue they commonly branch.

Regeneration. It is commonly said that elastic fibers that are destroyed are not regenerated. However, the author has observed the formation of new elastin in the repair of arteries damaged by experimentally produced calcium precipitations.

THE AMORPHOUS (NONFIBROUS) INTERCELLULAR SUBSTANCES

As noted previously, the fibrous kinds of intercellular substance are seldom found by themselves in the body; usually they are immersed in intercellular substances of the amorphous type. This was not generally appreciated until Sylvia Bensley in 1934, in some ingenious experiments, showed conclusively that the collagenic and the elastic fibers of ordinary loose areolar tissue are embedded in a ground substance which she was able to show possessed certain definite properties.

While histologists were engaged in working out ways and means of demonstrating amorphous intercellular substances among the fibrous types in the tissues of the body, a discovery was made that proved later to have considerable bearing on these amorphous intercellular substances. In 1928 Duran-Reynals discovered that when he injected rabbits' skins with an extract that had been made from a testis inoculated with a certain disease virus, he found that a very widespread disease of the skin developed in the rabbit. Further study showed that this spread was not due to any property of the virus contained in the testis but to some property of the testis tissue itself. It was found, for example, that mixing testicular extract with dye would, when the mixture was injected into the skin, cause the dye to spread widely throughout the intercellular substances of that tissue (Fig. 89). For these experiments Duran-Reynals postulated the existence of something that he called "spreading factor" to be found in testicular tissue. For many years the nature of this effect remained a mystery.

Shortly after the discovery of the spreading effect, a biochemist, Karl Meyer, began a series of studies on the chemistry of the amorphous intercellular substances. Before his work they were usually described as belonging to a chemically ill-defined group of substances called mucoids. These were supposed to be glycoproteins, that is, proteins with a carbohydrate prosthetic group. Meyer's illuminating researches resulted in a reclassification of these materials. Meyer has suggested that they should be called *mucopolysaccharides,* a term which suitably emphasizes the fact that they are essentially of a carbohydrate nature. Mucopolysaccharides consist of a complex mixture of hexosamines and hexuronic acids combined with protein, the precise nature of which has not yet been ascertained. Their physical state is either that of a sol or a gel.

The mucopolysaccharides are classified into 2 main groups according to whether or not they are esterified with sulfuric acid on the hexosamine part of the molecule. Hyaluronic acid and chondroitin (an isomere of hyaluronic acid) are representatives of the nonsulfated types, while chondroitin sulfates (chondroitin sulfuric acid) are representatives of the sulfated types.

Hyaluronic acid is a viscid material when it is polymerized into molecules of considerable size. Its distribution in the body has not yet been worked out in detail but it has been found to be present in the intercellular substances of many parts of the body as well as in the synovial fluid of joints and in the humors of the eye. The umbilical cord contains considerable amounts of it.

The next discovery of importance in relation to the amorphous intercellular substances occurred when Meyer found that certain kinds of bacteria made an enzyme that depolymerizes hyaluronic acid, thus making it less viscous. He named this enzyme *hyaluronidase.* Then, in 1939, two British workers, Chain and Duthie, observed that the spreading factor of testicular extract decreased the viscosity of synovial fluid, which was known by this time to contain hyaluronic acid. This, of course, raised the suspicion that the spreading factor discovered by Duran-Reynals some years before was the enzyme hyaluronidase, and indeed it was soon shown that testicular extract contains hyaluronidase.

This finding was important for this reason: Whereas it is of interest that certain bacteria can make hyaluronidase, which, in infections, could act to reduce the viscosity of the intercellular substance being invaded by the bacteria and so perhaps be a factor in the spread of an infection, it is of much greater interest that hyaluronidase can be produced by the normal tissues of the body, for this suggests that it has a physiologic function. How great this is has not yet been ascertained.

The sulfuric-acid-containing mucopolysac-

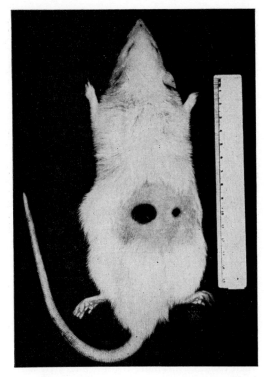

FIG. 89. The back of a rat, showing the spreading phenomenon. Two dark spots may be seen. The one at the right is the result of the injection of 0.1 ml. of saline and India ink into the site; the spot at the left is due to the injection of 0.1 ml. of India ink and an aqueous extract of rat testicle. The extract of testicle contains a spreading factor which permits the India ink to spread much more widely and much more quickly in the tissues than occurs when India ink is injected by itself. (W. R. Harris)

charides are also affected by enzymes which cause their depolymerization. At first it was thought that hyaluronidase performed this function, but it now seems to be established that it affects only some kinds of the sulfated types and that there are other enzymes more specific for other sulfated types. The sulfated types tend to be more viscid than hyaluronic acid and usually exist in tissues as very firm gels. This is probably because the sulfuric acid they contain permits a very firm union with a protein which is always associated with them. Being firm gels, the sulfated mucopolysaccharides can act as cement substances, and when they are present in great amounts, as in cartilage, they can participate with fibrous types of intercellular substances in providing support.

THE STAINING OF AMORPHOUS INTERCELLULAR SUBSTANCES

Ground substances (hyaluronic acid) are very difficult to fix and stain. In H and E sections the observer sees only relatively clear areas in the sites where they were present during life. The cement substances (usually chondroitin sulfuric acid) stain much better. In H and E sections chondroitin sulfuric acid is sometimes, but not always, colored blue or purple, but its staining with hematoxylin is somewhat erratic. The sulfated types of mucopolysaccharides are generally colored brilliantly by hemotoxylin, eosin and azure combinations.

Metachromasia. Both kinds of mucopolysaccharides stain metachromatically (*meta* = beyond; *chroma* = color). This means that when tissues containing them are treated with dyes of a certain type, they take on a color different from that of the dye employed. Only some dyes give this kind of reaction, and most that do are dyes of the sort which are said to illustrate a "dilution shift," that is, they change their color in relation to their concentration. Toluidine blue is commonly used for metachromatic staining. In the dilute solutions in which it is used for staining tissues it is blue. But in concentrated solutions it is reddish violet. If sulfated mucopolysaccharides are treated with a dilute (blue) solution of the dye, they turn reddish violet. It is presumed that substances which demonstrate metachromasia do so because they are able either to concentrate the dye or bring about some change in its molecular state or aggregation at its point of action which gives the same effect. Metachromatic staining methods have been useful in developing knowledge about the mucopolysaccharides of tissue, but the method is by no means as specific for them as is sometimes assumed.

It was believed for a time that the metachromasia of mucopolysaccharides depended on their having a sulfate group and hence that only the sulfated types exhibited this property. A thorough investigation of the matter was made in 1947 by Wislocki, Bunting and Dempsey, and they showed that hyaluronic acid (in tissues) also stained metachromatically, although this substance contained no sulfate group. The metachromasia of the mucopolysaccharides is, therefore, not dependent on a sulfate linkage. Nevertheless, the sulfated type in general evidences a more consistent and intense metachromatic reaction than the nonsulfated varieties.

THE PERIODIC ACID SCHIFF REACTION

The Feulgen reaction—a histochemical test for DNA—was described in the preceding chapter as being dependent on the Schiff reaction, which is an old-established test for aldehydes. The Schiff reagent is basic fuchsin which has been bleached with sulfurous acid. Aldehydes restore to the bleached dye the magenta (purple) color of unbleached basic fuchsin. The Feulgen reaction is specific for DNA only because the sections containing DNA are treated to a mild hydrolysis which liberates aldehydes from the sugar of DNA and not from that of RNA. It is obvious that if aldehydes could be liberated by other means from other substances they, too, would give a positive Schiff reaction.

Periodic acid is a strong oxidizing agent. Almost simultaneously three investigators, Hotchkiss, McManus and Lillie, discovered that this reagent could be used on tissue sections to liberate adlehydes from polysaccharides in such a fashion that the sites of aldehyde liberation could then be stained by means of the Schiff reaction. Periodic acid is believed to produce aldehydes from polysaccharides by acting on the 1,2 glycol (-CHOH-CHOH-) and α-amino-alcohol (C-CHOH-CHNH$_2$-) linkages of certain carbohydrates. (It will also liberate aldehydes from some amino acids placed at the end of protein chains.) The whole procedure, including the preliminary treatment of sections with periodic acid and the subsequent exposure of the section to the Schiff reagent, is commonly referred to as the *P.A. Schiff* or *P.A.S. Technic*. It is to be understood that periodic acid would liberate aldehydes from free soluble sugars as well as from polysaccharides, and these also would be stained if they were present in tissue sections. However, this complication is avoided because they, unlike the polysaccharides, are freely soluble and so are washed out of the sections by the aqueous reagents that are employed. It should be understood also that the results obtained with the technic must be interpreted with due caution (for details see references), because periodic acid may oxidize substances other than carbohydrates to aldehydes, and periodic acid does not react with all polysaccharides to produce aldehydes. Nevertheless, the P.A.S. technic has been a very important development in histology, and particularly with regard to the study of intercellular substances.

The ability of the P.A.S. technic to stain polysaccharides is perhaps best illustrated by its effectiveness in staining glycogen (Fig. 79). If there is any question as to whether or not any P.A.S. positive substance in tissue sections is glycogen the question may be settled by first treating a similar section with amylase, the enzyme present in saliva, before it is stained. This breaks glycogen down to freely soluble sugars that are easily washed from the section; hence, the "saliva test" removes glycogen as a possible cause of a positive reaction.

The P.A.S. Technic and the Staining of Intercellular Substances

Collagenic and, in general, elastic fibers are colored only faintly by the P.A.S. method; however, there is some evidence that elastic fibers in a few parts of the body, for example, in the skin, are P.A.S. positive. Reticular fibers are strongly P.A.S. positive. Many investigators, from their writings, seem to assume that hyaluronic acid or chondroitin sulfuric acid may be P.A.S. positive. The evidence for this is far from conclusive, being based, for example, on finding that the intercellular substance of cartilage is mildly P.A.S. positive and assuming from this that chondroitin sulfuric acid is P.A.S. positive. However, there is little basis in fact for assumptions such as these. Both Davies and Glegg, Clermont and Leblond have provided convincing evidence to the effect that pure hyaluronic acid is P.A.S. negative, and the latter group of investigators also provide very convincing evidence for thinking that this is true also of pure chondroitin sulfuric acid. They have shown that there is good reason for believing that when either hyaluronic acid or chondroitin sulfuric

acid seems to give a positive P.A.S. reaction, the reaction is due to a carbohydrate containing contaminant which we shall discuss in more detail presently.

Therefore, we may conclude that of the 5 main types of intercellular substance only reticular fibers are strongly P.A.S. positive.

When reticular fibers were described (a few pages back) it was suggested that certain of their staining reactions, including their P.A.S. positiveness, were actually due to an as yet ill-understood amorphous material with which they are intimately associated. We shall now discuss this matter somewhat further, and in particular we shall discuss the material with which they are commonly associated in basement membranes.

Basement Membranes. As will be described presently, all external body surfaces are covered or lined by membranes composed of epithelial cells. These cellular membranes always rest on, and are supported by, connective tissue which contains the usual types of intercellular substance. But at the boundary between an epithelial membrane and its supporting connective tissue there is generally a thin layer of a special kind of intercellular substance that constitutes what is termed a *basement membrane*. Basement membranes may also be formed between the epithelial elements of glands and the connective tissue that supports them, as in the kidney.

Basement membranes do not appear to advantage in H and E preparations (Figs. 128 and 132) but are colored a brilliant magenta color by the P.A.S. method; this is shown in Figure 464 which is a color plate of the kidney (the basement membrane is labeled). There has been much discussion about the nature of the material in basement membranes that is P.A.S. positive.

The first histologists who studied basement membranes believed them to consist of condensations of reticular fibers that were arranged in a closely knitted feltwork. Much later, von Ebner described them as being composed of a hyaline (glassy) amorphous material on which reticular networks abutted to provide support. Although these two views still persist, the author considers the second to be the true one for several reasons. (1) It is possible to devise procedures, as has been done by both Lillie and McManus, so that the

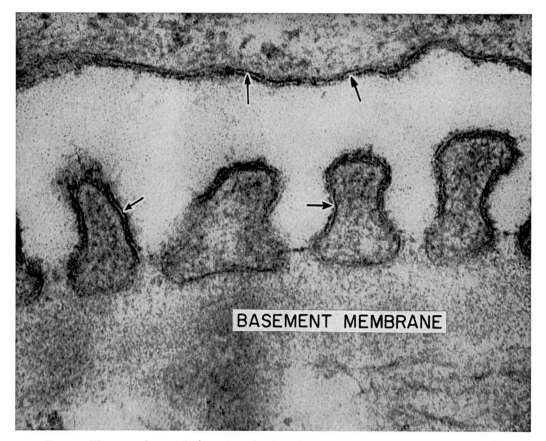

Fig. 90. Electron micrograph ($\times$ 160,000) of section of normal mouse kidney embedded in Epon and stained with lead hydroxide, showing a very small portion of a glomerulus. The basement membrane of the glomerulus runs across the illustration and consists of an amorphous material. The feet of podocytes rest on the basement membrane and these can be seen to be covered with a cell membrane which at this high magnification is seen to consist of two dark lines separated by a pale middle section. A cell membrane can also be seen toward the upper part of the picture and it also shows 3 layers. The arrows indicate sites where the layered structure of the cell membrane is seen to advantage. (Preparation by A. F. Howatson and J. D. Almeida)

hyaline basement membranes in the kidneys are colored differently from the reticular networks that abut on them. (2) Thin sections of glomerular basement membrane, viewed with the E/M, give no indication of any fibers within it that demonstrate periodicity (Fig. 90). If reticular fibers were actually throughout the hyaline membrane, it could be expected that the E/M would reveal them in sections.

The foregoing suggests that basement membranes actually consist of a hyaline amorphous intercellular substance and that this material is supported by networks of reticular fibers. What is the nature of the amorphous hyaline material? Since basement membranes are not metachromatic and are P.A.S. positive, the amorphous material in them would not seem to be either hyaluronic acid or chondroitin sulfuric acid. Since the material is so closely associated with reticular nets as to have been confused with them, it might be suspected with justification that it is the same kind of material that is commonly associated with reticular fibers elsewhere and is responsible for their seeming to be P.A.S. positive.

Some interesting work by Leblond and his group gives some intimation of the nature of this material. They hydrolyzed reticular and collagenic fibers obtained from several different parts of the body and found by means of paper chromatography that these materials yielded certain sugars, namely, galactose, fucose, mannose and glucose. Material from reticular fibers yielded more of these sugars than material from collagenic fibers, and in particular the material from reticular fibers yielded much more glucose. They concluded that it is this carbohydrate material that is responsible for the P.A.S. staining of reticular and collagenic fibers and that the reticular fibers stain more strongly than the collagenic because they have relatively more of it and, in particular, more glucose.

It is possible, of course, that the sugars obtained by Leblond and his group from reticular and collagenic fibers were derived from the fibers themselves, but it is also possible that they were components of a material with which the fibers were intimately associated. In our present state of knowledge this matter cannot be settled definitely, but the bulk of the evidence seems to suggest that there is an amorphous material that is P.A.S. positive that is associated intimately and abundantly with reticular fibers and constitutes the major material in basement membranes and that this material is associated to a much lesser extent with collagenic fibers. This material, the precise chemical nature of which is not yet understood, must be very permeable.

The Term "Reticulin." The term "reticulin" was first used in relation to reticular fibers in the same way as the term "collagen" was used in relation to collagenic fibers; reticulin was supposed to be the special scleroprotein of which the reticular fibers were composed. Reticulin is still defined this way—as a chemical term—in most medical dictionaries. But since the P.A.S. staining method has come into use for depicting reticular networks and basement membranes, the term "reticulin" has been used by many authors to designate the P.A.S. positive material in them; indeed, some authors refer to basement membranes as reticulin membranes.

Since reticular fibers have the same periodicity as collagenic fibers it seems questionable if pure reticulin would be different chemically from collagen. Since the P.A.S. positiveness of reticular fibers may be due to some carbohydrate-containing component commonly associated with them, this P.A.S. positive material, the chemical composition of which is not yet understood, which might be different from that of reticular fibers themselves, should not be termed reticulin. Since there are many reasons for considering that basement membranes are not constituted of reticular fibers but of an amorphous material there would seem to be no justification for terming basement membranes reticulin membranes.

P.A.S. Positive Pathologic Materials in Intercellular Substances. Ceroid, a pathologic pigment derived from oxidized unsaturated fats and found in cirrhotic livers (in rats) and in atheromatous lesions of arteries in man, is P.A.S. positive. Ceroid may be differentiated from other types of P.A.S. positive material because it stains with fat stains and does not dissolve out when sections are passed through alcohol and xylol. McManus says that the hyaline material seen in artery walls in some kinds of arteriosclerosis, and amyloid, which is an amorphous material that accumulates in intercellular spaces in certain pathologic states, is P.A.S. positive.

INTERCELLULAR SUBSTANCES AND AGING

Houses do not last forever, and the edifice of intercellular substance which houses the cells of the body is no exception to this rule. The passing of the years is inevitably associated with a deterioration of the intercellular substances of the body. The cells that produce intercellular substances can be most ingenious, on occasion, at patching up old intercellular substance with new, but a continuous renewal of *all* the intercellular substances of the body, with the old being completely removed and with new being substituted for it, seems to be beyond the capacities of the organism. In particular, much of the fibrous type of intercellular substance seems to persist through life, and it deteriorates with the years.

Perhaps the most obvious age change that

occurs in intercellular substance is the gradual diminution of the amount of the amorphous kind that it contains. The tissues of a fetus are jellylike because of their high content of amorphous intercellular substance, and those of a newborn infant have proportionately much less fibrous intercellular substance and much more of the amorphous kind than those of an adult. But as the years pass, the fibrous elements are built up, and thereafter the amount of amorphous intercellular substance gradually becomes lessened. The tissues of the aged contain so little that dyes spread through them more readily than they do in the tissues of the young; in the latter the free passage of dyes is impeded by the amorphous material that is present.

There is some difference of opinion as to the effects of aging on collagenic fibers. However, there is indication that the average size of collagenic fibers and bundles is increased, and their substance becomes more basophilic.

Pronounced changes occur in elastic fibers and laminae as an individual ages. Normal ones, obtained from the young, evidence no content of mineral by the micro-incineration method (Fig. 25), but they commonly contain mineral in the aged. Lansing (who should be read for details) has studied the structure of elastic fibers and laminae in great detail and has shown that there are various types of elastin in the body and that the elastin of the old is not the same as the elastin of the young. With the electron microscope elastin fibers appear to be amorphous (Fig. 88). With age, elastic fibers fray and fragment and develop an increased affinity for calcium salts. This, of course, is of the greatest importance in connection with the "hardening of arteries" (Fig. 330). It is probably that the sagging and the general lack of tone of the skin of the aged are due more to age changes in its elastic fibers than to changes in its collagenic fibers.

The relative proportion of amorphous and fibrous elements in intercellular substance, as well as the density and the size of collagenic fibers, is, at least in some parts of the body, greatly influenced by certain hormones. This matter will be discussed in Chapter 26. Further information about intercellular substances is given in Chapter 13.

REFERENCES

AMORPHOUS INTERCELLULAR SUBSTANCES AND ENZYMES AFFECTING THEM— SPECIAL REFERENCES

Bensley, Sylvia H.: On the presence, properties and distribution of the intercellular ground substance of loose connective tissue, Anat. Rec. 60:93, 1934.

Chain, E., and Duthie, E. S.: Identity of hyaluronidase and the spreading factor, Brit. J. Exper. Path. 21:324, 1940.

Day, T. D.: The nature and significance of the cementing substance in interstitial connective tissue, J. Path. & Bact. 95:567, 1947.

Dempsey, Edward W., Bunting, Henry, Singer, Marcus, and Wislocki, George B.: The dye-binding capacity and other chemohistological properties of mammalian mucopolysaccharides, Anat. Rec. 98:417, 1947.

Duran-Reynals, F.: Some remarks on the spreading reaction in Connective Tissue in Health and Disease, p. 103, ed. by G. Asboe-Hansen, Copenhagen, Munksgaard, 1954.

Edds, M. V., Jr.: Origin and structure of intercellular matrix in McElroy, W. D., and Glass, B. (eds.): The Chemical Basis of Development, p. 157, Baltimore, Johns Hopkins Press, 1958.

Hale, C. W.: Histochemical demonstration of acid polysaccharides in animal tissue, Nature 157: 802, 1946.

Hoffman, D. C., and Duran-Reynals, F.: Influence of testicle extract on intradermal spread of injected fluids and particles, J. Exper. Med. 53:387, 1931.

McManus, J. F. A.: Histochemistry of connective tissue in Connective Tissue in Health and Disease, p. 31, ed. by G. Asboe-Hansen, Copenhagen, Munksgaard, 1954.

———: Histological demonstration of mucin after periodic acid, Nature 158:202, 1946.

———: Histological and histochemical uses of periodic acid, Stain Technol. 23:99, 1948.

Meyer, Karl: The biological significance of hyaluronic acid and hyaluronidase, Physiol. Rev. 27:335, 1947.

———: The chemistry and biology of the mucopolysaccharides and glycoproteins, Cold Spring Harbor Symposium on Quantitative Biology 6:91, 1938.

———: Chemistry of connective tissue, polysaccharides in Connective Tissues, p. 88, ed. by C. Ragan, New York, Macy, 1950.

———: The chemistry of the ground substances of connective tissue in Connective Tissue in Health and Disease, p. 54, ed. by G. Asboe-Hansen, Copenhagen, Munksgaard, 1954.

———: Mucoids and glycoproteins in Advances

in Protein Chemistry, vol. 2, New York, Acad. Press, 1945.

Meyer, K., and Chaffee, E.: Mucopolysaccharides of skin, J. Biol. Chem. *138*:491, 1941.

Meyer, K., Smyth, E. M., and Dawson, M. H.: Isolation of mucopolysaccharides from synovial fluid, J. Biol. Chem. *128*:319, 1939.

Strauss, J., and Necheles, H.: Variations in dermal absorption with age, J. Lab. & Clin. Med. *33*:612, 1948.

Wassermann, F.: The intercellular components of connective tissue: origin, structure and interrelationship of fibers and ground substance, Ergebn. Anat. u. Entwicklungsg. *35*:240, 1956.

Wislocki, G. B., Bunting, H., and Dempsey, E. W.: Metachromasia in mammalian tissues and its relationship to mucopolysaccharides, Am. J. Anat. *81*:1, 1947.

FIBROUS INTERCELLULAR SUBSTANCES

Angevine, D. M.: Structure and function of normal connective tissue *in* Connective Tissues, p. 13, ed. by C. Ragan, New York, Macy, 1950.

Astbury, W. T.: X-ray studies of the structure of compounds of biological interest, Ann. Rev. Biochem. *8*:113, 1939.

Astbury, W. T., and Bell, F. O.: Molecular structure of the collagen fibres, Nature *145*:421, 1940.

Bear, R. S.: The structure of collagen molecules and fibrils, J. Biophysic. & Biochem. Cytol. *2*:363, 1956.

Bloom, P. M., Hartmann, J. F., and Vernier, R. L.: An electron microscope evaluation of the width of normal glomerular basement membrane in man at various ages, Anat. Rec. *133*: 251, 1959.

Cooper, Z. K.: Aging of the skin *in* Cowdry's Problems of Aging, edited by Lansing, ed. 3, p. 764, Baltimore, Williams & Wilkins, 1952.

Gross, J.: The structure of elastic tissue as studied with the electron microscope, J. Exper. Med. *89*:699, 1949.

Gross, J., and Schmitt, F. O.: The structure of human skin collagen as studied with the electron microscope, J. Exper. Med. *88*:555, 1948.

Jacobson, W.: Histological survey of the normal connective tissue and its derivatives *in* Nature and Structure of Collagen, p. 6, ed. by J. T. Randall and S. F. Jackson, New York, Acad. Press, 1953.

Keech, M. K.: The effect of collagenase and trypsin on collagen; an electron microscopic study, Anat. Rec. *119*:139, 1954.

Kramer, H., and Little, K.: Nature of reticulin *in* Nature and Structure of Collagen, p. 33, ed. by J. T. Randall and S. F. Jackson, New York, Acad. Press, 1953.

Lansing, A. I.: Aging of elastic fibers, J. Nat. Cancer Inst. *12*:217, 1951.

————: Chemical morphology of elastic fibers *in* Connective Tissues, p. 45, ed. by C. Ragan, New York, Macy, 1951.

Porter, K. R.: Repair processes in connective tissues *in* Connective Tissues, p. 126, ed. by C. Ragan, New York, Macy, 1951.

Schmitt, F. O., Hall, C. E., and Jakus, M. A.: Electron microscope investigations of the structure of collagen, J. Cell. & Comp. Physiol. *20*: 11, 1942.

————: The ultrastructure of protoplasmic fibrils *in* Frontiers of Cytochemistry, p. 261, ed. by N. L. Hoerr, Lancaster, Cattell, 1943.

Wassermann, F.: The intercellular components of connective tissue: origin, structure and interrelationship of fibers and ground substance, Ergebn. Anat. u. Entwicklungsg. *35*:240, 1956.

Wassermann, F., Roth, L. E., and Minick, O. T.: The fine structure of native collagen in thin sections, Exper. Cell Res. *13*:407, 1957.

Woessner, J. F., and Gould, B. S.: Collagen biosynthesis. Tissue culture experiments to ascertain the role of ascorbic acid in collagen formation, J. Biophys. & Biochem. Cytol. *3*:685, 1957.

Wyckoff, R. W. G.: The fine structure of connective tissues *in* Connective Tissues, p. 38, New York, Macy, 1952.

Zawisch, C.: Die Morphogenese der kollagenen Fibrille, Acta anat. *29*:143, 1957.

THE P. A. SCHIFF TECHNIC AND THE STAINING OF INTERCELLULAR SUBSTANCES

Bergeron, J. A., and Singer, M.: Metachromasy: an experimental and theoretical re-evaluation, J. Biophys. & Biochem Cytol. *4*:433, 1958.

Davies, D. V.: Specificity of staining methods for mucopolysaccharides of the hyaluronic acid type, Stain Technol. *27*:65, 1952.

Dempsey, E. W., Bunting, H., Singer, M., and Wislocki, G. B.: The dye-binding capacity and other chemohistological properties of mammalian mucopolysaccharides, Anat. Rec. *98*: 417, 1947.

Gersh, I.: Some functional considerations of ground substance of connective tissues *in* Connective Tissues, p. 11, New York, Macy, 1951.

Gersh, I., and Catchpole, H. R.: The organization of ground substance and basement membrane and its significance in tissue injury, disease and growth, Am. J. Anat. *85*:457, 1949.

Glegg, R. E., Clermont, Y., and Leblond, C. P.: The use of lead tetraacetate, benzidine, o-dianisidine and a "film test" to investigate the significance of the "periodic acid sulfurous acid" technique in carbohydrate histochemistry, Stain Technol. *27*:277, 1952.

Glegg, R. E., Eidinger, D., and Leblond, C. P.: Some carbohydrate components of reticular fibers, Science *118*:614, 1953.

———: Presence of carbohydrates distinct from acid mucopolysaccharides in connective tissue, Science *120*:839, 1954.

Hotchkiss, R. D. A.: Microchemical reaction resulting in the staining of polysaccharide structures in fixed tissue preparations, Arch. Biochem. *16*:131, 1948.

Leblond, C. P.: Distribution of periodic acid-reactive carbohydrates in the adult rat, Am. J. Anat. *86*:1, 1950.

Lillie, R. D.: Connective tissue staining *in* Connective Tissues, p. 11, New York, Macy, 1952.

———: Further exploration of the HIO$_4$ Schiff reaction with remarks on its significance, Anat. Rec. *108*:239, 1950.

———: Histochemistry of connective tissues, Lab. Investigation *1*:30, 1952.

McManus, J. F. A.: Histological and histochemical uses of periodic acid, Stain Technol. *23*:99, 1948.

———: The periodic acid routine applied to the kidney, Am. J. Path. *24*:643, 1948.

Robb-Smith, A. H. T.: The nature of reticulin *in* Connective Tissues, p. 92, New York, Macy, 1952.

Wislocki, G. B., Bunting, H., and Dempsey, E. W.: Metachromasia in mammalian tissues and its relationship to mucopolysaccharides, Am. J. Anat. *81*:1, 1947.

Chapter 6

Tissue Fluid

GENERAL CONSIDERATIONS

The great transportation system of the human body that is responsible for bringing food and oxygen to cells and for removing their waste products is the blood stream. This is contained by a system of tubes called *blood vessels*. These form a circuit through which blood is pumped in one direction by the heart (Fig. 328). The vessels that lead away from the heart have relatively thick and strong walls because they carry blood under considerable pressure; these vessels are called *arteries*. These branch and rebranch and finally empty their blood under low pressure into capillaries which are narrow tubes with very thin delicate walls. The capillaries empty their contents into veins which carry the blood back to the heart. Blood in the veins is not under much pressure; hence, the walls of veins are not as thick as those of arteries.

Most of the cells of the body lie *outside* blood vessels. So, to reach most cells of the body, nutritive substances and oxygen contained in the blood must leave the blood and pass through the walls of blood vessels and then through the intercellular substances of tissues to reach the cells that they nourish. The waste products formed by cells must make the same journey in an opposite direction.

The walls of arteries are much too thick to permit food substances or oxygen to pass through them. Therefore, arteries do not nourish tissues directly; their function is to carry blood to the very thin-walled capillaries and empty it into these capillaries under a greatly reduced pressure.

The walls of capillaries are thin enough to permit water, salts, oxygen and nourishment to pass through them to nourish the cells of the body that are outside them (Fig. 91 and 92).

The walls of capillaries are composed of very thin platelike cells that are curved in one direction so that they can be fitted together to form a tube. Since beginners commonly have some difficulty in understanding their structure, it is worth while to make a model

of a short section of one. To do this a cigarette paper is laid flat on a table, and an oval nucleus, about a quarter or a third of the width of the paper, is drawn in its central part. The paper now has become a model of an endothelial cell. It is very thin but relatively long and wide. It has a nucleus in its central part, and the rest of the paper represents the cytoplasm of the cell. The paper now is rolled into a tube, as if one were rolling a cigarette; it is then a model of a short section of a capillary, and it is obvious that over most of its extent its wall is no more than thin cytoplasm. (Capillaries often have some intercellular substance associated with them to give them support, as will be described later in this book.)

The edges of the cytoplasm of the endothelial cells of capillaries always fit closely together; indeed, it is probable that the edges of contiguous cells are cemented together with a cement substance. Accordingly, the living cells of capillaries provide a continuous living membrane which separates blood from the tissue that lies outside blood vessels. This endothelial membrane performs a function somewhat similar to that of a dialyzing parchment or collodion membrane. Under ordinary circumstances it does not permit the colloids of blood to pass through it but it does permit the passage of water and crystalloids. Generally, it is described as a living semipermeable membrane.

The fluid that passes from the blood through the endothelial cells of capillaries and out into the tissues is called *tissue fluid*. This fluid is in very intimate association with the intercellular substances of the tissues that are disposed outside capillaries, particularly with the amorphous kinds of intercellular substance. The relation between the tissue fluid that emerges from capillaries and the intercellular substance into which it emerges is different in different parts of the body. In some sites, where the amorphous intercellular substance is a sol, and fluid or semifluid, the tissue fluid is the medium in which the colloidal amorphous intercellular substance is dispersed, and the dilution of the amorphous intercellular

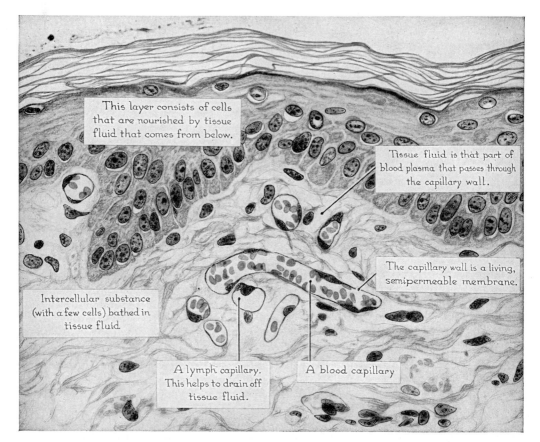

This layer consists of cells that are nourished by tissue fluid that comes from below.

Tissue fluid is that part of blood plasma that passes through the capillary wall.

The capillary wall is a living, semipermeable membrane.

Intercellular substance (with a few cells) bathed in tissue fluid

A lymph capillary. This helps to drain off tissue fluid.

A blood capillary

FIG. 91. High-power photomicrograph, lightly retouched, of a section cut through the outer part of the skin of a pig. This illustration shows the cellular epidermis above and capillaries surrounded by intercellular substance below. It shows how tissue fluid must migrate from capillaries to nourish adjacent cells.

substance in such sites depends in part on whether little or much tissue fluid is present. However, in sites where intercellular substances are rigid gels, the situation is different. Gelled intercellular substances contain a great deal of bound water. This is obtained, as the intercellular substances are formed, from the tissue fluid of the part. So, in the instance of gelled intercellular substances, tissue fluid becomes incorporated into them to become their bound water. This makes the gelled intercellular substances permeable because diffusion can occur through the bound water. However, there may be open passageways in gelled intercellular substances for free tissue fluid. For example, these are necessary in bone, for in it the gelled intercellular substance becomes impregnated with calcium salts; these probably displace the bound water, and so the inter-

cellular substance becomes impermeable. Accordingly, as we shall see, the intercellular substance of bone is provided with tiny little canals through which free tissue fluid can permeate.

Tissue fluid consists of that part of blood that can diffuse through the walls of capillaries. Blood consists of both fluid and cells. The fluid of blood is called *plasma* and it is a solution of both colloids and crystalloids. The endothelial walls of capillaries are permeable to solutions of crystalloids, so these pass out from the blood to comprise the tissue fluid. However, the walls of capillaries generally retain the cells of blood, and for the most part they also prevent any colloids in the blood from entering the tissue fluid. Tissue fluid, then, is of a different composition from blood plasma chiefly in that it does not contain very

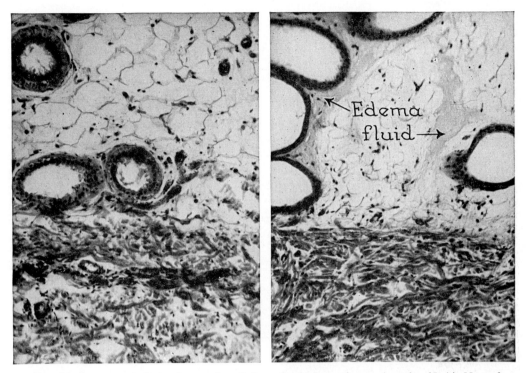

FIG. 93. Low-power photomicrographs of the subcutaneous tissue of a pig. (*Left*) Normal tissue. (*Right*) This tissue contains fluid which has leaked from capillaries because of a near-by area of tissue damage.

blood capillaries diffuses through their endothelial walls and once it has gained entrance to them is called *lymph* instead of tissue fluid. The capillaries of this second set, because they contain lymph, are termed *lymphatic capillaries*. They drain into larger lymph vessels, to be described later, and these, connecting with still other lymph vessels, eventually form two chief trunks that return the lymph collected from the whole body into large veins near the heart. Hence, that part of the tissue fluid absorbed by lymphatic capillaries eventually reaches the confines of the blood circulatory system again, but by a somewhat circuitous route.

Lymphatic capillaries are useful in regulating the *quality* of the tissue fluid as well as its quantity. At present, it is generally agreed that the endothelium of blood capillaries normally allows a little colloid to escape into the tissue fluid. It is also generally agreed that escaped colloid cannot diffuse back into blood capillaries. However, it can pass through the endothelial walls of lymphatics. The studies of Drinker and his associates have shown that if it were not for the lymphatic drainage of tissue fluid, colloid would accumulate in tissue fluid and by virtue of its osmotic pressure would tend to hold increasing amounts of water in the tissues. By more or less continually draining away colloid from tissue fluid, lymphatic capillaries exert a profound effect on the quality, as well as the quantity, of tissue fluid.

EDEMA

The many factors and instruments concerned in the production and the absorption of tissue fluid represent just as many possible causes for a disruption of the mechanism. Although it is conceivable that a disrupted mechanism could lead to there being too little tissue fluid, the common example of a disrupted mechanism is the swelling of tissue by an excess. A swelling of tissue from this cause is termed *edema* (*oedēma* = a swelling), and it is a very common clinical condition. If edematous tissue is examined under the micro-

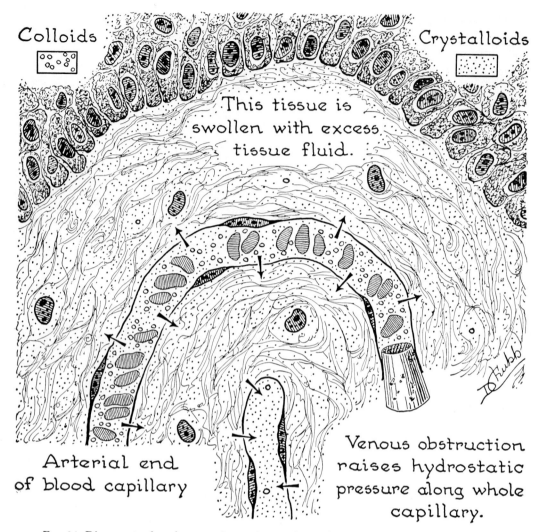

Colloids

Crystalloids

This tissue is swollen with excess tissue fluid.

Arterial end of blood capillary

Venous obstruction raises hydrostatic pressure along whole capillary.

Fig. 94. Diagram to show how an obstruction to the outflow of blood from capillaries (back pressure on veins) can cause an increased amount of tissue fluid to form from the capillaries and also interfere with its absorption.

scope, the cells and the structures within it are seen to be spread apart more widely than is usual (Fig. 93, *right*).

The amount of tissue fluid that can accumulate in tissues varies in relation to the type of tissue affected. Some tissues offer little resistance to being spread apart from within; others, because they are firmly knit together, offer more. In most sites edema tends to be self-limiting because the more the tissue becomes swollen, the more resistance it offers to becoming stretched further. When a certain point is reached, the hydrostatic pressure of

the fluid in the stretched tissue is almost as great as that within the capillaries, and as a result the production of tissue fluid in the part almost ceases.

It might be thought that the increased hydrostatic pressure of the tissue fluid in swollen tissue would collapse its lymphatic vessels and so interfere with lymph drainage. However, the studies of Pullinger and Florey indicate the opposite. The walls of lymphatic vessels are attached to fibers of intercellular substance that extend throughout the tissue. As tissues become spread apart by fluid, these

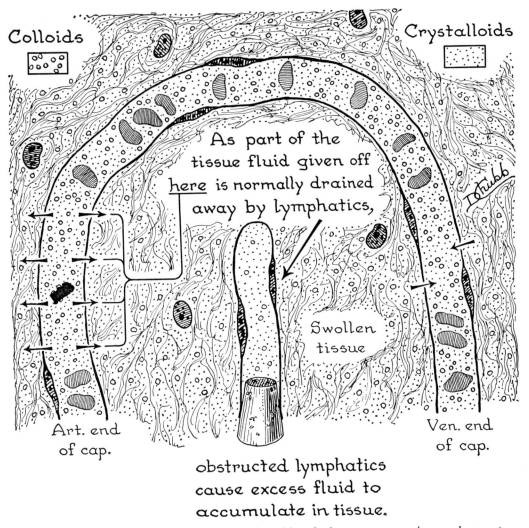

Colloids

Crystalloids

As part of the tissue fluid given off <u>here</u> is normally drained away by lymphatics,

Swollen tissue

Art. end of cap.

Ven. end of cap.

obstructed lymphatics cause excess fluid to accumulate in tissue.

Fig. 95. Diagram to show how the obstruction of lymphatics may cause an increased amount of tissue fluid to be present in the tissues they normally drain. It should be observed also that the amount of colloid in the tissue fluid becomes increased when lymphatics are obstructed because such colloid as normally escapes from capillaries is normally drained away by the lymphatics.

fibers are put on the stretch with the result that they pull on the walls of lymphtic vessels in various directions and so hold them open.

Some Causes of Edema

1. **Increased Hydrostatic Pressure in Blood Capillaries.** Theoretically, the hydrostatic pressure in blood capillaries would be raised either if blood were delivered to capillaries under increased pressure or if the free drain-age of blood from capillaries into veins were impeded. Arterial pressures high enough to raise capillary pressures sufficiently to cause edema are seldom encountered and, indeed, such pressures are scarcely compatible with life. Hence, increased hydrostatic pressure in capillaries is almost always due to some obstruction to the free drainage of blood into veins and back to the heart.

If a vein becomes obstructed, that portion of it between the obstruction and the capil-

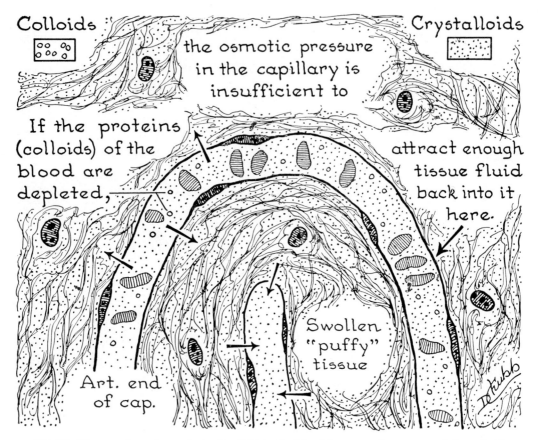

Colloids   the osmotic pressure in the capillary is insufficient to   Crystalloids

If the proteins (colloids) of the blood are depleted,

attract enough tissue fluid back into it here.

Art. end of cap.

Swollen "puffy" tissue

FIG. 96. Diagram shows how a lack of colloid in the blood increases the amount of tissue fluid.

laries soon becomes distended with blood, and the hydrostatic pressure within it rises. The increased hydrostatic pressure in the vein is transmitted back to the venous ends of those capillaries that drain into it and, as a result, the hydrostatic pressure at their venous ends becomes almost as great as at their arterial ends. Under these conditions, the whole capillary exudes tissue fluid, and none of the capillary absorbs it (Fig. 94).

There are many different ways in which the venous return of blood may be obstructed sufficiently to cause edema. The heart may be so diseased that it cannot pump away all the blood that is returned to it; hence, blood backs up in the veins to increase the hydrostatic pressure within them. Edema caused by such a mechanism is often said to be "dependent" because it tends to occur in the lowest parts of the body. Again, certain diseases cause

certain individual veins to become obstructed; the edema in this instance is roughly localized to the area normally drained by the affected vein.

2. **Lymphatic Obstruction.** As part of the tissue fluid produced at the arterial ends of capillaries is normally drained away by lymphatic capillaries, and obstruction to the drainage of lymph tends to lead to an increase of tissue fluid. Because the lymphatic capillaries are the normal means for draining away such colloids as escape from the blood into tissue fluid, the tissue fluid that accumulates when lymphatics are obstructed comes to contain an increasing amount of colloid, and this gradually raises its osmotic pressure. This contributes further to the edema (Fig. 95).

Lymphatic obstruction can be caused by several different disease processes. However, the most dramatic one is seen in the tropics

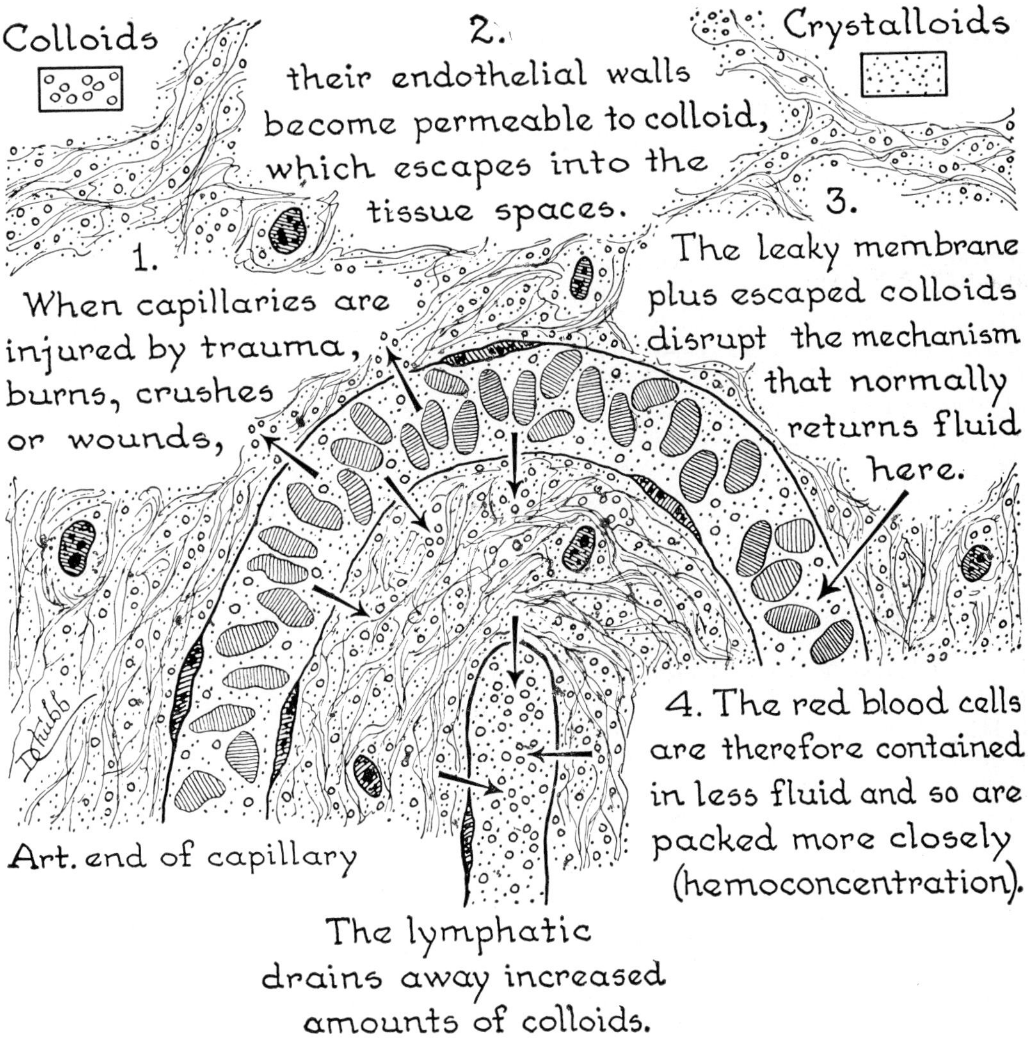

Colloids

2.
their endothelial walls
become permeable to colloid,
which escapes into the
tissue spaces.

Crystalloids

3.
The leaky membrane
plus escaped colloids
disrupt the mechanism
that normally
returns fluid
here.

1.
When capillaries are
injured by trauma,
burns, crushes
or wounds,

4. The red blood cells
are therefore contained
in less fluid and so are
packed more closely
(hemoconcentration).

Art. end of capillary

The lymphatic
drains away increased
amounts of colloids.

FIG. 97. Diagram shows how plasma escapes when the endothelial walls of capillaries are injured by burns, crushes, near-by wounds or other means. Notice that as plasma leaks away from the capillary the number of red blood cells in relation to plasma in it becomes increased. This is called hemoconcentration. Observe also how, under conditions of this sort, increased amounts of colloid are drained away by the lymphatic capillaries.

and is due to a small parasite that, on gaining entrance to the body, tends to occlude lymphatics. So, great persistent swelling of parts of the body (elephantiasis) may result.

3. **Insufficient Colloid in the Blood.** The absorption of tissue fluid at the venous ends of blood capillaries depends on the fact that the osmotic pressure of blood is greater than that of tissue fluid. This extra osmotic pressure possessed by blood depends on its colloid content. Therefore, a depletion of blood colloid diminishes the attraction of blood for tissue fluid and hence causes edema (Fig. 96).

The colloids of blood are proteins. Proteins, of course, are a most important and essential dietary ingredient; as noted previously, protoplasm consists chiefly of protein. So starvation, particularly protein starvation, can deplete the proteins of the blood with resulting edema. But more commonly, in countries where food is relatively abundant, a depletion of blood protein occurs when proteins are lost from the blood in some fashion faster than they can be replaced. This may happen, for example, in some kinds of disease of the kidneys. These organs filter out certain waste products from the blood. Normally, the filters in the kidney, to be described later, retain protein. But when injured in certain ways, they lose their ability to hold back protein, which, in consequence, escapes into the urine. Testing the urine for albumen—a very common procedure—gives information as to whether or not proteins are being lost this way. A low level of blood protein caused by the persistent escape of blood protein from diseased kidneys, then, can cause edema. Another way by which the blood proteins can become seriously depleted is by their seeping away from large, denuded areas of injured tissue (weeping wounds).

4. Increased Permeability of Blood Capillary Endothelium. Endothelial membranes differ from collodion or parchment membranes in being composed of living cells. Their ability to hold colloids is a vital activity. Hence, if capillaries become injured, they allow colloids as well as crystalloids to escape freely into the tissue fluid.

When capillaries leak colloid into the tissue fluid, its osmotic pressure becomes raised so that the difference between the osmotic pressure of blood and tissue fluid is eliminated. Therefore, tissue fluid is not returned at the venous ends of capillaries; hence, it accumulates even though lymphatics may drain away increased amounts of it. The lymph under these conditions contains more colloid than usual (Fig. 97).

Endothelium may leak colloid under a great many different conditions. Perhaps the most easily visualized condition in which this occurs is their injury by physical agents. For example, it is easy to understand how capillaries might be injured if tissue is exposed to great heat or cold or struck with a blunt instrument or crushed by a great weight.

If capillary injury is very widespread—for example, when much of the body surface is burned—a condition known as *surgical shock* tends to develop. The vessels of the circulatory system contain only a limited amount of fluid, and it is easily possible for enough plasma to leak away from capillaries in and

near the site of an extensive injury to deplete the circulatory system to the point where it can no longer function. As plasma continues to escape from vessels, less and less fluid is returned by the veins to the heart, with the result that its chambers do not fill properly between contractions. It is in the same situation as a pump on a well that is running dry. This results in a collapse of the circulation and death.

It is interesting to observe how the modern treatment of surgical shock represents the application of some simple laws of physics. Consider, for example, an individual who has had a considerable area of his body burned. Without treatment he would in all probability die from shock caused by extensive plasma loss in and about the injured area. To prevent this, two fundamental measures are taken. The first is directed toward preventing plasma loss by applying pressure bandages or otherwise encasing the injured members so the tissues within them are prevented from expanding further; thus they are put in a position in which they cannot allow any more tissue fluid to enter them. The second fundamental measure is that of injecting plasma obtained from other individuals into the veins of the injured one so as to maintain a full content of fluid in the vessels of his or her circulatory system; this is much the more important of the two.

REFERENCES

GENERAL

Cowdry, E. V.: Ageing of tissue fluids *in* Cowdry's Problems of Ageing, ed. 3, edited by A. J. Lansing, Baltimore, Williams & Wilkins, 1952.
Drinker, Cecil K., and Field, Madeleine E.: Lymphatics, Lymph and Tissue Fluid, Baltimore, Williams & Wilkins, 1933.
Rouvière, H.: Anatomy of the Human Lymphatic System, translated by M. J. Tobias, Ann Arbor, Edwards Bros., 1938.
Yoffey, J. M., and Courtice, F. C.: Lymphatics, Lymph and Lymphoid Tissue, Cambridge, Harvard Univ. Press, 1956.

SPECIAL

Chambers, Robert, and Zweifach, B. W.: Intercellular cement and capillary permeability, Physiol. Rev. 27:436, 1947.
Pullinger, B. D., and Florey, H. W.: Some observations on the structure and function of lymphatics, Brit. J. Exper. Path. 16:49, 1935.
————: Proliferation of lymphatics in inflammation, J. Path. & Bact. 45:157, 1937.

Chapter 7

The Cells of Blood

GENERAL CONSIDERATIONS

Blood is a fluid that has cells and fragments of cytoplasm suspended in it. The fluid is termed *plasma* and is a solution of both colloids and crystalloids. The blood cells are of two kinds: red and white. The fragments of cytoplasm that are in blood are called platelets; they play a part in clotting.

Although most blood cells are of greater specific gravity than the plasma in which they are suspended, they do not tend to settle in the blood stream because of its constant motion. However, they will slowly settle in blood that is removed from the body and kept fluid.

Certain diseases primarily affect the blood and/or the organs that form or destroy blood. The particular branch of medicine that deals with these is termed *hematology*. Those who specialize in this subject are called *hematologists*. But since disease in almost any part of the body affects the peripheral blood in some way, all physicians are interested in blood and must learn how to examine it properly.

Hematology is such an engrossing subject that it is not surprising that hematologists, like fond parents, should have overburdened the objects of their interest with too many names. Actually, the different types of blood cell with whose appearance the student must become familiar are not many. His chief difficulty is encountered in trying to remember which of many lengthy names should be attached to each. If the student attempts to memorize these names without inquiring into their respective meanings, he is more likely to be a source of amusement than satisfaction to his examiners. There is only one way to become conversant with the language of hematology and that is by learning the meaning of the various prefixes, roots and suffixes which the vocabulary of hematology employs. This is a relatively easy task because they are few; however, they are used in many different combinations.

For example, we shall presently discuss a cell known as a polychromatophilic erythrocyte. If one recalls, or learns, that *polys* means "many"; *chroma*, "color"; *philos*, "love"; *erythros* "red"; and *kytos* "cell"; the term becomes meaningful because it can be understood to refer to a red cell that loves many colors. Actually, next to red, it loves blue most; hence, it is a red cell with a blue tinge, which is the reason for such red cells being said to exhibit *basophilia*. The foregoing also explains why single solutions that, when applied to blood, color its different cells and their parts many different colors, are called *polychrome stains*.

In this section dealing with blood cells, and in a subsequent section dealing with the hemopoietic or blood-making tissues (*hemo* = blood; *poiesis* = a making), special attention will be given to the derivations of the words that are employed, so that the student

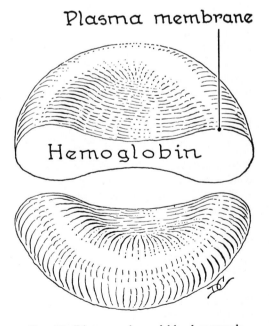

FIG. 98. Diagram of a red blood corpuscle that has been cut in half.

159

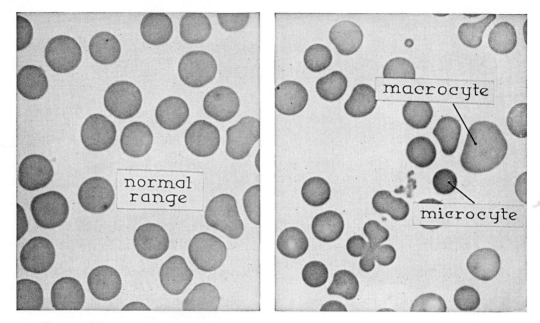

Fig. 99. Oil-immersion photomicrographs of stained films of rabbit's blood. (*Left*) Normal blood with the cells varying in size only slightly and, except where they have been pressed upon by other cells in the film, having a normal shape. (*Right*) Blood that was obtained from an animal with TNT poisoning. It shows a great range in the size of the red blood cells, with both microcytes and macrocytes present. It also shows red blood cells of different shapes.

will be able to relate them to particular cells.

The cells of blood are of two main types: red and white. They are so designated by their appearance in fresh, unstained blood. Actually, although red cells, *en masse*, are responsible for the red color of blood, they are straw-colored rather than red when seen individually under the microscope unstained. And white cells are colorless rather than white. Red cells are more properly termed *erythrocytes* and white cells *leukocytes* (*leukos* = white).

ERYTHROCYTES

Erythrocytes are from 500 to 1,000 times more numerous in blood than leukocytes.

Shape. The normal shape of the human erythrocyte is that of a *biconcave disk* (Fig. 98). The animal kingdom presents examples of other shapes. In certain diseases, human erythrocytes of altered shape make their appearance in the circulation (Fig. 99, *right*); hence, the determination of the shape of erythrocytes in any given sample of blood is of diagnostic importance.

As will be noted later, there probably is no supporting structural framework inside the erythrocyte to explain its shape, which, therefore, is determined and maintained by other factors. One is probably the molecular constitution of the material in its interior, because when this is abnormal cells of different shapes are seen. Another is the composition of the fluid in which the cell is suspended, for certain changes in the fluid may lead to the erythrocyte becoming spherical, as will be discussed in more detail when the behavior of erythrocytes in solutions of different osmotic pressure is considered.

Size. The diameter of erythrocytes usually is determined by spreading a drop of blood on a glass slide (this is called making a blood film) (Fig. 100) and then measuring the dried cells under high magnification by means of a micrometer eyepiece. Dried cells may not be of exactly the same diameter as cells suspended in plasma, but any difference in size is probably not great. If blood is normal the erythrocytes in a film are of an almost uniform diameter, not differing from one another by more than 1 μ (Fig. 102). If the size of each is ticked off on a properly prepared piece of graph paper it will be found that the greatest number are 7.2 μ wide and that almost all are within half a micron of this either way. If the sizes seen in a large sample are all indicated on graph paper, a curve can be drawn which shows at a glance whether the size range is normal, or whether the size of the cells as a whole is greater or less than normal, or whether the size range within the sample is greater than it should be. Such a curve is called a Price-Jones curve. Since there are certain disease states in which the size of erythrocytes is altered, Price-Jones curves are commonly used in clinical work.

Cells smaller than 6 μ are termed *microcytes (mikros = small)* (Fig. 99, *right*). Cells moderately larger than the normal, from 9 to 12 μ, are termed *macrocytes (makros = large)* (Fig. 103, *right*). The shift in size that occurs in certain blood diseases is usually either to the smaller or the larger side; when the average is smaller, the condition is termed *microcytic* (Fig. 103, *left*), when larger *macrocytic* (Fig. 103, *right*). In some conditions, both microcytes and macrocytes may be present (Fig. 99, *right*).

Structure and Composition. From the evidence that is available, it does not seem likely that there is any supporting framework within the erythrocyte other than that provided by the molecular constitution of the colloidal complex with which it is filled. This results in the cell being soft and elastic.

More than half of the erythrocyte consists of water (60%), the rest of solids. Of the solids, 90 per cent is the conjugated protein hemoglobin. This is said to be a conjugated protein because it consists of the protein *globin* joined to the pigment *heme*. Although only 4 per cent of hemoglobin actually consists of pigment (heme), its combination with globin results in the combined entity (hemoglobin) being colored; hence, hemoglobin is spoken of as a pigment. A little other protein and some fatty material also exist in the cell along with hemoglobin.

It may seem curious that erythrocytes containing only a soft jelly would maintain their biconcave shape, and that the molecular constitution of the jelly could be such as to be an important factor in making the cell assume this shape. However, the fact is that a change

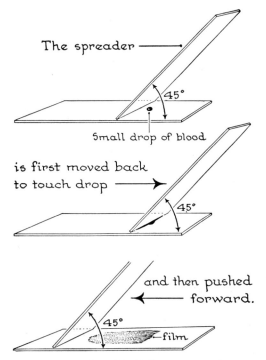

FIG. 100. How blood films are spread.

in the chemical constitution of hemoglobin can be responsible for the cells taking on a different shape. For example, there is a curious disease in which the erythrocytes may assume the form of sickles. In this form they are destroyed easily, and so individuals with this disease do not have enough erythrocytes. For many years no one knew what was responsible for the altered form of these cells. In 1949, however, Pauling and his colleagues discovered that the hemoglobin in them was of a slightly different composition from the normal, but the difference was sufficient to make the cells assume a shape different from that of biconcave disks. Hereditary factors are responsible for the condition; hence, this diseases provides an example of how an altered sequence in a DNA molecule (an altered gene) can determine a different amino acid sequence in protein molecules that are synthesized in a particular type of cell.

The substance of the erythrocyte is somewhat modified at its periphery to constitute the *cell* or *plasma membrane*. This is believed to be a lipoid-protein complex. Although its thickness is to be measured in molecules (it is therefore invisible with the light microscope), it normally acts to prevent the escape of the colloidal material of the cell into the plasma. It also exhibits great selectivity with regard to the passage of ions.

Behavior in Solutions of Different Osmotic Pressure. The osmotic pressure of plasma equals that of erythrocytes, and so plasma is said to be *isotonic* (*iso* = equal; *tonos* = tension) with regard to them. In plasma, then, there is no tendency for either the erythrocytes or the plasma to absorb water from each other. It is possible to prepare saline solutions that are isotonic with erythrocytes. If the salt concentration of a saline solution is below that of erythrocytes, it is said to be *hypotonic* (*hypo* = under); if above it, *hypertonic* (*hyper* = above, over).

Erythrocytes respond in somewhat different ways to the kind of solution in which they are immersed.

First, it already has been explained that the molecular structure of hemoglobin is an important factor in determining the biconcave shape of the cell. However, another factor is the nature, as well as the osmotic pressure, of the solution in which the cell is bathed. For example, if erythrocytes are washed and suspended in physiologic saline solution they become spheres and extend little projections out from them. The biconcave disk form can be restored to such cells by resuspending them in plasma or certain other solutions which are said to possess antisphering properties. Apparently, then, the molecular constitution of hemoglobin needs the help of certain substances which have some effect on the cell surface to bring about and maintain the biconcave shape of erythrocytes.

Secondly, erythrocytes can be shrunken or expanded by varying the osmotic pressure of the solution in which they are suspended. Erythrocytes are fairly resistant to slight changes in the osmotic pressure, but if the solution in which they are bathed is sufficiently hypotonic they assume a spherical shape and swell. When they become excessively swollen, another phenomenon occurs: their membranes become incapable of retaining hemoglobin, and this escapes into the surrounding fluid, coloring it. This is known as *hemolysis* (*lysis* = solution). Not all the substance of the erythrocyte escapes when he-

molysis occurs; enough remains to leave a "shadow" or "ghost" of the cell.

Hemolysis can be induced by means other than hypotonic solutions. Certain chemicals, particularly lipoid solvents, exert a hemolytic effect. Snake venom is a hemolytic agent. The plasma of some species hemolyzes the erythrocytes of others.

The erythrocytes in any given sample of blood are not equally susceptible to hemolysis. For instance, a solution of saline may be prepared of such concentration that it will hemolyze only some cells; for all to be hemolyzed, the strength of the solution must be reduced further. Hence, erythrocytes are said to vary with regard to their *fragility* (their susceptibility to hemolysis). The fragility of erythrocytes becomes altered in certain diseases; hence, fragility tests are of use in diagnosis.

If erythrocytes are immersed in a hypertonic solution, water is drawn from them into the solution. This results in the shrinkage of the erythrocytes and, as they shrink irregularly so that their outlines contain notches and indentations, they are said to be *crenated* (*crena* = a notch).

Function. Respiration is the basic metabolic process of life. For it to proceed without fatal interruption, the cells of the body require a continuous and substantial supply of oxygen. This is brought to them from the lungs by the blood in the circulatory system.

Oxygen does not dissolve to any great extent in water, or even in plasma. Hence, if the circulatory system contained only plasma, only a small fraction of the amount of oxygen needed by the cells of the body would dissolve into it as it passed through the lungs. To develop the great avidity that blood has for oxygen, Nature was forced to evolve a mechanism employing some other principle than that on which the ordinary solution of gases in fluids depends. This was accomplished by adding the protein hemoglobin to blood (within the erythrocytes).

Hemoglobin has the very important attribute of being able to combine with oxygen to form the compound *oxyhemoglobin.* A solution of hemoglobin, then, can continue to absorb oxygen until the hemoglobin it contains is converted into oxyhemoglobin, and this, of course, permits much more oxygen to be taken up than could be absorbed by blood plasma alone.

Hemoglobin, fortunately, is, in a sense, fickle in its liking for oxygen. In the lungs, where the oxygen tension (concentration) is high because of fresh air being constantly provided by the respiratory system, hemoglobin combines with oxygen avidly. But when oxygenated blood reaches the various tissues of the body, where the cells are constantly using oxygen so that its tension is low, hemoglobin releases a good part of its oxygen. When oxygen is thus divorced from oxyhemoglobin, the hemoglobin that remains is usually called *reduced hemoglobin* and this, on reaching the lungs, as it continues on its route through the circulatory system is, therefore, prepared to unite with oxygen and become oxyhemoglobin again.

WHY HEMOGLOBIN IS CONFINED
INSIDE ERYTHROCYTES

It is interesting to consider why hemoglobin is confined within the erythrocytes instead of being contained free in the plasma. Although hemoglobin is a protein, and in the nature of a colloid, it is not restrained by the endothelial membranes of the blood-vascular system to the same extent as the other colloids in the blood. Hence, when it is free, it escapes into the tissues and into the urine. This state of affairs occurs in "red-water fever," a disease of cattle in which a minute parasite invades the erythrocytes and so injures them that their hemoglobin escapes first into the plasma and then into the urine, which becomes colored sufficiently to justify the name of the disease. In certain human diseases, enough erythrocytes may be injured to produce a like condition.

It could be argued, of course, that Nature might have avoided the need for enclosing hemoglobin in cells by providing endothelial membranes of greater selectivity. But this would have made the ingress and the egress through capillary walls more difficult for many substances and would have disturbed the osmotic balance between blood and tissue fluid.

The cells that contain hemoglobin also have other uses. For example, as well as serving in the carriage of oxygen from the lungs to the tissues, erythrocytes are involved in the carriage of carbon dioxide from the tissues to the lungs. Their use in this respect is dependent on their containing an enzyme, carbonic

anhydrase, which, like hemoglobin, is confined within the erythrocyte (and in other cells as well). There are still other advantages in having hemoglobin confined to cells rather than in solution, and these, together with the details of its function in both oxygen and carbon dioxide transport, are best left to be considered in physiology.

Structure in Relation to Function. In addition to transporting large amounts of gases, the erythrocytes, to be efficient, must also absorb and release these gases very quickly. The absorption and the release of gases is a surface phenomenon; it occurs at an interface. Therefore, it is desirable that the interface between each erythrocyte and plasma should be as great as possible per unit of hemoglobin, and this desirable end is obtained by the biconcave form of the erythrocyte. The biconcave shape gives a surface area from 20 to 30 per cent greater than that of a sphere containing the same amount of hemoglobin. Furthermore, if erythrocytes were spheres, the average distance a gas would have to travel to reach the surface from the interior of the cell would be greatly increased. Hence, the biconcave shape is an ideal one for absorbing and releasing gases quickly.

The nonnucleated state of the erythrocyte is advantageous in that it allows the whole cell to contain hemoglobin and so be more efficient per unit volume.

The rounded edges of the erythrocyte protect it from injury, and its resilient elastic structure allows it to bend rather than break as it strikes bifurcations in capillaries. This phenomenon may be watched under the microscope in the web of a living frog's foot, suitably mounted, or in any thin living tissue possessing a good capillary bed and prepared in the same way. However, when examining such a preparation, it should be remembered that the microscope magnifies the speed of erythrocytes as much as it does their size; their movement is not actually as rapid as it seems.

It is the oxyhemoglobin in the erythrocytes in capillaries below the surface that imparts pinkness to cheeks and varying degrees of redness to lips and mucous membranes. The degree of color so imparted depends on many factors: the number of capillaries in operation, their closeness to the surface, the transparency of the overlying tissue and finally, the percentage of oxyhemoglobin in the blood.

Reduced hemoglobin, on the other hand, is blue rather than red. Normally, as blood passes through capillaries, not enough reduced hemoglobin is formed for the blue color to show. But if the oxygenation of blood in the lungs is seriously impaired so that blood containing a considerable amount of reduced hemoglobin is delivered to capillaries or if the circulation through the capillaries is slowed down so that a great deal of reduced hemoglobin forms and is not carried to the lungs fast enough, sufficient of this reduced hemoglobin (absolute amount—not percentage) may be present to impart a blue color to surfaces of the body that are ordinarily pink or red. This is termed *cyanosis* (*kyanos* = blue) and it is often a very important sign when detected on physical examination.

Hemoglobin is adversely affected by certain drugs and chemicals. Nitrites, for example, tend to cause hemoglobin to alter into a compound known as *methemoglobin*, which does not serve as a carrier for oxygen. Consequently, if this altered hemoglobin is present in the blood to too great an extent, there may not be enough hemoglobin left to support life. Moreover, methemoglobin, like reduced hemoglobin, imparts a dusky blue color to tissues, that is, in sufficient amounts it causes cyanosis.

Hemoglobin has a great affinity for certain other gases beside oxygen, most notably carbon monoxide. This gas forms a firm union with hemoglobin and so is not released to the tissues. Hence, a person breathing air containing even a low percentage of it gradually comes to have more and more of his hemoglobin bound to it and, therefore, valueless for the transport of oxygen. Carbon monoxide hemoglobin is a bright-red color, and the cherry-red lips of the carbon monoxide victim, whose tissues are in reality starved for oxygen, provide a sad paradox.

As the ability of the blood to transport oxygen efficiently is often impaired, an examination of the blood to ascertain its ability in this respect forms an important part of every physical examination.

Two of the procedures commonly employed, making an erythrocyte count and estimating the hemoglobin content of blood are learned about rather than learned thoroughly in the usual histology course. One reason for this is that making these tests requires the use of special equipment which students can scarcely be expected to purchase during their first year. A third procedure, which is of at least equal importance, the preparation, the staining and the examination of a blood film, requires no special instruments and should be learned thoroughly in a histology course. A fourth procedure, the making of a reticulocyte count, can also be learned to advantage at this time.

PRINCIPLES EMBODIED IN METHOD FOR COUNTING ERYTHROCYTES

To make an erythrocyte count the skin of the lobe of the ear or the finger is punctured. The first drop of blood that wells up from the wound is discarded because it may be diluted with tissue fluid. A special measuring pipette is used to draw up a known quantity of the second drop. The pipette is then placed in a special isotonic diluting fluid that does not destroy erythrocytes, and a considerably larger known quantity of this fluid is drawn up into the pipette and thoroughly mixed with the blood. A drop of the mixture is then introduced into what is known as a counting chamber; the bottom of this consists of a glass slide that is ruled into microscopic squares of known size, and its top of a coverslip which is separated from the ruled glass slide by a known distance. The counting chamber is then placed on the stage of a microscope, and the erythrocytes lying over the ruled squares are easily seen and their number per square counted. As the amount of blood taken, the amount of diluting fluid with which it is mixed, the thickness of the layer over the ruled squares and the size of the squares are all known quantities, the number of erythrocytes per cubic millimeter of blood can be calculated.

Under normal conditions, the blood of women should contain from 4,500,000 to 5,000,000 erythrocytes per cubic millimeter, that of men 5,000,000 to 5,500,000. However, the method employed in making the count is open to experimental error on many sides; hence, a blood count should always be read with a mental plus or minus reservation, the extent of which should bear a relation to the skill and the experience of the counter. Even under the best of circumstances the experimental error is considerable.

There is some evidence to suggest that counts made from blood obtained from different parts of the body differ and that the normal count varies somewhat throughout the day; it becomes increased after exercise and is somewhat higher in the newborn. The normal erythrocyte count of those who live in high altitudes is greater than that given above; less oxygen in the air is reflected by increased facilities for its absorption and transport.

Hemoglobin Content. This may be determined with different degrees of accuracy by several methods. Commonly, it is done by the use of the principle of colorimetry. This method, which is widely used clinically, involves the comparison of the color of blood with the color of a standard. Such a method is applicable when the color of a substance (for example, the hemoglobin in blood) changes in proportion to its concentration. As the amount of hemoglobin in blood becomes decreased or increased the color of the blood changes but its brick-red color is difficult to match. For this reason, blood is usually treated with acid to change its hemoglobin into acid hematin, which is of a reddish-brown color, much easier to match accurately. Similarly, stable pigments which can be readily matched can be produced by alkalies, carbon-monoxide, cyanide and other chemicals. In all these methods the color is compared with a standard, either by diluting the solution until it matches the standard when compared visually or by the use of a fixed dilution, which is examined in a photoelectric colorimeter. From the readings obtained it is easy to calculate the amount of hemoglobin that was present in the original sample of blood. Normal blood is said to contain about 15 gm. of hemoglobin per 100 ml. The normal amount varies in different geographic locations. Commonly, hemoglobin estimations are given in percentages. Just how many grams of hemoglobin is considered to constitute 100 per cent varies from community to community.

Preparation of a Blood Film. The study of a blood film is one of the foundation stones in the study of blood. However, to be useful, a film must be prepared understandingly and with great care. To make good blood films it is necessary to use a very clean slide. It is a time-tested procedure to wash new slides with soap and water and then, after rinsing them in several changes of clean water, to dry them with an old lint-free towel or rag that has been previously washed and rinsed many times and is kept for this purpose only. In drying them, they should be held by the edges so that their flat surfaces remain uncontaminated.

The cleaned ear or finger is then punctured lightly, and the first drop or two that well up are wiped away with sterile gauze. And then, as a *tiny* drop (the first drops are too large) wells up from the puncture, one surface of a clean slide, held by its edges, is applied to this (avoiding contact of the slide with the skin), so that most of the drop adheres to the slide midway between its sides and a short distance from one end (Fig. 100, *top*). A second slide, hereafter called the *spreader,* is now put in the position indicated in Figure 100. The edge of the spreader that touches the first slide should not be pressed against it firmly, but rather lightly. The spreader is now drawn back until the edge that is in contact with the first slide touches the drop of blood, which thereupon spreads quickly along the line of contact between the slides. The spreader is then pushed steadily forward, still without putting more than light pressure upon it, and by this means the drop of blood is spread out into a thin film.

The angle at which the spreader is held in relation to the first slide determines the thickness of the film to some extent. The greater the angle the thicker the film. Furthermore, the film is usually thicker toward the end of the slide from which the film is spread.

After a film has dried in air, it is generally stained with what is often called a "blood stain." Although there are different varieties of these, each commonly exists as a single solution. Enough blood stain is added to a slide to cover the film, and then after a very short time twice as much distilled water is added to dilute the stain. After the diluted solution has been allowed to act for a few minutes, the slide is rinsed in tap water and blotted. Then it can be studied with the oil-immersion objective, through oil, without a coverslip.

To stain blood films properly, the student must know something about the history and the nature of blood stains.

It will be recalled that most stains are classified as acid or basic and that these stain acidophilic and basophilic components, respectively (p. 8). In 1891, Romanovsky tried the effect of mixing an acid stain (eosin) with a basic stain (methylene blue). Curiously enough, the mixture acted as a better stain for blood than did the ingredients applied separately. With this mixture he was able to stain malarial parasites particularly well; indeed, one part of the parasite was colored a violet shade, which could not be attributed directly to eosin or methylene blue. He realized that the two dyes must have interacted chemically to produce still another dye. At about the same time, Unna discovered that if he treated methylene blue with alkali and heat, then it would impart a violet color to tissues which was not obtained with untreated methylene blue; hence, he decided that a new dye had formed as a result of the partial decomposition of methylene blue. Methylene blue treated to produce this new dye (or dyes) was said to be *polychromed*. Next, since Romanovsky had obtained such success with his mixture in which the polychroming of methylene blue occurred as a result of its being mixed with eosin, it was thought that mixing polychrome methylene blue and eosin might give still better results than Romanovsky's mixture and, when this was tried, it did.

However, there were so many practical disadvantages with regard to the use of the improved Romanovsky stain that it could scarcely be used except by an expert. The ingredients had to be mixed very exactly each time the stain was to be used, and even then they tended to react with each other very quickly to form a precipitate. These difficulties that restrained its common use were largely overcome by a further advance. The ingredients, mixed by experts, are allowed to precipitate. The precipitate is then dissolved and bottled in methyl alcohol, in which it keeps well. This is what is usually contained in the bottle of blood stain kept in the laboratory. Of course, in this form it is not an effective stain. But when water is added to it *on the slide,* the compound previously in solution in methyl alcohol partly passes into aqueous solution, and some dissociation occurs. So, for a brief period, the stain acts as if the ingredients had just been freshly mixed. Later on, of course, it tends to form a precipitate again, but by that time staining has been completed.

Anemia. If the amount of hemoglobin in circulating blood is reduced so that oxygen transport is impaired, the condition is said to constitute anemia (without blood). And, although the erythrocyte count and the hemoglobin estimation are of great importance in allowing the diagnosis of an anemia, it is difficult to assert just how great a reduction in either justifies the diagnosis.

There are different causes for anemia, and so there is some justification for saying that there are different kinds of anemia. An examination of the blood by erythrocyte counts, hemoglobin estimation and stained films are all of the greatest importance in establishing the type and the cause of any particular example of the condition. Until the cause is known rational treatment cannot be given. The investigation of anemia is a clinical problem, which the student will encounter later in his medical course. It is helpful if a few facts learned in histology are remembered well. These are:

Erythrocytes, although in most ways admirably suited to their purpose, are not very substantially constructed. Hence, they disintegrate after a certain length of time. There is a general but not precise agreement on their exact length of service in the blood stream, for different technics used to determine their life span give figures from 100 to 120 days. A common method for estimating their length of life is to remove some erythrocytes from an individual, label them with some radioactive material and then reinject them into the same individual and follow their length of life by technics which pick up their radioactivity. Another method hinges on the fact that erythrocytes of one individual may sometimes be sufficiently similar to those of another to permit them to live a normal life when they are injected into the blood stream of the other individual, and yet in this other individual they may retain certain specific properties by which they can be identified by agglutination tests. This latter technic, which does not require labeling the cells with radioactive material, indicates that their life span is about 120 days. After erythrocytes have lived their lives in the circulatory system they must be removed from it to prevent their disintegrating bodies from cluttering up the circulatory system. Worn-out erythrocytes are removed from the blood stream by certain phagocytic cells in the spleen, the bone marrow and the liver. The details of this process will be presented in later chapters.

It is obvious, of course, that if erythrocytes were constantly removed from the circulation, their numbers in the blood would steadily fall if new ones were not delivered into the blood at a corresponding rate. Indeed, the erythrocyte count must progressively fall or rise if the rate of their removal from blood is not in harmony with the rate of their liberation into blood. Furthermore, a little thought makes it apparent that the erythrocyte count need not be normal just because the rate of their removal from blood equals the rate of their liberation into blood. Such a circumstance would ensure that the count remained stationary, but it might remain stationary with only 2 million instead of 5 million erythrocytes per cubic milliliter of blood. Hence, a normal content of erythrocytes depends on the *level* at which the two processes of removal and liberation come into balance.

It is now easily seen that an anemia could occur as a result of a disturbance of either the rate of removal of erythrocytes from blood or the rate of their liberation into it. In other words, some anemias are due primarily to an increased rate of erythrocyte destruction; others, to a deficient rate of production.

In order to obtain information on either the rate of erythrocyte production or the rate of erythrocyte destruction, further tests must be made. Only the one that deals with the rate of their production will be considered at this time.

If a normal blood film, stained with a neutral blood stain, is examined with the oil-immersion objective, it will be seen that almost all the erythrocytes are of a clear pink color; they are acidophilic. But an occasional erythrocyte—anywhere from 1 out of 100 to 1 out of 1,000—will be slightly different in that, while fundamentally pink, it demonstrates a blue tinge. Such an erythrocyte is said to demonstrate basophilia and to be a *polychromatophilic erythrocyte* (Fig. 106) for reasons previously given.

From time to time it was argued that the basophilia of these cells indicated degeneration. This view is no longer accepted. Instead, it is agreed that basophilia in erythrocytes is a sign of youth. The reason for this will now be explained.

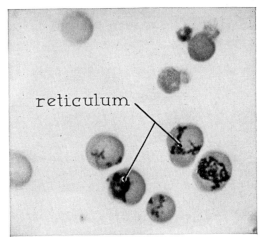

FIG. 101. Oil-immersion photomicrograph of a blood film stained with brilliant cresyl blue to show the so-called reticulum of the reticulocytes. The blood used was obtained from an animal which was regenerating large numbers of new erythrocytes.

The bone marrow cells that give rise to erythrocytes are of a rapidly growing undifferentiated type and, like other cells of this type, they have enough RNA in their cytoplasm to make it basophilic. Normally, the mother cells divide so many times before they become erythrocytes, their cytoplasmic RNA nucleoprotein becomes so divided up that it is lost. But when there is an increased need for erythrocytes some of the mother cells become erythrocytes before their cytoplasmic RNA is lost, and the erythrocytes that are formed this way are polychromatophilic.

Polychromatophilic erythrocytes in which basophilia is not very pronounced, so that they are only very faintly blue, are extremely difficult to identify in blood films stained with ordinary neutral blood stains. However, there is another way in which preparations may be made to show them much more distinctly. This is done by utilizing the supravital staining method (see p. 42). The dye used is brilliant cresyl blue. This may be employed in several ways but, in our experience, best results are obtained by preparing it in a 1 per cent aqueous solution to which 0.04 per cent potassium oxalate is added. A drop of this is placed in a freshly scooped-out, bowl-shaped depression in a block of paraffin wax, and to this a drop of fresh blood, taken with a pipette from a puncture, is added. After thorough mixing, a small drop is then put on a glass slide, and a film is made in the usual manner. Although the polychromatophilic erythrocytes are already stained by the cresyl blue, the film may then be stained with an ordinary neutral blood stain to color the other cells present.

Brilliant cresyl blue reacts with the newborn erythrocyte in freshly drawn and as yet undried or otherwise affected blood in a very curious manner: it appears to coagulate and concentrate the basophilic material previously spread through the cell so that this material comes to appear as a threadlike blue structure which, if abundant, may assume the form of a wreath or, if scanty, no more than scattered blue dots (Fig. 101). Because of this threadlike network, which was first thought to represent the staining of a previously existing reticular network inside the cell, the cells exhibiting it were termed *reticulocytes*. This name still persists even though it is generally agreed, first, that the network is an artefact due to cresyl blue coagulating and concentrating the basophilic material of the cells, and, secondly, that the reticulocyte is the same cell that would be termed a polychromatophilic erythrocyte if it were stained with an ordinary blood stain (Fig. 106).

By determining the percentage of reticulocytes among erythrocytes in a blood film, evidence can be obtained about the rate of erythrocyte production. Under normal conditions, less than 1 per cent of erythrocytes are reticulocytes, and, in our experience, the percentage of reticulocytes does not often closely approach 1 per cent, being considerably less.

Although some erythrocytes are born with basophilic material in them, it soon fades away. Exactly how long it lasts has been estimated by different procedures with different results; our experience, derived from making day-to-day reticulocyte counts on animals whose counts were falling from as high as 40 per cent, is in agreement with those estimates that put the time at one day or, at most, a very few days. Therefore, young reticulocytes show more reticulum than older reticulocytes; however, old reticulocytes are still very young erythrocytes. It is likely that only some erythrocytes, released into the circulation, are

released as reticulocytes. Probably under normal conditions many mature and so lose their basophilic material in the bone marrow before they are released into the circulation. But when erythrocyte production is increased, there is a tendency for the bone marrow to liberate erythrocytes in a less mature state than usual, so probably both the fact that more erythrocytes are being made and the fact that more of these are released as reticulocytes contribute to the increased percentage of reticulocytes when erythrocyte production is increased.

Under otherwise normal circumstances, any condition that causes an increased rate of erythrocyte destruction (or loss by hemorrhage) is compensated for, to at least some extent, by an increase in the rate of erythrocyte production. So if, for example, the reticulocyte count remains high day after day with no increase in the total number of erythrocytes in blood, it can be assumed that the rate of destruction is increased or that erythrocytes are being lost from the circulation in some other fashion. In other words, the reticulocyte count can often be used to deduce information about the rate of erythrocyte destruction or loss.

Although anemias are generally caused by the reduced production or the increased destruction of erythrocytes, it is usual to classify them according to the appearance of the erythrocytes in stained films. For example, sooner or later the student must learn to examine a blood film and say whether it indicates a *hypochromic microcytic anemia* or a *hyperchromic macrocytic anemia* or some other kind designated by this type of terminology. What do these terms mean?

Macrocytes and microcytes have already been defined. If, in any anemia, the erythrocytes tend to be substantially larger than normal, the anemia is said to be macrocytic; if they tend to be smaller than normal, microcytic; and if of normal size, normocytic. The terms "hyperchromic," "normochromic" and "hypochromic" require a more detailed explanation.

As the erythrocyte is a biconcave disk, it is thinner in its central portion than at its periphery. When stained and viewed from above, as is done when a dried film is examined under the microscope, the thinness of its

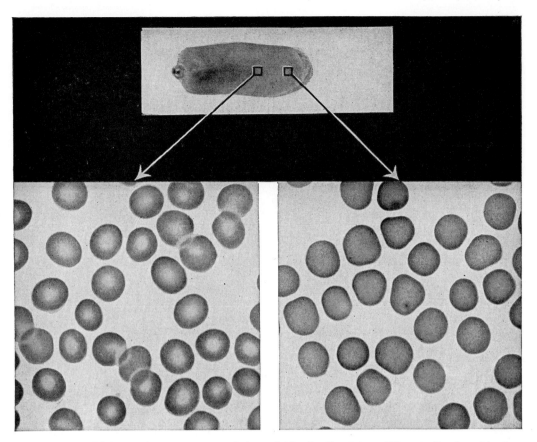

Fig. 102. Oil-immersion appearance of the red blood cells at two different sites in a blood film. (*Lower left*) These cells show the pale areas characteristic of normal cells. These pale areas show up only when the film is thick enough for occasional red cells to be superimposed on one another. (*Lower right*) Appearance of red cells at a place in the film where they are spread very thinly. Notice that no cells here are superimposed on one another and that in areas like this the central pale area, characteristic of the normal red cell, cannot be seen.

central portion is manifested by lighter staining than that which characterizes the peripheral zone of the cell (Fig. 102, *left*). Indeed, if the *proper part of a properly made film* is examined, the normal erythrocyte is seen to contain a central clear area that merges insensibly into the deeper-staining peripheral zone of the cell. In our experience, however, this clear portion is not to be seen in areas on a film where the erythrocytes are spread too thinly (Fig. 102, *right*). It is best seen in areas where they are spread fairly thinly but not so thinly that at least occasional cells are not superimposed on others (Fig. 102, *left*).

If the central pale area is not wider than a third, or slightly more, of the diameter of the erythrocyte and if the peripheral zone of the cell stains reasonably well, the erythrocytes are said to be *normochromic* (normal color) (Fig. 103, *center*). Some anemias are characterized by a reduction in the number of erythrocytes, but such cells as are present are normochromic; hence, they are said to be *normochromic anemias*. However, in a much more common type of anemia, the erythrocytes exhibit enlarged central pale areas and poorly stained peripheral zones (Fig. 103, *left*). The cells so altered are said to be *hypochromic* (undercolored); hence, the anemias with which they are associated, *hypochromic anemias*. In still other anemias there are few cells, and these are well filled with hemoglobin. It

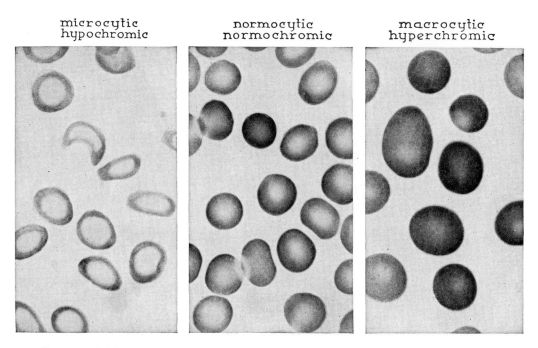

FIG. 103. Oil-immersion photomicrographs taken at the same magnification of 3 different films of human blood. (*Left*) This blood was obtained from a patient who had a microcytic hypochromic anemia due to iron deficiency, and the cells are seen to be small and their central pale areas greatly enlarged. (*Center*) Normal blood. (*Right*) Blood obtained from a person with pernicious anemia. In this condition the red blood cells, though fewer than normal, tend to be larger than usual and so they *appear* to be overfilled with hemoglobin.

is doubtful if red cells can be overfilled, so the reason for calling these anemias *hyperchromic* is that the cells are generally larger, and since they are well-filled they *appear denser* (Fig. 103, *right*).

Films of normal blood usually exhibit an occasional erythrocyte of abnormal shape. The general term for such a cell is *poikilocyte* (*poikilis* = manifold). In the anemias, poikilocytes are more common; hence, anemic blood is often said to exhibit poikilocytosis (Fig. 99, *right*). In some anemias, the cells of abnormal shape are named more specifically, for example, the type in which erythrocytes tend to be shaped like sickles, which has already been mentioned.

Inspection of the stained film is not the only method by which information can be obtained as to whether erythrocytes are hypochromic, normochromic or hyperchromic, and microcytic, normocytic or macrocytic. A determination of the ratio between the amount of hemo-globin and the number of erythrocytes present also tells whether the erythrocytes are hypochromic, normochromic or hyperchromic. Various types of ratios are used, but all give the same information. In one kind the number of grams of hemoglobin in 100 ml. of blood is divided by the number of erythrocytes per 100 ml. of blood; this gives the actual average amount of hemoglobin in each erythrocyte. This is called the Mean Corpuscular Hemoglobin Determination of Wintrobe (the M.C.H.). If the hemoglobin content and the erythrocyte count of blood are both expressed in percentages of what would be normal, and the former is divided by the latter, the ratio obtained is termed the color index (C.I.). Both ratios give the same kind of information and show at a glance whether the hemoglobin content of blood is reduced more or less than the number of erythrocytes in blood. There are 3 possibilities:

1. If the hemoglobin is reduced more than

the erythrocyte counts, the erythrocytes must have less than their normal content of hemoglobin and so must be hypochromic.

2. If the hemoglobin content and the erythrocyte count of blood are reduced proportionately, the erythrocytes, though fewer than normal may be present, must each have their full content of hemoglobin and so be normochromic.

3. If the hemoglobin content is reduced less than the erythrocyte count, the erythrocytes must each have more hemoglobin in them than is normal, and the only way they can do this is by being larger than normal. Therefore, this condition would be both hyperchromic and macrocytic.

In any given anemia knowing whether the hemoglobin is reduced more or less than the erythrocyte count is helpful in indicating the possible cause of the anemia. For example, iron is an essential ingredient of hemoglobin, so when iron is deficient the production of hemoglobin is reduced. However, iron is not so necessary for the production of erythrocytes as it is for hemoglobin, so in iron-deficiency anemias the hemoglobin content of blood is reduced more than the number of erythrocytes; hence, the cells are poorly filled with hemoglobin, and the anemia is said to be of the hypochromic type (Fig. 103, *left*). On the other hand, certain chemicals (vitamin B_{12} and folic acid) are essential for the building of the nucleic acids of cells; however, they are not so necessary for the building of hemoglobin, so that when either one of these substances is lacking there is more difficulty in producing cells than hemoglobin; hence, those cells that are produced under these conditions are literally overfilled with hemoglobin, and the anemia is of the *hyperchromic macrocytic* type (Fig. 103, *right*). The most important kind of this type is called *pernicious anemia,* and it is caused by an inability to absorb vitamin B_{12} from the stomach and the intestine. If the missing vitamin is supplied hypodermically to individuals they recover, and the condition recurs only if injections are discontinued. There is no point in feeding the vitamin by mouth because those afflicted cannot absorb it. (Vitamin B_{12} is present in liver extracts, and for those who might be interested it is probably the substance that. in the past,

has been called the extrinsic factor of Castle.)

Rouleaux Formation. If fresh blood is placed on a slide and covered with a coverslip, the broad surfaces of erythrocytes often adhere to one another with the result that numbers of erythrocytes may become arranged together like coins in a pile. These arrangements of adherent erythrocytes are termed *rouleaux formations,* and they are probably manifestations of surface tension forces. If circulating blood is examined under the microscope, rouleaux formations are sometimes seen in areas where the circulation is not rapid. Rouleaux formations are not permanent, and the erythrocytes in them can become separated from one another again with presumably no harm having been done to them. This is probably not true of sludges.

Sludging of Blood. By using the quartz-rod illuminator to study the circulating blood in laboratory animals and in man, Knisely and his associates were able to show a few years ago that a very curious condition, which they term *sludging,* develops as a result of certain disease conditions and after severe trauma. This condition is manifested by erythrocytes in the circulating blood becoming clumped together in the form of little irregular masses that are large enough to plug and otherwise obstruct the finer blood vessels of the body. It has been explained already that the capillaries near burned skin (or at the site of trauma, caused by other means), if they are not entirely destroyed, are injured enough to leak plasma. Moreover, trauma is prone to cause sludging of the blood, so that in addition to causing local damage, trauma may cause general damage because the circulation of blood through the finer blood vessels in distant parts of the body may become impeded by sludges. (See Knisely [1951] for a complete and concise account of the various kinds of damage caused by sludging.)

REFERENCES

Berlin, N. I., Waldmann, T. A., and Weissman, S. M.: Life span of the red blood cell, Physiol. Rev. *39*:577, 1959.

Bessis, M.: Cytology of the Blood and Blood-Forming Organs, tr. by Eric Ponder, New York, Grune, 1956.

Burt, N. S., Murray, R., and Rossiter, R. S.:

Nucleic acids of rabbit reticulocytes, Blood *6*:906, 1950.

Isaacs, R.: The erythrocytes *in* Downey's Handbook of Hematology, vol. 1, p. 1, New York, Hoeber, 1938.

Jordan, H. E.: Comparative hematology *in* Downey's Handbook of Hematology, vol. 2, p. 699, New York, Hoeber, 1938.

Kracke, R. R.: Color Atlas of Hematology, Philadelphia, Lippincott, 1947.

————: Diseases of the Blood and Atlas of Hematology, ed. 2, Philadelphia, Lippincott, 1941.

Tocantins, L. M. (ed.): Progress in Hematology, vol. 1, New York, Grune, 1956.

Whitby, L. E. H., and Britton, C. J. C.: Disorders of the Blood, ed. 8, London, Churchill, 1957.

Wintrobe, M. M.: Clinical Hematology, ed. 4, rev., Philadelphia, Lea & Febiger, 1956.

SLUDGING OF BLOOD

Bigelow, W. G., Heimbecker, R. O., and Harrison, R. C.: Intravascular agglutination of erythrocytes (sludged blood), vascular stasis, and the sedimentation rate of the blood in trauma, Arch. Surg. *59*:667, 1949.

Heimbecker, R. O., and Bigelow, W. G.: Intravascular agglutination of erythrocytes (sludged blood) and traumatic shock, Surgery *28*:461, 1950.

Knisely, M. H.: An annotated bibliography on sludged blood, Postgrad. Med. *10*:15, 1951.

Knisely, M. H., Bloch, E. H., Eliot, T. S., and Warner, L.: Sludged blood, Science *106*:431, 1947.

Knisely, M. H., Eliot, T. S., and Bloch, E. H.: Sludged blood in traumatic shock, microscopic observations and precipitation and agglutination of blood flowing through vessels in crushed tissues, Arch. Surg. *51*:220, 1945.

Chapter 8

The Cells of Blood

(Continued)

LEUKOCYTES

When studying erythrocytes in stained films of normal blood, the student may have seen, scattered sparingly among them, some cells with nuclei. These are the white cells of the blood, the leukocytes. The observant student may have noticed that although these are all nucleated, they are not all identical. Indeed, there are 5 different kinds of leukocytes, and the distinguishing characteristics of each must be learned well.

Although there are 5 kinds of leukocytes, they are the representatives of only 2 families of cells. The distinguishing trait of one family is *granular cytoplasm;* that of the other, *nongranular cytoplasm.* Hence, the leukocytes are classed as either granular or nongranular.

There are 3 kinds of granular leukocytes. Although they are similar in certain respects, they differ in others, most notably in the affinity of their respective granules for neutral, acid and basic stains. In fact, their difference in this respect accounts for their names, as they are called *neutrophilic, acidophilic* and *basophilic granular leukocytes,* respectively.

There are 2 kinds of nongranular leukocytes. The more numerous and usually smaller ones are called *lymphocytes* because they are to be found in lymph as well as in blood, for reasons to be explained later. The larger and less numerous ones are called *monocytes,* a term which is not very meaningful. Since these are long terms, neutrophilic granular leukocytes are generally referred to as *neutrophils.* They are also called *polymorphs,* for reasons which will be given when their nuclei are described. Acidophilic granular leukocytes are called *acidophils* or, more commonly still, *eosinophils,* because eosin is the usual acid stain employed to color their granules. Basophilic granular leukocytes are generally referred to as *basophils.*

Therefore, the leukocytes seen in stained smears of normal blood may be tabulated as follows:

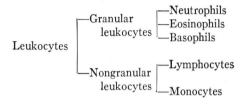

Before describing each of these cells in detail it may be helpful to give some general information about the functions of leukocytes.

WHY LEUKOCYTES ARE IMPORTANT

Almost everyone has had personal experience with a cut in his skin that has become "infected." While an unbroken skin surface keeps disease organisms from gaining entrance to the underlying tissues, a cut in the surface opens the door to them. So, if a cut is not treated properly, bacteria are prone to invade the tissues through it and, in this new environment, grow and multiply, but usually only for a short time. During this time the margins of the cut become red and swollen, and the infected area may feel hot and painful. In the language of pathology, the cut has become a site of inflammation. But then, instead of becoming worse, it is more likely that the redness and the swelling begin to decrease, and before long the cut has healed. Obviously, something happens to repel the bacterial invasion, first to localize it to the tissue immediately adjacent to the cut and then to overwhelm it completely.

For many years the significance of the changes occurring at the site of such an injury (redness, swelling, etc.) was not understood. John Hunter (1728-1793) was the first to understand that there was something purposeful about them—that they were the manifestations of the reaction of the host to injury and of a sort disposed to restore the part to normal. But beyond that little was known. However, as histologic methods improved, their precise nature was revealed by the microscope. Cohnheim (1839-1884), in particular, showed that

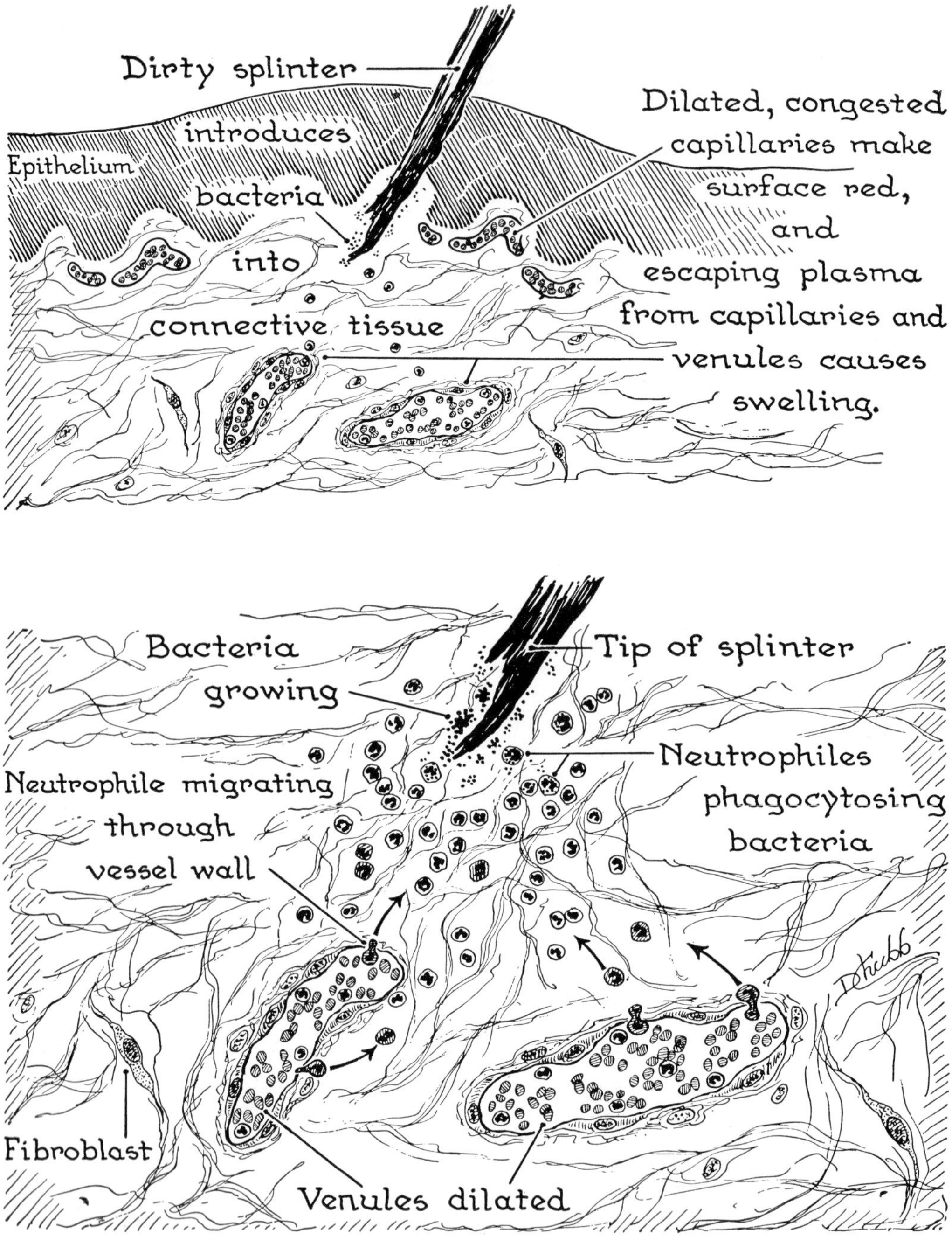

FIG. 104. Diagrams to show how neutrophils migrate from congested, dilated small blood vessels to combat bacteria introduced into the tissues by means of an injury.

the swelling of inflamed tissue is due to the endothelium of its capillaries leaking plasma because it is injured. Therefore, the swelling of inflamed tissue can be described as an inflammatory edema. The redness of inflamed tissue is due to the dilatation of its smaller blood vessels, allowing the tissue to contain an increased amount of blood (Fig. 104).

Cohnheim made many other accurate observations on the changes that occur in inflamed tissues. He observed, for example, that certain blood leukocytes migrated through the walls of injured capillaries and small venules to take up their residence in the tissue spaces (Fig. 104). However, the significance of this phenomenon was determined at a later date by Elias Metchnikoff (1845-1916), a Russian zoologist.

Metchnikoff's contribution to the study of inflammation in man was the outcome of a long series of investigations made on a great variety of simpler living creatures. He noted, for example, that unicellular organisms can ingest particulate matter and digest it within their cytoplasm and that any mildly noxious properties of certain particles seemed to disappear as the particles were digested by the chemical activity of the cytoplasm. When he then studied simple types of multicellular organisms wherein the cells had become variously specialized to perform different functions, he found that there were certain roving cells that were very adept at devouring and destroying particulate matter that gained entrance to their tissues; indeed, they could deal even with living particles such as yeast cells and bacteria. He termed these special cells *phagocytes* (*phago* = I eat), and their ability to engulf matter became known as *phagocytosis* (*osis* = increase, i.e., phagocytes have increased ability in this respect). In simple multicellular organisms whose tissues were divided into three layers—an outer one to provide covering, an inner one to line an intestine and a middle one between these two—he found the phagocytes confined to the middle layer. But when he studied organisms with circulatory systems, and the circulatory system evolves in the middle layer, he found that most of the phagocytes came to be contained in the blood, an arrangement that increases their mobility tremendously.

Metchnikoff's studies made the significance of many of the phenomena associated with inflammation much clearer. Because leukocytes are present in blood, they can be mobilized rapidly at any point of bacterial attack, make their way through the injured endothelium of the capillaries and the venules of that part and act to destroy the bacterial invader by phagocytosis, as is illustrated in Figure 104.

Metchnikoff observed that all the 5 kinds of leukocytes were not good phagocytes but only 2, the neutrophil and the monocyte, and that these seemed to be called into the tissues by different kinds of injuries.

Since infections constitute the largest single kind of human disease and since 2 of the leukocytes are such important agents in combating them, it is obvious that the study of leukocytes deserves our closest attention. It must not be thought, however, that phagocytosis is the only way in which the body copes with disease organisms. Although Metchnikoff's thesis has stood the test of time and it is agreed that phagocytosis is an extremely important mechanism of defense, there are other important mechanisms; in particular, antibodies which react against the disease agent are produced. Nor is it to be thought that the 2 phagocytic leukocytes, neutrophils and monocytes, serve the body only by phagocytosing bacteria; they may have other normal functions which are not yet clear.

How Leukocytes Are Studied

The Leukocyte Count. Usually a student is not required, in a histology course, to familiarize himself with the technic of making a leukocyte count. The procedure used resembles that employed in making an erythrocyte count but differs from it in the following respects: (1) the blood is not diluted to the same degree; (2) the diluting fluid is made up with a little acetic acid to destroy the erythrocytes and a little stain to color the nuclei of the leukocytes; and (3) the leukocytes are counted over the large-sized squares on the ruled slide.

A count between 5,000 and 10,000 leukocytes per cubic millimeter of blood is generally considered to be normal. As the method of making the count is open to a certain amount of experimental error, and as the count tends to vary somewhat throughout the day, each count should be read on a plus or minus basis. If the count is below normal limits, a *leukopenia* (*penia* = poverty) is said to exist; if above, a *leukocytosis* (*osis* = increase) is present.

Like a normal erythrocyte count, a normal leukocyte count depends on the rate of entry of leukocytes into the circulation balancing the rate at which they are removed. However,

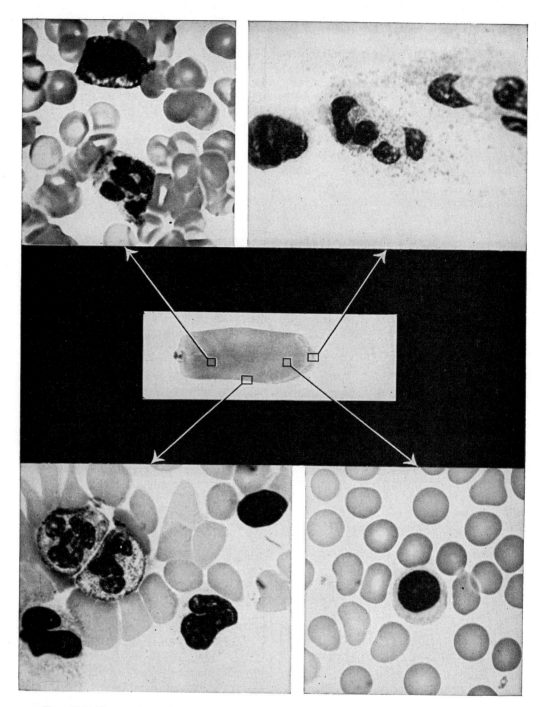

Fig. 105. The 4 photomicrographs in this figure show the way that leukocytes appear in different parts of a blood film. (*Upper left*) Picture taken from an area of the film in which the cells are thickly spread. The erythrocytes are seen to be superimposed on one another; leukocytes in such an area stain very poorly and are shrunken. Leukocytes should not be studied in such an area. (*Upper right*) Picture taken from the tail end of the film, where the leukocytes are pulled apart and their granules spread. This is not a good area for their detailed study. (*Lower left*) Picture taken from the edge of the film. Here the leukocytes tend to be crowded together and poorly stained. (*Lower right*) Picture taken from a thinly spread central part of the film and, although leukocytes are not numerous in this area, those seen are well stained and intact. This is the best place to study the cytology of leukocytes.

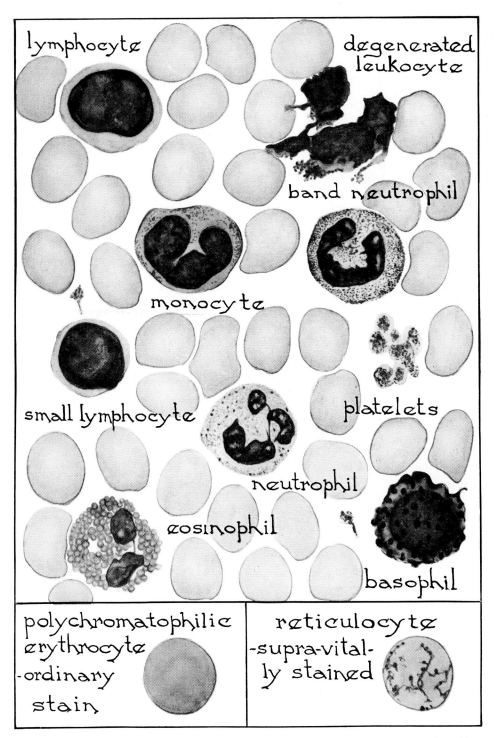

lymphocyte

degenerated leukocyte

band neutrophil

monocyte

small lymphocyte

platelets

neutrophil

eosinophil

basophil

polychromatophilic erythrocyte -ordinary stain

reticulocyte -supra-vital-ly stained

Fig. 106. The erythrocytes and the leukocytes of normal blood as they appear in a film stained with Hastings' stain.

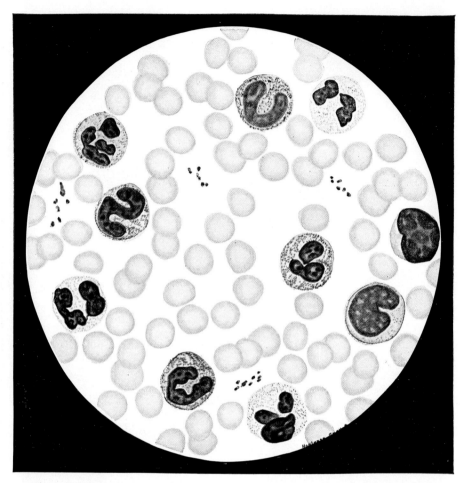

Fig. 107. Segmented band and juvenile neutrophils as they appear in a neutrophilic leukocytosis. A juvenile neutrophil may be seen at about 4 o'clock. Band neutrophils may be seen at 6:30, 9:30 and 12:30, respectively. With the exception of a lymphocyte present at 3 o'clock, the remaining leukocytes are segmented neutrophils. Several of the neutrophils in this illustration show toxic granulation. (Kracke, R. R.: Diseases of the Blood, ed. 2, Philadelphia, Lippincott)

the significance of the leukocyte count is somewhat different from that of the erythrocyte count, as will now be explained.

The erythrocytes perform their main function while in circulating blood, and when they become old and decrepit they are removed from the circulating blood. The leukocytes, on the other hand, probably do not perform their functions to any extent while in the circulating blood; they do their work after they leave the blood stream by passing through the walls of capillaries and entering the tissues. Therefore, the parts of their lives that leukocytes live in the blood stream is not their productive part; they are, as it were, merely in transit while they are in it. Accordingly, a *tissue* leukocyte count would be of more significance than a blood leukocyte count.

There is another factor that is related to blood leukocyte counts. While they are in the blood stream leukocytes can adhere to the walls of capillaries in certain organs, as it were, to hide out for a while and then later they can let go and once again appear in circulating blood. They do this particularly in the lungs, the liver and the spleen, and it is of interest that changes in breathing motions can affect the number that can remain hidden in the lung. Breathing motions can cause leukocytes to leave the lungs and enter the circulating blood, so breathing motions can affect the blood leukocyte count.

Moreover, it is obvious that the time that leukocytes spend in the blood stream gives no particular clue to their total life span as it does with erythrocytes. The time leukocytes spend in the blood stream is only a passing phase of their existence. Actually, it is very difficult to determine how long the different leukocytes normally remain in the blood stream; it is easier, as will be explained later, to obtain data on lymphocytes than on some of the other cells. Transfused leukocytes leave the blood stream of the individual into which they are transfused in a few hours, but it seems probable that most of an individual's own leukocytes remain in the blood stream for a somewhat longer period.

However, a count that does not lie within normal limits does have significance, and this is best determined by an examination of the stained blood film. The technic for doing this is one of the most important lessons applicable to the practice of medicine that is learned in histology.

THE STUDY OF LEUKOCYTES IN A STAINED BLOOD FILM

The way a blood film is made (Fig. 100) and stained with a Romanovsky-type blood stain has been described. With such a film the student can learn to identify the 5 kinds of leukocytes and also determine the percentage of each kind in the film; the latter procedure is known as making a *differential count*. Before describing each leukocyte in detail, so that the student can learn to identify each, we must discuss their staining reactions somewhat further.

The term *acidophilic* has already been explained (p. 8); hence, the student may rightly anticipate that the cytoplasmic granules of acidophils will attract the acid stain, eosin, of the mixture of eosin and polychrome methylene blue that comprises the Romanovsky type of blood stain. Since these granules attract eosin they are called eosinophilic granules, and the leukocytes that contain them generally are called eosinophils.

The term *basophilic* also has been explained previously (p. 8); hence, one could correctly expect the cytoplasmic granules of basophils to be colored blue by the basic stain, *methylene blue,* in the Romanovsky mixture.

The term *neutrophil* is more difficult to explain. It was coined by Ehrlich, who, in the early investigation of the staining reactions of leukocytes, devised many staining mixtures in an attempt to facilitate their identification. One of these mixtures, which stained the granules of the cells that he named neutrophils, was made by mixing a basic stain with two acid stains. The assumption probably was that the acid and basic stains interacted to form a neutral compound possessing staining properties different from either the acid or basic stains in the mixture, and that it was this neutral compound that colored the neutrophilic granules. Hence, the cells whose granules were thus stained were called neutrophils.

Leukocytes are now stained with Ehrlich's stains only for special reasons; stains of the Romanovsky type have superseded them for general use. These too could be designated as neutral stains in that they are mixtures of basic and acid stains. But the way they stain neutrophilic granules is not by forming a neutral stain. They usually color neutrophilic granules a light violet (lilac) shade; sometimes the color shifts toward pink. From MacNeal's work it would appear that the violet or purple shades imparted by these stains are due to the combined action of 3 different basic stains rather than to any neutral dyes that they contain.

As previously mentioned, polychroming methylene blue gives it the ability to color certain tissue ingredients a purple color, an ability not possessed by unpolychromed methylene blue. This is apparently due to the formation of 2 new dyes as a result of the breakdown of methylene blue in the polychroming process. One of these is methylene violet, the other methylene azure; indeed, there are 3 methylene azures in the mixture. So the violet and purple shades obtained by Romanovsky staining are due to the combined action of methylene blue, methylene violet and methylene azures, all of which are basic, not neutral, stains. Therefore, neutrophils are not named accurately.

The foregoing also explains why certain granules that sometimes appear in the cytoplasm of the nongranular leukocytes are called *azurophilic granules*. It seems contradictory to speak of the cytoplasmic granules of nongranular leukocytes; nevertheless, some monocytes and some lymphocytes possess lilac-pink and reddish-violet granules, respectively. Since azure means sky blue, the term azurophilic as applied to granules of a definitely reddish hue at first seems to be incorrect. However, as Michaelis (one of the two investigators who first discovered and described these granules) was strongly of the opinion that it was the methylene azure content of the then newly discovered Romanovsky stain which imparted a red-violet color to certain cell constituents, it was only natural that he should have called them azurophilic. Moreover, since MacNeal's more recent studies show that methylene azure is indeed one of the dyes that contribute toward producing this color, Michaelis' term seems to be justified.

Some General Instructions. Often the things that are most desirable require the greatest amount of work for their realization. This is certainly true with regard to finding good examples of all 5 kinds of leukocytes in a blood film. The method of making a film usually results in the film's being thicker at the end from which it is spread and thinner toward the end to which it is spread (Fig. 105). Leukocytes are more numerous and easier to find in the thicker part of the film. But wherever the film is thick (and this is indicated by erythrocytes being superimposed on one another to a great degree), the leukocytes do not stain sharply and hence are difficult to study (Fig. 105, *top, left*). They appear to much better advantage in the thinner part of the film. But here they are not as numerous as might be anticipated because, being somewhat larger than erythrocytes, they tend to be drawn to the edges of the film (Fig. 105, *bottom, left*), as well as toward the very end of it (Fig. 105, *top, right*). In either of these positions (the edge or the end), they may become distorted, and their cytoplasm may even be broken and scattered about them. Therefore, it is best to learn the appearance of normal leukocytes from the regions where they are most difficult to find (Fig. 105, *bottom, right*), and in order to find here good examples of each kind the student may have to study not only one film but several.

If a film is provided with a coverslip, it may be examined with low-power, high-power and oil-immersion objectives. If it has no coverslip the high-power objective does not reveal a clear image.

Leukocytes are conveniently detected with the low-power objective and centered with it, after which each should be studied with the oil-immersion objective.

When the student first searches a stained normal blood film for good examples of the 5 kinds of leukocytes, he can save much time by avoiding the following:

1. *Examining a degenerating leukocyte.* In every blood film there are many examples of partly broken-down leukocytes (Fig. 106), and it is a waste of time to try to identify their nature. So examine only well-formed and well-stained examples.

2. *Confusing clumps of platelets with leukocytes.* In every film there are many little bodies, called *platelets,* that commonly clump together. Most of each platelet is pale blue, but its central part may contain a dark-staining granule or granules (Fig. 106). Platelets will be considered in detail in the next chapter.

3. *Examining cells that are difficult to classify.* At first the student should examine only leukocytes that are easily recognized and disregard those that seem difficult to classify.

In the following description of the 5 kinds of leukocytes the student will learn that both the nuclei and the cytoplasm give important information that is useful in identifying any particular cell that is seen in a blood film.

GRANULAR LEUKOCYTES

NEUTROPHILS

Numbers. In a film of normal blood, neutrophils constitute from 60 to 70 per cent of the leukocytes. Therefore, they are the first kind of leukocyte that the student generally sees in a normal film.

Appearance. Neutrophils, as will be described in a subsequent chapter, develop in myeloid tissue (the bone marrow). In myeloid tissue they go through many developmental changes before they finally assume their mature form, and then they are liberated into the blood stream. In health only an occasional neutrophil is released into the blood stream before it is fully mature. Under conditions of disease, however, many immature ones may be released and so are seen in films made from peripheral blood. Therefore, it is necessary for the student to learn the appearance of both mature and immature neutrophils, so now both will be described, the mature type first.

Mature Neutrophils. These are from 10 to 12 μ in diameter, so they are slightly more than half as wide again as the erythrocytes in a film.

The nucleus of a mature neutrophil is divided into from 2 to 5 or more lobes (Fig. 106, *neutrophil*). The term "lobe" refers to a mass of nuclear material that is either completely separated from all other masses or connected to others by no more than *very delicate* strands (Figs. 106 and 108). The substance of the lobes is made up of coarse chromatin flakes that are rather densely packed (Fig. 106). As a consequence, the nuclear material stains fairly deeply with basic dyes, being colored a blue or blue-purple in the usual preparation. No nucleoli can be seen.

Since the nuclei of neutrophils may exhibit different numbers of lobes, sometimes neutrophils are called *polymorphonuclear leuko-*

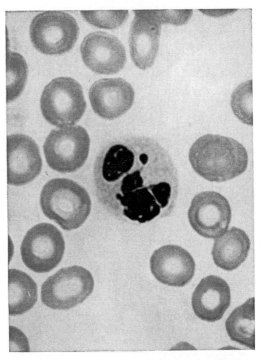

FIG. 108. Photomicrograph ($\times$ 1,750) of a stained film of the blood of a human female. The neutrophil in the center illustrates a characteristic "drumstick." (Davidson, W. M., and Smith, D. R.: Brit. M. J. 2:6).

cytes because their nuclei exhibit many forms (*morphi* = form). Since this is a long term, the abbreviation *polymorph* is commonly used in its place.

In 1954, Davidson and Smith demonstrated that it was possible to identify the chromosomal sex of an individual by the examination of blood films. It seems that the sex chromatin in the female, while it generally is contained in one of the lobes of the nucleus of a mature neutrophil, where it is very difficult, if not impossible, to identify because the chromatin is so packed, sometimes forms a separate tiny lobe which has the form of a drumstick (Fig. 108). According to Davidson and Smith this happens in about 1 out of every 38 neutrophils of females. Accordingly, to identify chromosomal sex from blood films many neutrophils must be examined, several examples of drumsticks must be found. Somewhat similar little bodies very occasionally are seen in the neutrophils of males but, on close scrutiny, most of these can be ruled out as examples of typical drumsticks. Furthermore, as many as 6 never are seen in a series of 500 neutrophils, and at least 6 always can be seen in 500 neutrophils obtained from females.

The cytoplasm of mature neutrophils occupies more space than the nucleus and reveals little structural detail except that it is fairly evenly and heavily sprinkled with very fine granules (Fig. 106). The granules in many preparations are so fine that they are difficult to resolve with the light microscope; hence, all that may be seen is that the cytoplasm has a granular appearance. Commonly, the granules either have or impart to the cytoplasm a lavender (lilac) color, but in old or poorly stained films the granules or the cytoplasm may veer toward the pink.

Immature Neutrophils. In order to describe immature neutrophils it is necessary to describe briefly how neutrophils develop in myeloid tissue. Here cells that are to become neutrophils have an indented ovoid nucleus and somewhat fewer granules than a mature neutrophil. At this stage of development the cell is called a neutrophilic metamyelocyte (for reasons to be explained in a later chapter) or a *juvenile neutrophil* (Fig. 107, *4 o'clock*). As this cell develops further its nucleus becomes increasingly indented until it becomes frankly horseshoe shaped, and at this stage of development it is termed a *band* or a *stab neutrophil* (Fig. 106, *band neutrophil,* and Fig. 107). Under normal conditions, the horseshoe-shaped nucleus of the band form becomes segmented to divide the nucleus into 2 or more lobes before the cell is released into the blood stream, for under normal conditions not more than 1 or 2 per cent of band forms are seen in films. But if there is a great need for neutrophils in the blood, as will be explained under function, some band and even some juvenile forms are released into the blood stream, so these are seen in blood films.

The nuclei of juvenile neutrophils do not stain as deeply as those of band forms (Fig. 107), and those of band forms do not stain as deeply as those of mature forms. Both juvenile and band neutrophils have cytoplasmic granules similar to those of mature neutrophils (Fig. 107).

From the above it is evident that *the maturity of a neutrophil is revealed by the shape of its nucleus* and to a lesser extent by how heavily the nucleus stains.

Fine Structure. Films of leukocytes cannot be studied with the E/M because whole flattened leukocytes are too thick to be penetrated by electrons. Accordingly, for the E/M, leukocytes must be cut into thin sections. In examining electron micrographs of leukocytes it is important to remember that one is looking at very thin slices cut through them, and not at whole cells, as one does when examining a blood film with the light microscope.

Leukocytes are obtained for sectioning in different ways. One way is to obtain tiny pieces of bone marrow from a puncture made into the sternum. The little pieces so obtained can be fixed in buffered osmium tetroxide and sectioned in the usual way. Sometimes it is helpful to drain the blood from the little pieces of bone marrow before fixing them. In sections prepared from bone marrow by these methods there are, of course, many immature cells of various kinds, but there are also most kinds of mature leukcoytes, and a sufficient search will reveal them. It is also possible to obtain sections of leukocytes from blood because if whole blood is allowed to settle, or if it is centrifuged in a tube, the erythrocytes go to the bottom of the tube, and the leukocytes form a layer (called the buffy coat) just above them. Bits of this can be fixed and sectioned for electron microscopy.

It is obvious that a thin section cut through a mature neutrophil would pass through only some of the lobes of the nucleus and that in all likelihood it would not pass through any of the strands that connect lobes. Hence, in electron micrographs neutrophils appear to have few lobes and these do not seem to be connected. The nuclei, in sections, appear granular, but of course the structures that appear as granules may be threads cut in section. The granules are more closely packed near the nuclear membrane, although some densely packed areas may be present in the more central parts of nuclear lobes. No nucleoli are visible in mature cells.

The cytoplasm, viewed with the E/M, reveals the following organelles: mitochondria, membranous vesicles, RNA granules and, in favorable sections, a Golgi apparatus. The most prominent inclusions seen are the specific granules.

The mitochondria are not very numerous and are identified easily by their cristae.

The specific granules, that in ordinary blood films are colored lilac, vary from around 0.1 to 0.2 μ in diameter; therefore, they are only about half the width of mitochondria (Fig. 109), and so it is not surprising that they are very difficult to see clearly with the light microscope. It is difficult to know whether the variation in size is only apparent, because of some granules being sliced through their greatest diameters and others through one side or the other, or real. However, there are so many small granules that it seems probable that the variation in size is real.

The internal cytoplasmic membranes (the endoplasmic reticulum) are composed chiefly of rounded vesicles that are scattered throughout the cytoplasm; therefore, the vesicles are of the distended rather than the flattened type. They vary greatly in size; many are very small, and the largest are of about the same size as the largest granules. Some appear empty, but others have material in them that varies, from vesicle to vesicle, in its density; indeed, there appears to be every transition between clear vesicles and granules. Under the best conditions granules that are covered with a single membrane can be seen, so that it seems probable, at this time, that the granules of the neutrophils are formed in cytoplasmic vesicles.

A Golgi apparatus can be identified in some sections of neutrophils examined with the E/M.

RNA granules are distributed somewhat sparingly, both on the walls of the intracytoplasmic vesicles and also between vesicles.

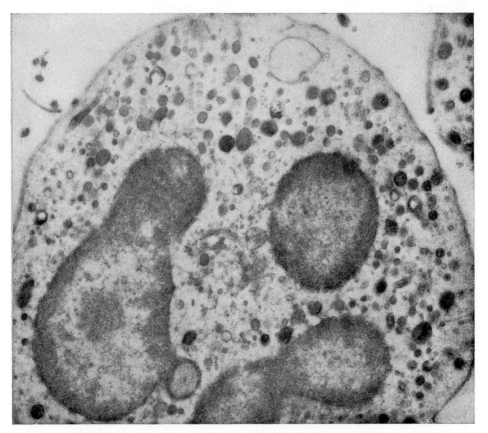

FIG. 109. Electron micrograph ($\times$ 18,000) of a section of a neutrophil obtained from the bone marrow of man. Three lobes of the nucleus may be seen. The specific granules are numerous and vary in size. Mitochondria are few in number and difficult to identify. Some Golgi material can be seen in the center of the cell. (Preparation by A. F. Howatson)

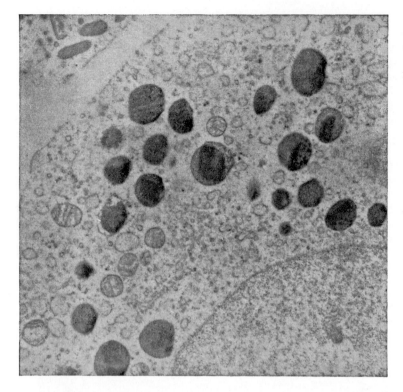

Fig. 110. Electron micrograph (× 30,000) of a section of an eosinophil obtained from the bone marrow of man. Note the large specific granules in the cytoplasm and the darker bodies that some contain. A few mitochondria, some rough-surfaced vesicles and some Golgi material are present in the cytoplasm. (Preparation by A. F. Howatson)

Function. Neutrophils serve as a mobile defensive force of cells that can migrate through capillary walls in any part of the body where inflammation has been set up by a bacterial invasion or by some other damaging agent. Neutrophils, in general, are called out of the blood stream and into the tissues by acute bacterial infections. Since they are mobile cells, they can move through the tissues; and since they are phagocytic, they can engulf bacteria in their cytoplasm and destroy them.

A severe infection in any part of the body results in a chemical message (the nature of this has been investigated by Menkin) being sent to the bone marrow, and the reception of the message results in the bone marrow liberating more neutrophils into the blood stream. Accordingly, in severe infections there is generally a *leukocytosis,* and a differential count will show that this is due to a great increase in the number of neutrophils in the blood. Therefore, a leukocyte and differential count can be used to help establish the presence of infection in the body. An examination of blood films from individuals who have severe infections also provides further information. If the infection continues to progress, the bone mar-

row sends out an increasing number of immature cells, neutrophils of the band type and even some juvenile neutrophils, as in Figure 107. (Some hematologists now term both types metamyelocytes). Accordingly, if in any patient, the examination of regularly obtained blood films shows that the percentage of immature cells is increasing, it is said that a shift to the left is occurring. If, however, it is found in regularly obtained films that the percentage of immature forms is decreasing, it is said there is a shift to the right. So, in a very general way, a shift to the left indicates that an infection is progressing, and a shift to the right indicates that it is subsiding.

EOSINOPHILS

Numbers. Eosinophils constitute from 1 to 3 per cent of the leukocytes seen in a film of normal blood.

Appearance. Eosinophils are from 10 to 15 μ in diameter; they tend to be slightly larger than neutrophils.

The nuclei of eosinophils commonly are composed of only 2 lobes (Fig. 106), and these may or may not be connected with a strand of nuclear material. The coarse clumps of chromatin are not so densely packed in the nuclei of eosinophils as they are in neutrophils; hence, eosinophil nuclei do not stain as deeply (Fig. 106).

The cytoplasm of eosinophils characteristically is packed with large refractile granules that in well-stained blood films are colored red or orange (Fig. 106). In poorly stained films their color may veer toward pink or a muddy blue. Even in poorly stained preparations they can be distinguished easily from the granules of neutrophils because they are more numerous—the cell seems to be packed with them—and because they are distinctly larger and more refractile (Fig. 106).

Fine Structure. The E/M reveals no special features in the nuclei. The cytoplasm is seen to contain mitochondria, specific granules, membranous vesicles, a Golgi apparatus and RNA granules.

The specific granules of the eosinophil, seen with the E/M, have a striking appearance, being dense and from 0.5 to 1 μ in diameter (Fig. 110). In immature eosinophils they are composed of a homogeneous material of considerable density. In mature eosinophils some of the granules are seen to contain still denser bodies in their more central parts (see inset in Fig. 110). These bodies, as seen in a section, may have the form of rough squares or rectangles. They sometimes occupy more and sometimes less than half of a granule.

Intracytoplasmic membranes are present in the form of distended vesicles. These range in size from very small ones to others which are of about the same size as the granules. The vesicles that are seen vary from being apparently empty to containing material of different degrees of density, and the most dense material seems to be similar to that of the granules. Accordingly, it seems probable that the granules of the eosinophils are formed inside membranous vesicles.

Eosinophils, with the E/M, reveal well-developed Golgi regions.

RNA granules are present in the cytoplasm; these are mostly distributed on the outer surfaces of the membranous vesicles.

Allergy. In order to discuss possible functions of eosinophils and the functions of mast cells (the latter will be described in Chap. 13), we must introduce the important topic of *allergy* (*hypersensitivity*).

It has been mentioned already that foreign macromolecules (see p. 40) have the ability, if they gain entrance to the tissues of the body, to incite the formation of substances that combine specifically with them. Because these foreign substances induce the formation of something that reacts against them they are called *antigens* (*anti* = against, *gen* = a thing produced). Likewise, the substances that are produced, which react specifically against antigens, are termed *antibodies*. In order to explain allergy and to discuss any role that eosinophils might play in this condition, it is necessary to explain that although the antibodies that form in response to any particular antigen are in a general way specific for that antigen, they actually represent a heterogeneous collection of molecules that have different degrees of affinity for the antigen. The firmness with which they combine with the antigen is expressed in terms of their avidity for antigen, so that antibodies may be spoken of as being of high avidity and low avidity. Indeed, in some instances the antibodies that form in response to an antigen have such different avidities for it and are so different in their physical properties that they can be separated by simple physical methods into fractions that have, respectively, much and little avidity for the antigen.

Since it is possible to separate or otherwise study these antibodies of different avidities, it has been shown that the antibody that at first forms in response to an antigen is always of very low avidity. However, antibody production, like so many other things, improves with practice, so that in a course of immunization which involves continued exposure, or many exposures, to the same antigen, the antibody that is produced over this period exhibits increasing avidity for the antigen (see Jerne). It has been shown also that the neutralizing capacity of antibodies that are formed against toxins increases during immunization; this holds also for antibodies that are formed against enzymes (see Cinader and Weitz, and Cinader and Pearce).

In our present state of knowledge there is reason to think that the individual who exhibits allergy to a particular antigen differs from the normal individual because on continued or frequent exposures to the antigen he or she does not respond by shifting sufficiently from producing antibody of low avidity to antibody of high avidity. The allergic individual tends, it is thought, to continue to produce too much antibody of low avidity (which does not precipitate antigen) and too little antibody of high avidity to effectively bind the antigen (high avidity antibody will actually precipitate antigen if the two are mixed). The way in which this results in allergic responses to an antigen will now be described with an example; namely, hay fever.

The antigen involved in hay fever is generally a pollen that is blown into the air from some plant, generally late in summer; ragweed is a common offender. When people breathe air containing pollen, tiny amounts of the latter may gain entrance to the substance of the body by passing through tiny imperfections in the lining of the upper respiratory tract. When pollen first gains entrance to the underlying connective tissues in this region, it incites the formation of antibody (the cells that do this will be described in Chapter 18). The antibody, as explained above, represents a heterogeneous collection of molecules which have different avidities for the antigen. In individuals who do *not* get hay fever, enough avid antibody molecules that can specifically precipitate the antigen develop. In those individuals who *do* get hay fever, the mixture of antibody molecules that are formed does not contain enough molecules that are sufficiently specific to precipitate the antigen but, instead, much low-grade antibody that only combines with the antigen loosely. This latter type of antibody acts as though it were sticky, for it becomes adherent to the cells that are scattered about in this region, probably on the endothelial cells of the capillaries, on mast cells and on others. The avid type of antibody does not form such firm or permanent attachments to cells; indeed, it can circulate in the fluids of the body without its having to be carried by cells.

Since the body fluids in the allergic individual do not contain enough of the avid antibody to bind any new pollen which gets through the epithelial lining in the upper respiratory tract, and since the cells of the part have antibody of low avidity attached to them, any further antigen that gains entrance to the part combines loosely with this antibody on cell surfaces. The presence of this loose dissociable antigen-antibody complex on cell surfaces leads somehow to the cells (particularly mast cells) releasing a substance called *histamine*. Histamine irritates the area in which it is liberated and, in particular, causes the capillaries of the part to leak plasma; this causes the mucous membranes of the nasal mucosa to swell, and the general irritation of the part causes the glands to secrete extra mucus and stimulates the sneeze reflexes.

Inheritance seems to play a part in determining whether any individual will respond normally to successive doses of antigens by making antibody of increasing avidity, or abnormally, by continuing to make too much antibody of the low avidity, and too little of the high avidity, type. But even those who inherit a relative inability to produce an increasing percentage of avid antibody on successive exposures to an antigen, and as a consequence are allergic or hypersensitive to that antigen, may improve in this connection. The fact that the prolonged production of antibody is associated in the normal with an improvement in the quality of the antibody also may hold to some extent for the allergic individual, and sometimes this can be taken advantage of by giving allergic individuals increasing infections of the antigen to which they are allergic so that eventually even they may produce a sufficiently avid antibody to combine with and so remove the antigen and thus prevent its forming loose combinations with low-grade antibody on cell surfaces.

What has allergy to do with eosinophils? About all that we know is that eosinophils are more numerous in the blood of individuals who suffer from allergic conditions than they are in normal individuals. Moreover, they are much more numerous in tissues that are inflamed as a result of the tissues being sites of allergic reactions than they are in normal tissues or in sites of inflammation caused, let us say, by physical agents, as for example, the inflammation in thermal burns. Eosinophils are linked somehow to the antigens or the antibodies involved in allergic reactions or to the histamine or similar substances that are released in these reactions. Since the eosinophils of at least some species have been shown to contain histamine, it seems more probable that they are concerned in liberating or absorbing histamine than with producing or carrying antibody. One finding that should be mentioned is that if the hormone, hydrocortisone, is administered to any individual, it immediately causes the eosinophils to leave the blood stream and enter the tissues. Since hydrocortisone acts fairly quickly to diminish allergic reactions in tissues, this might suggest that eosinophils, because they enter the tissues under these conditions, are to be associated with the depression of allergic responses (for example, they might absorb histamine). However, eosinophils are closely related to basophils, which are even more closely related to mast cells, and since mast cells, as will be explained in Chapter 13, are known to liberate histamine in allergic states, it seems probable that eosinophils do also and that hydrocortisone depresses allergic responses by some of its other effects (which will be described in Chap. 26) instead of its effect in sending blood eosinophils into the tissues.

In addition to their as yet mysterious function in allergic phenomena, eosinophils also can act as phagocytes, but their function in this respect is not comparable with that of the neutrophils.

BASOPHILS

Basophils comprise only about 0.5 per cent of the blood leukocytes; hence, to find a good example of one, it may be necessary to examine several hundred leukocytes and perhaps several different blood films. Basophils are usually from 10 to 12 μ in diameter; they are of about the same size as neutrophils. About half the cell consists of nucleus, which may be segmented, and, in any event, it often presents a very irregular shape. It is colored much less intensely than the nucleus of the neutrophil or the eosinophil and is overshadowed by the large, dark, blue-stained granules of the cytoplasm, which may be seen lying over the paler nucleus (Fig. 106). The granules of basophils are similar in appearance to those of mast cells; these cells and their functions will be described in Chapter 13. Basophils are said to contain about half of the histamine that is present in blood. Furthermore, basophils, like eosinophils, tend to leave the blood stream under the influence of certain hormones of the adrenal gland. In many respects they seem to be involved in allergic and stress phenomena in much the same way as eosinophils.

For the fine structure of basophils see the Fine Structure of Mast Cells in Chapter 13.

NONGRANULAR LEUKOCYTES

LYMPHOCYTES

Numbers. Lymphocytes constitute from 20 to 35 per cent of the leukocytes of normal blood. Therefore, next to neutrophils they are the commonest type seen in a normal film. The percentage of lymphocytes in the blood of mice and rats, which are so commonly used for experimental work, is much higher; indeed, lymphocytes are the commonest cell seen in their blood films.

Appearance. The usual or *small* lymphocyte (Fig. 106) is a relatively small cell, measuring from 7 to 12 μ in diameter. Most are only a little larger than erythrocytes.

The most striking feature of the small lymphocyte is that it consists almost entirely of nucleus. Even in films, where it is spread out and more or less flattened, and where such cytoplasm as was present would show to advantage, little cytoplasm generally can be seen. In sections of fixed tissue such lymphocytes as may be present are, of course, not flattened, *so in sections it is generally very difficult to see any cytoplasm at all around the nuclei of lymphocytes.*

The prominent nucleus of the lymphocyte is rounded or ovoid in shape but almost always exhibits a little indentation on one side, and on that side there is generally a little more cytoplasm than on the other (Fig. 106).

The chromatin of small lymphocytes is arranged into coarse clumps. This is an identifying feature of lymphocytes. The chromatin clumps stain deeply with basic dyes (Fig. 106).

As might be expected, nucleoli cannot be seen in the nuclei of lymphocytes stained in films by the Romanovsky technic, because the heavy chromatin masses would be almost sure to obscure them. Likewise, in ordinary H & E sections nucleoli cannot be seen. But, if *very* thin sections are cut from lymphocyte-containing tissue the nucleoli, that otherwise would be obscured by the condensed chromatin, can be seen.

As noted previously, most lymphocytes have only a narrow rim of cytoplasm around the nucleus; this generally is homogeneous and a clear pale-blue color.

Although most lymphocytes are small, around 10 per cent are of a larger type, ranging up to around 16 μ in diameter. These are

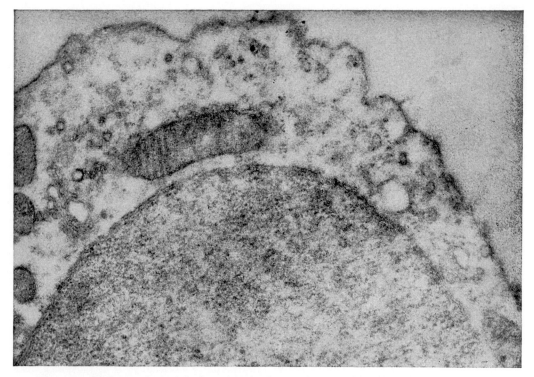

FIG. 111. Electron micrograph (× 45,000) of a section of a lymphocyte obtained from the bone marrow of an individual with lymphatic leukemia. The cytoplasm contains a few mitochondria, some vesicles and some RNA granules. The nucleus is relatively heavily granulated. (Preparation by A. F. Howatson)

termed *large lymphocytes* by some authors and *medium-sized lymphocytes* by others. The reason for some authors' referring to these as medium-sized instead of large is because they use the latter term for still larger cells which normally do not appear in blood but are present in lymphatic tissue; by others they are not referred to as lymphocytes but as lymphoblasts. Their larger size is due chiefly to their having more cytoplasm (Fig. 106, *lymphocyte*). However, their nuclei tend to be somewhat larger than those of the smallest lymphocytes and to have less densely packed chromatin.

Under favorable circumstances, a pale area representative of a negative Golgi image can be seen in the cytoplasm close to one side of the nucleus. With proper staining, centrioles can be demonstrated in its central part.

Some lymphocytes, particularly of the larger type, exhibit a few red-purple granules in their cytoplasm. These vary in size but are commonly coarse. They are called *azurophilic granules*. They are an inconstant feature of lymphocyte cytoplasm.

Lymphocytes are motile. In moving they often assume the appearance of a hand mirror or a tennis racquet.

Fine Structure. The nuclei of lymphocytes are more heavily granulated than the nuclei of most cells (Fig. 111). The granules are more closely packed toward the periphery of the nucleus than in its more central part (Fig. 111). With the E/M, sectioned lymphocytes show clearly that one or more indentations exist in the nuclear membrane.

The cytoplasm of a lymphocyte contains a few mitochrondria (Fig. 111); one estimate that has been made is 25 to 40. Intracytoplasmic membranes are arranged in the form of vesicles, but these are not numerous and are generally small (Fig. 111). A Golgi apparatus is present. A few RNA granules are distributed in the cytoplasm; they are both free and on the outer surface of the vesicles. There are enough of them to account for the slight basophilia exhibited by lymphocyte cytoplasm with the light microscope.

General Comments About Relations of Structure to Possible Functions. It should be emphasized that the quantity of cytoplasm of lymphocytes, and its relative lack of mitochondria and rough-surfaced vesicles of the endoplasmic reticulum, all suggest that the cytoplasm of lymphocytes is ill-equipped to perform any specialized function, for example, the synthesis of antibodies. On the contrary, the cytoplasm of cells of the plasma cell series appears under the E/M to be highly specialized for synthesizing protein. Accordingly, such functions as are performed by lymphocytes as such would seem not to depend on a specialized cytoplasmic function, but on their ability to differentiate into some other type of cells, or on their nuclei, or on their ability to transport materials that adhere to their cell surface. With this thought in mind we shall consider some of the theories regarding their function.

Theories of Life-Span and Functions. Lymphocytes, as will be explained in detail in Chapter 18, are made in the lymphatic tissue of the body; this consists of certain organs, the spleen and the thymus gland, a vast number of smaller depots, termed lymphatic nodes, that are distributed in many parts of the body, and vast numbers of smaller nonencapsulated nodules of lymphatic tissue that are scattered about in innumerable sites in the body. All these depots of lymphatic tissue manufacture lymphocytes to greater and lesser extents. In some of these depots lymphocytes are delivered directly into the blood stream, but in others, as will be explained in Chapter 18, the lymphocytes are delivered into lymphatic tubes which eventually empty their contents into the blood stream. By these means enormous numbers of lymphocytes enter the blood stream every day, yet under normal conditions they never accumulate in the blood stream, for the lymphocyte count remains relatively constant. Yoffey and his associates have studied this matter extensively, and they have shown that from one vessel alone (the thoracic duct) so many lymphocytes enter the blood stream each day that they could not remain there for more than a small part of a day without their numbers in the blood becoming much greater than they are. Therefore, they must leave the blood stream at the same rate as they enter it. The question is where do they go and what do they do?

We shall consider first the possible ways by which lymphocytes could be removed from the blood at the very rapid rate that would be necessary if their rate of removal is to match their rate of entry. First, according to Yoffey and his associates, many are strained out in the bone marrow. Secondly, many leave the blood capillaries in the gastrointestinal tract and migrate into and through the epithelial lining of the tract to become lost in its lumen. This can be studied easily in sections, for lymphocytes are often seen migrating *between* the lining cells of the gut and, indeed, they are often seen inside the epithelial lining cells; they are *very adept* at passing between cells and even into cells. In addition, some dying lymphocytes are commonly observed in many tissues, including lymphatic tissue. However, it seems improbable that the number of lymphocytes strained out in marrow and disposed of in the other ways mentioned could possibly be large enough to match the number that are poured into the blood stream by lymphatic vessels every day. This has given rise to the thought, for which there is some evidence, that many of the lymphocytes that leave blood capillaries, particularly in the intestinal tract, neither die in the tissue into which they have escaped nor leave the body through the intestinal lining but instead re-enter lymphatic capillaries which eventually empty them back again into the blood circulatory system. According to this concept lymphocytes recirculate; this means that many of the lymphocytes that are drained into the blood stream every day from the lymphatic channels are lymphocytes that left the blood stream a few days or even a few hours before.

The concept of the recirculation of lymphocytes makes it easier to account for many things that are otherwise difficult to explain. For example, if lymphocytes do not recirculate, they must die in the tissues or leave the tissues chiefly via the intestinal tract or turn into some other kind of cells in such tremendous numbers that their being disposed of in these fashions would surely be more obvious than it is. Furthermore, if they do not recirculate, their life in the blood stream and, indeed, their total life span as lymphocytes, no matter where they go, would be extraordinarily short—less than a day. It is obvious that if it could be shown that their life span was not short, this fact would argue strongly for the recirculation hypothesis. It is of interest in this connection that studies which have involved labeling newly formed lymphocytes with some radioactive tracer indicate that their life span is to be measured in weeks or months rather than in hours, and this, of course, provides support for the recirculation hypothesis.

It is difficult to be absolutely sure about almost anything relating to lymphocytes. For example, detecting label in lymphocytes over a period of some weeks, after it was given, does not prove conclusively that lymphocytes live this long, for it is just possible that the label does not stay in the same lymphocyte throughout this period. Pycnotic lymphocytes are to be observed in normal lymphatic tissue, and the question has been raised as to whether or not there might be a recirculation of some of the (labeled) components of lymphocytes from the dying to newly forming ones. In other words, is it possible that labeled material from a dying one might be incorporated into a newly forming one? If such a phenomenon does occur, it would mean that the life span of lymphocytes would not be as long as is suggested from studies involving a study of the length of time that labeled cells can be seen after its administration.

One fact that makes the possible utilization of the components of dying lymphocytes by new lymphocytes or even by other kinds of cells less improbable than it otherwise might seem is that lymphocytes are extraordinarily sensitive to many agents, responding to these by their almost immediate death. Radiation, even in small doses, nitrogen mustard, colchicine and the hormone hydrocortisone all seem to trigger off the pycnosis of lymphocytes. The fact that they die with slight provocation makes one wonder if one of their functions, unknown at present, is served not by their life but by their death. The one that immediately comes to mind in this connection is the possibility that they may be purveyors of DNA,

or of one of its components, to other cells which are dividing fairly rapidly and so may not be able for one reason or other to synthesize DNA completely by themselves. The fact that bacterial cells can assimilate into their own genetic constitution the DNA of other bacterial cells to which they are exposed (as was explained in connection with Cell Differentiation) makes one wonder whether or not lymphocytes might not serve as donors of normal DNA to other cells. However, there are other functions which they are generally conceded as serving, and for which they must be alive, and these will now be considered. However, these functions do not explain why lymphocytes should be so numerous as they are.

There is much evidence indicating that lymphocytes that have left the blood stream and have migrated into tissues which are the site of inflammatory reactions can develop into monocytes (these cells will be described later in this chapter) and macrophages. Indeed, in blood films cells that appear to be transitional forms between medium-sized lymphocytes and monocytes can often be seen. It then seems very probable that at least some lymphocytes, particularly the larger ones, can develop into monocytes.

Yoffey and his associates believe that lymphocytes that are filtered out in bone marrow undergo a metamorphosis into cells of great potentiality that can form many of the different kinds of blood cells that form in marrow. The concept that lymphocytes possess great mesenchymal potentiality was strongly supported in the past by Maximow. The concept that lymphocytes are motile cells of great potentiality has much attraction, but it is very difficult to reconcile this view of lymphocytes' being undifferentiated cells with the many findings that indicate that the small lymphocyte is a differentiated cell that has come almost to the end of its course and in many instances even appears to be unable to divide.

Another function that has been ascribed to lymphocytes is that they manufacture antibodies. The fine structure of their cytoplasm, revealed under the E/M, unlike that of plasma cells that *do* make antibodies, gives no indication of being adapted to synthesizing protein antibodies for secretion. There is much confusion about the relation between lympho-cytes and plasma cells. They evolve from closely related cell lineages, as will be described in Chapter 18; hence, it is difficult to be sure that antibody production ascribed to lympho-cytes is not to be explained by young plasma cells having been mistaken for lymphocytes. Furthermore, the mother cells that give rise to lymphocytes are so much like the mother cells that give rise to plasma cells, and the first cells that they give rise to along their respec-tive lines of differentiation are so similar, that it is easy to understand another view that is generally held, namely, that lymphocytes can turn into plasma cells. It seems possible that cells developing along the lymphocyte line could turn into plasma cells, but that is a different matter from differentiated small lym-phocytes turning into plasma cells. The prob-lem is still more confused by the probability that small lymphocytes may carry antibody on their cell surface. It seems very probable that antibody carried by lymphocytes into homologous or heterologous transplants, rather than circulating antibody in the plasma, is responsible for the destruction of the cells of these transplants. However, the fact that they carry antibody does not necessarily mean that they produce the antibody; the latter could be produced by plasma cells with which they live in close association in lymphatic tissue.

The student who tries to assemble his knowl-edge about lymphocytes may well feel despair at trying to organize a sound working hy-pothesis from so many uncertainties. The situ-ation will be resolved only by more research.

The formation of lymphocytes will be de-scribed in Chapter 18.

Monocytes

Numbers. Monocytes constitute only from 3 to 8 per cent of the leukocytes of normal blood; hence, a student may have to examine a great many leukocytes before a good ex-ample of a monocyte is found. A typical mono-cyte can be distinguished without undue diffi-culty. However, there are some difficulties associated with deciding whether some cells are monocytes or large lymphocytes and whether others are monocytes or juvenile neutrophils, as will be described.

Appearance. Although not all monocytes are larger than other kinds of leukocytes, the largest leukocytes seen in blood films are gen-erally monocytes (Fig. 106). They are from 12 to 15 μ in diameter when they are suspended in fluid and so permitted to assume a more or less spherical shape. When they are flattened, as they are in dried films, they measure up to 20 μ in diameter.

The nuclei of monocytes vary from being slightly indented ovals to kidney-shaped struc-tures (Fig. 106). In some instances the inden-tation becomes great enough to give the nucleus a horseshoe-shaped appearance. Some-times nuclei, particularly of the latter type, appear as if they had been twisted or folded in preparing the film. The chromatin of the nucleus is disposed in a network of granules and flakes; the network is of a finer texture than that in lymphocyte nuclei. The chromatin is colored a blue-violet shade in the usual preparation, and since it is finer and more spread out than that of lymphocytes it does not stain as intensely as that of lymphocytes. Nucleoli are not visible in the usual stained film but can be seen in monocytes examined with the phase microscope. There are often two in each nucleus.

The cytoplasm of monocytes is relatively abundant; it comprises the larger part of the cell. In blood films it is colored a pale gray-blue (Fig. 106). Fine lilac granules, similar in appearance to those seen in neutrophils, are sometimes present in the cytoplasm of mono-cytes (Fig. 106). These are called azurophilic granules because they have an affinity for the methylene azure of blood stains.

Monocytes are motile cells. One feature of their motility is their ability to extend from and withdraw to their ordinary boundaries, pseudopodia of cytoplasm. With supravital staining technics, which have been used ex-tensively in the study of monocytes, a rosette can be demonstrated surrounding the centro-some. This rosette is due to vacuoles concen-trating the supravital stain, and it occupies the same position as the Golgi apparatus when this is demonstrated by other means. The rosette made visible with vital staining is not specific for the monocyte: a few other kinds of cells may reveal the same appearance if treated by the same technic.

Fine Structure. The E/M confirms the fact

that the nuclei of monocytes have nucleoli. The cytoplasm has a fair sprinkling of mitochondria (Fig. 112). The intracytoplasmic membranes are fairly well developed. In part, they are present in the form of large, flattened vesicles which often show a linear arrangement. They are also in the form of small, rounded vesicles. RNA granules can be seen on the outer surfaces of both types, and there are also a few RNA granules distributed between vesicles in the cytoplasm. The Golgi apparatus is prominent in thin sections that are cut in the proper plane; it lies in the cytoplasm in the region of the indentation of the nucleus. No further detail about azurophilic granules has been elicited as yet with the E/M.

Function and Length of Life. The monocyte generally is regarded as a young cell that reaches its full development and attains its full capacity for function only when it leaves the blood stream and enters the tissues. In the tissues it develops into a somewhat larger cell which has great phagocytic powers. The larger cell generally is known as a macrophage but it has many other names. Macrophages will be discussed in detail in the chapter on connective tissues. Perhaps it should be pointed out here that the macrophages of connective tissue do not all develop from monocytes, for a certain number are born and remain as residents of connective tissue. However, monocytes provide an easily mobilized force of cells that can be

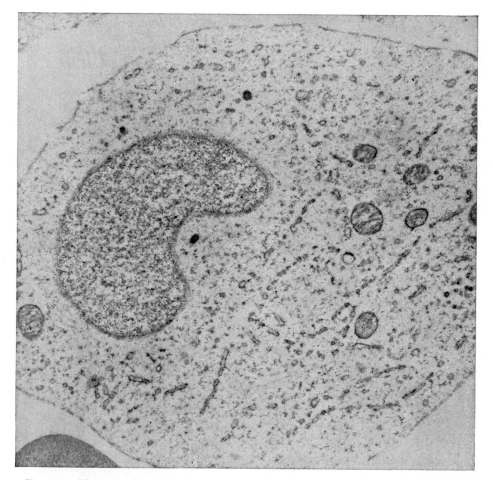

Fig. 112. Electron micrograph (× 12,000) of a section of a monocyte obtained from the bone marrow of man. The section probably passed through one side of the cell, so the nucleus appears relatively smaller than it should. A few mitochondria are present in the cytoplasm, which also reveals strings of vesicles. The section probably passed too far to one side of the center to pass through the Golgi region. (Preparation by A. F. Howatson)

easily marshaled from the blood stream, in any tissue where more macrophages are needed, and in that tissue they develop into macrophages.

The length of time that monocytes stay in the blood stream is not known.

SOME PROBLEMS ASSOCIATED WITH IDENTIFYING CERTAIN LEUKOCYTES SEEN IN A BLOOD FILM

We shall discuss first some simple problems that are likely to bother a beginner.

Two have been mentioned already. The student should learn to identify platelets and so learn to distinguish between clumps of platelets and leukocytes. The student also should be aware of the fact that platelets sometimes are superimposed on erythrocytes or even on leukocytes.

The beginner should pay no attention to degenerating or distorted leukocytes. Indeed, at first, the student should pay no attention to any leukocytes that do not closely resemble those seen in good illustrations.

A common mistake made by beginners who are eager to see an eosinophil is that of believing a neutrophil whose granules are a little on the pink side to be an eosinophil. Since there are relatively few eosinophils in normal blood the student must be prepared to examine a great many leukocytes before finding one. Once an eosinophil is seen it is easily recognized and seen to be obviously different from a neutrophil because its cytoplasm is literally stuffed with large, orange-red refractile granules, and its nucleus commonly has only two lobes. If in doubt about whether any given cell is a neutrophil or an eosinophil, compare it with other neutrophils and with other eosinophils; the latter may take some time.

Students, in their desire to find the elusive basophil, are likely to consider that some degenerating or poorly fixed cell, or even a neutrophil with a bluish tinge to its granules, is a basophil. When a true basophil is found the student will have no doubts, because it has large blue granules that overshadow its relatively pale nucleus. If the student is in doubt about whether or not any cell is an eosinophil or a basophil, the cell, in all likelihood, is neither.

A more serious difficulty is that of deciding whether certain cells are large lymphocytes or monocytes. In discussing this problem it should be mentioned that there are two schools of thought about the origin of monocytes. One school believes that they are formed from lymphocytes and hence that in blood there are cells that represent all transitions between the two types. If lymphocytes turn into monocytes, it is obvious that some cells will be seen in blood films that are halfway between the two types and hence impossible to classify definitely as one type or the other. The other school of thought about the origin of monocytes subscribes to the view that monocytes arise from a separate stem cell, the monoblast, and hence that lymphocytes and monocytes represent two different but closely related families of cells. Those who follow this school think that it is possible to distinguish large lymphocytes that otherwise resemble monocytes from monocytes by the character of the chromatin network in their nuclei. In lymphocytes this is a coarse network, and in monocytes it is a fine network. It takes experience to make this distinction.

If juvenile neutrophils are present in any numbers in blood—and this does not occur under strictly normal conditions—there may be difficulty in distinguishing them from monocytes that have granular cytoplasm. Here again the character of the nuclear chromatin is probably the most helpful guide, for it is of a coarser character in juvenile neutrophils than it is in monocytes. Moreover, the neutrophils have more granules in their cytoplasm than monocytes.

When abnormal blood is studied, as it will be when the student begins clinical work, other difficulties will be encountered, for in certain disease states immature cells of both the erythrocyte and the leukocyte series may be present in blood. To recognize these it is necessary to learn the appearance of the cells that normally are found only in myeloid and lymphatic tissue—the tissues where the mature cells are formed. The appearances of these cells will be described in subsequent chapters, and further comment will be made on this matter.

REFERENCES

GENERAL

Berlin, N. I., Waldmann, T. A., and Weissman, S. M.: Life span of the red blood cell, Physiol. Rev. *39*:577, 1959.

Bessis, M.: Cytology of the Blood and Blood-Forming Organs, tr. by Eric Ponder, New York, Grune, 1956.

Bloom, William: Lymphocytes and monocytes: theories of hematopoiesis *in* Downey's Handbook of Hematology, vol. 1, p. 373, New York, Hoeber, 1938.

Bunting, C. H.: The polymorphonuclear leucocytes *in* Downey's Handbook of Hematology, vol. 1, p. 159, New York, Hoeber, 1938.

Maximow, A. A.: The lymphocytes and plasma cells *in* Cowdry's Special Cytology, ed. 2, vol. 2, p. 603, New York, Hoeber, 1932.

Riley, J. F.: Mast Cells, Edinburgh, Livingstone, 1959.

Ringoen, A. R.: Eosinophile leucocytes and eosinophilia *in* Downey's Handbook of Hematology, vol. 1, p. 179, New York, Hoeber, 1938.

Tocantins, L. M. (ed.): Progress in Hematology, vol. 1, New York, Grune, 1956.

Trowell, O. A.: The Lymphocyte *in* Bourne, G. H., and Danielli, J. F. (eds.): Internat. Rev. Cytol., vol. VII, New York, Acad. Press, 1938.

Whitby, L. E. H., and Britton, C. J. C.: Disorders of the Blood, ed. 8, London, Churchill, 1957.

Wintrobe, Maxwell M.: Clinical Hematology, ed. 4, Philadelphia, Lea & Febiger, 1956.

Yoffey, J. M., and Courtice, F. C.: Lymphatics, Lymph and Lymphoid Tissue, Cambridge, Mass., Harvard Univ. Press, 1956.

SPECIAL REFERENCES ON LEUKOCYTES

Ackerman, G. A., and Bellios, N. C.: A study of the morphology of the living cells of blood and bone marrow in vital films with the phase-contrast microscope; I. Normal blood and bone marrow, Blood 10:3, 1955.

Bernhard, W., and Leplus, R.: La méthode des coupes ultrafines et son application à l'étude de l'ultrastructure des cellules sanguines, J. Suisse Méd. 38/39:897, 1955.

Bierman, H. R., Kelly, K. H., and Cordes, F. L.: The sequestration and visceral circulation of leukocytes in man, Ann. New York Acad. Sc. 59:850, 1955.

Bunting, C. H.: Functions of the leucocytes *in* Downey's Handbook of Hematology, vol. 1, p. 437, New York, Hoeber, 1938.

Code, C. F.: Histamine in blood, Physiol. Rev. 32:47, 1952.

Coons, A. H., Leduc, E. H., and Connolly, J. M.: Leukocytes involved in antibody formation, Ann. New York Acad. Sc. 59:951, 1955.

Davidson, W. M., and Smith, D. R.: A morphological sex difference in the polymorphonuclear neutrophil leucocytes, Brit. M. J. 2:6, 1954.

Garrey, W. E., and Bryan, W. R.: Variations in white blood cell counts, Physiol. Rev. 15:597, 1935.

Lillie, R. D.: Factors influencing the Romanovsky staining of blood films and the role of methylene violet, J. Lab. & Clin. Med. 29:1181, 1944.

McCutcheon, M.: Chemotaxis and locomotion of leukocytes, Ann. New York Acad. Sc. 59:941, 1955.

MacNeal, W. J.: Tetrachrome bloodstain, J.A.M.A. 78:1122, 1922.

Martin, S. P., McKinney, G. R., and Green, R.: The metabolism of human polymorphonuclear leukocytes, Ann. New York Acad. Sc. 59:996, 1955.

Menkin, V.: Factors concerned in the mobilization of leukocytes in inflammation, Ann. New York Acad. Sc. 59:956, 1955.

Pease, D. C.: An electron microscopic study of red bone marrow, Blood 11:501, 1956.

———: Marrow cells seen with the electron microscope after ultrathin sectioning, Rev. hémat. 10:300, 1955.

Rebuck, J. W., and Crowley, J. H.: A method of studying leukocytic functions *in vivo*, Ann. New York Acad. Sc. 59:757, 1955.

Richter, K. M.: Studies on leukocytic secretory activity, Ann. New York Acad. Sc. 59:863, 1955.

Sheldon, H., and Zetterquist, H.: Internal ultrastructure in granules of white blood cells of the mouse; a preliminary note, Bull. Johns Hopkins Hosp. 96:135, 1955.

Sieracki, J. C.: The neutrophilic leukocyte, Ann. New York Acad. Sc. 59:690, 1955.

Speirs, R. S.: Physiological approaches to an understanding of the function of eosinophils and basophils, Ann. New York Acad. Sc. 59:706, 1955.

Sundberg, R. D.: Lymphocytes and plasma cells, Ann. New York Acad. Sc. 59:1003, 1955.

Tompkins, E. H.: The monocyte, Ann. New York Acad. Sc. 59:732, 1955.

Valentine, W. N.: The enzymes of leukocytes, Ann. New York Acad. Sc. 59:1003, 1955.

Visscher, M. B., and Halberg, F.: Daily rhythms in numbers of circulating eosinophils and some related phenomena, Ann. New York Acad. Sc. 59:834, 1955.

Wright, C-S., and Dodd, M. C.: Phagocytosis, Ann. New York Acad. Sc. 59:945, 1955.

SPECIAL REFERENCES ON ANTIBODIES AND ALLERGY

Cinader, B., and Pearce, J. H.: Immunological approaches to the study of ribonuclease *in* Neuberger, A. (ed.): Symposium on Protein Structure, p. 240, London, Methuen, 1958.

Cinader, B., and Weitz, B.: Interaction of tetanus toxin and antitoxin, J. Hyg. *51*:293, 1953.

Humphrey, J. H., and Porter, R. R.: An investigation on rabbit antibodies by the use of partition chromatography, Biochem. J. *62*:93, 1956.

Jerne, N. K.: Study of avidity based on rabbit skin responses to diphtheria toxin-antitoxin mixtures, Acta path. et microbiol. scandinav., Suppl. *87*:3, 1951.

Kekwick, R. A., Record, B. R.: Some physical properties of diphtheria antitoxic horse serums, Brit. J. Exper. Path. *22*:29, 1941.

Kuhns, W. J.: Immunochemical studies of antitoxin produced in normal and allergic individuals hyperimmunized with diphtheria toxoid. IV. Differences between human precipitating and non-precipitating skin-sensitizing diphtheria antitoxin as shown by electrophoresis, J. Exper. Med. *99*:577, 1954.

Raynaud, M.: Heterogeneity of diphtheria antitoxin *in* Shaffer, J. H. (ed.): Mechanisms of Hypersensitivity, Henry Ford Hospital International Symposium no. 8, p. 27, Boston, Little, 1959.

Chapter 9

Platelets and Fibrin

The next mechanism to consider, that operates in blood, is the one that is automatically thrown into operation to seal off blood vessels when they are cut or bruised or have serious disease in their walls.

The vast importance of this mechanism is only fully appreciated when individuals in whom it is deficient are seen as patients. Those who are severly affected in this respect risk bleeding to death from trivial injuries. And even those who are not so severely affected are nevertheless much more serious risks than normal people if they have to undergo surgical operations. Those of us who have grown accustomed to counting on this mechanism from day to day can scarcely comprehend the difficulties that life presents to those in whom it is deficient.

Yet this helpful automatic mechanism is not an unmixed blessing. Particularly in middle and later life it may act too efficiently and automatically plug blood vessels that would be better left open. Usually the walls of the blood vessels that become occluded in this way are diseased; nevertheless, they generally are still functioning. The institution of the sealing-off process in vessels supplying the heart and the brain is a common cause of "heart attacks" and "strokes" in late middle and later life, and individuals in these age brackets have some cause to wish that the mechanism were not quite so automatic and efficient.

Actually two different phenomena occur in the usual sealing-off or plugging of an injured blood vessel. These are termed *coagulation* and *agglutination*. Although they differ from one another, they interact with each other in certain ways, as will be explained.

COAGULATION

Suppose a surgeon is operating on a bone, perhaps cutting a graft from it to be implanted elsewhere. When he removes the graft the bone saw, of course, cuts many little blood vessels contained in the substance of the bone; hence, some blood will seep into the cavity that remains after he detaches the piece he has cut. At first, this blood is fluid, but after a few minutes it changes into a firm clot. Figure 113 illustrates one that formed precisely in this way. From what elements in blood does such a clot arise?

In Chapter 6 the colloids of plasma were discussed, and it was stated that they were proteins. One of the plasma proteins is *fibrinogen*. In circulating blood this exists as a *sol*. But when plasma escapes into a wound, such as the one described above, the fibrinogen (*fibra* = a fiber; *gennao* = I produce) undergoes a transformation into a *gel* and in this state it assumes the form of a mesh of fibers (Fig. 113, *left*), which, however, may become added to, so as to form substantial ribbons (Fig. 113, *right*). Fibrogen having undergone a sol-gel transformation is called *fibrin*.

After fibrin has formed and served its purpose in some site of injury it is generally disposed of one way or another. Not uncommonly it is invaded and replaced by a young type of connective tissue, termed *granulation tissue*. When this occurs it is referred to as the organization of fibrin.

With the E/M, fibrin has been found to be composed of filaments around 600 Å in length and from 30 to 40 Å wide. These become arranged into threads in which axial periodicity is easily seen (Fig. 114), for the fibers have dense bands that alternate with lighter bands along their lengths. The distance between the middle of one dark band to that of the next is about 230 Å; therefore, the periodicity of fibrin threads is considerably different from that of collagenic fibrils. As fibrin forms, the filaments tend to become laterally associated to form the fibrin threads visible with the light microscope.

Factors Concerned in the Formation of Fibrin; the Clotting Mechanism

Why should fibrinogen undergo a sol-gel transformation when blood escapes into wounds but not while it is in the vessels of

194

fibrin threads

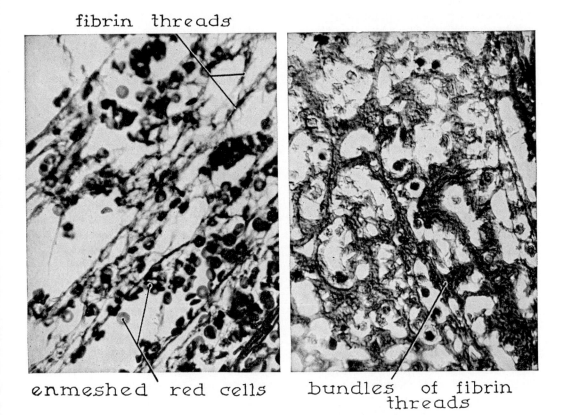

enmeshed red cells   bundles of fibrin
                                   threads

FIG. 113. High-power photomicrographs of sections cut through an area into which bleeding
had occurred. (*Left*) Fine threads of fibrin which are forming a mesh entangling many cells.
(*Right*) Fibrin threads arranged into coarser bundles.

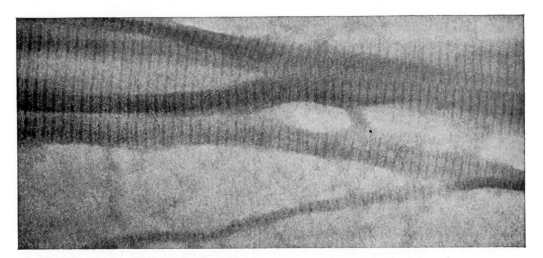

FIG. 114. Electron micrograph ($\times$ 115,000) of bovine fibrin, clotted in vitro by the addition
of thrombin to fibrinogen solution, stained with phosphotungstic acid. (Preparation by C. E. Hall)

the circulatory system? This is because fibrinogen becomes fibrin only under the influence of an enzyme called *thrombin*. Normally, there is only a little thrombin in blood, and the little that is present in the circulation is neutralized by a small amount of a substance that inactivates it, called *antithrombin,* which is also present in circulating blood.

It would appear, then, that the blood which escapes from vessels into a wound comes to contain, somehow, more thrombin, enough to induce the sol-gel transformation of fibrinogen. The extra thrombin produced at such a site is obtained from another material called *prothrombin,* which, although present in blood is not active and does not become active thrombin unless it is acted upon (in the presence of calcium ions) by still another substance called *thromboplastin* or *thrombokinase.* At first it was thought that this material was formed only by, or liberated from, injured tissues. But it was known that blood would clot under conditions where there was no injured tissue to provide thromboplastin, so it was accepted that thromboplastin could be produced in blood itself, and disintegrating platelets generally were believed to be its source. However, it was found that platelet extracts had only feeble coagulating powers, and so it was suspected that other factors in blood might be involved in the formation of thromboplastin. This view has now been proved to be correct, for over the past few years it has become known that the formation of thromboplastin requires the interaction of several substances, as will now be described. To explain how this was discovered we must briefly describe a curious disease.

Some Recent Advances in Knowledge Concerning the Clotting Mechanism. Undoubtedly, the student will have heard of hemophilia, a hereditary disease which, although transmitted by females, affects, with a few exceptions, only males. This is because the defective gene responsible for the condition is recessive and is carried on the X chromosomes. As was explained in Chapter 4, females have 2 X chromosomes, one from their father and one from their mother. Therefore, the chances are very great that even if one X chromosome has the defective gene the other will be normal. The normal one will act as the dominant one, and because it is dominant

the disease does not appear. But males, with their XY combination, have only one X chromosome in their cells. This, of course, comes from their mother, and so if this carried the defect they, unlike the female, have no normal gene of this type to compensate for the defective one, so they suffer from hemophilia. Individuals who have hemophilia are commonly termed "bleeders." Their blood does not clot promptly, and so they are disposed to bleed from simple cuts or injuries for much longer periods of time than normal individuals. Indeed, there have been many examples of hemophiliacs bleeding to death from having a tooth extracted or from undergoing a simple surgical operation. When the clotting mechanism of blood was understood reasonably well, it became apparent that the defect in hemophiliacs lay in their inability to produce thromboplastin; they lacked the trigger to set off the clotting mechanism. Understanding this helped in their treatment. To stop the bleeding one commonly employed measure was that of giving them transfusions of blood from normal individuals. However, in 1947, one investigator gave a hemophiliac a transfusion from another person who was also considered to be a hemophiliac and, probably much to his surprise, found that the blood from the second hemophiliac brought the coagulation time of the blood of the first to normal. In 1950 other investigators reported that after mixing blood from what were believed to be two different hemophiliacs the clotting time of the mixed blood had become normal. Soon afterward the reason for this reaction was discovered; it was that more than one factor is concerned in the formation of thromboplastin; and some individuals with bleeding disease lack one, and others the other. If blood from the two types were mixed, it would, of course, have both the factors necessary to make thromboplastin; hence, it would clot. As this matter was investigated in greater detail it came to light that the formation of thromboplastin was much more complicated than was previously believed. Now it seems to be fairly well established that the following materials enter into its production.

1. *Platelets,* to be described in detail later in this chapter, provide certain essential ingredients. When clotting occurs in plasma, in the absence of any injured tissue, this sub-

stance, with the next two materials to be described, forms thromboplastin.

2. A particular plasma protein termed *antihemophilic globulin* (*AHG*). This is the substance that is lacking in true hemophilia; this is why it was given its name—its presence prevents hemophilia.

3. A substance termed *plasma thromboplastin component* (*PTC*). Only recently it was discovered that this substance is essential for the formation of thromboplastin and that its absence (not that of AHG) from blood is the cause of about one third of all cases of what were in the past diagnosed as hemophilia. The name of the first patient in which a deficiency of this substance alone was responsible for the defect in clotting was Christmas, so PTC is called the *Christmas factor;* and the disease that results from a lack of it is termed *Christmas disease.*

It should be noted here that a deficiency of either AHG or PTC could cause a disease of clotting but by mixing blood from the two types of disease all the factors necessary for clotting would be present.

After it was established that a deficiency of either AHG or PTC could cause a bleeding disease, some examples of bleeding diseases caused by thromboplastin defects were found to be due to the absence of still other factors. One of the first of these factors to be discovered is called the *plasma thromboplastin antecedent* (*PTA*). This disease, like the other two types, is hereditary but, unlike them, is not due to the lack of a sex-linked factor.

When plasma is in contact with a rough or foreign surface the clotting mechanism is triggered by the activation of PTC. This acts with AHG to form an intermediate product which combines with the platelet factor in the presence of calcium to form thromboplastin. However, thromboplastin, at this stage of its formation, may not be completely active, and it has been suggested that another factor or other factors may be concerned in its activation.

When thromboplastin begins to convert prothrombin into thrombin, at first it does so slowly, but soon the rate increases because of certain accelerating mechanisms, which need not be discussed here, being set into motion.

Under normal conditions the fibrin clot that forms in a cut or the site of injury is in the form of a mesh, and various cells present in blood become entangled in the mesh (Fig. 113); indeed, the usual clot is red because so many erythrocytes are entangled in it (Fig. 113). Under normal conditions the fibrin strands contract, and this squeezes out the part of the blood plasma that still remains in the clot. The part of the plasma that is exuded from the clot lacks fibrinogen, but it contains the other proteins of the blood; this fluid is called *serum*, and it differs from plasma in the very important respect that it cannot clot.

AGGLUTINATION

This word is derived from two words that mean "to paste" or "to glue." Agglutination, then, refers to the phenomenon in which things become adherent. It is commonly used in bacteriology, where it refers to the adhesion and clumping of bacteria which occur in a fluid medium under certain circumstances. It can be used properly with reference to the clumping of the cells or of any particulate matter in blood. As a mechanism to seal off injured blood vessels, agglutination is very important, and it is informative to trace its evolution briefly.

In the lower vertebrates, the inner surface of an injured blood vessel seems to attract erythrocytes. These become sticky and adhere both to the vessel wall and to one another at the site of injury. In birds the mechanism is more specialized and is said to depend chiefly on certain cells called *thrombocytes* that are present in their blood. These are shaped something like erythrocytes but are smaller and of a different composition. They are believed to be highly specialized with regard to adhering and accumulating at points of injury along vessels. In mammals a further development of the mechanism is to be observed. Instead of there being specialized cells to perform this adhering function, there are still smaller bodies in circulating blood that are fragments of cytoplasm rather than complete cells. These are called *platelets* (*platum* = a plate, dish) because they look like little plates.

Platelets are more difficult to study than blood cells. When blood is obtained for a blood film by means of a puncture wound, the platelets tend to stick together, that is,

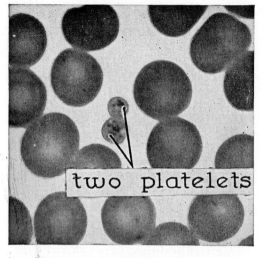

two platelets

FIG. 115. Oil-immersion photomicrograph of a stained film of human blood. Two platelets may be seen adherent to one another in the center of the picture.

so named because it is brightly colored after staining with dyes of the Romanovsky type. Its color after this treatment may be red or violet, or even blue-violet. The chromatomere may have the form of what seems to be a fairly solid central body in the platelet or, what is more common, it may be broken up into small granules which tend to occupy a more or less central position in the platelet (Figs. 106 and 115). The hyalomere comprises the relatively transparent substance in which the chromatomere lies and is colored a very pale blue by the usual Romanovsky stain (Fig. 106). When the chromatomere is granular, the hyalomere usually appears plate-shaped, but when the chromatomere is a fairly solid and relatively large central body, the hyalomere (in dried, stained films) may present varied forms; sometimes it is drawn out into spikelike processes. Furthermore, there are all sorts of gradations between these two types. For example, some platelets exhibit a chromatomere that consists of both granules and a larger body of chromatophilic material, and some platelets whose chromatomere is granular may be of a most irregular outline. However, platelets alter so quickly when removed from the blood stream that it is difficult to know just how much of the appearance they present in dried, stained films is due to artefact.

It may be that certain of the forms described above represent younger types, and other forms older types of platelets. Olef, from studying platelets in wet-fixed films, has proposed ways of distinguishing young from old platelets.

It has been of interest to investigate the chromatomere of platelets to determine whether it is nuclear or cytoplasmic material. If it contained nucleoprotein of either the DNA or the RNA type, it might be expected to stain with hematoxylin. In our experience it stains so faintly with this dye that it might be concluded that its stainability with blood stains is not due to nucleoprotein. Most investigators who have tried staining the chromatomere by the Feulgen technic have found it to be negative. In studies made on its histochemistry, Wislocki, Bunting and Dempsey did not find any evidence of the chromatomere's containing any substantial amount of RNA. We shall leave a further consideration of the composition of the chromatomere until

they are very prone to agglutinate. Hence, in an ordinary blood film, clumps of platelets are commonly seen lying among the blood cells (Fig. 106). Moreover, their form may change appreciably when blood is removed from the body and spread on a glass slide. There is considerable variation in the way platelets are preserved in different blood films.

Platelets, in circulating blood, are oval-shaped disks but they frequently appear in dried, stained blood films as rounded disks. They vary somewhat in size. Most of the more rounded ones seen in dried, stained blood films are about one half or slightly less than one half the diameter of the erythrocytes (Fig. 115), but they may be much smaller. However oval ones may be about three quarters of an erythrocyte's diameter in length. In examining a blood film, clumps of platelets may be mistaken for individual platelets. However, an adequate search will reveal isolated platelets so that the appearance of the individual platelet may be learned; thereafter the clumps of platelets will present no difficulty.

It is usual to describe a platelet (as seen in a dried and stained blood film) as having two parts, the *chromatomere* (*meros* = part), the colored part, and the *hyalomere* (*hyalos* = glass), the clear part. The chromatomere is

FIG. 116. Electron micrograph ($\times$ 33,000) of a section of a platelet that was in a capillary of a normal rat. A good example of a mitochondrion, showing cristae, can be seen at the left. Many large, round and ovoid granules are distributed throughout the platelet in the region of the chromomere; these probably account for the staining properties of the chromomere. Some membranous vesicles also can be seen. Note that the platelet is surrounded by a cell membrane and has some pseudopodia covered with the membrane. Only a few RNA granules are to be seen. (Preparation by W. Bernhard)

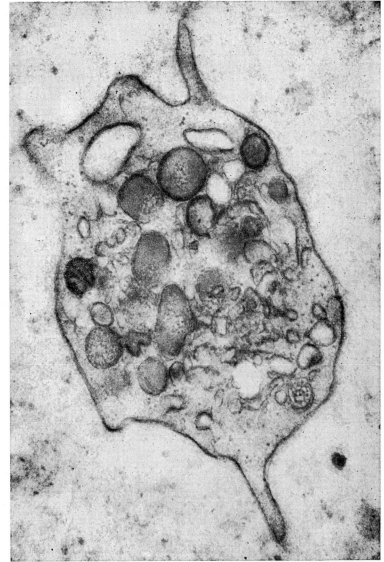

we have considered what has been learned about platelets with the E/M.

The Fine Structure of Platelets. Sectioned platelets have been studied with the E/M by several investigators, in particular by Bernhard and by Pease; the latter has published interesting electron micrographs of platelets aggregating to form thrombi.

In sectioned platelets the region of the chromatomere is seen to contain mitochrondria, distended membranous vesicles (which on the average are somewhat smaller than the mitochondria, although some may be as large)

and specific granules of a size comparable with that of the vesicles (Fig. 116). The origin of the specific granules, like that of the specific granules of the granular leukocytes, has not been settled, and there are two views on the matter: (1) that they represent transformed mitochondria, and (2) that they are formed by membranous vesicles accumulating a homogeneous material and eventually turning into granules.

Bernhard observed, in addition to the foregoing, a fine granularity in the region of the chromatomere but found relatively few RNA granules in his region. Pease reports finding RNA granules in abundance. At this stage of development of knowledge it would be unwise to attempt to draw too many conclusions from electron microscopy regarding the RNA content of the chromatomere and how much it is responsible for its staining qualities. However, the E/M has shown that there are specific granules in platelets, and since the specific granules of granular leukocytes are stainable it seems probable that the specific granules in platelets are responsible, to a considerable extent, for the staining properties of the chromatomere.

With the E/M, the hyalomere reveals no particular structural features. It is of interest, however, that the platelet as a whole is surrounded with a membrane comparable to the usual cell membrane (Fig. 116).

The formation of platelets will be described when myeloid tissue is considered.

In the examination of stained blood film it is not uncommon to encounter platelets superimposed on erythrocytes, an appearance that may be puzzling unless it is understood.

HOW PLATELETS ARE COUNTED

The tendency of platelets to clump together and adhere to any surface presented to them as soon as blood is drawn creates technical difficulties with regard to their enumeration. To keep them apart so that they may be seen as individuals and hence counted, it is necessary to mix blood taken from the body with an antiagglutinating fluid immediately. Fairly strong solutions of magnesium sulfate or weaker solutions of sodium citrate are both useful in preventing platelets from agglutinating. Antiagglutinating fluid of this type may be used in two ways—the direct and the indirect methods of making platelet counts.

In the indirect method a drop of sterile antiagglutinating solution is placed on the clean skin, and a puncture is made through the drop so that the blood wells up into the anti-agglutinant. A film of this mixture is then prepared and stained in the same manner as an ordinary blood film. The platelet count is estimated by noting the number of platelets in relation to the number of erythrocytes counted in several areas of the film; for example, if in one field 100 erythrocytes and 6 platelets are present, and if many other fields

give the same ratio, it is assumed that there are 6 platelets for every 100 erythrocytes in that specimen of blood. So, if an erythrocyte count is made, the number of platelets per cubic millimeter of blood can be determined.

With the direct method, no antigglutinating fluid is placed over the puncture site. Instead, a measured amount of blood is drawn up into a pipette containing a measured amount of antiagglutinant, and they are thoroughly mixed. As a little dye is added to the antiagglutinant to stain the platelets, they may be seen and distinguished from the erythrocytes when some of the mixture is examined in a counting chamber, where both an erythrocyte and a platelet count may be made from the same preparation with the ordinary light microscope.

The phase microscope has proved to be very useful for counting platelets, and probably the best method now available is a direct count made with this instrument.

It is very difficult to state exactly what constitutes a normal or an abnormal platelet count. The methods used in their enumeration are open to experimental error, and counts obtained by the indirect and the direct methods differ from each other considerably. Counts from arterial, venous and capillary blood are said to differ from one another, as are counts made from vessels supplying or leaving different organs and parts of the body. Platelet counts have a seasonal variation; they become altered with exercise and even vary throughout the day. (For details consult Tocantins' review.)

By the indirect method, the normal range is often considered to be between 250,000 and 350,000, or perhaps even between 200,000 and 400,000 per cubic millimeter of blood.

THE FUNCTIONS OF PLATELETS

Platelets exercise at least four functions:

1. Their primary function is that of agglutination. They tend to adhere to inner surfaces of blood vessels in sites where these are injured, and occasionally, when the current in a vein is slowed, they may even adhere in the absence of demonstrable injury to its wall. However, their general function in this respect is primarily protective and reparative; they seek to plug up leaks and cement over injured tissue. But as platelets, in exercising

their capacity to adhere or agglutinate, adhere to each other as well as to vessel walls, they tend to continue to attract further platelets as they accumulate and "melt" together. A mass of platelets, then, becomes thicker and thicker, and often the process is not arrested until the lumen of the affected vessel is almost or completely closed.

Such an agglutinated mass of platelets adhering to the inner surface of a blood vessel is known as a *white thrombus* (*thrombos* = a clot) because masses of platelets, in their fresh state, are white in color. It is obvious that a white thrombus can form only in flowing blood; it grows by abstracting fresh supplies of platelets from the blood that passes over it. Furthermore, it is obvious that it is very different in nature from the red clot that forms when still blood coagulates. Agglutination, then, tends to form a white clot, which consists primarily of fused platelets; coagulation, a red clot that consists primarily of strands of fibrin that enmesh innumerable erythrocytes.

2. The second function of platelets is manifested when they agglutinate or come into contact with a rough or foreign surface; they then liberate a substance which triggers the formation of thromboplastin, as has already been described. That they can do this helps account for the fact that white thrombi may very often be associated with red thrombi. For example, suppose a white thrombus forms and blocks a branch of a main blood vessel. The blood in this branch can no longer flow past the white thrombus; hence, the blood in that part of the branch between the thrombus and its point of origin from the main vessel comes to rest. Thromboplastic substances liberated from the agglutinated platelets of the white thrombus, and from the tissue injured by the shutting off of the circulation, set the coagulation mechanism into play in the blood that has thus come to rest; hence, a red thrombus forms between the white thrombus and the point of origin of the vessel. At this site, blood in the main vessel, flowing over the tail of the red thrombus, may begin depositing platelets on it, and this may continue until a sufficiently extensive white thrombus forms in this site to occlude the main vessel. This stops the circulation in this part of the main vessel, and a red thrombus then tends to form in the blood that comes to rest in it. By this mechanism, thrombi may grow until whole branching trees of blood vessels are occluded. In any event, it is easy to see why white thrombi have red tails.

3. The third function of platelets, and an extremely important one, as has been shown and stressed by Tocantins, is their ability to cause a coagulation (fibrin) clot to retract and become relatively solid and firm. It is to be appreciated that, when fibrin forms in a coagulation clot, many platelets are scattered throughout its meshes as well as many cells. Tocantins speaks of aggregations of platelets in the meshes of fibrin as "platelet knots" and describes how they act in this site to cause the fibrin strands to retract and become united into firmer and more adherent structures. Hence, although platelets are not essential for a coagulation clot to form, they probably accelerate its formation when they are present (second function), and they act still further to induce clot retraction (third function) and this is a very important factor in clots, serving to stop bleeding from a cut or otherwise injured vessel.

4. A fourth and more recently elucidated function of platelets is that they carry and so on occasion can liberate serotonin (5-hydroxytryptomine). Serotonin is produced by argentaffine cells (Fig. 407 A and C) of the intestine and is absorbed by platelets and carried this way in blood. When platelets agglutinate in a thrombus they spread and liberate the serotonin they carry. Since serotonin acts locally as a potent vasoconstrictor, it helps to reduce the size of the injured blood vessels of the part and this, of course, helps to arrest the bleeding. Serotonin liberated into the blood stream has another effect; it tends to reduce blood pressure, so it may help in this way also to restrain hemorrhage.

It is thus apparent that, although there are two fundamentally different types of thrombi, white and red, platelets are concerned in both. White thrombi depend for their formation on the agglutination of platelets and form only in flowing blood. Red clots depend for their formation on the fibrinogen of plasma undergoing a sol-gel transformation into fibrin and form only in still blood, either inside or outside blood vessels. The role of the platelets in the formation of white thrombi, therefore, is obvious. In red clots it is somewhat less definite. They assist to some extent in encouraging the formation of thromboplastin, but probably their most important function here is to induce retraction, consolidation and adherence of the fibrin mesh.

It is to be noted that the terms "thrombus" and "thrombosis" are reserved for agglutination and coagulation that occur intravascularly.

In the light of the foregoing it is interesting to inquire into exactly what happens in an ordinary skin cut which, as everyone knows, ceases to bleed after a few minutes. The severed ends of vessels attract platelets from the blood that flows from them. Thus there is a slight attempt at the formation of a white thrombus at the injured open ends of cut vessels. But the greater proportion of the clot that forms is a coagulation clot resulting from a fibrinogen-fibrin transformation in the escaping and escaped blood; this is set off by the thromboplastin liberated from the injured tissue and to some extent from that formed in the blood. If small arteries are cut, their muscular walls contract; this reduces the size of the hole that must be plugged by the clot. The fibrin that forms becomes adherent to the platelets that are deposited on the lining of the cut vessels, and also to the raw surfaces of the wound. The platelets in the clot induce its consolidation.

ORIGIN AND DESTRUCTION OF PLATELETS

Platelets are not complete cells; they are only fragments of protoplasm. Obviously, they must become detached from cells somewhere in the body and gain entrance to the circulation. The most commonly accepted theory ascribes their origin to certain large cells of bone marrow called *megakaryocytes;* these will be considered in Chapter 17.

The life of a platelet in the circulatory system is thought to be short; studies involving the tagging of platelets with radioactive chromium indicate a life of from 3 to 7 days in the blood stream.

Worn-out platelets are probably removed from the circulation similarly to worn-out erythrocytes, by phagocytic cells in the spleen, the liver and the bone marrow.

The normal content of platelets in blood, like the normal levels of erythrocytes, depends on the balance at a certain level between the liberation of platelets into blood and their removal from it. And, like the erythrocyte level, the platelet level may be depressed primarily because of increased removal of platelets from blood or from their decreased production.

A FEW ILLUSTRATIVE APPLICATIONS

The foregoing may help to illustrate what an ingenious and complicated mechanism is provided in blood to prevent individuals from bleeding to death when blood vessels are severed. It is a mechanism that depends on many factors, as has already been described. A deficiency of any one of these in blood may serve to keep the mechanism from functioning and so make an individual prone to abnormal bleeding. The following examples will show how different links in the chain may be involved:

It has already been explained that impaired clotting can be caused by a deficiency of either AHG, PTC (the Christmas factor) or PTA.

A deficiency of prothrombin is responsible for a condition called *hemorrhagic disease of the newborn*. This formerly mysterious disease, in which newborn infants were prone to bleed into their tissues and from various internal body surfaces, sometimes fatally, has been found to be due to a deficiency of vitamin K, a vitamin that is necessary for the synthesis of prothrombin. Curiously enough, this vitamin is synthesized by bacteria that normally live in the intestine, so the reason that newborn infants are particularly disposed to suffer from a vitamin K, and hence a prothrombin, deficiency is that their intestines have not yet had time to become contaminated with bacteria.

Since prothrombin is made in the liver, certain kinds of liver disease are associated with a defective production and hence with impaired clotting mechanisms.

Another condition in which individuals show an increased tendency to hemorrhage is known as *thrombocytopenic purpura* (*purphyreos* = purple), a condition in which affected individuals may exhibit purple patches in their skin caused by hemorrhages into their superficial tissues. These hemorrhages are caused by too small a number of thrombocytes (platelets) in the blood. Lest the student be given a false impression, it should be said that there are other kinds of purpura, resulting from causes other than a deficiency of platelets. In this condition, however, alleviation is usually obtained by removal of the spleen, an organ which, in this instance, seems to be particularly concerned in removing platelets from the circulation so that the number in the blood is kept at too low a level.

That a deficiency of calcium ions will prevent the clotting process is often taken advantage of for purposes of transfusion by mixing a certain amount of citrate solution with blood. Calcium ions in blood readily unite with the citrate ion to form a complex compound which does not dissociate into calcium ions. Hence, citrate removes calcium *ions* rather than calcium from the blood with which it is mixed.

REFERENCES

GENERAL

Biggs, Rosemary, and Macfarlane, R. G.: Human Blood Coagulation and Its Disorders, ed. 2, Oxford, Blackwell, 1956.

Blood Coagulation and Thrombosis: Brit. M. Bull., vol. 11, 1955, pub. by the Medical Dept., The British Council, 65 Davies St., London, England.

Stefanini, M., and Dameshek, W.: Hemorrhagic Disorders. New York, Grune, 1955.

(*See also* General References for Chapter 8)

SPECIAL

Aschoff, L.: Lectures on Pathology, XI. Thrombosis, New York, Hoeber, 1924.

Bernhard, W., and Leplus, R.: La méthode des coupes ultrafines et son application à l'étude de l'ultrastructure des cellules sanguines, J. Suisse de Méd. *38-39*: 897, 1955.

Hall, C. E.: Electron microscopy of fibrinogen and fibrin, J. Biol. Chem. *179*:857, 1949.

Hall, C. E., and Slayter, H. S.: The fibrinogen molecule: its size, shape, and mode of polymerization, J. Biochem. & Biophys. Cytol. *5*:11, 1959.

Hawn, C., and Porter, K.: The fine structure of clots formed from purified bovine fibrinogen and thrombin: a study with the electron microscope, J. Exper. Med. *86*:285, 1947.

Olef, I.: The enumeration of blood platelets, J. Lab. & Clin. Med. *20*:416, 1935.

Pease, D. C.: An electron microscope study of red bone marrow, Blood *11*:501, 1956.

Quick, A. J.: The Physiology and Pathology of Hemostasis, Philadelphia, Lea & Febiger, 1951.

Rand, M., and Reid, G.: Source of serotonin in serum, Nature *168*:385, 1951.

Rosenthal, N.: Blood platelets and megakaryocytes *in* Downey's Handbook of Hematology, vol. 1, p. 447, New York, Hoeber, 1938.

Silberberg, M.: The causes and mechanism of thrombosis, Physiol. Rev. *18*:197, 1938.

Tocantins, L. M.: The mammalian blood platelet in health and disease, Medicine *17*:155, 1938.

————: Platelets and the structure and physical properties of blood clots, Am. J. Physiol. *114*: 709, 1936.

Wislocki, G. B., Bunting, H., and Dempsey, E. W.: Further observations on the chemical cytology of megakaryocytes and other cells of hemopoietic tissues, Anat. Rec. *98*:527, 1947.

Wright, J. H.: Histogenesis of the blood platelets, J. Morphol. *21*:263, 1910.

PART THREE

The Four Primary Tissues
and Their Subdivisions

Chapter 10

The Four Primary Tissues
of the Body

GENERAL CONSIDERATIONS

There are only 4 basic types of tissue in the human body; everything in it is built of these. Each has a characteristic and distinguishing appearance. Hence, when a student views an unknown section, to recognize the tissues he sees therein does not require that a thousand possibilities be considered but only 4, and if he knows the fundamental differences between the 4 basic types well, he can decide with ease which of the 4 is represented. It is true that each of the 4 basic types contains subtypes, but the way a subtype of any one tissue varies from its basic plan will not be found to be very great. It cannot be emphasized too strongly that the most important step toward histologic and histopathologic competence is understanding the nature and knowing the appearance of the 4 basic tissues.

They are:

1. Epithelial tissue
2. Connective tissue
3. Muscular tissue
4. Nervous tissue

The 4 tissues represent 4 different types of specialization for the explicit performance of certain of the fundamental functions of protoplasm considered in Chapter 4.

Epithelial tissue (epithelium) is highly specialized to *protect, absorb* and *secrete*. In its protective role, epithelium exists in the form of *sheets* or *membranes* of cells which form *coverings* and *linings* for surfaces. For example, the outside of the body, the outer part of the skin, is an epithelial membrane. The intestine is lined by an epithelial membrane; so are the tubes and the primary passages of the respiratory system, the urinary system and so on. Some of these epithelial surfaces are not only protective, they are *absorptive,* as well. For example, certain of the cells in the epithelial lining of the intestine are responsible for absorbing nourishment into the body. Fur-

thermore, some of the cells of some epithelial membranes are *secretory*. But epithelial tissue, in the form of a covering or a lining membrane, cannot produce large amounts of secretion, so in sites where this is required, epithelial cells from membranes grow down into the underlying tissue and form structures called *glands* (Fig. 134), which are specialized arrangements of secretory cells. Hence, epithelial tissue exists in the form of covering or lining membranes and glands, as is described in detail in Chapters 11 and 12.

Connective tissue, as its name implies, is highly specialized for connecting other tissues together and for providing support for the body. Hence, connective tissues, on the whole, are characterized by containing a large amount of intercellular substance. Moreover, connective tissue conducts the vessels of the circulatory system throughout the body. Indeed, it is from very youthful connective tissue that the blood-vascular system develops. One subtype of specialized connective tissue (hemopoietic tissue) is responsible for manufacturing all the cells of the blood, and in this type cells are more prominent than intercellular substances.

Muscular tissue is highly specialized with regard to *contractility*. Muscle cells, to perform this function well, are elongated, so that the contraction of their protoplasm is effective. Furthermore, muscle tissue is highly specialized with regard to *conductivity*. When a stimulus is received at one part of a long muscle cell, a wave of excitation is conducted throughout the whole cell so that all parts of it contract.

Nervous tissue is highly specialized with respect to *irritability* and *conductivity*. Therefore, it is very receptive to various kinds of stimuli; when irritated by them, it conducts waves of excitation over long distances. For ease of stimulation, nervous tissue contains many special kinds of receptor nerve endings which are designed to be easily irritated by particular kinds of stimuli—light, sound, touch, pressure, etc. And, in order to conduct waves of excitation throughout the body to other tissues, for example, muscular and epithelial glandular tissue, that can respond to the stimulus received, part of the cytoplasm of nerve cells is drawn out into long processes called *nerve fibers*.

EMBRYOLOGIC ORIGIN OF TISSUES

At one early stage of development, the embryo is shaped something like a tube, the lumen of which is destined to become the intestinal canal. The embryo, at this time, is covered with a layer of cells termed the *ectoderm*. The tube is lined by another layer of cells, the *endoderm*, that is destined to form the lining of the intestine and certain glands. Between the ectoderm and the endoderm is the *mesoderm*. These 3 layers are referred to as the 3 primary germ layers.

Since the ectoderm covers, and the endoderm lines, the embryo, both ectoderm and endoderm are epithelial membranes; indeed, they serve as the origin for most of the epithelium that arises in subsequent development. Because of these facts, it becomes a temptation to use the word epithelium as if it had embryologic significance, inferring an origin from ectoderm and endoderm. But the fact is that a not inconsiderable amount of epithelium in the body (that of most of the urinary and the genital systems and that of the adrenal cortex) is derived from mesoderm. Therefore, the tissue that is termed epithelium in postnatal life is called *epithelium* because of its appearance and function and not because of its embryologic origin. However, many authors recognize two important exceptions to this rule. The cells that line the tubes of the blood vascular and lymphatic systems, while in appearance they resemble those of a typical epithelial membrane, develop from mesoderm and are generally referred to as endothelial cells (endothelium). The tissue that lines the great body cavities (pleural, pericardial and peritoneal) and covers the organs that fill these cavities, the lungs, the heart and the intestines, which also develops from mesoderm, in appearance also resembles a typical epithelial membrane; it is called mesothelium.

The reason for maintaining this distinction probably is not due entirely to these tissues developing from mesoderm, but because endothelium and mesothelium, under certain pathologic conditions, behave more like connective tissue cells than epithelial cells; hence, endothelium and mesothelium are sometimes considered as belonging to connective tissue. However, it seems to us that if tissue is to be called epithelium because of its morphology, we should be consistent and classify endothelium and mesothelium as epithelial tissues.

A NOTE ON HOW TO STUDY THE TISSUES

The student is strongly advised, after he completes the study of the 4 primary tissues and their various subdivisions (Chaps. 10 to 20 inclusive), to attempt to draw, on the left-hand side of a large piece of paper, a complete classification of the tissues similar to, or identical with, the one shown on an adjacent page. Then, on the right-hand side of the paper, the student should make a drawing of each and every subtype of the 4 primary tissues that are included on the chart. When a student can do this consistently from memory, and with some understanding as to why the microscopic structure of the different tissues must differ because of their various functions, he will be admirably equipped to begin the last part (Part Four) of the histology course. The student should realize that in the last part of the course, which deals with the microscopic anatomy of the different parts of the systems of the body, he will see no *new* tissues but only various arrangements of the basic ones with which he is already familiar.

Perhaps it should be noted that the thoughtful construction of an illustrated chart as described above constitutes an ideal way to study the histology of the tissues and also provides an ideal means for permitting the subject to be reviewed rapidly.

A VERY GENERAL ACCOUNT OF THE PROBLEMS OF TISSUE TRANSPLANTATION

It is a common practice in horticulture to graft shoots (scions) from trees that are not hardy but bear excellent fruit onto trees that are hardy but bear inferior fruit. By this

A MORPHOLOGIC CLASSIFICATION OF THE TISSUES

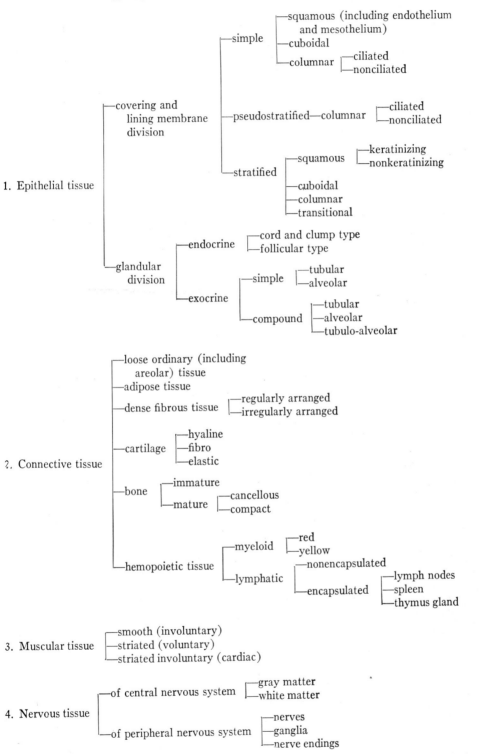

means it is possible to obtain a tree that is of hardy stock which also bears excellent fruit. This desirable aim is achieved because the stock retains its individual hardy character, and the growth resulting from the transplanted scion also retains its individual character and continues to produce the same kind of fruit that it would have produced had it never been severed from its parent plant. In other words, the transplanted tissue retains its own nature on transplantation; it merely uses its host as a source of nourishment.

It was inevitable, after it was known that grafting was a feasible procedure in the plant world, that attempts would be made to graft tissues from one part of an animal to another or from one animal to another. As research was performed in this field it became apparent that the problem was much more complicated in animals than in plants. Nevertheless, it is an exciting field for the investigator, and much research is currently being performed on the matter. Since the future surgeon may think about this matter with profit as he studies the tissues, we shall give a brief account of some of the problems associated with the transplantation of the tissues that we are about to study.

It has already been explained that if *foreign* molecules of a certain size range gain entrance to the tissues of a body they induce the formation of antibodies that react with them, and for this reason they are called *antigens*. We should pause here to ask "What is *foreign?*" Every body contains a vast assortment of macromolecules which do not incite antibody formation; this would seem to be because they were all present before the fetus or newborn animal developed the ability to make antibodies, for it would seem that any macromolecules, capable of inducing the formation of antibodies, that are present before the ability to make antibodies is developed, are accepted as normal constituents of that body. Only *further* and different macromolecules that gain entrance to the body after the body has developed an ability to make antibodies are regarded by the body as *foreign* and hence as antigens against which the body will react by producing antibodies.

Since the molecular constitution of all individuals, except those of identical twins, is different, everybody's tissues contain some macromolecules that would be foreign if they were injected or transplanted into someone else. Hence, if transplants of cells or tissues are made from one individual to another, the recipient will react to the foreign macromolecules in the donor tissue by making antibodies that will destroy the cells of the transplant.

The exception to this rule is in the instance of identical twins. Since identical twins both develop from the same egg, they both develop the same kinds of macromolecules, so any macromolecules from one, given to the other, are not recognized as foreign; therefore, tissue can be transplanted from one to the other without any of its molecules inducing the formation of antibodies.

It might be thought that blood must be an exception to the general rule given above, because almost everyone knows that blood is commonly transplanted from one individual to another by means of transfusions. But even blood cannot be transplanted from one individual to another indiscriminately; great care must be taken to see that the blood types (and these depend on the molecules in blood that could serve as antigens of the donor and the recipient) match. If the antigens in the blood of the donor are not possessed by the recipient, the latter will regard them as *foreign,* and produce antibodies against the transfused blood, and this can be fatal. It is possible to transplant blood from one individual to another within the limits of blood groups because there are only a small number of clinically important blood group antigens, so it is relatively easy to find other individuals with similar ones. In the instance of tissues other than blood the number of tissue antigens is so large that it is practically impossible to find donors and recipients who have the same ones. The antigens possessed by blood and by other tissues are inherited.

Man is not unique in the respect that all members of the species to which he belongs are different from one another; the same is true of all other species of mammals that, like man, engage in random breeding. In the laboratory, however, by means of inbreeding for generations, it is possible to produce strains of animals, the members of which, for all practical purposes, are identical. This has been done most extensively with mice, and there are now strains available for investigative work that have been inbred by means of brother-to-sister matings for 100 or more generations. Within such strains it is possible to transplant tissues from one animal to another without the transplant's calling forth an immune reaction from its host because the tissue antigens of the transplant are already possessed by the host and so they are not regarded as foreign.

Classification of Transplants. Transplants made from one part of the body to another part of the same body are said to be *autologous* or *autogenous* (*auto* = self). Transplants made from one animal to another of a pure inbred strain, as described in the preceding paragraph, are said to be *isologous* (*isos* = equal) because the animals involved are equal or the same as one another. Transplants made from one member of a species, in which random breeding has been practiced, to another animal of the same species are said to be *homogenous* or *homologous* (*homos* = same); and those made from an animal of one species to an animal of another species are said to be *heterogenous* or *heterologous* (*heteros* = another).

From the foregoing it might be concluded that homogenous and heterogenous transplants never would act as true living grafts in any species which indulges in random breeding. However, there are some interesting findings which will now be described briefly in a very general way; they are stimulating to those who are reluctant to give up the thought that some way may be found to make homologous transplantations successful. After this experimental work has been described, we shall explain why homogenous and even heterogenous transplants are sometimes used to good effect even though they do not function as true living grafts.

POSSIBLE WAYS OF OVERCOMING OR DIMINISHING IMMUNOLOGIC BARRIERS INVOLVED IN TISSUE TRANSPLANTATION IN EXPERIMENTAL ANIMALS

The Mechanism of Induced Tolerance. It has already been explained that in the instance of identical twins all of the molecules of each that could serve as antigens are possessed by the other. Hence, tissues transplanted from one to the other contain no antigens that the other will regard as foreign. On the contrary,

twins that are not identical do not come from the same ovum, but from two different fertilized ova; hence, unlike twins are genetically different, and so each has tissue antigens that are not possessed by the other. Accordingly, if tissue is transplanted from one to the other there will be some antigens in the donor tissue that are not possessed by the recipient; these will be regarded as foreign, and the recipient will make antibodies against them which will destroy the cells of the transplant. However, in 1945, Owens made a remarkable discovery in connection with unlike twins in cattle. He found examples of unlike twin cows, each of which had the other's type of red blood cells in its circulation as well as its own, and neither showed any immune reaction to the presence of its (unlike) twin's blood antigens. It became apparent that the reason for this is that unlike twins, in cattle, commonly share the same placenta, and this permits blood and even blood-forming cells from one to gain entrance to the other during fetal life. Some of the blood-forming cells from each twin take up residence in the other, and since this happens before the time the fetus develops the capacity to make antibodies, the cells from the unlike twin are accepted as part of the normal constitution of the animal in which they have taken up residence. The animal in which they thereafter reside is said to have acquired *immunologic tolerance* to the antigens possessed by the cells from the unlike twin.

Over the succeeding years, Billingham, Brent and Medawar showed that skin could be transplanted from unlike twin cattle that had shared a common circulation before birth and so it appeared that such animals were not only tolerant to each other's blood antigens but also to all the antigens in each other's skin. From the extensive research performed in this field since Owen's discovery it has become apparent that if enough of any of a great variety of antigens is given to a fetus before it is born the animal in later life will be tolerant to that antigen—that is, it will be incapable of producing antibodies against that antigen. The period of time over which an animal will accept an antigen as part of its own constitution ceases somewhere around the time of birth; thereafter, it will react to foreign antigens, not by developing tolerance to them, but by producing antibodies against them. In many animals, for example, the mouse and the rat, tolerance can still be induced for a short time after birth; hence, many experiments in connection with inducing tolerance are performed on newborn animals.

What appears to be tolerance can be induced in later life as follows: Animals given a lethal dose of whole-body radiation die chiefly because cell division ceases in their blood-forming tissues, and hence they are not able to make enough blood cells to support their existence. However, if such animals are given an intravenous injection of bone marrow from a nonradiated animal immediately after the radiation, they, for the most part, survive, because the transplanted blood-forming cells live and reproduce in their new hosts and supply them with blood cells. If radiated mice are thus injected with blood-forming cells from a rat, they subsequently come to have rat blood cells circulating in their blood stream. The previously radiated host does not seem to react to the foreign antigens in the blood cells from the donor animal even if its antibody-forming capacity recovers to some extent; and so it is assumed that even though its antibody-forming mechanism does recover, it does so in the presence of the donor's antigens and reacts to these antigens as would a fetus before its immunity mechanism had developed. However, the transplanted blood-forming (donor) cells contain cells capable of becoming antibody producers, and these soon begin to make antibodies against the antigens of the host. Hence, the radiated animal, transfused with foreign blood-forming cells, soon begins to manifest what is called secondary or runt disease, which is due to the donor antibody-forming cells making antibodies against the host cells, and this prevents many of the host cells from growing properly. Secondary (runt) disease can be avoided if the transplanted blood-forming cells are from an identical twin or an isologous animal, or from an animal that was injected with the recipient's tissues at birth, so that its antibody-forming cells would be tolerant to antigens of the recipient when they were injected into the latter.

By all of these various means it is possible for the tissues of one animal to live in the body of another. Such an animal is termed a *chimera* (in classical mythology a chimera was a fire-breathing monster with the fore-parts of its body being those of a lion, the middle parts those of a goat, and the hind parts those of a dragon. What a name for a poor little mouse!)

Why Homogenous Transplants Are Used in Man. It has already been mentioned that autogenous transplants, or transplants from an identical twin, are the most desirable type to use in man. However, it is sometimes impossible to obtain these, so homogenous transplants are used for many purposes; indeed, many hospitals maintain "banks" of homogenous tissue for transplantation. From what has been said in the preceding sections it might be thought that homogenous transplants would be of no value. While they do not function as true living grafts they are of value, as will now be explained.

Many tissues that are used for transplants consist chiefly of intercellular substance. This is true of bone, tendon, fascia, nerves, blood vessels and even the cornea of the eye. Intercellular substances are nonliving materials, and even though those of a homogenous transplant may act as mild antigens the antibodies that form against them cannot kill them because they are nonliving materials. So when homogenous transplants are made of tissues that consist chiefly of intercellular substance, such antibodies as develop may kill the cells of the transplant, but they cannot similarly destroy the nonliving intercellular substances of the transplant. Accordingly, the transplanted intercellular substance can act as a temporary bridge or support to substitute for destroyed tissue. Furthermore, it often acts to stimulate its replacement by new tissues made from the host. So the eventual fate of a successful homogenous transplant of a tissue that consists chiefly of intercellular substance is for it to serve a supporting role through a period while it is being replaced by new tissue made by cells of the host. So, although a homogenous transplant never becomes a true living graft, it can serve a very useful purpose. It is most important for anyone who wishes to think clearly on this matter to understand that homogenous transplants, even though they are useful, are not true living grafts; this fact is not always clearly stated in the literature.

How Autogenous Transplants Survive. In

using autogenous transplants it is of the greatest importance to understand thoroughly how the cells of the transplanted tissue are ordinarily nourished so that the best arrangements possible can be made when the tissue is transplanted to keep the cells of the transplant alive. Later, when we study skin, it will be explained that it is sometimes possible for plastic surgeons to transplant skin from one part of the body to another without ever severing it completely from its blood supply. But for most tissues to be transplanted requires that they be cut free from the body and its blood vessels; such transplants are termed free transplants. When these are moved to a bed and affixed in place, their cells can survive only if nutrients can diffuse through their substance from the tissue fluid of the bed to which they are attached. This mechanism of nutrition is adequate to keep transplanted skin alive until it is revascularized, and it is probably sufficient to keep the cells of transplanted cartilage alive. However, in the instance of many other tissues, severance from their blood supply leads to their death, and their cells do not continue to live after autogenous transplantation. Nevertheless, they may serve useful functions because of the persistence of their intercellular substance.

As each tissue and many organs and structures are considered in the remainder of this book, some attempt will be made to discuss briefly the particular problems that they present with regard to their transplantation.

REFERENCES

General—Transplantation of Tissues

Converse, J. M. (ed.): Second tissue homotransplantation conference, Ann. New York Acad. Sc. *64*:735-1073, 1957.

————: Fourth tissue homotransplantation conference, Ann. New York Acad. Sc. *87*:1-607, 1960.

Loeb, L.: The Biological Basis of Individuality, Springfield, Ill., Thomas, 1945.

Medawar, P. B.: Zoologic laws of transplantation *in* Peer, L. A. (ed.): Transplantation of Tissues, vol. 2, p. 41, Baltimore, Williams & Wilkins, 1959.

Merrill, J. P.: Transplantation of normal tissues, Physiol. Rev. *39*:860, 1959.

Peer, L. A.: Transplantation of Tissue, vols. 1 and 2, Baltimore, Williams & Wilkins, 1955, 1959.

Rogers, Blair O. (ed.): The relation of immunology to tissue homotransplantation, Ann. New York Acad. Sc. *59*:277-466, 1955.

————: Third tissue homotransplantation conference, Ann. New York Acad. Sc. *73*:539-868, 1958.

Special—Transplantation of Tissues

Since 1953 there has been a journal, the *Transplantation Bulletin,* which is devoted to the subject of tissue transplantation; it is published regularly. As well as publishing articles on the subject, this journal, from time to time, publishes extensive bibliographies of articles relating to the transplantation of different tissues.

Special References—Induced Immunologic Tolerance

Billingham, R. E.: Actively acquired tolerance and its role in development *in* McElroy, W. D., and Glass, B. (eds.): The Chemical Basis of Development, p. 575, Baltimore, Johns Hopkins Press, 1958.

Billingham, R. E., and Brent, L.: A simple method for inducing tolerance of skin homografts in mice, Transplan. Bull. *4*:67, 1957.

Billingham, R. E., Brent, L., and Medawar, P. B.: Quantitative studies on tissue transplantation immunity, III. Actively acquired tolerance, Phil. Tr. Roy. Soc. of London, Series B, *15*:357, 1956.

Billingham, R. E., Lampkin, G. H., Medawar, P. B., and Williams, H. L.: Tolerance to homografts, twin diagnosis, and the freemartin condition in cattle, Heredity *6*:201, 1952.

Burnet, Sir MacFarlane: The Clonal Selection Theory of Acquired Immunity, Nashville, Tenn., Vanderbilt University Press, and Cambridge, Eng., University Press, 1959.

Medawar, P. B.: A discussion of immunological tolerance—introductory remarks. Proc. Roy. Soc., Series B, Nov. 1956.

Owen, R. D.: Immunogenetic consequences of vascular anastomoses between bovine twins, Science *102*:400, 1945; Fed. Proc. *16*:581, 1957.

Chapter 11

Epithelial Tissue

It is convenient to classify epithelial tissue into two subtypes as follows:

Epithelial tissue
- 1. Covering and lining membranes
- 2. Glandular tissue

COVERING AND LINING MEMBRANES

Although all epithelial membranes are protective, the amount and the kind of protection that they must provide differs in various parts of the body, and this is reflected in their being of a somewhat different structure in various parts of the body. Furthermore, in some sites they perform additional functions—secretion and/or absorption—and in these sites their structure is modified further so that they can do these things as well as protect. Hence, while epithelial membranes all have certain features in common, it is obvious, because of their having to perform somewhat different functions in various parts of the body, that their structure will differ from part to part. First we shall consider the features that all have in common.

Some Features That Epithelial Membranes Have in Common. Epithelial membranes consist entirely, or almost entirely, of cells; these are fitted together so closely that epithelial membranes are true continuous membranes. The different factors concerned in holding the cells in an epithelial membrane so closely together will be discussed after some of the different types of epithelial membranes have been described.

Epithelial membranes contain no blood vessels. Epithelial cells, then, must obtain their nourishment as a result of food substances diffusing to them from the capillaries and the tissue fluid in the connective tissue which they overlie (Fig. 91).

All epithelial membranes are subjected to at least some wear and tear encountered in their normal function, and some in particular are often subjected to actual injury. For both these reasons epithelial membranes must be capable of regeneration. Since they are cellu-

lar in character, this means that at least some of their constituent cells must be capable of dividing and so furnishing new cells to replace those that are worn away because of normal wear and tear or as a result of injury. That the cells of epithelial membranes possess great capacity to divide and so maintain their full complement is illustrated in Figure 39, which shows the various stages of mitosis. All the cells in this figure are cells of an epithelial membrane. The cell turnover in many different epithelial membranes has been investigated in particular by Leblond and his associates (see Leblond and Walker for details).

Basement Membranes. Since living cells arranged into sheets do not constitute structures of much tensile strength, epithelial membranes must be attached firmly to a stronger supporting tissue if they are not to be pulled apart or otherwise torn from their position. Hence, epithelial membranes always rest on, and are attached to, connective tissue, the intercellular substance of which is adapted to providing the necessary support for them. At the surface between an epithelial membrane and the connective tissue, the intercellular substance of the connective tissue is generally modified to constitute what is termed a *basement membrane* for the epithelium (Fig. 122). A point which should be stressed here is that basement membranes are not epithelial membranes; they consist of intercellular substances and hence are described on page 143 in the chapter dealing with Intercellular Substances.

Some Differences Between Various Kinds of Epithelial Membranes. The different epithelial membranes of the body are so well adapted to the particular functions they perform that the thoughtful student can usually anticipate the kind of epithelial membrane that will be found on any given surface, provided that the following is kept in mind:

If there is little wear and tear on any surface, or if there must be absorption or filtration through the membrane that covers the surface, the membrane will consist of only a single layer of cells (it would be difficult for

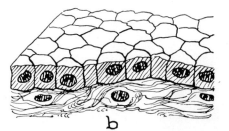

a

Simple squamous

b

Simple cuboidal

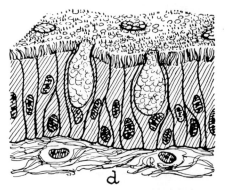

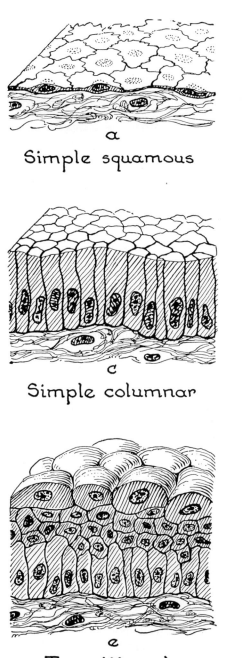

c

Simple columnar

d

Pseudostratified columnar ciliated

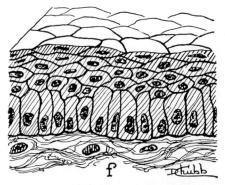

e

Transitional

f

Stratified squamous (nonkeratinized)

FIG. 117. Three-dimensional diagrams illustrating the different types of epithelial membranes found on wet surfaces.

effective absorption or filtration to occur through a thicker membrane). Epithelial membranes only one cell thick are said to be simple epithelial membranes. However, if there is considerable wear and tear at any surface, and no absorptive or filtering function to be performed by it, the epithelial membrane will be composed of several layers of cells. This is called *stratified epithelium*. For examples, the two upper pictures of Figure 117 show simple

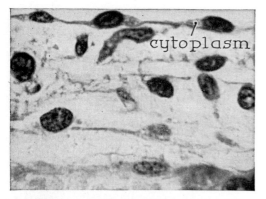

FIG. 118. High-power photomicrograph of a section of the medulla of the kidney cut parallel with the descending and the ascending loops of Henle. The simple squamous epithelium at the upper part of the photograph is that lining a loop of Henle.

epithelium; the two lower pictures, stratified epithelium.

Moreover, there is an extremely important difference between the epithelial membranes of *wet* and *dry* surfaces. It is possible for the surface cells of any stratified epithelial membrane to remain alive if the surface at which they are situated is always kept wet with a suitable fluid. For example, the surface cells of the epithelial membrane that lines the cheek remain alive because the inside of the mouth is always kept wet with saliva. If the student draws his finger across the inside of his cheek (it is not necessary to scratch it, the surface cells wipe off readily) and dabs the material so obtained on a glass slide and stains it, he will see surface cells complete with reasonably healthy appearing nuclei (Fig. 46).

However, in any stratified epithelial membrane which is exposed to air, such as the epithelium of the skin, the cells of the outermost layer cannot remain alive because they would become dehydrated. Hence, the surface cells of dry epithelial membranes fuse together and become converted into a horny material called *keratin*. Since this is an albuminoid, and hence relatively insoluble and impermeable, it forms a protective sheet of waterproof material which preserves the fluid environment of the epithelial cells of the deeper layers of the membrane (Fig. 132). Since the deeper living epithelial cells constantly reproduce them-

selves, new cells are constantly pushed toward the surface, and as they approach it they become converted into keratin to replace that which is worn away. So the process of keratinization is a continuous one.

Not all the epithelial surfaces that are in contact with air become keratinized, and very ingenious arrangements have been made to keep such nonkeratinized external surfaces wet. For example, if the outer layers of the membrane covering the front of the eye, through which one sees, became keratinized, the eye would be blinded, because keratin does not transmit light readily. Therefore, the surface of the eye is covered with epithelial cells that do not become keratinized; therefore, these must be kept wet with a thin film of moisture. This is accomplished by glands associated with the eye secreting small amounts of the same fluid that is seen more obviously when its secretion is stimulated by weeping. The right amount of this fluid, secreted normally, is kept spread over the surface of the eye by the frequent blinking of the eyelids that occurs automatically in a normal individual. But, apart from a few exceptions such as this, almost all epithelium that is constantly exposed to air is keratinized.

TYPES OF EPITHELIUM FOUND ON WET SURFACES

SIMPLE EPITHELIUM

Simple squamous epithelium consists of a single layer of thin, flat cells of irregular outline that fit together to form a continuous, thin membrane. A 3-dimensional view of simple squamous epithelium is given in Figure 117 a. If the simple squamous epithelium is not too thin, it appears in sections cut at right angles to the surface, as in Figure 118. If it is very thin, the cytoplasm is not visible, and all that can be seen are the flattened nuclei of cells scattered at intervals along the surface. Simple squamous epithelium is adapted to performing a dialyzing or filtering function. It is not adapted to withstanding wear and tear. As previously noted, the endothelium that lines the blood-vascular and lymphatic systems is morphologically simple squamous epithelium. So is the mesothelium that lines the great body cavities. The E/M has shown that there is a continuous membrane of simple

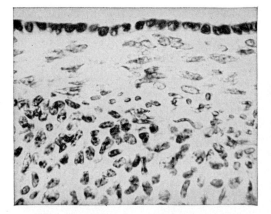

FIG. 119. Medium-power photomicrograph of a section of the ovary of a guinea pig. In maturity, the surface of the ovary is covered with cuboidal epithelial cells.

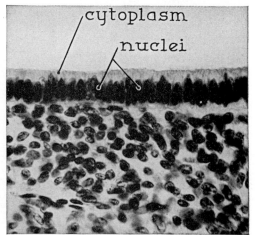

cytoplasm

nuclei

FIG. 120. Medium-power photomicrograph of a section of the cervix cut parallel with the cervical canal. The columnar epithelium seen (upper part) is that lining the cervical canal.

squamous epithelium present in and lining the air spaces in the lung. Oxygen, to enter blood, must pass through it and the endothelium of the lung capillaries. It is difficult to suggest examples of this type of membrane, other than endothelium and mesothelium, that the student can find and study with ease with the light microscope. The photomicrograph comprising Figure 118 was taken from the lower portion of a descending loop of Henle in the kidney. The student is perhaps best advised to postpone searching for simple squamous epithelium in this site until the kidney is studied.

Simple Cuboidal Epithelium. This is of a somewhat stouter character than simple squamous (Fig. 117 b). It is used in only a very few sites in the body; perhaps the student can find an example of it most easily in a section of ovary, for it forms a covering for that organ (Fig. 119). The cells of simple cuboidal epithelium are actually not cubes, as may be seen in Figure 117 b; the name "cuboidal" refers to the appearance of the cells when they are sectioned at right angles to the surface that they cover.

Simple Columnar Epithelium. This type of epithelium is composed of epithelial cells that are more or less hexagonal in cross section and fitted together side by side to form a relatively thick epithelial membrane (Fig. 117 c). The nuclei of the columnar cells are disposed toward the bases of the cells.

Although there are a few examples of simple columnar epithelial membranes in the body, which seem to serve no particular function except that of protecting the underlying tissue, the cells of nearly all simple columnar epithelial membranes are specialized for the performance of some specialized function in addition to that of providing protection. The first of these other functions that we shall consider is that of secretion.

All or only some of the cells in a simple columnar epithelial membrane may perform a secretory function. The material that they commonly secrete is *mucus;* this is a slippery protective material, chemically a sulfate-containing mucoprotein. In some simple columnar epithelial membranes all of the cells secrete mucus; examples of this are to be found in the surface epithelium of the stomach and the lining of the cervical canal (Fig. 120). In other sites, simple epithelial membranes contain two types of columnar epithelial cells that are interspersed with one another. Those of one type are specialized to secrete mucus, and those of the other to perform one of two other functions, either that of *selective absorption* or that of *moving mucus* along the free surface of the membrane by ciliary action. The most prominent example of the first combination is

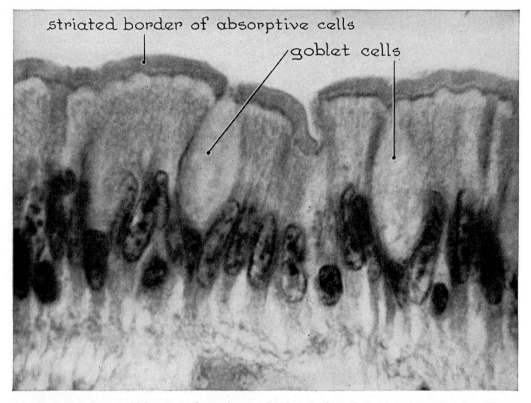

striated border of absorptive cells

goblet cells

FIG. 121. A very high-power photomicrograph of a section of the jejunum of a dog. The basement membrane is indistinct. A well-marked striated border is present on the absorptive cells. Two goblet cells opening through the striated border may be seen in this illustration.

the lining of the small and the large intestines, for both of these are both lined with simple columnar epithelial membranes in which some of the lining cells are specialized to secrete mucus and the others to absorb selectively the products of digestion or water (Fig. 121). A good example of the second example is to be found in parts of the upper respiratory tract where some of the lining cells are specialized to secrete mucus, while others are specialized to move the mucus along by ciliary action (Fig. 128). We shall consider the lining of the intestine first; here the cells that secrete mucus are called *goblet cells* and the others *absorptive cells* (Fig. 121).

Goblet Cells. Even in H and E sections it can be seen that the cells that are specialized to secrete mucus deserve the term "goblet cells" because the supranuclear portion of these cells commonly becomes so distended by the accumulating secretion that the cell assumes the form of a goblet (Figs. 121 and 122). Both the mucus in the goblet and that which has been secreted and lies on the free surfaces of the absorptive cells is colored brilliantly by the P.A.S. method (Fig. 122). There are other stains which also demonstrate mucus to advantage. Jennings and Florey have studied the formation of mucus in goblet cells by using a labeled precursor and radioautographs. They have found that radioactive label can be detected in the cells 3 hours after the labeled precursor is given. The label appears first in the cytoplasm, near the nucleus but between it and the free surface of the cell. After 6 hours the label appears in the bowl of the goblet, and after 12 to 24 hours in the mucus on the free surface.

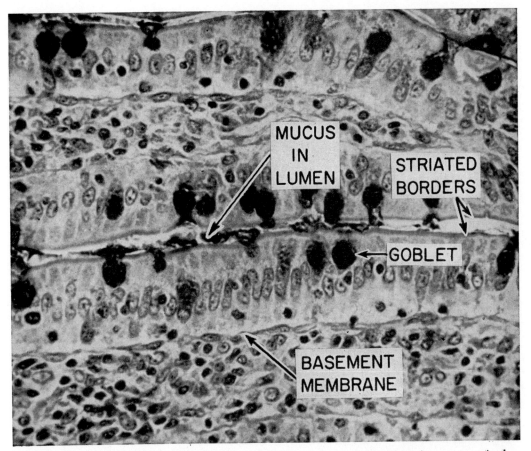

MUCUS IN LUMEN

STRIATED BORDERS

GOBLET

BASEMENT MEMBRANE

FIG. 122. High-power photomicrograph of a section of the small intestine of a mouse stained by the P.A.S. technic. The mucus in the lumen and in the goblet cells is colored red by this technic as is the basement membrane under the epithelium. In the illustration the red-colored mucus appears black, and the basement membrane appears as a dark, wavy line.

Fine Structure. Palay has shown the free surface of a *nonsecreting* goblet cell is covered with microvilli; the latter will be described presently (Fig. 123). When the goblet cell is discharging its secretion the microvilli disappear.

The E/M shows that the secretion in the goblet is collected in vesicles of the Golgi apparatus. Rough-surfaced vesicles of the endoplasmic reticulum are found in the deeper portion of the cell, extending from the region of the nucleus, along the sides of the deeper part of the goblet. Although it is not settled as to where the secretion is produced, it seems probable that the rough-surfaced vesicles are con-

cerned with its production, and that the smooth-surfaced vesicles of the Golgi apparatus are concerned primarily with its segregation and delivery.

Absorptive Cells, Striated Borders and Microvilli. In a well-fixed H and E section the free surfaces of the absorptive cells of the simple columnar epithelium of the intestine seem to be covered with a thin layer of some material of a different refractive index from that of the underlying cytoplasm (Figs. 121 and 122). When this was first noticed many years ago, it was believed to be of the nature of a protective cuticle. However, with improved methods it became possible, with the

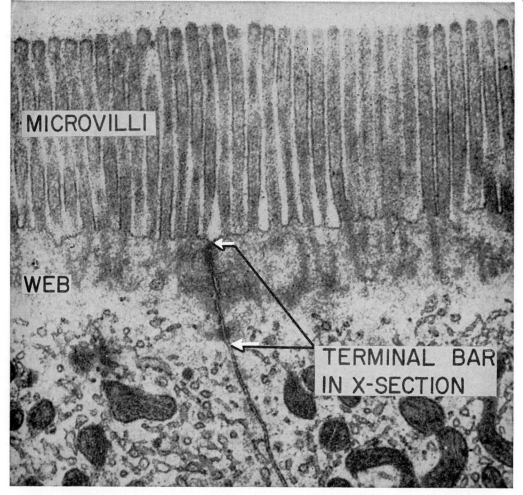

FIG. 123. Electron micrograph ($\times$ 41,000) of a section of the jejunum of man. Parts of the free ends of two absorptive cells, covered with microvilli, are shown. A terminal bar is cut in cross section between the upper parts of the two cells, and the terminal web can be seen to extend off across from each side of the bar. Notice mitochondria appear only in the cytoplasm under the web. (Preparation by Dr. H. Z. Movat and Dr. J. W. Steiner)

light microscope, to demonstrate fine striations that roughly paralleled the long axes of the underlying cells in this border, and so it was termed a striated border, and different theories were suggested for its nature. When thin-sectioning methods improved to the point where this border could be studied with the E/M, it was shown first by Granger and Baker and by Dalton that the appearance of striations was due to the cytoplasm, at the free surface of the cells, extending into the region of the border in multitudes of adjacent and very minute fingerlike projections which are termed microvilli (Fig. 123).

The microvilli are from 80 to 100 millimicrons in diameter and somewhat more than half a micron in length. Each is covered with the cell membrane and has a core of cytoplasm which is continuous with the cytoplasm of the main part of the cell. The cytoplasm in the cores appears to be somewhat denser than cytoplasm as a whole, and the denser cytoplasm of the cores of villi extend down into the cell for a short distance into the region of the terminal web, which structure will be described presently.

It is generally considered that the purpose of microvilli is to increase the surface area through which absorption can occur. Granger and Baker have estimated that a single cell may have 3,000 microvilli and that in a square millimeter of intestinal lining there may be 200,000,000 microvilli. Although it seems most reasonable to consider that microvilli serve in providing extra surface for absorption, they are found on many kinds of cells that are not noted for absorptive functions and so they may have other functions as well.

HOW THE CELLS IN EPITHELIAL MEMBRANES ARE HELD TOGETHER

Before considering further types of epithelial membranes we must begin to consider the problem of how the cells in epithelial membranes are held together. It so happens that some of the factors involved in this matter—which must be considered somewhere—can be described most easily in connection with simple columnar epithelium, and so we shall introduce this subject here and begin by describing terminal bars.

Terminal Bars. The name "terminal bars" was given to what seemed to be, from light

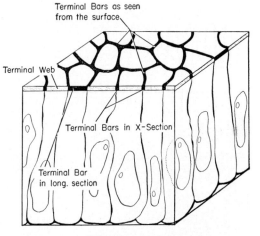

FIG. 124. Diagram to show a few columnar epithelial cells and the terminal bars that connect their free ends in 3 dimensions. The microvilli, which would be present on absorptive columnar epithelial cells, are not shown so that the sites of the terminal bars can be seen clearly.

microscope studies of sections of certain epithelial membranes stained for example with iron hematoxylin, little bars of cement substance that ran along, parallel with the cell

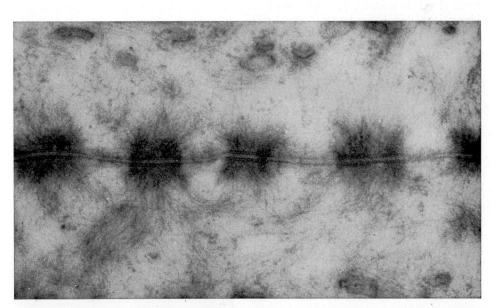

FIG. 125. Electron micrograph (× 50,000) showing several desmosomes scattered along the interface of 2 epidermal cells of *Ambystoma punctatum*. (Preparation by Dr. K. R. Porter)

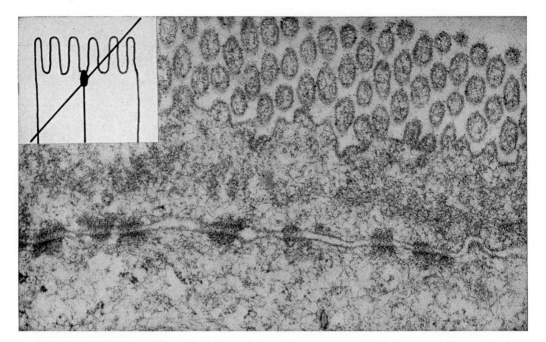

FIG. 126. Electron micrograph (× 70,000) of a section of the small intestine. The plane in which the section and the site through which it passed is illustrated by the straight dark line in the inset. As this shows, the section cuts a terminal bar in longitudinal section; this can be seen passing from one side of the illustration to the other and as the illustration shows, the terminal bar appearance is actually due to numerous desmosomes being distributed along the contiguous cell borders at this site. Immediately above and below the terminal bar that crosses the section is the cell web; the reason that the cytoplasm on both sides of the terminal bar reveals this appearance will become apparent from studying the inset (on both sides of the terminal bar the section passes through the cytoplasm at the very end of the cell where the terminal web is located). Microvilli, cut in oblique section, are seen at the upper part of the illustration. (Preparation by Dr. L. Zamboni)

surface, between the edges of the most super-ficial parts of the cells, just below the region of the microvilli (for clarity, the microvilli are not shown in Fig. 124, which is a diagram of terminal bars). Accordingly, if the *surface* of an epithelial membrane were examined in a suitably stained preparation the surface would appear much as a tile floor, with the terminal bars lying between the edges of ad-jacent tiles and so marking out the tiles by black lines (Fig. 124). In *very thin* sections of epithelial membranes, cut so that the columnar cells of the membrane are sectioned in a plane parallel with their long axes, the terminal bars would mostly be cut in cross and oblique section and so would appear as black dots between the edges of the cells at their free margins (Fig. 124). Through the

years there was a general belief that the ter-minal bars were bars of cement substance that served to hold adjacent cells together at their free margins. Before considering what the terminal bars have shown to be with the E/M we must first describe desmosomes.

Desmosomes. This word (derived from *desmos* = bond or fastening, and *soma* = body) has emerged from relative obscurity into common use as a result of the studies with the E/M on the attachments between cells. These studies have shown that there are little bodies that are often scattered along adjacent cell membranes of contiguous cells (Fig. 125) and seem to hold the cells tightly together at the sites where they exist. With the light microscope and special staining tech-nics, dark dots were seen at some of the sites

FIG. 127. Photomicrograph (× 1,000) of section of intestinal epithelium of rat stained by the tannic acid, phosphomolybdic acid and amido black method. The arrow points to a terminal bar cut in cross section, and others may be seen. The cell webs appear as dark lines running across the free edges of the cells, just below the region of the microvilli, from one terminal bar to another. (Puchtler, H., and Leblond, C. P.: Am. J. Anat. *102*:1)

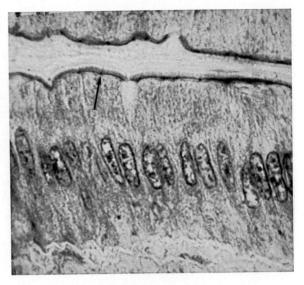

where desmosomes can now be identified with the E/M; indeed, for many years it was believed that there were tiny fibrils in the cytoplasm of cells, tonofibrils, which crossed from one cell to the other at these sites. The E/M has revealed that although there is a fibrillar content to desmosomes, there are no fibrils that cross from one cell to the other. Instead, each desmosome consists of the following: First, at the site of the desmosome, the cell membranes of the adjacent cells are thickened and so appear as dense dark lines (Fig. 125). Second, there is an accumulation of granular electron-dense material in the cytoplasm of each cell, close to the site of the thickening of the cell membrane (Fig. 125). Third, from the sites of thickened membrane and granular material, there are microfibrils that radiate out from the area into the cytoplasm for a short distance (Fig. 125).

Relation of Terminal Bars to Desmosomes. As noted before, terminal bars were once believed to be bars of cement substance. With the E/M it has been shown by Fawcett and others that terminal bars cut in cross section give the appearance of typical desmosomes (as can be seen in Fig. 123). Furthermore, if terminal bars are cut in longitudinal section desmosomes are seen close together along their course (Fig. 126).

The way that desmosomes serve to hold adjacent cells together is not understood.

The Terminal Web. Although there were occasional references through the years to the probable existence of some specialization of the cytoplasm of cells directly under their free surfaces, it was not until recent intensive studies were made on this matter in Leblond's laboratory that it was realized that there is a fibrillar component in the cytoplasm of many types of cells that deserves recognition as being a cytoplasmic organelle of importance. Leblond and his associates refer to this structure as the *terminal web*. It can be studied to advantage in the simple columnar epithelium of the intestine. If sections of the latter are stained by any one of several special staining methods but, in particular, by the tannic acid, phosphomolybdic acid and amido black technic, a heavy dark line is apparent at the free border of the cell, just below the microvilli (Fig. 127). This is the terminal web of the cell. It bears roughly the same kind of relation to the terminal bars that surround the free end of each cell as the skin of a drum does to the terminal hoop that surrounds the drum and to which the skin is attached and by which it is held tight.

In electron micrographs of intestinal epithelium the terminal web of the cell appears as a fibrillar area of cytoplasm, which extends across the free end of the cell directly below the microvilli and contains no mitochondria or vesicles of the endoplasmic reticulum (Fig. 123). The very delicate microfibrils or filaments in this region probably provide necessary internal support for the free end of the cell and serve as anchorage for the cytoplasmic

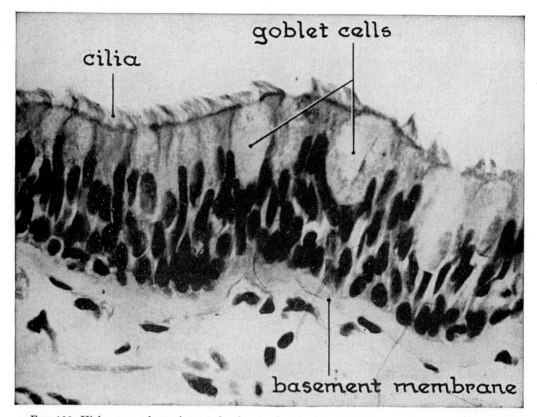

FIG. 128. High-power photomicrograph of a section cut from the human trachea. This shows pseudostratified ciliated columnar epithelium with goblet cells.

cores of microvilli, and the rootlets of cilia in ciliated cells. The fibrillar web connects all around the circumference of the cell with the terminal bars (desmosomes), and it seems very probable that the delicate microfibrils or filaments that extend out into the cytoplasm from desmosomes are of the same kind of material and more or less continuous with the microfibrils or filaments of the web. Leblond, Puchtler and Clermont have shown the existence of the web in many different kinds of cells, and in these it may assume different forms; their paper should be consulted for details.

Interdigitations of the cell membranes of contiguous cells as possible factors in helping to hold cells together will be described after the other types of epithelial membranes have been discussed.

Ciliated Epithelium. In the foregoing section simple columnar epithelium, the cells of which are either absorptive cells with striated borders or cells which secrete mucus and have the form of goblets, has been described. This type of epithelium lines the intestine. Another combination of cells in a simple columnar epithelial membrane is that of goblet cells intermixed with ciliated cells; the latter are characterized by little hairlike processes which project from their free surfaces and are called cilia (Figs. 117 d and 128). The cilia beat in harmony with one another and so move mucus along the membrane. This type of epithelium is found in some of the parts of the upper respiratory tract, but it is not as common here as another type which is called pseudostratified ciliated epithelium, and so we shall describe cilia in connection with this.

Pseudostratified Columnar Epithelium. Stratified epithelium is defined as consisting of two or more layers of cells. Pseudostratified epithelium does not quite fill this requirement.

Some of the cells in contact with the basement membrane do not reach the surface (Figs. 117 d and 128), but many do. It appears stratified, however, because sections cut at right angles to its surface show nuclei at two levels: the nuclei of the shorter cells that do not reach the surface are closer to the basement membrane than the nuclei of the longer cells that reach the surface. So, because the two rows of nuclei make this membrane *appear to be stratified*, and yet it is not, it is called *pseudostratified*. Pseudostratified columnar epithelium forms the lining for most of the upper respiratory tract and it is to be seen to advantage in a section cut from the trachea (Fig. 128).

In this type of epithelium the cells that reach the surface are either ciliated or goblet cells. The mucus, secreted by the latter, forms a film on the inner surface of the respiratory passages, and this serves as a dust-catcher to prevent dusts being inhaled into the lungs; it also moistens the dry air that is inspired. The cilia serve a very useful function by moving the mucus that contains the dust particles upward to where it can be swallowed or otherwise eliminated from the body.

The Fine Structure of Cilia. With the light microscope cilia can be shown, by special staining methods, to each have an axial filament, and to be more or less anchored in the superficial cytoplasm of the cells to little dense bodies called basal corpuscles. The E/M has illustrated further the structure of cilia; extensive studies have been made by Fawcett, by Porter, and by Rhodin and Dalhamn.

Each ciliated cell in the trachea has about 270 cilia. Each hairlike cilium is covered with a membrane that is continuous with the cell membrane and is about 70 Å thick. Each cilium has 11 filaments (2 single central ones and 9 double peripheral ones) disposed longitudinally in its core. The arrangement is easily seen in cross sections of cilia (Fig. 129). The filaments of the cilia pass into the substance of the cytoplasm of the cell and become continuous with a little body termed the basal corpuscle or body that underlies the cilium. Some microvilli commonly project from the free surface of ciliated cells in addition to the cilia.

In certain lower animals it can be shown that fibrillar rootlets of a material that shows

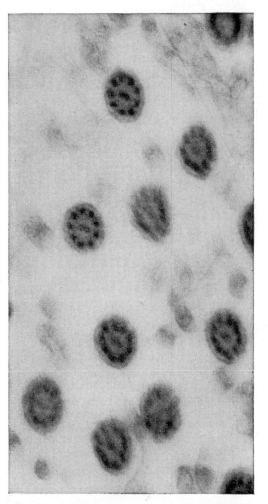

Fig. 129. Electron micrograph (× 65,000) of a cross section of the cilia of epithelial cells of the human oviduct. (Fawcett, D. W., and Porter, K. R.: J. Morphol. *94:221*)

cross banding, similar to but not identical with that of collagen, extend from the region of the basal corpuscles, more deeply into the cytoplasm. These, as well as the axial filaments, are probably related to the mechanism of ciliary movement, but the cause of the movement of cilia is not yet understood.

STRATIFIED EPITHELIAL MEMBRANES

Stratified epithelial membranes can withstand more wear and tear than simple membranes. But as they are stratified, they cannot serve efficiently as absorptive membranes;

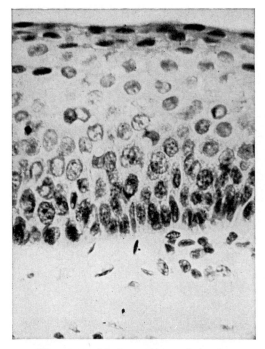

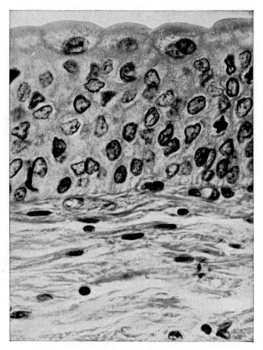

Fig. 130. Medium-power photomicrograph of a section cut from the human epiglottis. Its surface in this site is covered with stratified squamous nonkeratinizing epithelium. Notice that this type of epithelium has columnar cells in its basal part and thin, flattened squamous cells on its free border.

Fig. 131. Medium-power photomicrograph of a section cut from the bladder of a dog. Transitional epithelium, when contracted, is characterized by the innermost cells; these show rounded, free borders which give the surface a scalloped appearance.

furthermore, their stratified structure makes them ill-adapted to performing secretory functions. Hence, such secretion as is found on stratified membranes is provided by glands. Therefore, stratified membranes serve chiefly to protect, and the different ones of the body are dissimilar only because different kinds and degrees of protection are needed in different places.

Stratified squamous nonkeratinizing epithelium is provided on wet surfaces that are subjected to considerable wear and tear, and where little or no absorption is required. The fluid required to keep such a surface wet is usually provided by glands either in or below the membrane. The inside of the mouth and the esophagus are both lined with this type of epithelium, giving protection from coarse foods. Part of the epiglottis is covered with it, and the vagina is also lined with it. It is illustrated in Figures 117 f and 130.

Stratified squamous nonkeratinizing epithelium is not, as its name implies, composed of successive layers of squamous cells. The deepest cells in such a membrane (the basal layer that abuts on the basement membrane) are columnar. Just above these the cells are *polyhedral* (many-sided) and it is only toward the surface that the cells assume a squamous shape (Fig. 117 f). So only the more superficial cells in stratified squamous nonkeratinizing epithelium are actually squamous.

Stratified columnar epithelium is found on a few wet surfaces in the body that need more protection than that afforded by simple columnar epithelium but not as much as that provided by stratified squamous nonkeratinizing epithelium. For example, whereas ducts of moderate size are usually lined with simple columnar epithelium, the larger ducts of glands are commonly lined by stratified columnar epithelium.

Transitional epithelium is very much like

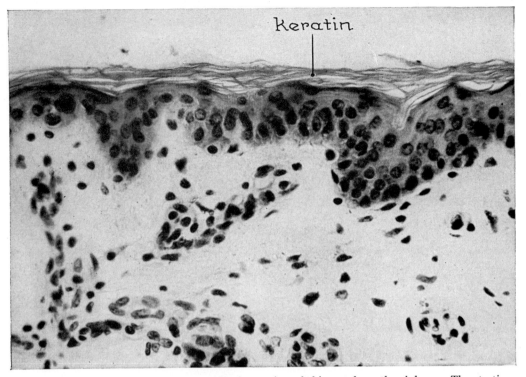

Keratin

FIG. 132. Low-power photomicrograph of a section of skin cut from the abdomen. The stratified squamous epithelium of thin skin, such as exists on the abdomen, is only a few cells thick.
It runs across the upper part of the illustration, and at the surface the epithelial cells undergo
a metamorphosis into keratin, which is labeled. The pale tissue on which the epithelium rests
is connective tissue; this is what the deeper layer of the skin, the dermis, is composed of.

stratified squamous nonkeratinizing epithelium
except that the more superficial cells of transitional epithelium tend to be large and
rounded rather than squamous in shape (Figs.
117 e, 131). This allows such a membrane
to be stretched without the superficial cells
breaking apart from one another; they merely
become drawn out into squamouslike cells
(Fig. 472). Hence, transitional epithelium is
well adapted to lining tubes and hollow structures that are subjected to being expanded
from within, and for this reason it constitutes
the lining of the urinary tract.

It was observed some years ago that such
mitotic figures as were seen in the surface
cells in the transitional epithelium of rodents
were very large. Subsequently, Leuchtenberger,
Leuchtenberger and Davis found that the
nuclei of the surface cells of the transitional epithelium in the urinary bladder
of man contained multiple amounts of
DNA; in other words, these cells demon-

strated polyploidy. Walker has studied the
development of this condition in the mouse
and has found that at around the 16th to the
17th day of embryonic life both binucleate
cells and polyploid nuclei become obvious in
the superficial layers of the urinary bladder.
Walker suggests that the chromosomes of
binucleated cells entering division become
grouped together, and as a result each of the
two daughter cells that results has double the
previous number of chromosomes.

STRATIFIED MEMBRANES ON DRY SURFACES

Stratified, squamous, keratinizing epithelium resembles stratified squamous nonkeratinizing epithelium except for the fact that the
more superficial cells of the membrane undergo a metamorphosis into a tough nonliving
layer of *keratin* which is tightly attached to
the underlying living cells of the epithelial
membrane. The outer layer of the skin provides a good example of stratified squamous

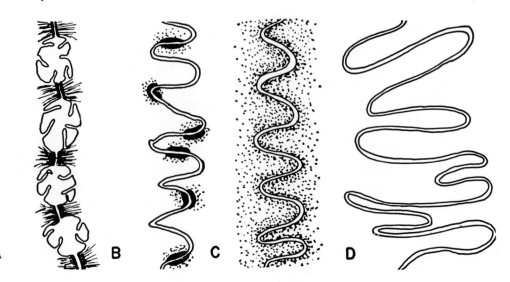

FIG. 133. (A) Drawing of attachments between cells in the stratified squamous epithelium of the rodent vagina. The cell surfaces are adherent at the sites of desmosomes but retracted between them. A few short microvilli project into the spaces that result from the retracted surfaces. (B) Drawing showing attachments between cells in the stratum spinosum of the tongue. The cells' surfaces show the corrugations of adjacent cells fitting one another. Desmosomes are scattered along the adjacent cell surfaces. (C) Drawing showing attachments between partly keratinized cells. The corrugated surfaces of adjacent cells fit each other, and no desmosomes are seen. (D) Drawing showing the elaborately corrugated surfaces between adjacent cells in the distal convoluted segment of the frog nephron. (Redrawn from Fawcett, D. W. *in* Palay, S. L. (ed.): Frontiers in Cytology, New Haven, Conn., Yale Univ. Press)

keratinizing epithelium (Fig. 132). In skin keratin serves several purposes. It is relatively waterproof; hence, it prevents fluid from evaporating from the living cells that lie beneath it; likewise, it keeps the body from imbibing water when one has a bath. Since it is tough and resilient it protects the underlying living epithelial cells from being injured by the ordinary wear and tear to which skin is exposed. It is relatively impervious to bacteria and hence is a first line of defense against infection. Over the soles of the feet and the palms of the hands the stratified squamous epithelium of the skin becomes thicker and, in particular, the keratin becomes very thick; this enables it to withstand the great wear to which these particular surfaces are exposed.

A further description of stratified squamous keratinizing epithelium and of the process of keratinization will be given in Chapter 22, which deals with skin.

Interdigitation of Adjacent Cell Surfaces.

The E/M has shown that in many types of epithelial membranes, the borders between adjacent cells are extraordinarily complex, with ridges or other protrusions of each cell extending into grooves or other types of depression on the surface of the other. Figure 133 illustrates some examples which have been described by Fawcett. Desmosomes are sprinkled along some of these contiguous cell borders (Fig. 133 A and B) but not along others (Fig. 133 C and D). These arrangements provide a much greater interface between adjacent cells that would be provided by relatively straight surfaces. This, of course, may be of biochemical significance, aiding the interchange of metabolites between cells. Moreover, there is an attraction between the surfaces of cells in which calcium ions are involved, and it could be reasoned that the greater the area of contact, the greater the adhesion. Finally, the interdigitations could have a frank mechanical function in keying cells to each other. The attachments between cells in the stratified squamous keratinizing epithelium of the skin and, in particular, the nature of the intercellular bridges seen so well in the prickle cell layer with the light microscope, will be described and illustrated in Chapter 22.

REFERENCES

CILIA

Fawcett, D. W.: Structural specifications of the cell surface *in* Palay, S. L. (ed.): Frontiers in Cytology, p. 19, New Haven, Conn., Yale Univ. Press, 1958.

Fawcett, D. W., and Porter, K. R.: A study of the fine structure of ciliated epithelia, J. Morphol. *94*:221, 1954.

Rhodin, Johannes, and Dalhamn, Tore: Electron microscopy of the tracheal ciliated mucosa in rat, Ztschr. Zellforsch. *44*:412, 1956.

Roth, L. E.: Aspects of ciliary fine structure in Euplotes patella, J. Biophysic. & Biochem. Cytol. (Supp.) *2*:235, 1956.

STRIATED BORDERS

Dalton, A. J., Kahler, H., and Lloyd, B. J.: The structure of the free surface of a series of epithelial cell types in the mouse as revealed by the electron microscope, Anat. Rec. *111*:67, 1951.

Fawcett, D. W.: Structural specifications of the cell surface *in* Palay, S. L. (ed.): Frontiers in Cytology, p. 19, New Haven, Conn., Yale Univ. Press, 1958.

Granger, B., and Baker, R. F.: Electron microscope investigation of the striated border of intestinal epithelium, Anat. Rec. *107*:423, 1950.

KERATIN

(*See* references for Chapter 22)

MESOTHELIUM

Odor, D. L.: Observations of the rat mesothelium with the electron and phase microscopes, Am. J. Anat. *95*:433, 1954.

TERMINAL WEB

Leblond, C. P., Puchtler, H., and Clermont, Y.: Structures corresponding to terminal bars and terminal web in many types of cells, Nature *186*:784, 1960.

Puchtler, H., and Leblond, C. P.: Histochemical analysis of cell membranes and associated structures as seen in the intestinal epithelium, Am. J. Anat. *102*:1, 1958.

DESMOSOMES

Fawcett, D. W.: Structural specifications of the cell surface *in* Palay, S. L. (ed.): Frontiers in Cytology, p. 19, New Haven, Conn., Yale Univ. Press, 1958.

GOBLET CELLS

Jennings, M. A., and Florey, H. W.: Autoradiographic observations on the mucous cells of the stomach and intestine, Quart. J. Exper. Physiol. *41*:131, 1956.

Palay, S. L.: The morphology of secretion *in* Palay, S. L. (ed.): Frontiers in Cytology, p. 305, New Haven, Conn., Yale Univ. Press, 1958.

Rhodin, J., and Dalhamn, T.: Electron microscopy of the tracheal ciliated mucosa in rat, Ztschr. Zellforsch. *44*:412, 1956.

TRANSITIONAL EPITHELIUM

Leuchtenberger, C., Leuchtenberger, R., and Davis, A. M.: A microspectrophotometric study of the desoxyribose nucleic acid (DNA) content in cells of normal and malignant human tissues, Am. J. Path. *30*:65, 1954.

Walker, B. E.: Polyploidy and differentiation in the transitional epithelium of mouse urinary bladder, Chromosoma *9*:105, 1958.

Chapter 12

Epithelial Tissue

(Continued)

GLANDULAR DIVISION

In the previous chapter the various types of epithelial covering and lining membranes of the body are described, and it is shown that in different locations these membranes must provide different amounts and types of protection and that, in addition, in some locations they must perform absorptive and/or secretory functions as well. It should now be reiterated that epithelial membranes are better adapted to performing protective and absorptive functions than they are to secretory ones. A cell highly specialized for secretion can scarcely be a sturdy protective cell. Furthermore, for its efficient functioning, the body needs so much secretion that its covering and lining membranes are not sufficiently extensive to accommodate within them the vast number of secretory cells required. In sites where secretion over and above that which can be provided by cells in a membrane is needed, cells from the membrane of the part turn inward and, during development, grow from the surface into the supporting connective tissue, there to form epithelial structures highly specialized to provide the full secretory requirements of the part. These epithelial structures are called *glands* because some of the first ones studied were shaped like acorns (*glans* = acorn).

CLASSIFICATION

The glands of the body are classified as *exocrine* or *endocrine*. The *crine* that appears in both these words is derived from *krino,* which means "I separate" and, in regard to glands, is taken to mean "secrete." So exocrine glands are those that secrete "out of" the body, and endocrine glands those that secrete into (within) the body. Both kinds, of course, are situated within the substance of connective tissue in the body. So exocrine glands, to secrete "out of" the body, must be provided with *ducts,* which are tubes that collect the secretion formed by the secreting cells of the gland and convey it to a surface where it can be delivered out of the substance of the body. Endocrine glands, because they secrete directly into the substance of the body (into capillaries), need no ducts, and for this reason they are commonly called *ductless glands.*

THE DEVELOPMENT OF GLANDS

The way in which both exocrine and endocrine glands develop is illustrated in Figure 134. Both kinds originate as a result of epithelial cells from a surface membrane growing, in the form of either a cord or a tubule, into the connective tissue beneath the membrane. The epithelial cells that thus invade the connective tissue, by means of their further proliferation and their subsequent differentiation, come to constitute a gland. In the instance of exocrine glands, the epithelial connection between the gland and the surface is retained (Fig. 134, *bottom, left*). The epithelial cells that thus connect the gland to the surface become somewhat differentiated to form the lining of a duct, which allows the secretion manufactured in the gland to be conveyed to and emptied upon the surface from which the gland originally developed. In the instance of endocrine glands, however, the epithelial cells that connect the gland to the surface and mark the path by which the gland developed disappear to leave the gland an epithelial island surrounded entirely by connective tissue (Fig. 134, *bottom, right*). Occasionally, however, little isolated groups of these connective cells persist, and later in life they may begin to secrete fluid in such a fashion that they come to surround the fluid they secrete; they form the covering for a sphere that is full of fluid. Such a structure is called a *cyst* (*kystis* = a bladder). Cysts, then, may sometimes form along the paths by which endocrine glands

EPITHELIAL TISSUE

Glandular Division

How Glands form from epithelial surfaces.

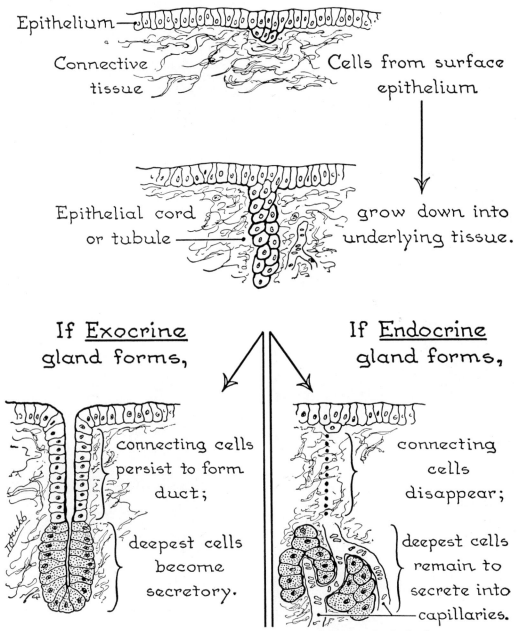

Epithelium

Connective tissue

Cells from surface epithelium

Epithelial cord or tubule

grow down into underlying tissue.

If <u>Exocrine</u> gland forms,

If <u>Endocrine</u> gland forms,

connecting cells persist to form duct;

deepest cells become secretory.

connecting cells disappear;

deepest cells remain to secrete into capillaries.

FIG. 134. Diagram showing how exocrine and endocrine glands develop.

developed. There are, of course, other kinds of cysts that develop for other reasons and in other ways.

Exocrine Glands

Although all the epithelial cells of an exocrine gland belong to the same family, and hence are closely related to one another, they are not all differentiated to the same degree or along quite the same lines. The more highly differentiated cells are those that are specialized to secrete, and the less highly differentiated cells those that line the duct or ducts which carry the secretion to the surface.

In the development of a gland, the cells near the termination or terminations of the epithelial growth that invades the connective tissue differentiate into secretory cells, and those between the secretory cells and the surface, into duct cells (Fig. 134, *bottom, left*). Therefore, the secretory cells are to be found at the termination of the duct or, if it is a branching duct, at the end of each branch. In this site, or in each of these sites, they are arranged to form a little cluster of secretory cells, which we shall call a *secretory unit*. Each secretory unit possesses some sort of central cavity or lumen into which the secretion of the cells that compose it can be liberated. This lumen or cavity of the secretory unit is continuous with the lumen of the duct to which the secretory unit is attached (Fig. 134, *bottom, left*).

Secretory cells wear out from time to time; hence, they must be replenished. There are two possible sources for new cells: (1) other secretory cells and (2) the cells of the duct to which the secretory unit is attached. As noted previously, differentiation usually entails some loss of reproductive capacity. And, as the cells of the ducts are not so highly differentiated as the highly specialized secretory cells, it is only natural that they should be able to reproduce themselves more readily, and that those nearest the secretory unit should differentiate into secretory cells and take the place of those that wear out. Hence, duct cells, particularly those nearest the secretory unit, serve as a source of new secretory cells. In some glands, however, it is not unlikely that secretory cells can reproduce themselves, to some extent at least, and so provide more secretory cells without the duct cells having to contribute all the new ones that are necessary.

Classification of Exocrine Glands. Exocrine glands may be classified several different ways. According to a classification made on one basis an exocrine gland may be said to be a tubular gland; according to a classification made on another basis, a compound gland, and so on. In stating the type of any particular gland, attention is usually paid to all the different bases for classification so that a gland may be called, for example, a compound, tubular, mucous gland. The various bases on which classifications are made and the types therein will now be considered.

Tubular, Acinous and Alveolar Glands. If the clusters of cells that constitute the secretory unit or units of a gland are tubular in shape (Fig. 135), the gland is said to be a tubular gland. But if the secretory units are more rounded in shape, the gland is said to be an *acinous* (*acinus* = grape, berry) or an *alveolar* (*alveolus* = a little hollow, a little hollow vessel) gland. For many years it was customary to distinguish between acini and alveoli, and hence between acinous and alveolar glands, the term acinus being used for secretory units that are rounded and somewhat resemble Florence flasks, and alveolus for those that are more conical and roughly resemble Erlenmeyer flasks (Fig. 135). But in the recent past it has become usual practice not to insist on this distinction and to call both acinous and alveolar glands by the latter name. However, there are a few exceptions to this rule, most notably the secretory units of the pancreas which are still commonly called acini. If glands contain both tubular and alveolar secretory units, or units that have some characteristics of each, they are called tubulo-alveolar glands (Fig. 135).

Simple and Compound Glands. Any exocrine gland in which the secretion formed by the secretory unit or units is collected and conveyed to a surface by an unbranched duct is said to be a *simple gland* (Fig. 135, *bottom, left*). If the duct branches, so as to form a duct system, the gland is known as a *compound gland* (Fig. 135, *bottom, right*).

As the trunk of a tree branches first into a few fairly large branches and then into increasingly smaller and more numerous ones, eventually to supply twigs for the leaves, so the main duct branches into increasingly smaller and more numerous branches to supply all of the almost innumerable secretory units

TYPES OF EXOCRINE GLANDS

<u>If secretory portion is</u>:

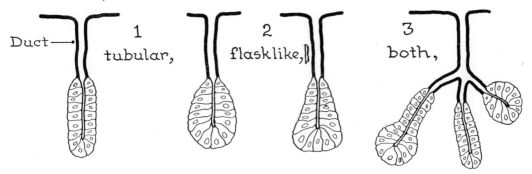

Duct → **1** tubular,   **2** flasklike,   **3** both,

it is a tubular
exocrine gland.

it is an alveolar or
acinous gland.

it is a tubulo-
alveolar gland.

<u>If duct doesn't branch</u>:

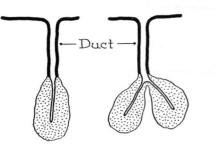

—Duct—

it is a simple gland.

<u>If duct branches</u>:

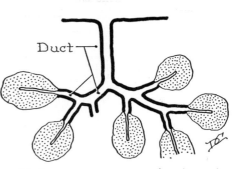

Duct—

it is a compound gland.

FIG. 135. Diagram showing the different kinds of secretory units of exocrine glands and the
difference between simple and compound glands.

of large compound glands. Large glands, then, all characteristically have extensive branching duct systems.

Large compound glands, being epithelial structures, need the support of connective tissue. This is provided by a capsule of connective tissue which surrounds the gland and also by partitions of connective tissue which divide the substance of the gland up into areas, which are thus "fenced off" in 3 dimensions by connective tissue. In some glands large areas so fenced off, particularly if cleavage has oc-

curred in the partition so that the fenced-off areas are somewhat separated from one another, are termed *lobes*; but if the fenced-off areas are not very large and are close to one another, they are called *lobules* (little lobes).

A connective tissue partition of the sort described above is termed a *septum*. Hence, connective tissue partitions between lobes are termed *interlobar septa*, and those between lobules, *interlobular septa* (Fig. 137).

The septa in some glands converge toward the point at which the main duct enters

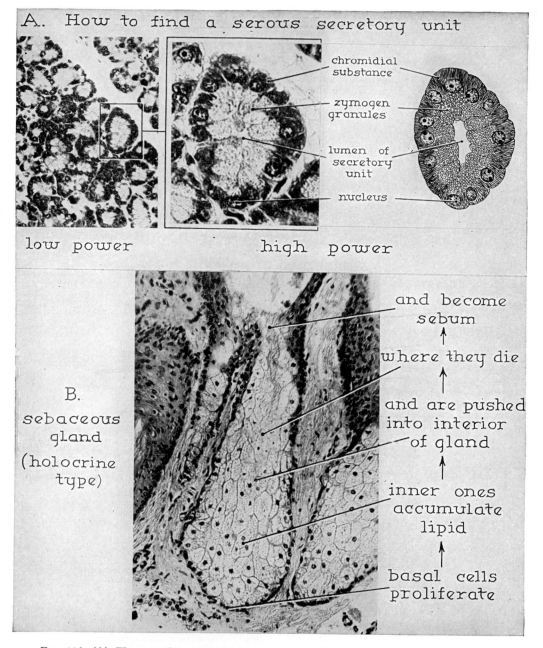

A. How to find a serous secretory unit

chromidial substance

zymogen granules

lumen of secretory unit

nucleus

low power   high power

B.
sebaceous
gland
(holocrine
type)

and become sebum

where they die

and are pushed into interior of gland

inner ones accumulate lipid

basal cells proliferate

FIG. 136. (A) The way that a section of pancreas (which contains serous secretory units) appears under low power is illustrated at the left. The pictures at the right show how individual secretory units appear under higher powers. (B) A medium-power photomicrograph of a sebaceous gland of the skin. These glands generally open into hair follicles and they make the fatty secretion, sebum. For details of structure see Chapter 23.

the gland. Hence, they provide an excellent means whereby the main branches of the duct may be conveyed and supported as they pass toward the gland's interior. As the larger branches of the duct system are thus conveyed in interlobular septa, they are termed *interlobular ducts* and they are easily recognized because they are large, have a thick epithelial

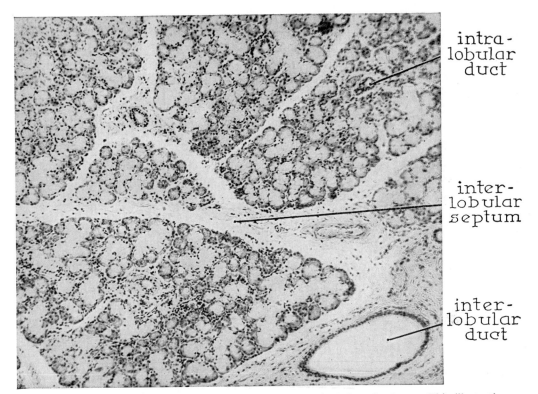

intra-
lobular
duct

inter-
lobular
septum

inter-
lobular
duct

Fig. 137. Low-power photomicrograph of a salivary gland of the mixed type. This illustration shows interlobular septa, interlobular and intralobular ducts and secretory units.

lining and are surrounded by the connective tissue of the partition which conveys them (Fig. 137). Branches from interlobular ducts leave the partitions to enter the substance of lobules, and, being *inside* rather than *between* lobules, are called *intralobular ducts*. They are smaller than interlobular ducts and are lined by epithelium that is not as thick as that of the corresponding interlobular ducts. Furthermore, they are not surrounded by as much connective tissue as are the interlobular ducts because they do not run in partitions. However, they may be surrounded by a certain amount of connective tissue, because the partitions usually send out prolongations of connective tissue into the substance of the lobules to afford them some support (Fig. 137).

Holocrine, Merocrine and Apocrine Glands. These terms refer to the manner in which the secretory cells of the glands elaborate their secretion. In holocrine glands the process is very drastic. A cell, to secrete, first accumu-

lates secretory products in its cytoplasm and then dies and disintegrates. Thereupon the dead cell is discharged to constitute the secretion (Fig. 136, *bottom*); in holocrine glands (*holos* = all), all of the cell is secreted. Holocrine glands are not common in the body. The sebaceous glands of the skin (Fig. 136) are convenient ones to study. It is obvious that, for a holocrine gland to maintain its full complement of cells, the less highly differentiated cells of the gland must constantly reproduce so as to provide a steady supply of cells which can differentiate into secretory cells. Merocrine glands are the opposite of holocrine glands in that, although *meros* means a part, they secrete without any part of the cell's being lost. It is to be recalled that secretory granules are in the nature of cytoplasmic inclusions; hence, although they are manufactured by the cytoplasm, they are not actually part of the cytoplasm. (Probably this was not understood when the name merocrine originated.) In merocrine glands, formed secretory

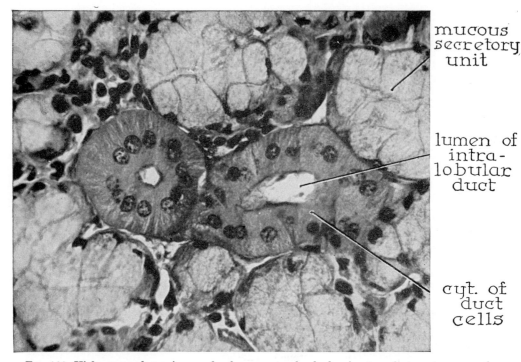

mucous secretory unit

lumen of intra-lobular duct

cut. of duct cells

Fig. 138. High-power photomicrograph of a mucous gland, showing two ducts cut more or less in cross section.

products, such as secretory granules, are passed through the free surfaces of secretory cells into the lumen of a secretory unit without any of the secretory cells' cytoplasm being lost in the process. In apocrine glands (*apo* = from), the process is much the same except that a little of the cytoplasm along the free secretory borders of the secretory cells is supposed to be lost as the formed secretory products are passed through them. However, these classifications were made from observations with the light microscope, and it is quite possible that from observations with the E/M which show secretion granules to be surrounded with a membrane that becomes continuous with the cell membrane as the secretion is delivered (see p. 106) that at least some glands, believed to be apocrine, will have to be reclassified.

SEROUS, MUCOUS AND MIXED GLANDS

This classification is not applicable to all exocrine glands but only to some. It is used particularly in classifying the salivary glands, those glands whose ducts open into the oral cavity and supply it with saliva.

This classification is based on the character of the secretion made by the gland. The word *serous* means "wheylike," and as whey is a clear, watery fluid, those glands in which secretion is of this nature are termed *serous glands*. Mucus is a slightly more viscid fluid. The glands that secrete mucin, the glycoprotein which, when mixed with water becomes mucus, are termed *mucous glands*. Any gland that produces a mixture of serous and mucous fluids is called a *mixed gland*.

However, the histology student will not be called upon to classify these glands from an investigation into the character of their secretion but from the appearance that sections cut through them present under the microscope. And since cells that make serous and mucous secretions, respectively, differ considerably from one another in appearance, the identification of sections cut from serous, mucous and mixed glands (in which both types are present) is a relatively easy matter.

A section cut through a highly specialized gland, such as one of the salivary glands, is at first a puzzling picture for the student to interpret, because secretory units and ducts are packed together, with only a slight amount of supporting connective tissue, in almost any way that allows the greatest number of secretory units, with their ducts, to be fitted into a limited amount of space. This is accomplished only by both secretory units and ducts being disposed in almost every conceivable plane; hence, a section through the substance of a gland cuts both ducts and secretory units in a vast variety of planes. The interpretation of such a section requires some thought.

With the low-power objective, the student, when he first studies a section of one of the salivary glands or of the pancreas (which is similar to the salivary glands in its general plan of construction but different in certain of its secretory functions), will be able to make out the outlines of lobules (Fig. 137). It is noted that lobules are not always complete, that is, lobules are not always, in any given section, completely surrounded by partitions of connective tissue. In glands, moreover, shrinkage often occurs along the line of the partitions between lobules; this is an artefact. With the low-power objective a few intralobular ducts (Fig. 138) may be seen within a lobule. These may be cut at right angles to their long axes, obliquely, or more or less longitudinally. (If necessary refer back to the section dealing with the appearance of tubes cut in different planes.)

When the section is examined with the high-power objective, secretory units may be seen (Fig. 136, *top*). In attempting to identify these, however, the student should remember that in every section they are cut in almost every conceivable plane, many of them obliquely. A search will soon reveal some cut approximately in cross section, and the diameter of one so cut is roughly comparable with that of one of the larger intralobular ducts (Fig. 138). Secretory units are separated from one another and from intralobular ducts by a minimal amount of delicate connective tissue (Fig. 139) which brings capillaries and nerves close to them.

Before examining secretory units in a section, it is perhaps helpful to visualize the appearance of the surface of a pie that has been cut into several pieces but not yet served. The individual pieces of pie are roughly triangular in shape, and their apices meet in the center. A cross section of a secretory unit presents a similar appearance, the individual cells of the unit, like the individual pieces of pie, presenting a more or less triangular appearance with their apices almost meeting in the center of the unit (Fig. 139). The apices of the different cells do not quite meet, because this region constitutes the lumen of the secretory unit. Often, however, the lumen cannot be seen because shrinkage causes the cells to obliterate it.

Serous Secretory Units. The nucleus of a serous secretory cell is usually rounded and lies toward, rather than at, the base of the cell (Figs. 58, 64). (Although all secretory cells contain nuclei, all do not exhibit them in a single thin section, so the slice may miss the nucleus.) At the base of the cell the cytoplasm contains chromidial substance (Fig. 64, and 136 A), the nature and the function of which were discussed in detail in Chapter 4. The fine structure of chromidial substance in this location is illustrated in Figure 65. Further toward the apex of each cell secretion granules are to be seen (Figs. 136, *top*, and 58). The fine structure of these is illustrated in Figure 73, and their formation and delivery from the cell is described on page 106.

The secretion granules are termed *zymogen* (*zym* has come to refer to enzyme and *gen* means "I produce"), because these are the forerunners of the enzymes that are present in the secretions of serous glands. In fixed tissue preparations these granules appear as small spheres of solid substance (Fig. 58), provided that the fixative and the stain employed in making the section are designed to present a "positive" picture of the granules (with a combination of some fixing and staining methods a "negative" picture of the granules is seen (Fig. 64, *left*); they are represented only by unstained spaces of the same size and distribution as granules). The positive picture, obtained by the use of some fixatives and stains, may give a false impression of their solidity, for studies made on living material suggest that they are semifluid in nature.

Zymogen granules are secreted through the apical region of secretory cells into the lumen of the secretory unit. This is very minute. When the granules enter the lumen of the secretory unit they dissolve and so lose their form.

Mucous Secretory Units. The appearance of a cross section of mucous secretory unit ex-

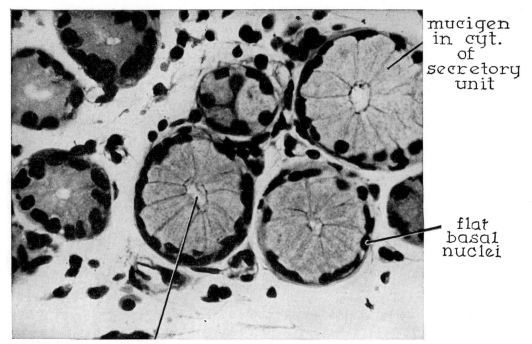

mucigen
in cyt.
of
secretory
unit

flat
basal
nuclei

lumen of mucous secretory unit

FIG. 139. High-power photomicrograph of a section of trachea, showing mucous secretory units cut in cross section.

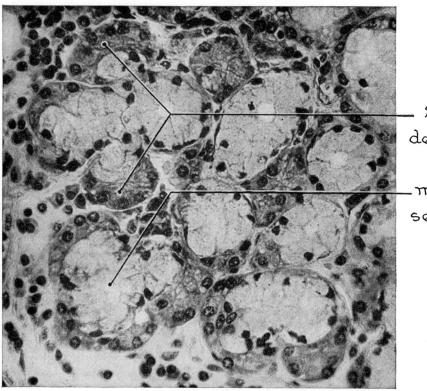

Serous

demilunes

on

mucous

secretory

units

FIG. 140. Medium-power photomicrograph of a mixed gland, showing mucous secretory units with serous demilunes.

hibits certain differences from that of a serous secretory unit. The nuclei are of a different shape and they occupy a different position in the cells. In serous cells they are rounded and situated near, but not at, the bases of the cells. In mucous cells they are flattened, almost to the point of becoming disks; furthermore, they are crowded against the bases of the cells that contain them (Fig. 139). The cytoplasm of mucous cells is also different from that of serous cells. There is less chromidial substance at the bases of the cells than there is in serous cells. That portion of the cytoplasm situated between the nucleus and the apex of a mucous cell contains, not zymogen granules, but a variable number of mucigen (mucigen is the forerunner of mucin) droplets which, in the usual preparation, present a negative picture and hence impart a vacuolated appearance to the very light-staining cytoplasm that contains them (Fig. 139).

Mucins from different sources vary in composition, but they all contain carbohydrate and are of the order of glycoproteins. Their carbohydrate component is believed to be responsible for their staining brilliantly in suitably fixed tissue with the P. A. Schiff technic (Fig. 122).

Radioautographic Studies. Bélanger has shown that after giving subcutaneous injection of S^{35} labeled H_2SO_4 radioactive sulfur enters and can be demonstrated by radioautographs in many tissues. Of interest to us here is the fact that the secretory cells of mucous glands take up the labeled sulfur in considerable amounts; indeed, in low-power radioautographs mucous glands stand out as a sprinkling of black ink drops on a white page. The uptake of radioactive sulfur by cells that secrete mucus is due to the fact that the mucoprotein that they synthesize has sulfur as one of its components; mucus probably contains some mucoitin sulfate.

Mixed Glands. Some glands, to be enumerated later, are of the mixed variety and so deliver both serous and mucous secretions through their ducts. This is accomplished by the glands possessing both serous and mucous units (Fig. 140) or by combinations of the two. Combinations usually consist of mucous units capped by crescent-shaped aggregations of serous cells called *serous demilunes* (half moons) (Fig. 140). Obviously, there must be passageways for the secretion of these serous

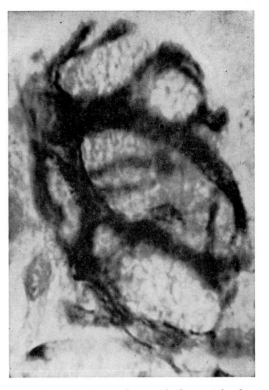

Fig. 141. Photomicrograph ($\times 2,250$) of myoepithelial (basket) cell in submaxillary gland of rat. The material was fixed in acetone and stained by the Gomori method for alkaline phosphatase. The cytoplasmic arms of the cell appear black in the illustration. (Leeson, C. R.: Nature *178*:858)

cells to gain entrance between the mucous cells which separate them from the lumen of the mucous unit. These passageways are probably in the nature of tiny intercellular canals situated between adjacent cells of the mucous secretory unit and are not evident in the ordinary preparation.

Myoepithelial Basket Cells. Secretory units of either the mucous or the serous type can be shown by special technics to be cradled in a loose basket made of the cytoplasmic processes of special cells that lie between the bases of the secretory cells and the basement membrane. These cells have a central cell body and many long cytoplasmic processes that encircle and so grasp the secretory unit (Fig. 141). Although these cells are of epithelial origin, it seems very probable that their cytoplasm is contractile, not only because of

ENDOCRINE GLANDS

How a clump of cells can become a follicle

Capillaries

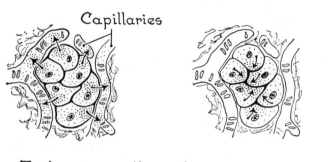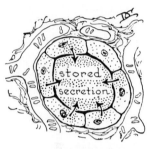

Endocrine cells commonly secrete into capillaries,

but, to store secretion, cells may secrete in opposite direction.

Then they expand the clump into a follicle.

Fig. 142. Diagram showing how different types of endocrine glands store secretion and how a clump of cells can become a follicle.

their shape and postition, but also because myofibrils have been seen in them with the E/M. Therefore, it is assumed that these cells function in some way to encourage the expression of secretion from secretory units into ducts. Leeson has shown that these cells are selectively demonstrated to advantage by the histochemical method employed for the demonstration of alkaline phosphatase (Fig. 141), which enzyme they contain in abundance.

ENDOCRINE GLANDS

The structure of endocrine glands is considerably simpler than that of exocrine glands because they possess no ducts. As their secretory cells discharge their secretions into capillaries, the secretory cells must be arranged in such a fashion that all abut on capillaries. This is accomplished by the secretory cells being disposed in either straight or irregular cords, separated from one another by capillaries, or in little clumps surrounded by capillaries (Fig. 134, *bottom, right*).

Intracellular Storage. All endocrine glands store their secretion to some extent. This is accomplished in most of them by intracellular

storage. For example, the endocrine cells that make insulin, the hormone so important in preventing an individual from having the disease diabetes, normally store within their cytoplasm enough of the hormone or its immediate forerunner to kill a person if it were all secreted at one time.

Extracellular Storage. If it is desirable for an endocrine gland to store secretion over and above that amount that can be accommodated by intracellular storage, another expedient is adopted. The cells of a clump secrete inwardly and so give rise to a pool of stored secretion (or precursor of secretion), which is extracellular but completely surrounded by the cells (Fig. 142). Such an arrangement of cells surrounding a little sphere of stored secretion is termed a *follicle* (a small bag).

Secretion Granules. The immediate forerunner of the secretion of some endocrine glands is evident in the cytoplasm of secretory cells as secretion granules (Fig. 142). These usually require very special histologic technics for their demonstration. Some endocrine glands that secrete fat-soluble hormones reveal droplets of fatty material in the cytoplasm, and these, in the usual paraffin section, appear as vacuoles (Chap. 26). It is not entirely clear how these are related to the secretory process of the gland concerned.

Endocrine glands are enclosed by capsules of connective tissue and usually some projections from these extend into the substance of the gland as *trabeculae* (little beams) to provide it with internal support and to carry blood vessels and nerves into it. These trabeculae account for the lobulated appearance that sections of some endocrine glands present under the microscope.

GLANDS THAT ARE BOTH EXOCRINE AND ENDOCRINE

The pancreas provides an excellent example of such a gland. This gland arises from an epithelial ingrowth that comes from the epithelial lining of the intestine. This epithelial ingrowth branches and branches to become a duct system, but also it gives rise to two kinds of secretory units: serous ones, in which the lumina of the secretory portions remain connected with the end branches of the duct system, and little groups of cells, called islets of Langerhans, that do not develop a lumen but become arranged into irregular cords and clumps richly provided with capillaries. These islands of cells which arise from the same source as the developing duct system may remain in contact with it but there is no continuity of the lumen of the duct system with them; hence, they must secrete directly into the many capillaries with which they are provided. They thus constitute the endocrine element of the pancreas.

The pancreas, then, contains numerous islands of endocrine tissue scattered through its substance, which is chiefly composed of serous secretory units that empty their secretion into its duct system. Therefore, it is both an endocrine and an exocrine gland, with different types of specialized cells to perform its two different functions.

REFERENCES

Bélanger, L. F.: Autoradiographic visualization of S^{35} incorporation and turnover by the mucous glands of the gastro-intestinal tract and other soft tissues of rat and hamster, Anat. Rec. *118*:755, 1954.

Bensley, R. R.: Studies on the pancreas of the guinea pig, Am. J. Anat. *12*:297, 1911.

Leblond, C. P., and Walker, B. E.: Renewal of cell populations, Physiol. Rev. *36*:255, 1956.

Leeson, C. R.: Localization of alkaline phosphatase in the submaxillary gland of rat, Nature *178*:858, 1956.

Leeson, C. R., and Jacoby, F.: An electron microscopic study of the rat submaxillary gland during its postnatal development and in the adult, J. Anat. (Lond.) *93*:287, 1959.

Montagna, W., and Noback, C. R.: Histochemical observations on the sebaceous glands of the rat, Am. J. Anat. *81*:39, 1947.

Palade, G. E.: Functional changes in structure of cell components *in* Hayashi, T. (ed.): Subcellular Particles, p. 64, New York, Ronald Press, 1958.

Palay, S. L. (ed.): The morphology of secretion *in* Frontiers in Cytology, p. 305, New Haven, Conn., Yale Univ. Press, 1958.

(*See also* references under Cytoplasm in Chapter 5)

Chapter 13

Connective Tissue

Introduction. Connective tissue was given its name because its chief function is to connect the other 3 tissues of the body (epithelial, muscular and nervous) together. Connective tissue is able to do this and to provide support because most kinds of it contain substantial amounts of the intercellular substances described in Chapter 5; indeed, many types of connective tissue consist chiefly of intercellular substance (dense fibrous cartilage and bone). Therefore, many of the cells of connective tissue must be of a type specialized to make intercellular substances. However, there are other types of connective tissue that have very little intercellular substance but instead consist chiefly of cells that have other functions. Since the latter tissues do not connect or support, it might be asked why they should be included in the connective tissue family. The reason is that their cells are close relatives of the cells that make intercellular substance; indeed, they all develop from the same mother cells. Even in the supporting kinds of connective tissue, where most of the cells are of a type specialized to make intercellular substance, generally there are a few of the other kinds of connective tissue cells that do other things.

From the foregoing it may be expected that different kinds of connective tissue will be found to have different microscopic appearances; for example, the types designed primarily for strength, as is the one illustrated in Figure 84, will appear to be different from the types that consist almost entirely of cells, as does the one illustrated in Figure 229.

THE DEVELOPMENT OF CONNECTIVE TISSUE

That the embryo, at one stage of its development, consists of 3 primary germ layers—ectoderm, mesoderm and endoderm—already has been noted in Chapter 10, as has the fact that most, but not all, of the epithelium of the body arises from ectoderm and endoderm. The connective tissue of the body, as might be assumed, develops from the middle layer of the embryo, the mesoderm. In particular, it develops from a subdivision of mesoderm called *mesenchyme* (middle infusion).

Mesenchyme is typically a loose, soft tissue which infiltrates between the various structures in the body that are developing from sources other than mesenchyme. It consists of both cells and intercellular substances. Its cells possess delicate, wavy cytoplasmic arms that extend out into the intercellular substance in which they lie (Fig. 143). Some think that there is cytoplasmic continuity between the arms of adjacent cells. Tiny fibrils, the forerunners of fibrous types of intercellular substance, may be demonstrated at the tips of some of the cytoplasmic arms by special methods. But the great bulk of the intercellular substance of mesenchyme is of the amorphous type, and it has only a few fibers scattered about in it (Fig. 143).

Mesenchyme illustrates well the capacity of amorphous intercellular substances to permit diffusion over considerable distances, for, in embryonic life, when the vascular system is developing, there may be considerable stretches of tissue which contain no small blood vessels. Yet the cells in mesenchyme thrive.

Potentiality and Differentiation of Mesenchymal Cells. When they first develop in the embryo and are as yet undifferentiated, mesenchymal cells have great potentiality; they have the capacity to differentiate along any one of several lines that lead to the formation of the many different kinds of cells in connective tissue (Fig. 144).

From the studies of Maximow, who contributed so much to our knowledge of the connective tissues, a very important concept arose, namely, that in the development of any kind of adult connective tissue all of the undifferentiated mesenchymal cells of the part do not differentiate. Therefore, in any adult connective tissue we might expect to find a few *undifferentiated mesenchymal cells.*

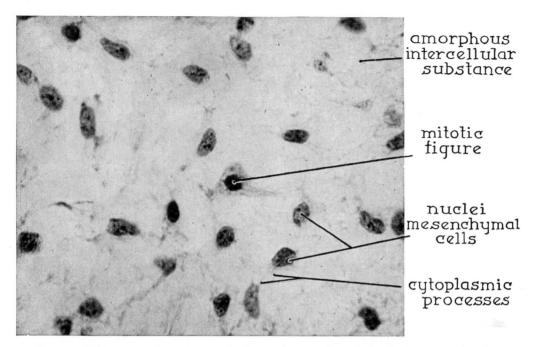

amorphous
intercellular
substance

mitotic
figure

nuclei
mesenchymal
cells

cytoplasmic
processes

Fig. 143. High-power photomicrograph of a section cut through developing connective tissue (mesenchyme) of an embryo. This tissue is characteristically soft because the cells are separated by a jellylike, amorphous type of intercellular substance.

Furthermore, in connective tissues there is a tendency for cells to exist in different states of differentiation, from undifferentiated, through partly differentiated cells, to fully differentiated cells.

Summary. In at least some types of connective tissue there may be (1) undifferentiated cells, (2) differentiated cells and (3) cells in *all stages* of differentiation between the undifferentiated mesenchymal cells and the fully differentiated ones. Moreover, it should be kept in mind that the undifferentiated cells have great potentiality and can differentiate along any line of differentiation to form any kind of cell found in any kind of connective tissue, but that on differentiating they lose potentiality. The farther they move down any line of differentiation the less able they become to form cells of any other family type; finally, most of them become restricted to producing one type of cell within the connective tissue family.

Metaplasia in Connective Tissue. It sometimes appears under certain pathologic conditions as if one specialized type of connective tissue turned into another kind. This phenomenon is called *metaplasia*. It should be understood that although mesenchyme (which is unspecialized) can change into any specialized type of connective tissue, any of the specialized adult types of connective tissue cannot actually change into any other specialized type. As Adami pointed out so clearly many years ago, there is no metamorphosis of one adult type of tissue into another adult type. What really happens when this seems to occur as, for example, when bone forms in the abdominal wall, is that there is a replacement of the old type of tissue by a new type that is born within it. The new type of tissue arises from cells that have never completely differentiated and so have retained much of their original mesenchymal potentiality. In understanding how this could occur, it is helpful to remember that the environment of cells plays a very important role in affecting their differentiation. So, if some new, potent environmental influence appears in a special kind of connective tissue, it may induce the undifferentiated cells that remain in that tissue to

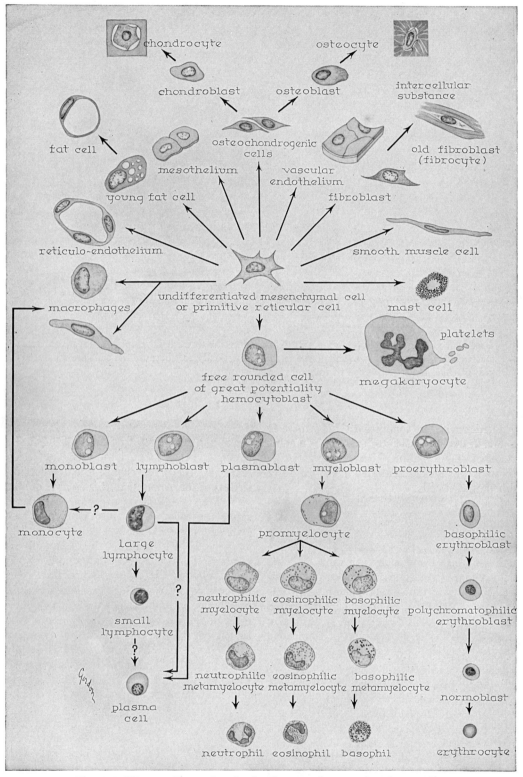

FIG. 144. Diagram illustrating the family tree of connective tissue cells.

differentiate along a different pathway from their customary one, and the new cells of a different type that arise in this way may gradually replace those of the former tissue, thus giving the impression that the previous type of tissue has changed into another type. Actually, it has been replaced by another.

Growth in Connective Tissues. In at least some special types of connective tissue the most highly specialized cells that develop not only lose their potentiality for differentiating into other kinds of connective tissue cells but also their ability to divide (an example of differentiation being attained at the expense of reproductive capacity). So, as a general rule, cell division, on which growth depends, is the function of the somewhat less highly specialized cells in any connective tissue. However, the progeny of these less highly specialized cells, by further differentiation, can add to the numbers of the most highly specialized cells.

CLASSIFICATION OF CONNECTIVE TISSUES

It is convenient to classify the connective tissues into certain main types and to classify some of these further into subtypes.

Mesenchyme, an important connective tissue of the embryo, has already been considered. In the classification that follows we shall list those connective tissues that are encountered in postnatal life.

1. Loose ordinary (including areolar)
   (both supporting and cellular)
2. Adipose
   (primarily cellular)
3. Dense fibrous ⌐regularly arranged
   └irregularly arranged
   (primarily supporting)
4. Cartilage ⌐hyalin
   ├elastic
   └fibro
   (primarily supporting)
5. Bone ⌐immature
   └mature ⌐cancellous
   └compact
   (primarily supporting)
6. Dentin
   (primarily supporting)
7. Hemopoietic ⌐myeloid
   └lymphatic
   (primarily cellular)

LOOSE ORDINARY CONNECTIVE TISSUE (INCLUDING AREOLAR TISSUE)

Why Loose Connective Tissue Is Commonly Studied First. This type of connective tissue has a connecting function, and so intercellular substances are an important component of it. However, in addition to having intercellular substances and the cells that make intercellular substances, it also has cells that perform other functions. Therefore, loose connective tissue is more or less halfway between the two main kinds of connective tissue that are composed either chiefly of intercellular substance or chiefly of cells.

The term *loose* refers to the arrangement of the intercellular substance in a connective tissue. For a tissue to be loose, the fibers of its intercellular substance should be neither numerous nor woven together in such a way as to prevent the tissues being stretched in any direction. Moreover, the amorphous intercellular substance in which the fibers are embedded should be of a soft jellylike character so that the tissue is pliable as well as stretchable. The term *ordinary* is used in contrast to special; the latter term is used with reference to certain connective tissues such as cartilage and bone that have special supporting properties and are disposed in only certain sites in the body. In contrast with special connective tissues, the ordinary varieties are widely distributed throughout the body.

Distribution. The student will study loose ordinary connective tissue in sections and in teased preparations. Perhaps the easiest way to study loose connective tissue in sections is to study some sections that have been cut through the epithelial membranes or the secretory units of glands. The connective tissue that abuts on and nourishes the epithelial structures generally is loose (except at the line of junction between epithelium and connective tissue where it may become condensed into a basement membrane). Since epithelium contains no capillaries, the connective tissue that supports epithelium must contain an abundance of capillaries and be loose enough to permit nourishment to diffuse from the capillaries to the epithelial cells. Moreover, the connective tissue must be loose enough to permit the epithelial structure some movement.

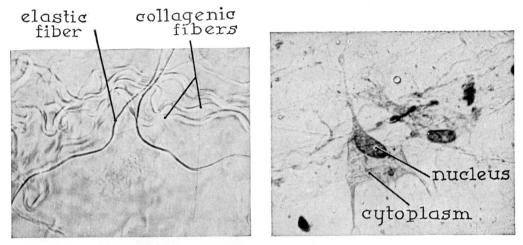

elastic fiber   collagenic fibers   nucleus   cytoplasm

FIG. 145. (A, *Left*) Collagenic and elastic fibers as seen in a fresh, unstained, teased preparation of areolar tissue with the light cut down. The elastic fibers are more refractile than the collagenic. (B, *Right*) High-power photomicrograph of a spread of areolar tissue stained lightly with methylene blue. Two fibroblasts may be seen in the central part of this picture. Notice that the cytoplasm of the fibroblasts is apparent in this type of preparation.

Loose connective tissue of this type is illustrated in Figures 91 and 139.

In addition to being disposed beneath epithelial membranes and around the secretory units of glands, loose ordinary connective tissue is distributed widely as a sticky but elastic glue between many nonepithelial body structures, such as muscle and fascia, that are normally adherent to one another and around lymph nodes, blood vessels and nerves to join them to adjacent tissues. When such structures are separated in the dissecting room, it may be noticed that the tissue, along the line where it is being pulled apart, develops a white bubbly appearance just before it breaks; this is due to air bubbles being sucked into it as it becomes stretched. The older anatomists called this tissue *areolar tissue* because it was believed to have little areas (areolae) in it.

How Areolar Tissue Is Studied. Areolar tissue commonly is in such thin films that it is difficult to study it in sections; generally, it appears only as thin lines. To explore it to advantage and to learn more about the cells and the intercellular substances of loose ordinary connective tissue in general, it is desirable to cut little pieces of it from the body and tease these apart on slides. Such preparations can be made easily in the laboratory from animals; for example, one mouse will provide enough material for a whole class. The skin and the subcutaneous tissue are reflected from the muscles of the thigh; this tears the areolar tissue along the line at which the separation is effected, and small pieces of tissue from this site may be grasped with forceps, cut with scissors and mounted on slides. Pieces containing obvious fat should be avoided. Some pieces should be mounted dry, and others placed in saline, and they should be teased apart. The dry preparations can be fixed and stained with one of the Romanovsky blood stains. Some of the saline preparations should be treated with some 1 per cent methylene blue or toluidine blue for a minute or two. These preparations and those mounted only in saline should be covered with coverslips, using saline as a mounting fluid and petroleum jelly to seal the edges of the coverslip.

Intercellular Substances of Areolar Tissue. Areolar tissue contains both intercellular substances and cells. The intercellular substances consist of rather fine collagenic fibers that are woven loosely with single elastic fibers, and both are embedded in a ground substance (Fig. 145 A). The ground substance can be demonstrated only in mounts of tissue that have been specially stained to demonstrate metachromasia. If this is done, some metachromatic material can be seen throughout the preparation, and this is the ground substance. Without special staining the ground substance cannot be seen. However, it can be demonstrated in the animal that is being used to provide areolar tissue before this tissue is removed, for it will be found (as Sylvia Bensley showed in 1934) that saline injected into areolar tissue cannot be recovered subsequently as a free fluid; it will have become "soaked up," as it were, by the ground substance of the areolar tissue.

The fibers of the intercellular substance of areolar tissue should be studied in the unstained teased preparations mounted in saline. Of course, in this type of preparation, these fibers can be studied to better advantage with a phase or interference microscope, but these instruments may not be available. In using the ordinary light microscope for their study, it is advisable to diminish the size of the condenser diaphragm; this improves the contrast between the two kinds of fibers and between the fibers and the mounting media. The fibers appear as in Figure 145 A, where it may be seen that the collagenic fibers are thicker, more wavy and more numerous than the elastic fibers. The collagenic fibers, in contrast with the elastic fibers, have a fibrillar appearance because they are made up of fibrils.

The Cells of Loose Ordinary Connective (Including Areolar) Tissue

As has already been mentioned, the cells of loose ordinary connective tissue are more or less representative of those found in all the various kinds of connective tissue; hence, in studying the cells of loose ordinary connective tissue we more or less obtain a preview of what will be seen in the special kinds of connective tissue that will be studied later.

I. Stem or Mother Cells. Loose connective tissue develops from mesenchyme with the mesenchymal cells differentiating into the types that will now be described. However, it seems very probable that a few mesenchymal cells persist in loose connective tissue in at least a relatively undifferentiated state. However, it is doubtful if these could be recognized for they would appear much like young fibro-

blasts. That they persist in loose connective tissue is not to be proved by their recognition with the microscope but because of what they *do* under certain circumstances.

In the type of connective tissue termed hemopoietic, which we shall study presently, the undifferentiated mesenchymal cells that persist are commonly fixed in position by reticular networks; hence, they commonly are called *primitive reticular cells* (Fig. 144). In these tissues they commonly give rise to cells that are not fixed to the reticular network; these are called *free* cells. Because they are free they tend to assume a rounded form, and because they retain most of the potentiality of the fixed cells from which they arise they are termed *free rounded cells of great potentiality* (Fig. 144). They are also called by other names, as will now be described.

According to one school of thought, the free rounded cells that arise from the fixed mesenchymal cells have sufficient potentiality to form any kind of blood cell; hence, the members of this school term them *hemocytoblasts* (Fig. 144). However, the members of another school consider that the fixed cells give rise not to a single type of rounded cell but to several types, each of which has a somewhat restricted potentiality. These are termed *monoblasts, lymphoblasts, plasmoblasts, myeloblasts* and *proerythroblasts* and are supposed to give rise to the different lines of blood cells illustrated in Figure 144. Such controversy as exists about this matter is primarily of academic importance and is very difficult, if not impossible, to settle. To the author it seems most probable that the fixed cells give rise first to rounded cells that are true hemocytoblasts, and these cells have the potentiality to form the various secondary free stem cells indicated in Figure 144.

The formation of rounded cells from fixed cells of great potentiality and the formation of cells of different lines from these free rounded cells occurs chiefly in hemopoietic tissue. However, the reason we are considering this matter here is that it occurs also to some extent in the development of loose connective tissue; hence, in this tissue there are occasional free rounded cells of great potentiality that can give rise to some monocytes, lymphocytes and/or plasma cells.

To sum up, in loose connective tissue there

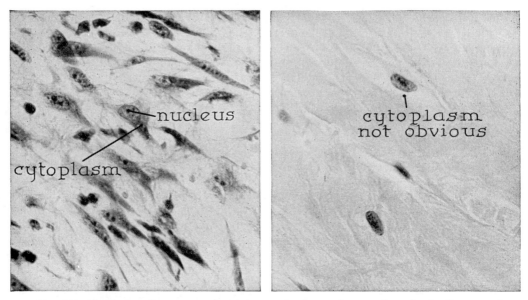

FIG. 146. (*Left*) A medium-power photomicrograph of a section cut through a healing wound, where young fibroblasts are growing rapidly. Observe that the cytoplasm of young, actively growing fibroblasts is apparent in H and E sections. (*Right*) Picture taken from a section of mature connective tissue in the deeper part of the skin. Most of the tissue in this illustration consists of collagenic fibers. Only the nuclei of the old fibroblasts present in such tissue can be seen to advantage.

can be a few representatives of two kinds of stem or mother cells: undifferentiated mesenchymal cells, which tend to be fixed in position, and free rounded cells of great potentiality, which tend to be free.

2. Fibroblasts. These are the most numerous cells in loose connective tissue. They are so named because those who first observed them believed that they made the fibers of the intercellular substance. Now it is generally accepted that they are indeed responsible for the production of fibers and, in all probability, for most of the amorphous components of intercellular substance as well.

In fresh preparations of areolar tissue stained with methylene blue, fibroblasts are more or less spread out and appear as rather large cells, as is illustrated in Figure 145 B. In teased preparations such as this, the cytoplasm of the cells is clearly evident and can be seen extending out from the main cell body in the form of irregular processes.

In stained H and E sections fibroblasts have a different appearance from the one they present in teased stained fresh preparations.

Before describing them as they appear in sections, it should be pointed out that fibroblasts exist in tissues in different stages of differentiation. In this sense it is permissible to speak of young and old fibroblasts; the latter are sometimes termed fibrocytes to distinguish them from those that are younger and less differentiated.

Fully differentiated fibroblasts have completed their work of producing intercellular substance and generally are surrounded by that which they have made. Since the production of intercellular substance is an activity of the cytoplasm, and since this activity is finished in the instance of old fibroblasts, there is no need for them to possess much cytoplasm. Indeed, in H and E sections, it is difficult to see any cytoplasm associated with the nuclei of old fibroblasts; therefore, they appear in sections as almost naked nuclei (Fig. 146, *right*). On the other hand, young fibroblasts that are actively producing intercellular substance have abundant, basophilic cytoplasm that is seen easily in H and E sections, as is shown in Figure 146, *left*. Since the formation of intercellular substance is an example of protein synthesis, it is to be expected that the cytoplasm of young active fibroblasts would contain considerable amounts of chromidial substance which, of course, would make the cytoplasm basophilic.

The nucleus of a fibroblast is a fairly large, somewhat flattened, ovoid body, sometimes indented on one side (Figs. 145 B, 146). Its outline in sections depends upon the plane in which it is cut. One cut longitudinally at right angles to its lesser diameter exhibits in a section a plump, oval outline with an indentation sometimes present on one side. If cut longitudinally, but at right angles to its greater diameter, it presents in a section a somewhat thinner oval outline. And if it is cut in cross section, it presents in a section an oval outline but one smaller than either of the foregoing.

The nucleus of a fibroblast stains lightly in an H and E section because its chromatin granules are fine rather than coarse and are scattered like dust throughout the nucleus. One or more nucleoli may be seen lying among the chromatin granules (Fig. 146, *left*).

DEVELOPMENT OF KNOWLEDGE REGARDING FIBER FORMATION. Through the years there has been much discussion as to whether fibrils of collagen were formed as such within the cytoplasm of fibroblasts and then extruded, or whether they were formed outside of cells by means of the cells secreting precursor substances which outside the cell became polymerized into fibrils and fibers. The significant observations in this field will now be reviewed briefly.

Stearns, in 1939, actually watched the formation of collagenic fibers in transparent chambers in rabbits' ears. She found that fibers developed at sufficient distances from fibroblasts and sufficiently rapidly to rule out the possibility of their necessarily having an intracellular origin.

In the last few years, the formation of fibers has been investigated with the E/M, in particular by Porter, Wasserman and Jackson. One of Jackson's electron micrographs showing fiber formation by fibroblasts appears as Figure 147.

Jackson investigated this matter by studying the morphogenesis of avian tendon in embryos of increasing ages by means of thin sections and electron microscopy. She found that, early in the development of a tendon, mesenchymal cells were close together and formed a syncytium; the boundaries between individual cells were by no means distinct. As development proceeded, dense little dots appeared; these were about 80 Å in diameter and were seen close to the cell boundaries that were, by this time, becoming dimly apparent. That the dots were cross sections through collagenic filaments was established from sections in which they could be visualized longitudinally (Fig. 147). As development proceeded, further filaments were seen; these became gathered into bundles. Some filaments seemed to be in the cytoplasm immediately beneath the cell surfaces, while others were seen clearly between cells (Fig. 147). The periodicity of the filaments was at first about 210 Å; only later did the typical periodicity of collagen become apparent. Throughout development the individual filaments became thicker and thicker, even though most were then clearly outside cells.

Porter investigated the same problem in tissue cultures and found that fibrils developed at, or immediately beneath, the cell surfaces. Wassermann found that what he terms "primary fibrils" may be synthesized inside the cytoplasm, but true fibrils are formed in intercellular sites. As more and more E/M studies continue to be made on this subject the evidence for intracellular fiber formation becomes less and less convincing, and it now seems clear that collagen fibers are synthesized at cell surfaces or even farther away from the cells.

The formation of dentin in the developing tooth offers particular advantages for studying the formation of collagen. The process of dentin formation will be described in detail in Chapter 23; for our purpose here it is enough to observe that the cells in this region that are the counterparts of the fibroblasts of ordinary tissue are called odontoblasts. Odontoblasts are more or less columnar in form and are lined up beside each other around the inner surface of the shell of the tooth; the latter becomes steadily thicker because of collagen and other intercellular substances being laid down at the ends of the odontoblasts that abut on the inner surface of the shell. Since collagen appears at only one end of each odontoblast (the end that abuts on the den-

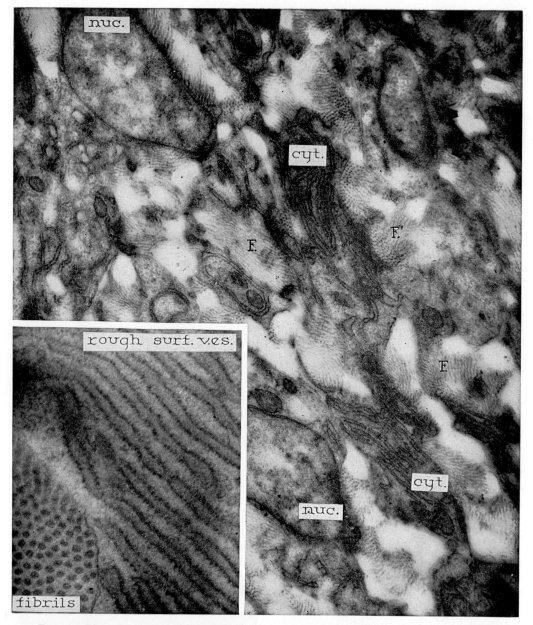

FIG. 147. Electron micrograph (× 27,000) of a section of developing tendon of fowl, showing fibroblasts with their cytoplasmic processes forming a network. Collagenic fibrils appear at the edges of the processes and so are deposited in the interstices of the cytoplasmic network. (*Inset*) Electron micrograph (× 54,000) showing the association between flattened rough-surfaced membranous vesicles of the cytoplasm and collagenic fibrils that have formed at the cell surface. (Jackson, S. F.: Proc. Roy. Soc., London, s.B *144*:556)

tin), its formation is relatively easy to follow, and Carneiro and Leblond have taken advantage of this fact and have studied its formation by giving young mice labeled glycine, an amino acid that enters into the composition of collagen, whose passage they followed by radioautographs prepared from animals at different times after the labeled glycine was given. They found that the label appeared in the cytoplasm of the odontoblasts 30 minutes after the labeled glycine was given. By 4 hours the label had moved outside the cell into the site where collagen was forming, and in 35 hours it was out in the organized intercellular substance of the dentin proper. The rapid passage of the label from the cytoplasm of the cell into the site where collagenic intercellular substance was appearing could scarcely be explained by fibrils being formed within the cell and then extruded. The findings strongly support the concept that some precursor substance in which glycine is incorporated is synthesized in the cytoplasm and secreted through the end of the cell where it becomes polymerized into collagen.

With the E/M, the cytoplasm of fibroblasts that are synthesizing collagen or its precursor contain abundant flattened rough-surfaced vesicles (Fig. 147). As has already been pointed out, rough-surfaced flattened vesicles generally are associated with the synthesis of protein for secretion, so it might be expected that the basophilia, obvious with the light microscope in fibroblasts that are producing precursor substances for fibril formation, would be shown by electron microscopy to be due to an abundance of rough-surfaced flattened vesicles in the cytoplasm.

The formation of the amorphous components of intercellular substance has not been studied as yet as effectively as the formation of fibrils. However, it seems very probable that at least part of it is synthesized simultaneously with fibrils. Some of it acts to cement fibrils together so that they can become fibers. In loose connective tissue it could be assumed that amorphous material made by fibroblasts would also act as a ground substance in which the fibers would lie.

3. Macrophages. Next to fibroblasts these are the commonest cells of connective tissue. They are often termed *histiocytes*. Less commonly there are termed *resting wandering cells* or *clasmatocytes*.

They may be either ovoid or irregular in shape, with many cytoplasmic processes. In freshly made teased preparations of areolar tissue stained either with methylene blue or one of the Romanovsky-type blood stains, or in sections of ordinary material, ovoid macrophages sometimes can be distinguished by their shape. But if they are not ovoid, or if their

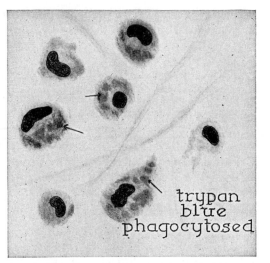

FIG. 148. Drawing of a group of macrophages (under oil-immersion) which have phagocytosed trypan blue in an area of loose connective tissue into which trypan blue and some bacteria were injected. Observe that the nuclei of macrophages tend to be indented, smaller and more deeply stained than those of fibroblasts.

cytoplasm does not show to advantage, an inspection of their nuclei may serve to identify them. The *nucleus* of a macrophage differs from that of a fibroblast with regard to its size, shape and staining reaction. It is smaller, indented on one side and more deeply stained (Fig. 148).

The easiest way to study macrophages in areolar tissue is to take advantage of their phagocytic abilities and inject the areolar tissue of a living animal with a suspension or a solution of some material that will be phagocytosed and therefore will come to lie within their cytoplasm and so serve to identify them. They readily phagocytose certain colloidal dyes termed *vital stains*. Trypan blue is one of these, and if a freshly made 1 per cent solution of this dye is injected into the areolar tissue of an experimental animal, sections cut from the site of injection a day or two afterward will reveal large numbers of macrophages in the area, with their cytoplasm containing accumulations of the injected trypan blue. (Fig. 148). If H and E sections are prepared from such material, it may be difficult to distinguish the phagocytosed trypan blue, which is in the cytoplasm of the macrophages, from their nuclei, which are colored blue by the hematoxylin. However, a little practice will soon enable the observer to make the distinction readily between the phagocytosed trypan blue and the nuclear material.

If trypan blue is injected into the areolar tissue of a normal animal, as described above, and if sterile precautions are purposely avoided so that some bacteria, as well as trypan blue, are injected into the areolar tissue, the injected material incites a pronounced inflammatory reaction in the areolar tissue and results in an increase in the number of macrophages in and about the injured area. Some of the extra macrophages that appear in inflammatory reactions have a local, and others a hematogenous, origin. Some develop locally as a result of cell division of the pre-existing macrophages of the part; others may arise locally from the free rounded mesenchymal cells of great potentiality of the part. However, many have a hematogenous origin, arising from monocytes that leave the capillaries and the venules of the part to migrate into the inflammed area.

FINE STRUCTURE. The E/M has revealed interesting detail in macrophages, particularly with regard to the configuration of the cell membrane; this is probably of significance with regard to the mechanism of the phagocytosis.

The cell membrane of a macrophage is characteristically uneven because it extends outward from the cell body to cover pseudopodia and inward into the cytoplasm to line pits and clefts. When macrophages are fitted closely together, as they may be in lining sinusoids (in this site they would also be known as reticuloendothelial cells), the pseudopodia of one may fit into the clefts of the next, as has been shown so beautifully by Palade, one of whose illustrations is Figure 246. When pseudopodia that extend into clefts of adjacent cells are sectioned, either at right angles or obliquely, circular or oval areas surrounded by a double membrane may be seen (Fig. 246). The outer layer of the double membrane is the cell membrane that lines the cleft into which the pseudopodium extends,

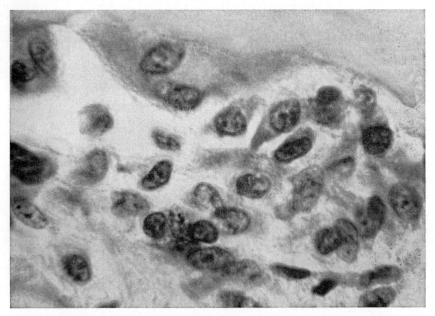

FIG. 149. High-power photomicrograph of an H and E section cut from the subcutaneous tissue of a rabbit at the site where some fragments of dead bone had been implanted. A portion of a fragment may be seen at the top of the illustration. Young connective tissue cells are multiplying beneath the fragment, and at the upper left some have fused to form 2 small giant cells. The cells to the right of the middle are preparing to fuse. Note that any intercellular substance that would lie between them would be incorporated into the giant cell that would result from the fusion.

and the inner layer of the double membrane is the cell membrane that covers the pseudopodium that extends into the cleft.

When macrophages are not fitted closely together, the shape of their pseudopodia is not limited by the shape of the clefts into which they must fit. Under these conditions the pseudopodia may have the form of thin, flat sheets that extend out from the main cell body more or less parallel with one another (Fig. 150). When leaflike pseudopodia are cut in section they present an appearance somewhat similar to that seen when one views a Venetian blind from one end; however, the leaves of cytoplasm are relatively longer than the leaves of a Venetian blind. Each leaflike pseudopodium is *covered* with the cell membrane; therefore, this *lines* the grooves between each two pseudopodia. Phagocytosis probably occurs as follows: the particle that is to be phagocytosed comes to lie in the bottom of the groove between two leaflike pseudopodia. Next, either one of two things can happen, or, what is more probable, a combination of the two happens. Either the leaflike pseudopodia meet and fuse over the particle, or the bottom of the groove in which

the particle lies sinks deeply into the cytoplasm, and the edges of the groove above the particle meet and fuse. By either mechanism, or by a combination of the two, the particle comes to lie in the cytoplasm surrounded by a membrane which shortly before was cell membrane. Palade has pointed out that strings of smooth-surfaced membranous vesicles commonly are seen extending into the cytoplasm from the bottoms of the grooves between pseudopodia; this is regarded as evidence, as was explained in Chapter 4, that smooth-surfaced vesicles develop from the cell membrane as a result of invaginations of the cell membrane becoming pinched off in the cytoplasm. The smooth-surfaced vesicles that contain phagocytosed material probably originate in the same manner. Therefore, for a time each phagocytosed particle is surrounded by a membrane, but later the membrane disappears, as it has around the phagocytosed material in Figure 246.

Foreign Body Giant Cells. Any foreign material that gains entrance to loose connective tissue and does not consist of particles small enough to be phagocytosed by individual macrophages may incite the formation of *for-*

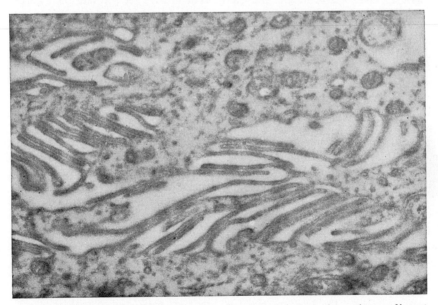

Fig. 150. Electron micrograph ($\times$ 24,000) of a section cut from tissue adjacent to where agar-agar had been injected into the subcutaneous tissue of a rabbit. This picture shows the cell borders of macrophages that, in all probability, are fusing to form a giant cell. Note the thin platelike processes that extend from the surfaces of the macrophages and how they interdigitate with one another. (Preparation by A. F. Howatson)

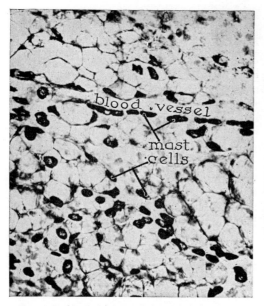 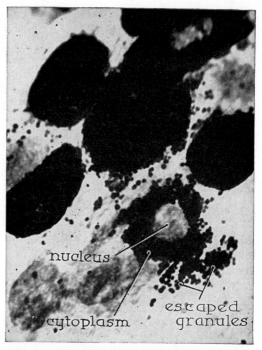

FIG. 151. (A, *Left*) Low-power photomicrograph of a spread of fat tissue (from a rat) containing a blood vessel. It was stained lightly with methylene blue. At this magnification, the mast cells show as dark-blue blotches. It is to be observed that many of them are distributed along the blood vessel, which courses across the tissue. (B, *Right*) Oil-immersion photomicrograph of a spread of areolar tissue (from a rat) stained with methylene blue. Several dark-stained mast cells may be seen. Granules are so densely packed in most that no details can be seen. However, the lowermost one is broken up, and some of its granules can be seen to have escaped into the adjacent area. Its nucleus is also apparent.

eign body giant cells. These, as their name implies, are very large and contain a great many nuclei (Fig. 149). There is no evidence to suggest that they form as a result of the repeated division of the nucleus of a macrophage without the cytoplasm subsequently dividing, because mitotic figures are not seen in them. The usual view is that they originate from the fusion of monocytes or macrophages, and indeed this phenomenon has been observed in tissue cultures. Their purpose would seem to be that of providing a cell large enough to enclose or wall off masses of debris that cannot be incorporated into a single phagocyte.

It is very easy to produce these cells experimentally by injecting foreign material, such as agar-agar, into the loose connective tissue of an animal. Foreign body giant cells soon form around the margins of the larger masses of injected foreign material and completely surround the smaller masses. If this procedure is performed in animals that are being given vital stains such as trypan blue, the vital stain can be found later in some of the foreign body giant cells. Sometimes this is taken as an indication that foreign body giant cells are phagocytic. The finding of vital stain in them could be an indication, not that they themselves are actively phagocytic, but that the cells that fused to form them were phagocytic and had accumulated some vital stain in their cytoplasm before they fused. In our opinion, foreign body giant cells, once they have formed, are not very active.

The formation of foreign body giant cells is illustrated in Figure 149, and fully formed ones (osteoclasts) are shown in Figure 175.

FINE STRUCTURE. From some thin sections that we have studied with the E/M, there is evidence to suggest that as a prelude to fusion the cytoplasmic processes of adjacent macrophages interdigitate with each other in a very extensive manner (Fig. 150). Hence, in a sense, giant cell formation may be an expression of the cells attempting to phagocytose each other's processes.

4. Mast Cells. These are large mesenchymal-derived cells which often give the impression of being overstuffed with granules. The word *mast* is derived from the German and is related to feeding. Ehrlich, who first described them, thought they represented an overnourished variety of connective tissue cell.

Distribution. Mast cells are much more numerous in areolar and certain other types of connective tissue than is suggested by the study of routine H and E sections because their granules may not show up clearly in this type of preparation. With proper staining they are commonly seen in many connective tissues but are particularly numerous along blood vessels and also along lymphatics and small nerves. Their distribution differs somewhat in relation to species. They are very numerous in the capsule of the livers of the ox, the pig and the dog. Padawer has pointed out that peritoneal fluid is a good source of mast cells for study.

Form and Staining Properties. The areolar tissue of rodents contains many mast cells, and it is easy to study them by injecting some 1 per cent methylene blue into the areolar tissue of a rat and then making a teased preparation of the injected tissue. Under low power the mast cells appear as large, dark, oval cells that are scattered diffusely throughout the areolar tissue as well as being arranged along blood vessels (Fig. 151 A). Closer inspection of mast cells in such a preparation is often disappointing because neither the centrally placed round-to-oval nucleus nor the cytoplasmic granules show to advantage. The cytoplasm is so stuffed with granules that the centrally placed nucleus is hidden; furthermore, the granules are so tightly packed together that their individual outlines cannot be seen. However, in making this type of preparation, many mast cells are usually ruptured and their granules escape into the surrounding tissue, and in these instances their granules are clearly evident (Fig. 151 B).

In sections also mast cells are so commonly stuffed with granules that their nuclei are hidden. However, in thin sections in which mast cells are actually cut into slices, their nuclei can often be seen (Fig. 152). The nu-

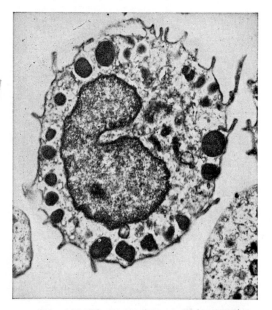

FIG. 152. Electron micrograph ($\times$ 2500) of section of a young mast cell from the peritoneal fluid of a rat. The nucleus is obvious with the Golgi apparatus adjacent to it on the right. In the cytoplasm are some dark granules which vary in size. At the cell surface, the cell membrane forms microvilli. Granular endoplasmic reticulum and free RNA granules are scarce. In a fully mature mast cell, the cytoplasm contains many more granules than are seen here. (Preparation by Dr. A. L. Burton)

clei can also be seen well in mast cells that have extruded most of their granules (Fig. 153).

In relation to other types of cytoplasmic granules, those of the mast cells are large. They vary somewhat in size, the larger ones being about twice the size of the smaller ones. They possess the property of staining *metachromatically* (described in Chapter 5). Commonly toluidine blue and azure A are employed to demonstrate their metachromasia, and with these blue dyes they are colored red. Moreover, the granules of mast cells obtained from man are generally P.A.S. positive. Bensley has shown that pinacyanol erythrosinate is a very effective stain for the granules of mast cells.

In order to discuss mast cells further it is necessary to comment on a material known as *heparin*, because, as we shall see, this material can be extracted from mast cells.

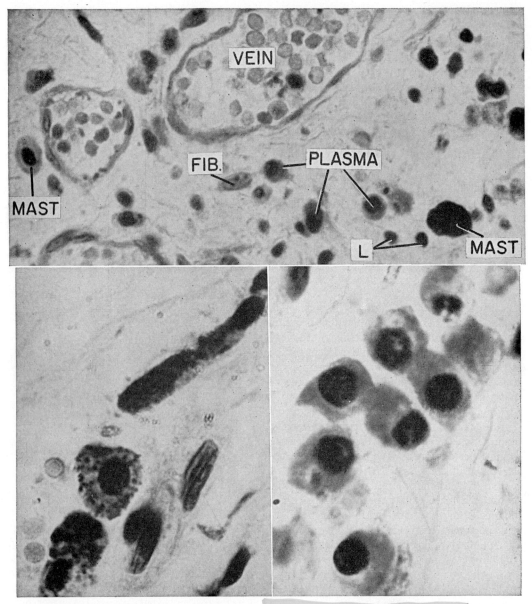

FIG. 153. Photomicrographs of sections of loose connective tissue (areolar tissue) near a lymph node. The upper picture shows two venules with erythrocytes in them. At the left a mast cell that has lost most of its granules can be seen. The little dots in the wall and lumen of the venules beside it stain like mast cell granules and may represent the passage of granules through the wall of this blood vessel. A fibroblast nucleus (FIB) can be seen near the center. To the right of this are three plasma cells and then a mast cell that is so stuffed with granules its nucleus is obscured. At the lower left, mast cells, and at the lower right, plasma cells, are seen at higher magnification in the same kind of tissue.

HEPARIN. In 1916, in the course of some experiments being carried on in Howell's laboratory, in which extracts from different organs were being tested with regard to their ability to hasten the clotting of the blood with which they were mixed, McLean discovered that one particular extractive of liver, obtained by the use of certain solvents and procedures, did not hasten the clotting of blood but instead delayed it. Howell and Holt carried this work further and succeeded in preparing extracts of liver that had a very potent anticoagulant effect. They named the active principle in this extract *heparin* (*hepar* = liver). Subsequently, it has been discovered that heparin may be extracted from many different organs and tissues; also, that the relative amount in different organs and tissues varies considerably with regard to species and that it seemed to prevent the clotting of blood in a test tube by exerting an antithrombin or perhaps an antiprothrombin effect.

Since many deaths are caused by thrombosis occurring in the arteries and the veins of man, the discovery of heparin aroused hopes that it might find a use in preventing thrombosis (intravascular clotting) and, indeed, this hope was realized for it was shown that, in addition to acting as an anticoagulant, it also helps in keeping platelets from agglutinating, and administration of heparin to individuals threatened with fatal thrombosis has saved many lives. It has also greatly enlarged the scope of blood-vessel surgery. It is to be realized that operations on blood vessels involve a great risk of thrombi forming at the sites where the cut ends of vessels are sutured together. Heparinizing individuals has made feasible operations formerly considered to involve too great a risk of thrombosis, and, pioneered by Murray, surgery in this field has made great advances.

Another action of heparin has been discovered recently; if it is injected into animals it acts to clear the blood of fat.

RELATION OF HEPARIN TO MAST CELLS. In our discussion of the amorphous intercellular substances it was pointed out that one group of them was sulfated. Sulfated polysaccharides have been referred to by several European workers for some years as sulfuric acid esters of great molecular weight. In 1936, Lison discovered that these substances stained metachromatically; for example, toluidine blue colored them red. A year or so later Jorpes found that heparin also exhibited metachromasia and this, with further work on his part, together with the studies of Charles and Scott, have shown that heparin is this type of substance: a sulfuric acid ester of high molecular weight. Since the cytoplasmic granules of mast cells were known to be metachromatic, it is not surprising that they soon came to be suspected as the source of heparin. Holmgren

and Wilander, and later Wilander alone, made studies in this connection and showed that the amount of heparin that could be extracted from an organ or tissue was related to the number of mast cells it contains, so, for this reason, in addition to the fact that both mast-cell granules and heparin are metachromatic, these workers suggested that mast cells manufacture heparin. Of course, the fact that heparin can be extracted from mast cells does not prove that they produce it, for it could be argued that they merely segregate it or some sulfated compound from the intercellular substance.

Riley and his co-workers have shown that mast cells contain considerable amounts of histamine, which, it will be recalled, seems to be involved in allergic and inflammatory reactions. Indeed, it has been shown that a profound hypersensitivity reaction (called anaphylactic shock) is associated with the discharge of both histamine and heparin from mast cells. Also, histamine has been found in considerable amounts in the basophilic leukocytes of the blood, the granules of which, like those of mast cells, are metachromatic.

More recently still it has been shown that mast cells contain serotonin, the action of which was described in connection with platelets.

Origin and Maintenance of the Mast Cell Population. There is general agreement that mitotic figures are not seen in mast cells. It has been suggested that they may divide by amitosis, but it seems more probable that all mast cells develop from less differentiated cells that can divide and so maintain a population of cells from which mast cells can develop. There is no universal agreement as to which cells of the mesenchymal family serve as a source of mast cells; it could be the undifferentiated mesenchymal cell as is indicated in Figure 147 or perhaps the free rounded cell of great potentiality or one of its less differentiated descendants.

Fine Structure. With the E/M the cytoplasm of mast cells is packed with granules, except in a narrow zone surrounding the nucleus where they occur sparingly or not at all. Figure 152 illustrates a young mast cell, and it shows relatively few granules.

Each granule has a district boundary which suggests enclosure in a membranous vesicle. The internal structure of granules has been described by various authors as filamentous, reticular or vacuolar. In any given mast cell, the granules vary in size and density. Mitochondria are few and most common immediately adjacent to the nucleus. A Golgi apparatus is sometimes seen, and it also is close to the nucleus. In contrast with the fibroblast, granular endoplasmic reticulum and free RNA granules are both scarce. The cell membrane usually shows microvilli, and these are thought by Burton and Bensley to participate in pinocytosis. These authors have suggested that the function of mast cells is to remove and segregate abnormal or altered substances in the environment rather than to synthesize and secrete. Certainly, the scarcity of granular endoplasmic reticulum would indicate that synthesis of material for secretion is not a major function of these cells.

SUMMARY OF FUNCTION. Since heparin is an antiagglutinant and an anticoagulant found in mast cells, and since mast cells may lie along blood vessels, it might be thought that there is good evidence for considering that mast cells secrete heparin into the blood stream where it acts normally to keep blood from clotting and, indeed, appearances suggestive of mast cell granules passing through the wells of small blood vessels can be seen in properly stained sections. However, so far, it has been impossible to demonstrate that there is a sufficient quantity of heparin in normal blood to be able to assign this function to mast cells.

The function of mast cells as histamine liberators now seems to be well established, although they are not the only cells that can liberate histamine. The release of histamine and some discussion of its effects in allergy is given on page 184.

The reason for mast cells containing serotonin is as yet obscure. The functions of serotonin are discussed in connection with platelets in Chapter 9.

Asboe-Hanson's studies indicate a relationship between mast cells and the hyaluronic acid content of tissue. He points out, for example, that there are a great many mast cells in synovial membranes, and it is known that the hyaluronic acid of synovial fluid must be produced in these membranes. It is obvious that in our present state of knowledge it is quite difficult to be very precise about all of the possible functions of mast cells.

5. Plasma Cells. It is difficult to decide whether they should be considered as a type of connective tissue cell or as one of the cell types of hemopoietic tissue. They are found in connective tissues, especially in those that support wet epithelial surfaces, but they are much more abundant in hemopoietic tissue, particularly lymphatic tissue. Therefore, we shall consider these briefly here and reserve a full description of them for our discussions of lymphatic tissue in Chapter 18.

Plasma cells are specialized to produce antibodies. Plasma cells develop from precursor cells in sites to which new antigens gain entrance; this is why they are seen so often under wet epithelial surfaces through which absorption occurs (Fig. 153) and in areas that are sites of inflammation.

MICROSCOPIC APPEARANCE. Plasma cells can be seen in sections stained by ordinary methods.

To recognize a plasma cell, the student should look for a rounded cell that has an eccentrically placed spherical nucleus (Figs. 153, 235). The latter contains coarse, angular, densely staining flakes of chromatin that sometimes (but only sometimes, too much has been made of this) are arranged in the nucleus like the hours on the face of a clock or like the spokes of a wheel; accordingly, the nucleus

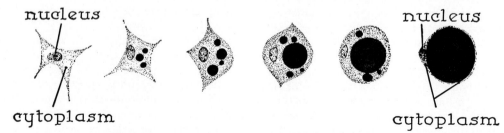

nucleus   nucleus

cytoplasm   cytoplasm

FIG. 154. Diagrams showing the changes in appearance caused by a cell's taking in globules of fat until it finally becomes a typical fat cell with a "signet-ring" appearance.

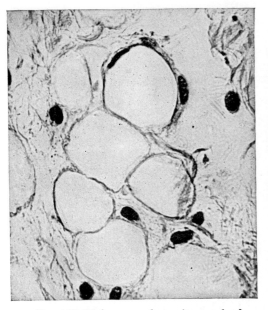

FIG. 155. High-power photomicrograph of a section of areolar tissue that contained several fat cells.

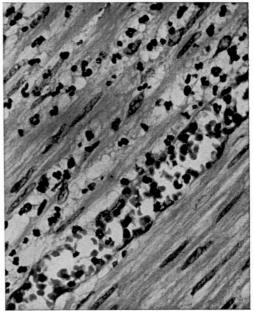

FIG. 156. High-power photomicrograph of a section through the muscular part of the wall of an appendix that was acutely inflamed and removed at operation. A small venule runs from the lower left corner to just above the middle of the right border. It contains both erythrocytes and leukocytes. Neutrophilic leukocytes can be seen migrating through the wall of the vessel out into the swollen spaces between the smooth muscle fibers. The neutrophils can be recognized by their lobed nuclei.

is said to have sometimes a clockface or cartwheel appearance. The cytoplasm generally is strongly basophilic and reveals a pale area in the region where the centrosphere or Golgi apparatus would be located (Fig. 153). The pale area sometimes is rounded with ill-defined edges, but it may be crescentic (Fig. 153), following the curved border of the nucleus but removed from it by a very short distance.

Most plasma cells *seen in sections* may be crowded against each other; if so, they may be pressed out of a spherical shape into other shapes (Fig. 153). Furthermore, the nucleus may not have the classic eccentric position in the cell but may lie more toward its center, and the pale area in the cytoplasm may not be very obvious.

The comparative size of plasma cells and mast cells is shown in Figure 153.

The origin, the fine structure and the details of the function of plasma cells are given in Chapter 18.

6. Fat Cells. These cells are a normal component of areolar tissue. They occur singly or in clumps (Fig. 155). Before a fat cell stores fat it resembles a fibroblast (Fig. 154). This has led to the view that fat cells are nothing more than fibroblasts that have stored

fat in their cytoplasm. But it seems more likely that fat cells, though resembling fibroblasts, represent a special strain of mesenchymal cells that are more specialized than fibroblasts with regard to storing fat in their cytoplasm.

In storing fat, a cell accumulates small droplets in its cytoplasm (Fig. 154). The accumulated droplets fuse, and, as the cell continues to take in more, they too fuse with the fat already accumulated. Finally, the cell contains one huge droplet (Fig. 154, *right*). This greatly expands the cell, with the result that the cytoplasm becomes reduced to little more than a peripheral film. In sections, the site of the nucleus is indicated by a slight bulge and this, together with the ringlike appearance of the cytoplasm that surrounds the droplet, gives the fat cell a "signet-ring" appearance (Figs. 154, *right,* and 155).

7. Blood Leukocytes. As was noted in Chapter 8, leukocytes do not perform their chief function in the blood stream; they use it merely as a means for being transported to the parts of the body where they leave it to enter the connective tissue. Therefore, it is to be expected that blood leukocytes sometimes will be seen in some of the loose connective tissue of the body. When they are seen their significance must be assessed, as will become apparent in the following section.

NEUTROPHILS are seen only occasionally in normal loose connective tissue. When encountered in sections their cytoplasm generally does not show up clearly; hence, they must be recognized by their nuclei, which usually have 3 tiny lobes (Fig. 156). Isolated neutrophils sometimes are seen among the cells of the epithelial membranes which they are traversing. Even a small accumulation of neutrophils in loose connective tissue indicates the existence of an acute inflammatory process in that tissue. For example, if the vermiform appendix is removed from an individual following a diagnosis of acute appendicitis, the removed appendix is sectioned in a pathology laboratory and examined with the microscope. A very important criterion as to whether the diagnosis was correct or incorrect is whether or not accumulations of neutrophils can be found in the loose connective tissue that supports the epithelial lining of the appendix.

Acute appendicitis is an example of an acute infection. To cause it bacteria gain entrance somehow through the epithelial lining of the appendix and multiply, first in the inner part of the wall. But they may spread throughout the whole wall. The tissues of the appendix react to this infection by demonstrating the classic signs of acute inflammation. The blood vessels become dilated and engorged, and the smaller ones leak plasma. Neutrophils are delivered into the blood from the bone marrow at an increasing rate and come to the appendix in great numbers. They stick to the walls of the smaller blood vessels (Fig. 156) and migrate through the walls of the blood vessels into the adjacent tissue (Fig. 156) where they phagocytose bacteria and so aid in overcoming the bacterial invader. Plasma cells help also

by making antibodies that react against the bacteria and their toxins (see Chap. 18).

EOSINOPHILS may be seen in many of the different loose connective tissues of the body, particularly in those that support wet epithelial membranes. The presence of a few scattered eosinophils is not regarded as being of pathologic significance. If they are numerous it may indicate an allergic reaction, or, if very numerous, a subacute type of inflammatory condition in that tissue.

LYMPHOCYTES are relatively common in loose connective tissue; indeed, in the loose connective tissue that supports wet epithelial membranes they often are seen in the form of little nonencapsulated nodules. Nodules of lymphocytes, as we shall learn when lymphatic tissue is considered, constitute one of the structural arrangements in which lymphatic tissue is disposed in the body; hence, a nodule of lymphocytes in loose connective tissue generally is regarded as a small depot of lymphatic tissue inserted, as it were, into loose connective tissue. This is a normal phenomenon. As we shall learn later, the lymphocytes in nodules are produced in the nodules; they do not come to the nodules by way of the blood stream. When lymphocytes are scattered diffusely in loose connective tissue the microscopic picture is more difficult to interpret because it may be of pathologic significance. Generally, it is assumed that lymphocytes that are not arranged into typical nodules but are scattered about in loose connective tissue arrived in the tissue by way of the blood stream. Such accumulations may be of physiologic or pathologic significance. For example, lymphocytes accumulate regularly around the rapidly forming secretory units of the breast in the early stages of pregnancy; since this is usual it is assumed that they play some physiologic role in the process. But accumulations of lymphocytes in loose connective tissue, where they are not usually present, is taken to indicate the existence of a low-grade or a chronic inflammatory reaction in that tissue. It takes a considerable amount of experience to be able to assess the importance of accumulations of lymphocytes in loose ordinary connective tissue.

MONOCYTES are rare in normal loose connective tissue. Macrophages, of course, are

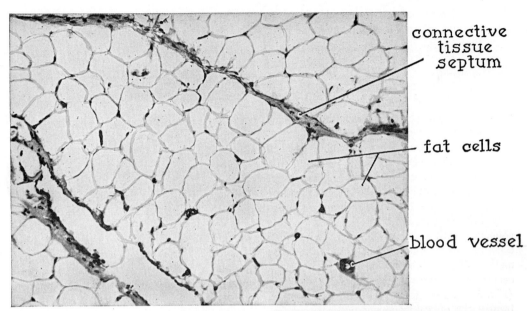

connective
tissue
septum

fat cells

blood vessel

FIG. 157. (A, *Top*) Low-power photomicrograph of a section of the omentum of a dog. It shows aggregations of fat cells (small lobules) separated from one another by partitions of connective tissue which carry blood vessels throughout the tissue. (B, *Bottom*) Medium-power photomicrograph of a section cut from the brown fat of a rat. In this type of fat the nuclei of the fat cells tend to be located more centrally, and the globules of fat do not all fuse together. Therefore, such cytoplasm as is present has a vacuolated appearance.

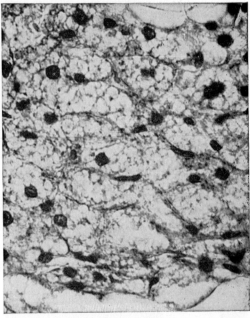

normal residents of such tissues. The presence of numerous monocytes indicates the presence of an inflammatory process.

ADIPOSE TISSUE

This differs little from areolar tissue except that it contains a much higher percentage of cells of the type disposed to store fat. For support it has partitions of collagenic and elastic fibers running through it (Fig. 157 A). Fibroblasts, macrophages and mast cells are present in it, but by far the great majority of its cells are fat cells. These are more or less organized into lobules separated by the partitions of connective tissue mentioned above (Fig. 157 A). The partitions carry arteries and veins into the adipose tissue and from these partitions arterioles and venules enter the lobules themselves. Here the arterioles break up into extensive capillary networks which supply the fat cells; these are necessary, for fat cells must obtain the fat they store from capillaries immediately adjacent to them.

Adipose tissue is more or less concentrated in certain parts of the body, and these parts are called *fat depots* (for example, the subcutaneous tissue of the belly and the buttocks).

In rodents in particular, fat cells of a special character are present in certain sites. In these, the individual fat droplets in the cytoplasm do not become confluent (Fig. 157 B). This type of fat is termed *brown fat* and it makes up the so-called hibernating glands of these animals.

Transplantation of Adipose Tissue. Peer has studied the fate of free transplants of adipose tissue. He found that adipose tissue from one person transplanted to another always atrophied and, in the end, all that remained was a fibrous scar. On the other hand, he found that transplanted autogenous adipose tissue survived in part. The circulation in the free grafts became re-established rather soon, probably because capillaries of the host became connected with vessels of the transplant, which thereupon functioned again; this is the same method of revascularization that we observed occurring in full-thickness skin transplants (Fig. 372). Peer found that, on the average, transplants of autogenous adipose tissue became reduced in size to approximately one half their original bulk, so it would seem that roughly half of the cells of the transplant survive transplantation. Peer believes that if the transplant later increases in size it is due to the cells accumulating more fat and not to their multiplying.

DENSE FIBROUS TISSUE

Most of the mesenchymal cells that form this type of connective tissue develop into fibroblasts. These form abundant quantities of collagen and in some instances some elastin. The production of fibers is so great in this type of tissue that intercellular substance becomes its prominent feature. Such tissue has great tensile strength. Since it is composed chiefly of intercellular substance, it requires little blood supply. Therefore, dense fibrous connective tissue is supplied only sparingly with capillaries; it is a relatively nonvascular tissue.

If tensile strength is required in only one direction, as in a tendon, the bundles of collagenic fibers of the tissue are disposed in that direction. This type is called *regularly arranged dense fibrous tissue* (Fig. 84). In longitudinal sections it reveals parallel bundles of collagenic fibers with adjacent bundles separated from each other by rows of flattened fibroblast nuclei (Fig. 84). In cross sections, the fibroblasts appear star-shaped because

their processes extend out between the various bundles that surround them.

If tensile strength is required in several planes, bundles of collagenic fibers are disposed in several planes and interwoven with one another to form a dense cohesive tissue. Fibroblasts are disposed in the interstices between bundles. The deeper part of the skin provides a good example for studying this type of tissue (see Chap. 22).

Dense fibrous tissue comprises tendons, most of the skin, aponeuroses, deep fascia, the capsules of many organs and many other parts of the body. In some sites, collagenic bundles of which it is composed are woven in such a way, and provided with enough elastic fibers, to permit a certain amount of stretch. Macrophages and undifferentiated mesenchymal cells are scattered through dense fibrous tissue but they are not so numerous as they are in areolar tissue.

SOME DETAILS ABOUT TENDONS

Development. Tendons, as they develop in the embryo, first appear as dense bundles of fibroblasts that are oriented in the same plane and packed closely together. The fibroblasts proliferate to permit the growth of the tendon. But, as development proceeds, more and more fibers appear between the fibroblasts which become arranged into rows (Fig. 84), and eventually the character of the structure changes from being primarily cellular to being primarily intercellular substance.

Blood Supply. During development, when tendons are cellular, they have a reasonably good blood supply; it is obvious that intercellular substances cannot be built from nothing, and the materials for the construction of the fiber bundles must be brought to the fibroblasts by capillaries. But when the fiber bundles of collagen become built up, the capillary blood supply within the tendon bundles almost entirely disappears. The fibroblasts which lie between the fiber bundles become dormant, and, of course, the intercellular substance itself requires no nourishment.

Tendon Sheaths. Some tendons, in certain sites, where they otherwise might rub against bone or other friction-generating surfaces, are enclosed in sheaths. Actually, a tendon sheath consists of two sheaths. The outer one is a connective tissue tube, and its exterior is attached to the structures that surround it. The inner sheath directly encloses the tendon and is firmly attached to it. There is a space between the inner and the outer sheaths, and this is filled with ground substance diluted with tissue fluid; this makes a slippery sol. This is termed *synovial fluid,* and it is discussed in detail in Chapter 16 of this book.

The inner surface of the outer tendon sheath and the outer surface of the inner sheath do not possess a continuous lining of cells, so the surfaces that glide over one another are mostly surfaces of intercellular substances, chiefly collagen, along which, however, some cells are scattered (Fig. 220). The synovial fluid between the two sheaths is an excellent lubricant.

Regeneration of Tendons. The severance of tendons is of common occurrence in accidents, and it is fortunate that, if they are properly treated, they heal excellently and in due course become as strong as before. Soon after a tendon is cut, fibroblasts from the inner tendon sheath or, if the tendon has no proper sheath, from the loose connective tissue around its periphery, grow into the gap, proliferating all the while. Gradually, they become orientated in the axis of the tendon. Here they reinact the same scenes that are to be witnessed when a tendon develops. At first they have a good capillary blood supply and they produce much collagen which becomes deposited in bundles between them, and so arranged in the long axis of the tendon. Some of the cells grow into the cut ends of the tendon and cement the new collagen that is being formed to the old. As more and more collagen is deposited between the fibroblasts the capillary blood supply diminishes, and the site of the repair eventually becomes almost free of capillaries. It is not generally believed that the fibroblasts between the fiber bundles of the original tendon contribute very much to the repair process; most of the fibroblasts that repair the tendon, as noted before, come from the inner tendon sheath, or if there is no sheath, from the loose connective tissue at the periphery of the tendon. We shall find that broken bones are repaired in much the same way.

Tendon Insertions. Near tendon insertions the fibroblasts between the fiber bundles of a tendon are somewhat different from ordinary fibroblasts in that they exhibit certain of the properties of the cells that produce cartilage or bone. Hence, at their points of insertion, some tendons consist of a tissue which has the properties of both dense regularly arranged fibrous tissue and cartilage; this is called *fibrocartilage* (Fig. 162). The way that tendons are inserted into bones by means of *Sharpey's fibers* is illustrated in Figure 389 and into cartilage in Figure 219, but it is described more conveniently after we have studied cartilage and bone.

The Transplantation of Fascia and Tendon. Fascia and tendon consist chiefly of the intercellular substance collagen, and the fibroblasts that each contains are mostly of a mature type, having completed their work of producing the intercellular substance that surrounds them. The question arises as to whether or not the fibroblasts of fascia and tendon live after free transplantation. Also, there is the question of whether or not they can divide, with the daughter cells they produce manufacturing new intercellular substance.

The evidence obtained from experimental studies in this field is very conflicting. In many studies healthy appearing cells have been seen in transplanted autogenous fascia and tendon, but it is difficult to know whether these represent the original cells of the transplanted tissue or new ones that have invaded it from the region into which the tissue was transplanted. Perhaps it is not very important to settle this point, because the value of these transplants hinges chiefly on the persistence of their intercellular substance. It seems more probable that the cells that produce the new intercellular substance which cements the transplant to whatever it is attached come from younger fibroblasts in the region rather than from the transplant itself.

The problem of transplanting tendon to bone is an involved one because this requires that the fibers of the transplanted tendon either become buried in bone substance or attached to something that is already well anchored in bone. A subsequent discussion on Sharpey's fibers will be informative on this matter.

Homogenous transplants of fascia and tendon sometimes are used. The cells of these would not survive, but the intercellular substance could persist, and it is possible that it could be replaced gradually by new intercellular substance made by cells of the host. Since even foreign intercellular substances can act as antigens, it would seem that, even if the cells of autogenous transplanted fascia and tendon do not survive, it would be better to employ autogenous transplants whenever this is possible.

Peer gives a comprehensive review of the controversial literature on this subject.

REFERENCES

GENERAL REFERENCES ON CONNECTIVE TISSUE

Asboe-Hansen, G.: Connective Tissue in Health and Disease, Copenhagen, Munksgaard, 1954.

———: Hormonal effects on connective tissue, Physiol. Rev. *38*:446, 1958.

Baker, B. L., and Abrams, G. D.: The physiology of connective tissue, Ann. Rev. Physiol. *17*:61, 1955.

Bennett, G. A.: Pathology of connective tissue, fibrinoid degeneration *in* Ragan, C. (ed.): Connective Tissues, p. 44, New York, Macy, 1950.

Bloom, W.: Bindegewebe und blutbildende Gewebe *in* v. Mollendorff: Handbuch mikroskopischer Anatomie des Menschen, vol. 2, p. 232, Berlin, Springer, 1927.

———: Morphology of the mesenchymal reactions, Arch. Path. *4*:557, 1927.

SPECIAL REFERENCES ON CONNECTIVE TISSUE

Intercellular Substances—See References for Chapter 6.

FIBROBLASTS AND FORMATION OF INTERCELLULAR SUBSTANCES

Bloom, W.: Fibroblasts and histiocytes *in* Downey's Handbook of Hematology, vol. 2, p. 1335, New York, Hoeber, 1938.

———: Studies on fibers in tissue culture, Arch. exper. Zellforsch. *9*:6, 1929.

Carneiro, J., and Leblond, C. P.: Role of osteoblasts and odontoblasts in secreting the collagen of bone and dentine as shown by radioautography in mice given tritium-labelled glycine, Exper. Cell Res. *18*:291, 1959.

Gross, J., and Schmitt, F. O.: *In vitro* fibrogenesis of collagen *in* Metabolic Interrelations, p. 32, New York, Macy, 1952.

Grossfeld, H., Meyer, K., and Goodman, G.: Differentiation of fibroblasts in tissue culture, as determined by mucopolysaccharide production, Proc. Soc. Exper. Biol. & Med. *88*:31, 1955.

Jackson, S. F.: Fibrogenesis *in vivo* and *in vitro* *in* Randall, J. T., and Jackson, S. F. (eds.): Nature and Structure of Collagen, p. 140, New York, Acad. Press, 1953.

———:The formation of connective and skeletal tissues, Proc. Roy. Soc., London, s. B *142*:536, 1954.

———: The morphogenesis of avian tendon, Proc. Roy. Soc., London, s. B *144*:556, 1956.

Jackson, S. F., and Smith, R. H.: Studies on the biosynthesis of collagen. I. The growth of fowl osteoblasts and the formation of collagen in tissue culture, J. Biophys. & Biochem. Cytol. *3*:897, 1957.

Lewis, M. R.: Development of connective tissue fibers in tissue culture of chick embryos, Contrib. Embryol. *6*:45, 1917.

Maximow, A.: The development of argyrophile and collagenous fibers in tissue cultures, Proc. Soc. Exper. Biol. & Med. *25*:439, 1928.

———: Development of nongranular leucocytes (lymphocytes and monocytes) into polyblasts (macrophages) and fibroblasts *in vitro*, Proc. Soc. Exper. Biol. & Med. *24*:570, 1927.

———: Relation of blood cells to connective tissue and endothelium, Physiol. Rev. *4*:533, 1924.

Muller, T.: The effect of estrogen on the loose connective tissue of the albino rat, Anat. Rec. *111*:355, 1951.

Parker, R. C.: The races that constitute the group of common fibroblasts; differences determined by origin of explant and age of donor, J. Exper. Med. *58*:401, 1933.

Porter, K. R.: The morphogenesis of collagen fibers, Anat. Rec. *112*:74, 1952.

———: Repair process in connective tissues *in* Connective Tissue, p. 126, New York, Macy, 1952.

Porter, K. R., and Pappas, G. D.: Collagen formation of fibroblasts of the chick embryo dermis, J. Biophys. & Biochem. Cytol. *5*:153, 1959.

Porter, K. R., and Vanamee, P.: Observations on the formation of connective tissue fibers, Proc. Soc. Exper Biol. & Med. *71*:513, 1949.

Schmitt, F. O.: Structural proteins of cells and tissues *in* Advances in Protein Chemistry, vol. 1, p. 26, New York, Acad. Press, 1944.

Stearns, M. L.: Studies on the development of connective tissue in transparent chambers in the rabbit's ear, Am. J. Anat. *66*:133, 1939; *67*:55, 1940.

Vorbrodt, A.: Histochemically demonstrable phosphatases and protein synthesis, Exper. Cell Res. *15*:1, 1958.

Wassermann, F.: Fibrillogenesis in the regenerating rat tendon with special reference to growth and composition of the collagenous fibril, Am. J. Anat. *94*:399, 1954.

Wassermann, F., and Kubota, L.: Observations on fibrillogenesis in the connective tissue of the chick embryo with the aid of silver impregnation, J. Biophys. & Biochem. Cytol. (Supp.) 2:67, 1956.

Wolfe, J. M., Burack, E., Lansing, W., and Wright, A. W.: The effect of advancing age on the connective tissue of the uterus, cervix, and vagina of the rat, Am. J. Anat. 70:135, 1942.

MACROPHAGES AND GIANT CELLS

Chèvremont, M.: Recherches sur l'origine, la distribution, les caractères cytologiques et les propriétés biologiques des histiocytes et des macrophages par la méthode de la culture des tissus, Arch. Biol. 53:281, 1942.

Clark, E. R., and Clark, E. L.: Relation of monocytes of the blood to tissue macrophages, Am. J. Anat. 46:149, 1930.

Evans, H. M.: The macrophages of mammals, Am. J. Physiol. 37:243, 1915.

Evans, H. M., and Scott, K.: On the differential reaction to vital dyes exhibited by the two great groups of connective tissue cells, Contrib. Embryol. 10:1, 1921.

Felix, M. D., and Dalton, A. J.: A comparison of mesothelial cells and macrophages in mice after the intraperitoneal inoculation of melanin granules, J. Biophys. & Biochem. Cytol. (Supp.) 2:109, 1956.

Haythorn, S. R.: Multinucleated giant cells with particular reference to the foreign body giant cell, Arch. Path. & Lab. Med. 7:651, 1929.

Maximow, A.: Development of nongranular leucocytes (lymphocytes and monocytes) into polyblasts (macrophages) and fibroblasts in vitro, Proc. Soc. Exper. Biol. & Med. 24:570, 1927.

———: The macrophages or histiocytes in Cowdry's Special Cytology, ed. 1, p. 425, New York, Hoeber, 1928.

———: Relation of blood cells to connective tissue and endothelium, Physiol. Rev. 4:533, 1924.

Odor, D. L.: Uptake and transfer of particulate matter from the peritoneal cavity of the rat, J. Biophys. & Biochem. Cytol. 2:105, 1956.

Palade, G. E.: Relations between the endoplasmic reticulum and the plasma membrane in macrophages, Anat. Rec. 121:445, 1955.

Sampaio, M. M.: The use of thorotrast for the electron microscopic study of phagocytosis, Anat. Rec. 124:501, 1956.

MAST CELLS

Asboe-Hansen, G.: The mast cell, Internat. Rev. Cytol. 3:399, 1954.

Bensley, S. H.: Pinacyanol erythrosinate as a stain for mast cells, Stain Technol. 27:269, 1952.

Best, C. H., Cowan, C., and MacLean, D. L.: Heparin and the formation of white thrombi, J. Physiol. 92:20, 1938.

Bloom, F.: Spontaneous solitary and multiple mast cell tumors (mastocytomata), Arch. Path. 33:661, 1942.

Charles, A. F., and Scott, D. A.: Studies on heparin: IV. Observations on the chemistry of heparin, Biochem. J. 30:1927, 1936.

Fawcett, D. W.: An experimental study of mast cell degranulation and regeneration, Anat. Rec. 121:29, 1955.

Hedbom, A., and Snellman, O.: Isolation and analysis of the large cytoplasmic granules of tissue mast cells, Exper. Cell Res. 9:148, 1955.

Holmgren, H., and Wilander, O.: Beitrag zur Kenntniss der Chemie und Funktion des Ehrlichschen Mastzellen, Ztschr. mikr. anat. Forsch. 42:242, 1937.

Howell, W. H., and Holt, F.: Two new factors in blood coagulation, heparin and pro-anti thrombin, Am. J. Physiol. 47:328, 1918.

Jaques, L. B.: L'héparine en médecine, Rev. hémat. 7:74, 1952.

Jorpes, E., and Bergström, S.: Heparin: a mucoitin polysulfuric acid, J. Biol. Chem. 118:447, 1937.

———: On the relationship between the sulphur content and anti-coagulant activity of heparin preparations, Biochem. J. 33:47, 1939.

Julen, C., Snellman, O., and Sylvén, B.: Cytological and fractionation studies on the cytoplasmic constituents of tissue mast cells, Acta physiol. scandinav. 19:289, 1950.

Lison, L.: Etudes sur la métachromasie, Arch. biol. 46:599, 1935.

Mergenthaler, D. D., and Paff, G. H.: Peritoneal mast cells as a possible source of circulating heparin in the rat, Anat. Rec. 126:165, 1956.

Michels, N. A.: The mast cells in Downey's Handbook of Hematology, vol. 1, p. 231, New York, Hoeber, 1938.

Mota, I., Beraldo, W. T., Ferri, A. G., and Junqueira, L. C. U.: Intracellular distribution of histamine, Nature 174:698, 1954.

Murray, D. W. G., and Best, C. H.: Heparin and thrombosis; present situation, J.A.M.A. 110:118, 1938.

Murray, D. W. G., Jaques, L. B., Perret, T. S., and Best, C. H.: Heparin and thrombosis of veins following injury, Surgery 2:163, 1937.

Padawer, J.: Studies on mammalian mast cells, Trans. New York Acad. Sc. Ser. II, 19:690, 1957.

Paff, G. H., and Bloom, F.: Vacuolation and the release of heparin in mast cells cultivated in vitro, Anat. Rec. 104:45, 1949.

Paff, G. H., and Mergenthaler, D. D.: Vacuolation in normal mast cells and in mast cells treated with protamine sulfate, Anat. Rec. *121*: 579, 1955.

Riley, J. F.: Histamine in tissue mast cells, Science *118*:332, 1953.

——: Riddle of mast cells; tribute to Paul Ehrlich, Lancet *1*:841, 1954.

——: The Mast Cells, Edinburgh, Livingstone, 1959.

Riley, J. F., and West, G. B.: The presence of histamine in tissue mast cells, J. Physiol. *120*:528, 1953.

Smith, D. E., and Lewis, Y. S.: Electron microscopy of the tissue mast cell, J. Biophys. & Biochem. Cytol. *3*:9, 1957.

PLASMA CELLS

Coons, A. H., Leduc, E. H., and Connolly, J. M.: Studies on antibody production: I. A method for the histochemical demonstration of specific antibody and its application to a study of the hyperimmune rabbit, J. Exper. Med. *102*:49-60, 1955.

Kautz, J., Demarsh, Q. B., and Thornburg, W.: A polarizing and electron microscope study of plasma cells, Exper. Cell Res. *13*:596, 1957.

Leduc, E. H., Coons, A. H., and Connolly, J. M.: Studies on antibody production: II. The primary and secondary responses in the popliteal lymph node of the rabbit, J. Exper. Med. *102*: 61-71, 1955.

ADIPOSE TISSUE

Clark, E. R., and Clark, E. L.: Microscopic studies of the new formation of fat in living adult rabbits, Am. J. Anat. *67*:255, 1940.

Hausberger, F. X.: Quantitative studies on the development of autotransplants of immature adipose tissue of rats, Anat. Rec. *122*:507, 1955.

Menschik, Z.: Histochemical comparison of brown and white adipose tissue in guinea pigs, Anat. Rec. *116*:439, 1953.

Napolitano, L., and Fawcett, D.: The fine structure of brown adipose tissue in the newborn mouse and rat, J. Biophys. & Biochem. Cytol. *4*:685, 1958.

Peer, L. A.: Loss of weight and volume in human fat grafts, Plast. & Reconstruct. Surg. *5*:217, 1950.

——: Transplantation of Tissues, vol. 1, Baltimore, Williams & Wilkins, 1955.

Wassermann, F.: Die Fettorgane des Menschen; Entwicklung, Bau und systematische Stellung des sog. Fettgewebes, Ztschr. Zellforsch. *3*:235, 1926.

Wells, H. G.: Adipose tissue, a neglected subject, J.A.M.A. *114*:2177, 1940.

DENSE CONNECTIVE TISSUE

Buck, R. C.: Regeneration of tendon, J. Path. *66*:1, 1953.

Ingelmark, B. E.: The structure of tendons at various ages and under different functional conditions, Acta anat. *6*:193, 1948.

Jackson, D. S.: Chondroitin sulfuric acid as a factor in the stability of tendon, Biochem. J. *54*:638, 1953.

Peer, L. A.: Transplantation of Tissues, vol. 1, Baltimore, Williams & Wilkins, 1955.

Chapter 14

Cartilage

Cartilage is a special kind of dense connective tissue. The dense kinds of connective tissue that we have studied so far, although they possess great tensile strength, would bend if they were called upon to bear weight. Cartilage was designed to overcome this deficiency. It has a fairly dense network of collagenous fibers, and in some instances, elastic fibers, to give it tensile strength, but they are embedded in, and perhaps even chemically united to, a considerable quantity of an amorphous type of intercellular substance which exists in the state of a very firm gel. This arrangement gives the intercellular substance of cartilage a consistency not unlike that of a fairly firm plastic, and so it is capable of bearing a certain amount of weight without bending. Like some of the newer plastics, its surfaces can take a high polish; hence, cartilaginous surfaces, if kept lubricated, move against each other with very little friction and wear. Cartilage, then, is superbly adapted for coating the articulating ends of bones in movable joints.

Cartilage may be classified into 3 main types:

Cartilage
- hyaline
- elastic
- fibro

Of the 3 types, hyaline is the most common and serves best as the prototype of the group. Hence, it will be considered first and in detail, after which the other types will be described briefly.

The word "hyaline" is derived from the Greek *hyalos,* which means "glass." Hyaline cartilage was so named because it has, in the gross, a pearly white, glassy, translucent appearance. This appearance is due entirely to the special character of its intercellular substance.

Microscopic Appearance. Hyaline cartilage consists of cells and intercellular substance.

The *cells* are called *chondrocytes* and reside in little spaces in the intercellular substances called *lacunae* (Fig. 158). In some instances, a lacuna contains but a single chondrocyte. In others, pairs, or even larger numbers of chondrocytes may be present. When many chondrocytes are present in a single lacuna, it is said to constitute a *cell nest.* Often when several cells are present in a single large lacuna, very fine partitions of intercellular substance may exist between the individual cells so that a large primary lacuna, which is still called a cell nest, is thereby broken up into a number of smaller secondary ones (Fig. 158). Typically, chondrocytes have a rounded nucleus with one or more nucleoli. In life, their cytoplasm fills the lacunae in which the cells reside. However, in stained sections the cytoplasm is commonly seen to be shrunken away from the sides of the lacunae. Glycogen and fat may be demonstrated in the cytoplasm of large chondrocytes. Chondrocytes vary considerably in size and shape. Young chondrocytes, like the lacunae that contain them, instead of being spherical are often flattened (Fig. 158). Old or, more precisely, fully differentiated cartilage cells tend to be large and rounded (Fig. 158). Size, then, is an important indication of the degree to which any given chondrocyte has differentiated. Small, more or less flattened chondrocytes are to be regarded as not nearly so well differentiated as the large hypertrophied rounded ones.

The *intercellular substance* of hyaline cartilage is a firm gel. Although it appears to be homogeneous both in the gross and in most ordinary kinds of microscopic preparations, it contains considerable quantities of both formed and amorphous kinds of intercellular substance. The formed kind is represented by collagen fibers, and a considerable quantity of these are present. However, they are immersed in a relatively large quantity of amorphous intercellular substance. Most of this is one of the sulfated mucopolysaccharides described in Chapter 5 and is known as *chondroitin sulfuric acid.* This probably is bound to a protein (see Chap. 5) which is as yet unknown, and the complex between the mucopolysaccharide and the unknown protein is either mixed with, or chemically united to, the collagen which is also present. The intercellular substance of cartilage may be mildly P.A.S. positive. Since chondroitin sulfuric acid

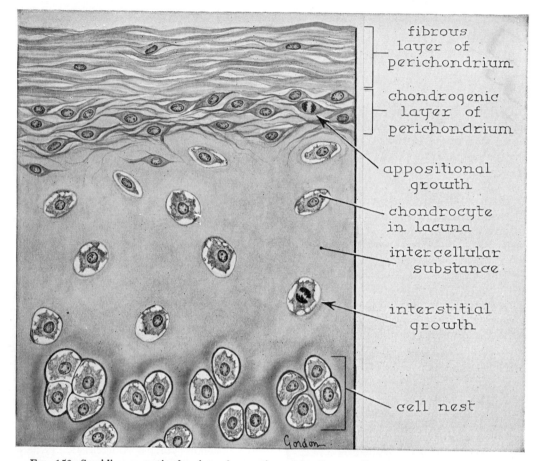

FIG. 158. Semidiagrammatic drawing of a section of hyaline cartilage covered with perichondrium. It illustrates the processes of both appositional and interstitial growth.

is not P.A.S. positive, there is probably some other as yet imperfectly understood carbohydrate component present (see Chap. 5). The amorphous intercellular substance of cartilage is of approximately the same refractive index as the collagen fibers which lie in it; hence, the collagen fibers cannot be seen at all distinctly unless the amorphous intercellular substance is dissolved away. The lining of each lacuna seems to consist of an intercellular substance of a somewhat different consistency from that present throughout most of the substance of cartilage (Fig. 158). If cartilage is stained with toluidine blue, strong metachromasia is evidenced by the thin layer of intercellular substances that lines each lacuna. This suggests that it is largely chondroitin sulfuric acid because this substance stains metachromatically with toluidine blue. Frequently, this

lining layer of the lacuna is referred to as the *capsule* of the cartilage cell.

Perichondrium. Except at articular surfaces, where cartilaginous surfaces are exposed to one another or to other connective tissues in the joint, each piece of, or structure of, cartilage in the body is completely surrounded by a connective tissue membrane called its *perichondrium* = about cartilage (Fig. 158). The outer part of this membrane is composed of densely arranged collagenous connective tissue. The inner part of it shows some cartilaginous characteristics; indeed, it is often difficult to decide exactly where the inner border of the perichondrium stops and the cartilage begins. In other words, the inner surface of the perichondrium usually exhibits a gradual transition from ordinary connective tissue into cartilage. This is because the cells in the inner

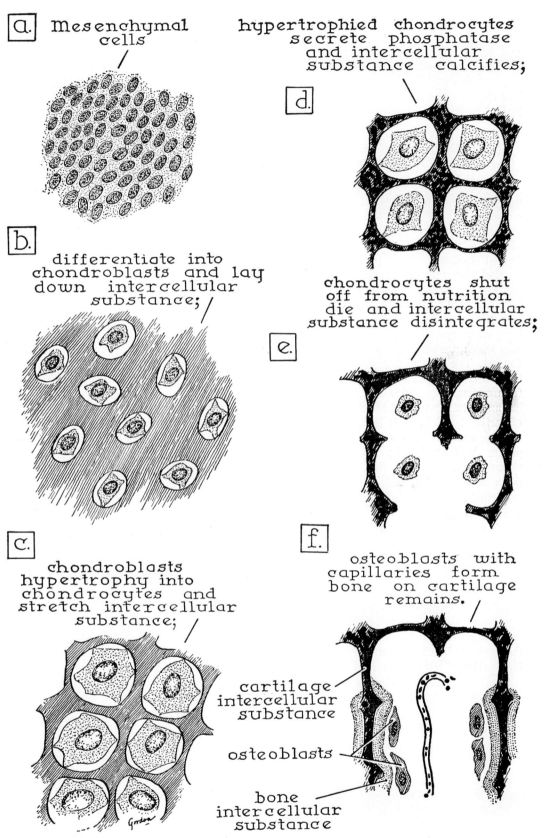

a. Mesenchymal cells

b. differentiate into chondroblasts and lay down intercellular substance;

c. chondroblasts hypertrophy into chondrocytes and stretch intercellular substance;

d. hypertrophied chondrocytes secrete phosphatase and intercellular substance calcifies;

e. chondrocytes shut off from nutrition die and intercellular substance disintegrates;

f. osteoblasts with capillaries form bone on cartilage remains.

cartilage intercellular substance

osteoblasts

bone intercellular substance

FIG. 159. Diagrams to show the development, the life history and the usual fate of cartilage in the body.

part of the membrane have the potentiality of becoming chondroblasts, and, as we shall see, their continued growth and differentiation into chondrocytes can cause a piece of cartilage to become larger.

THE DEVELOPMENT OF CARTILAGE

Cartilage, like the other connective tissues, develops from mesenchyme. In an area of mesenchyme where cartilage is to develop, the mesenchymal cells lie in an amorphous type of intercellular substance which contains few formed elements. To form cartilage, the mesenchymal cells first come closer together and lose the processes which, up to this time, have extended off from their cytoplasm. Soon, then, the area in which cartilage is to form becomes composed of rounded mesenchymal cells which are packed closely together (Fig. 159, a). The next change to be observed is that these cells gradually become separated from one another again. This is due to their beginning to form the intercellular substance of cartilage which, as it is laid down in increasing amounts between the cells, gradually pushes them apart (Fig. 159, b). Since the mesenchymal cells have now differentiated and lie in lacunae in intercellular substance, they are called *chondrocytes* (cartilage cells).

The mesenchyme surrounding the area in which cartilage develops remains closely applied to the forming cartilage and becomes its perichondrium. In the outer part of this mesenchyme, the mesenchymal cells tend to differentiate into fibroblasts and to form collagenous fibers. In the inner part of the perichondrium, that is, the part applied closely to the cartilage tissue, the mesenchymal cells of the perichondrium do not differentiate into fibroblasts but remain in a relatively undifferentiated state, retaining their capacity to form chondroblasts and chondrocytes. When they exercise this capacity, there is, of course, a gradual transition between connective tissue and cartilage in the inner part of the perichondrium.

The Growth of Cartilage. Young cartilage can grow in 2 different ways: (1) by interstitial growth and (2) by appositional growth.

Since *interstitium* means a small hole in the substance of a tissue, the word *interstitial* refers to the cells in the lacunae in the substance of the cartilage. These cells (the chondrocytes), unless they have become greatly hypertrophied and very mature, retain their ability to divide; hence, more chondrocytes can form within the substance of cartilage. The new cells that are formed by this growth mechanism can give rise to new and more intercellular substance. The formation of new cells with their subsequent formation of intercellular substance within the substance of cartilage causes the cartilage to expand from within (Fig. 158). A piece of cartilage growing by the mechanism of interstitial growth increases in size in much the same way as dough "rises" when bread is made. For this type of growth to occur in cartilage, it is obvious that the intercellular substance must be sufficiently malleable to allow the cartilage to expand from within when internal cells divide and make new intercellular substance. It is obvious that cartilage in which the amount of intercellular substance is not yet great permits interstitial growth to occur much more readily than cartilage which has become older and in which the intercellular substance has become great in amount and stiff with collagen. Interstitial growth, then, is limited to moderately young cartilage.

The second mechanism by which any piece of cartilage can increase in size is known as *appositional* growth. As the name implies, this means a mechanism whereby new layers of cartilage are apposed to one of its surfaces. Appositional growth depends upon activity in the inner part of the perichondrium. In this there is first a division of the deeper cells of the perichondrium which increases their numbers. Some of the cells so formed then differentiate into chondroblasts and then into chondrocytes, and, as they do so, they surround themselves with intercellular substance. By this mechanism a new layer of cartilage is laid down under the perichondrium on the surface of the cartilage model. Furthermore, since the deeper cells of the perichondrium divide before differentiation occurs, their numbers are not depleted by the process, and so there are plenty more should additional growth by this mechanism be necessary. (Fig. 158 illustrates the appositional growth of cartilage.)

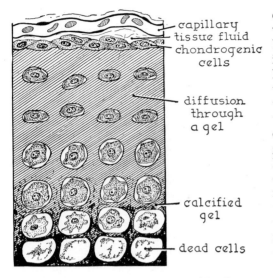

capillary
tissue fluid
chondrogenic
cells

diffusion
through
a gel

calcified
gel

dead cells

FIG. 160. Diagram of a section of hyaline cartilage. A capillary which forms tissue fluid is shown outside the limits of the cartilage. For the cells of the cartilage to be nourished, substances, dissolved in tissue fluid, must diffuse through the gelled intercellular substances of the cartilage to deeply buried cells. If the intercellular substance becomes calcified, as is indicated in the lower part of the diagram (black), diffusion cannot occur and the cells die. (Ham, A. W.: J. Bone & Joint Surg. **34A**: 701)

THE NUTRITION OF CARTILAGE

Cartilage is a nonvascular tissue; it contains no capillaries within its substance to provide it with nourishment. The invasion of cartilage by capillaries generally is associated with its calcification and death. Blood vessels, without associated calcification, are seen occasionally in cartilage in some sites (e.g., epiphyseal plates), but they lie in special protected canals and only pass through the cartilage on their way to a destination elsewhere. Therefore, the capillaries that supply cartilage with nourishment are outside the perichondrium of cartilaginous structures (Fig. 160). Consequently, chondrocytes are nourished by means of substances diffusing through the gelled intercellular substance that surrounds them (Fig. 160). The tissue fluid of cartilage is the bound water—the dispersion medium—of the gelled intercellular substance.

The Calcification of Cartilage. Although

cartilage can bear a moderate amount of weight, it is not strong enough to constitute, by itself, the skeleton of a large, heavy organism. So, as organisms become heavier and larger, Nature had to find some way of providing a tissue that would bear more weight than hyaline cartilage. It would almost seem that the first experiment Nature tried in this connection was that of impregnating the organic intercellular substance of hyaline cartilage with mineral salts, chiefly insoluble salts of calcium (Fig. 159, d). At first thought, it might seem that this would be an excellent idea, for, if the intercellular substance of cartilage were impregnated with mineral salts to make it stonelike in character, obviously it could bear much more weight than it could in an uncalcified state. But like so many good schemes, that of calcifying the intercellular substance of cartilage did not work as well as might have been hoped. In the preceding paragraph it was pointed out that chondrocytes depend on receiving substances essential for their welfare by diffusion through the bound water of the gelled intercellular substance surrounding them. When this intercellular substance becomes calcified, that is, thoroughly impregnated with a mineral deposit, it no longer permits the ready diffusion of gases or ions. The result of this is that the chondrocytes in their lacunae are shut off from their normal source of nutrition, so they die (Fig. 159, e). This might seem to be of no consequence since it might be assumed that the strong calcified intercellular substance would remain. But living cells seem to be necessary for the permanence of calcified intercellular substance in the body, for, when the chondrocytes die, the calcified intercellular substance tends to dissolve away (Fig. 159, e, f). Hence, the fate of calcified cartilage is almost always that of resorption. In the following chapter it will be explained how Nature overcame this difficulty by inventing bone, a tissue which permits calcification of an organic intercellular substance without causing the death of the cells in its substance by shutting them off from their nutrition.

Although calcifying cartilage did not solve the problem of providing a permanent tissue for weight-bearing in the body, calcified cartilage has proved to have an extremely important use in serving as a temporary weight-bearing tissue while the bony skeleton is being constructed. The problem of building a bony skeleton in a human being is not unlike that of building a sturdy permanent bridge across a stream. Often before a permanent bridge is begun a temporary wooden bridge is constructed so that the materials for the permanent bridge can be conveyed and deposited where they are needed. Then, as the permanent bridge assumes form, the temporary one is removed piece by piece. Much the same plan is used in building most of the bony skeleton. Temporary cartilage models of the future bones are constructed first (Fig. 180). Next, as will be described in detail in the following chapter, parts of these become calcified, and then, as calcification of the cartilage proceeds, bone formation follows in its wake (Fig. 159, f). As bone is formed, the temporary calcified cartilage is removed piece by piece. Calcified cartilage, then, is a very important tissue in the body during the time the bony skeleton is forming and growing. Further, the calcification mechanism that operates in cartilage is very similar to that which operates in bone. We shall consider this important mechanism in some detail at this time.

As a preliminary it is important to appreciate that the calcification in cartilage refers to the calcification of the intercellular substance only; the cells are not calcified in the calcification process; they die, not because they become calcified, but because they are shut off from food and oxygen. Furthermore, it should be remembered that not all cartilage in the body normally becomes calcified. For example, the cartilage present on the articular surfaces of bones shows no tendency to become calcified at any point close to the articulating surface. Whether cartilage becomes calcified or not seems to depend on the size of its chondrocytes. If the cells are small, calcification does not tend to occur in their surrounding intercellular substance. However, if the cartilage cells become large and hypertrophied (Fig. 159, d), calcification tends to occur in their surrounding intercellular substance.

Bone Salt. The mineral that deposits into the organic intercellular substance of cartilage is believed to be the same as that which deposits into the organic intercellular substance of bone; hence, it is called *bone salt*. The composition of bone salt has been studied over the years by many technics, including x-ray diffraction, and, generally, it is agreed that it has the structure of an apatite. Apatites were so named because often they were mistaken for other minerals (*apatē* = deceit.). They are complexes of $Ca_3(PO_4)_2$ with other calcium compounds, for example, calcium carbonate or tricalcium phosphate hydrate; however, the precise nature of the calcium compounds is still a matter of debate which is difficult to settle because the composition of bone salt probably differs in different sites and in different animals, and the salt probably becomes remodeled after its initial deposition. Since $Ca_3(PO_4)_2$ is such a basic component of the salt, it is convenient, in describing some of the factors that may affect the deposition of bone salt, to consider how those factors would affect the deposition of $Ca_3(PO_4)_2$; we shall do this in the following section.

The Mechanism of Calcification in Mature Cartilage and in Bone. The mineral that is deposited in the cartilage and the bone of the skeleton must be obtained from the food and the water consumed in the diet. It must be absorbed through the wall of the intestine, pass into the blood vessels and be carried by these to sites of calcification. Here it must leave the blood vessels and pass out into the tissue fluid of the part; then it must diffuse into the organic intercellular substance of cartilage and bone and in this medium be laid down in concentrated form as bone salt. It is remarkable that enough relatively insoluble mineral could be carried by the blood to mineralize the skeleton without any mineral precipitating out into the walls of the blood vessels that carry the mineral. In this respect there is a certain margin of safety provided for transporting this mineral; however, the margin is limited because it can be exceeded by certain experimental procedures, as by giving animals large doses of vitamin D or parathyroid hormone or even by giving them large amounts of certain calcium salts in their diet. Under these conditions mineral will precipitate out into the walls of the blood vessels that are carrying it and so cause arterial disease. Therefore, there must be some specific mechanism in the sites where cartilage, bone and teeth become calcified, which somehow concentrates mineral in these sites. Probably several factors are involved in concentrating mineral in the sites of normal calcification, as will now be described.

Calcium phosphate is a relatively insoluble salt, and generally it is assumed that under normal conditions the blood, while not saturated with it, is nearly so. Accordingly, since calcium phosphate would diffuse out into tissue fluid, it could be assumed that a nearly saturated solution of calcium phosphate would exist in the organic intercellular substance of any tissue that is bathed in tissue fluid and is about to become calcified. Hence, if there were any mechanism that could liberate further calcium or phosphate ions in mature cartilage or forming bone, the concentration of calcium and phosphate ions could be raised to the point where precipitation would occur in the mature cartilage or forming bone. Now we shall describe the evidence which suggests that a mechanism exists in calcifying tissues that would operate to bring about a local increase in PO_4 ions in those tissues.

Shortly after the turn of the century it was discovered that sodium phosphate, added to fermenting sugar, greatly increased the rate of fermentation. Harden and Young then showed that the added phosphate actually entered into the fermentation process, that sugar did not turn into alcohol directly, but that first it was converted to a compound of sugar and phosphate. Robison then became interested in compounds of sugar and phosphate (phosphoric esters and sugar phosphates) and in whether they played any role in calcification. One interesting thing about these compounds of sugar and phosphate is that although they are soluble they are not ionized; hence, they can be present in an almost saturated solution of calcium phosphate without their causing precipitation of calcium phosphate. Robison and his associates discovered that hypertrophied cartilage cells and the cells that produce the intercellular substance of bone both manufacture an enzyme termed *alkaline phosphatase* and that this enzyme hydrolyzes sugar phosphates and frees PO_4 ions from them. Accordingly, a theory arose to the effect that the calcification of mature cartilage and forming bone was dependent on the cells of these tissues producing alkaline phosphatase that acted on sugar phosphates to free extra PO_4 ions from them. Since the tissue fluid of the part already would be almost saturated with calcium phosphate, the extra PO_4 ions from the sugar phosphates would cause a precipitation of calcium phosphate in the organic intercellular substance adjacent to the cells that make alkaline phosphatase.

One difficulty with this theory was that there did not seem to be any explanation for there being a substantial amount of sugar phosphate in calcifying cartilage or bone. However, it has been shown that hypertrophied cartilage cells contain glycogen and, more recently, that they make another enzyme, phosphorylase, which conceivably could act to convert the glycogen of the cells into a sugar phosphate which then could serve as a substrate for alkaline phosphatase. Gutman and his associates have shown that interference with phosphorylase activity blocks the calcification mechanism *in vitro*. Although the matter is too complex to be dealt with in any detail in a book of this kind, there does seem to be evidence to the effect that phosphorylase and glycogen are involved in providing a substrate for alkaline phosphatase in the very site in cartilage where extra PO_4 ions could institute calcification.

Calcifying cartilage has been sectioned and studied with the E/M by Robinson and Cameron. They found that crystals measuring 250 to 750 Å $\times$ 50 to 75 Å were deposited singly or in groups in the site where calcification was occurring. The crystals appeared in sites occupied by cement substance (amorphous intercellular substance) and were not arranged in any particular relation to the fibers or fibrils that were present in the organic intercellular substance. (This is in contrast with bone, where the crystals that form as bone calcifies tend to be arranged along and in the collagenic fibrils and in a particular relation to the periodicity of the fibrils.)

The deposition of various elements into the intercellular substance of cartilage can be investigated to advantage by means of radioautographs and by the use of different radioactive compounds. Bélanger has made extensive use of radioactive sulfur which enters into the composition of the sulfated mucopolysaccharides of cartilage intercellular substance; this permits the formation of the amorphous intercellular substance to be followed. The calcification of the organic inter-cellular substance can be visualized in radio-autographs by giving animals radioactive calcium, strontium or phosphorus. Leblond and his group have shown that radioactive carbon labels organic intercellular substance as it forms.

The organic intercellular substance of mature cartilage and that of newly forming bone has an affinity for bone salt. It is not known whether this is primarily a physical or a chemical affinity. Dead cartilage, implanted into certain sites in animals, tends to become calcified even if there are no cells in the vicinity to make alkaline phosphatase.

To sum up, the mechanism of normal calcification of mature cartilage probably depends on many factors, including the availability of mineral from the blood stream, the local production of alkaline phosphatase, the local production of a substrate for the phosphatase and an affinity of the amorphous intercellular substance of cartilage for bone salt. The process is not thoroughly understood as yet, and there are many different points of view on many aspects of the process.

A Further Note on Phosphatase. The phosphatase that is concerned in the calcification of cartilage and bone is effective in an environment which is on the alkaline side of neutrality; hence, it is termed an *alkaline phosphatase*. There are other phosphatases that work best in more acid environments; these are termed *acid phosphatases*. Since Robison made his original studies, phosphatases have been found to have a wide distribution in the body and to be deeply involved in the metabolism of many types of cells. A very important development that has permitted them to be studied advantageously was the devising by Gomori of a histochemical method for detecting these enzymes in tissue sections. The way that this method demonstrates sites of phosphatase activity in sections of calcifying cartilage and bone is illustrated in Figure 189.

The importance of alkaline phosphatase in the calcification of cartilage and bone was illustrated dramatically some years ago in the most unusual instance of a 3-week-old boy who was admitted to the Hospital for Sick Children at Toronto. This child suffered from a condition that was believed to represent a

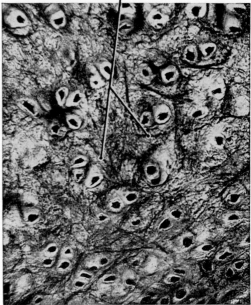

elastic fibers
in intercellular subst.

Fig. 161. Low-power photomicrograph of a section cut through the external ear. Elastic fibers may be seen as dark, fine lines in the intercellular substance.

hitherto-undescribed developmental anomaly (hypophosphatasia)—an almost complete inability to produce phosphatase. In contrast with normal children, whose blood contains phosphatase that originates from the bones, the blood of this child contained almost no phosphatase, and after death very little was found in its bones. However, under these conditions the organic substance of both cartilage and bone had formed; but they had become calcified in only a few sites. The histologic picture of the bones, sections of which the author was privileged to examine, was very similar to that of severe rickets, a condition which will be described in the next chapter and in which phosphatase is abundant but in which cartilage and bone do not become properly calcified for another reason—because there is not enough mineral in the blood.

As the student progresses to the study of pathology, he will learn that the subject of pathologic calcification is a matter of considerable interest. In disease processes the calcification of tissues other than cartilage and bone

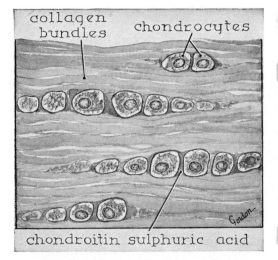

FIG. 162. High-power drawing of an H and E section of fibrocartilage that was taken from a tendon close to its point of insertion.

may occur. In general, there are two kinds of pathologic calcifications and neither seems to depend on phosphatase activity. In the first kind, tissues other than cartilage and bone degenerate and develop a physical or chemical affinity for calcium salts. In the second kind, the blood comes to contain more calcium and phosphate ions than it can retain in solution, with the result that calcium precipitates settle into otherwise normal tissues (Fig. 330). More information will be given on this when the parathyroid gland, whose secretion controls the level of the calcium of the blood, is considered.

Elastic Cartilage. Although hyaline cartilage is elastic to some degree, it is not as elastic as cartilage that is made with considerable numbers of elastic fibers in its intercellular substance. In some sites, for example, in the external ear and in the epiglottis, it is desirable that there should be a stiff tissue present yet one that is very elastic. In these sites elastic cartilage is found. In many respects it is similar to hyaline cartilage, but its intercellular substance, in addition to collagen fibers and chondroitin sulfate, contains elastic fibers that are scattered throughout it (Fig. 161).

Fibrocartilage. Because hyaline cartilage contains collagen, its intercellular substance possesses a certain degree of tensile strength.

However, in some sites in the body, it is desirable to have a tissue which has the general stiffness of cartilage but which, in addition, has great tensile strength, as, for example, in a tendon insertion. In these sites a type of cartilage called *fibrocartilage* commonly is employed. This is much like hyaline cartilage except that there is an excessive amount of collagen in its intercellular substance. Moreover, the collagen fibers tend to be disposed in a plane parallel with the pull made on the structure (Fig. 219). The chondrocytes tend to be disposed in rows between the strong collagenous bundles (Fig. 162).

The intercellular substance that is between the cells that are arranged in the rows, and between them and the fiber bundles, is more basophilic than the intercellular substance in the fiber bundles and hence is probably predominately chondroitin sulfuric acid (Fig. 162).

Hyaline cartilage and fibrocartilage will both be considered further in connection with joints.

GENERAL CONSIDERATIONS ABOUT THE TRANSPLANTATION OF CARTILAGE

Autogenous transplants of cartilage commonly are obtained from the cartilages of the ribs or the nose. The cells of free autogenous transplants of cartilage seldom divide but they may remain alive for at least many years, and, as a result, the transplant may persist for long periods of time. Since cartilage does not require capillaries within its substance, cartilage transplants do not have to be vascularized for their cells to live. Furthermore, cartilage cells probably do not require any oxygen but live anaerobically by glycolysis; this probably makes it easier for them to be nourished by diffusion phenomena, which could continue to operate after free transplantation.

The fact that cartilage cells live by diffusion, which occurs through the intercellular substance, probably accounts for the fact that the cells of homogenous transplants also may survive for a comparatively long time. It is probable that the intercellular substance prevents antibodies that might form in response to the transplant from reaching the cells deep within a transplant. In any event, the cells of homogenous transplants of cartilage survive much better than those of homogenous transplants of other types of tissue, and the same is true, to some extent, of heterogenous transplants.

Cartilage treated in any way to kill its cells represents, on transplantation, nothing more than a transplant of intercellular substance. Such transplants do not seem to persist as well as autogenous transplants with living cells; the latter would seem to be the transplant of choice.

The repair of cartilage is considered on page 353.

REFERENCES

CARTILAGE REFERENCES OTHER THAN THOSE ON CALCIFICATION

Amprino, R.: Uptake of S^{35} in the differentiation and growth of cartilage and bone *in* Wolstenholme, G. E. W., and O'Connor, C. M. (eds.): Ciba Foundation Symposium on Bone Structure and Metabolism, p. 89, London, Churchill, 1956.

Bélanger, L. F.: Autoradiographic studies of the formation of the organic matrix of cartilage, bone and the tissues of teeth *in* Wolstenholme, G. E. W., and O'Connor, C. M. (eds.): Ciba Foundation Symposium on Bone Structure and Metabolism, p. 75, London, Churchill, 1956.

Benninghoff, A.: Form und Bau der gelenkknorpel in ihren Beziehungen zur Funktion, Ztsch. Zellforsch. 2:783, 1925.

Fell, H. B.: Skeletal development in tissue culture *in* Bourne, G. H. (ed.): The Biochemistry and Physiology of Bone, p. 401, New York, Acad. Press, 1956.

Laskin, D. M., Sarnat, B. G., and Bain, J. A.: Respiration and anaerobic glycolysis of transplanted cartilage, Proc. Soc. Exper. Biol. & Med. 79:474, 1952.

Leblond, C. P., and Greulich, R. C.: Autoradiographic studies of bone formation and growth *in* Bourne, G. H. (ed.): The Biochemistry and Physiology of Bone, p. 325, New York, Acad. Press, 1956.

Martin, A. V. W.: Fine structure of cartilage matrix *in* Randall, J. T., and Jackson, S. F. (eds.): Nature and Structure of Collagen, p. 129, New York, Acad. Press, 1953.

Montagna, W.: Glycogen and lipids in human cartilage with some cytological observations on the cartilage of the dog, cat, and rabbit, Anat. Rec. 103:77, 1949.

Peer, L. A.: Transplantation of Tissues, vol. 1, Baltimore, Williams & Wilkins, 1955.

Pritchard, J. J.: A cytological and histochemical study of bone and cartilage formation in the rat, J. Anat. 86:259, 1952.

Robinson, R. A., and Cameron, D. A.: Electron microscopy of cartilage and bone matrix at the distal epiphyseal line of the femur in the newborn infant, J. Biophys. & Biochem. Cytol. (Supp.) 2:253, 1956.

Scott, B. L., and Pease, D. C.: Electron microscopy of the epiphyseal apparatus, Anat. Rec. 126:465, 1956.

Sylvén, B.: The ground substance of connective tissue and cartilage in Bourne, G. H. (ed.): The Biochemistry and Physiology of Bone, p. 53, New York, Acad. Press, 1956.

CALCIFICATION OF CARTILAGE

Bélanger, L. F.: The entry of CA^{45} into the skin and other soft tissues of the rat: An autoradiographic and spodographic study, J. Histochem. Cytochem. 5:65, 1957.

Bourne, G. H.: Phosphatase and bone *in* The Biochemistry and Physiology of Bone, p. 251, New York, Acad. Press, 1956.

Dixon, T. F., and Perkins, H. R.: The chemistry of calcification *in* Bourne, G. H. (ed.): The Biochemistry and Physiology of Bone, p. 287, New York, Acad. Press, 1956.

Durning, W. C.: Submicroscopic structure of frozen-dried epiphyseal plate and adjacent spongiosa of the rat, J. Ultrastr. Res. 2:245, 1958.

Gutman, A. B., and Yu, T. F.: Concept of the role of enzymes in endochondral calcification *in* Reifenstein, E. C., Jr. (ed.): Tr. of the Second Conference on Metabolic Interrelations, p. 167, New York, Macy, 1950.

――――: A further consideration of the effects of beryllium salts on *in vitro* calcification of cartilage *in* Reifenstein, E. C., Jr. (ed.): Tr. of the Third Conference on Metabolic Interrelations, p. 90, New York, Macy, 1951.

――――: Further studies of the relation between glycogenolysis and calcification in cartilage *in* Reifenstein, E. C., Jr. (ed.): Tr. of the First Conference on Metabolic Interrelations, p. 11, New York, Macy, 1949.

Hass, G. M.: Pathological calcification *in* Bourne, G. H. (ed.): The Biochemistry and Physiology of Bone, p. 767, New York, Acad. Press, 1956.

McLean, F. C., and Urist, M. R.: Bone; An Introduction to the Physiology of Skeletal Tissue, Chicago, Univ. Chicago Press, 1955.

Rathbun, J. C.: Hypophosphatasia, a new developmental anomaly, Am. J. Dis. Child. 75:822, 1948.

Robison, R.: The Significance of Phosphoric Esters in Metabolism, New York, New York Univ. Press, 1932.

Sheldon, H., and Robinson, R. A.: Studies on cartilage: electron microscope observations on normal rabbit ear cartilage, J. Biophys. & Biochem. Cytol. 4:401, 1958.

Wells, H. G.: Chemical Pathology, ed. 5, Philadelphia, Saunders, 1925.

(*See also* references on Calcification of Bone, next chapter)

Chapter 15

Bone

THE DIFFERENCES BETWEEN CALCIFIED CARTILAGE AND BONE

In the preceding chapter it was intimated that Nature, in an attempt to improve the weight-bearing capacity of hyaline cartilage, tried the expedient of impregnating its intercellular substance with mineral salts (Fig. 159, d). The experiment was not successful, however, because calcium deposits interfere with the ready diffusion of gases, food substances and waste products throughout its intercellular substance. The cells of calcified cartilage thereby are deprived of their means of existence, so they die (Fig. 159, e). Calcified cartilage, then, soon becomes dead cartilage, and dead cartilage for some reason tends to disintegrate and dissolve away (Fig. 159, e, f).

The evolution of bone overcame this peculiar deficiency of calcified cartilage. In many respects it is similar to cartilage. It consists of cells in lacunae surrounded by intercellular substances of much the same sort as are present in cartilage. But there are certain very important fundamental differences between the two tissues, and these will now be described.

1. Bone Has a Canalicular Mechanism. First, the intercellular substance of bone, unlike that of cartilage, is permeated by a system of tiny canals called *canaliculi* (Figs. 163 and 164). These extend from one lacuna to another and to bony surfaces where capillaries are situated. Tissue fluid originating from the capillaries permeates into and fills the canaliculi and such space as is left in the cell-filled lacunae. Oxygen and food, brought by capillaries to bony surfaces, diffuse through the tissue fluid contained in the canaliculi to nourish the cells in the lacunae. The waste products of the cells in lacunae are removed by the same mechanism. By this unique mechanism the cells of bone are enabled to remain alive even though the intercellular substance surrounding them becomes calcified (Fig. 163, d).

How Bone Canaliculi Are Formed. The canaliculi that permeate the intercellular substance of bone are formed by the mechanism illustrated in Figure 163. As this shows, the cells destined to form the organic intercellular substance of bone are provided with long cytoplasmic processes (Fig. 163, a). The organic intercellular substance formed by such cells is formed around these processes (Fig. 163, b). When the organic intercellular substance "sets," the processes may be withdrawn (probably not immediately but later when the bone matures) with the result that tiny canals (canaliculi) are left permeating the intercellular substance (Fig. 163, c). Unfortunately, canaliculi cannot be seen in H and E sections. On the other hand, certain basic dyes that stain bone brilliantly sometimes stain canaliculi selectively; this suggests that they are lined with a sulfated mucopolysaccharide (Fig. 164).

2. Bone Is Vascular. As might be expected, the canalicular mechanism is not a very efficient one and it cannot maintain the life of cells over very great distances. This means that no bone cell can survive if it is very far removed from a capillary. This necessitates that bone be exceedingly well supplied with capillaries. Even what appears to the naked eye to be dense solid bone will be found, on microscopic examination, to be built on such a plan that no bone cell is more than a fraction of a millimeter from a capillary (Fig. 199). The second fundamental difference between cartilage and bone is, then, that bone, in contrast to cartilage, is a vascular tissue—its substance is richly supplied with capillaries.

3. Bone Can Grow Only by the Appositional Mechanism. In its normal state, the organic intercellular substance of bone is calcified. In other words, under normal conditions, the formation of the organic intercellular substance of bone is followed almost immediately by its calcification. This feature of bone is another point of difference between it and cartilage. The latter tissue, it will be recalled, can exist in the body in an uncalcified state, and in that state its intercellular substance is sufficiently malleable to permit interstitial growth to occur. On the other hand, bone, since its intercellular substance becomes calcified almost as soon as it forms, is not malleable enough to expand. So, for all practical purposes, any given piece of *bone can increase in size only because new bone is added to one of its surfaces.* Bone grows only by the appositional mechanism (Fig. 165).

The almost immediate calcification of forming bone probably is due to the cells concerned in the process acquiring the ability to secrete phosphatase almost simultaneously with their ability to manufacture organic intercellular substance. However, the calcification of bone is dependent on adequate supplies of calcium and phosphorus being present in the blood and tissue fluid as well as on phosphatase. So, if growing animals are given inadequate amounts of calcium or phosphorus, forming bone may remain uncalcified until the diet is remedied; in this state it is commonly called *osteoid tissue*. However, under normal conditions newly formed bone exists in an uncalcified or osteoid state for only a transitory period.

4. The Fine Structure of Bone Intercellular Substance Is Different from That of Cartilage. The organic intercellular substance of bone consists chiefly of collagen. The fibrils of the collagenic fibers are embedded in some kind of a cement substance. It seems probable that part of this is a sulfated mucopolysaccharide, but the precise nature of the cement substance or substances in bone has not yet been settled.

Robinson and Cameron have studied calcifying cartilage and calcifying bone with the E/M and have shown that there are several points of difference between the fine structure of the two tissues. In calcifying cartilage the fibrils are farther apart than they are in bone, so there is relatively more cement substance in cartilage than in bone. Moreover, they show that calcification—the deposition of crystals—begins in cartilage intercellular substance at some distance from the hypertrophied chondrocytes, and the crystals that appear in the cement substance are not in any particular relation, or even close, to the fibrils. Since the crystals are deposited in the cement substance and since there is relatively more cement substance in cartilage the latter tissue can take up more mineral than bone.

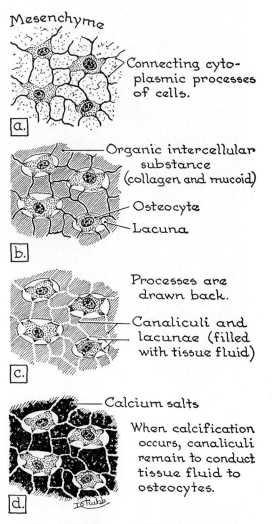

FIG. 163. Diagrams to show how a very small island of bone develops and how the cytoplasmic processes of the cells account for canaliculi.

In bone, the mineral is deposited in the cement substance between fibrils but generally in closer association with the fibrils. The cross-banding of the collagenic fibrils is seen much more clearly in bone than in cartilage (it may not be demonstrable in cartilage). The fibrils in the bones of the young are fine but they become thicker throughout life. The water content of bone becomes less throughout life, and the crystals of bone salt become larger throughout life. The crystals have the form of plaques, and those in the bones of the middle-aged measure about 400 Å by 200-

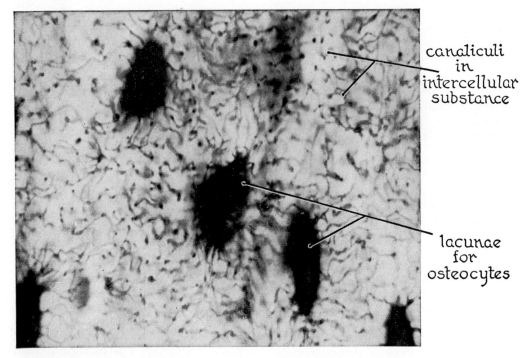

canaliculi
in
intercellular
substance

lacunae
for
osteocytes

FIG. 164. High-power photomicrograph of a section cut from the rib of a rabbit and stained with Giesma's stain. The canaliculi that pass between the different lacunae may be seen in this type of preparation. (Ham, A. W.: *In* Cowdry's Special Cytology, vol. 2, ed. 2, New York, Hoeber)

300 Å by 25-50 Å. The crystals form primarily in the cement substance between fibrils but sooner or later become arranged along and within the collagenic fibrils in some relation to their periodicity. This aspect of the problem requires further study, particularly to assess its significance.

From the foregoing it may be concluded that studies with the E/M reveal certain fundamental differences in the intercellular substance of cartilage and bone.

5. Bone Is a More Permanent Tissue. The foregoing, it is hoped, will prevent the student from making one or both of two very common errors: that of thinking that cartilage on becoming calcified becomes bone, and that calcification is the same thing as ossification. It should be realized that bone is a very special tissue that was evolved to solve the problem of maintaining the life of cells buried in a calcified intercellular substance (Fig. 163). That the life of the cells within a calcified intercellular substance can be preserved has important effects; the most notable one is that

of making the tissue more or less permanent. A possible reason for this is that the living cells continue to manufacture the enzyme phosphatase, which, in turn, maintains a high phosphate ion concentration in the tissue fluid in the canaliculi and so prevents the ionic concentration from falling to a point where bone salt would go back into solution.

SPECIAL TYPES OF PREPARATIONS USED FOR BONE STUDY

The heavy mineral deposit in the intercellular substance of bone precludes its being cut into sections as readily as other tissues. Consequently, special procedures are employed to obtain suitable preparations of it for microscopic study. No single type of preparation provides complete information about this tissue. Consequently, several different types of preparations are commonly employed for the study of bone. It is important that the student should know the general principles of the methods employed to obtain these if he is to use them or even to study the illustrations in a textbook effectively.

The commonest type of preparation used is a section of decalcified bone. To prepare one, bone tissue, after fixation, is immersed in a solution of a decalcifying agent (5 per cent nitric acid is a common one) until all of its mineral is dissolved away. Then the acid is washed out of it, and it is sectioned in paraffin or celloidin like any other tissue.

It is important to realize that only the inorganic constituents of bone dissolve away in the decalcification process. Consequently, the cells and the organic intercellular substance of bone persist after decalcification. Further, the procedure illustrates the fact that it is the organic intercellular substance that gives form to a bone. A decalcified bone closely resembles one with its mineral contents present. Unlike it, however, it may be bent and even tied into knots (Fig. 166).

Prolonged treatment with decalcifying agents tends to cause artefacts in bone tissue and, in general, it interferes with its proper staining. In H and E sections of decalcified bone, the cells usually are shrunken, and the canaliculi cannot be seen. However, the canaliculi often can be demonstrated in sections of decalcified bone by means of special stains or special impregnation methods (Fig. 164).

Although sections of decalcified bone are very useful, they do not tell the whole story. Consequently, they often are supplemented in the usual histology course with other types of preparations that are made from bone that still contains its mineral. Three methods are commonly employed to make these.

1. The bones of very young animals are not very heavily mineralized, and, if special precautions are observed, they may be sectioned in celloidin without previous decalcification. Such sections of undecalcified bone are very useful for demonstrating the sites of mineral deposition in growing bones. Figure 190 is an example of one.

2. Pieces of certain very thin bones of the nose and the skull of embryos and very young animals may be stained and mounted whole on glass slides. These, if they are thin enough, show to advantage the cytoplasmic processes of osteocytes and canaliculi.

3. Thin slices of mature, heavily calcified bone may be cut with a saw and then ground down to great thinness by means of abrasives. Such preparations are termed *ground-bone sections*. They may be prepared so that they are thin enough to be studied effectively with the microscope. However, they are better adapted for illustrating the layered calcified

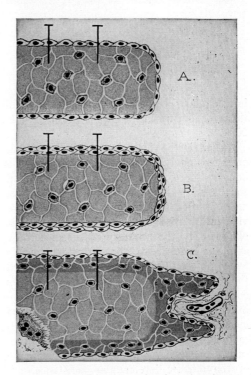

Fig. 165. Diagrams showing that bone cannot grow by the interstitial mechanism, but only by appositional growth which requires new layers of bone being deposited on surfaces. (A) This shows that a trabecula of bone is covered on all surfaces with a layer of osteogenic cells (or osteoblasts). (B) This shows that the surface cells can proliferate so as to increase their numbers. (C) This shows that the innermost layer of surface cells can form a new layer of bone by secreting organic intercellular substance about them, and that the surface still remains covered by a continuous layer of osteogenic cells except at sites of resorption where osteoclasts are present. One is shown at the lower left corner. At the right end, the diagram illustrates how new bone can be laid down on surfaces, extending the length of a trabecula to surround a capillary, so that the cells of the newly formed bone will have a source of nutrition. (Ham, A. W.: J. Bone & Joint Surg. **34A**:701)

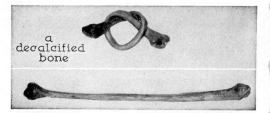

a
decalcified
bone

FIG. 166. This illustration shows that although a decalcified bone closely resembles a calcified bone, it may be tied into knots, as is illustrated in the upper picture.

intercellular substance of bone and canaliculi than for illustrating the cells of bone (Fig. 200).

Although the foregoing methods are the ones commonly employed for the study of bone in the teaching laboratory, the student should know that there are certain special methods used in research studies which provide information over and above that to be obtained by the ordinary methods. For example, a special dye, alizarin, which may be fed or injected into living animals, colors all the mineral deposited in bone while it is being administered, red. Likewise, the deposition and interchange of mineral in the bones of experimental animals may be studied by the use of radioactive isotopes. Radioactive sulfur and carbon have been used to study the formation of the organic intercellular substance, and radioactive calcium, strontium and phosphorus have been used to study the calcification process and mineral interchange. The fine structure of bone has been investigated by several electron microscopists by different methods.

THE DEVELOPMENT OF BONE

SOME GENERAL CONSIDERATIONS

The process by which bone is formed in the body is termed osteogenesis or ossification.

For osteogenesis to occur in any part of the body it is necessary for special cells of mesenchymal origin, called *osteoblasts*, to make their appearance in that part of the body, for only osteoblasts can secrete, or otherwise form, the special organic intercellular substance of bone.

As has been mentioned already, the cell bodies of osteoblasts have many fine cytoplasmic processes extending out from their cell bodies, and these processes join with those of adjacent osteoblasts. When osteoblasts produce organic intercellular substance they generally surround both their cell bodies and their processes with it (Fig. 163). Thereafter the cell bodies come to lie in little spaces in the organic intercellular substance called lacunae; after this has happened the cells are termed *osteocytes*. The processes of the cells lie in tiny passageways in the intercellular substance called canaliculi (Fig. 163).

The organic intercellular substance produced by osteoblasts is commonly termed bone matrix. It has 2 main components: (1) collagenic fibrils and (2) amorphous cement substance. As has been noted already, mineral, in the process of calcification, is deposited in the cement substance between the fibrils, but the crystals of mineral become arranged along the sides of the fibrils. Under normal conditions, bone matrix begins to calcify as soon as it is formed and is well calcified, but not completely, in a relatively short time. Hence, under normal conditions, it exists in an uncalcified state for only a very transitory period.

The structure of calcified matrix is very much like that of reinforced concrete. The collagenic fibrils in calcified matrix are comparable to the rods of iron in reinforced concrete, and the calcified cement substance is comparable to the concrete itself.

The hardness of bone and its opacity to x-rays both depend on its content of mineral; this, in turn, is limited by the amount of cement substance that is available in the matrix. It might be thought that the proportion of collagen to cement substance always would be constant in bone, but this is not so. Baker, Pritchard and Weinmann and Sicher all have placed great and deserved emphasis on the fact that there are 2 kinds of bone, as will now be described.

IMMATURE BONE

The first bone that develops in embryonic development or in the repair of bone fractures, as well as the bone that generally forms in certain types of bone tumors, is termed immature bone. It has proportionately more cells and more collagen and less cement substance and mineral than the mature bone that forms later and makes up most of the adult skeleton. Immature bone is also termed *woven bone* or *coarsely bundled bone* because of its large content and arrangement of collagenic fibers. This type of bone is commonly very cellular (Fig. 167), and the lacunae in which the osteocytes reside are not as flattened as they are in mature bone (Fig. 168). The intercellular substance is characterized by relatively thick bundles of collagenic fibrils which are not disposed in any regular arrangement but in an irregular and often interlacing fashion. The content of cement substance in the intercellular substance is proportionally less than in mature bone; hence, immature bone takes up less mineral than mature bone, so it is neither as strong nor as opaque to x-rays as mature bone.

The matrix of immature bone stains very unevenly but it often demonstrates a patchy basophilia; hence, areas of immature bone that have become surrounded by mature bone may be spotted easily on low-power examination (Fig. 168).

Almost all the immature bone that forms during embryonic life is later replaced with mature bone, which will be described next. Pritchard, who gives an excellent and comprehensive account of types of bone, states that some immature bone persists in tooth sockets, near cranial sutures, in the osseous labyrinth and near tendon and ligament attachments, but that in these sites it usually is mixed with mature bone.

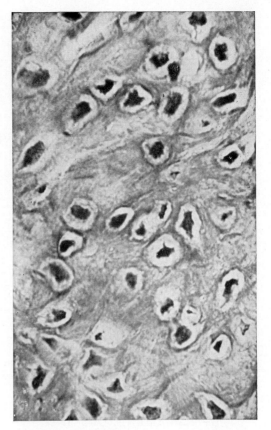

FIG. 167. High-power photomicrograph of an H and E section of decalcified immature bone.

MATURE BONE

It has been pointed out already that cartilage can exist in the body in an uncalcified state and that such cartilage can grow by the interstitial mechanism. Unlike cartilage, bone cannot expand from within because its matrix begins to become calcified (and hence rigid) almost as soon as it is formed. For all practical purposes, therefore, bone, even immature bone, cannot grow by the interstitial mechanism, but only by the appositional—by having new layers added to one or more of its surfaces (Fig. 165).

In the formation and growth of mature or lamellated bone, new layers are added to bony surfaces in an orderly way (Fig. 165). Each layer, according to Weinmann and Sicher, is from 4 to 12 μ thick. The osteoblasts responsible for producing the successive layers of lamellated bone become incorporated as osteo-

cytes within the layers or between the layers of bone matrix that they form. In general, the direction of the fibrils in any given layer is usually at an angle to that of the fibrils in immediately adjacent layers. Sometimes the direction of the fibrils in one layer is at right angles to the direction of those in the next. Since the direction of the fibrils in immediately adjacent layers is not the same, adjacent layers may appear to be optically different.

Mature bone is to be distinguished from immature bone because it stains evenly and lightly (Fig. 168), by the regularity of its lamellae, by the fact that the direction of fibrils in immediately adjacent lamellae is different, by its relatively greater content of cement substance and mineral and by its fewer cells, which are more regularly arranged and in flatter lacunae than they are in immature bone (Fig. 168).

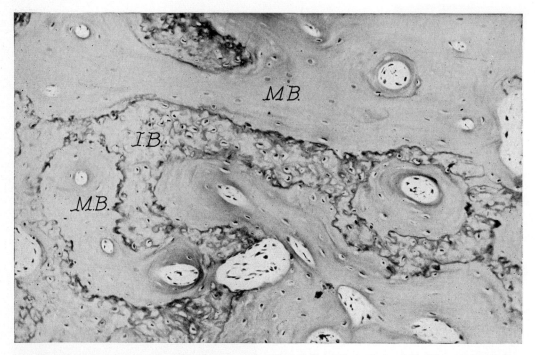

Fig. 168. Low-power photomicrograph of an H and E section of decalcified bone, showing areas of immature bone (I.B.) that have been surrounded or otherwise encroached upon by mature bone (M.B.) that formed later.

INTRAMEMBRANOUS AND ENDOCHONDRAL OSSIFICATION

In the embryo, osteoblasts become differentiated from mesenchymal cells in two general environments. In the first, and this is seen to advantage in connection with the development of the flat bones of the skull, they appear in what are called *membranous areas*. This term is justified by the fact that certain of the mesenchymal cells in these areas already have differentiated into fibroblasts which have formed some collagenic fibers to give the areas a membranous character. However, for ossification to begin, it is necessary for some of the mesenchymal cells to differentiate into osteoblasts, which thereupon secrete or otherwise form the characteristic organic intercellular substance of bone. Since the general environment in which this occurs is sometimes membranous, in that some collagenic fibers may be present, the process is spoken of as *intramembranous ossification*. Moreover, bones that form in these areas sometimes are referred to as *membrane bones*. This is an unfortunate term because it suggests false inferences—for

example, that membrane turns into bone, or that the bone formed in these areas has a special membranous character.

However, most of the skeleton of the body is not formed in membranous areas but, instead, in cartilaginous ones. This is accomplished as follows:

In sites to be occupied later by most of the bones of the skeleton, Nature first builds cartilage models of the bones-to-be. Subsequently, and gradually, the cartilage models are replaced by bone, which forms as a result of ossification occurring along the sides and in the interior of the cartilage models. Ossification occurring in a cartilaginous environment is described as *endochondral*, and the bones that result from it are often referred to as *cartilage bones*. This latter term is unfortunate because it conveys the impression that cartilage changes into bone. Actually, in endochondral ossification cartilage does not change into bone. Instead, osteoblasts developed from mesenchyme appear in the vicinity of the cartilage models, and as the models become calcified, bit by bit, the dead cartilage is replaced by new bone formed as a result of the activi-

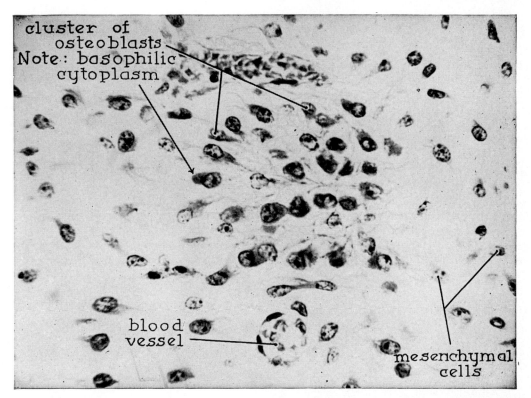

FIG. 169. A cluster of osteoblasts differentiating from mesenchyme in the developing skull of a pig embryo.

ties of the osteoblasts that surround and invade the cartilage models.

Under pathologic conditions, in postnatal life, bone sometimes forms in tissues other than those comprising the skeleton. Little pieces of bone may develop in the scars of wounds, in the tonsils, in the kidney or in other sites. Such bone forms as the result of what is called *heteroplasia* (*heteros* = other; *plasis* = forming), and is spoken of as *heteroplastic bone*. This term is apt because it is the other (than membrane or cartilage) kind of environment in which bone can form.

Since the literature dealing with bone is not always clear about this matter, it is important for the student to keep in mind the fact that the terms intramembranous, endochondral and heteroplastic, when applied to ossification, refer only to the environments in which the process occurs. It is to be emphasized that other adult tissues, for example, cartilage or muscle, never undergo mysterious transformations into bone. In every instance where bone forms, special bone-building cells, the osteo-

blasts, must first make their appearance—these cells alone are capable of manufacturing the special organic intercellular substance of bone. Such bone as develops in any site is a result of their progressive activity; it is not the result of a tissue transformation. Commonly, in embryonic development the first bone to form in any site is of the immature type, but as growth of bone continues mature bone forms and replaces the immature. For this reason, large deposits of bone are never formed quickly. Bones always form a little at a time. Intramembranous and endochondral ossification will now be considered in detail.

INTRAMEMBRANOUS OSSIFICATION

This process is illustrated beautifully by the formation of the bones that come later to comprise the vault of the skull. Sections show that the areas in which these bones develop are occupied first by mesenchyme. Some fibers appear in this to give it a *membranous* character. Intramembranous ossification begins when a

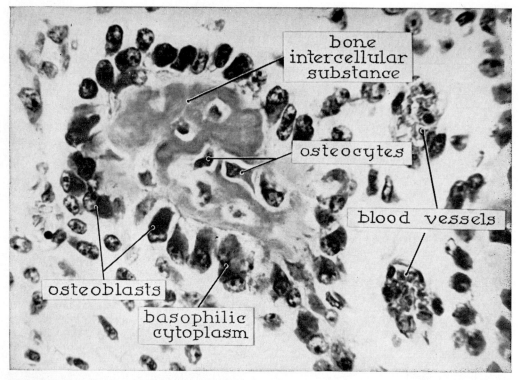

Fig. 170. High-power photomicrograph of a section cut through a newly formed spicule of bone in the developing skull of a pig embryo. Observe that some of the osteoblasts have differentiated into osteocytes and have surrounded themselves with intercellular substance so that they have come to reside in lacunae. Note that osteoblasts are arranged around the periphery of the spicule, where they are engaged in increasing its extent.

cluster of mesenchymal cells differentiate into osteoblasts; these are plump cells with abundant and very basophilic cytoplasm (Figs. 169, 170, and 205). Their borders may show a prickly outline (Fig. 70); the prickles are the roots of cytoplasmic processes which generally cannot be seen in H and E sections. The nuclei of osteoblasts often are disposed eccentrically. In good preparations, a pale area, the negative image of the Golgi net, often can be seen beside the nucleus (Fig. 70).

The E/M has shown that osteoblasts, as would be suspected from the basophilia they exhibit with the light microscope, contain an abundance of rough-surfaced flattened vesicles (Fig. 171); these probably are related to the function of the cell in synthesizing bone matrix. The E/M also has demonstrated sizable Golgi areas in osteoblasts. Fibrils of collagen are formed both in the cytoplasm close to the cell surface and immediately outside the cells. Whether or not there is a demon-

strable precursor of the cement substance in the cytoplasm has not yet been clearly established.

The sites where clusters of osteoblasts first appear are spoken of as centers of ossification. There are usually two centers for each of the bones of the vault of the skull.

After the osteoblasts appear, it is not very long before some of them secrete or otherwise form the characteristic organic intercellular substance of bone. If they completely surround themselves with this, so that they come to lie in the lacunae, they are said to have become osteocytes (Fig. 170). However, not all the osteoblasts that arise from mesenchyme differentiate immediately into osteocytes. Instead, many proliferate to increase the numbers of those in the region. These remain fairly closely applied to the margin of the bone already formed, with some of them continuing to proliferate and others secreting intercellular substance about themselves to

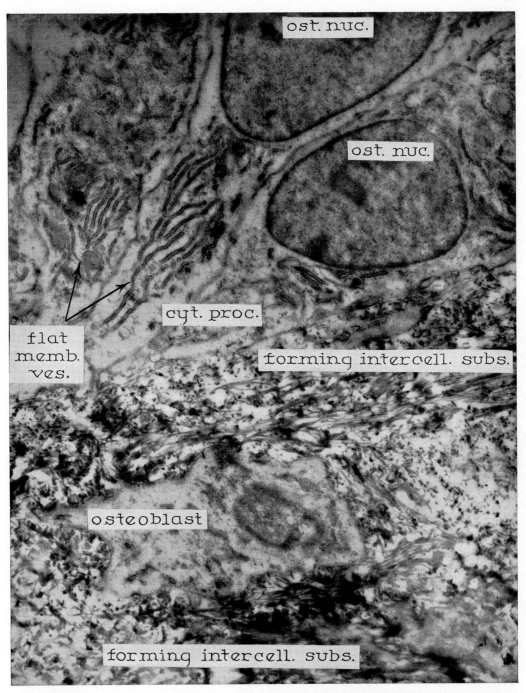

Fig. 171. Electron micrograph ($\times$ 18,000) of a section of undecalcified bone of a fowl embryo, illustrating periosteal osteoblasts depositing bone matrix. The lower osteoblast is embedded in the matrix that it has formed. Fine collagenic fibrils cut in various planes can be seen in the intercellular substance; these form in association with cell surfaces. (Jackson, S. F.: Proc. Roy. Soc., London, s.B *146*:270)

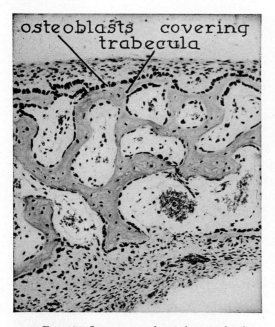

osteoblasts covering trabecula

FIG. 172. Low-power photomicrograph of a section cut from the skull of a pig embryo somewhat more developed than that in Figure 170. This picture illustrates trabeculated (cancellous) bone, with the trabeculae arranged so as to enclose spaces. Observe the osteoblasts, with their dark-staining cytoplasm, arranged along the surface of the trabeculae.

become osteocytes. Osteoblastic activity on the periphery of the first-formed bone is greater at some points than at others. At the sites where osteoblasts proliferate and differentiate more rapidly, spiderlike processes of new bone, radiating out from the first bone formed, soon are developed. These are called *spicules*. Figure 170 is a cross section of one. Figure 165 shows how one forms.

The spicules that radiate out from the ossification center are termed *trabeculae* (*trabs* = a beam). This term is apt because individual trabeculae (beams) of bone commonly are joined together in much the same way that beams of wood are joined together to form a scaffolding (Fig. 172). Bone that consists of a scaffolding of trabeculae joined together is called *cancellous* (*cancellus* = a grating) bone.

As has been noted before, osteoblasts manufacture organic intercellular substance and phosphatase more or less simultaneously;

hence, bone intercellular substance, in a normal individual, begins to become calcified almost as soon as it is formed. Nevertheless, a little time is required for newly formed intercellular substance to become impregnated thoroughly with mineral salts, so, in very rapidly forming membrane bones, a superficial layer of intercellular substance, which has a somewhat lighter staining reaction than that beneath it, may be seen sometimes, probably because it is not fully calcified (Fig. 170).

Osteoblasts cover both the sides and the free ends of the individual trabeculae in a cancellous network (Fig. 172). If the covering osteoblasts continue to proliferate, with some of their members differentiating into osteocytes, new bone is added both to the free ends and to the sides of the trabeculae of the network. The new bone added to the free ends of the trabeculae increases their length and so accounts for the spread of osteogenesis from the center of ossification. The new bone that is added to the sides of the trabeculae usually is deposited in the form of fairly even *lamellae* (*lamella* = a plate).

Although the initial bone that is formed in intramembranous ossification is of the immature type (Fig. 168), the subsequent bone that forms is of the mature type. By the time networks of cancellous bone have formed, like the one illustrated in Figure 172, the type of bone that is being formed is predominately of the mature variety. If new lamellae are added to the sides of trabeculae in a cancellous network, the spaces between the trabeculae are correspondingly narrowed. If it is remembered that the scaffolding of trabeculae that comprise cancellous bone is a 3-dimensional one, it will be easy to understand that the continued deposition of lamellae on the trabeculae sooner or later will change the character of the bone in that it will change from a structure consisting of large spaces with little bone (Fig. 172) to one of narrow spaces with much bone (Fig. 173). When bone substance (instead of spaces) becomes the predominant feature of the tissue, it is said to be *compact* or *dense* bone. It is obvious from the foregoing that the continued deposition of lamellae on the trabeculae of cancellous bone gradually converts it into dense or compact bone.

The Relation of the Structure of Bone Tissue to its Blood Supply. It has already been said that the canalicular mechanism is relatively inefficient, and that the distance over which it will operate effectually is no more than a fraction of a millimeter. Such measurements as have been made by the author in the bones of dogs suggest that one fifth of a mm. is about the greatest distance over which it can maintain the life of osteocytes. But this is unusual, for the great majority of osteocytes, in both cancellous and compact bone, are at most no more than one tenth of a mm. from a capillary. The fact that the canalicular mechanism cannot operate effectively over greater distances explains much that otherwise might seem meaningless with regard to the microscopic structure of both cancellous and compact bone, as will now be described.

1. **Cancellous Bone.** The trabeculae of cancellous bone are bathed in tissue fluid which is derived from the capillaries of the spaces between the trabeculae. Within each trabecula, canaliculi extend out from each lacuna and anastomose with canaliculi from all adjacent lacunae (Fig. 165). Moreover, canaliculi from the more superficial lacunae extend to the exterior of the trabecula and so permit tissue fluid to enter the anastomosing canalicular system of the trabecula. Consequently, food substances, to reach the bone cells in the middle of a trabecula that is one fifth of a mm. in thickness must diffuse along the canalicular system for one tenth of a mm. In the experience of the author, trabeculae of more than one fifth of a mm. in thickness generally have blood vessels disposed in canals near their middles to provide the more deeply disposed bone cells with nourishment. Accordingly, the thickness of solid trabeculae is limited. If too many layers are deposited on the surface of one, the osteocytes that are disposed deeply within it are separated too far from capillaries to survive. Hence, the trabeculae of cancellous bone generally do not become more than about one fifth of a mm. in thickness without their having blood vessels present in canals in their substance.

2. **Compact Bone.** As has been explained already, the development of the bones of the skull is associated first with the formation of trabeculae (Fig. 170) and next with the trabeculae anastomosing with one another so that they enclose spaces (Fig. 172). Each space, of course, contains a blood vessel (Fig. 172).

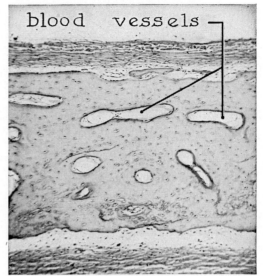

FIG. 173. Low-power photomicrograph of a section cut through the skull of a child. The trabeculated bone shown in Figure 172 has become filled in to constitute a plate of compact bone, as is shown here. The former spaces in the trabeculated area are reduced to canals which transmit the blood vessels.

The trabeculae that become arranged into networks are very thin (Fig. 172) in intramembranous ossification. Hence, several layers of new bone can be added to the trabeculae—and this, of course, correspondingly diminishes the sizes of the spaces between trabeculae—without the osteocytes in the original trabeculae becoming too far removed from the central blood vessel of the space to be nourished by the canalicular mechanism (Fig. 173). Even when the spaces are nearly filled in with bone, the osteocytes in the original trabeculae are no more than about one tenth of a mm. away from the central blood vessel of the space. Hence, the procedures by which cancellous bone is converted to compact bone are such that they generally permit all the osteocytes of the bone to be close enough to the blood vessel of the central canal to exist by means of the canalicular mechanism.

At birth the ossification process has not advanced sufficiently to make the bones of the skull complete. However, it has advanced far enough so that over most of their periphery the individual bones approach one another so

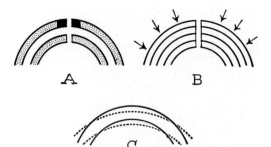

FIG. 174. (A) Diagram to show how appositional growth in sutures could enlarge the vault of the cranium. The new bone is black. (B) Diagram to show how appositional growth on the convex surfaces of the bones could enlarge the cranium without new bone being deposited in the sutures. It is to be understood that resorption would occur from the concave surfaces as new bone is laid down on convex surfaces. (C) Diagram to show how apposition at some sites and resorption from others could change the curvature of a skull bone.

closely that they are separated from one another only by narrow seams of relatively undifferentiated connective tissue. An arrangement whereby adjacent bones are joined by connective tissue is termed a *suture* (Fig. 212). However, at points where more than 2 bones meet, the sutures are wide, and such areas are termed *fontanelles*. There are 6 of these membranous areas in the skull of the newborn infant. The most prominent one, the anterior or frontal fontanelle, is situated at the point where the 2 parietal bones and the bone advancing from the 2 centers of ossification of the frontal bone meet. Its inspection, in an infant, can give valuable information as to whether ossification is proceeding normally.

The vault of the skull enlarges in postnatal life by appositional growth. However, there are somewhat different views as to whether the appositional growth that is primarily responsible occurs in the sutures (Fig. 174 A) or on the convex surfaces of the bones that comprise the vault. As Figure 174 B illustrates, appositional growth on the convex surfaces alone could account for the individual bones becoming larger (resorption on their inner surfaces would keep them from getting much thicker) without bone actually being deposited *in* the sutures. Weinmann and Sicher favor

sutural growth and say that in some sutures more bone is added to one bone than the other. Brash, however, favors the second view.

As the cranium enlarges the curvature of its bones must decrease. This requires that the bones of the skull be remodeled continuously as they grow, and this involves the deposition of bone on some surfaces and resorption of bone from others. Figure 174 C shows how deposition and resorption, at different sites, could change the curvature of a skull bone. We shall now consider the resorptive process.

BONE RESORPTION

There are certain facts about bone resorption that students must learn. In addition to these there is much to speculate about. In the following section we shall first present material which the student should learn well and afterward comment on some very interesting problems which are not yet settled.

SOME FACTS TO BE LEARNED ABOUT BONE RESORPTION

It has been explained already that any bone can become increased in size only by having new layers of bone added to one or more of its surfaces. Bone growth is a surface phenomenon. Likewise, the resorption of bone is a surface phenomenon. Hence, we may postulate that all alterations in the shapes of bones that occur through their development and growth (their remodeling) are the result of bone being added to surfaces and resorbed from surfaces.

Its Importance in the Growth and Remodeling of Bones. Under normal conditions, the two processes of formation and resorption are nicely balanced, for example, as successive new layers of bone are added to the outside of a shaft of a long bone during the growing period, to make the shaft increasingly wider bone must be resorbed simultaneously from the inside of the shaft to make the lumen (marrow cavity) increasingly wider. If the two processes of growth and resorption get out of balance with one another, bones become abnormal. For example, there is a disease of man called *osteopetrosis*, or *marble bone disease*, which is characterized by the resorptive processes falling behind the growth processes, and, as a consequence, the shafts of bones become thicker than usual and marrow cavities are not widened and variously expanded as they should be. It is of interest that there are certain strains of mice and rats in which this, or a very similar condition, is congenital, and these experimental animals demonstrate very effectively the problems that arise if bone resorption does not occur at a normal rate. Moreover, there is another disease of man called *generalized osteitis fibrosa* which is characterized by a greatly increased rate of bone resorption occurring in many parts of the skeleton. This condition generally is caused by one or more of the parathyroid glands secreting much more hormone than is normal. In this condition bone tissue tends to be resorbed and replaced with fibrous tissue.

It is of interest that the administration of extra parathyroid hormone increases the rate of bone resorption in mice and rats with osteopetrosis and so permits them to grow more normally. Moreover, removal of the offending parathyroid gland or glands in man, if done in time, usually will cure generalized osteitis fibrosa and permit the skeleton to become normal again. It is obvious that in some fashion the hormone of the parathyroid gland is concerned in controlling the process of bone resorption.

Resorption Reduces Opacity to X-Rays. Another important fact about bone resorption is related to the interpretation of roentgenograms of bones. It has been noted already that the relative opacity of bones to x-rays is dependent on their mineral content. When some bone or portion of a bone demonstrates less opacity than is normal, it can be inferred that the bone contains less mineral than normal. The question then arises as to whether this is always due to the amount of bone tissue being reduced from a normal quantity or whether the organic substance is normal in amount but has a lessened mineral content. This is a relatively complex matter, as will now be shown.

It has been noted already that newly formed bone matrix passes through a transitory period when it is calcifying and that for a short time it has a smaller mineral content than that of older bone. Furthermore, it has been mentioned already that by certain experimental procedures, for example, using diets that cause a considerable reduction of the blood phosphorus level, all new bone matrix

that forms subsequently will remain relatively uncalcified until the defect in the diet has been remedied. The bone matrix formed under the experimental conditions is not opaque to x-rays but it becomes so very shortly after the diet is remedied. Therefore, it is clear that a *lack* of calcification of newly formed bone matrix can be one possible reason for bone not being as opaque to x-rays as is normal.

The question now arises as to whether or not a reduced opacity to x-rays ever can be caused by fully calcified bone matrix losing part of its mineral content without losing any of its organic substance. In other words, is it possible for calcified bone matrix to become physiologically decalcified? Some radiologists postulate that a physiologic decalcification of bones (they term this halisteresis) can occur and that this process is sometimes responsible for a loss of opacity in bones. However, histologists find no grounds for this belief; they believe that for fully calcified bone to lose mineral it is necessary that the bones lose also the organic intercellular substance that holds the mineral, and, therefore, for mineral to be obtained from bones it is necessary that bone substance (both organic and inorganic) be resorbed. Therefore, we conclude that bone resorption not only occurs at surfaces but that it also entails the almost simultaneous resorption of both the mineral and the organic matter of bone at those surfaces.

The foregoing provides a basis for some generalizations about the cause of a bone or part of an adult bone becoming less opaque to x-rays:

1. Lessened opacity is not due to mineral being withdrawn from organic matrix with the organic matrix remaining in a less calcified state.

2. Lessened opacity generally is due to a reduction in the amount of bone matrix.

3. Lessened opacity of an adult bone, under special circumstances, could be due to there being as much matrix present as before but with some of it having a reduced mineral content. This does not negate the first generalization but is to be explained as follows: Adult bones are slowly, but more or less continuously, being broken down and rebuilt. If conditions arise which prevent the matrix formed by replacement growth from being calcified

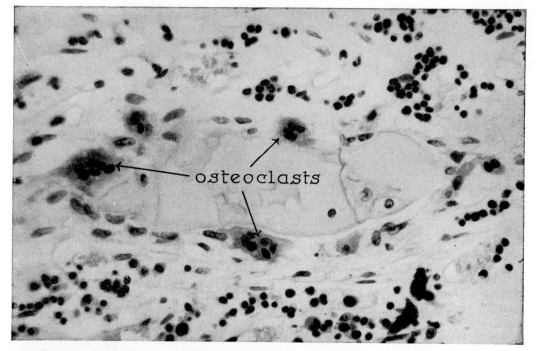

Fig. 175. High-power photomicrograph of a section cut through a trabecula of bone in the marrow cavity of a long bone of a dog. The trabecula occupies the middle of the picture. It is covered with osteogenic cells except in 4 sites where osteoclasts are present. The dark-staining nuclei in the periphery of the picture are those of cells concerned in producing red blood cells and granular leukocytes. (Ham, A. W.: *In* Cowdry's Special Cytology, vol. 2, ed. 2, New York, Hoeber)

properly it is possible for a bone or part of a bone to become composed gradually of a mixture of old, fully calcified mature bone and new imperfectly calcified bone. Such a bone or part of a bone would be less opaque to x-rays than normal. That such a condition conceivably can develop is not to be interpreted to mean that mineral can be withdrawn from bone without its organic matrix also being removed.

Osteoclasts. Next, bone resorption does not occur on surfaces that are covered and hence protected with osteogenic cells and/or osteoblasts. Bone resorption occurs only on naked bony surfaces that are neither protected nor being built upon by osteogenic cells or osteoblasts. Furthermore, multinucleated cells, called osteoclasts (Fig. 175), are usually present over the naked areas where bone is being absorbed; often they occupy little cavities, termed Howship's lacunae (Fig. 177 A), which they appear to have eroded. There is a time-honored view to the effect that these large cells

are the specific agents for bone resorption. There is, however, much interesting controversy about the origin, the nature and the function of these cells, and, indeed, the process of bone resorption is not understood as thoroughly as we might wish. The student probably need not concern himself with the details of this controversy; however, he should learn some of the facts about osteoclasts upon which there is general agreement, which will now be described.

Osteoclasts, seen in the usual section of bone that is being remodeled, may seem to have anywhere from one to many dozen nuclei (Figs. 175 and 176); most show about half a dozen. However, it must be remembered that osteoclasts are large cells; hence, what appears as an osteoclast in a section is only a slice cut through one, and that if an osteoclast were cut into serial sections it would be found to contain many more nuclei than would be apparent in any single slice cut through it.

The nuclei in any osteoclast are usually

similar to one another, but those of different osteoclasts may be different. In what are interpreted as young osteoclasts the nuclei are ovoid. The nuclear membranes are smooth, the chromatin granules are fine and evenly distributed, and each nucleus contains 1 to 2 nucleoli. In older osteoclasts the nuclear membranes are wrinkled, and the nuclei are more darkly stained; indeed, they may be pyknotic.

The cytoplasm of very young osteoclasts may be slightly basophilic, but the typical osteoclast has acidophilic cytoplasm. The acidophilia becomes pronounced as the cell ages. The cytoplasm of many osteoclasts has a frothy appearance (Fig. 176); at least part of this appearance is due to vacuoles.

Shrinkage artefact must be a factor in producing the appearance that most osteoclasts have, because pronounced shrinkage spaces commonly are seen on one side or the other of them. Shrinkage is sometimes responsible for osteoclasts being widely separated from bony surfaces.

Differences Between Osteoclasts and Megakaryocytes. As will be learned in a subsequent chapter, the bone marrow contains large cells, called megakaryocytes, that at first glance may seem so similar to osteoclasts that the student may have difficulty, when studying sections that contain both, in distinguishing one from the other. However, there are several important differences between the 2 types of cells:

Their position is different. Megakaryocytes commonly are disposed throughout the substance of bone marrow while osteoclasts commonly are disposed along bone surfaces. Sometimes, however, osteoclasts may be removed some little distance from bone. These may be distinguished from megakaryocytes by their nuclei and their cytoplasm, as follows: At first glance megakaryocytes seem to be multinucleated. However, it will be found, by focusing the microscope up and down, that the structures that appear as individual nuclei are in reality the lobes of a single continuous nucleus; this particular type of nucleus is characteristic of the megakaryocyte. Furthermore, the cytoplasm of megakaryocytes is generally basophilic.

The Striated or Brush Borders of Osteoclasts. There is another feature of osteoclasts which, although exhibited by only some of

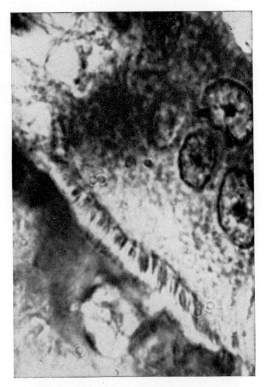

Fig. 176. Oil-immersion photomicrograph of an osteoclast, showing a well-developed striated border. The bone is lower left, the osteoclast is above. (Preparation by W. Wilson)

them, is regarded as being both important and specific; this is that they have, on the surface which they expose to bone, a *striated or brush* border. With the light microscope this appears to be constituted of fine hairlike processes that extend out from the cell and reach toward the bone (Fig. 176). Moreover, it has been generally assumed that this border is instrumental in facilitating the osteoclast's ability to resorb bone.

However, there is some question as to whether or not the striated border is actually the border of the osteoclast or the border of the bone that is being resorbed. There are several points relating to this controversy that should be considered.

1. Striated borders do not surround osteoclasts but are seen only on their surfaces that abut on bone. This fact could indicate that the border actually belongs to the bone or that there is something peculiar about the surface of bone that makes osteoclasts form

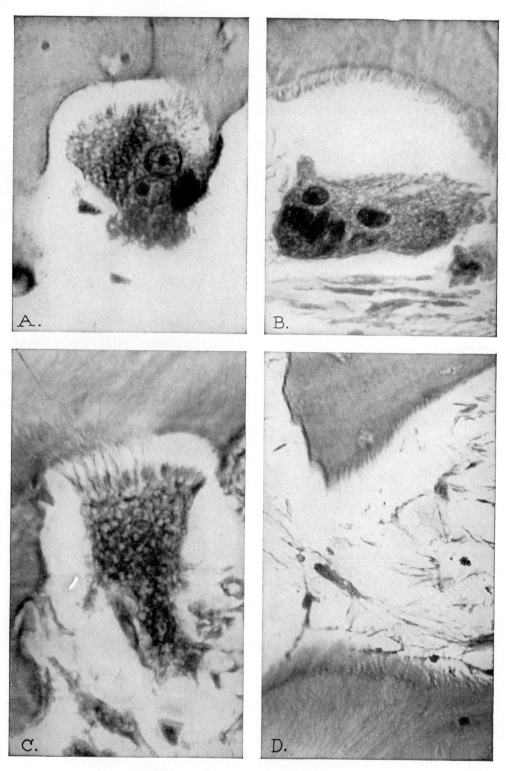

FIG. 177. (*Legend on opposite page.*)

a striated border only when they abut on bone and not on other surfaces.

2. When osteoclasts shrink away from bone, striated borders sometimes remain adherent to the osteoclast (Fig. 177 A) and sometimes to the bone (Fig. 177 B). This finding creates doubt about the ownership of the border.

3. With the phase microscope it is sometimes possible to trace striations from the border on into the bone (Fig. 177 C), where the striae become the collagenic fibrils of the matrix. Furthermore, striated borders are not seen to advantage at surfaces that are parallel with the fibrils of the matrix. Striated borders are seen to best advantage at surfaces where the fibrils in the bone matrix are disposed more or less at right angles to the bone surface.

4. Appearances similar to brush borders sometimes are seen in resorbing bone where no osteoclasts are present (Fig. 177 D).

In view of the above findings, the author, a few years ago, concluded that the brush or striated borders, so commonly attributed to osteoclasts, were in reality the borders of resorbing bone, and the striations in the borders were actually the exposed ends of collagenic fibrils that ran to the resorbing surface roughly at right angles. It was visualized that the ends of these fibrils became exposed, to form a striated surface, because the cement and the mineral substance between the fibrils dissolved a little in advance of the fibrillar material. Although this interpretation of the nature of the striated border—as seen with the light microscope—is, we think, still correct, recent studies with the E/M have shown that the osteoclast itself also has a striated border. We shall elaborate.

There are many technical difficulties involved in obtaining thin sections of bone for study with the E/M that contain osteoclasts with striated borders as well as the bone substance on which the striated border abuts. However, Bronetta Scott, working with Pease, has studied such osteoclasts with the E/M and describes the brush border as an intricate infolding of the plasma (cell) membrane. This investigator suggests that an association of the membrane with mineral resorption is suggested by the presence of crystals between its folds and by associated cytoplasmic vacuoles.

The fact that macrophages, seen with the E/M, exhibit intricate folds of their cell membranes (Fig. 150) makes it easy to believe that osteoclasts would have similar folded membranes. However, a problem arises as to whether or not the folded cell membrane of the osteoclast, seen with the E/M, is what is seen as a striated border with the light microscope. The individual striae observed with the light microscope (Fig. 176) are much coarser than folds of cell membrane, such as those of macrophages (Fig. 150); indeed, it is doubtful if the latter could be resolved with the light microscope. Accordingly, since there is so much evidence indicating that freed collagenic fibrils of resorbing bone are the striae seen with light microscope, the most probable explanation for the seemingly conflicting evidence is that both the resorbing bone surface and the surface of the osteoclast have striated borders. This is the conclusion that Pease has reached (personal communication). Since collagenic fibrils are much thicker than folds of cell membrane, it seems most probable that the striae seen readily with the light microscope are those of the bone.

Hancox points out that the view to the effect that the striated border consists of two components, one of collagenic fibrils and one of cytoplasmic processes, was suggested originally by Pommer in 1883. Hancox, in his recent comprehensive review of osteoclasts (which, however, was written before the E/M studies of Scott and Pease became available),

---

FIG. 177. (A) Photomicrograph ($\times$ 1250) of an osteoclast in a Howship's lacuna. The surface of the osteoclast facing the bone exhibits a striated border. (B) Photomicrograph ($\times$ 1250) of an osteoclast which has shrunken away from the bone. The striated border is present on the bone surface instead of on the osteoclast. (C) Oil-immersion photomicrograph, taken with the phase microscope, of an osteoclast. This shows that the striations of its striated border continue into the intercellular substance of the bone as collagenic fibers and fibrils. (D) Photomicrograph ($\times$ 1250) of striated borders of resorbing bone surfaces in sites where osteoclasts are not present. (Ham, A. W.: J. Bone & Joint Surg. **34A**:701)

stresses the evidence indicating that exposed collagenic fibrils are a component of the border, but considers that it has cytoplasmic components as well.

Origin, Nature and Function of Osteoclasts. So far, we have considered the morphology of osteoclasts. We shall now inquire into their origin, nature and function. In doing this there is one very important question that must be considered: this is whether or not they are fundamentally different from foreign body giant cells, which were described in Chapter 13, which, as every pathologist knows, are prone to develop around or in association with foreign bodies that gain entrance to, or develop in, the tissues. Haythorn, in his most extensive review of foreign body giant cells, classed osteoclasts as one type, and it is probable that most pathologists would subscribe to this view. The adoption of this view leads to the important concept that *naked bone* in the body may be treated as a foreign body. In considering this view it is most important to recall that, except where resorption is occurring, all bone surfaces in the body normally are covered or lined, and hence protected, with a continuous layer of either osteogenic cells or osteoblasts. It is only where breaks in their surface develop—where bone matrix is left naked—that osteoclasts appear.

Two reasons have been suggested for considering that osteoclasts are different from foreign body giant cells. The first is that osteoclasts sometimes have striated borders. We have investigated this problem by placing dead bone chips, cartilage fragments and foreign bodies such as agar-agar into the soft tissues of rabbits and dogs. The reaction that develops around these foreign bodies already has been described (p. 253). In our opinion the reaction is similar whether the foreign body is a dead bone chip or agar-agar. However, some of the giant cells that line up against bone surfaces develop striated borders (Fig. 176), but only on the particular surface of the giant cell that abuts on the bone. Therefore, we consider that there is something peculiar about a bone surface that is responsible for the appearance of the striated border, and an osteoclast is no more than a foreign body giant cell that happens to abut on bone.

The second point of difference that is some-times said to exist between foreign body giant cells and osteoclasts is that the former are phagocytic and the latter are not. Much of the evidence for this view has been obtained from investigations in which vital stains have been injected intravenously into experimental animals. Since, under these conditions, the cytoplasm of some foreign body giant cells is found to contain dye, sometimes it is assumed that they are phagocytic. Since, under the same conditions, osteoclasts have not been reported to contain dye, it has been assumed that they are a different kind of cell. We have performed many experiments in this field. It should be emphasized that it is possible to administer a great amount of vital stain without marking many foreign body giant cells. It is true that some vital stain sometimes may be found in foreign body giant cells, but we question if this is not due to some of the cells that fused to form the giant cell having phagocytosed the dye before they fused. Furthermore, we have seen osteoclasts with vital dye in their cytoplasm; we think for the same reason. Our experience suggests that vital staining does not reveal such a clear-cut difference between foreign body giant cells and osteoclasts as might be assumed from such studies as are on record, and whether or not any giant cell contains dye is due primarily to whether or not the cells that fused to form the giant cell had dye in their cytoplasm.

If osteoclasts are no more than foreign body giant cells, a view to which we subscribe, it could be expected that their origin would be similar to that of foreign body giant cells. It should be emphasized here that the formation of osteoclasts is not limited to cells associated specifically with bone, because perfectly typical osteoclasts with striated borders will develop in the subcutaneous tissue and muscle of dogs into which dead bone chips have been planted (Fig. 177) and around which there is no sign of bone formation. We believe that osteoclasts arise from relatively undifferentiated cells that have sufficient potentiality to differentiate either into macrophages or fibroblasts. Since we believe that osteogenic cells have considerable mesenchymal potentiality, we think they probably serve as an important source for osteoclasts in bony tissues, as could also the reticular cells of the marrow.

Many different kinds of function have been

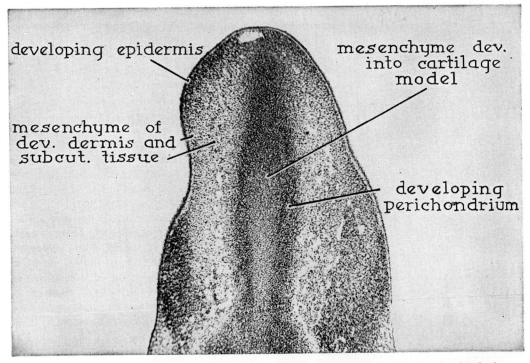

developing epidermis

mesenchyme dev.
into cartilage
model

mesenchyme of
dev. dermis and
subcut. tissue

developing
perichondrium

Fig. 178. Low-power photomicrograph of a longitudinal section cut through the developing toe of an embryonic rabbit. In the central part of the developing toe the mesenchyme is becoming condensed and is beginning to differentiate into the cartilage model of the terminal phalanx.

suggested for osteoclasts. The problem requires further study. From the evidence available, it seems unlikely that they remove bone by phagocytic actions. It has been suggested that they produce an enzyme, such as hyaluronidase, that dissolves the cement substance that holds the mineral in bone matrix. In our opinion, an important reason for considering the possibility of their producing an enzyme is that cells fuse to form osteoclasts. Mitotic figures are not encountered in them; therefore, osteoclasts must form by the fusion of cells, and for cells to melt together suggests that some proteolytic enzyme has been liberated. Another indication of this is that in certain sites there is intercellular substance associated with the cells that fuse to form osteoclasts, and, as fusion occurs, the intercellular substance seems to melt into the cytoplasm of the osteoclasts.

It might be asked whether cells that fuse continue to live. Evidence from tissue culture studies suggests that osteoclasts are living cells. Studies of sections would suggest that if they are alive their life span is very limited,

and we doubt very much if those that have wrinkled dark nuclei are alive. The fact that nuclear detail remains visible is no indication that a multinucleated cell is alive; we have seen fused cells in transplanted tissues, previously killed by 3 freezings and thawings, show reasonably good nuclear detail when they were sectioned several weeks after they were implanted. Therefore, we conclude that many osteoclasts seen in sections are dead cells, and such enzyme activity as they manifest is manifested around the time when individual cells fuse against the naked bone surface that they regard as a foreign body.

THE FURTHER GROWTH OF THE SKULL

Remodeling procedures, dependent both on the addition and the removal of bone from surfaces, are responsible for the decrease in the curvature of the bones of the vault of the skull as this enlarges in postnatal life. The bones that are remodeled in this fashion are, for some time after birth, composed of only a single plate of bone which, however, contains some spaces filled with mesenchyme and thin-

cartilage   perichondrium

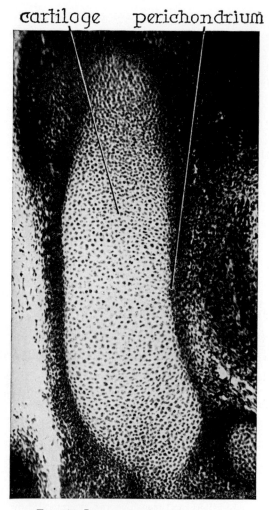

FIG. 179. Low-power photomicrograph of a longitudinal section of a developing leg (rabbit). In the middle of this picture a cartilage model is differentiating from the mesenchyme. In its more central part, the cartilage is fairly well developed. The mesenchyme along the sides of the cartilage model forms a sheath for it; this is called the perichondrium.

walled veins (Fig. 173). As the growth of the skull continues, the remodeling process gradually converts these single plates of bone, over most of the skull, into double plates of compact bone, with cancellous bone and a considerable amount of marrow between them. The layer of cancellous bone and marrow between the 2 plates of compact bone is termed the *diploe,* and it comes to contain many large, thin-walled veins called the *diploic veins.* The double plate arrangement over most of the skull is attained in childhood (around the age of eight). Later on, in adult life, the bones meeting at the various sutures become fused, and it becomes possible for diploic veins to pass from one bone to another.

ENDOCHONDRAL OSSIFICATION

Most of the skeleton forms as a result of endochondral ossification. The process can be followed to advantage in observing the histologic changes that occur in the limb buds of an embryo as they form and grow.

In the various sites where bones are to form, the mesenchyme of a limb bud begins to differentiate into cartilage (Fig. 178). The result is that cartilage models of the bones-to-be make their appearance (Fig. 179). The mesenchyme immediately adjacent to the sides of each cartilage model becomes arranged into a surrounding membrane for the model; this is called its *perichondrium* (Fig. 179). This has 2 ill-defined layers. The cells in the outer part of this membrane differentiate into fibroblasts, and these form collagen. The outer part of the perichondrial membrane thus becomes a connective tissue sheath. The mesenchymal cells in its inner part (between its fibrous layer and the cartilage of the model) do not differentiate to any great extent. Instead, they remain relatively undifferentiated and so possess almost all the potentiality of the mesenchymal cells from which they are derived. They constitute the inner or chondrogenic layer of the perichondrium (see Fig. 158).

The Growth of the Model. Cartilage models increase in length by the mechanism of interstitial growth. This entails division and hypertrophy of chondrocytes in the substance of the cartilage. Moreover, the models grow in width. Although interstitial growth may be a factor in this, it is likely that most growth in width is accomplished by the appositional mechanism; that is, new layers of cartilage are added to the surface of the sides of the model by the proliferation and differentiation of the cells of the chondrogenic layer of the perichondrium.

The interstitial growth responsible for the increase in length of any model tends to occur nearer its end than in its midsection. Hence, as growth continues, the chondrocytes left in the midsection of the model have time to ma-

hypertrophied
chondrocytes

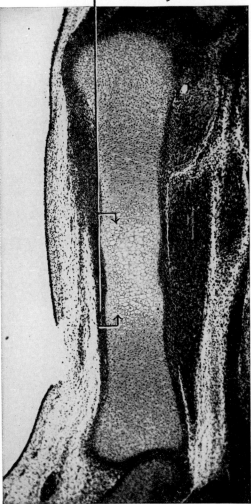

FIG. 180. Low-power photomicrograph of a longitudinal section of a developing leg (rabbit). This shows a cartilage model in a somewhat more advanced stage than that shown in Figure 179. The form of the bone-to-be is well outlined. Furthermore, the cartilage cells in the central part of the model have become hypertrophied and are about to secrete phosphatase.

calcified cartilage

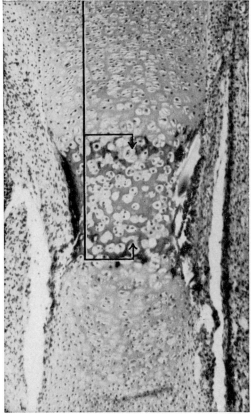

FIG. 181. Low-power photomicrograph of a longitudinal section of a developing phalanx (human). At this stage of development, the cartilage cells in the central part of the model have become hypertrophied and have secreted phosphatase. This has resulted in the calcification of the organic intercellular substance of the cartilage in this part of the model. The calcified cartilage appears in sections as somewhat darker than the uncalcified, which constitutes the remainder of the model.

ture. As they become larger, the intercellular substance about them becomes somewhat thinned out (Fig. 180), and when they have become sufficiently hypertrophied to manufacture phosphatase, it becomes calcified (Fig. 181). With the consequent death of the cells, the intercellular substance, particularly in the central part of the midsection of the model, begins to break up and some of it dissolves away to leave cavities within the substance of the model (Fig. 183).

During the period in which the changes described above are taking place in the midsection of a cartilage model, the progressive development of the vascular system of the embryo is responsible for the perichondrium

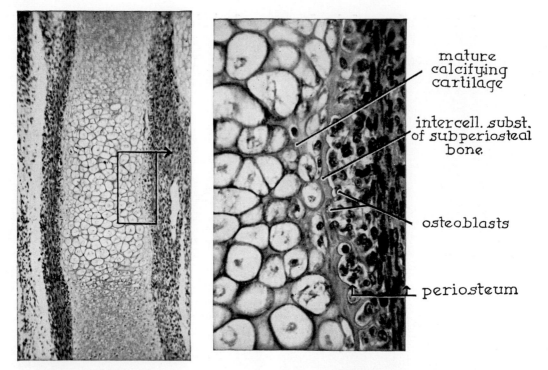

mature
calcifying
cartilage

intercell. subst.
of subperiosteal
bone.

osteoblasts

periosteum

FIG. 182. At the left is a low-power photomicrograph of a longitudinal section of the developing leg of a rabbit. The cartilage cells in the central part of the model are seen to be hypertrophied and are presumably secreting phosphatase, which is bringing about the calcification of the intercellular substance about them. Furthermore, as may be seen in the picture at the right, which is a high-power photomicrograph of the area indicated by a rectangle in the picture on the left, the osteogenic cells of the perichondrium have differentiated into osteoblasts and have laid down a thin layer of bone intercellular substance (subperiosteal bone) on the side of the model.

of the model being invaded by capillaries. Before their appearance, the relatively undifferentiated cells of the inner (chondrogenic) layer of the perichondrium, by proliferation and differentiation into chondroblasts and cartilage cells, have been adding new layers of cartilage to the sides of the model (appositional growth). However, the appearance of capillaries in the perichondrium profoundly affects the differentiation of the relatively undifferentiated cells of its inner layer. For, instead of continuing to differentiate into chondroblasts and chondrocytes, they, in the presence of capillaries, begin to differentiate into osteoblasts and osteocytes, with the result that a thin layer or shell of bone is soon laid down around the model (Fig. 182). Since the perichondrium thereafter covers bone tissue, its name is changed from perichondrium to *periosteum.*

It should be kept in mind that the differentiation of the cells of the inner layer of the perichondrium into osteoblasts at this period of development does not represent a change in the nature of these cells so much as it does a change in their environment brought about by the invading capillaries. Indeed, the cells of the inner layer of the periosteum retain their ability to differentiate into chondroblasts and form cartilage even into adult life. This is easily demonstrated in the repair of broken bones, for, when bones are fractured, the cells of the inner layer of the periosteum situated close to the break proliferate vigorously and, in sites where capillaries are unable to keep up with their rapid growth, differentiate into chondroblasts and so form cartilage (Fig. 208). However, in other sites, where capillaries are able to keep up with their growth, they differentiate into osteoblasts and so form bone.

These relatively undifferentiated cells of

mesenchymal origin that are first encountered mixed with chondroblasts in the inner layer of the periosteum, usually are termed *osteogenic* cells. This name does not suggest their cartilage-forming capacities. It would be better to term them *osteochondrogenic* cells. However, we shall use the shorter term with the understanding that the term osteogenic cell refers to a cell somewhat less differentiated than the chondroblast or osteoblast and which differentiates into either, depending on the environment in which it differentiates.

At this stage of development, then, the calcified cartilage in the midsection of the model is beginning to break down, and the shaft of the model has gained a surrounding shell of bone which has been laid down by the recently vascularized perichondrium which is now termed the periosteum. The inner layer of the periosteum at this time consists of osteogenic cells and osteoblasts which have formed from them. It also contains capillaries. As the calcified cartilage in the midsection of the model begins to disintegrate, osteogenic cells and osteoblasts, together with capillaries, begin to grow from the inner layer of the periosteum into the breaking down midsection of the cartilage model (Fig. 183). The invading osteogenic cells, osteoblasts and capillaries constitute what is called the *periosteal* bud.

When the osteogenic cells, osteoblasts and capillaries of the periosteal bud reach the interior of the midsection of the cartilage model, they are said to constitute a center of ossification. In this area the osteoblasts gather round such remnants of calcified cartilage as still remain and lay down bone intercellular substance on them (Fig. 184). The calcified cartilaginous intercellular substance that still remains at this time is, in this part of the model, in the form of an irregular network riddled with spaces; so, since the first bone that is formed in this area is deposited on the remnants of the cartilaginous network, the first formed bone in this area is, therefore, cancellous in type, with its individual trabeculae having cores of calcified cartilage. In a good H and E section, this makes a very pretty picture because the cores of cartilage intercellular substance are blue while the bone covering them is pink or red. The osteoblasts applied to the surface of the trabeculae are blue.

spaces in breaking-down calcified cartilage

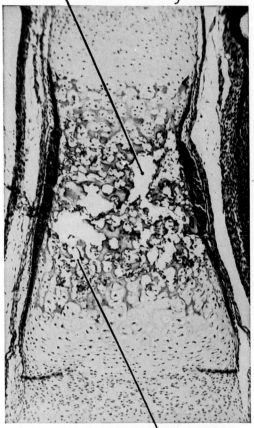

being invaded by blood vessels and osteoblasts of periosteal bud

FIG. 183. Low-power photomicrograph of a longitudinal section cut through a developing human phalanx. At this stage of development the calcified cartilage in the central part of the model has broken down and this has resulted in the formation of spaces in this area. Subperiosteal bone has formed along the sides of the model; this stains more darkly than the cartilage which it covers. Furthermore, osteogenic cells and blood vessels from the periosteum have grown into the spaces in the breaking-down cartilage, and the osteogenic cells in this area are beginning to differentiate into osteoblasts and lay down bone on what is left of the old calcified cartilage matrix.

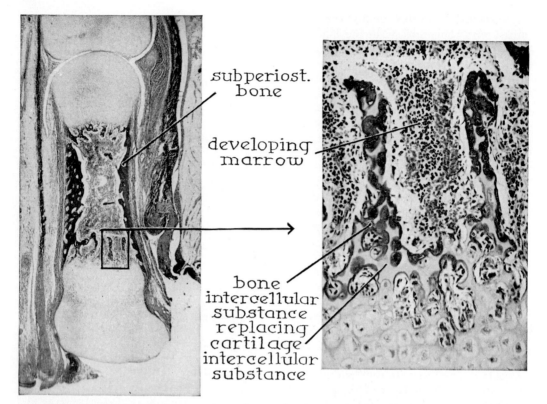

subperiost.
bone

developing
marrow

bone
intercellular
substance
replacing
cartilage
intercellular
substance

FIG. 184. (*Left*) A low-power photomicrograph of a longitudinal section of a developing human phalanx. This shows a stage somewhat more advanced than that illustrated in Figure 183. The amount of subperiosteal bone is increased, and the cartilage of the entire central part of the model has disappeared. Marrow now occupies the central part of the model. Bone formation is advancing toward each end. (*Right*) The photograph shows the characteristic picture of bone being deposited on cartilage remnants. The bone intercellular substance is dark, that of the cartilage is light.

Up to this time the only cartilage in the model that has matured, become calcified, and died, is that part which was situated in its midsection and whose remnants by this time are covered with bone. The cartilage at each end of the model continues to grow by means of the interstitial growth mechanism, and in these sections of the model the cartilage cells tend to be arranged in longitudinal rows. The continued growth at the ends of a cartilage model tends to increase the total amount of cartilage in the model and would do so if it were not for the fact that those cartilage cells next to the bone that has formed from the ossification center continue to mature. They become large and hypertrophied, manufacture phosphatase, and so cause the intercellular substance about them to become calcified. This brings about their death. When this occurs

the calcified cartilage intercellular substance breaks up into cavities and these are rapidly invaded by capillaries, osteogenic cells and osteoblasts that are extending up and down the model from the center of ossification. The osteoblasts that invade these cavities in the cartilage quickly line up along those remnants of cartilage intercellular substance that still persist and lay down bone on them to form trabeculae similar to those in the ossification center itself. By this mechanism the process of ossification gradually extends into each of the growing ends of the cartilage models (Fig. 185).

While bone formation is extending from the ossification center toward each end of a cartilage model, the periosteum continues to add further bone to the sides of the model. As the periphery of the model thus becomes stronger,

cartilaginous
epiphysis

developing ossification
center in epiphysis
epiphyseal disk

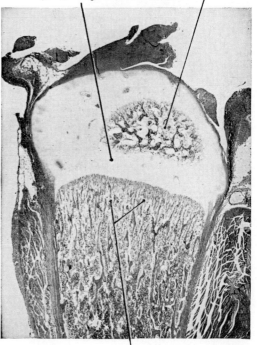

trabeculae on diaphyseal
side of epiphyseal disk

Fig. 186. Low-power photomicrograph of a longitudinal section of the upper part of the tibia of a kitten. This shows the stage of development shortly after the appearance of a center of ossification in an epiphysis. The cartilage that remains between the bone that forms from the epiphyseal center of ossification and that from the diaphyseal center constitutes an epiphyseal disk.

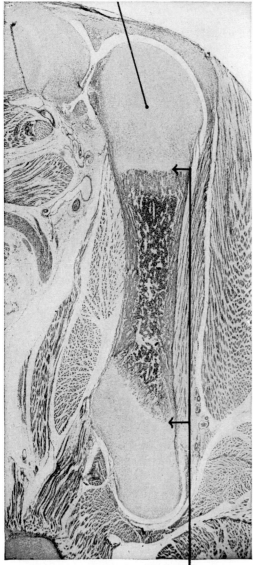

bony
diaphysis

Fig. 185. A very low-power photomicrograph of a longitudinal section of the developing thigh of a rabbit. At this stage the cartilage of the model is replaced by bone except at its ends. The bone that has formed from the periosteum and periosteal bud constitutes the diaphysis. The cartilage left at each end constitutes the epiphyses.

the cancellous bone in its central part is no longer necessary for support, so it tends to dissolve away and leave a cavity that is called the marrow cavity (Figs. 184 and 185). This soon becomes filled with the various cells that are concerned in making erythrocytes, granular leukocytes and platelets, as will be described in a subsequent chapter. However, during the postnatal growing period, the marrow cavity never extends quite all the way to the cartilaginous ends of a model but instead is always separated from each cartilaginous end by a

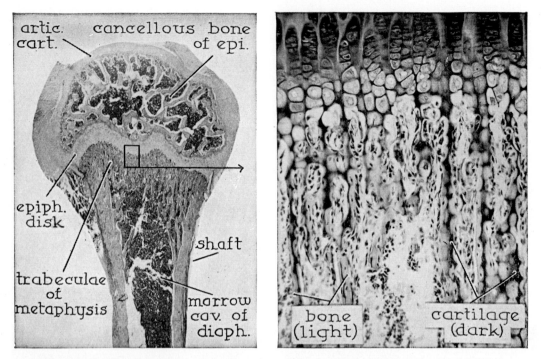

FIG. 187. At the left is a low-power photomicrograph of a longitudinal section cut through the end of a long bone of a growing rat. At this stage of development osteogenesis has spread out from the epiphyseal center of ossification so that only the articular cartilage above and the epiphyseal disk below remain cartilaginous. On the diaphyseal side of the epiphyseal plate are the metaphyseal trabeculae, which, as may be seen from the high-power picture on the right, consist of cartilage cores on which bone has been deposited. The cartilage cores of the trabeculae formerly were partitions between columns of cartilage cells in the epiphyseal disk.

zone of cancellous bone (Fig. 186) in which trabeculae are disposed longitudinally.

An ossification center that arises in the midsection of a cartilage model, as has been described, is spoken of as a *diaphyseal center* of ossification since it gives rise to the shaft or diaphysis of the bone concerned. However, the development of many bones of the body is complicated by the development of further centers of ossification in their cartilage models. In the long bones these further centers of ossification appear in the growing cartilaginous ends of the models and are termed *epiphyseal centers* of ossification (Fig. 186). These are responsible for forming the bone that comes to exist in the epiphyses or ends of the bones.

The development of an epiphyseal center of ossification is heralded by the maturation of the cartilage cells situated in and near the central part of the cartilaginous end of a model. As the chondrocytes enlarge and make

phosphatase, the intercellular substance about them becomes thinned out and calcified and they die. The intercellular substance about them then breaks up to form cavities which soon are invaded by capillaries, osteogenic cells and osteoblasts. The latter lay down bone on the remnants of the cartilage intercellular substance. Meanwhile, the living chondrocytes immediately surrounding this area have begun to mature and die; hence, the process of ossification is able to spread out from the center in all directions. However, ossification stops short of replacing all the cartilage in the end of a model. Enough is left at each articulating end of a model to constitute an articular cartilage (Fig. 187). Furthermore, a transverse disk or plate of cartilage is left between the bone derived from the epiphyseal center of ossification and that from the diaphyseal center. This transverse disk or plate of cartilage that separates epiphyseal bone from diaphys-

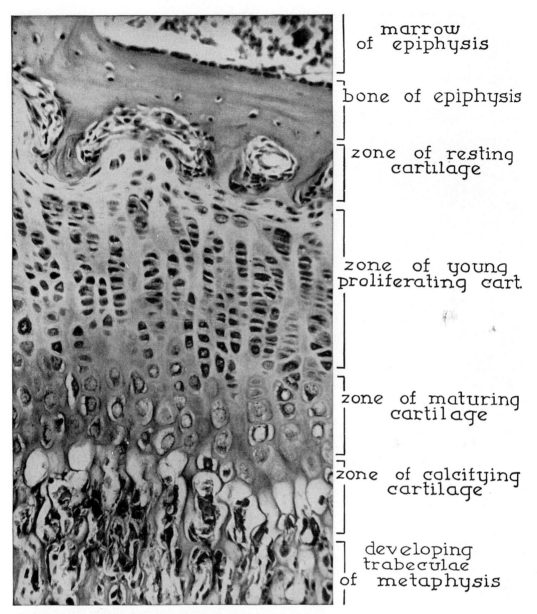

marrow
of epiphysis

bone of epiphysis

zone of resting
cartilage

zone of young
proliferating cart.

zone of maturing
cartilage

zone of calcifying
cartilage

developing
trabeculae
of metaphysis

FIG. 188. High-power photomicrograph of a longitudinal section cut through the upper end of the tibia of a guinea pig. This picture illustrates the different zones of cells in the epiphyseal plate.

eal bone is termed the *epiphyseal disk or plate* (Figs. 186 and 187), and it persists until the postnatal longitudinal growth of bones is completed; only then is it replaced by bone.

The route by which capillaries and osteogenic cells gain entrance to the central part of an epiphysis probably is indicated later by the course of the larger blood vessels that supply that epiphysis. The blood supply of epiphyses will be described later in connection with the blood supply of bones.

Further Growth of the Model. The further longitudinal growth of a model of a long bone in which epiphyseal centers of ossification have appeared is accounted for by the continuance of the interstitial growth of cartilage

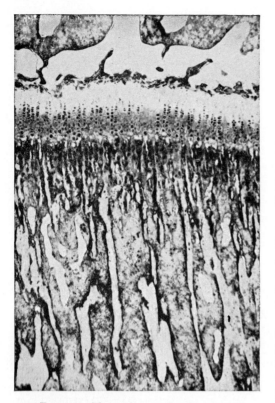

FIG. 189. Photomicrograph of a section of the growing zone of a tibia of a normal rat. The section was prepared so that the darkened areas are due to the presence of alkaline phosphatase. Notice that there is a dark band of phosphatase activity in the region of the hypertrophied cartilage cells in the plate and another in the region of the osteoblasts that are invading the diaphyseal side of the plate. Notice that the zone of calcified cartilage is relatively free from phosphatase (it contains few living cells). (Morse, A., and Greep, R. O.: Anat. Rec. I I I :193)

ration, death and replacement of cartilage on the diaphyseal side of the disk. Hence, in an epiphyseal disk there is a persistent race between 2 processes: (1) interstitial growth, which tends to thicken it, and (2) calcification, death and replacement of cartilage at its diaphyseal surface, which tends to thin it.

An epiphyseal disk and that part of the diaphysis adjacent to it constitute what is termed a *growing zone* of a long bone. In a child, this zone is the site of tremendous cellular activity. Many different processes (the interstitial growth, maturation, calcification, death and disintegration of cartilage, and the formation, calcification and destruction of bone) are at work in this area simultaneously. Any interference with any one of these different processes, while the others continue, is quickly reflected by an alteration in the normal histologic picture of the part.

Since different abnormal states (for example, dietary deficiencies and endocrine gland imbalances) affect different processes at work in this region and so produce different kinds of alteration in the histologic picture in the part, we shall consider the growing zone of long bones in some detail.

If a longitudinal section of a growing bone is placed under the microscope and examined so as to allow the eye to sweep across the thickness of the epiphyseal disk from its epiphyseal to its diaphyseal aspect (Fig. 188), the cartilage of the disk will be seen to present 4 successively different appearances. Accordingly, the epiphyseal disk is divided into 4 different zones. From the epiphysis to the diaphysis these zones are: (1) The zone of resting cartilage, (2) the zone of proliferating young cartilage, (3) the zone of maturing cartilage, (4) the zone of calcified cartilage. These 4 zones are not distinctly separated from one another but more or less merge into one another. Their special characteristics and functions will now be described.

1. The layer of resting cartilage is that layer situated immediately adjacent to the bone and the marrow spaces of the epiphysis. Chondrocytes of moderate size are scattered irregularly throughout its intercellular substance. The part of the cartilage of this zone that actually touches the bone or marrow spaces of the epiphysis sometimes has a perichondrial-like appearance.

cells in the epiphyseal disk. Since epiphyseal disks separate bony epiphyses from bony diaphyses, interstitial growth in them (Fig. 191) constantly tends to separate the bone of the epiphyses from the bone of the diaphysis. The result is that the total length of the model becomes increased. However, the thickness of the epiphyseal disks does not become increased because of interstitial growth within them. This is because another process, one tending to reduce the thickness of the disk, is at work simultaneously, namely, the continuing matu-

This zone of cartilage does not participate in the growth of the epiphyseal plate. It serves merely to anchor the plate to the bone of the epiphysis and to insulate the cells of the next zone to be described from capillaries present between it and the bone and which probably nourish the disk. (See the section on the blood supply of bones for further information on this latter point.)

2. The second zone is composed of young proliferating cartilage cells. These are commonly thin and many of them are wedge-shaped. The cells in this zone are more or less piled on top of one another like stacks of coins so that they form columns whose long axes are parallel with that of the bone (Fig. 188). In a growing bone, mitotic figures can be found among these cells. The plane in which mitosis occurs exhibits considerable variability. It seems likely that the column arrangement is maintained because of the bundles of collagen fibrils in the partitions of intercellular substance between the columns. The function of this zone is cell proliferation (Fig. 191). This is the site where a sufficient number of new cells must be produced to replace those that hypertrophy and die at the diaphyseal surface of the disk, as will be described.

3. The third zone or layer contains cartilage cells that are in various stages of maturation. These, too, are arranged in columns. Those nearest the zone of proliferating cartilage are the least mature and those nearest the diaphysis are the oldest and most mature (Fig. 188).

The cells in this zone were originally in the proliferating zone but were left behind as their neighbors on their epiphyseal side continued to proliferate and so drew away from them. The cells left behind in this zone gradually mature. In this process they become larger and accumulate glycogen in their cytoplasm. In becoming larger they take up more space and hence expand the epiphyseal disk longitudinally. The epiphyseal plate then is expanded in the long axis of the bone by the proliferation of cells in the second zone and by the maturation of cells in the third zone. Moreover, the cells of this zone produce phosphatase, as may be demonstrated in sections by histochemical methods (Fig. 189). The phosphatase brings about the calcification of the intercellular substance that surrounds the hypertrophied cells so that the latter die and

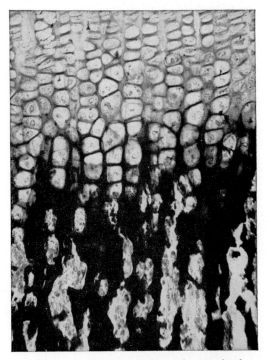

FIG. 190. Low-power photomicrograph of a longitudinal section of the end of the tibia of a young rat. This section was cut without the bone's being decalcified and has been stained by von Kossa's method, by which the phosphate of the calcium phosphate reacts with a silver salt to become blackened. The blackened material seen in the illustration represents the calcified cartilage of the epiphyseal plate and the calcified bone underlying it.

disappear. When this happens the third zone has turned into the fourth zone which will now be described.

4. The fourth zone is very thin, being only one or a few cartilage cells thick. This zone abuts directly on the bone of the diaphysis. Most of the cells in this zone are dead because they have previously hypertrophied (in the adjacent zone of maturing cartilage) to the point where they made phosphatase, and this has brought about the calcification of the intercellular substance about them and, hence, their death (Fig. 188). If sections of undecalcified bone are stained with silver salts, the phosphate of the recently deposited calcium phosphate in the cartilaginous intercellular substance in this zone reacts with the silver to form black silver phosphate (Fig. 190).

This clearly marks the zone of calcifying cartilage.

Osteogenesis is very active at the diaphyseal side of the epiphyseal disk and results in bone being formed in very intimate contact with the cartilage of the disk (Figs. 187 and 191). It is important to understand exactly where this bone is formed. A glance at the zones of maturing and calcified cartilage of a disk will show that the partitions of cartilaginous intercellular substance between the columns of cartilage cells vary somewhat in thickness but that in general they are thicker than the partitions between the individual cells in any single column. Hence, as the cartilage cells in the zone of calcification die and the inter-

cellular substance about them begins to disintegrate, the partitions between the cells of any column and the thinner partitions between columns are the first to melt away. Only the stouter partitions between columns remain and these are immediately utilized as sites for bone deposition (Figs. 191 and 193). Osteoblasts from the diaphysis invade the breaking-down cartilage and line up along the sides of these stouter partitions and quickly deposit bone on their surfaces. This results, on the diaphyseal side of the epiphyseal disk (the metaphysis), in the formation of longitudinally disposed bony trabeculae with cartilaginous cores (Figs. 191 and 193). Since the cartilaginous cores of these trabeculae are continuous with the car-

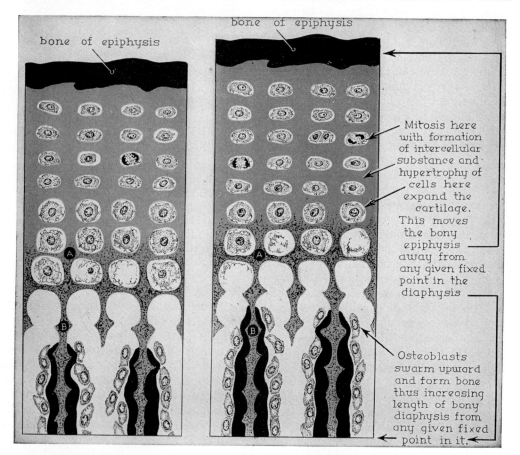

Fig. 191. Diagrams of 2 longitudinal sections cut through the same epiphyseal plate and part of the diaphysis of growing long bone. The diagram on the right illustrates the changes that occur in what is represented in the left over a short space of time. Cartilage is gray, calcified cartilage is stippled and bone is black. The sites labeled A and B are fixed points and remain at the same level in both diagrams. Note, however, that "bone of epiphysis" has moved upward in the diagram on the right and that the level of calcified cartilage and bone is also higher in the diagram on the right. (Ham, A. W.: J. Bone & Joint Surg. 34A:701)

tilaginous intercellular substance of the disk (partitions between columns), the newly formed bony trabeculae are united firmly with the cartilaginous disk. By this arrangement the metaphysis of a bone is joined firmly to the epiphyseal disk.

The part of the metaphysis in direct contact with the epiphyseal disk in a growing bone is a site of active osteogenesis. This is the region wherein new bone is added to the ends of the diaphysis by means of osteoblasts advancing into the breaking-down cartilage in the zone of calcification of the epiphyseal disk and there laying down bone on the stouter cartilaginous partitions to extend the length of the bony trabeculae. They make phosphatase also; this brings about the calcification of the organic intercellular substance that they form (see Fig. 189 for the intense band of phosphatase activity in this zone; the osteoblasts are responsible for this). This is the only mechanism by which the diaphysis can become lengthened. Bone cannot grow by interstitial growth. It can grow only by appositional growth, and the new bone that is "apposed" and accounts for the growth in length of the diaphysis is added to the tips of the prolongations of bone that extend into the cartilage; this increases the penetration of the cartilage and makes the metaphysis longer (Fig. 191).

Since the ends of the bony trabeculae in this zone are constantly being added to by the deposition of bone in the zone of calcification of the cartilaginous disk, it might be thought that the zone of trabeculated bone in the metaphysis would become increasingly elongated. Instead, however, except at its periphery, this zone of trabeculated bone is maintained at a fairly constant thickness during

the growing period (see Fig. 193). This can only mean, then, that as rapidly as bone is added to the ends of the metaphyseal trabeculae in the zone of calcification, bone is resorbed from their free ends that project toward the marrow cavity of the diaphysis. Osteoclasts commonly are seen here; often they

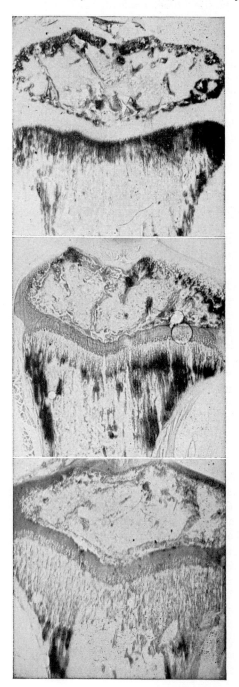

FIG. 192 (*Top*) Coated radioautograph of a safranin-stained section of the end of a tibia of a 50-Gm. rat sacrificed 5 minutes after injection of radiophosphorus. (*Middle*) Similar preparation from rat sacrificed 2 days after the injection. (*Bottom*) Similar preparation from rat sacrificed 8 days after the injection. (All 3 preparations from Leblond, C. P., Wilkinson, G. W., Bélanger, L. F., and Robichon, J.: Am. J. Anat. **86**:289)

are wrapped around the free ends of the trabeculae.

That the trabeculae that are present under the more central part of an epiphyseal disk of a growing animal at any given time are not the same ones that are present several days later is illustrated beautifully by means of radioautography. Leblond, Wilkinson, Bélanger and Robichon, by means of administering radiophosphorus, have shown that although there is some exchange between circulating phosphate and the phosphate in bones, there is a substantial precipitation of administered radiophosphorus into bone that is forming and calcifying at the time the radiophosphorus is administered. This precipitated radiophosphorus is sufficiently stable to permit the fate of the bone into which it precipitates to be followed thereafter by means of radioautographs. As a glance at Figure 192, *top,* will show, radiophosphorus, 5 minutes after it is injected into a young growing rat, is deposited in the new bony trabeculae that are forming and calcifying on the diaphyseal side of epiphyseal disks. This, for the practical purposes with which we are concerned, removes the radiophosphorus from the circulation. However, the bone continues to grow in length, and so new bone is added continuously to the ends of the trabeculae—the ends that extend into the epiphyseal disk—and this new bone is not marked by radiophosphorus because now there is not enough in the circulation to mark it. A considerable band of new unmarked bone is already present 2 days after the administration of the radiophosphorus (Fig. 192, *middle*). Meanwhile, the marked bone of the trabeculae has been dissolving from the free ends of the trabeculae, so that the average total length of marked bone in the trabeculae is shorter than it was 2 days previously. After 8 days, all the marked bone has been eroded from the trabeculae under the central part of the disk (Fig. 192, *bottom*); hence, the trabeculae that are present at this time (8 days after the radiophosphorus was administered) are composed of bone that has formed and calcified during the 8 days; therefore, they are not the same trabeculae that were present 8 days before. However, it is to be noted that Figure 192, *bottom,* shows the persistence of some of the marked bone under, and some distance away from, the *peripheral* portion of

the epiphyseal disk; the significance of this will be discussed soon.

Under the *periphery* of the epiphyseal disk, the fate of the metaphyseal trabeculae is different from that described for the trabeculae under its more central part. However, an explanation of what happens to these involves a discussion of how a long bone *as a whole* changes during the growing period, so we shall discuss this matter first.

THE GROWTH OF A LONG BONE AS A WHOLE

Although there are a few exceptions to the rule, it can be stated as a generalization that the growth in length of bones that develop in cartilage is fundamentally dependent on the ability of the cartilage that persists in them and on their ends to grow by the interstitial mechanism, as follows:

The growth in length of short bones, which have no epiphyseal disks, depends on such interstitial growth as occurs in their articular cartilages (Fig. 184).

In long bones that have epiphyseal disks, the interstitial growth of the articular cartilages provides only for the growth in size of the epiphyses and not for the growth of the diaphysis. However, articular cartilage may provide for growth in width of the epiphysis as well as for its growth in length (Fig. 193).

In long bones that have epiphyseal disks the interstitial growth of the cartilage in the disks does not assist in the growth of the epiphysis after the bony epiphyses are reasonably well developed. After an epiphysis is well developed the cartilage of an epiphyseal disk is no longer replaced with bone on its epiphyseal side but only on its diaphyseal side (Fig. 188). Hence, the interstitial growth of cartilage in epiphyseal disks accounts only for the growth in length of diaphyses during all but the early stages of the growing period (Fig. 193).

With these facts established we can now consider some further points about the growth of a long bone as a whole.

The diaphyses of many long bones funnel outwardly as they approach their epiphyses; hence, many bones are of a much greater diameter in their metaphyseal regions (the metaphysis is the part of the shaft responsible for growth in length: the epiphyseal disk and the trabeculae on its diaphyseal side) than in their midsections (Fig. 193). As may be seen by comparing the left and the right sides of Figure 193, the site, along the longitudinal axis of a bone, that is occupied by the flared metaphyseal portion of the diaphysis will, as the bone continues to elongate, be occupied later by the tubular and considerably nar-

rower portion of the shaft. This means that as growth in length continues, the diameter of the portion of the shaft that is flared at any given time subsequently must become decreased. This requires that bone be resorbed continuously from the exterior of the flared portion and built up continuously on its inner aspect so that it can become a narrower shaft.

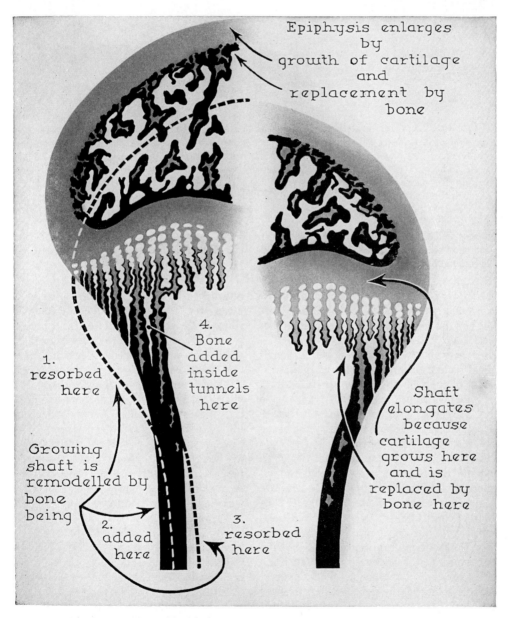

Epiphysis enlarges
by
growth of cartilage
and
replacement by
bone

4.
Bone
added
inside
tunnels
here

1.
resorbed
here

Growing
shaft is
remodelled by
bone
being

2.
added
here

3.
resorbed
here

Shaft
elongates
because
cartilage
grows here
and is
replaced by
bone here

FIG. 193. Diagram showing surfaces on which bone is deposited and resorbed to account for the remodeling that takes place at the ends of growing long bones that have flared extremities. (Ham, A. W.: J. Bone & Joint Surg. **34A**:701)

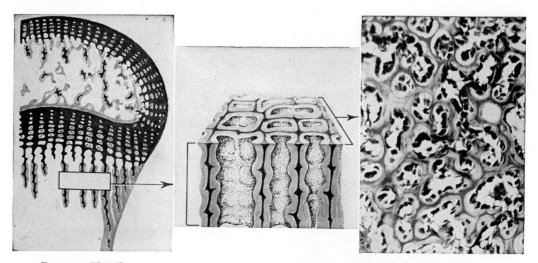

FIG. 194. The diagram at the left illustrates the appearance seen in a longitudinal section of the end of a growing long bone. The trabeculae appear stalactitelike in such a preparation. However, if they could be seen in 3 dimensions, as is illustrated in the drawing in the middle, it would be seen that, close to the plate, the structures that appear as trabeculae in a longitudinal section are slices that have been cut through walls that surround spaces; they are slices cut through the walls of tunnels. The photomicrograph at the right represents what is seen in a cross section cut through the metaphysis of a growing long bone of a rabbit, close to the epiphyseal disk. In it the trabeculae of bone have cartilaginous cores and they surround spaces. These spaces under the periphery of the disk become filled in to form haversian systems, and such compact bone as is present in the flared extremities of bone is built by spaces such as these becoming filled in.

We shall now consider how bone is built up on the inner aspect of the flared portion so that bone can be resorbed safely from its outer aspect.

It is easy to get the impression from longitudinal sections of growing bone that the trabeculae of the metaphysis are like stalactites, hanging down from the diaphyseal side of the plate. However, if cross sections are cut of the metaphyses of larger mammals, close to the plate, it will be found that only the free ends of the trabeculae are stalactitelike. Closer to the plate the structures that in longitudinal sections appear as stalactitelike trabeculae are revealed in cross sections to be connected together to constitute a network that is honeycombed with spaces (Fig. 194). Why the newly formed bony trabeculae (which have cartilaginous cores) appear isolated from one another in longitudinal sections should appear, when they are seen in cross section, to comprise a cancellous network will now be explained.

To explain why the newly formed bone should exist in a honeycomblike cancellous network in this area it is necessary to refer again to the way in which the calcified cartilage in the epiphyseal plate disintegrates.

In the zone of maturing cartilage the cartilage cells are arranged in longitudinal rows that are separated from one another by partitions of intercellular substance. If this area is visualized in 3 dimensions, it will be obvious that the rows of cells are contained in longitudinal tunnels and that the partitions of intercellular substance between the rows of cells are the walls of these longitudinally disposed tunnels. As the cartilage cells in a tunnel mature and die at its diaphyseal end, the thinner partitions between tunnels tend to dissolve, and by this means tunnels only one cartilage-cell wide fuse with others of the same size to become relatively large tunnels (Fig. 191), which are invaded from the diaphysis by osteogenic cells, osteoblasts and capillaries. The osteoblasts line up along the sides of the tunnels and deposit bone on the tunnel surfaces (Fig. 191). Hence, in a longitudinal section, the wall between 2 adjacent tunnels will appear as a trabecula with a cartilage core that is covered on each side by a layer of bone (Fig. 194). In other words, the bone seen covering the cartilaginous cores of the trabeculae in longitudinal sections is the bone that in cross section is seen to line the tunnels of cartilage (Fig. 194). The osteoblasts that cover the trabeculae of longitudinal sections similarly are the osteoblasts that line the insides of the tunnels that are seen in cross sections. And the capillaries and osteogenic tissue that fill the spaces between the trabeculae of longitudinal sections are the contents of the tunnels seen in cross section.

On the diaphyseal side of the more central part of the epiphyseal disk only a single layer of bone is commonly deposited inside the cartilaginous tunnels. Hence, the trabeculae seen in a longitudinal section of this area are narrow. However, at the periphery of the disk successive layers of bone are deposited inside the tunnels. This narrows their lumens and imparts a lamellar appearance to their thickened walls. The successive layers of bone deposited inside the tunnels are the result of appositional growth. The osteoblasts lining the tunnel proliferate by mitosis to increase their numbers. Simultaneously some of them differentiate into osteocytes and in doing so surround themselves with intercellular substance. This results in a layer or lamella of bone being deposited inside the tunnel. The osteoblasts that remain to line the tunnel then repeat the full procedure, so a second layer of bone is deposited. Finally, after several layers have been deposited, the tunnel is reduced to a narrow canal, which contains a blood vessel, some osteoblasts or osteogenic cells and perhaps a lymphatic. This arrangement of a canal with concentric layers of bone surrounding it is called a *haversian system* (Fig. 199). Haversian systems, in a sense, are units of structure of compact bone. Each has a blood vessel in its canal and this provides tissue fluid to nourish the osteocytes in the surrounding lamellae. Haversian systems are limited with regard to the number of lamellae they can contain by the distance over which the canalicular mechanism can nourish osteocytes. This, of course, is not very great; hence, commonly a haversian canal is surrounded by less than half a dozen concentric lamellae (Fig. 199).

A haversian system can develop only by means of a tunnel being filled in from its

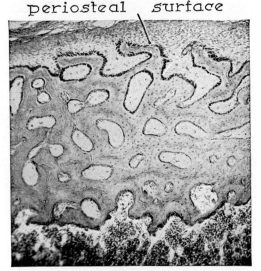

periosteal surface

FIG. 195. Low-power photomicrograph of a cross section of the radius of a growing puppy. It is to be noted that the periosteal surface is not smooth but consists of longitudinally disposed ridges and grooves. The ridges are covered by osteoblasts and the grooves are lined by them. Developing haversian systems can be seen throughout the substance of the shaft.

inside with concentric layers of bone. A haversian system, then, is in the nature of a bony tube with thick walls and a very narrow lumen. However, if tubes are bundled together side by side, crevices are left between them. Compact bone, though made of longitudinally disposed haversian systems, does not exhibit such crevices. With what are they filled?

Since the first compact bone that forms under the periphery of a disk is the result of a cartilaginous tunnel being filled in with bone, the crevices between the haversian systems that form in this manner are filled with cartilage. Hence, in the shaft of a very young growing bone, irregular bits of cartilage commonly will be seen (Fig. 193). It should be kept in mind by any student who wishes to understand bone growth well, that each of these bits of cartilage seen incorporated into the shaft of bone and situated between haversian systems was once part of a partition between rows of cartilage cells in the epiphyseal plate and somewhat later was the cartilaginous core of a metaphyseal trabecula under

How haversian systems are added to periphery of young shaft

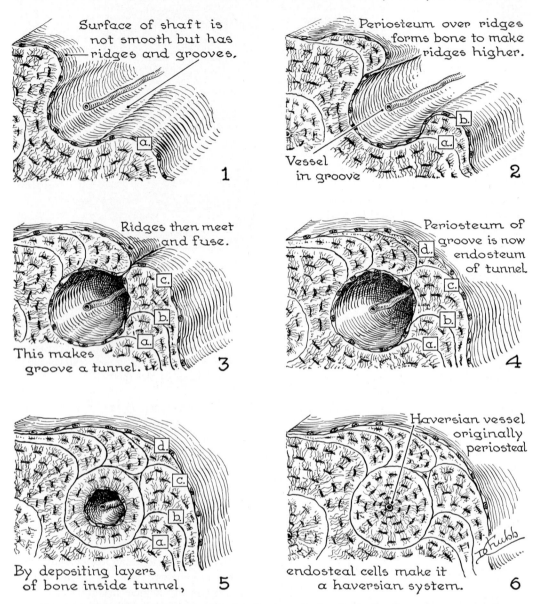

FIG. 196. Three-dimensional diagrams showing how the longitudinally disposed grooves on the exterior of a growing shaft become roofed over to form tunnels and how these become filled in to form haversian systems which thereupon are added to the exterior of the shaft. These diagrams also show how the blood supply of a shaft of a long bone comes to be derived, when it is fully grown, to a great extent from the periosteum by means of vessels having been buried in its substance.

How haversian systems can be added to older shafts

Osteoclasts

Osteogenic cells

Outer circumferential lamellae

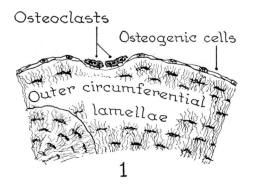

1

Longitudinal groove

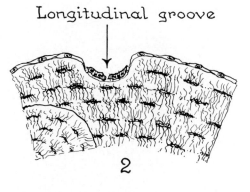

2

Groove becomes deepened.

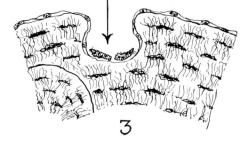

3

Periosteum with periosteal vessel descends into groove.

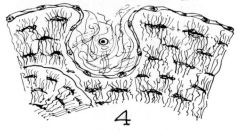

4

Periosteum forms bone to make groove a tunnel.

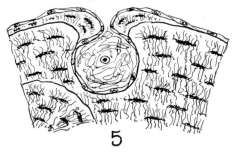

5

Tunnel is filled in to become haversian system.

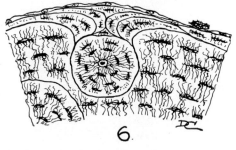

6

FIG. 197. Diagrams of cross sections of the shaft of a bone showing how haversian systems are laid down under the periosteum in older bones to replace outer circumferential lamellae.

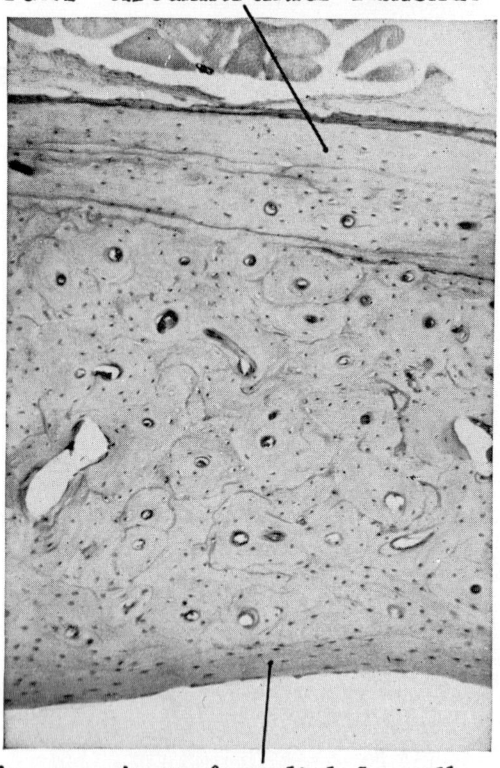

outer circumferential lamellae

inner circumferential lamellae

FIG. 198. Low-power photomicrograph of a cross section of the radius of a dog. This picture shows outer circumferential lamellae in its upper part, inner circumferential lamellae in its lower part and haversian systems with haversian lamellae, separated by interstitial lamellae, in the middle.

the periphery of the plate. In the shafts of older bones the crevices between adjacent haversian systems are filled with what are termed interstitial lamellae (Fig. 199); the origin of these will be described later.

HOW SHAFTS OF BONES GROW IN WIDTH

A long bone does not grow in length alone; it also grows in width. This is accomplished by new layers of bone being added to the outside of the shaft while at the same time bone is dissolved away from the inside of the shaft. The result of these two processes proceeding simultaneously is that, although the shaft as a whole becomes wider, its walls do not be-

come unduly thick, and the width of the marrow cavity gradually increases.

The shaft of a bone grows in width by the appositional mechanism (Fig. 165). New bone is laid down under the periosteum by the osteogenic layer of that membrane. However, if a cross section through the shaft of a young bone that is growing in width is examined, it will be seen that much of the new bone that is being added under the periosteum is in the form of haversian systems. It has been explained that haversian systems always are formed as a result of tunnels (not necessarily cartilaginous ones) being filled in from their inside. How, then, can bony tunnels, to be subsequently filled in from their insides, be formed under the periosteum of a young growing bone?

A brief study of the periphery of a cross section of an actively growing shaft will reveal how this occurs. The surface of such a shaft is not smooth; instead, it demonstrates a series of longitudinal ridges with grooves between them (Fig. 195). The osteoblasts of the periosteum cover the tops of ridges and extend down to the bottoms of the grooves between them. The periosteum here also contains blood vessels (Fig. 196, 1). Longitudinal tunnels form from this arrangement as follows: the osteoblasts of the periosteum covering the ridges proliferate and lay down bone so as to gradually extend the ridges over toward one another (Fig. 196, 2) till they meet (Fig. 196, 3). This converts the groove that formerly existed between 2 ridges into a tunnel. Since the groove was lined with periosteum containing osteoblasts and blood vessels, the tunnel now contains a lining of osteoblasts with a blood vessel somewhere in its lumen. As is shown in Figure 196 (4, 5 and 6), the continued proliferation of the osteoblasts lining the tunnel with their subsequent differentiation into osteocytes, results in the tunnel being converted into a haversian system. It is in this manner that new haversian systems are added under the periosteum to the periphery of a young actively growing shaft.

As the growth in width of a bone slows down, the surface of the shaft becomes smoother. Appositional growth occurring under the periosteum, then, tends to add smooth, even layers to the surface of the shaft (Fig. 197). These are called *circumferential lamellae*

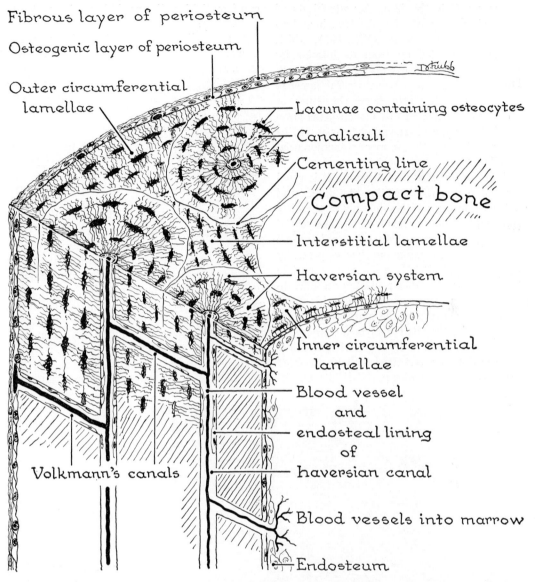

Fibrous layer of periosteum

Osteogenic layer of periosteum

Outer circumferential
lamellae

Lacunae containing osteocytes

Canaliculi

Cementing line

Compact bone

Interstitial lamellae

Haversian system

Inner circumferential
lamellae

Blood vessel
and
endosteal lining
of
haversian canal

Volkmann's canals

Blood vessels into marrow

Endosteum

Fig. 199. A 3-dimensional diagram showing the appearance of both a cross and a longitudinal section of the various components that enter into the structure of the cortex of the shaft of a long bone. It should be kept in mind, of course, that there would be many more haversian systems in the cortex than are shown here. The diagram shows the different kinds of lamellae that are present and the relation between the blood vessels of the periosteum, Volkmann's canals, haversian canals and the marrow cavity.

because they tend to surround the whole shaft. It is obvious that, if several circumferential lamellae were laid down under the periosteum, the cell farthest away from the periosteum (in the deepest lamellae) soon would be unable to receive enough nourishment by the canalicular mechanism for their survival.

Hence, lamellar bone of this type does not tend to persist if it becomes thick. Sooner or later it is replaced by haversian systems. The replacement is brought about by means of longitudinal troughs being eroded on the surface of the shaft. Osteoclasts may be seen in these (Fig. 197). When a longitudinal trough becomes sufficiently deep, the osteoblasts of the periosteum roof over the trough and so convert it into a tunnel (Fig. 197), which thereupon is filled up from its interior by osteoblastic activity. By this means, bone consisting originally of circumferential lamellae can be converted into bone consisting of haversian systems. In this instance, the crevices between the haversian systems would be the remains of the former circumferential lamellae.

As a bone attains its full width, it is usual for the osteoblasts covering its outer, and lining its inner, surfaces to smooth these by adding a few more or less final circumferential lamellae. These are called the "outer" and the "inner" circumferential lamellae respectively (Figs. 198 and 199). In a sense, they are like the finishing coats that a plasterer applies to the walls of a room as he completes his work. Between the outer and the inner circumferential lamellae, the shaft of a bone consists of haversian systems (Fig. 199). The crevices between these (interstitial lamellae) are filled either with the remaining parts of old outer cir-cumferential lamellae or old haversian systems (Fig. 199).

It seems likely that the haversian systems in a shaft of compact bone have a limited life span. It could be expected that the canalicular mechanism would not always function perfectly and hence that areas of osteocytes contained in the lamellae of a system, from time to time, would die. With their death the intercellular substance of the lamellae about them tends to dissolve away and this, of course, enlarges the canal. Furthermore, it is highly unlikely that a whole system would die at any one time. More likely, only a part of it would suffer; for example, one side might die while the other side might remain healthy. For this reason, the new tunnels that form because parts of haversian systems dissolve away do not necessarily represent or occupy exactly the same position as the original canal that was filled in to form the system. However, osteoblasts from the original canal proliferate to line the new one and lay down lamellae in it to form a new haversian system. As new systems form in this fashion, it is easy to see that parts of the old systems that still

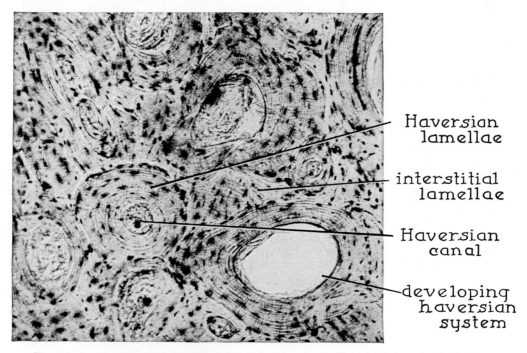

Haversian
lamellae

interstitial
lamellae

Haversian
canal

developing
haversian
system

FIG. 200. Low-power photomicrograph of a ground cross section of dried, undecalcified bone. This shows both fully formed and developing haversian systems. The haversian systems of bone can be seen to good advantage in this type of preparation.

remain would come to constitute the interstitial lamellae between the new systems. For this reason, the majority of interstitial lamellae in older bones are the remnants of old haversian systems. Haversian systems and interstitial lamellae are seen to advantage in "ground" cross sections of undecalcified bone (Fig. 200).

As the two processes of bone deposition and bone resorption, on the outside and inside of a shaft respectively, continue through the growth period, it comes to pass that the bone of the original shaft is all resorbed and that the shaft comes to be composed entirely of bone that has been deposited under the periosteum during the growing period. Since each haversian system that forms under the periosteum is built around a periosteal vessel (Fig.

196), the blood supply of the shaft, as growth in width continues, would seem to be derived more and more from the periosteum. It will be recalled that haversian systems are added to the outer surfaces of a bone by means of troughs containing periosteal vessels being roofed over. However, the roof that forms over each trough is not quite complete. A hole is left in it at the site at which the periosteal vessel descends into the trough. As the successive haversian systems are added to the surface, the first-formed ones become more deeply buried, and so what were originally only holes in the roofs of troughs become elongated to constitute canals which run at right angles to the haversian systems between them and the periosteum. These canals that convey periosteal vessels into the haversian canals are

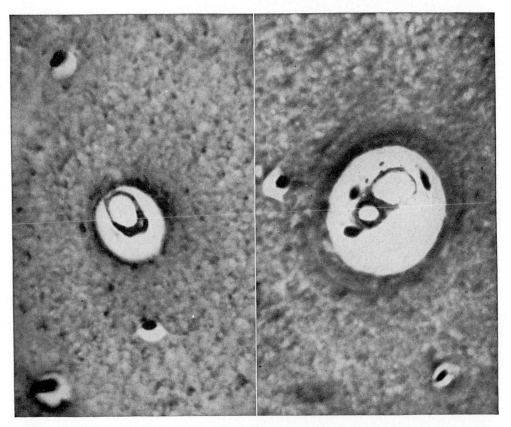

Fig. 201. Photomicrographs ($\times$ 800) of blood vessels in haversian canals as they appear in cross sections of the radius of a dog. (*Left*) The canal in the center contains a single vessel which is a large capillary. (*Right*) The canal in the center contains 2 vessels, a very small arteriole and a very small venule. The stippled appearance of the bone intercellular substance is due to the presence of canaliculi that are cut in cross section and obliquely. A few bone cells in lacunae may be seen. (Ham, A. W.: J. Bone & Joint Surg. **34A**:701)

called "Volkmann's canals" (Fig. 199). Because of the way they are formed, they are not surrounded by concentric lamellaelike haversian canals.

From the foregoing account of how a bone grows in width, it would seem that most of the blood vessels of the cortex of the diaphysis of a fully grown bone would be derived from the periosteum. However, the circulation is more complicated that it seems, as we shall now describe.

THE BLOOD SUPPLY OF A LONG BONE

First, it should be understood that compact bone is a very vascular tissue. Since haversian systems tend to run longitudinally, the blood vessels in their central canals also run longitudinally, and since the systems are of such a limited width, the longitudinally disposed blood vessels in haversian canals are relatively close together, generally not more than one fifth of a mm. apart and often closer. Consequently, the capillary bed of compact bone is of an extraordinary magnitude.

Most haversian canals contain only a single blood vessel (Fig. 201, *left*) and this is generally of the order of a large capillary. However, some canals contain 2 vessels; these generally consist of a small arteriole and a small venule (Fig. 201, *right*). Lymphatics have been described as being present in some haversian canals. Volkmann's canals, of course, contain larger vessels (Fig. 199).

The frequency of anastomoses between the blood vessels of adjacent haversian systems does not seem to have been worked out in detail. However, anastomoses do not seem to be very numerous. This, of course, is important in relation to fractures. If a bone is broken, the vessels in the haversian system are interrupted, and clotting occurs at their torn ends. The circulation in them stops on each side of the break at least back to the point where they anastomose with a vessel that is still functioning. Because of the scarcity of anastomoses between the vessels of adjacent haversian systems, the osteocytes in the shaft of a bone generally die for a distance of at least a few millimeters away from the site of a fracture, and sometimes they die over a much greater distance.

We shall now consider how the small vessels in bone substance are supplied and drained by larger vessels.

Of course, the larger blood vessels that enter any bone can be identified by dissection. The precise area that each supplies can be investigated by injecting different ones with India ink or other materials and then ascertaining where the India ink or other material has lodged. The particular parts of bone that each large vessel supplies can be studied also by tying off different vessels or sets of vessels in living animals and then, from histologic sections determining which parts of the bone have died from a lack of blood supply. Lastly, the extent to which the process of repair is affected by tying off different vessels also helps to identify the respective territories commonly supplied by the different vessels.

By using these and additional technics in extensive experiments, Johnson, in 1927, investigated the blood supply of bones. More recently, Brookes has made many illuminating studies in this field. There are 3 sets of vessels involved in supplying a long bone. These are:

1. **The Nutrient Artery or Arteries.** It will be recalled that a diaphyseal center of ossification is set up in a cartilage model of a developing bone by a periosteal bud or buds that invade the cartilage. The blood vessels of the periosteal bud or buds become larger, as development proceeds, to become eventually the nutrient artery and vein of the diaphysis. The diaphysis of some bones, for example, the femur, normally has several nutrient arteries, while the diaphysis of others, for example, the tibia, has only one.

2. **The Metaphyseal and the Epiphyseal Vessels.** The segment of a long bone occupied by an epiphyseal disk and by the adjacent newly forming trabeculae on the diaphyseal side of the disk is called a *metaphysis*. In many bones, as is illustrated in Figure 193, the shaft, as it passes from the diaphysis into a metaphysis, widens to become more or less funnel-shaped. Since the trabeculae of the metaphysis are parallel with the longitudinal axis of the bone, they form acute angles with the side of the funnel (Fig. 193). Likewise, the longitudinally disposed spaces between the trabeculae also form angles with the sides of the funnel, so they provide ready communica-

tion between the interior and the exterior of the bone (Fig. 193). Therefore, at this site, blood vessels from the exterior of the bone could easily enter the interior of the bone, and it seems probable that the many small vessels that enter the shaft in this region, that constitute the metaphyseal vessels, use this route of entry.

The blood supply of different epiphyses differs. One kind of epiphysis is completely covered with articular cartilage; the latter is continuous with that of the epiphyseal disk (Fig. 202). The head of the femur is an example of this kind of epiphysis. The vessels that supply such an epiphysis, according to Dale and Harris, who have investigated this matter in our laboratory by means of injecting the vessels of experimental animals, enter the epiphysis along the line where the articular cartilage meets the cartilage of the epiphyseal disk (Fig. 202, A). In the other kind of epiphysis the articular cartilage does not extend to the cartilage of the epiphyseal disk, and in the gap between the 2 cartilages the sides of the epiphysis are bony. In such epiphyses, blood vessels can enter and leave the bony sides (Fig. 202, B).

Dale and Harris have found that there is a great difference in the fate of these 2 types of epiphyses if they become separated from their diaphyses. Separations of epiphyseal disks sometimes occur as a result of trauma and for other reasons. Harris has confirmed Haas's observations to the effect that the line of separation effected by the usual trauma is across the zone of mature but as yet uncalcified cartilage of the epiphyseal disk (Fig. 188). When epiphyses that are completely covered with cartilage are separated from their diaphyses, the vessels that enter them, along the line where the articular cartilage meets the cartilage of the disk (Fig. 202, A), generally are ruptured. As a result, both the bone and the marrow of the epiphysis die. When the other type of epiphysis is separated from its diaphysis it continues to live because the vessels that enter through its bony sides are not ruptured by the separation. The bulk of an epiphyseal disk remains attached to a separated epiphysis. Briant, Dale and Harris, working in our laboratory, have found that if a detached living epiphysis is left undisturbed in a living animal, the epiphyseal disk continues to

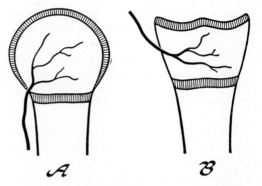

FIG. 202. Drawings to show the 2 types of epiphyseal blood supply. When separation of the epiphyseal plate occurs in A, the blood vessels are torn and the bone of the epiphysis dies. (Preparation by G. Dale and W. R. Harris)

thicken. This suggests that the zone of proliferating cartilage (Fig. 188) is fed from the vessels occupying the canals in the zone of resting cartilage (Fig. 188), as has been suggested previously by the author.

After growth in length is over, the cartilage of epiphyseal disks is resorbed and replaced by bony trabeculae. The spaces between the latter permit ready communication between the interior of the epiphysis and the metaphysis. Under these conditions, anastomoses between the epiphyseal and the metaphyseal vessels occur (this has been investigated by Trueta and Harrison in the head of the femur in man), and the complex of epiphyseal and metaphyseal vessels that enter and leave the bone in this region then generally are referred to as the *metaphyseal-epiphyseal* vessels.

3. **The Periosteal Vessels.** It has been explained already that, because of the way that bone grows in width, periosteal vessels become successively buried in the cortex of the diaphysis as central vessels of haversian systems, and they retain their connection with the periosteum or more superficial haversian vessels through Volkmann's canals (Fig. 199).

Results of Experiments Indicating Respective Roles of the 3 Sets of Vessels in Adult Animals. Johnson's studies revealed that the nutrient artery will maintain the life of the marrow and the inner two thirds of the cortex of the diaphysis. Moreover, he showed that there are excellent anastomoses between the branches of the nutrient artery and the metaphyseal vessels, and that the metaphyseal-epiphyseal complex of vessels would maintain the life of the marrow and the inner half of the bone of the cortex (there are some results that conflict with this latter finding). The periosteal vessels alone would maintain the life of only the outer half of the cortex of the bone.

DeHaas, working with Macnab, in the Department of Surgery, University of Toronto, recently has made further extensive studies of the blood supply of bones. In these studies all of the various technics mentioned previously were employed, and evidence was found that suggested that the blood supply of a bone is perhaps more complex than was realized previously. In most studies of this kind it is usually deemed sufficient to trace the course of the arterial side of the circulation and assume that blood passes back by the same route in companion veins. However, deHaas and Macnab point out that a nutrient vein is generally smaller than its companion artery, and this, as well as certain of their experimental results, suggests that there is normally some flow of the blood that reaches the marrow from the nutrient artery out through the cortical vessels to the periosteum. More recently, Brookes and Harrison have reported that the normal flow of blood in the cortex is from the medullary arteries out through the cortex to the capillaries of the deep periosteal layer and from there into veins. However, if there is a lack of blood flow in the medullary arteries the flow through the cortex can be reversed, with blood from the periosteal vessels flowing through the vessels of the cortex to the medullary cavity. This reversal of blood flow, which occurs when the medullary circulation is impaired has been demonstrated in ischemic bones in man and experimentally in bones of rabbits by Brookes.

HOW DISTURBANCES OF MINERAL METABOLISM AFFECT GROWING BONES

Rickets. The mechanism of calcification has been described as being dependent on the concentration of calcium and phosphate ions in the vicinity of calcifying bone or cartilage exceeding their solubility product. It has been shown that in general this condition is not attained in a growing infant if the product obtained by multiplying the number of milligrams of calcium per 100 cc. of serum by the number of milligrams of phosphorus per 100 cc. of blood is less than 40. It is to be noted that a reduced level of calcium *or* phosphorus in the blood does not necessarily interfere with calcification; it is the concentration of the product of the two ions that determines whether precipitation will continue in the sites of calcification.

In a baby the growing skeleton normally absorbs large amounts of calcium phosphate. For the CaP product of the blood to be maintained above 40 consequently necessitates that the infant's diet contain an adequate amount of calcium and phosphorus. Further, for these minerals to be absorbed into the blood stream, the infant also requires an adequate supply of vitamin D.

If an infant's diet is deficient in these essentials, the CaP product of the blood may fall below 40, with the result that a condition known as *rickets* develops. Rickets is associated with characteristic changes in the growing zones of long bones. The earliest one to be seen is that the calcification of cartilage almost ceases in the epiphyseal disks. If the intercellular substance about the cells in this zone fails to become impregnated with mineral, the cells of this zone are not shut off from nutrition. Hence, they do not die but continue to live. The result is that, since growth continues in the growing zone of the disks, the epiphyseal disks become thicker than normal (Fig. 203). Inasmuch as calcification is not entirely arrested but occurs in a few sites on the diaphyseal sides of the disk, the thickening of the disks tends to be irregular (Fig. 203). In the meantime, osteoblasts continue to lay down the organic intercellular substance of bone in the metaphysis, but this also does not become calcified because of the low CaP product. Instead, it exists in an uncalcified state until the diet is remedied. New bone, during the time it remains uncalcified, is termed *osteoid tissue* (Fig. 203). Furthermore, it would seem as if the osteoblasts of the periosteum in the region of metaphysis realized that calcification was not proceeding normally, for they increase their activities and lay down large amounts of osteoid tissue in

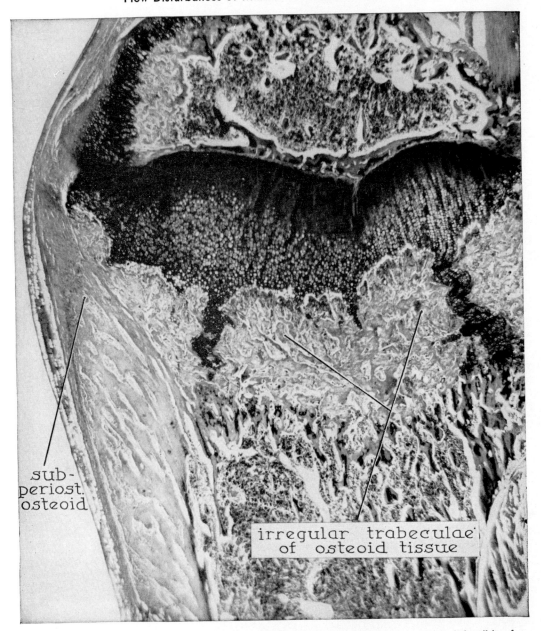

sub-
periost.
osteoid

irregular trabeculae
of osteoid tissue

FIG. 203. Low-power photomicrograph of a longitudinal section of the upper end of the tibia of a young rat that had been fed a Steenbock diet with calcium carbonate added to produce a blood-calcium level of 10 mg. and a blood-phosphorus level of 2 mg. per 100 cc. Since the product of calcium and phosphorus was only 20, proper calcification did not ensue on the diaphyseal side of the epiphyseal plate. This has resulted in the cartilage cells living much longer than they should, and as a result the epiphyseal disk has become thicker than normal and in some sites very thick. Furthermore, such trabeculae as have formed on the diaphyseal side of the disk are irregular and poorly calcified (osteoid tissue). Osteoid tissue also may be seen to have formed under the periosteum at the left side of the picture. This is an example of severe low-phosphorus rickets.

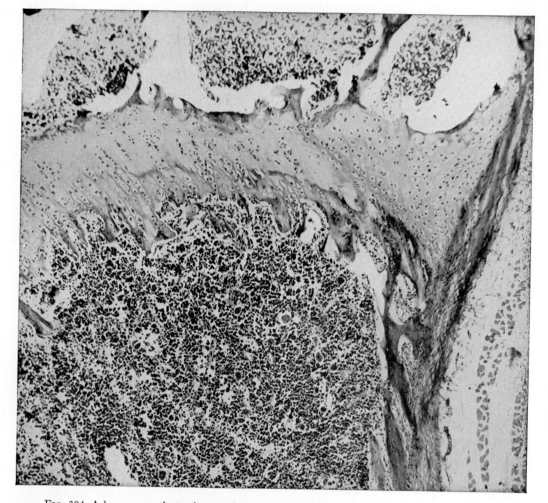

Fig. 204. A low-power photomicrograph of a longitudinal section of the upper end of the tibia of a guinea pig that for some weeks had been fed a diet containing an inadequate amount of vitamin C. Under conditions of prolonged vitamin C deficiency, bone building almost ceases on the diaphyseal side of the disk, and, as a result, the epiphyseal plate is not supported by a proper number of trabeculae. Furthermore, bone building almost ceases in the shaft, and, as a result, it becomes fragile and breaks easily. (Ham, A. W., and Elliott, H. C.: Am. J. Path. 14:323)

the metaphyseal region under the periosteum. This makes the metaphyseal regions knobby. The knobs so produced at the growing ends of the ribs are responsible in a rachitic child's chest for what is termed the "rachitic rosary."

It is to be kept in mind that the changes that occur in the growing zones of bone in rickets are the result of growth continuing while calcification fails. For this reason, a disturbed mineral metabolism will cause more severe rickets in a child that is actively growing than in one that is not. The poorly calcified intercellular substance of bone, seen in rickets, bends with weight bearing. Hence, rachitic children may be bowlegged.

Osteomalacia. The characteristic alteration in bone in rickets can be produced only while growth continues. However, there is a condition, called *adult rickets*, better termed *osteomalacia*, that occurs after growth of bones is over. To understand this, it is necessary to remember that the formation of new bone tissue in the body does not cease when the bones of the skeleton reach their full development. As has been explained previously, haversian systems probably have only a limited life, and as older ones disintegrate new ones must be formed to replace them if the skeleton is to be maintained. The formation of new bone that proceeds slowly, but more or less constantly, in the skeleton commonly is referred to as maintenance growth. Under an unfavorable mineral metabolism the new bone that is formed in maintenance growth may be imperfectly calcified. If the unfavorable mineral metabolism persists for long periods, a substantial part of the skeleton may come to consist of osteoid tissue. Under these conditions, bones become less opaque to x-rays, as has already been explained.

Osteoporosis and Allied Conditions. As noted previously, the normal growth of bone depends upon several processes occurring more or less simultaneously in the metaphysis. In contrast to rickets, which is commonly due to a deficiency of vitamin D in the diet and in which calcification is primarily affected, a deficiency of vitamin C in the diet interferes with the health of osteoblasts and their production of organic intercellular substance. In deficiencies of vitamin C, calcification is unimpaired. If the deficiency is only moderate in degree, a bone continues to grow in length but with a deficient production of trabeculae on the diaphyseal side of the epiphyseal disk (Fig. 204); consequently, the disk is poorly supported and may fracture. Furthermore, the haversian systems of the diaphysis are not properly built up (Fig. 204); the result of this is that the shaft fractures easily.

Other factors besides a deficiency of vitamin C can interfere with the proper production of the organic intercellular substance of bone. Individuals past middle life (women, in particular) suffer not uncommonly from impaired skeletal maintenance. Too little new bone is formed to replace that which breaks down, and, as a result, the bones of the skeleton become relatively fragile. The condition is termed *osteoporosis*. The evidence suggests that a lack of certain hormones may be, at least in part, responsible for the condition.

A local osteoporosis occurs in the condition termed *atrophy of disuse*. If, for example, an arm or a leg is paralyzed, or even put in a cast which prevents all movement for a long time, the bone of the part becomes less dense. It is not known whether this is due principally to an increased resorption or to an almost complete cessation of maintenance growth. However, that bones put at rest tend to become less dense, illustrates very clearly that the structure of bone is actively related to the function it is called upon to serve.

WOLFF'S LAW

Moreover, bone responds to increased function or altered function with structural changes. That the internal architecture and the external form of a bone are related to its function and change with altered function was observed many years ago by Wolff, whose particular postulate regarding this general principle, which is somewhat too detailed to be quoted here, is often spoken of as "Wolff's law." Sir Arthur Keith has fittingly likened osteoblasts to architects. Certainly the arrangement of trabeculae in the upper end of the femur is a magnificent demonstration of engineering principles put into practice.

PERIOSTEUM AND ENDOSTEUM

Those students who have occasion to read the older literature on bone will find that there have been many arguments as to whether or not periosteum is osteogenic or merely a fibrous limiting membrane. The probable reason for much confusion in this field is that many surgeons have regarded the fibrous membrane that they could strip from bones as the complete periosteum of those bones. Histologists regard the periosteum as having 2 layers: an outer fibrous layer and an inner osteogenic or osteoblastic layer (Fig. 205). If "periosteum" is stripped from bone the inner osteogenic layer is prone to adhere to the bone. Hence, the layer that is stripped, which some surgeons have called the (whole) periosteum, is only the outer fibrous layer of what the histologists term periosteum. This argument, which confused matters for a long time, seems now, however, to be fairly well resolved, for there is now much more complete agreement to the effect that the periosteum has 2 layers. The inner layer becomes less noticeable with age.

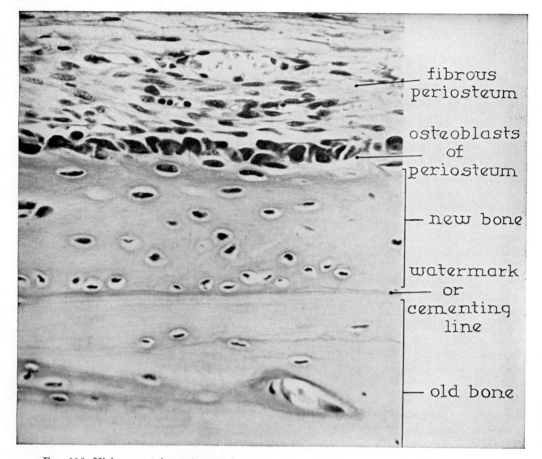

fibrous periosteum

osteoblasts of periosteum

new bone

watermark or cementing line

old bone

FIG. 205. High-power photomicrograph of an *active* periosteum near the site of a fracture. Observe the difference between the cell types in the fibrous and the osteogenic layers. Notice the intense basophilia of the cytoplasm of the osteoblasts that abut on the bone (RNA) and the difference between the appearance of newly formed bone and the pre-existing bone. Observe how osteoblasts are being surrounded by intercellular substance to become osteocytes.

The endosteum is the cellular membrane that lines the marrow cavities of bone and all haversian canals of bone. It develops from the periosteal bud and is composed of osteogenic cells that can become active osteoblasts when required.

The cells of the inner layer of the periosteum and of the endosteum form a continuous covering for all bony surfaces that are not undergoing resorption. The osteogenic cells that make up the membrane that covers and lines bone surfaces are direct descendants of the cells of the inner layer of the perichondrium of bones that develop in cartilage, so it should not be surprising that these cells, that multiply to repair fractures, can produce cartilage as well as bone.

THE REPAIR OF FRACTURES

The healing of broken bones is a matter of concern to every practicing doctor. Consequently, the process by which fractures heal receives considerable attention in medical schools. A student ordinarily receives instruction and is interrogated about this matter in every year of his medical course. The time when it is easiest to grasp the fundamentals of the process is when the facts of the development and the growth of bone are still fresh in the mind. For this reason, the repair of fractures will be considered briefly at this time.

In the usual fracture a single bone is broken into 2 parts, each of which is termed a *frag-*

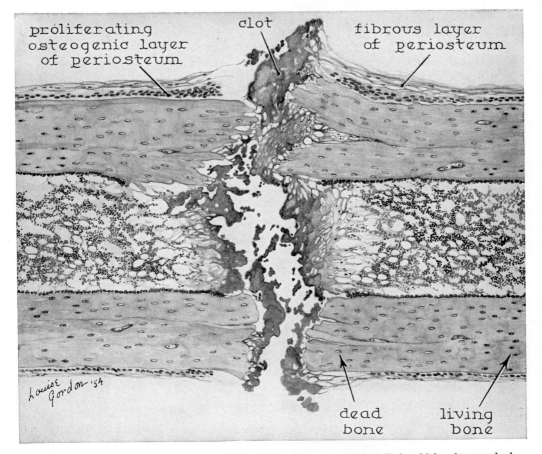

FIG. 206. A drawing of a longitudinal H and E section of a rabbit's rib in which a fracture had been healing for 48 hours. The territory encompassed by the drawing was that which could be seen with a very low-power objective, but the detail has been depicted at higher magnification to obviate the necessity of making several drawings at different magnifications. (Ham, A. W., and Harris, W. R.: *In* Bourne's Biochemistry and Physiology of Bone, New York, Acad. Press)

ment. Further, in the usual fracture the periosteum is torn and the fragments are displaced so that their ends are not in perfect apposition to one another. Because of this, it is usually necessary for fractures to be reduced; that is, the fragments are led back, usually by manipulation but sometimes by an open operation, so that their broken ends are in apposition to one another and the line of the bone is restored.

The student may think, and indeed he should be entitled to think, that by this time the repair of fractures would have been studied enough for the accounts of the process given in modern books dealing with surgery, pathology, histology and even bone itself to be very much alike. Unfortunately, they are

not, and the best way to resolve any confusion resulting from reading different accounts of the process is to study a set of sections cut from fractures that have healed for different lengths of time. Such a set can be prepared easily from the ribs of rabbits.

THE REPAIR OF A SIMPLE FRACTURE

Effects of the Injury

In a simple fracture there is both direct and indirect injury to tissue. The trauma itself causes direct injury; it breaks the bone and tears the soft tissues associated with the bone. As a result of the trauma, all the blood vessels crossing the fracture line are torn. The first result of this is that blood pours from their torn ends into the fracture area. This blood soon coagulates to form a clot in and about the site of the fracture (Fig. 206, *clot*). The next and second type of injury caused by a fracture is indirect; it depends on the fact that when the ends of the torn blood vessels are sealed off by agglutination and coagulation (see Chap. 9), circulation stops in all these vessels back to sites where they anastomose with still functioning vessels. Cessation of circulation in these vessels—an indirect cause of tissue damage—leads to considerable death of tissue as follows.

It has been explained already that the life of the osteocytes in any haversian system is precarious, being dependent on diffusion through canaliculi from the central vessel or vessels of the system. The latter run more or

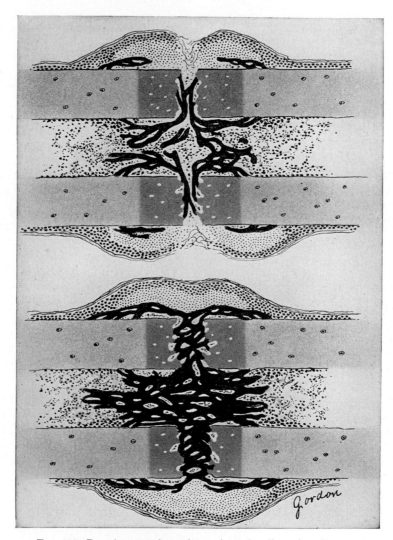

Fig. 207. Drawings to show the periosteal collars that form, approach each other and fuse in the repair of a fracture. The drawings also show the formation of internal callus and how the trabeculae become cemented to the original fragments. Living bone of the original fragments is light gray, dead portions of the original fragments are dark gray, and new bone in the external and the internal callus is black. In the external callus, cartilage is stippled lightly, and proliferating osteogenic cells are stippled darkly.

less longitudinally in bone. When the bone is broken, these vessels in haversian systems are all torn at the fracture line, and circulation in them stops back to sites where they anastomose with other haversian vessels. Since anastomoses between vessels of adjacent haversian systems are probably not overly abundant, this means that circulation ceases in haversian vessels for some distance each side of the fracture line. This results in the death of the osteocytes for a considerable distance from each side of the fracture line (Fig. 206). Hence, when a fracture occurs, bone dies, not only at the fracture line from the direct effects of trauma, but also for a considerable distance from each side of the fracture line because of the interruption of circulation in the haversian vessels that cross the fracture line.

The same factors that cause the death of bone are also responsible for the death both of periosteal tissue and some marrow tissue on each side of the fracture line. However, since both these tissues have a better blood supply

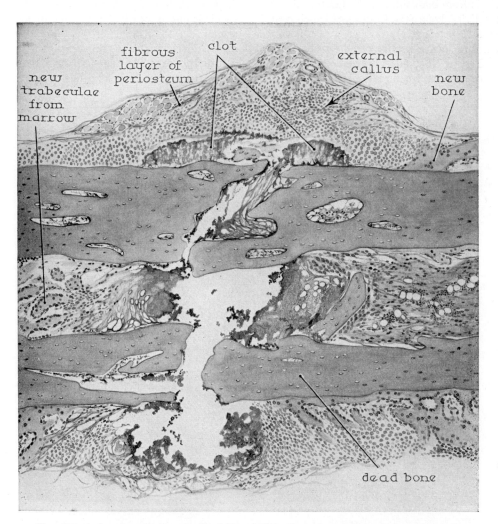

Fig. 208. A drawing of a longitudinal H and E section of a rabbit's rib in which a fracture had been healing for 1 week. The territory encompassed by the drawing was that which could be seen with a very low-power objective, but the detail has been filled in at higher magnification to obviate the necessity of making several drawings at different magnifications. (Ham, A. W., and Harris, W. R.: *In* Bourne's Biochemistry and Physiology of Bone, New York, Acad. Press)

than the bone itself, the periosteal tissue and the marrow tissue do not die for as great a distance from each side of the fracture line as does the bone (Fig. 206).

Dead bone is generally recognized because dead osteocytes undergo lysis; hence, in most dead bone the lacunae appear to be empty (Figs. 206, 207 and 208). However, the osteocytes, before dissolving, sometimes become pyknotic (dark and rounded). After 48 hours, the irregular line of demarcation between the dead bone (with empty lacunae), that extends from both sides of the fracture line, and the living bone (the lacunae of which contain normal osteocytes), farther away from the fracture line, generally can be recognized, as in Figures 206, 207, 208 and 209. The distance from a fracture line over which bone

dies as a result of its blood supply being interrupted differs depending on the site of the fracture in the bone and the particular bone that is fractured.

Early Stages of Repair

The Term Callus. A fracture is repaired by a growth of the new tissue that develops in and around the site of the fracture; this new tissue, which soon or late forms a bridge between the fragments so that they are united (Figs. 207, 208 and 209), is termed a *callus*. A great amount of literature dealing with bone repair is unnecessarily complicated by authors attempting to distinguish different stages of callus development by different names such as provisional callus, temporary callus, bridging callus and permanent callus. These terms

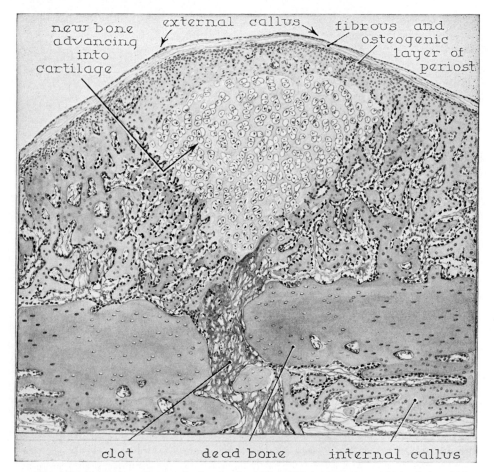

Fig. 209. A drawing of part of a longitudinal H and E section of a rabbit's rib in which a fracture had been healing for 2 weeks. (Ham, A. W., and Harris, W. R.: *In* Bourne's Biochemistry and Physiology of Bone, New York, Acad. Press)

suggest that different calluses exist at different times with each being replaced by another. Actually, what happens is that only one callus develops and it, like any bony structure, is remodeled as it grows. However, there is one classification that is helpful in describing callus formation; that is to speak of the callus that forms *around* the opposing ends of the bone fragments as the *external callus* and that which forms between the 2 ends of the bone fragments and between the 2 marrow cavities as the *internal callus* (Fig. 209).

The Origin of Callus. Many accounts of fracture healing describe the first important step in the repair process as depending on the invasion of the blood clot by a growth of new young capillaries and fibroblasts (granulation tissue). This alleged phenomenon often is described also as bringing about the formation of a temporary or transient callus. Many authors, having described the formation of a temporary callus, are vague about its subsequent fate, whether it is replaced by or turns into permanent callus. We think there is no temporary callus. Furthermore, so far as the external callus is concerned, invasion and replacement of the blood clot is *not* an early or important step in the healing of the fracture; in fact, the blood clot remains more or less intact for days and seems only to be in the road of the repair process (Figs. 206, 208 and 209). So far as the internal callus is concerned, such blood clot as exists between the 2 marrow cavities is soon invaded by osteogenic cells from the endosteum and from marrow cells of great potentiality; both of these types of cells form new bone trabeculae, so there is nothing temporary about the callus tissue they build (Fig. 207, *bottom*).

How does a fracture become repaired? Forty-eight hours after a fracture, or even sooner, the cells that will be responsible for the repair are actively dividing by mitosis and increasing rapidly in numbers. These cells are: (1) the osteogenic cells of the deep layer of the periosteum (Figs. 206 and 208), and (2) the cells of the endosteum of the marrow cavity and the undifferentiated cells of bone marrow (Figs. 206 and 207). After 48 hours the cells of the deep layer of the periosteum of both fragments close to, but not directly adjacent to, the line of fracture have proliferated so extensively that they form a layer several cells thick (Fig. 206). As a result of this growth, the fibrous layer of the periosteum, which remains relatively inactive, is lifted away from the bone in this site (Fig. 206). The cells of the endosteum that line the marrow cavity, or cover any trabeculae in the marrow cavity that are close to the line of fracture, also proliferate, and this causes the endosteal layer, which is normally only 1 cell thick, to become composed of 2 or more layers. Moreover, the endosteal cells grow toward the fracture line with their numbers being augmented by undifferentiated cells of the marrow. During the first week after the fracture, these cells have begun to form some new trabeculae of bone in the marrow cavity close to the line of fracture (Fig. 208). These trabeculae may be cemented, at one end, to one fragment or the other (Fig. 207, *top*).

Over the next few days, the proliferation of osteogenic cells continues in both periosteal and endosteal regions, but those cells in the deep layer of the periosteum show the greater activity. They proliferate so rapidly that they soon form a distinct collar around each fragment close to the line of the fracture (Fig. 207, *top*). In addition to proliferating, these cells now begin to manifest signs of differentiation. To understand how they differentiate it is necessary to recall that the deep layer of the periosteum normally contains some capillaries. When the osteogenic cells begin to proliferate after a fracture the capillaries among them also proliferate, but they do not seem to grow as quickly as the osteogenic cells. As a result, the osteogenic cells that are more deeply disposed in the collars (those closest to the bone) differentiate in the presence of a blood supply; consequently, they become osteoblasts and form bony trabeculae in this region (Fig. 208). The new trabeculae that develop are cemented firmly to the bone matrix of the fragment, even though the bone of the fragment may be dead (Fig. 208). Those osteogenic cells in the more superficial parts of a collar (those farther away from the bone) seem to grow so quickly that the capillaries from the periosteum cannot keep up with them. When these osteogenic cells differentiate they must do so in a nonvascular environment, so they tend to differentiate into chondroblasts and chondrocytes, and, as a result, cartilage develops in the outer parts of the collars (Fig. 208).

Two comments should be made about the significance of cartilage in the external callus. (1) Its development here should not be unexpected because the osteogenic cells that cover bone surfaces, which proliferate to repair a fracture, are direct descendants of the cells of the perichondrium of embryonic bones where they, of course, once formed cartilage. (2) The amount of cartilage that forms in a callus is probably dependent on how quickly the callus tissue grows; if it grows very rapidly, capillaries probably cannot keep up with it, so its outer parts become nonvascular and cartilaginous. However, if callus tissue develops more slowly, new capillaries can keep pace with the osteogenic cells, so the osteogenic cells in such a callus differentiate in a vascular environment and so form bone. There also may be other factors that influence the amount of cartilage that forms, for example, species and movement.

When the collars resulting from the growth and the differentiation of the osteogenic cells of the deep layer of the periosteum are well developed, they generally exhibit 3 layers that merge into one another (Figs. 207 and 208). The layer closest to the fragment consists of bony trabeculae that are cemented to the bone; the next and intermediate layer consists of cartilage which merges imperceptibly into the outer parts of the bony trabeculae on one side and into the third and outer layer of the callus on the other. The third and outer layer consists of proliferating osteogenic cells.

The collars continue to grow chiefly because of the proliferation of osteogenic cells in their outer layer and to a lesser extent because of the interstitial growth of cartilage in their middle layers. Such growth as occurs in the collars makes them thicker and makes them bulge toward each other. Sooner or later the collars from the 2 fragments meet and fuse (Fig. 207); when this occurs union of the fragments has been achieved. Union is also achieved in the marrow cavity by developing trabeculae there forming a bridge (Fig. 207). Soon the histologic picture of the healing fracture comes to resemble that illustrated in Figure 209.

The Fate of the Cartilage. The cartilage that develops in a callus normally has a temporary existence only; like that which develops in embryonic bones, it is eventually replaced with bone. Those cartilage cells that are closest to the newly formed bone mature and begin to secrete phosphatase; this brings about a calcification of the intercellular substance around them and their death. The region in which this occurs is seen as a V-shaped line in a longitudinal section of a fracture at this stage of healing (Fig. 209). As the cartilage becomes progressively calcified it is replaced progressively with bone; this makes the angle of the V become increasingly acute. Finally the cartilage is all replaced with bone that is of the cancellous type. It is to be observed that the trabeculae of this cancellous bone that replace the calcified cartilage have cores of cartilage as do those that replace calcified cartilage on the diaphyseal side of an epiphyseal plate.

The Remodeling of the Callus. To understand the remodeling process it is important to realize that those trabeculae of bone that form close to the original fragments are firmly cemented to the fragments. Since they also connect with one another, the 2 fragments are firmly bridged by a cancellous network (Fig. 207, *bottom*). Moreover, it is important to realize that osteoblasts in building new trabeculae can lay down their matrix on dead portions of the fragments (as well as on living portions of them), so that by this means new trabeculae of bone become firmly cemented here and there to dead bone. However, between these trabeculae there are spaces, and the matrix of the dead bone is dissolved away in these spaces. By this mechanism the matrix of the dead bone is slowly etched away (except where new trabeculae fasten onto it). Next, osteoblasts grow into the spaces that have been deepened into the matrix of the dead bone by this process and lay down new living bone in them. By this means the matrix of the dead bone eventually is almost all replaced with new living bone.

At this stage the callus constitutes a fusiform mass of cancellous bone around the 2 fragments from which most of the dead bone has been resorbed. We have already described how cancellous bone can be converted into compact bone, and this phenomenon occurs in the cancellous bone that is directly between the 2 fragments and around their immediate periphery. This makes the bone very strong in this site, and, as a consequence, the trabeculae in the periphery of the callus are no longer necessary to provide strength so they are gradually resorbed. Eventually, the original line of the bone may be so well restored by this process that the site of the fracture can no longer be felt as a bony thickening.

It should be remembered that these various steps in the remodeling procedure merge into one another and proceed simultaneously to some extent.

The Healing of Fractures in Which Only One Fragment Remains Alive. As was explained in the blood supply of bones, a fracture near an epiphysis sometimes may destroy the blood supply to that epiphysis. A common example of this phenomenon is seen in many fractures of the neck of the femur in older people. In treating this type of fracture, the head of the femur, which is often left without any blood supply, is commonly attached to the neck, which has a blood supply, with some kind of metallic pin. In such a fracture all the callus tissue, which is generated to repair the fracture, must come from the living neck. There is a good amount of cancellous bone in this area, and osteogenic cells from the trabeculae, together with blood vessels from the spaces between the trabeculae, grow slowly into the dead cancellous bone and dead marrow of the head. Here the osteogenic cells become osteoblasts and form new trabeculae that become firmly cemented to the dead trabeculae of the head. This process brings about union between the dead head and the living neck. Gradually, osteogenesis extends farther and farther into the head, and under the best conditions the dead trabeculae of the head are almost all replaced with new living bone. The dead marrow likewise is replaced with living marrow. Curiously enough, the articular cartilage covering the head may live through the whole process because it obtains its nourishment from the synovial fluid and not from the blood supply of the head that was destroyed.

Do Fibroblasts Form Bony Callus? Some of the ways in which different accounts of fracture healing differ from one another have already been described. Another and most important way in which they differ is related to the extent to which they attribute the formation of bony or cartilaginous callus to the activities of fibroblasts.

In our account we have stressed what we believe is the extremely important role of the osteogenic cells that normally cover and line surfaces. The view has been taken that these cells represent a special family of cells that develop from mesenchyme, and the members of this family inherit an innate capacity to form tissues of the bone and cartilage types in the repair process. However, some investigators do not seem to think that these cells are any different from fibroblasts because of their inheritance but that they only seem different because of their environment, and if fibroblasts were in the same environment (against bone) they would be as competent at forming bone.

The student may be interested in what gave origin to the idea that environment is all-important. This idea seems to have arisen because pathologists occasionally found that little areas of bone had developed in sites where there were normally no osteogenic cells but in which there was a pathologic deposit of calcium salts such as in the scar of an old abdominal wound, a diseased tonsil or a calcified and sclerotic artery. Here, some reasoned, bone developed from fibroblasts growing up against the calcified material; this provided an environmental stimulus that made the fibroblasts turn into osteoblasts. Then Huggins made the very interesting discovery that transplanting the mucosa of the urinary bladder of a dog to its abdominal wall would cause bone to form in the wall; this seemed to be a true example of experimentally induced bone formation. Since then many experimenters have tried many means to obtain extracts or materials, calcified and otherwise, that on injection into different soft tissues would induce bone formation.

There is no question about the fact that bone sometimes develops in sites far removed from the skeleton. However, this does not prove that fibroblasts are as competent at forming bone as the cells that cover and line bone surfaces. Indeed, such examples of heteroplastic bone formation as occur are to be explained more readily, we think, by the presence of occasional undifferentiated mesenchymal cells in these tissues that are led to differentiate along the osteogenic-osteoblastic line than by assuming that any fibroblasts can form bone under the right stimulus.

We shall discuss this matter somewhat further when we consider bone transplantation. Here, however, we should like to point out that many investigators have shown that if they strip the covering and lining cells from bone, fractures almost never become repaired properly. Furthermore, even if the periosteum is not disturbed, if there is a sufficiently large gap between the fragments of a fracture, so that the collars of osteogenic cells from the fragments take too long a time to meet and fuse, fibroblasts from nearby tissues may grow through the gap between the fragments and fill it in, not with bone, but with ordinary dense connective tissue; this gives rise to a fibrous union which, of course, does not provide a proper repair. So, despite the fact that bone sometimes forms in ordinary connective tissue, we think it is unjustifiable to reason from this fact that fibroblasts can repair bone as effectively as the covering and lining cells of bone. Furthermore, we think that in our present state of knowledge it would be calamitous for an orthopedic surgeon to put his trust in fibroblasts and induction phenomena for bone repair instead of in the heredity of the covering and lining cells of bone.

THE TRANSPLANTATION OF BONE

Bone transplants often are used when fractured bones fail to heal by the ordinary method. They are also used when substantial parts of a bone are destroyed by accident or disease. They are useful in permitting certain reconstructions of the face to be made by plastic surgeons. They are sometimes employed to bring about bony union between 2 bones separated by a joint which has become diseased. Indeed, the transplantation of bone has become a common surgical operation.

The fate of a piece of compact bone that is transplanted in the body is a matter about which there has been considerable dispute. In the earlier days of bone grafting, it was believed by many who utilized the procedure that transplanted compact bone continue to live in its new site. More recently, however, it has become fairly generally realized that most of the osteocytes of a piece of compact bone that is transplanted die, and that sooner

or later the dead transplanted bone is replaced by new bone.

When a graft of compact bone is cut, it is, of course, severed from its blood supply. When it is fitted into its new position, its osteocytes, if they are to live, must obtain all their oxygen and nourishment from such tissue fluid as penetrates canaliculi. Hence, the only osteocytes that survive after a piece of compact bone is transplanted are those that are close enough to a supply of tissue fluid to permit the canalicular mechanism to function. This means that at best only a few surface osteocytes survive in transplanted bone.

However, the osteogenic cells of the periosteum and such endosteal cells as are present on a graft, being situated at surfaces, are more likely to be sufficiently well bathed in tissue fluid to survive than the osteocytes of the graft. Indeed, some of the covering and lining cells of compact bone do survive and grow if they are in a suitable environment, and they contribute toward osteogenesis, which, however, comes mostly from the bones into which the graft is inserted (Fig. 210).

If most of the osteocytes of a transplanted piece of bone die, it might be thought that a bone transplant would be of little use. However, bone transplants are of the greatest use even if most of their constituent cells do die. Bone transplants are placed so that each of their ends extends well into living bone tissue of the 2 fragments they bridge. Cells from the osteogenic layer of the periosteum, the endosteum and the marrow of the host bone proliferate and push out toward the transplant, forming new trabeculae of bone (Fig. 210), and, in some instances, cartilage. After a time the bony trabeculae, increasing in length and breadth by new bone being deposited on their surfaces, reach the transplant and unite with it (Fig. 210). It is to be understood that new bone deposited on dead bone becomes firmly cemented to it, as the new bone that is deposited on the calcified cartilage on the diaphyseal side of the epiphyseal plate becomes firmly cemented to the cartilage. This step in the history of a compact bone transplant is illustrated in Figure 210 and shows that new trabeculae from the host have firmly united with the dead bone of the transplant. It is also obvious in this

HISTORY OF A COMPACT BONE GRAFT

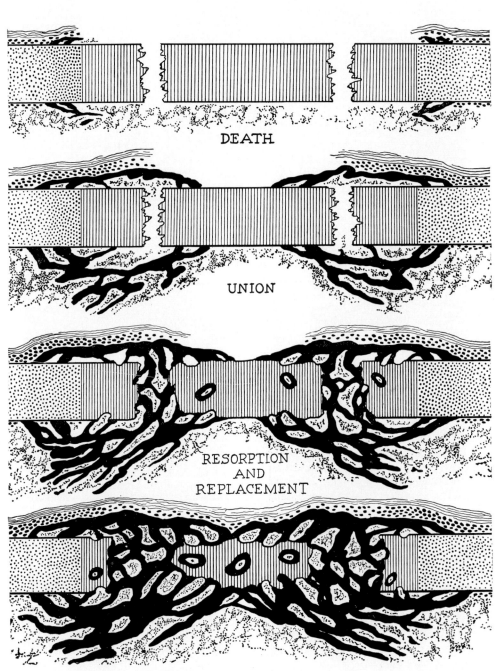

DEATH

UNION

RESORPTION
AND
REPLACEMENT

Fig. 210. Diagrams to show the steps in the history of a block of cortex of a bone which is cut free from its blood supply and placed back into the defect its removal caused. The periosteal surface is above and the marrow surface is below in each of the 4 pictures. Pre-existing bone still alive is shown in medium stipple, dead bone is lined and new bone is black. (Ham, A. W.: J. Bone & Joint Surg. **34A**:701)

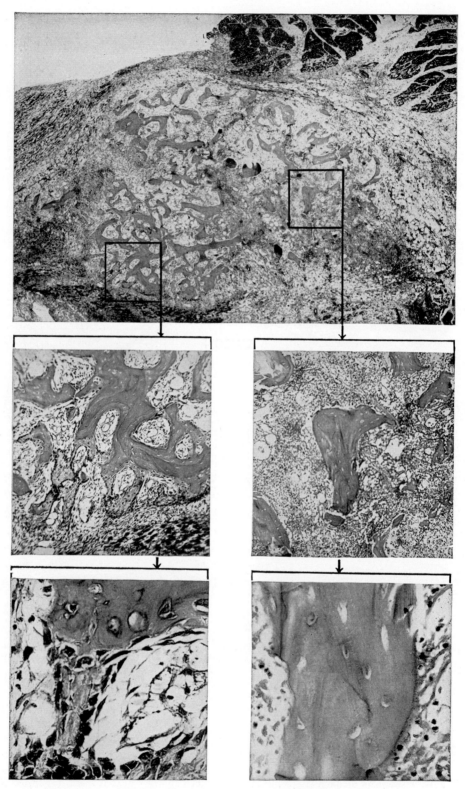

Fig. 211. (Legend at bottom of facing page.)

illustration that the osteogenic cells and osteoblasts from which these new trabeculae arose came from some little distance behind the dead edge of the graft bed.

After the transplant is united to its host it must be resorbed slowly and replaced with new bone. Resorption occurs in 2 general sites: (1) on the outer surfaces of the transplant in between areas where trabeculae of new bone have become cemented to it and (2) on the inner surfaces of haversian canals (Fig. 210, *bottom*).

It is to be understood that functioning blood vessels are as necessary for the resorption of bone as for the deposition and maintenance of the life of bone. Accordingly, little resorption can occur from the inner surfaces of the haversian canals of a transplant until there are functioning blood vessels in these haversian canals. Commonly it takes many weeks for new blood vessels to grow into the haversian canals of a compact bone graft.

The growth of new blood vessels into the haversian canals of the transplant is associated with both the resorption of dead bone from the canals, which widens them (Fig. 210), and also with the deposition of new bone on the sides of the canals, which narrows them again (Fig. 210). The same 2 processes operate simultaneously on the exterior of the transplant and also at the dead edges of the graft bed, so before long the transplant and the edge of the bed both become a conglomerate of living and dead bone (Fig. 210, *bottom*). Eventually, nearly all, if not all, of the dead bone is resorbed with new bone being substituted for it, but this takes considerable time because the dead bone always must be resorbed from a *free* surface and the new bone

deposited on a *free* surface. This has been termed the "creeping replacement" of a transplant.

As the dead bone of a compact bone transplant is irregularly eroded at different sites around its outer surface, and as its haversian canals become opened up by resorptive processes occurring within them, it tends to resemble cancellous bone as much as it does compact bone. But the deposition of new bone on all these surfaces eventually takes precedence over resorptive phenomena, so it once more begins to resemble compact bone, thus providing another illustration of the fact that the filling in of spaces surrounded by trabeculae converts cancellous bone to compact bone.

TRANSPLANTS OF CANCELLOUS BONE

It might be thought that the bone cells in a transplanted cancellous trabecula would have a much better chance of surviving transplantation than the bone cells in a block of compact bone. No bone cell in a small cancellous trabecula is very far away from a free surface, and, when a trabecula is transplanted, the free surface conceivably could be bathed in tissue fluid. But the canalicular mechanism for diffusion is evidently so inefficient that even though a cancellous trabecula is transplanted into an area close to functioning capillaries nearly all the bone cells of the trabecula die. Gordon and the author, in an extensive experiment, followed the day-to-day appearance of autogenous cancellous fragments transplanted into both bone defects and muscle and have concluded that, for all practical pur-

FIG. 211. The upper picture is a very low-power photomicrograph of a site in a dog's muscle where cancellous fragments obtained from the crest of the ilium had been planted 7 days before. The 2 lower left pictures are higher-power views of an area where the transplanted fragments were situated close to capillaries in living tissue and hence bathed in reasonably fresh tissue fluid. Under these conditions, although the osteocytes of the transplanted fragments have died and left empty lacunae, as may be seen in the left middle picture, the covering and lining osteogenic cells and osteoblasts have survived and have grown toward the capillaries in the living tissue. Osteoblasts with their basophilic cytoplasm may be seen in the lower left picture. The 2 lower right pictures are higher-power representations of fragments transplanted to a site in the muscle where they were far removed from living capillaries and hence from a fresh supply of tissue fluid. Under these conditions both the osteocytes within the fragments and the covering and lining cells of the fragments all have died. (Gordon, S., and Ham, A. W.: The Gallie Addresses, Toronto. Univ. Toronto Press)

poses, the cells in transplanted cancellous fragments fail to survive transplantation (Fig. 211) and hence that the ultimate fate of the substance of the transplanted bone is resorption.

Although the osteocytes of cancellous fragments survive transplantation little better than the cells of compact bone, the possibilities with regard to the survival and the growth of the covering and the lining cells of cancellous fragments is much greater than those of compact bone. The first reason for this is that cancellous trabeculae are completely covered with osteogenic cells and osteoblasts, and since the trabeculae themselves are small there is a relatively high proportion of surface cells to bone cells in cancellous bone. This is in contrast with compact bone (and in particular with chips from adult compact bone) wherein the proportion of surface cells to bone cells is very low. Accordingly, vast numbers of surface cells are available when cancellous trabeculae are transplanted, and since the surface cells cover all aspects of the trabeculae, they face in every direction and so are able to take advantage of such nutritive tissue fluid as may exist in the site to which they are transplanted (Fig. 211, *left*).

It is to be understood, of course, that even without any of the surface cells of cancellous fragments surviving transplantation, cancellous fragments serve a very useful purpose in bone defects. This is because they stimulate the osteogenic cells, the osteoblasts and the undifferentiated marrow cells of the host bone to grow into their midst and lay down bone on many of their surfaces. By this means the dead transplanted fragments become incorporated into a new network of cancellous bone that connects them with the bone of the host. However, the dead fragments do not persist indefinitely in such a network, but are resorbed.

In addition to stimulating and conducting osteogenesis, cancellous fragments can perform another function under very suitable circumstances—that of setting up new centers of osteogenesis. They can do this if they are transplanted into living tissue where there is a sufficiently good capillary bed to provide their surface cells with adequate tissue fluid. In order to prove that their surface cells can survive transplantation and give rise to new bone, the common experiment performed is to transplant them into muscle where there are no other cells of a bony origin to confuse the issue. Gordon and the author have done this several times and have found repeatedly that when a mass of cancellous chips is placed in a muscle, the surface cells of the fragments that are around the periphery of the mass of fragments, close to functioning capillaries in the muscle, live and give rise to new bone which tends to grow toward the capillaries of the muscle (Fig. 211, *left*).

It could be argued that cancellous or compact bone chips have still another function—that of inducing bone formation by metaplasia from fibroblasts. The author and Gordon have investigated this matter recently by studying the fate of thrice-fast-frozen-and-thawed autogenous cancellous fragments transplanted into muscle. In contrast with untreated fragments, about which some new bone formed in each animal, no new bone was found to develop in association with any of the thrice-frozen-and-thawed fragments. Since the repeated fast-freezing of a tissue probably destroys its cells by physical means and does not alter its chemical constituents nearly as much as other procedures which destroy cells, our experiment shows, we think, that the bone that forms around cancellous fragments transplanted into muscle originates from the covering cells of the chips and not from fibroblasts by metaplasia. This experiment, like many others, suggests that those who seek osteogenesis should, in our present state of knowledge, continue to put their trust in the cells that cover and line bone surfaces and their close relatives in the bone marrow rather than on cells such as fibroblasts that are specialized for other functions.

REFERENCES

COMPREHENSIVE GENERAL REFERENCES ON BONE

Bourne, G. H.: The Biochemistry and Physiology of Bone, New York, Acad. Press, 1956.

Weinmann, J. P., and Sicher, H.: Bone and Bones: Fundamentals of Bone Biology, ed. 2, St. Louis, Mosby, 1955.

OTHER GENERAL REFERENCES ON BONE

Greep, R. O., *et al.*: Recent advances in the study of the structure, composition and growth of mineralized tissues, Ann. New York Acad. Sc. *60*:543, 1955.

Ham, A. W.: Some histophysiological problems peculiar to calcified tissue, J. Bone & Joint Surg. *34A*:701, 1952.

McLean, F. C.: Bone, Scientific American *92*:84, 1955.

McLean, F. C., and Urist, M. R.: Bone: An Introduction to the Physiology of Skeletal Tissue, Chicago, Univ. Chicago Press, 1956.

Stein, Irvin, Stein, Raymond O., and Beller, Martin L.: Living Bone in Health and Disease, Philadelphia, Lippincott, 1955.

Wolstenholme, G. E. W., and O'Connor, C. M.: Ciba Foundation Symposium on Bone Structure and Metabolism, London, Churchill, 1956.

SPECIAL REFERENCES ON SPECIAL TECHNICS, EXCEPT ELECTRON MICROSCOPY, USED FOR THE STUDY OF BONE

Amprino, Rodolfo: Uptake of S^{35} in the differentiation and growth of cartilage and bone *in* Bone Structure and Metabolism, London, Churchill, 1956.

Armstrong, Wallace D.: Radiotracer studies of hard tissues, Ann. New York Acad. Sc. *60*:670, 1955.

Axelrod, Dorothy J.: An improved method for cutting undecalcified bone sections and its application to radio-autography, Anat. Rec. *98*: 19, 1947.

Bélanger, L. F.: Autoradiographic studies of the formation of the organic matrix of cartilage bone and the tissues of teeth *in* Bone Structure and Metabolism, London, Churchill, 1956.

———: Autoradiographic visualization *in vitro* exchange in teeth, bones, and other tissues, under various conditions, J. Dent. Res. *32*:3, 1953.

Bélanger, L. F.: and Leblond, C. P.: Method for locating radioactive elements in tissue by covering histological sections with photographic emulsion, Endocrinology *39*:8, 1946.

Bevelander, G., and Johnson, P. L.: A histochemical study of membrane bone, Anat. Rec. *108*:1, 1951.

Comar, C. L., Lotz, W. E., and Boyd, G. A.: Autoradiographic studies of calcium, phosphorus and strontium distribution in the bones of the growing pig, Am. J. Anat. *90*:113, 1952.

Davies, D. V., and Young, L.: The distribution of radioactive sulphur (S^{35}) in the fibrous tissues, cartilages and bones of the rat following its administration in the form of inorganic sulphate, J. Anat. *88*:174, 1954.

Davies, H. G., and Engstrom, A.: Interferometric and x-ray absorption studies of bone tissue, Exper. Cell Res. *7*:243, 1954.

Dempster, W. T., and Liddicoat, R. T.: Compact

bone as a nonisotropic material, Am. J. Anat. *91*:331, 1952.

Fell, Honor B.: Skeletal development in tissue culture *in* The Biochemistry and Physiology of Bone, New York, Acad. Press, 1956.

Gomori, G.: The distribution of phosphatase in normal organs and tissues. J. Cell. & Comp. Physiol. *17*:71, 1941.

Leblond, C. P., Wilkinson, G. W., Bélanger, L. F., and Robichon, J.: See under references on Growth, etc.

Morse, A., and Greep, R. O.: Effect of abnormal metabolic states upon the histochemical distribution of alkaline phosphatase in the tibia of the albino rat, Anat. Rec. *111*:193, 1951.

Pritchard, J. J.: A cytological and histochemical study of bone and cartilage formation in the rat, J. Anat. *86*:259, 1952.

Sognnaes, R. F.: Microstructure and histochemical characteristics of the mineralized tissues, Ann. New York Acad. Sc. *60*:545, 1955.

Trautz, Otto R.: X-ray diffraction of biological and synthetic apatites, Ann. New York Acad. Sc. *60*:696, 1955.

SPECIAL REFERENCES ON THE DEVELOPMENT OF BONE

Baker, S. L.: Introduction to the Pathology of Bone for X-ray Diagnosis, ed. 2, Philadelphia, Saunders, 1952.

Bertelson, A.: Experimental investigation into post-foetal osteogenesis, Acta orthop. scandinav. *15*:139, 1944.

Bevelander, G., and Johnson, P. L.: An histochemical study of the development of membrane bone, Anat. Rec. *108*:1, 1950.

Fell, H. B.: Osteogenesis *in vitro,* Arch. exper. Zellforsch. *11*:245, 1931.

———: Skeletal development in tissue culture *in* The Biochemistry and Physiology of Bone, New York, Acad. Press, 1956.

Felts, W. J. L.: The prenatal development of the human femur, Am. J. Anat. *94*:1, 1954.

Gardner, Ernest: Osteogenesis in the human embryo and fetus *in* The Biochemistry and Physiology of Bone, New York, Acad. Press, 1956.

Ham, A. W., and Gordon, S. D.: The origin of bone that forms in association with cancellous chips transplanted into muscle, Brit. J. Plast. Surg. *5*:154, 1952.

Huggins, C. B.: The formation of bone under the influence of epithelium of the urinary tract, Arch. Surg. *22*:377, 1931.

Jackson, Sylvia Fitton: The structure of developing bone in the embryonic fowl, Proc. Roy. Soc., London, s.B *146*:270, 1957.

Johnson, F. R., and McMinn, R. M. H.: Transitional epithelium and osteogenesis, J. Anat. *90*:106, 1956.

Lacroix, P.: L'os et les méchanismes de la formation, J. physiol. Paris *43*:385, 1951.

————: Recent investigations on the growth of bone, Nature *156*:576, 1945.

Levander, Gustav: Tissue induction, Nature *155*: 148, 1945.

Pritchard, J. J.: The osteoblast *in* The Biochemistry and Physiology of Bone, New York, Acad. Press, 1956.

Strangeways, T. S. P., and Fell, H. B.: Experimental studies on the differentiation of embryonic tissues growing *in vivo* and *in vitro,* Proc. Roy. Soc. London *99*:340, 1926.

Urist, M. R., and McLean, F. C.: Osteogenic potency and new bone formation by induction in transplants to the anterior chamber of the eye, J. Bone & Joint Surg. *34A*:443, 1952.

SPECIAL REFERENCES ON THE CALCIFICATION
OF BONE

Arnold, J. S., and Webster, J.: The optical activity of collagen fibers and calcification of bone matrix, Anat. Rec. *118*:373, 1954.

Bourne, G. H.: Phosphatase and bone *in* The Biochemistry and Physiology of Bone, New York, Acad. Press, 1956.

Dixon, T. F., and Perkins, H. R.: The chemistry of calcification *in* The Biochemistry and Physiology of Bone, New York, Acad. Press, 1956.

Fell, Honor B.: The histogenesis of cartilage and bone in the long bones of the embryonic fowl, J. Morphol. *40*:417, 1925.

————: Osteogenic capacity *in vitro* of periosteum and endosteum isolated from the limb skeleton of fowl embryos and young chicks, J. Anat. *66*:157, 1932.

Fell, Honor B., and Robison, Robert: The development and phosphatase activity *in vivo* and *in vitro* of the mandibular skeletal tissue of the embryonic fowl, Biochem. J. *24*:1905, 1930.

Ham, A. W.: Mechanism of calcification in the heart and aorta in hypervitaminosis D, Arch. Path. *14*:613, 1932.

Hass, George M.: Pathological calcification *in* The Biochemistry and Physiology of Bone, New York, Acad. Press, 1956.

Logan, M. A.: Recent advances in the chemistry of calcification, Physiol. Rev. *20*:522, 1940.

Logan, M. A., and Taylor, H. L.: Solubility of bone salt, J. Biol. Chem. *119*:293, 1937: *125*: 377, 1938; *127*:704, 1938.

McLean, F. C., and Bloom, W.: Calcification and ossification: calcification in normal growing bone, Anat. Rec. *78*:333, 1940.

McLean, F. C., and Urist, M. R.: See General References.

Newman, W. F., and Lullyran, B. J.: The surface

chemistry of bone, J. Biol. Chem. *185*:705, 1950.

Robson, R.: Bone phosphatase, Ergebn. d. Enzymforsch. *1*:280, 1932.

————: The possible significance of hexosephosphoric esters in ossification, Biochem. J. *17*: 286, 1923.

Sheldon, H., and Robinson, R. A.: Electron microscope studies of crystal-collagen relationships in bone. IV. The occurrence of crystals within collagen fibrils, J. Biophys. & Biochem. Cytol. *3*:1011, 1957.

Sobel, Albert E.: Local factors in the mechanism of calcification, Ann. New York Acad. Sc. *60*: 713-732, 1955.

(*See also* References on Calcification of Cartilage and References on the Parathyroid Gland)

SPECIAL REFERENCES ON THE STRUCTURE OF
BONE INCLUDING FINE STRUCTURE

Baker, S. L.: Introduction of the pathology of bone *in* X-ray Diagnosis, ed. 2, Philadelphia, Saunders, 1952.

Barbour, E. P., and Cook, S. F.: The effects of low phosphorus diet and hypophysectomy on the structure of compact bone as seen with the electron microscope, Anat. Rec. *118*:215, 1954.

Bell, G. H.: Bone as a mechanical engineering problem *in* The Biochemistry and Physiology of Bone, New York, Acad. Press, 1956.

Carlstrom, D., and Engstrom, A.: Ultrastructure and distribution of mineral salts in bone tissue *in* The Biochemistry and Physiology of Bone, New York, Acad. Press, 1956.

Eastoe, J. E.: The organic matrix of bone *in* The Biochemistry and Physiology of Bone, New York, Acad. Press, 1956.

Enstrom, Arne: Structure of bone from the anatomical to the molecular level *in* Bone Structure and Metabolism, London, Churchill, 1956.

Harris, W. R., and Ham, A. W.: The mechanism of nutrition in bone and how it affects its structure, repair and fate on transplantation *in* Bone Structure and Metabolism, London, Churchill, 1956.

Jackson, S. Fitton: The fine structure of developing bone in the embryonic fowl, Proc. Roy. Soc., London, s.B *146*:270, 1957.

Jackson, S. F., and Randall, J. T.: Fibrogenesis and the formation of matrix in developing bone *in* Bone Structure and Metabolism, London, Churchill, 1956.

Martin, A. V. W.: Electron microscope studies of collagenous fibers in bone, Biochem. et Biophys. Acta *10*:42, 1953.

Meyer, Karl: The mucopolysaccharides of bone *in* Bone Structure and Metabolism, London, Churchill, 1956.

Neuman, W. F., and Neuman, M. W.: The nature

of the mineral phase of bone, Chem. Rev. *52*:1, 1953.

Pritchard, J. J.: General anatomy and histology of bone *in* The Biochemistry and Physiology of Bone, New York, Acad. Press, 1956.

Robinson, R. A.: An electron microscopic study of the crystalline inorganic component of bone and its relationship to the organic matrix, J. Bone & Joint Surg. *34A*:389, 1952.

Robinson, R. A., and Cameron, D. A.: Electron microscopy of cartilage and bone matrix at the distal epiphyseal line of the femur in the newborn infant, J. Biophys. & Biochem. Cytol. (Supp.) *2*:253, 1956.

Robinson, R. A., and Watson, M. L.: Collagen-crystal relationships in bone as seen in the electron microscope, Anat. Rec. *114*:383, 1952.

———: Crystal-collagen relationships in bone as observed in the electron microscope: III. Crystal and collagen morphology as a function of age, Ann. New York Acad. Sc. *60*:596, 1955.

———: Electron micrography of bone *in* Reifenstein, E. C. (ed.): Metabolic Interrelations, New York, Macy, 1953.

Rouiller, C., Huber, L., Kellenberger, E., Majno, G., and Rutishouser, E.: Etude de la structure de l'os au microscope électronique, Cong. Microscopie Electronique, Paris, 1950, Rev. Optique, p. 697, 1953.

Ruth, Elbert B.: Bone Studies: I. Fibrillar structure of adult human bone, Am. J. Anat. *80*:35, 1947.

———: Bone Studies: II. An experimental study of the Haversian type vascular channels, Am. J. Anat. *93*:429, 1953.

———: Gross demonstration of the vascular channels in bone, Anat. Rec. *98*:59, 1947.

Sandison, J. C.: A method for the microscopic study of the growth of transplanted bone in the transparent chambers of the rabbit's ear, Anat. Rec. *49*:41, 1928.

Stack, Maurice V.: The chemical nature of the organic matrix of bone, dentin and enamel, Ann. New York Acad. Sc. *60*:585, 1955.

Watson, M. L., and Robinson, R. A.: Collagen-crystal relationships in bone: II. Electron microscope study of basic calcium phosphate crystals, Am. J. Anat. *93*:25, 1953.

Special References on the Growth of Bone

Asling, C. W., Simpson, M. E., Li, C. H., and Evans, H. M.: The effects of chronic administration of thyroxin to hypophysectomized rats on their skeletal growth, maturation and response to growth hormone, Anat. Rec. *119*:101, 1954.

Bhaskar, S. N.: Growth pattern of the rat mandible from 13 days insemination age to 30 days after birth, Am. J. Anat. *92*:1, 1953.

Brash, J. C.: Some problems in the growth and developmental mechanics of bone, Edinburgh M.J. *41*:305, 365, 1934.

Frandsen, A. M., Nelson, M. M., Sulon, E., Becks, H., and Evans, H. M.: The effects of various levels of dietary protein on skeletal growth and endochondral ossification in young rats, Anat. Rec. *119*:247, 1954.

Gans, B. J., and Sarnat, B. G.: Sutural facial growth of the Macaca rhesus monkey: a gross and serial roentgenographic study by means of metallic implants, Am. J. Orthodont. *37*:927, 1951.

Giblin, N., and Alley, A.: Studies in skull growth: Coronal suture fixation, Anat. Rec. *88*:143, 1944.

Haines, R. W.: Cartilage canals, J. Anat. *68*:45, 1933.

Ham, A. W.: Some histophysiological problems peculiar to calcified tissues, J. Bone & Joint Surg. *34A*:701, 1952.

———: The variability of the planes of cell division in the cartilage columns of the growing epiphyseal plate, Anat. Rec. *51*:125, 1931.

Harris, H. A.: Bone Growth in Health and Disease, London, Oxford, 1933.

Lacroix, P.: The Organization of Bones, translated from the amended French edition by Stewart Gilder, New York, Blakiston Division of McGraw-Hill, 1951.

Lacroix, P.: The histological remodelling of the adult bone: an autoradiographic study *in* Bone Structure and Metabolism, London, Churchill, 1956.

Leblond, C. P., and Greulich, Richard C.: Autoradiographic studies of bone formation and growth *in* The Biochemistry and Physiology of Bone, New York, Acad. Press, 1956.

Leblond, C. P., Wilkinson, G. W., Bélanger, L. F., and Robichon, J.: Radio-autographic visualization of bone formation in the rat, Am. J. Anat. *86*:289, 1950.

Moss, M. L.: Growth of the calvaria in the rat; the determination of osseous morphology, Am. J. Anat. *94*:333, 1954.

Murray, P. D. F.: Bones, A Study of the Development and Structure of the Vertebrate Skeleton, London, Cambridge, 1936.

Scott, B. L., and Pease, D. C.: Electron microscopy of the epiphyseal apparatus, Anat. Rec. *126*:465, 1956.

Sisson, H. A.: Experimental determination of rate of longitudinal bone growth, J. Anat. *87*: 228, 1953.

———: The growth of bone *in* The Biochemistry and Physiology of Bone, New York, Acad. Press, 1956.

SPECIAL REFERENCES ON THE RESORPTION OF BONE AND ON OSTEOCLASTS

Arey, L.: Phagocytosis by osteoclasts, Anat. Rec. *13*:269, 1917.

Arnold, J. S., and Jee, W. S. S.: Bone growth and osteoclastic activity as indicated by radioautographic distribution of plutonium, Am. J. Anat. *101*:367, 1957.

Barnicott, N. A.: The local action of the parathyroid and other tissues on bone in intracerebral grafts, J. Anat. *82*:233, 1948.

Bhaskar, S. N., Mohammed, C. I., and Weinmann, J. P.: A morphological and histochemical study of osteoclasts, J. Bone & Joint Surg. *38A*:1335, 1956.

Chang, Hwei-Ya: Grafts of parathyroid and other tissues to bone, Anat. Rec. *111*:23, 1951.

Cooley, L. M., and Goss, R. J.: The effects of transplantation and x-irradiation on the repair of fractured bones, Am. J. Anat. *102*:167, 1957.

Dodds, G. S.: Osteoclasts and cartilage removal in endochondrial ossification of certain mammals, Am. J. Anat. *50*:97, 1932.

Greep, R. O.: A hereditary absence of the incisor teeth, J. Hered. *32*:397, 1941.

Ham, A. W., and Gordon, S. D.: Nature of the so-called striated border of osteoclasts, Anat. Rec. *112*:147, 1952.

Hancox, N. M.: The osteoclast, Biol. Rev. *24*: 448, 1949.

————: The osteoclast *in* The Biochemistry and Physiology of Bone, New York, Acad. Press, 1956.

Kroon, D. B.: The bone-destroying function of the osteoclasts (Koelliker's "brush border"), Acta anat. *21*:1, 1954.

McLean, F. C., and Bloom, W.: Calcification and ossification; mobilization of bone salt by parathyroid extract, Arch. Path. *32*:315, 1941.

Molnar, Z.: Development of the parietal bone of young mice. I. Crystals of bone mineral in frozen-dried preparations, J. Ultrastr. Res. *3*: 39, 1959.

Scott, B. L.: Electron microscopy of the epiphyseal apparatus, Anat. Rec. *124*:470, 1956.

Scott, B. L., and Pease, D. C.: Electron microscopy of the epiphyseal apparatus, Anat. Rec. *126*:465, 1956.

Shipley, P. G., and Macklin, C. C.: Some features of osteogenesis in the light of vital staining, Am. J. Physiol. *42*:117, 1916.

Weinmann, J. P., and Sicher, H.: The gray-lethal mouse and the "incisor absent" rat *in* Bone and Bones, ed. 2, p. 163, St. Louis, Mosby, 1955.

SPECIAL REFERENCES ON THE BLOOD SUPPLY OF BONES

Brookes, M.: Femoral growth after occlusion of the principal nutrient canal in day-old rabbits, J. Bone & Joint Surg. *39*:563, 1957.

————: Sequelae of experimental parietal ischemia in long bones of the rabbit, J. Anat. *94*: 552, 1960.

Brookes, M., and Harrison, R. G.: The vascularization of the rabbit femur and tibiofibular, J. Anat. *91*:61, 1957.

Dale, G., and Harris, W. R.: Canad. J. Surg. (in press).

deHaas, W. G., and Macnab, I.: Blood supply of the tibia (in press).

Ham, A. W.: Some histophysiological problems peculiar to calcified tissues, J. Bone & Joint Surg. *34A*:701, 1952.

Jackson, R., and Macnab, I.: Fractures of the tibia. A clinical and experimental study, Am. J. Surg. *97*:543, 1959.

Johnson, R. W.: A physiological study of the blood supply of the diaphysis, J. Bone & Joint Surg. *9*:153, 1927.

Trueta, J., and Harrison, M. H. M.: The normal vascular anatomy of the femoral head in adult man, J. Bone & Joint Surg. *35*:442, 1953.

SPECIAL REFERENCES ON THE EFFECTS OF CERTAIN METABOLIC ALTERATIONS ON BONE

Albright, F., Bloomberg, E., and Smith, P. H.: Post-menopausal osteoporosis. Tr. A. Am. Physicians *55*:298, 1940.

Albright, F., Smith, P. H., and Richardson, A. M.: Post-menopausal osteoporosis; its clinical features, J.A.M.A. *116*:2465, 1941.

Asling, C. W., and Evans, H. M.: Anterior pituitary regulation of skeletal development *in* The Biochemistry and Physiology of Bone, New York, Acad. Press, 1956.

Bailie, J. M., and Irving, J. T.: Changes in the metaphysis of the long bones during the development of rickets, Brit. J. Exper. Path. *29*: 539, 1948.

Barnicot, N. A., and Datta, S. P.: Vitamin A and bone *in* The Biochemistry and Physiology of Bone, New York, Acad. Press, 1956.

Bourne, Geoffrey H.: Vitamin C and bone *in* The Biochemistry and Physiology of Bone, New York, Acad. Press, 1956.

Dodds, G. S., and Cameron, H. C.: Studies on experimental rickets in rats, Am. J. Path. *14*: 273, 1939; *15*:723, 1939; *19*:169, 1943; Am. J. Anat. *55*:135, 1934.

Fitch, L. W. N.: Osteodystrophic diseases of sheep in New Zealand: I. Rickets in hoggets; with a note on the aetiology and definition of the disease, Australian Veter. J. *19*:2, 1943.

Follis, R. H., Jr.: Diseases, particularly of bone, associated with derangements of calcium and phosphorus metabolism *in* Fifth Conf. on

Metabolic Interrelations, New York, Macy, 1954.

Hall, Kathleen: Changes in the bone and cartilage of the symphysis pubis of the mouse during pregnancy and after parturition, as revealed by metachromatic staining and the periodic acid-Schiff technique, J. Endocrinol. *11*:210, 1954.

Ham, A. W., and Elliott, H. C.: The bone and cartilage lesions of protracted moderate scurvy, Am. J. Path. *14*:323, 1938.

Harris, Leslie J.: Vitamin D and bone *in* The Biochemistry and Physiology of Bone, New York, Acad. Press, 1956.

Hess, A. F.: Collected Writings, Springfield, Ill., Thomas, 1936.

———: Rickets, Including Osteomalacia and Tetany, Philadelphia, Lea & Febiger, 1929.

Howard, J. E.: Present knowledge of parathyroid function, with especial emphasis upon its limitations *in* Bone Structure and Metabolism, pp. 206-221, London, Churchill, 1956.

McLean, Franklin C.: The parathyroid glands and bone *in* The Biochemistry and Physiology of Bone, New York, Acad. Press, 1956.

Munson, Paul L.: Studies on the role of the parathyroids in calcium and phosphorus metabolism, Ann. New York Acad. Sc. *60*:776, 1955.

Murray, P. D. F., and Kodicek, E.: Bones, muscles and vitamin C: I. The effect of a partial deficiency of vitamin C on the repair of bone and muscle in guinea pigs, J. Anat. *83*:158, 1949.

———: Bones, muscles and vitamin C: II. Partial deficiencies of vitamin C and mid-diaphyseal thickenings of the tibia and fibula in guinea pigs, J. Anat. *83*:205, 1949.

———: Bones, muscles and vitamin C: III. Repair of the effects of total deprivation of vitamin C at the proximal ends of the tibia and fibula in guinea pigs, J. Anat. *83*:285, 1949.

Silberberg, Martin, and Silberberg, Ruth: Steroid hormones and bone *in* The Biochemistry and Physiology of Bone, New York, Acad. Press, 1956.

Wilkins, Lawson: Hormonal influences on skeletal growth, Ann. New York Acad. Sc. *60*:763, 1955.

Wolbach, S. B., and Bessey, O. A.: Tissue changes in vitamin deficiency, Physiol. Rev. *22*:233, 1942.

SPECIAL REFERENCES ON THE REPAIR AND TRANSPLANTATION OF BONE

deBruyn, P. P. H., and Kabisch, W. T.: Bone formation by fresh and frozen, autogenous and homogenous transplants of bone, bone marrow and periosteum, Am. J. Anat. *96*:375, 1955.

deHaas, W. G., and Macnab, I.: Fractures of the neck of the femur: method of assessing the viability of the femoral head, South African M. J. *30*:1010, 1956.

Gallie, W. E., and Robertson, D. E.: The repair of bone, Brit. J. Surg. *7*:211, 1920.

Gordon, S., and Ham, A. W.: The fate of transplanted cancellous bone *in* The Gallie Addresses, p. 296, Univ. Toronto Press, 1950.

Haas, S. L.: The importance of the periosteum and the endosteum in the repair of transplanted bone, Arch. Surg. *8*:535, 1924.

Ham, A. W.: An histological study of the early phases of bone repair, J. Bone & Joint Surg. *12*:827, 1930.

———: *See 1952 reference under* Special References on Growth, etc.

Ham, A. W., and Gordon, S. D.: *See reference under* Special References on the Development of Bone.

Ham, A. W., and Harris, W. R.: Repair and transplantation of bone *in* The Biochemistry and Physiology of Bone, New York, Acad. Press, 1956.

Ham, A. W., Tisdall, F. F., and Drake, T. G. H.: Experimental noncalcification of callus simulating non-union, J. Bone & Joint Surg. *20*:345, 1938.

Keith, A.: Menders of the Maimed, Philadelphia, Lippincott, 1952.

Pritchard, J. J.: Repair of fractures of the parietal bone in rats, J. Anat. *80*:55, 1946.

Pritchard, J. J., and Ruzicka, A. J.: Comparison of fracture repair in the frog, lizard and rat, J. Anat. *84*:236, 1950.

Simpson, M. E., van Dyke, D. C., Asling, C. W., and Evans, H. M.: Regeneration of the calvarium in young normal and growth hormone-treated hypophysectomized rats, Anat. Rec. *115*:615, 1953.

Urist, M. R., and Johnson, R. W.: Calcification and ossification: IV. The healing of fractures in man under clinical conditions, J. Bone & Joint Surg. *25*:375, 1943.

Urist, M. R., and McLean, F. C.: Calcification and ossification: I. Calcification in the callus in healing fractures in normal rats, J. Bone & Joint Surg. *23*:1, 1941.

———: Calcification and ossification: II. Control of calcification in the fracture callus in rachitic rats, J. Bone & Joint Surg. *23*:283, 1941.

———: Calcification and ossification: III. The role of local transfer of bone salt in the calcification of fracture callus, J. Bone & Joint Surg. *24*:47, 1942.

Wilkinson, G. W., and Leblond, C. P.: The deposition of radiophosphorus in fractured bones in rats, Surg., Gynec. & Obst. *97*:143, 1953.

Chapter 16

Joints

INTRODUCTION

Diseases of joints constitute the greatest single cause of disability in the civilized world. The microscopic study of the different parts of the various types of joints is therefore a matter of great importance, not only for permitting one to understand how they function, but also in providing a proper basis for understanding the nature of the various types of pathologic lesions to which they are subject.

Definition and Function. The words *articulation* (*articulare* = to connect) and *joint* (*jungere* = to join) are used synonymously with reference to those structural arrangements that exist to connect two or more bones together at their site of meeting. It is by means of joints that the individual bones of the body are connected together to form a skeleton. Although many joints permit movement between the two or more bones that they connect, the permitting of movement is not essential for a connecting structure to be termed a joint; indeed some joints become as solid as the bones they connect. Another function of joints, which will be described later, is that they make it possible for the structures they connect to grow in extent.

Classification. Joints may be classified in several ways: according to how they develop (on an embryologic basis), according to their structure (on a morphologic basis) or according to the kind of movement they permit (on a physiologic basis). We shall classify them on a morphologic basis, and, accordingly, there are 5 kinds:

1. Syndesmoses
2. Synchondroses
3. Synostoses
4. Symphyses
5. Synovial

The above terms are not so difficult to understand and remember as at first might be thought. It is easy to associate the prefix *syn* with joints because it means *together*. The term *desmosis* refers to a *band* or a *bond,* but in connection with joints the term has become restricted to imply bands or bonds of dense connective tissue. Syndesmoses, then, are joints wherein bones, at their site of meeting, are held together by bands of dense fibrous tissue. It is important to understand that in a syndesmosis the bands of dense connective tissue extend from one *bare* bony surface to another; if the bones that are connected with dense fibrous tissue are capped with cartilage, another term, as we shall see, is employed to describe them. *Synchondroses*, as might be supposed, are joints wherein two bones are connected with cartilage. Likewise, since *osteon* means *bone, synostoses* are joints wherein two bones are cemented together with bone. A synostosis, in effect, makes two bones into one, but synostoses are thought of as joints because they connect bones that developed separately and remained individual through the growing period, during which time they were connected by some other tissue (cartilage or fibrous tissue). The term *symphysis* means literally a *growing together;* actually the term is used with reference to joints wherein bones that are capped with cartilage at the joint site are held together (through the medium of their cartilage caps) by dense fibrous tissue or fibrocartilage. In one sense, then, a symphysis is a type of syndesmosis, but it is easier to think of it as a different type of joint, the difference lying in the fact that the dense fibrous tissue of the joint, in a syndesmosis, is inserted into bone tissue, and in a symphysis, into the cartilage that caps the bones of the joint at their site of meeting. The term *synovial* is derived from *syn* and *ovum*. Ovum, as used here, refers to the egg of the domesticated bird, and in particular, to the "white" of the egg, which is a glairy fluid. Synovial joints, then, are joints wherein a glairy fluid is present (in a closed cavity, called a synovial cavity) between the ends of the bones that participate in the joint. The glairy fluid, as we shall see, is of the nature of a lubricant to allow the smooth surfaces of the cartilage-capped bones that meet in the joint to slide freely on one another. Synovial joints, then, represent a specialized type

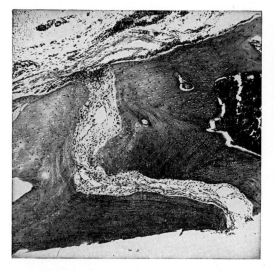

FIG. 212. Low-power photomicrograph of a section cut through the parietotemporal joint of an adult rat. This is an example of a suture and a syndesmosis.

of joint for free movement. Synovial joints, moreover, are sometimes termed *diarthroses* (*di*-apart, *arthron*-joint) because the two bones entering into one are, in a sense, kept *apart* by the synovial cavity. Furthermore, any of the first 4 types given in our classification can be termed a *synarthrosis* because in this type 2 bones are not kept apart, but *together*, by the joint.

The particular features of the various types of joints will now be described.

SYNDESMOSES

The sutures of the skull are good examples of this type of joint. The way in which membrane bones develop, grow and give rise to sutures has already been described (page 268). Individual membrane bones, it will be recalled, develop from separate centers of ossification and thereafter grow in extent because new bone is continuously added to their edges by means of the appositional growth mechanism. As a result of this, the young connective tissue situated between the edges of 2 adjacent bones becomes reduced eventually to a narrow band (Fig. 212). This narrow band of connective tissue joins the edges of the 2 bones together; hence, a suture is a syndesmosis. Osteoblasts along the edges of the 2 bones in the suture

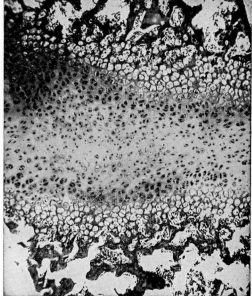

FIG. 213. Low-power photomicrograph of a section cut through the basisphenoid joint of an adult rat. Notice that the cartilage is being replaced by bone on both its sides.

can still proliferate and differentiate into bone cells. Because of the latter phenomenon layers of new bone can be added to the edges of the bones in the suture, and this permits the 2 bones that meet at the suture to grow in extent. Therefore, a syndesmosis provides a site wherein membrane bones can increase in extent by means of the appositional growth mechanism. When growth is over, the connective tissue in a suture may be replaced by bone; thus the syndesmosis becomes converted into a synostosis. When this occurs, the 2 bones that meet at the joint can no longer grow in extent.

Suture lines are commonly irregular; the edges of the bones concerned may be serrated or they may interlock by means of toothlike processes. When a suture is cut in cross section, the suture line is usually seen to be oblique (Fig. 212). Not uncommonly an isolated ossicle, called a Wormian bone, may be seen in the connective tissue of a suture; such a bone forms as a result of the detachment of a little group of osteoblasts or a little spicule from the edge of one of the bones that meet in the suture.

SYNCHONDROSES

Epiphyseal disks, which were described at great length when the development and growth of long bones were considered, are good examples of synchondroses because they consist of hyalin cartilage and connect bony epiphyses with bony diaphyses. It is to be understood that in most epiphyseal plates any substantial growth of bone occurs only on the diaphyseal side of the plate. But such new bone as forms in the epiphysis, as it grows larger, is due mostly to osteogenesis advancing into the articular cartilage and replacing it as it grows; the articular cartilage serves, as it were, as the "epiphyseal disk" for the growth of the epiphysis. However, the synchondrosis between the basioccipital and the basisphenoid bones is unlike an epiphyseal plate in this respect, for it provides for the growth of both of the bones that meet at this joint; in sections, then, it appears as a "double-sided" epiphyseal disk (Fig. 213).

SYNOSTOSES

When growth is over, most syndesmoses and synchondroses become synostoses. This is emphatic evidence to the effect that the chief function of the first two described types of joint is to permit growth rather than movement. It is of interest that operative procedures (including the use of bone transplants) are often employed to convert symphyses and synovial joints into synostoses when pathologic conditions arise which make movement undesirable.

SYMPHYSES

In a symphysis, the ends of the bones meeting in the joint are each capped with hyaline cartilage, and in turn the cartilage caps are joined by strong fibrous tissue which blends with the hyalin cartilages through a transitional zone of fibrocartilage. This arrangement provides great strength with a limited amount of movement.

In the *symphysis pubis* the tissue between the cartilage caps of the bones concerned consists almost entirely of fibrocartilage. A tiny slitlike space exists in the fibrocartilage, and in women during pregnancy this becomes larger, thus allowing for greater movement between the pubic bones during the passage of the fetus through the birth canal. In some lower animals the pubic bones actually become separated during pregnancy. Hall and her associates have studied the process in pregnant mice and have investigated the effects of hormones on the process (see references).

The *intervertebral joint* or, as it is often called, the *intervertebral disk* is a specialized type of symphysis. In each of these joints the flat bony surfaces of the bodies of the vertebrae concerned are capped with a layer of hyaline cartilage; the cartilage of one is joined to that of the other by fibrocartilage and dense fibrous tissue that is disposed so as to form a ring around the periphery of the joint (Fig. 214, A and B). This ring, called the annulus fibrosus, surrounds a central space that is filled with a pulpy semifluid material; this central space, so-filled, is termed the nucleus pulposus (Fig. 214, A and B). The nucleus pulposus is believed to represent a remnant of the notochord. It contains cells (at least in the young) and intercellular substance, and under normal conditions it is under pressure; this, since the annulus fibrosus is slightly elastic, makes the spine more resilient than it would be otherwise. In the aged, the nucleus pulposus loses some of its water content and so becomes smaller. This change is partly responsible for the spine becoming shorter and less resilient in old age.

In recent years it has become recognized that the nucleus pulposus may herniate through the annulus fibrosus into the spinal canal, where it may press on the roots of the spinal nerves. These herniations or extrusions of the nucleus pulposus commonly occur between the 4th and the 5th lumbar vertebrae or between the 5th lumbar and the 1st sacral vertebrae. Pressure on the roots of the 5th lumbar or the 1st sacral nerve as a result of this condition is a common cause of a painful condition known as sciatica. Extrusions of the nucleus pulposus through the annulus fibrosus may also occur in the cervical region, where the extrusion may compress the entire spinal cord or the roots of the nerves of the brachial plexus. Sometimes the nucleus pulposus herniates through the hyaline cartilage covering the body of a vertebra into the cancellous bone of its substance; this causes a

FIG. 214 A. (*Top*) Very low-power photomicrograph of a horizontal section cut through an intervertebral disk. The circularly disposed fibers in the annulus fibrosus may be seen in the periphery of the picture. The central dark area is the nucleus pulposus. (*Middle*) Very low-power photomicrograph of a vertical section cut through the bodies of 2 vertebrae and the disk between them. The fibers of the annulus fibrosus may be seen near the edges of the disk; the paler material in the more central part of the disk is the nucleus pulposus. (*Bottom*) Very low-power photomicrograph of a vertical section cut through 2 vertebrae and the disk between them. The nucleus pulposus has ruptured into the substance of the body of the vertebra below. (Dr. William Donohue)

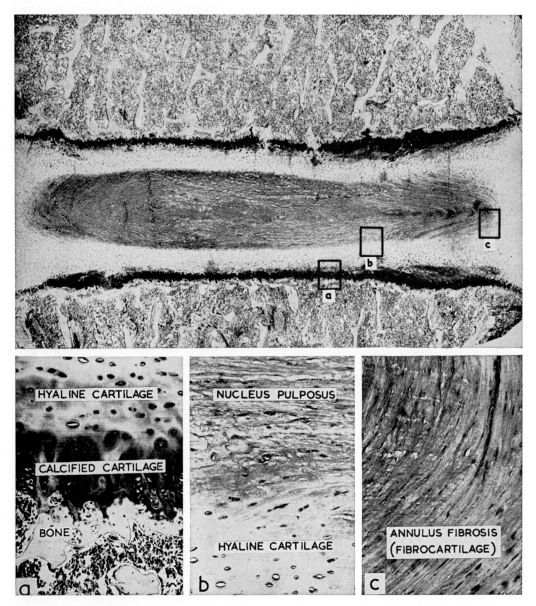

Fɪɢ. 214 B. Very low and medium power photomicrographs of an H and E section of an intervertebral disk of a young child. The areas marked a, b and c in the upper picture are shown in higher magnifications in the lower pictures

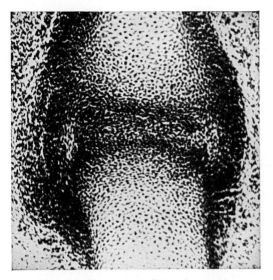

FIG. 215. Low-power photomicrograph of a longitudinal section cut through the developing interphalangeal joint in a 20-mm. human embryo. The developing cartilaginous ends of the 2 bones-to-be are pale. The dark-staining material that extends across the middle of the picture is the condensed mesenchyme that makes up the articular disk. The dark-staining stripes that run up and down each side of the ends of the developing cartilage models represent the condensed mesenchyme that is destined to form the capsule of the joint. The little clear areas seen in the dark-staining, otherwise condensed, mesenchyme of the disk represent the beginnings of the synovial cavity.

characteristic lesion called a Schmorl's nodule (Fig. 214, A, *bottom*).

SYNOVIAL JOINTS

Development. It has been explained already that the central mesenchyme in the limb buds of embryos gradually differentiates into cartilage in such a way that cartilage models of the bones-to-be are formed (Figs. 179 and 180). It has also been explained that the mesenchyme immediately surrounding the shaft of a cartilage model becomes arranged into an indistinctly 2-layered membrane, the perichondrium, that the outer layer of this membrane assumes a fibrous nature, and that the inner remains cellular and chondrogenic so that by the appositional growth mechanism it can add

further layers of cartilage to the sides of the shaft, thus causing the shaft to grow in width. We shall now consider the series of events that transpire in regions where the ends of cartilage models approach one another and where synovial joints develop.

The mesenchyme between the ends of two developing models becomes condensed; this ill-defined area of condensed mesenchyme between the two ill-defined ends of the developing cartilage models of the bones-to-be is called the *articular disk of mesenchyme* or the primitive joint plate (Fig. 215). And, in a fashion similar to that in which the perichondrium forms around the shafts of the cartilage models, the mesenchyme that surrounds the whole area in which the two ends of the cartilage models are developing also becomes condensed to form the counterpart of the perichondrium in this region (Fig. 215). This latter condensation of mesenchyme around the joint area is the forerunner of what is called the *capsule* of the joint. This fits like a sleeve over the end of each of the cartilage models that enters into the joint and extends along the sides of their ends for a sufficient distance to become continuous with the perichondrium that covers and is adherent to the sides of their shafts.

As development proceeds, the jellylike amorphous intercellular substance and tissue fluid disposed between the mesenchymal cells of the articular disk begin to increase, and as a result, the cells in the disk become widely separated from one another in at least certain areas in the disk. The continuance of this process soon leads to the appearance of fluid-filled clefts in the substance of the disk; these gradually fuse with one another so that soon or late a continuous cavity, the *synovial cavity,* comes to occupy the site formerly occupied by the bulk of the disk. This permits the ends of the two cartilage models to come into contact and articulate with each other.

The process which accounts for the formation of a synovial cavity is not confined to the area between the two ends of the models; the same process operates to cause the cavity to extend along the sides of the ends of the two models for some distance. The condensed mesenchyme which surrounds the joint area and which is the counterpart of the perichondrium of the shafts of the models, thereby becomes separated from the sides of the ends of the models. However, the developing joint capsule becomes continuous with the tightly attached perichondrium (or periosteum as the case may be) that covers the shaft of the models some little distance back from the end of each model.

As development continues, differentiation occurs in the forming joint capsule. The mesenchyme comprising its outer and thicker layer tends to differentiate into dense fibrous tissue, while that of its inner layer becomes more or less specialized to constitute its synovial layer, or, as it is often called, the *synovial membrane* of the joint. Its finer structure will be described presently.

To summarize: Since the synovial cavity is nothing more than a large cleft that forms in the substance of mesenchyme, it can scarcely

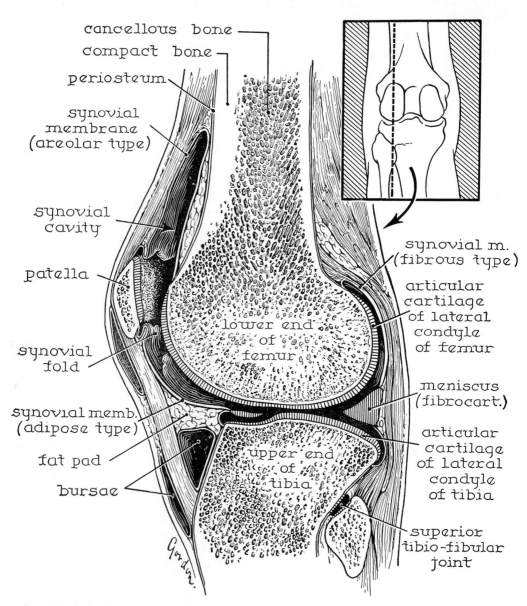

Fig. 216. A drawing of a longitudinal section of a knee joint of an adult man. The plane of the section that is illustrated in the main drawing is indicated in the insert (*upper right*).

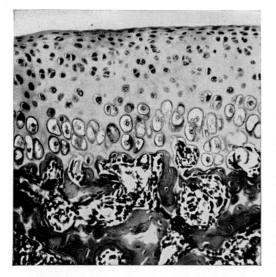

FIG. 217. Low-power photomicrograph of a longitudinal section cut through the upper end of the tibia of a guinea pig. This picture illustrates the appearance of normal articular cartilage.

be expected to have a continuous cellular lining of mesothelium like that possessed by the great body cavities. Moreover, its contents (synovial fluid) should be expected to be what might be termed diluted intercellular substance, and, indeed, a good way to regard synovial fluid is to think of it as ground substance (hyaluronic acid) diluted with tissue fluid. Because of the way the joint capsule forms, the latter structure could be expected to have many of the properties of perichondrium and periosteum.

General Structure. The appearance of a longitudinal section of a synovial joint—the knee joint of man—is illustrated in Figure 216. This figure shows the various structures that are involved in a complex synovial joint and their relations to one another. This figure should be consulted frequently as the microscopic structure of various components of a synovial joint are considered in the following section.

Articular Cartilage. This is a typical example of hyaline cartilage. It has no blood vessels, nerves or lymphatics. The cells in it are arranged in 3 ill-defined layers (Fig. 217): (1) a superficial layer in which the cells are flattened and small and are disposed with their long axes running parallel with the articular surface; (2) an intermediate layer in which the cells are somewhat larger and more nearly round and often are disposed in columns that run at right angles to the surface; (3) a deep layer that is composed of large cells. In the deepest part of this layer it is assumed that the cells make phosphatase, for the intercellular substance about them is calcified and stains more deeply even in decalcified H and E sections than does the intercellular substance that surrounds the cells in the outer part of this layer. During the period of growth this layer is more or less constantly being replaced by bone, while the cartilage cells in the more (but not the most) superficial layers proliferate by mitosis and grow away from the advancing bone.

The intercellular substance of articular cartilage consists of collagenic fibers embedded in a sulfated amorphous type of intercellular substance (chondroitin sulfuric acid). In sections cut from the articular cartilages of young animals the fibers are effectively masked by the amorphous intercellular substance. But in older animals, the fibers are demonstrated more readily and can be seen (Fig. 218) to form coarse bundles that, deep in the cartilage, run at right angles to the surface between the rows of cells. As the fibers approach the surface, however, they become separated into smaller bundles which eventually spread out in a fountainlike fashion to run parallel with the surface (Fig. 218). This creates a densely tangled network of fibers immediately under the surface; this network probably is suited to bear the constantly altered stresses to which a joint surface is subjected.

NOURISHMENT AND METABOLISM OF ARTICULAR CARTILAGE. Since articular cartilage is nonvascular, nourishment must diffuse into its cells from outside its substance. The calcification of its intercellular substance in its deeper layers probably shuts off nutriment from the capillaries of the cancellous bone that underlies it; it is said, however, that there are certain sites where some nourishment may percolate through to it by this route. Around its periphery articular cartilage probably obtains some nourishment from the vessels of the synovial membrane in a manner to be described presently. But the greater part of the articular cartilage obtains its nourishment from the synovial fluid. It has been demonstrated repeatedly that fragments of cartilage, detached by injury or disease and floating freely in the synovial fluid, not only can survive, but also in many instances can grow and increase greatly in size. Furthermore, in experimentally produced fractures of the necks of the femurs of dogs, in which the heads are separated completely from all blood supply and then pinned in place, the articular cartilages of the heads, over the succeeding months, as seen in sections, seem generally to survive. When good results are obtained in such fractures the dead bone and marrow of the head is all replaced, as has been described in connection with the healing of a fracture, and new bone develops to support the living articular cartilage which has survived through the whole procedure. Since a head has no blood supply until it is revascularized, and since the region directly beneath the articular cartilage is the last part of the head to be revascularized, it seems evident that the synovial fluid is capable of supporting the life of the chondrocytes of articular cartilage. This suggests that synovial fluid, under normal circumstances, provides the chief source of nourishment for most of the cells of articular cartilage.

Chondrocytes probably have a low metabolic rate. There is evidence indicating that their metabolism is of the anaerobic type, for their oxygen consumption is almost negligible (Bywaters). Moreover, their oxygen consumption diminishes with advancing age (Rosenthal).

GROWTH, MAINTENANCE AND REPAIR OF ARTICULAR CARTILAGE. As has been noted before, the articular cartilage provides for the growth of the bony epiphysis in the same way that an epiphyseal disk provides for the growth in length of a bony diaphysis; indeed, in short bones in which there are no epiphyseal disks, the articular cartilages serve as the sites wherein the bones as a whole grow in length. During the growing period, mitotic figures are to be observed among the chondrocytes of articular cartilage, not in the most superficial layer of flat cells (which might otherwise be assumed to be the youngest cells in the cartilage), but somewhat deeper, in about the third or fourth layer of cells below the surface. Deep to this layer the chondrocytes of articular cartilage are more mature, and still deeper, next

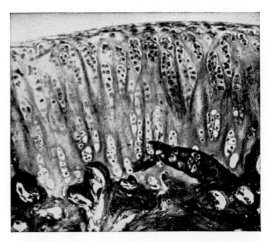

FIG. 218. Low-power photomicrograph (taken with the phase microscope) of a section cut through the upper end of the tibia of an aged rat. The direction of the collagenic fibers in the articular cartilage may be seen.

to the bone, they are hypertrophied, and the intercellular substance surrounding them is calcified. During the period of active growth this zone of calcified cartilage is continuously being replaced by bone, which forms from osteogenic cells and osteoblasts, which invade this layer of cartilage from the bone below.

However, when the epiphysis has grown to its full size these 2 processes—the growth of the cartilage and its replacement by bone—appear to cease. It is the author's experience that mitotic figures can no longer be found in the articular cartilage after growth is over. Elliott, when a graduate student with the author, could not find mitotic figures in the articular cartilages of adult animals even if they were specially exercised.

From the foregoing it seems dubious if there is enough maintenance growth in articular cartilage to compensate for much wear, so it is generally assumed that under normal conditions articular cartilage wears only slightly and gradually. Rosenthal and his associates have shown that the number of cells in articular cartilage decreases in relation to the amount of intercellular substance throughout life; this may mean that some wear and tear is compensated for by such cells as persist continuing to produce more intercellular substance.

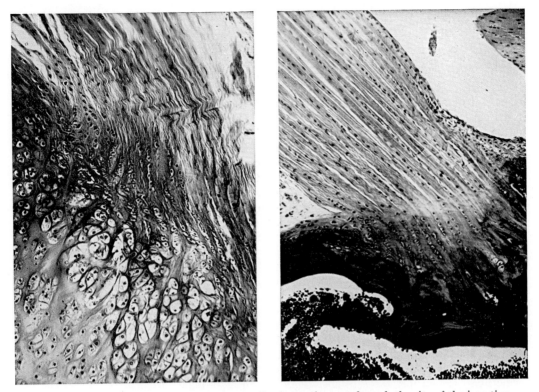

Fig. 219. (*Left*) Low-power photomicrograph of a section cut through the site of the insertion of the patellar tendon of an adult rat. (*Right*) Low-power photomicrograph of a section cut through the site of the insertion of the anterior cruciate ligament of an adult rat. Observe the bundles of collagenic fibers buried in bone (Sharpey's fibers).

The foregoing suggests that once that growth is over the regenerative capacity of the cells of articular cartilage would not be great, and this suggestion is borne out by the experimental evidence. Superficial wounds, made anywhere except around the edges of articular cartilage or close to any other attachment of synovial membrane, apparently remain quiescent and unhealed for long periods of time; the chondrocytes of the articular cartilage appear to be too highly differentiated to give rise to new tissue which would heal the defect. However, if the wounds are deep and extend to and through the bone of the epiphysis which supports the articular cartilage, healing occurs. Such wounds, however, represent the healing of the fractured bone below the articular cartilage rather than the healing of articular cartilage itself, for osteogenic cells, osteoblasts and capillaries grow up into the wound from the bone below. This results in the filling of the defect in the cartilage with what amounts to a callus; this, of course, may contain calcified cartilage and bone as well as uncalcified cartilage, and these other types of tissue are not suitable for an articular surface. Hence, although fractures through the articular cartilage into its supporting bone below will heal, the end result commonly leads to the development of an arthritic condition in the joint at a later date.

If wounds are made in articular cartilage at sites close to the attachment of the synovial membrane, the cells of the latter, being relatively undifferentiated, respond by producing fibrocartilage, and this leads to healing. This is further evidence to the effect that the synovial membrane (the lining of the joint capsule) is in many respects similar to the osteogenic layer of the perichondrium or periosteum.

Joint Capsule. As noted before, this consists of 2 layers: an outer fibrous layer which commonly is called the fibrous capsule of the joint and an inner layer which commonly is called the synovial membrane of the joint (Fig. 216).

The fibrous capsule of a joint is continuous with the fibrous layer of the periosteum of the bones that meet at the joint (Fig. 216). It is composed of sheets of collagenic fibers that run from the periosteum of one bone to that of the other. It is relatively inelastic and hence makes a contribution to the stability of the joint. Occasionally, gaps are present in fibrous capsules; if so, the synovial membrane rests on muscles or such other structures as surround the joint. The ligaments of a joint represent cordlike thickenings of the capsule. These may be incorporated in the capsule or may be separated from it by bursae that are formed by outpouchings of the synovial lining (Fig. 216, *bursae*). Near their attachments the structure of ligaments undergoes a transition into fibrocartilage (Fig. 219). The collagenic fibers become associated with increased amounts of amorphous intercellular substance, and the fibroblasts become encapsulated and resemble chondrocytes (Fig. 219). The collagenic fibers extend into the substance of the bone to which they are attached as typical Sharpey's fibers (Fig. 219, *right*). It is to be remembered that bundles of collagenic fibers can become buried in bone as Sharpey's fibers to serve as an anchorage for tendons, muscles or the periodontal membrane only when the fibers are formed before or as bone intercellular substance is deposited around them and onto the surface of the bone (appositional growth mechanism) by the osteoblasts which lie between the fiber bundles close to the bone. In this sense, a tendon serves as the periosteum of a bone at the site of its insertion (see also Sharpey's fibers, p. 565 and Fig. 389).

The synovial membrane, the inner layer of the joint capsule, lines the joint everywhere except over the articular cartilages (Fig. 216). The inner surface of the synovial membrane is usually smooth and glistening and it may be thrown into numerous processes; some of these are termed *villi*. It is abundantly supplied with blood vessels, nerves and lymphatics, as will be described presently.

The cells in this membrane are called synovial cells. They are of a relatively undifferentiated type and tend to be concentrated along the inner border of the membrane; indeed, in some instances, they may be so concentrated as to give the appearance of forming a continuous cellular membrane. However, the careful microscopic study of such a membrane will show that the cells disposed along its inner surface lie *in among* rather than *on* the collagenic fibers which also participate in forming the inner lining of the membrane.

The inner lining of the joint capsule, which contains the synovial cells, may lie directly on the fibrous capsule of the joint or may be separated from the fibrous capsule by a layer of areolar tissue or a layer of adipose tissue (Fig. 216). Accordingly, Key distinguishes 3 morphologic types of synovial membrane: (1) fibrous, (2) areolar and (3) adipose. These are illustrated in Figures 216 and 220 and will now be described.

The fibrous type is found over ligaments and tendons and in other areas where the synovial lining is subjected to pressure (Fig. 216). The surface cells are characteristically widely separated from one another (Fig. 220, *top*), and although they are slightly larger and more numerous than the fibroblasts that are farther removed from the surface, it is often difficult to distinguish them from ordinary fibroblasts in sections. Since intercellular substance, rather than cells, comprises most of the lining of this type of synovial membrane, this type of membrane provides strong evidence in favor of the concept that synovial cavities are of the nature of connective tissue spaces.

The areolar type of synovial membrane is found where the membrane is required to move freely over the fibrous capsule of the joint, as, for example, in the suprapatellar pouch of the knee joint (Fig. 216). The surface cells are grouped fairly closely together in this type of lining (Fig. 220, *middle*), usually in 3 or 4 rows, and are embedded in a layer of collagenic fibers which blend smoothly into those of the areolar tissue. Usually many elastic fibers are present in this type of lining; these usually are arranged in a lamina and this probably serves to keep synovial projections from being nipped between the articular cartilages (Davies).

The adipose type of synovial lining covers the intra-articular fat pads (Fig. 216) and most closely resembles a true cellular lining

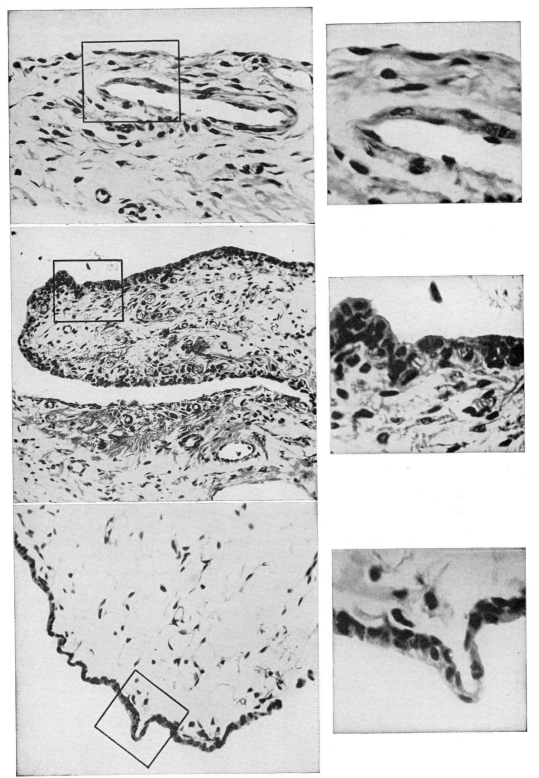

FIG. 220. (*Top*) Low- and high-power photomicrographs of a section of synovial membrane of the fibrous type. (*Middle*) Low- and high-power photomicrographs of a section of synovial membrane of the areolar type. (*Bottom*) Low- and high-power photomicrographs of a section of a synovial membrane of the adipose type. All of the sections are of rat tissue.

membrane in appearance. The surface cells are usually formed into a single layer which appears to rest on the adipose tissue (Fig. 220, *bottom*). However, careful inspection will reveal that the surface cells are more or less embedded in a thin layer of collagenic fibers, as are the surface cells in the other two types of lining membrane.

Synovial cells vary quite a bit in appearance, as might be expected if they represented a mesenchymal-derived family of cells the members of which were in different stages of differentiation. Recently Asboe-Hansen has observed that there are numerous mast cells in synovial membranes, and he believes that they produce the hyaluronic acid of the synovial fluid.

Transition Zone. At the site of attachment of the synovial membrane to the periphery of the articular cartilage, the synovial cells undergo a transition into chondrocytes. This region is known as the *transition zone*. In this site a fold or fringe of synovial tissue may be seen to overlie the articular cartilage for a short distance. This fold, which is cut in cross section in a longitudinal section of a joint, appears wedge-shaped (Fig. 221). The tip of the wedge is relatively noncellular and the base is cellular. The areolar tissue that underlies the base of the wedge undergoes an abrupt change into fibrous tissue as it nears the articular cartilage, and this tissue, in turn, merges with the articular cartilage.

Since the synovial cells are relatively undifferentiated, synovial tissues are capable of rapid and complete repair. It is helpful to know this fact because synovial tissues must be removed in certain types of operations on joints. Key found that following the removal of a portion of the synovial lining from the knee joints of rabbits, there was a rapid deposition of fibrin in the wounded area and that this quickly became organized by young connective tissue cells which grew in from the fibrous capsule. These soon differentiated into synovial cells, so that within 60 days the newly formed synovial lining could not be distinguished from that of undamaged adjacent areas.

Intra-articular Menisci. These structures (Fig. 216) develop from portions of the articular disk of mesenchyme (Fig. 215) which once occupied the space between the develop-

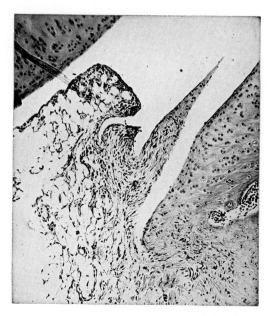

Fig. 221. Low-power photomicrograph of a section cut through the border of the patella of a rat. The synovial fold is wedge-shaped in this section.

ing articular cartilages of the joint concerned. In these, the mesenchyme tends to differentiate into fibrocartilage. They may have a free inner border, as they have in the knee joint, or they may traverse the joint, dividing it into 2 separate synovial cavities, as in the sternoclavicular joint.

The menisci of the knee joint may be torn as the result of an injury, and it is common practice to excise an affected meniscus. Following the removal of a meniscus, a new one sometimes forms, growing in from the fibrous capsule of the joint. The new structure that forms in this fashion is an almost complete duplicate of the former meniscus but it consists of dense fibrous tissue rather than of fibrocartilage. New menisci that form in this fashion may themselves become injured and require removal; indeed, it was because of this that it was found that intra-articular menisci can regenerate (Smillie).

Blood Vessels and Lymphatics. Synovial joints have a relatively rich blood supply. The branches of arteries that approach a joint commonly supply 3 structures, one goes to the epiphyses, a second to the joint capsule and a third to the synovial membrane. In these sites they supply capillary beds. There are arteriovenous anastomoses in joints; the significance of these has not yet been determined.

The synovial membrane has a very rich supply of capillaries and in many sites these approach the inner surface of the membrane very closely. As a result blood may escape into the synovial fluid from a relatively minor injury to the joint.

Blood vessels are arranged in a circular network at the periphery of the articular cartilage in the transition zone; this arrangement constitutes the circulus articuli vasculosus of Hunter.

Gardner's papers should be consulted for details regarding the blood supply of joints.

The lymphatic plexus lies somewhat more deeply from the synovial surface than the blood capillaries. The lymphatic capillaries begin as blind tubes; these are often enlarged at their blind ends. After piercing the elastic lamina of the synovial lining they converge into larger vessels which pass in the general direction of the flexor aspect of the joint. Here they anastomose freely with the periosteal lymphatics and then empty into the main lymphatic vessels of the limb (Davies).

Nerve Supply. The student will find it easier to understand the following section if he returns to it after reading the section on nervous tissue. Hilton's law, first enunciated by John Hilton* in 1863, continues to be the fundamental statement about the nerve supply of joints: "The same trunks of nerves whose branches supply the muscles moving a joint also furnish a distribution of nerves to the skin over the insertions of the same muscles, and . . . the interior of the joint receives its nerves from the same source." Articular cartilage contains no nerve endings. The capsular structures contain different types of endings, as will now be described.

Joints are supplied with both myelinated and nonmyelinated fibers.

The larger myelinated fibers that reach joints are those of afferent neurons. These terminate for the most part in the joint capsule. The nerve endings on these fibers, according to Gardner, are mostly of the Ruffini type, and these, in this site, are sensitive to changes

in pressure and probably other types of stimuli concerned in providing a proprioceptive function. The endings are aggregated chiefly in sites in the capsule that are most likely to be compressed by joint movements.

Small myelinated fibers pass to the joint capsule and to the ligaments of the joint where they end in free endings. These fibers are concerned with the sense of pain. There are very few of these free endings in the connective tissue of the synovial membranes, hence it would not seem to be very sensitive to pain. That the synovial membrane is not very sensitive to pain has been confirmed at operations in which joints have been opened under local anesthesia. The free endings in the capsule and ligaments of joints seem to be stimulated most easily by stretching or twisting these structures. Small myelinated fibers also form free endings in the adventitia of blood vessels; these are probably vasosensory and, at least, some probably are concerned with the sense of pain. Endings of this type in the adventitia of blood vessels are probably the only kind of free afferent endings in synovial membranes.

Nonmyelinated sympathetic fibers, which, of course, are efferent, end in the smooth muscle of the blood vessels of joints to regulate flow through them.

Fibers reach larger joints from many spinal nerves, and any given nerve may supply more than one joint. Joint pain is generally poorly localized.

Gardner has made extensive studies on the nerve supply of joints, and his papers should be read to obtain detailed information on this subject.

Synovial Fluid. Since the synovial cavity develops as a connective tissue space, it should contain a ground substance and be perfused with tissue fluid. This concept of the cavity and its contents has been supported by the investigations of Bauer and his colleagues, who showed that synovial fluid was an ultrafiltrate or dialysate of blood (as is tissue fluid) plus mucin. Meyer identified the mucin of synovial fluid as hyaluronic acid. In synovial fluid, in contrast to the aqueous humor, hyaluronic acid is highly polymerized; this accounts for the viscous quality of synovial fluid and doubtless adds to its lubricating qualities.

The various projections of the synovial

---

* Hilton, J.: Rest and Pain, ed. 5, London, Bell.

membrane that extend into the synovial cavity and the closeness of the capillaries to the surface of the cavity make it easy to understand how tissue fluid readily could gain access to the cavity. The presence of hyaluronic acid in synovial fluid is to be explained by the fact that synovial cells produce it, and that which is produced constitutes the ground substance of the synovial membrane and also gains entrance to the synovial fluid. Asboe-Hansen believes the mast cells of the synovial membrane produce the hyaluronic acid of the synovial fluid.

The cell content of synovial fluid appears to vary considerably from joint to joint and from species to species. Key points out that it tends to become increased after death. Counts of from 80 to several thousand cells per cubic millimeter have been found by different investigators. Key found a typical differential count to yield 58 per cent monocytes, 15 per cent macrophages, 14 per cent ill-defined types of phagocytes, 1 per cent primitive cells, 3 per cent synovial cells and 5 per cent of other types of blood leukocytes.

The passage of substances into and out of the synovial fluid depends upon their size. Crystalloids diffuse readily in both directions. This is of importance in the treatment of joint diseases, for soluble drugs given an individual can quickly enter the synovial fluid. Gases also diffuse readily in both directions. Hence, in caisson disease (the bends), nitrogen bubbles frequently appear in joint cavities. This disease occurs when divers or other people working under high atmospheric pressure return too quickly to normal atmospheric pressure. The sudden decompression of the individual as a whole causes a too sudden release of gases dissolved in the blood stream and other fluids, just as carbon dioxide bubbles from soda water when the cap is removed from a bottle.

Proteins, with their large colloidal molecules, leave synovial fluid by way of lymphatics. Particulate matter must be removed from synovial fluid by phagocytosis. Although synovial cells have some phagocytic powers, most of the phagocytosis of particulate matter introduced into synovial fluid is brought about by macrophages. The removal of particulate matter from joints is a slow process, and phagocytes containing hemosiderin may be

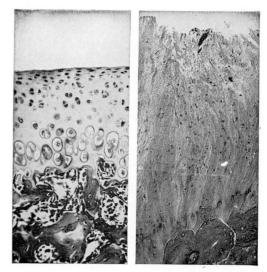

FIG. 222. (*Left*) Low-power photomicrograph of a section of the upper end of the tibia of a guinea pig. This is the normal appearance. (*Right*) Low-power photomicrograph of a section of the head of a first metatarsal bone removed at operation; note the fibrillation of the articular cartilage.

seen in the synovial tissues of joints months after blood has escaped into the synovial fluid.

Age Changes. A condition called *osteoarthritis* tends to develop in joints as individuals age. This condition is so common that its development to some degree is considered, by some investigators, to be a normal consequence of the aging process. Should the condition develop prematurely or in a severe form, it is, of course, considered to be pathologic. It consists essentially of a curious combination of degenerative and proliferative phenomena.

The degenerative changes that occur are seen to best advantage in the more central parts of articular cartilages (rather than at the periphery of articular cartilages). The cement substance of the cartilage (chondroitin sulfuric acid) appears to be involved and to change in character. As a result, the collagenic fibers and even the fibrils of the intercellular substance of the cartilage become unmasked and visible in sections (Fig. 222, *right*). As the condition progresses, the collagenic fibers become freely exposed on the articular surface; this gives the surface an appearance like the "pile" of a carpet, and the condition is termed fibrillation of the cartilage (Fig. 222, *right*).

The proliferative changes occur around the edges of the articular cartilage, particularly in the transition zone and at the sites of attachment of tendons and ligaments. Cartilage proliferates in these regions and is replaced by bone in such a fashion that bony spurs, termed *osteophytes,* grow so as to form lips around the joint. It may be that these outgrowths represent Nature's attempt to restrain movement in the joint.

This combination of degenerative and proliferative changes, although it occurs commonly in the aged, may occur in younger individuals, particularly if the direction of a stress borne by a joint has been altered by some kind of an injury. Hence the condition appears to be the consequence of joints having to perform too much, or the wrong kind of, work.

Effects of Compression on Articular Cartilage. Salter, having observed that degenerative changes were sometimes associated with joints that had been immobilized in forced positions, has made an experimental study with Field and shown that artificially induced compression on joint cartilages will lead to their degeneration. Moreover, they have shown experimentally that if joints are immobilized in forced positions degeneration will occur. Degenerative changes may appear as soon as 6 days after the compression has been applied. They think that the effects of compression interfere with the nutrition of the cells of the articular cartilage which, as has been explained, is probably dependent on diffusion through the synovial fluid and then through the intercellular substances of the cartilage. It would seem logical to assume that the maintenance of a joint in one position with a compression of the cartilage would interfere with this mechanism of nutrition which, it might be thought, would ordinarily be facilitated by movement, which would result in surfaces being more or less continuously coated with fresh synovial fluid.

REFERENCES

REFERENCES FOR JOINTS
GENERAL REFERENCES

Davies, D. V.: The anatomy and physiology of joints *in* Copeman's Textbook of the Rheumatic Diseases, ed. 2, p. 40, Edinburgh, Livingstone, 1955.

SPECIAL REFERENCES ON JOINTS

Adkins, E. W. O., and Davies, D. V.: Absorption from the joint cavity, Quart. J. Exper. Physiol. *30*:147, 1940.

Asboe-Hansen, G.: The mast cell *in* Inter. Rev. Cytol., ed. 3, New York, Acad. Press, 1954.

Bauer, W., Ropes, M. W., and Waine, H.: The physiology of articular structures, Physiol. Rev. *20*:272,1940.

Bennett, G. A., Waine, H., and Bauer, W.: Changes in the Knee Joint at Various Ages, New York, Commonwealth Fund, 1942.

Benninghoff, A.: Form und Bau der Gelenkknorpel in ihren Beziehungen zur Funktion (II), Ztschr. Zellforsch. u. mikr. Anat. *2*:783, 1925.

Bradford, F. K., and Spurling, R. G.: The Intervertebral Disc, Springfield, Ill., Thomas, 1941.

Bywaters, E. G. L.: The metabolism of joint tissues, J. Path. & Bact. *44*:247, 1937.

Clark, W. E. LeGros: The Tissues of the Body, ed. 2, Oxford, Clarendon, 1945.

Davies, D. V.: Anatomy and physiology of diarthrodial joints, Ann. Rheumat. Dis. *5*:29, 1945.

Elliott, H. C.: Studies on articular cartilages. I. Growth mechanisms, Am. J. Anat. *58*:127, 1936.

Gardner, E.: The anatomy of the joints, Am. Acad. Orthop. Surgeons, Instructional Course Lectures, vol. 9, Ann Arbor, Edwards, 1952.

————: Blood and nerve supply of joints, Stanford M. Bull. *11*:203, 1953.

————: The innervation of the elbow joint, Anat. Rec. *102*:161, 1948.

————: The innervation of the hip joint, Anat. Rec. *101*:353, 1948.

————: The innervation of the knee joint, Anat. Rec. *101*:109, 1948.

————: The innervation of the shoulder joint, Anat. Rec. *102*:1, 1948.

————: The nerve supply of diarthrodial joints, Stanford M. Bull. *6*:367, 1948.

————:Physiology of movable joints, Physiol. Rev. *30*:127, 1950.

Gardner, E., and Gray, D. J.: Prenatal development of the human hip joint, Am. J. Anat. *87*:163, 1950.

Grant, J. C. B.: Interarticular synovial folds, Brit. J. Surg. *18*:636, 1931.

Haines, R. W.: The development of joints, J. Anat. *81*:33, 1947.

Hall, Kathleen: The effect of hysterectomy on the action of oestrone on the symphysis pubis of ovariectomized mice, J. Endocrinol. *7*:299, 1951.

————: The effect of oestrone and progesterone on the histological structure of the symphysis pubis of the castrated female mouse. J. Endocrinol. 7:54, 1950.

Hall, Kathleen, and Newton, W. H.: The action of "Relaxin" in the mouse, Lancet 1:54, 1946.

————: The effect of oestrone and relaxin on the x-ray appearance of the pelvis of the mouse, J. Physiol. 106:18, 1947.

————: The normal course of separation of the pubes in pregnant mice, J. Physiol. 104:346, 1946.

Hilton, J.: Rest and Pain, ed. 5, London, Bell, 1920.

Key, J. A.: The reformation of synovial membrane in the knees of rabbits after synovectomy, J. Bone & Joint Surg. (N.S.) 7:793, 1925.

————: The synovial membrane of joints and bursae *in* Cowdry's Special Cytology, ed. 2, p. 1053, New York, Hoeber, 1932.

Lanier, R. R.: The effects of exercise on the knee-joints of inbred mice, Anat. Rec. 94:311, 1946.

Lever, J. D., and Ford, E. H. R.: Histological, histochemical and electron microscopic observations on synovial membrane, Anat. Rec. 132:525, 1958.

McDermott, L. J.: Development of the human knee joint, Arch. Surg. 46:705, 1943.

Meyer, K., Smyth, E. M., and Dawson, M. H.: The nature of the mucopolysaccharide of synovial fluid, Science 88:129, 1938.

Paulson, S., Sylvén, B., Hirsch, C., and Snellman, O.: Biophysical and physiological investigations on cartilage and other mesenchymal tissues. III. The diffusion rate of various substances in normal bovine nucleus pulposus, Biochem. et biophys. acta 7:207, 1951.

Ropes, M. W., and Bauer, W.: Synovial Fluid Changes in Joint Disease, Cambridge, Mass., pub. for Commonwealth Fund by Harvard Univ. Press, 1953.

Rosenthal, O., Bowie, M. A., and Wagoner, G.: Studies in the metabolism of articular cartilage. I. Respiration and glycolysis of cartilage in relation to its age, J. Cell. & Comp. Physiol. 17:221, 1941.

Ruth, Elbert Bresee: Metamorphosis of the pubic symphysis. I. The white rat (Mus norvegicus albinus), Anat. Rec. 64:1, 1935.

————: Metamorphosis of the pubic symphysis. III. Histological changes in the symphysis of the pregnant guinea pig, Anat. Rec. 67:409, 1937.

————: A note on the fibrillar structure of hyaline cartilage, Anat. Rec. 96:93, 1946.

Salter, R. B., and Field, P.: The effects of continuous compression on living articular cartilage, J. Bone & Joint Surg. 42A:31, 1960.

Sigurdson, L. A.: The structure and function of articular synovial membranes, J. Bone & Joint Surg. 12:603, 1930.

Smillie, I. S.: Injuries of the Knee Joint, Edinburgh, Livingstone, 1946.

Sylvén, B., Paulson, S., Hirsch, C., and Snellman, O.: Biophysical and physiological investigations on cartilage and other mesenchymal tissues. II. The ultrastructure of bovine and human nuclei pulposi, J. Bone & Joint Surg. 33-A:333, 1951.

Walmsley, R., and Bruce, J.: The early stages of replacement of the semilunar cartilages of the knee joint in rabbits after operative excision, J. Anat. 72:260, 1938.

Whillis, J.: The development of synovial joints, J. Anat. 74:277, 1940.

Chapter 17

Hemopoietic Tissue

Neither red nor white cells live in the blood stream for very long. Most leukocytes probably leave it after a matter of hours or days to enter the tissues. However, all erythrocytes, and some leukocytes, end their days in the blood stream. There would be a danger of their disintegrating bodies plugging small blood vessels if it were not for the fact that provision is made for removing their bodies from the blood as they die. Provision is also made for replenishing those that wear out. Since most kinds of blood cells cannot divide, most blood cells must be made outside the blood stream and delivered into it at the same rate as they die or leave it.

In general, the functions of producing new blood cells for the blood stream and removing worn-out ones from it go hand in hand in the body. These two functions are carried out by a special kind of tissue whose name, *hemopoietic* tissue, relates to only one of them, blood-making. Hemopoietic tissue, then, may be defined as a variety of connective tissue that is highly specialized both for the production of blood cells and for the removal of worn-out blood cells from the blood stream. Moreover, it should be noted that within hemopoietic tissue further specialization has resulted in there being two somewhat different varieties of it, termed *myeloid* and *lymphatic* tissue, respectively. In postnatal life myeloid tissue produces erythrocytes, granular leukocytes (neutrophils, eosinophils and basophils) and platelets. Lymphatic tissue produces at least most of the nongranular leukocytes (lymphocytes and monocytes).

MYELOID TISSUE

Types and Distribution. Myeloid tissue, under normal circumstances, is confined to the marrow cavities of bones, where it is called bone marrow. In the adult, there are two kinds of bone marrow—red and yellow. Red marrow derives its color from vast numbers of red blood cells in various stages of formation. Red marrow, then, is marrow that is actively pro-ducing blood cells. Yellow marrow derives its color from the large quantity of fat it contains. Although yellow marrow has the potentiality to manufacture red blood cells, the fact that it is not red indicates that it is not actively engaged in doing so and the fact that it is yellow indicates that it has taken on the more leisurely work of storing fat.

In the fetus the marrow of most bones is red. But during the growing period in post-natal life the marrow of most bones becomes yellow so that, in the adult, red marrow is found only in the diploe of the bones of the vault of the skull, in the ribs and the sternum, in the bodies of the vertebrae and in the cancellous bone of some of the short bones and at the ends of long bones. The marrow in all other sites is yellow and, from the standpoint of producing red blood cells, inactive. However, it must be remembered that yellow marrow has the potentiality to resume the production of red cells. Under conditions in which there is an urgent and prolonged need for increased red blood cell production, yellow marrow becomes reconverted to red marrow.

THE DEVELOPMENT OF MYELOID TISSUE

The common view is that myeloid tissue develops from mesenchymal cells that gain entrance to the developing marrow cavities of bones along with the blood vessels. In endochondral ossification marrow cells appear almost as soon as bone is deposited on the calcified cartilage.

The author has been impressed with the fact that typical marrow cells develop along with new trabeculae of bone in the callus of a repairing fracture. Typical bone marrow also can develop in association with heterotopic bone. When autogenous transplants of cancellous bone are made in an individual under good conditions so that some of the surface cells of the trabeculae remain alive and grow, marrow often forms in association with the new bone. All in all, there is a very close association between osteogenesis and the formation of myeloid tissue, and the author has come to the conclusion that at least some of the covering and lining cells of bone (osteogenic cells) must be sufficiently undifferentiated to be able to form marrow cells as well as bone cells and that such cells, in periosteal buds, are responsible for marrow formation. There is, of course, abundant evidence to the effect that the least differentiated marrow cells can form bone as readily as they can form marrow cells. If they are not identical, the mother cells of skeletal tissue and the mother cells of marrow are at least not very different from one another; both have almost unrestricted mesenchymal potentialities. However, the mother cell of marrow generally is not termed an undifferentiated mesenchymal cell but a *primitive reticular cell*. This is because there are some reticular fibers in bone marrow, and the primitive cells are supposed to be more or less attached to them.

LINES OF CELL DIFFERENTIATION IN MYELOID TISSUE

It has been explained already that hemopoietic tissues have two main functions, that of removing worn-out cells from the circulation and that of adding new cells to the circulation. In order to perform these two functions the primitive reticular cells of developing marrow differentiate along two main lines, as is illustrated in the following chart.

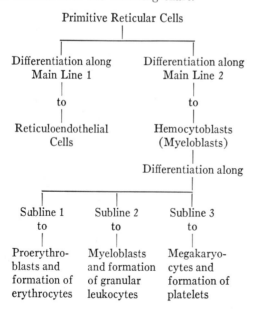

In differentiating along Line 1, they form the cells and the structures responsible for removing worn-out cells from the circulation. In differentiating along Line 2, they form free cells that produce the various kinds of blood cells. So, the differentiation of primitive reticular cells along two different lines is to provide cells to perform the two different functions of hemopoietic tissue, that of removing cells from and that of adding cells to the circulation.

The Cells That Form Along Line 1

In differentiating along Line 1, primitive cells become increasingly specialized for phagocytosis and for lining blood passageways. After they have become thus specialized they are called *reticuloendothelial cells*. The reticuloendothelial cells of hemopoietic tissue are the counterparts of the macrophages that develop in loose connective tissue. However, reticuloendothelial cells, while phagocytic like macrophages, are a little different from them. In addition to lining blood passageways (to be described presently), they have the capacity to make networks of reticular fibers. Both they and the primitive cells are held in these networks. Their ability to make fibers is responsible for the *reticulo* part of their name. As has been mentioned already, they tend to arrange themselves so as to become the walls of the blood passageways that connect the arterial side of the circulation to the venous side in bone marrow. These blood passageways are termed *sinusoids* (Fig. 223). Sinusoids occupy the same position in relation to arterial and venous vessels that capillaries do in most parts of the body. However, they are much wider than capillaries, and their lining cells do not fit together so well. Since all other kinds of blood vessels in the body are lined by endothelial cells (which are not phagocytic), it was thought that these phagocytic lining cells of sinusoids should also have *endothelial* attached to their name, so they were called reticuloendothelial cells.

Primitive Reticular Cells and Reticuloendothelial Cells. As is so usual in connection with hemopoietic tissue, there is much confusion in the literature about the terminology of the cells that we have described as being involved in Line 1. Some authors make no distinction between primitive reticular cells and reticuloendothelial cells, and, as a consequence, many

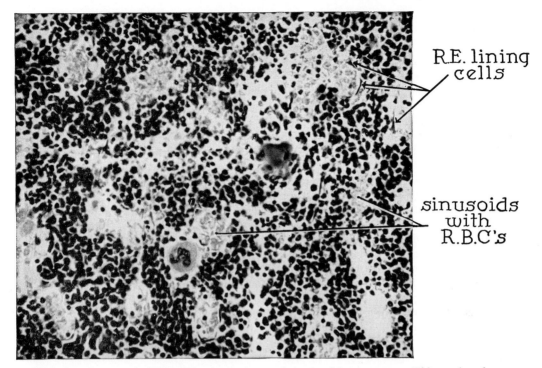

R.E. lining cells

sinusoids with R.B.C's

FIG. 223. Low-power photomicrograph of a section of red bone marrow. This section shows numerous sinusoids, most of which contain red blood cells. These are the lighter areas in the photograph. Between them are innumerable cells of the red blood cell and granular leukocyte series. One megakaryocyte is present in the lower middle part of the picture. In a few sites, the thin, flattened reticuloendothelial lining cells of the sinusoids may be seen.

authors describe reticuloendothelial cells as the mother cells of bone marrow. Other authors distinguish only what they term *reticular cells*. In considering this matter, it might be said that a fully developed reticuloendothelial cell that is phagocytic evidences a large amount of differentiation, and it would be surprising if such a cell could function as a mother cell for marrow. However, it might be argued that less differentiated reticuloendothelial cells could function as mother cells. But undifferentiated reticuloendothelial cells are not reticuloendothelial cells; they are primitive cells. The term reticuloendothelial cell should be reserved for cells *that have differentiated* to the point where they can make reticular fibers and phagocytose. Confusion about this matter has arisen for two main reasons: (1) there are not merely primitive reticular cells and reticuloendothelial cells along Line 1, but many intermediate stages, and (2) the cells in all these stages from the primitive to the differentiated members of the

family are in close association with one another. Hence, if some cell along a sinusoid does something to indicate that it has great potentiality, it should not be concluded that reticuloendothelial cells have great potentiality but that a primitive cell was present and responsible for the act.

The Appearance of Sinusoids in Sections. Red marrow is riddled with sinusoids. In the tissue between sinusoids, erythrocytes, granulocytes and platelets all are produced, and the cells that are produced gain entrance to the circulation through the leaky walls of the sinusoids. The lining cells of sinusoids are difficult to distinguish in sections because they are pressed upon by the cells of the surrounding tissue (Fig. 223). Furthermore, their walls are so thin that they are easily collapsed, and many are probably partially or completely collapsed in the living state. When a block of bone marrow is cut for sectioning, the blood tends to run out of the sinusoids; subsequently, when the block is fixed the empty sinusoids may be squeezed and closed and, consequently, difficult to see when the block is sectioned (Fig. 229). Sinusoids generally are easier to see in the marrow of a section of a whole bone, for in this they are filled with blood (Fig. 223); the reason for this is that if a whole bone is put in fixative the blood cannot run freely out of the sinusoids. Sinusoids are particularly easy to see in the bone marrow of animals that have been subjected to a near lethal dose of total body radiation. In the first few days following severe total body radiation, nearly all the cells concerned in forming blood cells in the marrow are destroyed and disappear. As a result of the radiation, the sinusoids become congested with blood and, since the cells in the tissue between them are mostly destroyed, they show up very clearly in sections (Fig. 224).

With the light microscope, the reticuloendothelial cells that line sinusoids have ovoid nuclei arranged so that the long axis of each follows the curve of the sinusoid wall (Fig. 224). The chromatin granules are fine and numerous, so each nucleus stains evenly and with moderate intensity. The cytoplasm seems to extend off from each pole of the nucleus in a long thin sheet. The sinusoidal walls generally appear to be continuous; the cytoplasm of one lining cell generally can be traced into that of the next.

Pease has described their fine structure. With the E/M, the cytoplasm of the reticuloendothelial lining cells is seen to extend along the sinusoid walls in the form of *pseudopodia,* and there are small but distinct gaps between the pseudopodia from adjacent cells at sites where they intermesh. Pease has micrographs showing blood cells entering the sinusoids through the gaps between the cytoplasmic pseudopodia of adjacent cells. The E/M appearance of these cells explains why the sinusoid walls can appear to be continuous with the light microscope and yet be permeated with openings, because it could be visualized that in the thicker sections used for light microscopy, imperfectly fitting, but overlapping, pseudopodia of adjacent cells would

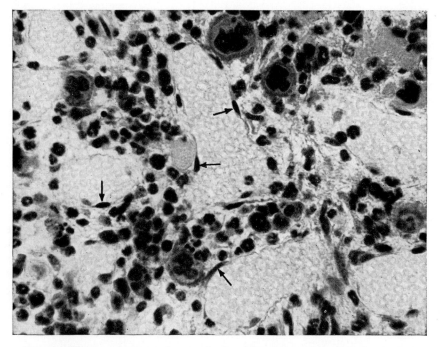

Fig. 224. High-power photomicrograph of an H and E section of the bone marrow of a mouse 24 hours after the mouse was given a dose of radiation sufficient to kill most of the mice so treated. Notice that the various cells between sinusoids are undergoing pyknotic changes and that the sinusoids are congested. The arrows point to the nuclei of reticuloendothelial cells that are lining sinusoids.

appear as a continuous thin band of cyto-plasm.

With the E/M, Pease finds the nucleoli of reticuloendothelial cells to be well developed. The mitochondria are large, the internal membranes of the cytoplasm are only moderately well developed, and the content of RNA granules is low. Phagocytosed material can be demonstrated in their cytoplasm.

The Cells That Form Along Line 2

The tissue that occupies the space between the sinusoids will be considered now. This is where primitive reticular cells differentiate along the second main line of differentiation to form red blood cells, granular leukocytes and platelets.

The tissue between sinusoids is poorly supported. Occasional small arteries or veins are seen in it, and the connective tissue associated with these, as well as the walls of the vessels themselves, provide a basic, though weak, framework for the tissue. Some reticular fibers run from the connective tissue associated with arteries and veins to connect with those reticular fibers that surround the sinusoids. Hence, most of the tissue between sinusoids is supported by no more than a delicate mesh of reticular fibers. The meshes of this network are packed with cells that range all the way from primitive reticular cells to erythrocytes and granular leukocytes.

In the mesh the mother cell is the primitive reticular cell, and it is generally assumed that this is a *fixed cell,* having some attachment to the reticular net. The first step in primitive reticular cells forming blood cells is for them to differentiate into free cells; these become detached from the reticular net and, as a consequence, they "round up" and lie among the other cells in the interstices of the net. The change from a fixed cell to a free cell is not associated with any great loss of potentiality, and, as a consequence, the first free cell that develops has the potentiality to form any of the cells that are produced in marrow (Fig. 144). Since it is the mother cell of blood cells it is called a hemocytoblast, and since it is the mother cell of the cells produced in myeloid tissue it is also properly called a myeloblast.

Some hematologists think that the primitive fixed cell of marrow gives rise, not to a single kind of free stem cell, but to two kinds. One

of these is visualized as the mother cell of the red blood cell series, and the other as the mother cell of the granulocyte series. This creates a problem in terminology, for they use the term "myeloblast" for the mother cell of the granulocyte series.

It is very difficult for universal agreement to be reached on matters of this kind. We take the view that the most primitive free cells that form from primitive reticular cells have the potentialities to form either red blood cells or granulocytes. Since the term "myeloblast" now is used so commonly for the mother cell of the granulocyte series, we think it is perhaps preferable to designate this primitive free cell as a hemocytoblast, although the term "myeloblast" is a perfectly correct designation for it. In Figure 144 and in the chart on page 362, the hemocytoblast is shown as giving rise to several different mother cells for the different lines of blood cells, and the mother cell of the granulocyte line is labeled as a myeloblast in accordance with the terminology now being used by so many hematologists. Since in previous editions and in Figure 225, which was taken from a previous edition, we have used the term "myeloblast" to indicate the free rounded mother cell that can form cells of either the red blood cell or granulocyte series, it is necessary to comment briefly on why we are now using it for a different purpose.

The word "myeloblast," from its origin, means the germinative cell of marrow, and it was used by the earlier hematologists to indicate the mother cell that could produce all the cells of marrow, both those of the red blood cell and the granulocyte lines. But the cells that develop granules in their cytoplasm were named *myelocytes* (which means no more than marrow cells), and, as a consequence, an overwhelming association has been developed between "myelo" and "granules." After anyone develops an association between "myelo" and "granules" he is prone to associate the term "myeloblast" only with cells that have granules, and, although a myeloblast has no granules itself, it is now commonly defined as the cell that produces only the cells of the granulocyte series.

As matters now stand, some authors use the term "myeloblast" for a cell with potentiality to form both red cells and granular leukocytes. Other authors use it for cells with more restricted potentiality—cells that can form only the granular leukocytes.

The formation of free rounded mother cells in the meshes of the reticular network represents the first step in the differentiation of primitive reticular cells into hemocytoblasts along Line 2. However, from this point on, differentiation proceeds along 3 separate sublines (see chart on page 362). Along the first of these, hemocytoblasts eventually form erythrocytes; along the second, granular leukocytes; along the third, large cells known as megakaryocytes. But hemocytoblasts do not form red blood cells or granular leukocytes directly. Instead, between hemocytoblasts and erythrocytes and hemocytoblasts and granular leukocytes there are many intermediate steps, with each being represented by a type of cell somewhat different from the one that precedes it and the one that follows it (Figs. 144 and 225). All these various cells intermediate between hemocytoblasts and red blood cells and hemocytoblasts and granular leukocytes are to be found in the meshes of myeloid tissue. Therefore, it is not surprising that myeloid tissue is so packed with cells that individual ones can scarcely be distinguished (Fig. 223).

To decide how the various free cells found in the meshes of myeloid tissue are related to one another, in the sense of which gives rise to which, is not an easy matter, and indeed, there is much controversy about it. Yet this matter is of very practical importance because, in certain important diseases, the cells that are intermediate between mother cells and mature erythrocytes or granular leukocytes, or even hemocytoblasts themselves, may enter the circulation and so be seen in films made from peripheral blood. The discovery in blood films of cells ordinarily confined to myeloid tissue may be of the greatest diagnostic importance, and for this reason the student must learn how to recognize these various cells and know something of their position on the myeloid family tree.

Technics for Studying the Cells of Marrow. The fact that the practicing physician is interested in detecting free cells of myeloid tissue in blood films stained with blood stains makes it important for the student to learn the appearance of these cells as revealed by blood stains. For this reason, ordinary H and E sections of myeloid tissue are not adequate for learning the appearance of the free cells of marrow because H and E do not color these cells the same way as blood stains. Furthermore, sections are not very satisfactory for this purpose because the mesh of marrow is so packed with cells that individual cells cannot be seen to advantage (Figs. 223 and 229). Consequently, the appearances of the various cells of marrow usually are learned either from thin films or thin imprints of fresh marrow that are stained with blood stains. Imprints are made by touching fresh marrow lightly to glass slides. Films are made either by smearing the marrow lightly on a slide or by mixing the marrow with blood serum and then spreading the resulting mixture on a glass slide by the same method employed in making a blood film. Imprints or films can be stained rapidly with ordinary blood stains. Students using preparations of this sort to study the free cells of marrow should not try to ascertain the nature of every cell that they see because many cells are altered in some way in the making of this kind of preparation. It is better for students to examine only reasonably perfect cells until typical appearances become familiar to them.

The Cells Concerned in the Formation of Erythrocytes (Subline 1)

Since erythrocytes arise through many intermediate steps from hemocytoblasts, we shall consider this cell first. A hemocytoblast (labeled myeloblast in Fig. 225) is a large cell commonly measuring anywhere from 12 to 20 μ in diameter (Fig. 225). Its nucleus is ovoid and it may show some indentation, but indentation, as a general rule, is not pronounced. With blood stains, its nucleus is red but with a purple tinge to it. The chromatin granules are fine and distributed rather lightly throughout the nucleus with the result that the nucleus as a whole is rather pale. From 2 to 5 nucleoli of a pale-blue color may be seen in the nucleus. The cytoplasm is a light to moderate shade of blue and is scanty to moderate in amount. In some instances it is vacuolated.

The fine structure of the free mother cell has been described by Pease. The E/M shows the nuclei to have large nucleolar masses. The mitochondria are large. The Golgi apparatus is well developed, but other intracytoplasmic membranes are only poorly developed. However, RNA granules are numerous, being scattered diffusely through the cytoplasm; this type of arrangement, as has been pointed out already, is common in cells that are synthesizing protein for growth.

Hemocytoblasts in the meshes of myeloid tissue, in differentiating along the red blood cell route (the first subline), divide and give rise to somewhat smaller cells. These are called *proerythroblasts* (Fig. 225) and measure usually from 12 to 15 μ in diameter. The chromatin in their nuclei is somewhat coarser than that in the nucleus of the hemocytoblast. The staining reaction of the nucleus on the whole is somewhat more basophilic than that of the hemocytoblast, so the nucleus is somewhat more purple and not quite so red as that of the hemocytoblast. Two prominent nucleoli are commonly present. The cytoplasm of the proerythroblast is somewhat more basophilic and less in amount than that of the hemocytoblast.

Proerythroblasts divide and give rise to cells known as *erythroblasts*. More specifically, the cell that the proerythroblast gives rise to is called a *basophilic erythroblast* (Fig. 225) because of the color of its cytoplasm. The basophilic erythroblast is somewhat smaller than the proerythroblast. The chromatin of its nucleus is more dense and appears in the form of coarse granules which often are clumped. Sometimes the clumped granules are arranged like the spokes of a wheel. The staining reaction of the nucleus is still more basophilic than that of the proerythroblast. Consequently, the red color of the nucleus apparent in the hemocytoblast is not seen in the nucleus of the basophilic erythroblast. No nucleoli can be seen in its nucleus. The cytoplasm is more basophilic than that of the proerythroblast and ranges from a moderate to a deep blue in color.

Basophilic erythroblasts divide and give rise to cells which are somewhat smaller. These are called *polychromatophilic erythroblasts* (Fig. 225). This name has been given to them because their cytoplasm "loves many colors" in the limited sense that it takes up both the acid and the basic components of blood stains. As is demonstrated by the preceding cell (the

basophilic erythroblast), the cytoplasm of cells encountered along the red blood cell route is fundamentally basophilic; this is due to cytoplasmic RNA. The cause of acidophilia of the cytoplasm, which becomes apparent first in the cytoplasm of the polychromatophilic erythroblast, is hemoglobin, which is being synthesized by, and so comes to be mixed with, the fundamentally basophilic cytoplasm. The net result is that the cytoplasm takes on a muddy-gray or green-violet color. The nucleus of the polychromatic erythroblast is somewhat smaller than that of the basophilic variety, and its chromatin is in the form of coarse granules which commonly are clumped so that the nucleus as a whole is very basophilic. No nucleoli can be seen in it.

Polychromatophilic erythroblasts experience 1 of 2 different fates. Occasionally under ordinary circumstances (probably less than once in 100 times), and more often when erythroid activity is increased because of a need for more red cells, the nucleus of the polychromatophilic erythroblast becomes pyknotic and is extruded while the cytoplasm is still polychromatophilic. This results in the formation of a polychromatophilic erythrocyte, as is shown in Figure 225. As has been described already, the polychromatophilic erythrocyte is called a reticulocyte when it is stained by supravital technics; the RNA still present in its cytoplasm shows up under these conditions as if it were in the form of a reticulum.

The other and common fate of polychromatophilic erythroblasts is for them, as they continue to divide, to lose their cytoplasmic RNA so that their cytoplasm loses all its former basophilic properties. When this has happened, the cell is termed a *normoblast* because it is going to give rise to a normocytic erythrocyte. By this time a normoblast has a small spherical dark-staining pyknotic nucleus (Fig. 225). Normally, this is lost by extrusion; recently Pease has published electron micrographs of the process. The fate of extruded nuclei is still somewhat of a mystery; there was an older view, to which we were somewhat sympathetic, that they might become platelets, but the E/M has shown convincingly, as will be described presently, that platelets arise from a different source. The many extruded nuclei of normoblasts seem to disappear very quickly from marrow. Occasionally, small particles of the nucleus are left behind in erythrocytes; these are called Howell-Jolly bodies. When a nuclear remnant is in the form of a ring it is called a Cabot ring.

The process of the formation of red cells has been studied recently in our laboratory by Howatson and McCulloch with the E/M. Proerythroblasts (Fig. 226) contain large finely granulated nuclei, in which the nucleoli can be identified readily. The cell also has a prominent Golgi region, but few mitochondria; some of the latter are elongated, and their matrices are of low density (Fig. 226). The cytoplasmic vesicles are few and rounded (Fig. 226). RNA granules are numerous and are mostly spread diffusely through the cytoplasm (Fig. 226). With the process of maturation, the nucleolus is lost, and the chromatin becomes clumped (Fig. 227). The cytoplasmic structures also become altered. The Golgi apparatus disappears, and the mitochondria become less numerous and often appear to be degenerate. Hemoglobin shows up as a gray background, which seems to consist of evenly dispersed fine particulate matter; this is distinct from the larger and darker RNA granules, which can be seen until the cell is near maturity. The continued increase in hemoglobin content is associated with a gradual loss of all other cytoplasmic components.

In the preceding account, red blood cells are described as being formed from free cells (hemocytoblasts) in the reticular mesh of marrow. That is, they are described as being formed *extravascularly* and so, to do their work in the body, they must somehow gain entrance to the circulatory system. This could be conceived of as occurring by their penetrating through the sievelike walls of the sinusoids. Possibly the pressure of the accumulating cells in the extravascular tissue be hind them is a factor in forcing them through the sinusoid walls.

Not all hematologists have believed that red blood cells are formed extravascularly; many, at least until now, have subscribed to another view that visualized them as being formed intravascularly—within capillaries in the bone marrow. Bone marrow is so packed with cells that it is very difficult to determine by means of light microscopy whether forming cells are inside or outside very delicate capil-

laries. However, the E/M gives promise of settling this controversy. Pease, in his recent comprehensive study of marrow with the E/M, finds no support for the intravascular theory, finding that red blood cells are indeed formed extravascularly and that they subsequently gain entrance to the circulation by migrating through the imperfect walls of sinusoids. However, since the intravascular theory has held so much attention in the past, it will now be described briefly.

The first reason for anyone's suspecting that red cells might be formed intravascularly in the red marrow of postnatal life is that they are formed intravascularly in early embryonic life. One of the first examples of red blood cell formation occurs in the yolk sac where the cells of the mesenchyme give rise to little clumps of rounded basophilic cells, called blood islands. However, it is not long before the cells of the blood islands come to be enclosed in blood vessels. The walls of the latter develop from the outermost cells of the blood islands and also from the mesenchymal cells that lie between blood islands. Some degree of differentiation occurs in the cells of the blood islands (now enclosed in blood vessels), and as a result some hemoglobin appears in their cytoplasm. Moreover, their numbers are added to from the lining cells of the vessels in which they lie. Although these cells could be called endothelial cells because they line blood vessels, they are at this stage of development relatively undifferentiated, and in all probability they retain almost full mesenchymal potentiality. In any event, they not uncommonly become swollen and detached to float free in the lumens of the vessels, where they become rounded. These rounded cells divide and give rise to further rounded cells which develop hemoglobin in their cytoplasm. It is clear from studies on hemopoiesis, made in the yolk sac of the young embryo, that the lining cells of primitive blood vessels can give rise to primitive red blood cells.

As development continues in the embryo, the liver becomes an important source of new red blood cells. Later in fetal life, the spleen takes on the function of producing red blood cells, and only later still does the bone marrow of the fetus become highly specialized for this work and do most of it. At birth red blood cell production usually is limited to bone mar-

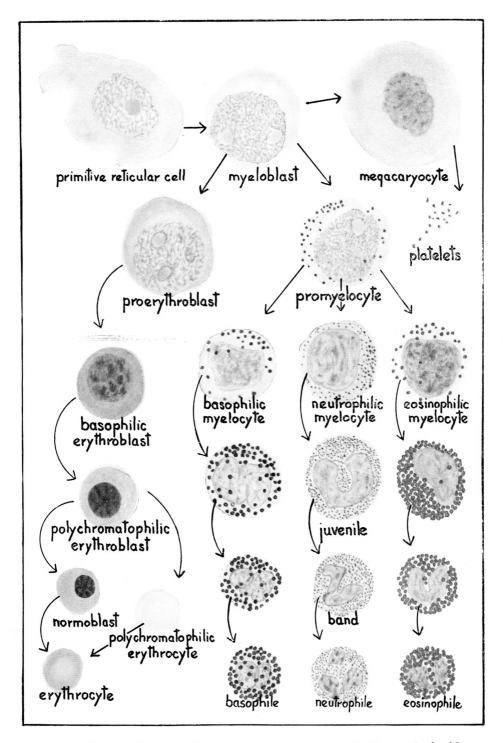

FIG. 225. The normal, free cells of marrow as they appear in films stained with a Romanovsky-type stain (Hastings).

row, but the distribution of red marrow is more extensive in the bones of the newborn than in the adult.

Support for the intravascular theory was provided by Doan, who studied the blood vessels of the marrow of birds by starving the birds. This tends to convert red marrow into fatty marrow. Then, when feeding is resumed (Doan, Cunningham and Sabin), fatty mar-

row becomes gelatinous in character; then, shortly afterward, as feeding is continued, red cell production begins, and this, for a time, is not accompanied by the production of granular leukocytes. By these methods Doan and his associates have obtained a fairly clear view of the vascular pattern of marrow and the relation of the blood vessels to red blood cell formation. Doan describes the nutrient artery

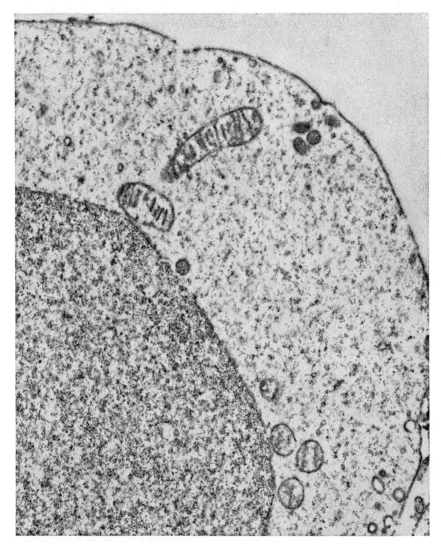

FIG. 226. Electron micrograph (× 32,000) of part of a section of a proerythroblast obtained from human bone marrow. The granular nucleus is at the lower left. The cytoplasm contains a few mitochondria of different sizes. There are only a few membranous vesicles and these tend to be rounded (*lower right*). RNA granules are spread diffusely through the cytoplasm; these account for diffuse basophilia. Compare with Figure 227. (Preparation by A. F. Howatson and E. A. McCulloch)

of the marrow as dividing into two main branches that are directed toward each end of the bone. These branch and from the branches of the third and the fourth orders, capillaries, which he terms "transition capillaries," are given off. These open into a network of venous sinusoids which in turn drain into veins. Doan finds the number of sinusoids so great in marrow that it would be impossible for them all to be open simultaneously. Many of them normally are collapsed, and in this state they resemble capillaries.

Doan, from injection experiments, does not find that the sinusoids of bone marrow have sievelike walls; instead he thinks they are lined with continuous endothelium. Both Sabin and Doan believe that the endothelium of these sinusoids is erythrogenic; that is, it gives rise to red cells. Moreover, they indicate that erythrogenesis occurs primarily in the collapsed sinusoids. Since these resemble capillaries, they are termed erythrogenic capillaries. The lining cells of these are described as dividing, with the innermost cells resulting from the divisions becoming free and rounded. These take up a position close to the endothelium from which they were derived. In birds, these free cells that develop from the endothelial cells are termed *megaloblasts*. These are large cells possessing characteristics not unlike those we have described for proerythroblasts. Megaloblasts are said to be not so common in mammalia; here the endothelial cells of the erythrogenic capillaries give rise more commonly to basophilic erythroblasts. Toward the more central part of the

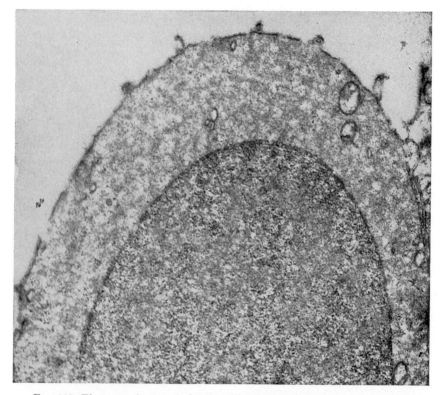

FIG. 227. Electron micrograph ($\times$ 32,000) of part of a section of a polychromatophilic erythroblast from normal human bone marrow. Observe that the chromatin is becoming clumped and dense. Only a very few mitochondria are visible in the cytoplasm and they do not appear to be healthy. Membranous vesicles also are very few in number. The cytoplasm is thoroughly infiltrated with pale finely granular material which is hemoglobin. RNA granules are becoming few in number at this stage of development. (Preparation by A. F. Howatson and E. A. McCulloch)

capillaries the erythroblasts give rise to polychromatophilic erythroblasts and normoblasts. As hemopoiesis occurs, an erythrogenic capillary gradually becomes swollen with cells. When the cells contained in it become mature, the capillary becomes opened to the circulation, and its contents are swept away. An erythrogenic capillary restored to the circulation becomes an open sinusoid. Therefore, sinusoids are regarded as alternating between open and collapsed states, being erythrogenic in the latter. The intravascular theory of red blood cell formation permits one to conceive of a mechanism whereby nonmotile red cells are formed and delivered into the circulation without having to pass through the walls of sinusoids. However, as has been mentioned already, Pease, in his studies with the E/M, finds no evidence of the existence of these erythrogenic capillaries in the mammals that he has studied.

The Control of Erythropoiesis. The bone marrow can respond to a lack of red cells in peripheral blood by increasing its production of erythrocytes. Under normal conditions the rate of production and liberation of erythrocytes by the marrow evenly matches the rate of their destruction by the reticuloendothelial system, so the normal level of red cells in the circulation is maintained. If the number of red cells in blood is reduced, as a result either of hemorrhage or of their being destroyed at an increased rate, the marrow can increase its production up to 10 times in order to maintain the balance. The method by which this matter is regulated is only partly understood. However, it is certain that anoxia (lack of oxygen) increases red cell production, for people who live at high altitudes, where the air is thin, have unusually high erythrocyte counts. However, it is doubtful if changes in oxygen content of the blood that reaches marrow could provide a regulation as fine as that which must exist. There is now much evidence that anoxia stimulates erythopoiesis in the marrow indirectly by its secretion, causing an increase in the formation of a substance called *erythropoietin*, which is the agent that directly stimulates red cell production. Convincing evidence of the existence of this factor was provided by an experiment in which parabiotic pairs (a parabiotic pair is a pair with joined circulations) of rats were placed in chambers so that one of the pair breathed normal air, and the other air with only 8 per cent oxygen. Both animals of each pair developed hyperplasia of their red marrow.

Where erythropoietin comes from is not known. The pituitary gland has been implicated but it cannot be the only source.

Anemia. An understanding of the factors described above is essential to the systematic investigation of anemia, for in anemia the balance between production and destruction has been disturbed, and the number of cells in the blood becomes reduced. This may result from blood loss or an increased rate of destruction of erythrocytes or from some failure of the marrow to produce erythrocytes. For example, if the marrow is destroyed, or replaced by some other kind of tissue, it will be unable to produce cells, and anemia develops. Or, if red marrow is available, but if a sufficient supply of raw materials for the manufacture of cells is not, the marrow cannot produce enough cells. This happens in *pernicious anemia*; in this condition the marrow does not receive enough vitamin B_{12}. Only minute quantities (about 1 gamma or .000001 G) of this vitamin are required daily. However, for this to be absorbed from the food, a specific substance, probably a mucopolysaccharide, must be secreted by the stomach. Certain individuals seem unable to secrete this latter material and so are unable to absorb sufficient B_{12} from their intestine. The role of B_{12} is that of a coenzyme in the biosynthesis of nucleic acid; it is needed for the formation of DNA and RNA. Under these conditions of a B_{12} deficiency, cell production in the marrow is slowed, and such cells as are produced, in the erythrocyte series, are larger than normal, and the chromatin of their nuclei remains finely granular, even after their cytoplasm accumulates hemoglobin. The cells that develop under these conditions, which are comparable with the proerythroblasts seen under normal conditions, are called *megaloblasts*, and, in the absence of B_{12}, the whole family of erythrogenic cells that arise from these are larger than normal; the terms early, intermediate and late megaloblasts are used for these cells. When these cells eventually lose their nuclei and appear in the blood stream, they are larger than normal (Fig. 103, *right*), and the anemia is described as a macrocytic anemia.

Curiously enough, the mother cells of the red blood cell series that are present in early embryonic life are similar to the megaloblasts that appear in pernicious anemia. This has led some hematologists to consider the megaloblast as a normal cell. However, it seems best to consider the megaloblast a normal cell only for embryos, for in postnatal life the widespread replacement of proerythroblasts by megaloblasts in the marrow, and the appearance of the latter cells' progeny in the blood stream, indicates that the marrow is deficient in some material required for the building of normal protoplasm.

When the number of red cells in the blood dwindles in some kinds of anemic states, it is common for the bone marrow to discharge the nucleated, developing forms of blood cells into the circulation. Hence, normoblasts, erythroblasts and even younger forms may be detected in blood films made from patients with at least certain kinds of severe anemias. In pernicious anemia, as has been explained already, the immature nucleated cells of the red blood cell series that appear are larger than usual.

Iron is an ingredient of hemoglobin, hence hemoglobin cannot be made without iron. Under normal conditions, the body is very economical of iron and uses that obtained from old, worn-out red cells in the synthesis of hemoglobin in new ones. But, under certain conditions, the body may suffer from a deficiency of iron, and as a result an iron-deficiency anemia can occur. This is commonly of the hypochromic type (Fig. 103, left).

The Formation of Granular Leukocytes (Granulopoiesis) (Subline 2)

The three kinds of granular leukocytes that develop in the reticular mesh of red marrow are all descendants of hemocytoblasts and are produced as a result of differentiation proceeding along what we have termed Subline 2 (see chart). In forming granular leukocytes, the first cell formed along this line of differentiation by the hemocytoblast is now generally termed a myeloblast, and this in turn gives rise to the next type that is known as a promyelocyte (Fig. 225). This cell is very similar in appearance to the myeloblast; indeed, it differs from it only in containing a few granules in its cytoplasm. Some fastidious observers distinguish three kinds of promyelocytes: neutrophilic, eosinophilic and basophilic, depending on whether the few granules in their cytoplasm are violet, red or blue. But this is a very difficult distinction for the student to make because the first granules seen in the cells of this series do not stain so specifically as those that appear in cells farther along in the line. Consequently, the student is not advised to try to distinguish three kinds of promyelocytes in bone marrow films or imprints. It is enough to identify cells that closely resemble myeloblasts but which have a few granules in their cytoplasm.

The second step in differentiation along Subline 2 is represented by the formation of myelocytes from promyelocytes. This step involves changes in both the nuclei and the cytoplasm of the cells and a slight reduction in their size (Fig. 225). Whereas the nucleus of the promyelocyte is only slightly indented (like that of the myeloblast), the nucleus of the myelocyte exhibits a moderate degree of indentation. Furthermore, the chromatin of the nucleus is more condensed. Hence, the nucleus stains somewhat more darkly than the nucleus of the myeloblast or the promyelocyte. But the nuclei of the cells seen along Subline 2 do not stain nearly so darkly as those seen along Subline 1 (the red blood cell route). The cytoplasm of the myelocyte in which the granules lie is not so basophilic as that of myeloblasts and promyelocytes and is inclined to take on a pale-red color with blood stains. Generally, a cell is not called a myelocyte unless it has at least a dozen granules in its cytoplasm. However, myelocytes may be loaded with granules. Moreover, at this stage of development, the granules may be identified as being neutrophilic, eosinophilic or basophilic; hence, there are three kinds of myelocytes (Fig. 225). Students, particularly those with deficient color vision, should remember, as has been described previously for the three kinds of granular leukocytes, that the three kinds of granules differ from one another in size and shape as well as in their color.

The three kinds of myelocytes form the three kinds of granular leukocytes (Fig. 225). Some authors describe an intermediate metamyelocyte stage. The changes that occur in the nucleus of a neutrophilic myelocyte as it becomes a neutrophilic leukocyte are not precisely the same as those that occur in the nucleus of an eosinophilic myelocyte as it becomes an eosinophilic leukocyte, and these in turn are not precisely the same as those that occur in the nucleus of a basophilic myelocyte as it becomes a basophilic leukocyte. Consequently, the formation of the three kinds of leukocytes from the three kinds of myelocytes will be described separately.

Formation of Neutrophilic Leukocytes. A fairly mature neutrophilic myelocyte (neutrophilic metamyelocyte) has an indented nucleus, and its cytoplasm contains a goodly complement of fine, violet granules. Although cells of this type are confined to bone marrow under normal conditions, they may appear in the circulating blood when the body is reacting to an infection. When detected in blood films, they are called *juvenile neutrophils* (Fig. 108). Normally, however, the nucleus of this cell undergoes certain changes before the cell is liberated into the blood stream. Essentially, this change is brought about by an increasing indentation of the nucleus so that it becomes somewhat darker and assumes the shape of a thin horseshoe. Folding of the horseshoe-shaped nucleus may produce still other appearances. A cell containing such a nucleus is known as a *band* or *filamented* neutrophil (Figs. 106, 108 and 225). Some neutrophils are released from the bone marrow under normal conditions at this stage of development. But further nuclear changes occur before most neutrophils are released. Essentially, these are due to the long, then horseshoe-shaped nucleus developing constrictions at one or more points. This causes the chromatin to become somewhat more dense, hence it stains more deeply. At the sites of a constriction, the nucleoplasm is reduced to a thin thread, and sometimes this thread becomes broken. Constrictions result in a nucleus having a multilobed appearance. Cells with such nuclei are commonly termed *segmented neutrophils* (Figs. 106, 108 and 225). The degree of lobulation (from 1 to 5 or more lobes) generally is regarded as an index of maturation.

Formation of Eosinophilic Leukocytes. In forming an eosinophilic leukocyte the slightly indented nucleus of the eosinophilic myelocyte generally develops a deep constriction at the metamyelocyte stage of development. This deepens to divide the nucleus of the eosinophil into two lobes that usually remain joined together only by a strand of nucleoplasm (Figs. 106 and 225). As the constriction develops, the chromatin of the nucleus becomes somewhat condensed, and as a result the chromatin takes up a little more stain than the nucleus of a myelocyte. But the condensation of chromatin that occurs is not so great as that which occurs in the neutrophil, hence the nuclei of eosinophils are paler than those of neutrophils.

Formation of Basophilic Leukocytes. In forming a basophilic leukocyte the nucleus of a mature basophilic myelocyte (metamyelocyte) undergoes less change than occurs in the formation of either a neutrophil or an eosinophil. Irregular constrictions may appear in it to give it an irregular outline. But, in general, it does not become broken up into lobes to the same extent as neutrophils or eosinophils. Since its chromatin does not become condensed, it stains only very lightly. In contrast, its granules stain deeply, and as a result those that lie in the cytoplasm that is spread over the nucleus tend to obscure it (Fig. 225).

The Fine Structure of Cells Involved in Granulocytopoiesis. The E/M appearance of the cells of bone marrow have been investigated on this continent particularly by Pease, Howatson and McCulloch and De Marsh and Kautz and in Europe by Bessey and Bernhard.

The hemocytoblast (myeloblast) has prominent nucleoli. The mitochondria are large, and the Golgi apparatus is well developed. Although the cytoplasm contains numerous RNA granules the membranous vesicles of the cytoplasm are not particularly well developed at the hemocytoblast stage, so most of the granules are spread diffusely through the cytoplasm rather than being attached to membranous vesicles. As the cell becomes first a promyelocyte and then a myelocyte, rough-surfaced membranous vesicles become very much more numerous; this development seems to be associated with the synthesis of granules. Many of the rough-surfaced vesicles are of about the same size as the granules, and this, of course, gives some suggestion that the specific granules of the cells of the granulocyte series are synthesized inside rough-surfaced vesicles (Fig. 228). Another view is that specific gran-

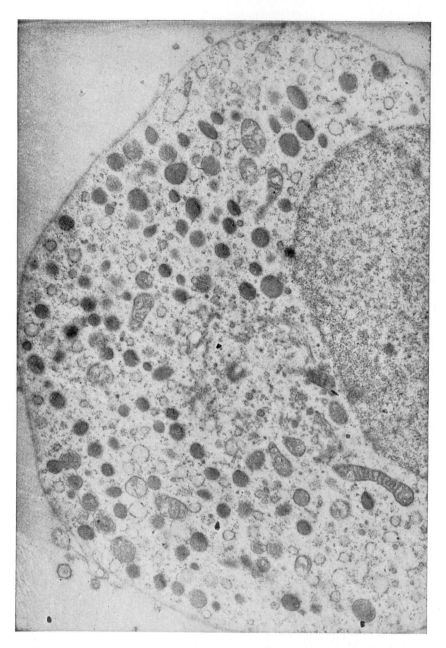

Fig. 228. Electron micrograph (× 29,000) of part of a section of a neutrophilic myelocyte obtained from the bone marrow of an individual with pernicious anemia. The finely granular nucleus can be seen on the right. The cytoplasm shows a well-developed Golgi apparatus to the left of the nucleus, a little below the middle of the picture. A moderate number of mitochondria can be seen in the cytoplasm. Moreover, the cytoplasm contains a large number of rounded rough-surfaced membranous vesicles as well as many specific granules of about the same size and shape. Both the vesicles and the granules vary in size. RNA granules, as well as being distributed around the membranous vesicles, are also spread throughout the cytoplasm. (Preparation by A. F. Howatson and E. A. McCulloch)

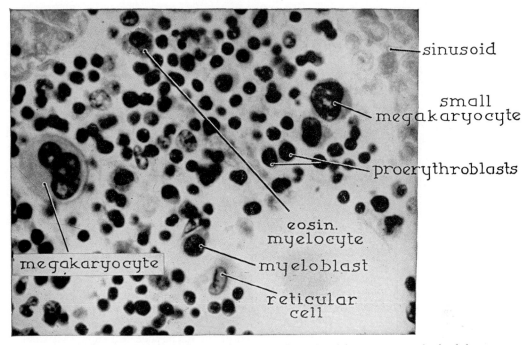

FIG. 229. High-power photomicrograph of a section of red bone marrow obtained from an infant. The cells in this specimen are less tightly packed than is usual, and in this photograph a primitive reticular cell, a myeloblast, some megakaryocytes and a myelocyte can be distinguished. The smaller nuclei are those of erythroblasts and normoblasts.

ules represent transformed mitochondria. At this time the origin of specific granules of these cells cannot be settled definitely. The Golgi apparatus is still well developed at the myelocyte stage (Fig. 228). The specific granules of developing neutrophils vary in size and in their affinity for osmium tetroxide and hence in their density (Fig. 228). The specific granules that appear in developing eosinophils, which may contain dense disklike bodies, have already been described in the chapter on blood. Pease has described the granules of basophils as seeming to have a laminated structure, but he notes that these granules are particularly difficult to fix.

About the time that the cells are developing specific granules in their cytoplasm, the nucleoli disappear from their nuclei. Furthermore, after the granules are formed, both the rough-surfaced membranous vesicles and the mitochondria in the cytoplasm become much fewer in number. RNA granules scattered throughout the cytoplasm persist.

Some General Principles Useful for Identifying Different Types of Marrow Cells. The more primitive stem cells of marrow (blast cells) have large nuclei which are colored a red-purple color with Wright's stain. The chromatin granules in these nuclei are *fine* and *evenly dispersed,* and *several pale blue* nucleoli are generally present. The cytoplasm is a pale to a moderate shade of blue and contains no granules.

Along the erythrocyte line of development the cells become increasingly smaller. The nuclei become smaller and darker with increasingly condensed chromatin, and the nucleoli are lost. The cytoplasm at first becomes more basophilic but later becomes polychromatophilic as hemoglobin forms in it. Eventually it becomes acidophilic as the RNA is lost from it in the final stages of development. Lastly, the nucleus is extruded.

Along the granulocyte line of development the primitive cell becomes only somewhat smaller. The striking feature of development

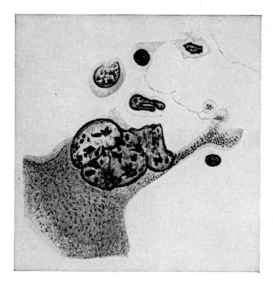

FIG. 230. A black-and-white photograph of one of Wright's colored illustrations of the appearance of megakaryocytes forming platelets in a section of the bone marrow of a kitten, stained with Wright's special stain. The picture shows a pseudopodium extending through a thin-walled blood vessel and liberating 2 platelets. (Wright, J. H.: J. Morphol. *21*:263)

along this line is the appearance of granules in the cytoplasm. The first granules that form cannot be identified as neutrophilic, eosinophilic or basophilic. As development proceeds the three types of granules can be distinguished by their size and staining reactions. As neutrophils and eosinophils mature, that is when they have become well-filled with their specific granules, nucleoli can no longer be seen in their nuclei. But of even greater importance is the fact that as these cells mature their nuclei become increasingly indented and finally lobulated. Hence, a glance at the shape of their nuclei enables one to judge their degree of maturity. Cells of the basophilic series are identified by the fact that they contain large irregular basophilic granules and that these tend to overshadow the nucleus.

MEGAKARYOCYTES AND THE FORMATION OF PLATELETS (SUBLINE 3)

It is generally believed that hemocytoblasts differentiate along a third subline to form megakaryocytes (cells so-called because they possess great nuclei), and that these cells give rise to the platelets of the blood.

Both sections and imprints of red marrow are usually employed for the study of megakaryocytes. The student is advised to become familiar with the appearance of these cells in sections before he tries to identify them in imprints.

In H and E sections of red marrow, studied with the low-power objective, megakaryocytes appear as huge cells scattered throughout the marrow (Fig. 229). Under high power each one can be seen to be many times the size of a hemocytoblast (Fig. 229). The nucleus is colored a deep blue with hematoxylin. The nucleus of a megakaryocyte may be ovoid in shape or it may be lobulated in a fashion reminiscent of the nucleus of the segmented neutrophil. Since the nucleus is so large, a megakaryocyte with a lobulated nucleus may, at the first focus at which it is examined, seem to be a multinucleated cell. But careful focusing of the microscope will show that what at first appear to be separate nuclei are in reality connected to one another. Since osteoclasts are sometimes present in marrow, and are of an order of size comparable to megakaryocytes, this test (focusing) may be used to help tell the two cells apart because osteoclasts (Fig. 175) are truly multinucleated cells. The cytoplasm of megakaryocytes seen in H and E sections is pink and of an even texture. Some cells have large amounts of it but others have scarcely any.

In imprints of bone marrow stained with blood stains, megakaryocytes are not very sharply outlined. Their nuclei are a deep blue-purple color and their cytoplasm is pale blue (Fig. 225). It may be stippled with fine granules that may be colored anywhere from red to blue.

It was not until 1906 that evidence was obtained suggesting that megakaryocytes manufacture platelets. At that time Wright devised a special strain (a variation of the polychrome methylene blue and eosin mixture) and stained thin sections of red marrow, particularly that of kittens and puppies, with it. He observed that megakaryocytes not commonly extended cytoplasmic pseudopodia into the sinusoids of the marrow and further that the cytoplasmic pseudopodia stained identically with platelets in that the red granules of the pseudopodia resembled the granular chromatomere of the platelet and that the substance of the pseudopodia stained similarly to the hyalomere of the platelet (Fig. 230). Moreover, he pointed out that only those animals that possess megakaryocytes have platelets. Many observers have since shown that in certain diseased states there is a rela-

tion between the number of platelets in the blood and the number of megakaryocytes in the marrow.

Final proof that platelets are detached portions of megakaryocyte cytoplasm has come from E/M studies. The study of platelets with the E/M, as was explained in Chapter 10, revealed that each is surrounded by a "cell"

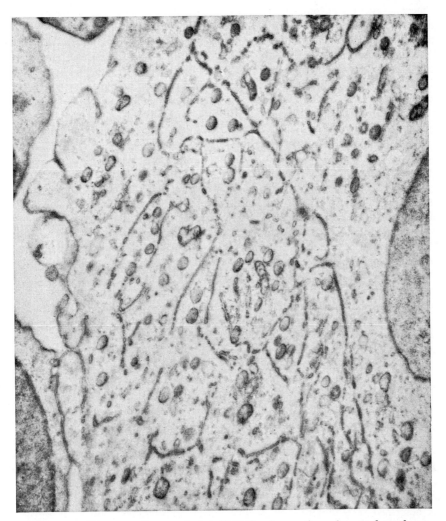

FIG. 231. Electron micrograph ($\times$ 21,000) of a section of normal rat bone marrow. Most of the field is occupied by megakaryocyte cytoplasm; a portion of the nucleus is at the right, and the cell membrane is at the left. Between the two, the cytoplasm is being divided up into compartments by a great development of flattened smooth-surfaced membranous vesicles which are mostly so flattened that they appear as single lines at this magnification. In a few sites their double nature is apparent. Each small compartment of cytoplasm separated off by membranes in this fashion will become a platelet, and each, like a platelet, contains a few mitochondria and some specific granules. Compare with Figure 116, which shows a platelet at higher magnification. (Preparation by W. Bernhard)

membrane. Studies of megakaryocyte cytoplasm, made with the E/M, have shown how each fragment of cytoplasm could become completely surrounded with a "cell" membrane while the cytoplasm from which the fragments become detached could remain covered with a cell membrane, as will now be explained.

Yamada, in 1955, described how the cytoplasm of megakaryocytes becomes divided up into small compartments by an extensive development within the cytoplasm of smooth-surfaced membranous structures. In Chapter 4 we described how smooth-surfaced membranous vesicles probably form directly under the cell membrane by means of invaginations of the cell membrane becoming pinched off within the cytoplasm. It seems that in megakaryocytes vesicles of this nature are very extensive and become greatly flattened within the cytoplasm; indeed, the vesicles become so flattened that they appear as double and sometimes even as single membranes (Fig. 231). These double membranes develop so extensively that they demarcate tiny areas of cytoplasm, each of which is to become a platelet (Fig. 231). Such demarcated portions of cytoplasm as abut on the cell surface would be covered on their outer aspect by the cell membrane, and on all other surfaces by double membranes. All that would be needed for such a superficial portion of cytoplasm to become detached, and so become a platelet, would be for separation to occur between the two layers of the double membrane. One layer of the latter then would provide a covering for the platelet, and the other, which would remain attached to the megakaryocyte, would become its cell membrane. It seems probable that this is the way that platelets form, why each is covered with a continuous membrane and why the megakaryocyte continues to be covered with a cell membrane when platelets break away from it.

As was described in Chapter 10, platelets have specific granules in them and these probably are responsible for the staining of the chromatomere. These specific granules are to be seen in the cytoplasm in megakaryocytes, and each developing compartment has a quota of them (Fig. 231).

Megakaryocytes often exhibit blebs on their surface (Fig. 231), and it might be thought that these blebs would be extruded to constitute platelets. But the blebs commonly do not contain the specific granules, so it seems improbable that they become platelets. All the evidence suggests that platelets develop from the portions of cytoplasm that become separated into compartments by the development of intracytoplasmic smooth-surfaced flattened membranous vesicles.

OTHER CELLS IN BONE MARROW

Lymphocytes. Yoffey's extensive studies suggest that many lymphocytes are filtered out of the blood stream in the bone marrow, and for this reason lymphocytes are relatively common members of the marrow cell population. It should be emphasized that lymphocytes are not normally produced in bone marrow but in lymphatic tissue, as will be explained in the next chapter.

Yoffey has suggested that the function of lymphocytes in the marrow is to serve as stem cells for the production of other types of blood cells. This matter was discussed in Chapter 8, and it was indicated that this concept probably would require a considerable amount of confirmation before it was accepted. Another possible function of lymphocytes in the bone marrow might be to provide, through their nuclei, structural elements for the formation of the many new nuclei that are produced by mitosis in this very active tissue.

Plasma Cells, Mast Cells and Monocytes. All these cells are not uncommon in normal marrow. All the evidence points to the fact that the plasma cells and the mast cells of normal marrow are produced there, probably by the lines of differentiation indicated in Figure 144. It seems probable that some of the monocytes of marrow come there from other sites in the body, and also that some are produced in bone marrow from hemocytoblasts.

Fat Cells. The fat cells of bone marrow doubtless arise from cells that are differentiating along Main Line 1. It seems probable that a cell anywhere along this line could differentiate into one.

THE STUDY OF BONE MARROW IN CLINICAL MEDICINE

The diagnosis of many diseases is facilitated by studying the cells of the affected person's bone marrow. Red bone marrow is soft to semifluid in consistency; hence, it is possible

FIGURE 232

BONE MARROW*
(NORMAL: HYPERLASTIC: APLASTIC)

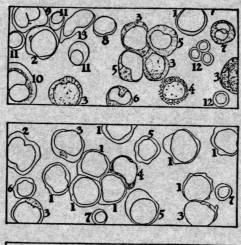

Top: Normal Bone Marrow:
1. Myeloblast
2. Premyelocyte
3. Neutrophilic myelocytes
4. Eosinophilic myelocyte
5. Juvenile neutrophils
6. Band neutrophil
7. Segmented neutrophil
8. Lymphocyte
9. Monocyte
10. Megakaryocyte
11. Macroblasts
12. Normoblasts
13. Primitive free cell (?)

* Drawn from serum spread

Center: Hyperplastic Bone Marrow with Maturation Arrest at Myeloblastic Level (from Patient with Acute Myeloblastic Leukemia):
1. Myeloblasts
2. Myeloblast in division
3. Premyelocytes
4. Myelocyte
5. Megaloblasts
6. Macroblast
7. Normoblasts

Bottom: Aplastic Bone Marrow (from Patient with Aplastic Anemia):
1. Lymphocytes
2. Primitive free cell (?)
3. Degenerating cells

FIGURE 232

BONE MARROW*

(NORMAL: HYPERPLASTIC: APLASTIC)

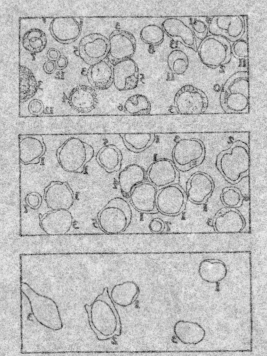

Top: Normal Bone Marrow
1. Myeloblast
2. Premyelocyte
3. Neutrophilic myelocytes
4. Eosinophilic myelocyte
5. Juvenile neutrophils
6. Band neutrophil
7. Segmented neutrophil
8. Lymphocyte
9. Monocyte
10. Megakaryocyte
11. Macroblasts
12. Normoblasts
13. Primitive free cell (?)

* Drawn from serum spread

Center: Hyperplastic Bone Marrow with Maturation Arrest at Myeloblastic Level (from Patient with Acute Myeloblastic Leukemia):
1. Myeloblasts
2. Myeloblast in division
3. Premyelocytes
4. Myelocyte
5. Megaloblasts
6. Macroblast
7. Normoblasts

Bottom: Aplastic Bone Marrow (from Patient with Aplastic Anemia):
1. Lymphocytes
2. Primitive free cell (?)
3. Degenerating cells

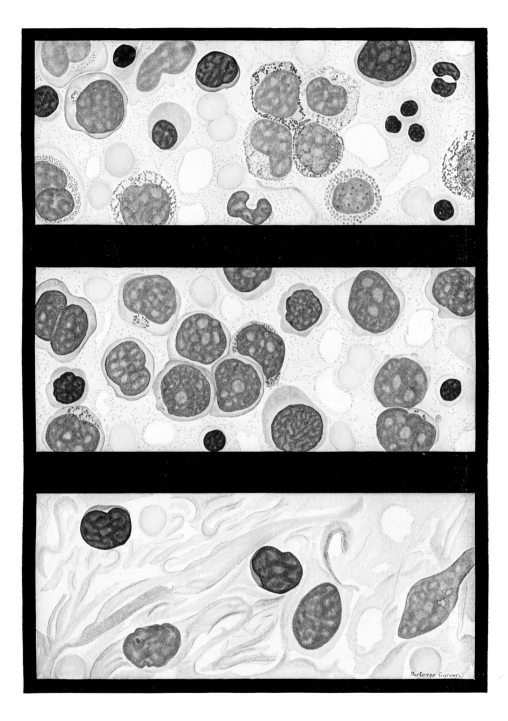

Hortense Garver.

to aspirate it from certain sites. Commonly, bone marrow is obtained in the clinic by means of a *sternal puncture*. Sometimes it is obtained from an iliac crest. Other sites may be utilized, particularly in children.

Bone marrow so obtained generally is studied by means of making films or imprints of it and staining these with blood stains. As was explained in Chapter 8, the cells of marrow can also be concentrated and sectioned.

The student will find that in most hospital laboratories a particular terminology and a particular chart of the percentage distribution of the different cells in marrow are employed. Therefore, we shall make only a few general comments on the cells that are seen in a preparation of normal marrow, such as the one illustrated in Figure 232, *top*.

Few myeloblasts (labeled 1) are present. Promyelocytes (labeled 2) are more numerous. Myelocytes and metamyelocytes (labeled 3-4) are the most numerous of all cells. Granular leukocytes are fairly numerous, and, as might be expected, neutrophils (labeled 5, 6 and 7) are more numerous than acidophils, and acidophils are more numerous than basophils. Cells of the red blood series (labeled 11-12) are fairly numerous, and the more highly differentiated ones (normoblasts) are much more numerous than the less differentiated ones (proerythroblasts and erythroblasts). A few lymphocytes (labeled 8) and monocytes (labeled 9) may be present, as well as an occasional megakaryocyte (labeled 10).

The way that the bone marrow picture, as seen in films, becomes altered in disease will now be illustrated by two examples.

Myeloid Leukemia. Leukemia is a disease characterized by a great overproduction of leukocytes. One main kind is termed myeloid or myelogenous leukemia; in this type, leukocytes from myeloid tissue are overproduced.

Myeloid leukemia occurs in what are described as acute or chronic forms. In the acute and generally rapidly fatal form, the bone marrow becomes very overactive in producing granular leukocytes and pours these into the blood stream, where their numbers may become increased up to 60 or even more times. The production and the liberation of leukocytes is so rapid that many immature forms appear in the blood (band neutrophils, juve-

nile neutrophils [metamyelocytes], myelocytes and even myeloblasts). Many of the leukocytes leave the blood to infiltrate tissues; this often crowds the tissues that they infiltrate and causes damage in them. The production of leukocytes in the marrow generally becomes so extensive that cells of the erythrocyte series and megakaryocytes are literally crowded out of the marrow; hence, anemia and thrombocytopenia tend to develop in the later stages of the disease, and the latter defect leads to hemorrhages. An examination of the bone marrow in this condition shows a greatly increased percentage of myeloblasts and a general shift toward increased numbers of immature cells in the granular leukocyte series (Fig. 232, *center*).

Aplastic Anemia. The former example is one of an overproductive bone marrow. There are other conditions in which the bone marrow becomes underproductive. For example, there are certain toxic chemicals which, if absorbed by the body in sufficient amounts, literally destroy cell activity in the marrow, and it becomes unable to produce blood cells and platelets in sufficient numbers. In this condition the numbers of erythrocytes, granular leukocytes and platelets in the blood all become reduced. An examination of the bone marrow reveals the reason; films show that it contains only very few cells (Fig. 232, *bottom*).

REFERENCES

MYELOID TISSUE—GENERAL REFERENCES

Bessis, M.: Cytology of the Blood and Blood-forming Organs, translated by E. Ponder, New York, Grune, 1956.

Diggs, L. W., Sturm, D., and Bell, A.: The Morphology of Human Blood Cells, Philadelphia, Saunders, 1956.

Downey, H.: Handbook of Hematology, New York, Hoeber, 1938.

Root, W. S. (ed.): Hematopoietic mechanisms, Ann. New York Acad. Sc. *77*:407-820, 1959.

(*See also* References for Chapters 7, 8 and 9)

SPECIAL REFERENCES ON FORMATION OF RED BLOOD CELLS AND GRANULAR LEUKOCYTES

Ackerman, G. A., and Bellios, N. C.: A study of the morphology of the living cells of blood and bone marrow in vital films with the phase contrast microscope: I. Normal blood and bone marrow, Blood *10*:3, 1955.

————: A study of the morphology of the living cells of blood and bone marrow in supravital films with the phase contrast microscope: II. Blood and bone marrow from various hematologic dyscrasias, Blood 10:1183, 1955.

Astaldi, G., Bernardelli, E., and Rondanelli, E. G.: Proliferation rhythm of primitive embryonic erythroblasts, Acta haemat. 9:1, 1953.

Bloom, W., and Bartelmez, G. W.: Hematopoiesis in young human embryos, Am. J. Anat. 67:21, 1940.

Coleman, D. H., Stevens, A. R., Jr., Dodge, H. T., and Finch, C. A.: Rate of blood regeneration after blood loss, A.M.A. Arch. Int. Med. 92:341, 1953.

Cunningham, R. S., Sabin, F. R., and Doan, C. A.: The development of leukocytes, lymphocytes and monocytes from a specific stem cell in adult tissues, Contrib. Embryol. 16:277, 1925.

Doan, C. A.: Capillaries of bone marrow of the adult pigeon, Bull. Johns Hopkins Hosp. 33:222, 1922.

————: The circulation of the bone marrow, Contrib. Embryol. 14:27, 1922.

————: On the origin and developmental potentialities of blood cells, Bull. New York Acad. Med. 15:668, 1939.

Downey, H.: The myeloblast—its occurrence under normal and pathological conditions and its relations to lymphocytes and other blood cells, Folia haemat. 35:65, 145, 1927.

Erslev, A. J.: Analytical review; physiologic control of red cell production, Blood 10:954, 1955.

Erslev, A. J., and Lavietes, P. H.: Observations on the nature of the erythropoietic serum factor, Blood 9:1055, 1954.

Goldeck, H.: 24-Stunden-rhythmische Blutmauserung bei der Ratte, Acta med. scandinav. (Supp. 278) 145:83, 1953.

Gordon, A. S.: Endocrine influences upon the formed elements of blood and blood-forming organs, Rec. Progr. Hormones Res. 10:339, 1954.

Grant, W. C., and Root, W. S.: Fundamental stimulus for erythropoiesis, Physiol. Rev. 32:449, 1952.

Harris, P. F., Menkin, V., and Yoffey, J. M.: The action of leukocytosis-promoting factor on the blood and bone marrow of the guinea pig, Blood 11:243, 1956.

Hodgson, G., and Tohá, J.: The erythropoietic effect of urine and plasma of repeatedly bled rabbits, Blood 9:299, 1954.

Isaacs, R.: Formation and destruction of red blood cells, Physiol. Rev. 17:291, 1937.

Jacobson, L. O., Plzak, L., Fried, W., and Goldwasser, E.: Plasma factor(s) influencing red cell production, Nature 177:1240, 1956.

Jones, O. P.: Morphologic hematology, Blood (Special Issue), vol. I, 1947.

————: Morphologic, physiologic, chemical and biologic distinction of megaloblasts, Arch. Path. 35:752, 1943.

Jordan, H. E.: Extramedullary blood production, Physiol. Rev. 22:375, 1942.

Osgood, E. E., and Seeman, A. J.: The cellular composition of bone marrow as obtained by sternal puncture, Physiol. Rev. 25:46, 1944.

Piney, A.: The anatomy of bone marrow, Brit. M.J. 2:792, 1922.

Ponder, E., et al.: Some aspects of red cell production and destruction, Ann. New York Acad. Sc., vol. 48, 1947.

Rheingold, J. J., and Wislocki, G. B.: Histochemical methods applied to hematology, Blood 3:641, 1948.

Roofe, P. G., Bingham, H., and Comer, R.: A quantitative study of normal hemopoiesis in the albino rat, Anat. Rec. 121:495, 1955.

Root, W. S.: Stimulus for erythropoiesis, J. Mt. Sinai Hosp. 20:331, 1954.

Sandkühler, S., and Gross, E.: Normal bone marrow total cell and differential values by quantitative analysis of particle smears, Blood 11:856, 1956.

Seip, M.: Humoral factors in regulation of reticulocyte level and erythropoiesis in man, Acta paediat. 44:507, 1955.

————: Liberation of red blood corpuscles from bone marrow into peripheral blood and production of erythrocytes elucidated by reticulocyte investigations, Acta med. scandinav. (Supp. 282) 146:1, 1953.

Steinberg, B., and Hufford, B.: Development of bone marrow in adult animals, Arch. Path. 43:117, 1947.

Thorell, B.: Studies on the formation of cellular substances during blood cell production, Acta med. scandinav. (Supp. 200) 129:1, 1947.

Weicker, H.: Exakt Kriterien des Knochenmarks: Die Mas- und Mengenrelationen der Erythroblasten als Ausdruck der Reifungsund Teilungsgesetze der Erythropoese, Schweiz. med. Wchnschr. 84:245, 1954.

Wislocki, G. B., Bunting, H., and Dempsey, E. W.: Further observations on the chemical cytology of megacaryocytes and other cells of hemopoietic tissue, Anat. Rec. 98:527, 1947.

Wislocki, G. B., and Dempsey, E. W.: Observations of the chemical cytology of normal blood and hemopoietic tissues, Anat. Rec. 96:249, 1946.

Yoffey, J. M., Ancill, R. J., Holt, J. A. G., Owen-Smith, B., and Herdan, G.: A quantitative study of the effects of compound E, compound

F and compound A upon the bone marrow of the guinea pig, J. Anat. *88*:115, 1954.

Special References on Megakaryocytes and Platelets

Campbell, E. W., Small, J., and Dameshek, W.: Metabolic activity of human blood platelets, J. Lab. & Clin. Med. *47*:835, 1956.

Humphrey, J. H.: Origin of blood platelets, Nature *175*:38, 1955.

Pisciotta, A. V., Stefanini, M., and Dameshek, W.: Studies on platelets: X. Morphologic characteristics of megakaryocytes by phase contrast microscopy in normals and in patients with idiopathic thrombocytopenic purpura, Blood *8*: 703, 1953.

Storti, E., Perugini, S., and Soldati, M.: Cytochemical investigations of normal megakaryocytes and platelets, Acta haemat. *10*:144, 1953.

Thiery, J. P., and Bessis, M.: The formation of platelets by megakaryocytes observed in living cells, Compt. rend. Acad. sc. *242*:290, 1956.

Witte, S.: Megakaryozyten und Thrombozytopoese bei der experimentellen thrombozytopenischen Purpura, Acta haemat. *14*:215, 1955.

Wright, J. H.: The histogenesis of the blood platelets, J. Morphol. *21*:263, 1910.

Zajicek, J.: Studies on the histogenesis of blood platelets: I. Histochemical investigations of the acetylcholinesterase activity of megakaryocytes and platelets in different animal species, Acta haemat. *12*:238, 1954; II. Quantitative determination of acetylcholinesterase activity in single megakaryocytes from various mammals, Acta haemat. *15*:296, 1956.

Special References on Fine Structure (Electron Microscopy) of Bone Marrow and Blood Cells

Aleksandrowicz, J.: Les états fonctionnels des plaquettes sanguines, au microscope électronique, Le Sang *25*:67, 1954.

Bernhard, W., Hagenau, F., and Leplus, R.: Coupes ultrafines d'éléments sanguins et de ganglions lymphatiques étudiées au microscope éléctronique, Rev. hémat. *10*:267, 1955.

Bernhard, W., and Leplus, R.: La méthode des coupes ultrafines et son application à l'étude de l'ultrastructure des cellules sanguines, J. Suisse Méd. *85*:897, 1955.

Bernhard, W., Leplus, R., and Elbers, P. E.: Étude de coupes ultrafines de globules rouges humains au microscope électronique, Acta haemat. *11*:265, 1954.

Bessis, M.: Microscopie électronique des cellules du sang, Gassetta Sanitaria *9*:1, 1953.

Bloom, G.: The morphology of human blood platelets and the coagulation of blood in vitro; an electron-microscopical examination, Ztschr. Zellforsch. *42*:365, 1955.

Braunsteiner, H., Fellinger, K., and Pakesch, F.: Elektronmikroskopische Untersuchungen des Knochenmark, Deutches Arch. Klin. Med. *200*:541, 1953.

———: Structural changes in the platelets as observed by electron microscopy, Blood *9*:595, 1954.

Grey, E. C., and Biesele, J. J.: Thin-section electron microscopy of circulating white blood cells, Rev. hémat. *10*:283, 1955.

Howatson, A. F., and McCulloch, E. A.: The fine structure of normal and leukemic marrow cells, Anat. Rec. *124*:460, 1956 (abstr.).

Kautz, J., and De Marsh, Q. B.: An electron microscope study of sectioned cells of peripheral blood and bone marrow, Blood *9*:24, 1954.

———: Electron microscopy of sectioned blood and bone marrow elements, Rev. hémat. *10*: 314, 1955.

Pease, D. C.: An electron microscopic study of red bone marrow, J. Hemat. *11*:501, 1956.

———: Marrow cells seen with the electron microscope after ultrathin sectioning, Rev. hémat. *10*:300, 1955.

Rinehart, J. F.: Electron microscope studies of sectioned white blood cells and platelets, Am. J. Clin. Path. *25*:605, 1955.

Sheldon, H., and Zetterquist, H.: Internal ultrastructure in granules of white blood cells of the mouse; a preliminary note, Bull. Johns Hopkins Hosp. *96*:135, 1955.

Watanabe, Y.: An electron microscope study of the leukocytes in bone marrow of guinea pig, J. Electron Microscopy *2*:34, 1954.

Yamada, E.: Some features of the fine structure of megakaryocytes in the mouse spleen, Anat. Rec. *121*:458, 1955 (abstr.).

Chapter 18

Hemopoietic Tissue
(Continued)

LYMPHATIC TISSUE

Relationship of Its Structure and Function to Myeloid Tissue. Lymphatic tissue is the second, and only other, variety of hemopoietic tissue. Like myeloid tissue, it produces *blood* cells and filters worn-out blood cells and other kinds of particulate matter from the fluids to which it is exposed. With regard to the production of blood cells, the lymphatic tissue of man is restricted in postnatal life to producing lymphocytes and monocytes (the plasma cells it produces are not blood cells). However, in prenatal life, some lymphatic tissue (the spleen) produces other kinds of blood cells as does the lymphatic tissue of some animals in postnatal life. With regard to a filtering function, lymphatic tissue performs a broader function than myeloid tissue. Lymphatic tissue exists in different structural arrangements to filter tissue fluid, lymph and blood, respectively, while myeloid tissue filters only blood. Therefore, lymphatic tissue performs a very important function in preventing undesirable materials that gain entrance to the tissues of the body from reaching the blood stream via tissue fluid and lymph. But, even if they do reach the blood, it helps the myeloid tissue to filter them from it.

In addition to producing *blood* cells and filtering the various fluids of the body lymphatic tissue is highly specialized for producing plasma cells—the cells that are primarily concerned with making antibodies in response to the antigens that gain entrance to the body. The production of plasma cells is, of course, not limited to lymphatic tissue, for they are produced to some extent in loose connective tissue and also in myeloid tissue. It should be emphasized here that plasma cells are *not* a form of blood leukocyte; they do not gain entrance to the circulation under ordinary circumstances but remain in the tissue where they were produced and in this site they give off antibodies which gain entrance to the circulation.

The Basic Structure of Lymphatic Tissue. The structural arrangements in lymphatic tissue are basically very similar to those learned for myeloid tissue because the cells of lymphatic tissue lie in a network of reticular fibers with some of them being attached to the fibers and others existing as free cells in the meshes of the fibers. The delicate reticular fibers of lymphatic tissue can be demonstrated by several different special technics (for example see Fig. 87), and by these technics they are seen to be arranged either in closely knit meshes or loosely knit meshes. Both types are illustrated diagrammatically in Figure 237, *top.* In H and E sections, which are commonly used for the study of lymphatic tissue, the reticular fibers of these meshes are not seen; hence, they must be imagined when H and E sections are being studied. However, occasional collagenic trabeculae, which convey blood vessels into lymphatic tissue and provide support for the reticular meshwork, can be seen in H and E sections.

The various kinds of cells that are supported by the meshes of reticular fibers in lymphatic tissue are all related. The mother cell is the primitive reticular cell; this is sometimes called a reticular cell. The mother cell is attached to the reticular network. The mother cell can divide, and its progeny differentiate along two main lines. Along one line the cells become increasingly specialized for phagocytosis and are called reticuloendothelial cells or macrophages. These cells are generally but not always attached to the reticular network. Along the other line of differentiation the progeny of the mother cells become free cells that are not attached to the mesh but are contained by it. The morphology of both these and reticular cells will be described presently. The first *free* cell to form should be called a

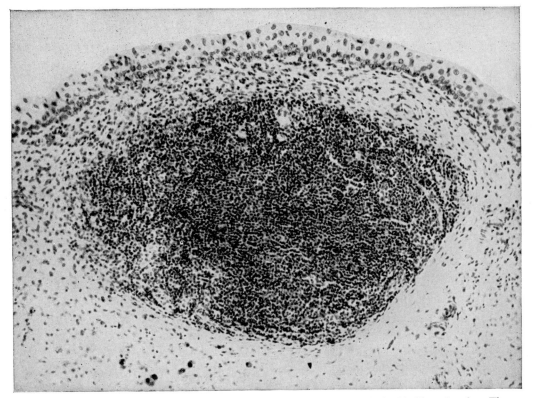

Fig. 233. Low-power photomicrograph of a section of the wall of the bladder of a dog. The surface seen at the upper part of the picture is covered with transitional epithelium. In the connective tissue below this there is an ovoid nodule of lymphocytes. Such nodules are called lymphatic, primary or malpighian nodules.

hemocytoblast because it has great potentiality. However, many authors refer to it as a lymphoblast. This first formed *free cell* can differentiate along three different lines to form eventually lymphocytes, monocytes and plasmoblasts, respectively. The family relationships of all these cells are illustrated in Figure 144.

As has been mentioned already, lymphatic tissue exists in the body in three structural arrangements to filter tissue fluid, lymph and blood, respectively. However, in all of these arrangements we shall find structures known as primary (malpighian) nodules; these are what might be considered the basic units of structure of all lymphatic tissue. Primary nodules are concerned more with the production of cells than with filtering, and although some reticuloendothelial cells for filtering purposes are present within the primary nodules, most of them are outside the nodules. In lymph nodes and the spleen, the reticuloendothelial cells that are outside nodules are disposed in special arrangements for filtering lymph and blood, respectively.

Since the primary nodule is a basic unit of structure of all lymphatic tissue, we shall consider its histologic structure first and then later see how primary nodules are fitted into the various special arrangements of lymphatic tissue.

The Primary Nodule. A primary nodule is roughly spherical and may measure from a few hundred microns to a millimeter or more in diameter (Fig. 233). In an H and E section a primary nodule appears, under low power, as a dark blue area (Fig. 233). Under higher magnification the blue appearance is seen to be due to the nodule's being packed with cells of the lymphocyte series; since these cells have little cytoplasm, there is a great

primary   germinal
nodule   center

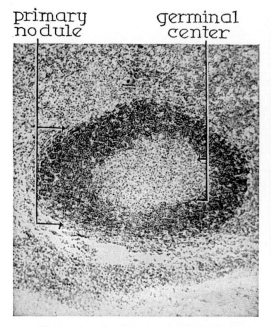

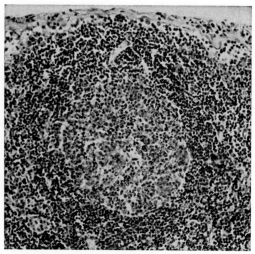

Fig. 234 B. Low-power photomicrograph of a primary nodule that contains a germinal center which is not pale but basophilic. On close inspection it would be seen to contain many mitotic figures (see Fig. 235 for higher-power views of this type of germinal center).

Fig. 234 A. Low-power photograph of a section of a lymph node of a dog, showing a primary nodule. The central part of this contains a pale germinal center.

concentration of nuclei in the nodule; and since the densely packed nuclei are all colored blue, the whole nodule stands out as a rounded blue area. Indeed, the dense blue staining of primary nodules is so obvious when a section is inspected with the naked eye that the student can generally diagnose the presence of lymphatic tissue when he holds a section to the light and does his preliminary inspection of it with the naked eye.

The next point about a primary nodule that should be emphasized is that its periphery is not sharply defined (Fig. 233). The reason for this is that the lymphocytes (and some plasma cells) that are produced in the nodules are pushed out from its periphery into whatever kind of tissue the nodule happens to be in, so at the periphery of the nodule the appearance gradually changes from that of a dense concentration of lymphocytes to a decreasing concentration in the adjacent tissue. Another point that should be made is that lymphatic nodules are *not* encapsulated; they lie naked in whatever tissue they are in. To avoid misunderstanding it should be noted that the *lymph nodes* (that filter lymph) and the *spleen*

(that filters blood) *are* enclosed by connective tissue capsules. However, the primary nodules that lie within these organs are *not* encapsulated.

Germinal Centers. Beginning only in postnatal life, the more central part of a primary nodule commonly but not always takes on a somewhat different appearance from the remainder of the nodule. When this happens the primary nodule is said to have developed a *germinal center.* The germinal center is sometimes referred to as a *secondary nodule*, the secondary nodule being the one that lies within the primary nodule. Under low-power inspection the germinal center is often paler than the remainder of the nodule (Fig. 234, A). However, it often is not; instead, it may be moderately deep blue in color (Fig. 234, B). However, even though it is blue, its appearance differs from the peripheral part of the nodule because the nuclei within it are *fewer* and *farther apart* than in the primary nodule. Much of the deep blue appearance is due not only to the large blue nuclei that are present but also to the fact that many of the cells in the germinal center have considerably

Fig. 235. High-power photomicrographs of somewhat different magnifications of different parts of a mediastinal lymph node of a rat.

A. An active germinal center. Arrows indicate cells in mitosis.

B. A germinal center. Arrow indicates the nucleus of a reticular cell. Note that its cytoplasm is very indistinct.

C. Edge of a germinal center. Arrow indicates a large cell with a ring of basophilic cytoplasm that has a sharp edge. This is a free, rounded cell, either a lymphoblast or a plasmoblast.

D. A medullary cord. Arrows indicate some of the plasma cells that are present. Note the negative Golgi areas in their cytoplasm.

E. A medullary sinusoid. Arrows indicate reticuloendothelial cells.

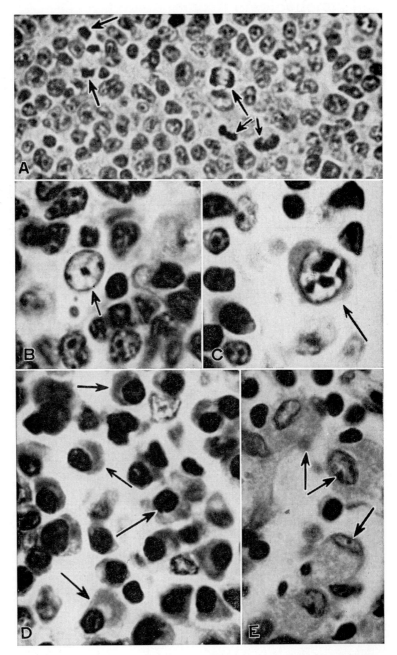

more cytoplasm than ordinary lymphocytes, with this cytoplasm being very basophilic.

Germinal centers, particularly when they demonstrate the basophilia mentioned above, reveal many mitotic figures (Fig. 235) and so are active sites of formation of cells of the lymphocyte and plasma cell series. However, cells of both the lymphocyte and the plasma cell series can be formed in primary nodules that do not have germinal centers. Since it is easier to see the various cells concerned in these lines of differentiation in germinal centers than it is in nodules without germinal centers, it is suggested that the student study a basophilic type of germinal center to see the cell types that will now be described.

The primitive reticular cell can be recognized because only its nucleus can be seen

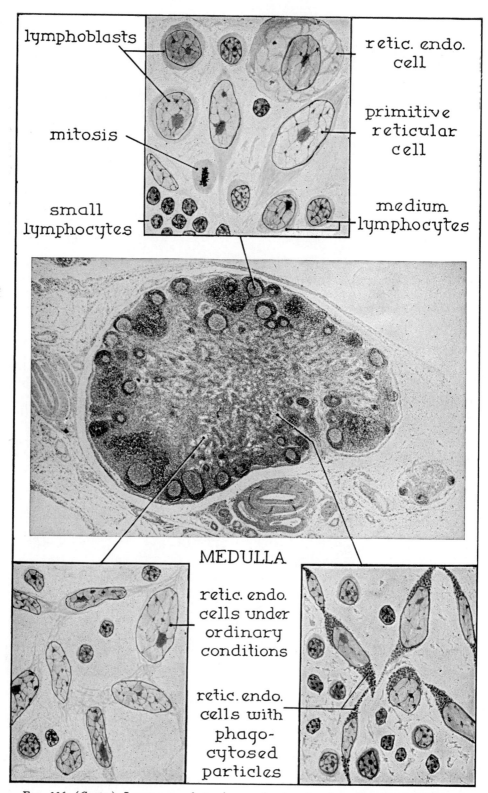

lymphoblasts

retic. endo. cell

mitosis

primitive reticular cell

small lymphocytes

medium lymphocytes

MEDULLA

retic. endo. cells under ordinary conditions

retic. endo. cells with phago-cytosed particles

FIG. 236 (*Center*) Low-power photomicrograph of a lymph node. (*Top*) High-power drawing of cells in germinal center. (*Bottom*) High-power drawings of reticuloendothelial cells in mesh of medulla.

(Figs. 235, 236); such cytoplasm as it has is exceedingly pale and indefinite and, in particular, its edge cannot be determined. The nucleus is oval. The nuclear membrane is thin and hence not heavily stained. A single nucleolus is commonly present, and the chromatin content of the nucleus, being spread over a comparatively large area, because the nucleus is large, shows up poorly (Figs. 235, 236). Having identified the primitive reticular cells by their nuclei, the student should look next for the youngest types of free cells which form from the reticular cells. These can be distinguished because they have nuclei that are as large or almost as large as those of reticular cells, and in addition they have basophilic cytoplasm that has a sharply defined edge (Figs. 235, 236). It is probable that the largest of these cells, which have the palest cytoplasm and the least well-defined edges, are hemocytoblasts, and that the progeny of these which are somewhat smaller and have less but more darkly stained cytoplasm are lymphoblasts and plasmoblasts. The nucleoli of the lymphoblasts and the plasmoblasts are very prominent; this fact is probably related to the fact that RNA, which makes the cytoplasm of these cells so basophilic, is synthesized chiefly in the nucleolus, and as a result the nucleolus is large. Since the plasmoblast will form cells that will have much more RNA in their cytoplasm than the cells that the lymphoblasts will form, it is probable that the cells at this stage that reveal the largest and heavily stained nucleoli are plasmoblasts (Fig. 235) and those that have smaller, multiple and not so deeply stained nucleoli are lymphoblasts (the nucleoli of the latter do not have to make as much RNA as the nucleoli of plasmoblasts).

The two cell types described above divide and some of the progeny of the lymphoblasts become medium-sized lymphocytes (Fig. 236), and some of the progeny of the plasmoblasts become young plasma cells, which can be recognized by their possessing a relatively large amount of basophilic cytoplasm and a tendency for the nucleus to shift to an eccentric position. The medium-sized lymphocytes sometimes enter the circulation as such, either indirectly through lymphatics or directly through blood capillaries. In blood they are termed large lymphocytes. Here again, we must pause to try to prevent confusion about what are termed medium-sized and large lymphocytes. The lymphocytes that are seen in blood are generally referred to as small or large lymphocytes. Those seen in lymph nodes are often referred to as small, medium-sized and large lymphocytes. However, we and many others refer to what some term the large lymphocytes of lymphatic tissue as lymphoblasts; these do not enter the circulation under normal conditions. What we refer to as medium-sized lymphocytes of lymphatic tissue do gain entrance to the blood stream and then they are termed the large lymphocytes of the blood. However, most of these cells remain in nodes for further division and then they give rise to small lymphocytes and these too may enter the circulation either indirectly or directly.

The young plasma cells, after further divisions, give rise to mature plasma cells. The small lymphocytes and the mature plasma cells are most numerous in the peripheral part of the nodule. In lymph nodes we shall see that they both enter medullary cords. The central part of a nodule, whether it has a germinal center or not, contains more of the less differentiated cells, described above, than of the mature cells which always tend to be in the periphery of a nodule.

Neither primary nodules nor germinal centers are necessarily permanent structures; they come and go throughout life. Furthermore, germinal centers pass through phases of activity. A germinal center of the basophilic type, which actively produces cells, may change into one of the pale type, which shows much less mitotic activity and in which reticuloendothelial cells can be seen as is shown in Figure 236.

Having described primary nodules and germinal centers, we shall now describe how these units of lymphatic tissue are disposed in the arrangements which filter tissue fluid, lymph and blood, respectively.

The Different Types of Lymphatic Tissue. As noted before, lymphatic tissue is designed and distributed in the body to filter tissue fluid, lymph and blood. The lymphatic tissue that is designed to filter tissue fluid is somewhat different from that designed to filter lymph and this in turn is somewhat different from that designed to filter blood. The general constitution and distribution of lymphatic tissue designed to filter each of these three body fluids will now be considered.

Character and Distribution of Lymphatic Tissue Designed to Filter Tissue Fluid

A few moments' reflection is enough to make one realize that the tissue fluid formed in certain parts of the body might be contaminated more easily than that formed in others. For example, it is obvious that the tissue fluid formed directly under body surfaces is in much greater danger of being contaminated (from the outside world) than that formed deep within the substance of muscles or organs. Furthermore, it is obvious that the danger of contamination is much greater in the instance of tissue fluid formed directly under wet epithelial surfaces than that formed directly under dry epithelial surfaces because the latter are protected by keratin. Hence, it could be anticipated that the lymphatic tissue designed to filter tissue fluid would be distributed chiefly under those wet epithelial surfaces that are exposed to contamination from the outside world; that is, directly under the epithelium that lines the alimentary canal and, to a lesser extent, that which lines the respiratory and the urinary passages.

The nodules of lymphatic tissue that are distributed under these wet epithelial surfaces are not encapsulated (Fig. 233). Therefore, tissue fluid formed in these sites is able to percolate through the lymphatic tissue with little hindrance before entering either blood or lymphatic capillaries.

Impressive examples of lymphatic tissue situated directly under wet epithelial surfaces and designed to filter the tissue fluid formed, and to produce lymphocytes in that area, and plasma cells to produce antibodies against antigens that gain entrance to the tissue through the epithelial surfaces, are offered by the palatine, the pharyngeal and the lingual tonsils, and by Peyer's patches in the ileum, all of which are large aggregations of lymphatic tissue containing many primary nodules. But the student should not be surprised to see smaller depots of lymphatic tissue under any wet epithelial surfaces. In all these structures some plasma cells will be seen; the purpose of these as noted above is to make antibodies in response to the antigens that percolate into the tissue.

Loose Lymphatic Tissue. Although it is customary to consider lymphatic tissue and loose connective tissue as two different types of connective tissue, it is obvious that nodules of lymphatic tissue that form under wet epithelial surfaces must develop from cells of the loose connective tissue, and hence that cells of the latter have the potentiality to form the cells of the lymphocyte series. Sometimes the potentiality of loose connective tissue for forming cells of lymphatic tissue is not expressed by the formation of true primary nodules but instead by the formation of cells of the lymphocyte series in a less well-organized way, so that a tissue appears that has loose connective tissue as its basis but contains, in addition, many cells of the lymphocyte series. Such a compromise between loose connective tissue and lymphatic tissue is sometimes termed loose lymphatic tissue. However, one must be on guard about designating connective tissue which contains many lymphocytes as loose lymphatic tissue because, under conditions of chronic inflammation, any connective tissue may become infiltrated with lymphocytes that come to the affected part by way of the blood stream. The lymphocytes in such an area represent a reaction against an injurious agent; therefore, such a tissue is not normal and should not be termed loose lymphatic tissue. Accordingly, unless the student can see definite primary nodules in loose connective tissue, he should hesitate when he sees lymphocytes in a diffuse distribution to conclude immediately that he is looking at loose lymphatic tissue, for the lymphocytes may indicate no more than that the connective tissue is the site of a chronic inflammatory process.

In lymph nodes and the spleen lymphocyte-forming and lymphocyte-containing tissue that is not in the form of primary nodules can be spoken of with confidence as loose lymphatic tissue.

Character and Distribution of Lymphatic Tissue Designed to Filter Lymph

As has been described in the section of this book dealing with the formation and the absorption of tissue fluid (Chap. 6), a certain amount of the tissue fluid formed in many parts of the body is drained away by means of lymphatic capillaries (Fig. 92). These begin from blind endings and join with one another to form lymphatic vessels of a larger caliber and with thicker walls. Eventually, these all empty into two main lymphatic trunks—the thoracic duct and the right lymphatic duct. The thoracic duct empties, and so returns the lymph it carries, into the venous system at the point of junction between the left subclavian and the left internal jugular veins. The right lymphatic duct returns the lymph collected by it into the venous system at the point of junction of the right subclavian and the right internal jugular veins. Hence, all the lymph collected in the body is restored to the blood circulatory system to help maintain the fluid content of the blood.

Most of the lymph collected by the lymphatic capillaries of the body, before being returned to the blood circulatory system by the thoracic or right lymphatic duct, passes through one or more little round, oval or bean-shaped structures called *lymph glands* or *nodes*. The student should understand that while the word "gland" means "acorn-shaped," it is used to designate any structure that secretes. Lymph glands may be acorn-shaped but they do not secrete. Since the word "gland" has gradually come to be defined on a physiologic rather than a morphologic basis, and since many lymph glands are not shaped like acorns, they should not be called glands; therefore, we shall refer to them from now on as lymph nodes. However, the student in using this term must be careful to distinguish between nodes and nodules, the latter have been described already.

Lymph nodes are distributed along the various lymphatic vessels that lead to the thoracic or right lymphatic duct. In order to pass through a lymph node, lymph must percolate through a coarse reticular mesh on which many reticuloendothelial cells are suspended (Fig. 237); hence, lymph nodes tend to filter and purify the lymph that flows through them.

Many lymph nodes are situated in the axilla and in the groin. Also, a great many are distributed along the great vessels of the neck, and a considerable number in the thorax and the abdomen, particularly in association with the great vessels and the mesentery. A few are associated with the popliteal vessels, and also a few are at the elbow. In general, then, lymph nodes are distributed, not where lymph

originates (like lymphatic tissue that filters tissue fluid), but rather along the course of the main tributaries that flow into the thoracic and the right lymphatic ducts. Their chief function is to filter the lymph that is picked up by the lymphatic capillaries before it is returned to the blood stream and to produce antibodies in response to the antigens that reach them. They also add lymphocytes to the lymph that flows through them. Once it was believed that they also act to concentrate lymph, but the evidence for this view is not convincing. The problem relating to the recirculation of lymphocytes was discussed in Chapter 8.

The Microscopic Structure of Lymph Nodes. They may be round, ovoid or bean-shaped. They vary greatly in size; some are as small as seeds; others are as large as almonds. Each is said to consist of two main parts: a cortex and a medulla. The cortex (bark) is the outer part, and the medulla (marrow) the inner. Since bean-shaped nodes are common and facilitate description by possessing convex and concave surfaces, in the following we shall describe the intimate structure of a node of this shape.

A lymph node is surrounded by a connective tissue capsule (Figs. 236 and 237). Since lymph nodes commonly lie in fat tissue, some fat usually adheres to the outer part of the capsule (Fig. 237, *bottom*) when they are dissected out for sectioning. This provides an aid in distinguishing between a section of a lymph node and one of spleen (which has a somewhat similar microscopic appearance) because the latter has a smooth peritoneal surface. Lymphatic vessels penetrate the capsule covering the convex aspect of the node (Fig. 237) and leave from the deepest part of the indentation. This area is called the *hilus*. The lymphatic vessels that bring lymph *to* the node are called *afferent lymphatics,* and those that *bring it out* from the node are called *efferent lymphatics*. Both kinds are provided with valves so that the lymph in them cannot pass backward toward its point of origin. Refer to Figure 237 to see these features.

The connective tissue capsule is usually somewhat thicker in the region of the hilus, and in this site it gives rise to trabeculae of connective tissue that extend into the substance of the node to provide support and carry blood vessels (Fig. 237). Trabeculae of

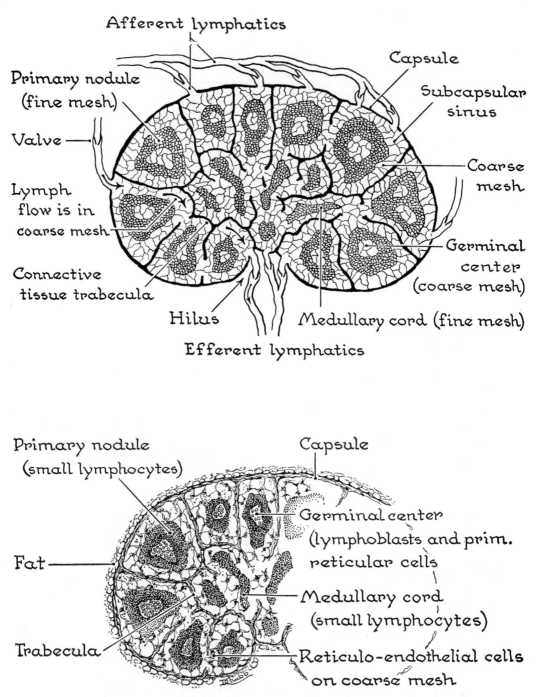

Afferent lymphatics

Primary nodule (fine mesh)

Valve

Lymph flow is in coarse mesh

Connective tissue trabecula

Capsule

Subcapsular sinus

Coarse mesh

Germinal center (coarse mesh)

Hilus

Medullary cord (fine mesh)

Efferent lymphatics

Primary nodule (small lymphocytes)

Capsule

Germinal center (lymphoblasts and prim. reticular cells

Fat

Medullary cord (small lymphocytes)

Trabecula

Reticulo-endothelial cells on coarse mesh

FIG. 237. Diagrams showing the structure of lymph nodes. (*Top*) The framework of the node as it would appear if the lymphocytes were removed from it. (*Bottom*) The distribution of lymphatic nodules, with or without germinal centers, in the node and also the distribution of medullary cords.

connective tissue also extend in from the capsule covering the convex aspect of the node (Fig. 237).

Within the node, a mesh of reticular fibers, on which many reticuloendothelial cells are suspended, extends like a continuous cobweb to fill all the space between the various trabeculae and between them and the capsule. In the cortex, there are rounded areas in which the mesh is finer than it is in the remainder of the cortex (Fig. 237, *top*). These areas of fine mesh constitute the sites of primary nodules (a fine mesh holds small lymphocytes better than a coarse mesh). In the medulla also areas of fine mesh may be seen; these are in the nature of extensions into the medulla of fine mesh from the edges of primary nodules. However, these are not rounded but have an irregular, elongated form and are called *medullary cords* (Fig. 237, *bottom*). Their fine mesh, like that of the lymphatic nodules in the cortex, also tends to hold lymphocytes. The cords commonly branch and anastomose with one another as well as connecting with the primary nodules of the node.

The primary nodules of the cortex are separated from the capsule by a coarse reticular mesh on which many reticuloendothelial cells

are suspended. This zone of coarse mesh is commonly called the *subcapsular sinus* (Fig. 237, *top*). It should be realized that this particular sinus, unlike the sinuses of certain other organs, is not in the nature of a tube with a clear lumen; it is merely a zone of coarse mesh through which fluid can easily percolate. Lymph emptied into it by the afferent lymphatics for the most part seeps deeper into the gland by way of the coarse mesh situated between the primary nodules and the trabeculae or that between primary nodules that are adjacent but not in direct contact with one another. Because primary nodules have a fine mesh and are packed with lymphocytes, their substance does not offer as easy a passage to lymph as does the coarse mesh that surrounds them. On reaching the medulla of the gland,

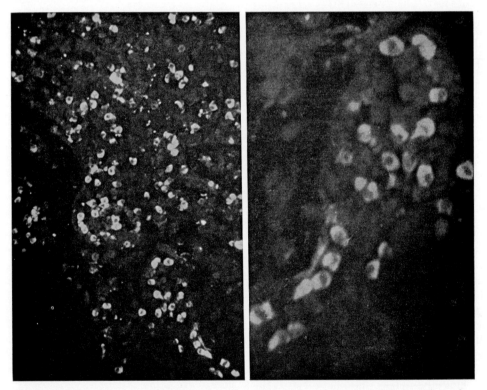

FIG. 238. Low-power and high-power photomicrographs of sections of a portion of a popliteal lymph node of a rabbit after it had received a second injection of diphtheria toxoid. The photomicrographs were taken, not from frozen sections as described in the text, but from paraffin sections prepared by a new method devised by G. Sainte-Marie which permits immunofluorescence studies to be made on this type of section. The photomicrographs were taken using an ultraviolet source of light, and sites where antibody was present appear in the photomicrographs as bright areas. Careful inspection of the picture on the right will show that antibody is present in the cytoplasm of cells which have the characteristic structure of young plasma cells. (Preparation by G. Sainte-Marie)

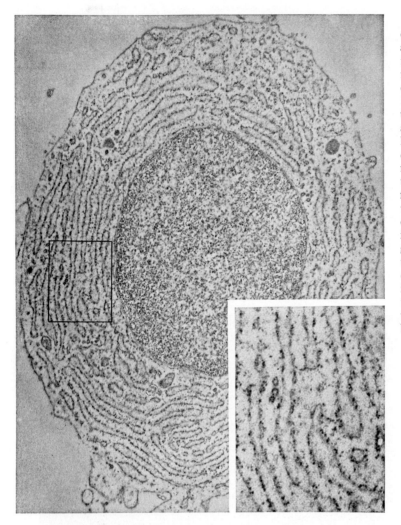

Fig. 239. Electron micrograph of a section of a plasma cell obtained from human bone marrow. The magnification of the main picture is × 20,000 and that of the inset × 48,000. The area from which the enlarged inset was taken is outlined in black in the main picture. Notice the tremendous number of flattened rough-surfaced vesicles in the cytoplasm of the plasma cell; this is characteristic and suggests a function of synthesizing protein for secretion. Also, notice the irregular cell surface and the heavy granulation of the nucleus. (Preparation by A. F. Howatson)

the lymph, for the most part, passes through the coarse mesh disposed between the medullary cords and the trabeculae and finally enters the efferent lymphatics.

There is some difference between the microscopic appearance of lymph nodes taken from different parts of the body. In some nodes the lymph nodules of the cortex are highly developed, and little medulla is apparent. In a section of a node of this type, the student will have difficulty finding medullary cords and typical coarse mesh filtering tissue. In nodes taken from other parts of the body, particularly those from the mesentery, the medulla rather than the cortex is well developed. These should be used for the study of medullary cords. The character of the filtering coarse mesh tissue that lies between them can also be studied to advantage in these.

The microscopic appearance of any given lymph node probably varies from time to time. There is reason to believe that lymphatic nodules are not constant structures, and that old ones disappear, and new ones form in the cortex throughout life. Germinal centers are not present in lymphatic nodules at birth and they are by no means constant structures thereafter. They exhibit different degrees of functional activity under different circumstances. In some instances, germinal centers may be seen that constitute almost the whole of a lymphatic nodule; in other instances they are small, and in still others, absent.

THE FUNCTIONS OF LYMPH NODES

Even a cursory examination of a section of a lymph node suggests that it has two main functions.

Filtering Lymph. First, its architectural arrangements are such that lymph, which enters it by way of the afferent lymphatics (Fig. 239), would percolate most readily through the node via the coarse mesh of reticuloendothelial cells that exist first in the subcapsular sinus, then between the primary nodules of the cortex and, finally, between the medullary cords of the medulla before it entered the efferent lymphatics that leave the hilus. Since the reticuloendothelial cells are phagocytic it is obvious that particulate matter could be strained effectively from lymph during its passage through the node; and indeed, sections of the lymph nodes that filter that lymph that flows from the lungs of city-dwellers commonly contain large accumulations of carbon (smoke) particles that have been phagocytosed from the lymph that flows through them. Figure 238 (*lower right*) illustrates the filtering function of reticuloendothelial cells.

Producing Cells. Secondly, the presence of primary nodules, with or without germinal centers, in the cortex of the nodes, and the very considerable mitotic activity that can be easily observed in primary nodules (Fig. 235, *top*), including their germinal centers, indicates that a second very important function of lymph nodes is the production of cells. These are of two chief types: lymphocytes and plasma cells. The production of lymphocytes has been described in this chapter, and possible functions of lymphocytes were discussed in Chapter 8.

Although some lymphocytes are probably delivered directly into the blood stream, because they pass through the walls of the capillaries of the node, most lymphocytes that enter the blood stream from lymph nodes do so by an indirect route; they are, as it were, washed from the node by the lymph that passes through it and hence leave the node by its efferent lymphatics (Fig. 237). Since the lymphatics eventually drain into the blood circulatory system, the lymphocytes in the lymph from lymph nodes eventually reach the blood stream. It should be noted that fresh lymph, before it has drained through a lymph node, may not contain lymphocytes; most lymphocytes of lymph are picked up in the nodes through which the lymph drains.

Next, we shall discuss the production and the function of plasma cells (plasmocytes).

Plasma Cells and the Formation of Anti-bodies. Over the past decade there has been a tremendous growth of knowledge about antigens and antibodies. In the past it was more or less assumed that reticuloendothelial cells made the antibodies that formed in response to antigens that gained entrance to the body; this view was aided by the fact that reticuloendothelial cells could be seen to phagocytose various types of particulate matter, including some kinds of bacteria against which the body would produce antibodies. Another view which later came into prominence was that lymphocytes made the antibodies; an important basis for this theory was the finding that giving an animal a large dose of the hormone hydrocortisone, which causes the disintegration of vast numbers of lymphocytes, temporarily increases antibody titer, and it was assumed that this was due to the release of antibody from the breakup of cells that were producing the antibody. However, in 1948 Fagraeus had assembled and published very convincing evidence to the effect that plasma cells were the chief cells involved in antibody production. More recently Coons and his associates, by their application of fluorescence microscopy to the problem, provided convincing proof that antibodies are indeed produced within plasma cells.

Fluorescence microscopy has been described in Chapter 3, and it is assumed that the student will already be familiar with the explanation given there of how the presence of antigens can be detected and localized in sections. The way that sites of antibody formation can be detected employs the same technics and is roughly as follows: An injection, or repeated injections, of some particular antigen are given in some part of an animal. After an appropriate length of time the lymph nodes along the lymphatics that drain this part of the body are removed, immediately frozen, and sectioned while frozen so that no shift in antibody can occur. Then the sections are dried and fixed. Next, they are flooded with the particular antigen that was used in the experiment, and this antigen, of course, attaches itself to all specific antibody that has formed in any of the cells in the tissue in response to the antigen that was injected into the animal some time before. The section, after washing, is then flooded with antibody that has been labeled with a fluorescent dye. The labeled antibody attaches itself to any specific antigen that is present, and the only antigen that is present after the washing is that which, when the section was flooded with antigen, sought out and attached itself to any specific antibody that was in cells. Hence, the only sites where labeled antibody will be attached and remain after further washing, and so will fluoresce when the section is examined subsequently in the fluorescence microscope, will be those sites where antibody formed in cells in response to the *injected* antigen. Figure 238 illustrates what is seen by the fluorescent technic in a lymph node sectioned after an animal received two doses of diphtheria toxoid, and it shows that the antibody that formed in response to this antigen is within the cytoplasm of plasma cells.

Fine Structure of Plasma Cells. The concept of plasma cells producing antibodies is also strongly supported by the appearance that they present under the E/M, for their cytoplasm contains a great abundance of more or less flattened rough-surfaced vesicles of endoplasmic reticulum (Fig. 239). The great abundance of cytoplasmic RNA granules strongly suggests that they synthesize much protein, and the great abundance of flattened vesicles of the endoplasmic reticulum strongly suggests that the protein that they synthesize is destined for delivery outside of the cell. Accordingly, their E/M appearance is what might be expected if they synthesize antibodies for secretion. Moreover, their E/M appearance shows the reason for their cytoplasm's evidencing so much basophilia with the light microscope—it contains a great abundance of RNA granules. It might be mentioned also that people who have diseases that are associated with a change in nature of their plasma cells or with a lack of plasma cells are very deficient in antibody production.

The Specificity of Plasma Cells. In the preceding section we have given reasons for believing that plasma cells are chiefly responsible for producing antibodies when antigens are given an animal; furthermore, that the fine structure of their cytoplasm gives every evidence for considering that it is structurally specialized to perform such a function. However, in the instance of plasma cells it would seem that specialization is carried a step further in that plasma cells are not merely specialized to make antibodies in general; on the contrary, individual plasma cells (or families of plasma cells) are generally specialized for making antibody against a single antigen. (Many elegant experiments have been carried out in this connection.) There is evidence suggesting that it is possible for a cell sometimes to make antibody against two different antigens (Attardi *et al.*), but in general (White) there are different plasma cells for making antibodies to different antigens. Any interested student who wishes to explore this further should read Nossal and Lederberg, White and Attardi, Cohn and Lennox.

What Happens in Lymphatic Tissue When an Animal Is Given an Antigen? When an animal is given an antigen in fetal life or, in the instance of some species, in the early days of postnatal life, the animal does not react to the antigen by making antibodies to it; instead, the administration of the antigen at this time renders the animal *unable* to make antibodies against this antigen later in postnatal life. The animal is said under these conditions to have developed acquired immunologic tolerance to the antigen. This was discussed in some detail in Chapter 10.

When an animal is given its first injection of an antigen anytime in postnatal life, after the few days are past during which tolerance can be established it reacts to the antigen by manifesting what is termed a *primary response*. This takes several days to develop; and when it has developed, some antibody to the antigen appears in the circulation.

When an animal that has been given an injection of antigen as described above and has experienced a primary response is, after a suitable length of time, given a second injection of the same antigen, it responds in a much shorter time than that required for a primary response, by producing antibody to the antigen, and it produces much more than it did in the primary response. This response is termed the *secondary response*.

Coons (1958), using the immunofluorescence technic, has studied lymph nodes in various stages of primary and secondary responses to an antigen.

First, Coons showed that an hour after an antigen is given it can be detected in thousands of cells in the lymph node draining the region where the antigen is given. By the 4th day, in a comparable section of the node, only about 50 cells can be seen that are producing antibody to the antigen, and their numbers do not appear to increase over the next 4 days. There is, then, a wide exposure of cells to an injected antigen, but only a few respond by making antibody in the primary response; indeed, it is not certain that the response actually occurs in the kind of cells that originally take up the antigen.

Next, in a secondary response Coons finds that hundreds of cells demonstrating a little antibody appear by the 2nd day in an area where only about 50 appeared in the primary response by the 4th day. His observations suggest that these cells spring up independently; they do not appear to develop as colonies or clones from the 50 or so cells that could be seen in a comparable area in the primary response. However, later on in the secondary response these cells do form groups and colonies as they proliferate.

How do the histologic findings contribute toward explaining the shorter time taken for the secondary response and its greater vigor? The findings suggest that one step, that takes a certain amount of time and is not required in the secondary response, must occur in the primary response. This step (although this is by no means clearly established) may be that of the antigen acting directly, or indirectly through other cells, as an inducing agent on precursor cells of the plasma-cell series, so that a line of cells is established to make antibody against, and only against, the administered antigen. In other words, the first step in the primary response would be in the nature of an induction of a special cell type. The second part of the primary response would be the differentiation of only relatively few of these cells of the special type into functioning types that actually produce antibody. The evidence suggests further that the rapid and effective response observed on a second exposure to the antigen, when a great many more and widely scattered cells develop quickly into antibody formers, coud be explained by cells having been induced in the primary response so that they are able to react specifically to this antigen, so that on a second exposure to it they react promptly by both proliferating and differentiating into mature functioning cells.

A way by which an antigen could induce the formation of a family of cells to make antibody against this antigen was described in connection with Cell Differentiation in Chapter 4. The fact that a cell specialized to make antibody to a special antigen does not make antibodies to other antigens is in keeping with the behavior of other specialized cells in the body because the specialization of a cell along one line generally inhibits or terminates its capacity for specializing along some other line. An epithelial gland cell, specialized for producing mucus, does not produce zymogen granules, or vice versa, although both types of cells are closely related and often develop in the same gland. It would then be in accord with other cell types for cells of the plasma-cell series that have become specialized for making antibody to a given antigen not to respond to other antigens by making or attempting to make antibodies against them.

The next two problems that must be considered in any discussion such as this are related. They are (1) Why do plasma cells not develop in the fetus and make antibodies against the innumerable substances that are formed as a fetus develops which would act as antigens if they were injected into an adult host? (2) Why does an animal in postnatal life have immunologic tolerance to any antigenic substance to which it is exposed in fetal life?

The first question is the easier to attempt to answer. The total various potentialities of the ovum are unfolded in an orderly way in the successive generations of cells that form from it. Some types of specialized cells appear sooner than others; indeed, full development of some organs is not completed until after birth. For example, secretory units do not develop in the salivary glands until after birth. Therefore, it is possible that the reason for plasma cells not appearing in the body until around the time of birth is that this is part of the schedule of development that is inherent in the embryo, and it accounts for erythropoiesis occurring at one time, the development of cartilage at another, bone at another, the gallbladder at another, and so on.

Even if we grant that plasma cells cannot develop until around the time of birth (although there is probably some difference between species), we are faced with trying to explain why, when they do develop, they do not begin immediately to make antibodies against all the substances then present in the body that would serve as antigens if they were injected into another body. Why does the body remain immunologically tolerant to all these substances that are present before birth?

One theory about this matter which has received a great deal of consideration suggests (if we interpret it correctly) that a great host of stem cells, which in later life could give rise to antibody-forming cells, develop in the fetus and that these stem cells are already so variously specialized before birth that there are special ones to form cells that could make antibody against each conceivable antigen to which a body could be exposed. However, if any of these stem cells are exposed in fetal life to the special antigen to which they are preadapted, they do not respond by producing cells that make antibodies against that antigen but, instead, their premature union with that antigen results in their death. Accordingly, each new possible antigen that appears in embryonic and fetal life destroys the particular stem cell or cells that would have been able later, in postnatal life, to make cells that could synthesize antibody adapted to that special antigen. So, at the time of birth, there are no cells left that can respond to any antigens to which the fetus has been exposed; however, there are all the stem cells required to make antibody-forming cells against every other possible antigen to which the body could be exposed.

To us, in our present state of knowledge, it would seem to be more in keeping with other data from the field of experimental embryology if the specialization required for making antibody against a special antigen were acquired only after the precursor cells of the plasma-cell series were exposed to that antigen. Of course, such a theory does not require that precursors of antibody-forming cells be *predetermined* as to their specificity; the specificity occurs only after a nonspecific cell has been induced to be specific by an antigen. However, if this is the way that plasma cells become specific, there must be another kind of explanation for nonspecific precursor cells that are exposed to antigens in fetal life not responding to these antigens by producing antibody-forming cells and antibodies, but instead by being affected in some fashion so that any future antibody-forming response to these antigens is inhibited in them. Theories that would explain how this could happen have

been suggested; those who wish to pursue this matter further should read Jerne and Cinader and Dubert.

Auto-antibodies. Whatever the mechanism is that accounts for immunologic tolerance, the mechanism prevents us from making antibodies against any of the possible antigens that have developed within us until around the time of birth, provided that these possible antigens have been dissolved in, or carried by, the body fluids. However, there are some substances that form in the body that are segregated from the circulation, as will be explained when the thyroid gland is considered later; if these previously segregated substances gain access in later life to the fluids of the body they may act as antigens and, as a result, the body will make antibodies against one of its own components. Such antibodies are termed *auto-antibodies*. Indeed, it is now believed that there are several mechanisms that can act to cause auto-antibodies to form, and a growing number of hitherto not understood diseases are being considered as being due to this cause. This matter will be considered somewhat further in the section that deals with the thyroid gland, for it provides a good example on which a discussion can be based.

Lymphocytes and Antibodies. Evidence obtained by the immunofluorescence technic and from other sources, some of which will be described presently, indicate that lymphocytes may have antibody in them or on them. This evidence is sometimes interpreted as indicating that lymphocytes actually produce antibodies. We take a very simple position on this matter. We think that it is inconceivable that any cell could synthesize antibody unless its cytoplasm was provided with the machinery for synthesizing protein for secretion; hence, any cell that produces antibody would have an abundance of rough-surfaced vesicles of endoplasmic reticulum in its cytoplasm. This is the kind of cytoplasm that characterizes plasma cells (Fig. 239). The cytoplasm of the typical lymphocytes (Fig. 111) is poorly equipped with this type of organelle. The nature and the amount of cytoplasm are the only definitive criteriae by which lymphocytes and plasma cells can be distinguished. We cannot conceive of a cell without typical rough-surfaced vesicles of endoplasmic reticulum synthesizing antibody, and we think that if any cell of the lymphocyte-plasmocyte family has this kind of cytoplasm, it should be considered as being in the plasma-cell series.

There are some examples of immune reactions occurring in the body that are not easily explained by the amount of antibody that is present in the blood. For example, if skin is transplanted from one animal to another of the same species, the transplant is rejected in due course, and the rejection of the transplant seems to be associated more with an accumulation of lymphocytes beneath and around the transplant than with any substantial concentration of antibody to the antigens of the transplant in the serum of the host. One explanation for the role of lymphocytes in this type of response is that they take up and carry the antibody from lymphatic tissue (where the antibody is made by plasma cells) to the site where the antigen is located, without the antibody's being free in the serum; this produces a high local concentration of antibody at the site where the antibody would be most effective. Another possibility is that some of the less well-differentiated lymphocytes that migrate into the part develop into cells of the plasma-cell series and produce antibody which remains fairly well localized in the area of the transplant.

The last discussed possibility brings up the vexing problem of whether or not lymphocytes can become transformed into plasma cells. In considering this question, it must be remembered that many authors refer to what we have termed lymphoblasts as large lymphocytes. These cells are so like plasmoblasts that they could be expected to have sufficient potentiality to differentiate into cells of the plasma-cell series under proper stimulation. It is possible also that the potentiality to form plasma cells is retained by at least some medium-sized lymphocytes but, in general, it might be expected that even if this potentiality exists in the less differentiated cells of the lymphocyte series it would diminish with each step in differentiation along the lymphocyte route. Accordingly, before accepting that small lymphocytes can develop into plasma cells, very substantial evidence should be available. However, much investigation is being carried out in this field at the moment, and doubtless some of these problems will be removed from the realm of speculation in the near future.

The Blood Supply of Lymph Nodes. Arteries enter and veins leave a lymph node at its hilus. The branches of the arteries are carried to the various parts of the node by the trabeculae that extend into it from the hilus. Arterioles leave the trabeculae and, supported by an ensheathment of condensed reticular tissue derived from the mesh, branch into capillary nets. Capillaries, while present throughout the reticular mesh, are particularly abundant in the peripheral parts of the lymphatic nodules, and in this site some lymphocytes enter the blood stream by penetrating through the capillaries' rather thick walls. The capillaries empty into venules. These traverse the mesh to open into the veins of the trabeculae which carry the blood back to the hilus.

NATURE AND DISTRIBUTION OF LYMPHATIC TISSUE DESIGNED TO FILTER BLOOD

Most mammals have, in addition to lymph nodes, a much smaller number of structures that are similar except that they are yellow or red instead of gray in color. On section, these structures resemble lymph nodes except that they have somewhat better-defined channels in their coarse mesh, and either some of these channels or all of them are filled with blood instead of lymph. If only some are filled with blood and others with lymph, the structure is called a *hemal lymph node*. If all the channels are filled with blood, it is called a *hemal node*.

There is some question as to whether hemal lymph nodes or hemal nodes are constant structures in man, but they have often been described as commonly occurring in the prevertebral peritoneal tissue, in the root of the mesentery, near the rim of the pelvis and occasionally in other sites. There are not enough of them in man to filter very much blood, but it is important to know of them, lest, on being discovered at operation or at autopsy, they be mistaken for pathologically altered tissue.

The Spleen

With the possible exception of a few hemal and hemal lymph nodes, all the lymphatic tissue of the body that is specialized to filter blood is concentrated in one organ, the spleen.

Galen described the spleen as an organ full of mystery. A student who reads all the accounts of those who have tried to determine the precise course by which blood circulates through it might come to the same conclusion.

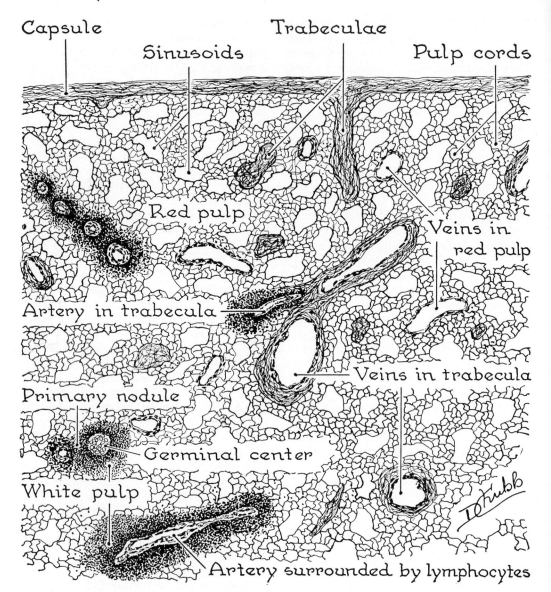

Capsule　　　Trabeculae

Sinusoids　　　Pulp cords

Red pulp

Veins in red pulp

Artery in trabecula

Veins in trabecula

Primary nodule

Germinal center

White pulp

Artery surrounded by lymphocytes

Fig. 240. Diagram of a section cut at right angles to the surface of a distended spleen. Notice that the white pulp (*left lower corner*) consists of nodules and aggregations of lymphocytes and that the red pulp is an open mesh with sinusoids running through it. A trabecula with veins may be seen in the central part of the illustration.

But much has been learned about the spleen. It removes most of the worn-out red blood cells of the body from the circulatory system. From the hemoglobin of these worn-out cells it manufactures bilirubin (bile pigment), which it liberates into the blood, from which the liver collects it. It also extracts the iron from the hemoglobin of the worn-out cells and liberates this into the blood stream in a form that permits it to be used over again in the manufacture of new red blood cells in the red bone marrow. The spleen, because of its ability to form plasma cells, produces antibodies that give protection from various disease organisms. It also produces many of the lymphocytes and probably most of the monocytes that are present in blood. It also acts to some extent like an automatic transfusion bank in that, particularly in animals that are called upon for great bursts of activity, it can

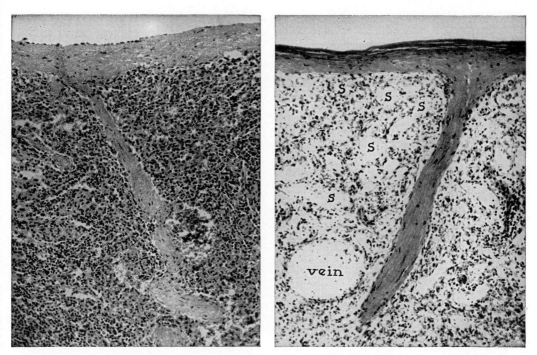

Fig. 241. Low-power photomicrographs of 2 sections cut at right angles to the capsule of the spleen. (*Left*) Picture taken from a section of collapsed spleen. The capsule and also a trabecula extending in from the capsule may be seen. (*Right*) Picture taken from a spleen that was distended with fixative through its veins. Notice that the red pulp has been opened up by this procedure and that the sinusoids are apparent.

quickly liberate stored blood into the circulatory system. Yet, with all these functions, the spleen is not essential to life. This is not because its functions are not valuable but because most of them are taken over by the other hemopoietic tissues when the spleen is removed.

Gross Characteristics. The spleen is roughly the size and the shape of a clenched fist. It lies in the shelter of the left 9th, the 10th and the 11th ribs, with its long axis parallel with them. Its purple color is due to its great content of blood. It is soft in consistency and more friable than most organs. A long fissure may be seen close to its medial border; this is termed the hilus. On approaching this, the splenic artery divides into several branches that enter the substance of the spleen separately at different points along the elongated hilus. Veins leave the spleen in association with the arteries that enter it and later unite to form the splenic vein.

Before beginning the microscopic study of this organ, the student should examine, with the naked eye or a magnifying glass, the sur-

face of a slice cut through the spleen. The spleen will be seen to be surrounded by a connective tissue capsule (the capsule has smooth muscle fibers in it also but these cannot be seen with the naked eye). Trabeculae of the same material as the capsule will be seen extending into the substance of the organ both from the hilus and to a lesser extent from the capsule. The remainder of the interior of the spleen is filled with what is called splenic pulp. Two kinds of pulp can be seen with the naked eye: white and red. The white pulp is distributed as tiny little firm gray islands, somewhat less than 1 mm. in diameter, among the soft, red pulp that fills all the remaining space.

General Microscopic Structure. If sections cut from a block of splenic tissue, cut at right angles to the capsule, are examined with the microscope, it will be obvious that the little nodules of gray pulp observed on the cut surface of the spleen with the naked eye are lymphatic nodules (Fig. 240). These, then, are the chief sites of lymphocyte production in the spleen. Moreover, it will be seen that

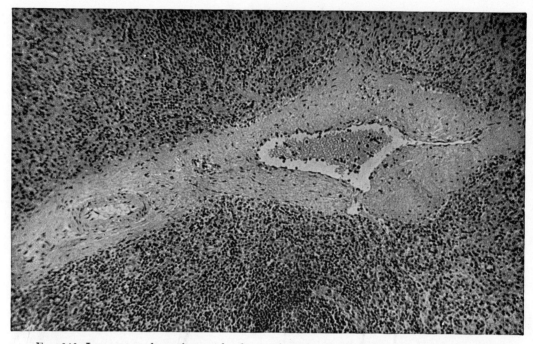

Fig. 242. Low-power photomicrograph of a section of collapsed spleen cut near its center. The picture shows a large trabecula containing an artery on the left and a vein on the right.

the red pulp (Fig. 240) that surrounds the lymphatic nodules contains vast numbers of red blood cells in its mesh and so represents the part of the lymphatic tissue of the spleen that is designed to act as a filter. In the spleen then, as in lymphatic tissue in general, the two functions—lymphocyte production and filtering—tend to be segregated from one another; the white pulp makes the lymphocytes and the red pulp filters.

Before studying the white and the red pulp in more detail, the student should examine the capsule of the organ (Figs. 240 and 241). This consists of collagenic and elastic fibers in which fibroblasts and some smooth muscle cells are distributed. In some animals there is much more smooth muscle in the capsule of the spleen than in man, and its contraction can materially assist the smooth muscle of the trabeculae in contracting the spleen and so forcing the blood it contains into the circulatory system in times of emergency. It is doubtful if there is enough smooth muscle in the capsule of the spleen of man to function very efficiently in this respect.

The capsule is covered with a serous (peritoneal) coat of mesothelium; this consists of a single layer of squamous cells. The cytoplasm of the mesothelial cells is too scant to be seen in sections, but their nuclei may be seen occasionally.

Next, the student should examine the trabeculae that are scattered through the substance of the spleen (Figs. 240, 241 and 242). Since these extend in from the hilus like a branching tree and pass in various directions to connect with those that extend in from the capsule (though not all do), they will be cut, in any section, in almost every plane. Most of them, of course, will be cut obliquely. They consist, like the capsule, of dense connective tissue in which there is a fairly high percentage of elastin. They also contain a few muscle cells, but, as is true of the capsule, the amount of smooth muscle in them is not as great in man as in certain other animals.

In the trabeculae both arteries and veins, as well as nerves, may be seen. In general, the largest trabeculae are seen near the hilus, and these contain the largest vessels. Although the detailed microscopic structure of arteries and veins will not be considered until a later chapter, it should be said here that arteries have thicker walls (composed chiefly of cir-

FIG. 243. Low-power photomicrograph of a section of a human spleen. In this particular section an artery that has left a trabecula and is passing through the red pulp is cut longitudinally. Many lymphocytes, disposed in a fine reticular mesh, are to be seen above the artery. Toward the left-hand side of the picture, the lymphatic tissue accompanying the artery is expanded into a primary nodule. The artery at the site of the primary nodule has given off a branch called the follicular artery, which may be seen in the central part of the nodule.

cularly disposed smooth muscle) and smaller lumens than their corresponding veins. By using these criteria the student should readily distinguish the vein from the artery in most trabeculae (Figs. 240 and 242).

Arteries. The arteries that travel in from the hilus in the larger trabeculae branch into small branches *that leave the trabeculae* (the smaller trabeculae, therefore, contain only veins) to enter the pulp. To support these, the reticular tissue of the pulp becomes condensed along one side of them, and to some extent around them, to provide them with fairly substantial sheaths. The reticular fibers in these sheaths are disposed so as to hold lymphocytes in their meshes, and as a result the sheaths are heavily infiltrated with lymphocytes (Fig. 243). While the supporting sheaths of these arteries, infiltrated with lymphocytes, are not true lymphatic nodules along most of their course, the sheath does become expanded (usually at one side) from time to time to

form true lymphatic nodules (Fig. 240, *lower left*; Fig. 243, *left*), which may contain germinal centers. The white pulp of the spleen, then, is distributed along the arteries that leave the trabeculae.

In each site where the surrounding reticular sheaths of the arteries are expanded into lymphatic nodules, the artery gives off a branch to supply the nodule (Fig. 243, *left*). This is termed a follicular artery (in the spleen, lymphatic nodules are often termed lymphatic follicles).

A follicular artery gives off branches to supply the capillary beds of the lymphatic nodule which contains it and then emerges from the follicle into the surrounding red pulp. On entering the red pulp, each follicular artery, according to Solnitzky, divides into from 2 to 6 branches which radiate out in different directions from their point of origin. Since these arterial branches are straight, they are called *penicillar arteries* or *penicilli*. Each of these,

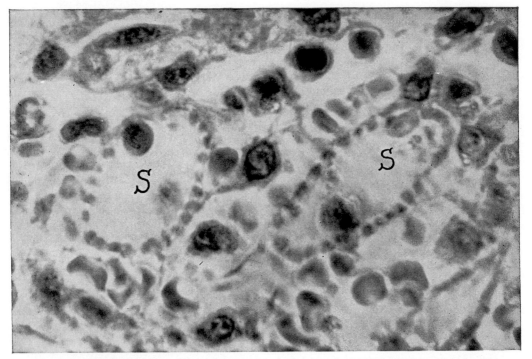

Fig. 244. Oil-immersion photomicrograph of a section of distended spleen taken with the phase microscope. In this picture 2 sinusoids are cut in cross section. These are marked S. Their longitudinally disposed stavelike lining cells are cut in cross section and can be seen to be slightly separated from one another.

according to Solnitzky, divides into 2 or 3 arterioles, most of which soon enter curious little structures called ellipsoids, whereupon they lose all their arteriolar characteristics (muscular and elastic walls) to become capillaries. Before considering further the structure of ellipsoids or the course of the blood, it is helpful to describe first the structure of the red pulp.

General Structure of Red Pulp. The framework of the red pulp consists of a mesh of reticular fibers which are continuous with the collagenic fibers of the trabeculae and the capsule. The reticular mesh of red pulp, though of an open type itself, is permeated by passageways that measure from 12 to 40 μ in width. Since these passageways drain into veins they are termed the venous sinusoids of the red pulp (Figs. 240 and 241). The walls of at least some of these are made of long, narrow reticuloendothelial cells that bulge somewhat into the lumen of the sinusoid in the region of their nuclei. The long, narrow cells lining the sinusoids are arranged

something like the staves of a barrel, in particular, a barrel whose staves were fashioned from imperfectly seasoned wood and has been left empty in the sun, for the sides of the cells lining the sinusoids are separated from each other by longitudinal slits (Fig. 244). To carry the analogy still further, it will be recalled that the staves of barrels usually are supported by surrounding iron hoops. The reticuloendothelial staves of the venous sinusoids are somewhat similarly surrounded and supported by hoops of reticular fibers.

In a single section, the red pulp situated between two adjacent sinusoids often resembles a cord (Fig. 240, *top, right*); indeed, these areas have been termed *Billroth* or *pulp cords*. However, the student who has zealously practiced 3-dimensional visualization will quickly realize that true cords of pulp do not exist between sinusoids any more than cords exist between the holes made by poking two fingers into dough.

Neither the red pulp between sinusoids nor the sinusoids themselves can be studied to

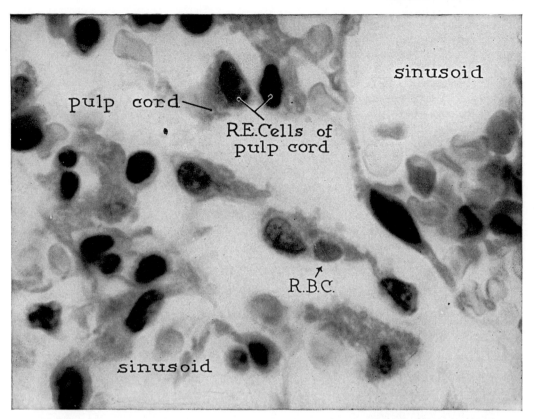

FIG. 245. Oil-immersion photomicrograph of a section of distended human spleen removed to alleviate excessive red blood cell destruction. Sinusoids may be seen at the lower left and the upper right; between them is a pulp cord. In this, several reticuloendothelial cells may be seen. One near the center has phagocytosed a red blood corpuscle which is lying in its cytoplasm. The spotty appearance of the cytoplasm of the cell immediately below it is due to granules of pigment formed as a result of the breakdown of hemoglobin in its cytoplasm.

advantage in ordinary sections of spleen. The reason for this is that the spleen collapses to some extent either before or after death, and this compresses the red pulp and obscures its microscopic structure (Fig. 241, *left*). A much better picture of the structure of the red pulp can be obtained if the spleen is re-distended to its original size, particularly by injecting fixative into the splenic vein (Fig. 241, *right*). Robinson, in his studies, has not only studied distended spleens but has studied thick sections of the red pulp of distended spleens with a binocular microscope arranged to give stereoscopic vision. He describes the pulp between the sinusoids as consisting of a vast, delicate network of starlike reticulo-endothelial cells having long, irregular proto-plasmic processes running in all directions and uniting one cell with another. The inter-stices of this cellular network he visualizes as a vast cavernous system of intercellular spaces that are in free communication with the venous sinusoids through the longitudinal slits in the walls of the latter (Fig. 244).

In examining the red pulp, particularly that of a distended spleen, the student will see many types of cells in the interstices of the pulp cords. Red blood cells abound in this situation. If the student is fortunate, he may see reticuloendothelial cells that have phago-cytosed worn-out red blood cells (Fig. 245). In the cytoplasm of the reticuloendothelial cells (both fixed ones and free macrophages), the hemoglobin of phagocytosed red blood cells is broken down to an iron-containing pigment of a golden-brown color (hemosiderin) and a non-iron-containing pigment variously called hematoidin, bilirubin or bile pigment. The latter pigment is readily soluble and diffuses out of cells as quickly as it is made, but hemosiderin lingers long enough for it to be seen at least sometimes in the cytoplasm of the cells that form it.

Fine Structure. Palade has obtained electron micrographs of phagocytic cells lining a sinusoid in the spleen of the rat (Fig. 246). The cells in this illustration do not appear to be of the barrel-stave type, for they fit together closely by means of pseudopodia from adjacent cells being invaginated into the cytoplasm of each other. When a pseudopodium from one cell invaginates the next, it either pushes the cell membrane of the second cell ahead of it or fits into an already existing cleft in the second cell so that the cytoplasm in any pseudopodium is separated from the cytoplasm of the invaginated cell by two cell membranes, one that covers the pseudopodium and the other that lines the cleft. Therefore, invaginated pseudopodia cut in cross section, demonstrate two rings of cell membranes around them (Fig. 246, *invag. pseudo.*).

With the E/M the cytoplasm of the lining cells of sinusoids reveals granular bodies that probably represent iron-containing pigment (Fig. 246, *phago. mat.*). In addition, rough-

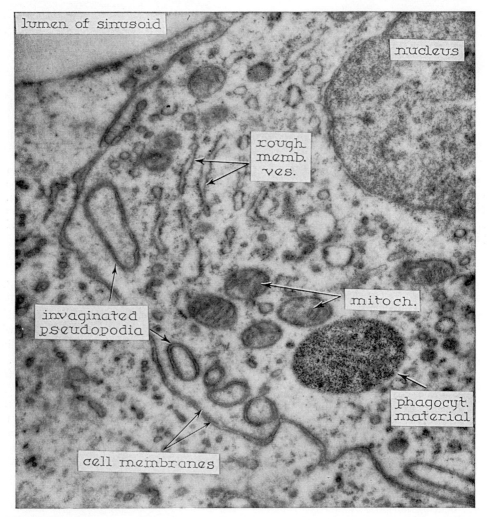

Fig. 246. Electron micrograph (× 42,000) of a section of parts of 2 cells lining a splenic sinusoid in a rat. The labeling has been added. (Palade, G. E.: J. Biophys. & Biochem. Cytol. (Supp.) 2:85)

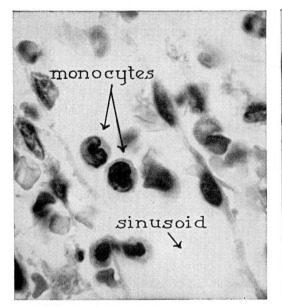

FIG. 247. Oil-immersion photomicrograph of a section of distended spleen. A sinusoid may be seen running from the upper left to the lower right portion of the picture. Two monocytes are present in the sinusoid. It is likely that many monocytes develop in this situation.

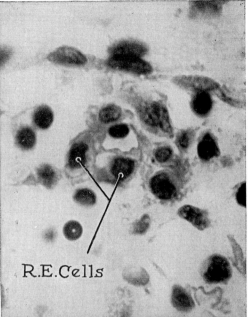

FIG. 248. Oil-immersion photomicrograph of a section of distended human spleen. An ellipsoid, cut in cross section, may be seen in the center of the illustration. It consists of an arrangement of reticuloendothelial cells surrounding a capillary. The lumen of the capillary may be seen immediately above the labeled reticulonedothelial cells. A lymphocyte is present in the lumen of the capillary.

surfaced flattened vesicles, RNA granules and mitochondria are all evident.

Monocytes and Other Cells. In addition to red blood cells and fixed and free reticuloendothelial cells, many lymphocytes may be seen in the pulp. It is likely that most of the monocytes of the blood stream are normally formed in the pulp cords and the venous sinusoids of the spleen as a result of the differentiation of monoblasts or lymphoblasts (Fig. 247). Plasma cells may also be encountered as they may in any kind of lymphatic tissue. Various numbers of neutrophils and eosinophils may also be seen in the interstices of the pulp cords. Worn-out cells of the granular leukocyte series as well as red blood cells probably are strained out here to some extent by the reticuloendothelial phagocytes.

The reticular fibers of the red pulp can be seen to advantage only in silver or other special types of preparations.

It will be recalled that before we began the foregoing general description of the structure of red pulp we had succeeded in tracing the course of arterial blood through the spleen to the point where it had reached the ellipsoids of the red pulp. Furthermore, in our description of the red pulp, it became apparent that blood delivered into the venous sinusoids would pass by way of the veins of the red pulp to the trabecular veins and hence to the splenic vein. To complete the account of the circulation of blood through the spleen, we have only to trace the course of blood from the ellipsoids to the venous sinusoids. There are differences of opinion about the course that it takes over this short distance. Before discussing the matter, we shall comment very briefly on the structure of ellipsoids.

Ellipsoids are developed to different degrees in different species. Those of man are not very highly developed. So to study the structure and the function of ellipsoids, many investigators have turned to the cat, whose ellipsoids are extremely well developed. Ellipsoids have

CIRCULATION OF BLOOD THROUGH THE SPLEEN

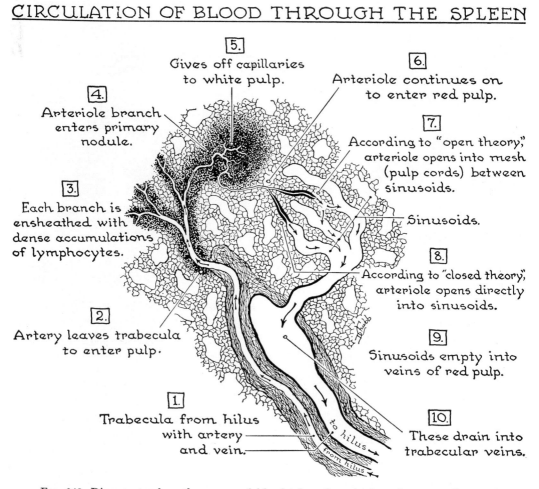

5. Gives off capillaries to white pulp.

6. Arteriole continues on to enter red pulp.

4. Arteriole branch enters primary nodule.

7. According to "open theory," arteriole opens into mesh (pulp cords) between sinusoids.

3. Each branch is ensheathed with dense accumulations of lymphocytes.

Sinusoids.

8. According to "closed theory," arteriole opens directly into sinusoids.

2. Artery leaves trabecula to enter pulp.

9. Sinusoids empty into veins of red pulp.

1. Trabecula from hilus with artery and vein.

to hilus
from hilus

10. These drain into trabecular veins.

FIG. 249. Diagram to show the course of blood taken through the spleen according to the open and the closed theories of circulation. The legends on the figure should be read in a clockwise fashion.

been suspected of being nervous structures, muscular organs and other things, but the general opinion derived from the more recent studies is that the ellipsoid represents nothing more than a condensation of reticular fibers and reticuloendothelial cells around a capillary (Fig. 248). However, in distended cat spleens, there are openings through the sides of the ellipsoids through which blood can escape from the central vessel of the ellipsoid; but in contracted cat spleens, the side openings of the ellipsoids probably are closed. In this sense the ellipsoids of the cat spleen act as arterial sphincters. But their sphincterlike action probably is not due to the cells of the ellipsoids

being possessed of contractile powers. It seems more likely that the ellipsoids of the cat open out and shrink down passively along with the whole spleen. In this connection it is of interest that ellipsoids seem to be more highly developed in those species that have much muscle in the capsules and the trabeculae of their spleens; and in these animals it is not unlikely that the ellipsoids cut down the amount of blood entering the spleen when the smooth muscle of the capsule and the trabeculae contract in emergency and certain other conditions (for example, exercise). It is doubtful if the more or less rudimentary ellipsoids in the spleen of man act to any extent even as passive sphincters. What then is their function? The most reasonable explanation is that since they have openings between their reticuloendothelial cells through which blood from the central capillary can escape they serve as the first filters that arterial blood encounters in the spleen. Robinson has shown that certain foreign particles injected into the blood stream are first seen in the spleen adherent to the reticuloendothelial cells of the ellipsoids.

Ellipsoids are situated in the pulp tissue (pulp cords) between the venous sinusoids. Although blood can escape into the pulp through the side openings of the ellipsoids, most of the blood that comes to an ellipsoid passes through it in its central capillary, which then opens into the intercellular pulp spaces. Since openings exist between contiguous cells in the pulp, blood delivered into it by the capillary can circulate through it to some extent.

The description of the passage of the blood through the spleen given above constitutes a statement of the *open circulation theory* (Fig. 249). This theory is called the open one because it suggests that blood in circulating through the spleen is not confined to a *closed* system of endothelial-lined vessels as it is elsewhere in the body. In a sense, the open theory suggests that from the capillaries of the ellipsoids, hemorrhages occur into the tissue of the pulp cords and that this extravasated blood is transfused back into the vascular system through the openings in the walls of the venous sinusoids (Fig. 245).

It is obvious that the filtering function of the spleen would be extremely efficient under conditions of an open circulation. By having red blood cells delivered into the interstices of the pulp where they can move only slowly and in the small spaces of which they come into contact with many reticuloendothelial cells, the worn-out ones can be phagocytosed much more readily than if they were being swept along a vessel even if it were lined with reticuloendothelial cells. Robinson has shown that the reticuloendothelial cells of the pulp attract and so filter from the circulation particles bearing negative charges.

Many students of the spleen do not agree that the circulation through it is of the open type but think instead that the capillaries

from the ellipsoids or other arterial vessels deliver blood directly into the venous sinusoids (Fig. 249). Those who subscribe to the closed theory explain the numerous red blood cells present in the pulp cords as being due to their being forced out through the openings between the cells of the walls of the venous sinusoids.

Another opinion is to the effect that the circulation can be either closed or open, depending on circumstances. According to this view, the beginnings of the venous sinusoids which appear as tubular structures in a contracted spleen may, in a distended spleen, exhibit so many openings between the cells of their walls that they cease to be structures and become no more than fairly open passageways through a reticuloendothelial meshwork that abounds with communicating spaces. In other words, some consider that the first parts of the venous sinusoids, when they are distended, are so leaky that they are only spaces in a meshwork, and hence that the circulation under these conditions is open. But when the spleen is contracted, the cells of the walls of the sinusoids come close enough together to justify the view that they are tubular structures; under these conditions, the circulation is closed.

All the evidence concerning the circulation through the spleen that has been discussed so far has been obtained by means of the study of sections of fixed tissue. In 1936, however, a new approach to the problem was made by Knisely when he utilized the quartz-rod illuminator to study the passageways by which blood circulates between the arteries and the veins in the living animal. Knisely found that the arterial capillaries branch after passing through the region of ellipsoids, and that some of the branches pass directly to the veins. These capillaries (see Fig. 250, *capillary shunts*), which are controlled by sphincters, provide a *by-pass* or *shunt* circulation so that blood can pass through the spleen without being emptied either into the red pulp or the sinusoids. Knisely found that the other set of capillary branches empty into the sinusoids; in this respect Knisely's findings support the closed circulation theory. But Knisely found also that there were sphincters at each end of the sinusoids and that, depending on

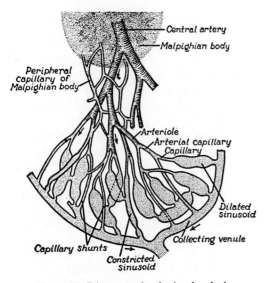

FIG. 250. Diagram of splenic circulation, according to Knisely. (Peck, H. M., and Hoerr, N. L.: Anat. Rec. *109*:447)

the contraction or the relaxation of these sphincters, sinusoids exhibit different states of form and function which he termed phases (Fig. 250). With both sphincters open, a sinusoid would be relatively narrow; in this state it would be said to be in a conducting phase. With the efferent sphincter contracted and the afferent one open a sinusoid is said to be in a *filtration-filling* phase with its walls retaining erythrocytes but allowing plasma to escape into the pulp cords. When the sinusoid becomes filled with erythrocytes the afferent sphincter closes, and the sinusoid enters the *storage* phase. Then when both sphincters open it enters the *emptying phase,* and the red blood cells that are packed in it are washed into the circulation.

The study of the circulation of the living spleen by the quartz-rod illuminator is a difficult technic. In their use of this method MacKenzie, Whipple, and Wintersteiner were unable to confirm many of Knisely's findings. Accordingly, Peck and Hoerr made a further study of both the method and the problem. Their work emphasized the necessity for very exacting precautions if the method is to yield information of value, and they found that when these precautions are taken the intermediary circulation in the spleen is essentially as Knisely described it.

The function of the human spleen in stor-

ing blood and delivering stored blood into the circulation under certain circumstances is not as significant as that of the spleens of certain other species. The human spleen is somewhat larger in life than it is after death (when it has contracted), but this difference is not nearly so great as that seen in laboratory animals and probably not nearly so great as is sometimes inferred from studies made on these other animals. Nevertheless, as Barcroft and his associates have shown, the human spleen has a definite function in storing blood and liberating stored blood under certain circumstances when extra blood would be helpful. It is not likely that there is enough smooth muscle in the capsule and the trabeculae of the human spleen to explain its contraction under these circumstances. The release of blood from the human spleen is more in the nature of a passive act that occurs when the smooth muscle fibers that encircle its arteries and arterioles contract and so restrict the amount of blood entering the spleen. This permits the stretched elastic fibers of the trabeculae and the capsule, aided to some extent by smooth muscle fibers of the same structures, to contract and so squeeze blood out of the pulp spaces of the spleen into the venous sinusoids, and out of them and the trabecular veins into the circulation.

THE ORIGIN OF MONOCYTES

There are different views about the origin of monocytes, as will now be described.

1. **From Reticuloendothelial Cells.** Although not avidly phagocytic in the blood stream, monocytes can quickly develop into macrophages with great phagocytic powers if they leave the blood stream and enter the tissues at a site of inflammation. Macrophages, as has been indicated in our study of hemopoietic tissues, are, in a sense, free reticuloendothelial cells. Since monocytes are so closely related to the latter, it is only natural that the view would arise to the effect that the reticuloendothelial cells of hemopoietic tissues give rise to the monocytes of the blood. However, the experimental evidence for this widely held view is not very convincing. Bloom points out that although some reticuloendothelial cells become detached from their moorings as blood sweeps through the spleen, and may be found in the blood of the splenic vein, they are dissimilar from monocytes. These

probably are strained out of the blood stream by the narrow capillaries of the lungs.

2. From Ordinary Endothelial Cells. This is an old view that is no longer generally accepted; however, it accounts for the sometimes used term endothelial leukocyte or even *endothelial cell* to designate the cell we refer to as a monocyte.

3. From Special Cells Called Monoblasts. Sabin, Doan and Cunningham and others have described certain cells in the spleen, bone marrow and other tissues which, though similar in appearance to lymphoblasts and myeloblasts are, they think, sufficiently different to be considered as representatives of a separate kind of free stem cell. They term these "monoblasts" and think that they give rise to monocytes (Fig. 144). The concept of these being a special stem cell for the monocyte series is now widely held.

4. From Lymphocytes. Both Maximow and Bloom have been able to demonstrate all transition stages between lymphocytes and monocytes in the sinusoids of the spleen and the liver in sections of these tissues. Bloom has studied the development of monocytes in a disease of rabbits (infection with *Listeria monocytogenes*) in which a monocytosis develops and has traced their origin to lymphocytes. Moreover, Bloom has shown that monocytes develop from lymphocytes in tissue cultures.

To Sum Up. In this confusing field we think that the simplest view for the student to take is that monocytes can and do arise from free rounded cells of great potentiality and somewhere along the line of differentiation that leads to their formation there is a cell that could properly be termed a monoblast (Fig. 144). It seems most probable that they can also arise from the younger (least differentiated) lymphocytes.

In the foregoing section the kinds of lymphatic tissue that filter tissue fluid, lymph and blood, respectively, have been considered. The next important depot of lymphatic tissue that is to be considered is not primarily concerned with a filtering function; indeed, its function is poorly understood; this depot of lymphatic tissue is an organ termed the thymus gland.

THE THYMUS GLAND

Shape and Site. The thymus gland is a pinkish-gray, broad, flat bilobed mass of tis-

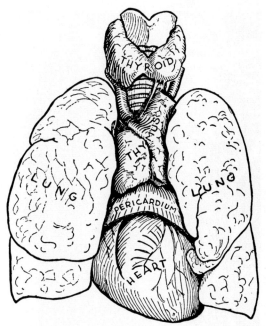

FIG. 251. The thymus gland of a child. (Grant, J. C. B.: A Method of Anatomy, ed. 4, Baltimore, Williams & Wilkins)

sue. The bulk of the organ lies in the thorax immediately beneath the upper part of the sternum (Fig. 251). Its upper part extends up into the neck. Each of the two lobes of the gland resembles a thyme leaf; they are disposed one on each side but are in apposition along the mid-line.

Size. The size of the thymus gland varies greatly in relation to age. It is largest—in relation to the remainder of the body—during fetal life and in the first 2 years of postnatal life. From the 2nd year onward and until the time of puberty, it continues to increase in size but not so rapidly as the remainder of the body. After puberty it begins to involute (*involvere* = to roll up) and as a consequence it slowly becomes smaller as an individual ages.

For many years the size and the weight of a normal thymus gland in childhood were underestimated. This was probably because the average figure did not represent the normal. This is to be explained by the fact that serious diseases tend to bring about the premature involution of the gland. Since so many children from whom surveys were made in the past had had serious diseases, the average

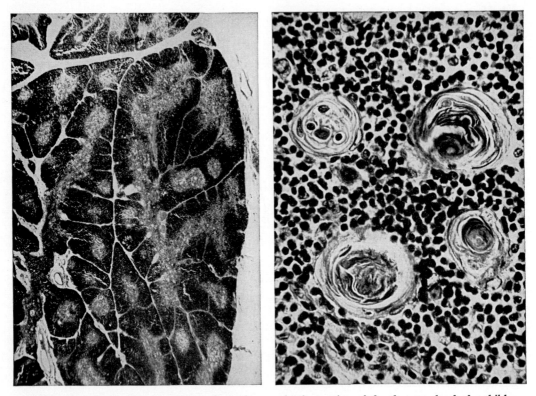

FIG. 252. (*Left*) Very low-power photomicrograph of a section of the thymus gland of a child. The septa appear as clear lines. The cortex of the lobules is dark; the medulla is light. Observe that the medulla of one lobule is continuous with that of another. (*Right*) High-power photomicrograph of an area of medulla. Four Hassal's corpuscles are shown.

figure compiled from them was then not representative of the normal. At the time of birth a normal thymus gland weighs about 10 to 15 gm. and at the time of puberty 30 to 40 gm. From then onward its weight slowly declines.

Development. The thymus gland develops as a result of tubes of epithelial cells growing out into mesenchyme from the third pharyngeal pouches. These epithelial tubes soon become solid cords, and as development proceeds they are pulled down into the thorax and lose their connections with their points of origin. At this stage of development the thymus resembles an endocrine gland because it is composed of cords of epithelial cells. These proliferate and send out side branches which are the forerunners of lobules. The arrangement of the epithelial cells then begins to change. Here and there little groups of cells become arranged around a central point, much as football players pile up around and over a loose ball. These little groups of cells are known as Hassal's corpuscles (Fig. 252, *right*).

Other epithelial cells (although it is not perfectly clear as to what happens at this time) seem to become arranged into a loose network of branching cells; these networks extend out and into the mesenchyme which now tends to surround the developing lobules. Some mesenchymal cells develop into the capsule and into the septa; but others, along with lymphoblasts to which they give rise, become incorporated into the epithelial network of reticular cells to provide cells of mesenchymal origin for the further production of lymphocytes. Lymphocytes are produced in the gland in large numbers, chiefly in the peripheral parts of lobules.

Microscopic Structure. Each lobe is surrounded by a thin capsule of connective tissue. This extends into the substance of each lobe to form septa and to divide the lobes into lobules which are usually from 1 to 2 mm. in width (Fig. 252, *left*). The septa, on penetrating into the substance of each lobe, meet and fuse with other septa but not extensively enough to surround the thymic tissue of each lobule completely (although they may appear to do so in a single section); hence, the thymic tissue of each lobule is continuous in the more central part of each lobe with that of other lobules (Fig. 252, *left*).

Lymphocytes are not spread evenly throughout the substance of each lobule; instead, they tend to be concentrated toward those borders of each lobule that abut on the capsule or on interlobular septa. The peripheral part of each lobule, heavily infiltrated with lymphocytes, is termed its cortex (Fig. 252, *left*), and the more central part of the lobule that does not contain so many lymphocytes is called its medulla (Fig. 252, *left*). Since lymphocytes are concentrated in the periphery of lobules only where the lobule abuts on the capsule or on an interlobular septum, and since lobules are not completely surrounded by connective tissue, each lobule has one side that is deficient in cortex, and at this site the medulla of the lobule is continuous with the medullary tissue of other lobules (Fig. 252, *left*).

Lymphocytes are so numerous in the cortex that they obscure the network of reticular cells on which they lie.

Although lymphocytes are numerous in the medulla, they are not so densely packed as to obscure the cells of the network of reticular cells on which they lie. The nuclei of the cells of this reticulum are large, and although they contain nucleoli, they do not contain very much chromatin and hence they stain lightly. The cytoplasm of these cells is pink. That they are arranged in a network is not very clearly shown in sections cut from postnatal glands.

Hassal's corpuscles are numerous in the medulla. The centers of these usually consist of nonliving material: pyknotic and broken-up nuclei, keratin and nondescript hyalin material (Fig. 252, *right*). The remainder of each corpuscle consists of a few layers of concentrically arranged epithelial cells; the innermost ones may be dead (Fig. 252, *right*). The fact that the reticular cells of the medulla form Hassal's corpuscles suggests that the reticular cells here are epithelial in nature. Moreover, it seems probable, since so many lymphocytes are produced in the cortex that the reticular cells in the cortex are chiefly mesenchymal.

Blood vessels supported by connective tissue may be seen in the substance of lobules.

They are more numerous and are seen to better advantage in the medulla. Veins are common in septa.

The Production of Lymphocytes in the Thymus Gland. Sainte-Marie and Leblond have recently made detailed studies of the production of lymphocytes in the thymus gland. They describe 4 cell types in the cortex that are involved in the process: reticular cells, large lymphocytes, medium-sized lymphocytes and small lymphocytes. Their large lymphocytes, we think, are what we would term lymphoblasts. These are derived from reticular cells, which, of course, can divide. Each large lymphocyte (lymphoblast), as a result, first of its own and then of its progeny continuing to divide, yields 128 mature small lymphocytes. The medulla also contains reticular cells, large lymphocytes (lymphoblasts) and medium-sized and small lymphocytes. Sainte-Marie and Leblond find that reticular cells are more abundant in the medulla than in the cortex but that the various types of lymphocytes are less abundant than in the cortex. Most of the lymphocytes seen in the medulla are probably formed in the cortex. In the medulla, lymphocytes pass through the walls of the lymphatic vessels that run along with the blood vessels in the medulla, and by this means lymphocytes can leave the medulla of the thymus and eventually enter the circulation.

Relation to Endocrine Glands. The growth hormone of the pars anterior and the thyroid hormone both stimulate the growth of the thymus gland. Most steroid hormones on the other hand—if sufficient quantities of them are present in the blood stream—tend to bring about the involution of the gland. Hence the appearance of substantial quantities of sex hormone in the circulation at the time of puberty is probably an important factor in causing the thymus gland to begin to involute at this time. Selye believes that the premature involution of the gland observed in children who suffer from serious diseases or other forms of stress is caused by the oversecretion of adrenal cortical steroid hormones that occurs as a result of the disease or stress condition. A deficiency of either adrenal cortical hormone or sex hormone in an animal, brought about by removing the endocrine glands responsible for these hormones, is associated with the hypertrophy of the thymus gland. Speaking generally, then, there seems to be an inverse reciprocal relationship between the amount of steroid hormones in the circulation and the size of the thymus gland.

Possible Functions. The thymus gland does not perform any filtering functions. The parenchyma is not thought to contain lymphatic vessels; those that are present are confined to the connective tissue septa and their immediate environment. Moreover, according to Yoffey, the thymus gland does not contain any plasma cells under normal conditions, and he quotes evidence indicating that extracts of it normally do not contain antibody.

Different results from removing the thymus gland from growing animals have been claimed by different investigators. It is not generally conceded that any of these results indicate that the thymus gland normally makes a hormone. One very curious effect of removal of the thymus is that it lowers the incidence of spontaneous leukemia in mice, as is described at the end of this Chapter.

Many types of extracts have been made from thymic tissue and injected into animals. Many different types of results have been claimed, but none has stood the test of time. One recent result which deserves thorough exploration is that of Metcalf, whose experiments indicate that a factor that stimulates lymphocytosis can be recovered from the thymus. For short, this is termed L.S.F.—the lymphocytosis stimulating factor.

Individuals with thymic tumors and hyperplasias have been investigated for possible indications of the effects of a thymic secretion. The results in this field of investigation have been interesting. Bell made a survey of 56 cases of a curious condition called myasthenia (*mys* = muscle; *asthenia* = weakness) gravis, in which condition the muscles, beginning usually with those of face and throat, become weak without becoming greatly diminished in size. He found that nearly half of the individuals with this condition had either a thymic tumor or an enlarged thymus. It has been shown that the disease represents a disturbance of the mechanisms involved in the chemical mediation of the nervous impulse (see Chap. 20) at the sites where nerve fibers make contact with muscle fibers. The mechanism by which an enlarged thymus or a thymic tumor exerts an effect on this is as yet obscure, but

knowledge that it does has had application in treating the condition.

Status Thymicolymphaticus. It has been observed for centuries that certain children—often of an angelic countenance—who have a general overgrowth of lymphatic tissue, including enlarged thymus glands, seem to have only a tenuous hold on life and may die suddenly under conditions that their more sturdy counterparts would survive. The condition is called status thymicolymphaticus. It is believed to be constitutional in nature and that the lymphatic hyperplasia seen in it is associated with other defects, including an underdeveloped circulatory system and underdeveloped adrenal cortices. Why those with status thymicolymphaticus should be unduly susceptible to sudden death has been explained many ways. An early explanation was that the enlarged thymus gland pressed against the trachea and so caused suffocation. Explanations that have been offered since are numerous and complex. Indeed, the original concept of status lymphaticus has itself come to have no more than a tenuous hold on its further existence as a true medical entity, for many authorities deny that such a condition occurs. But certainly many constitutional defects make life less certain. A generalized hyperplasia of lymphatic tissue may well be an indication of some kind of constitutional defect, but it is not clear that this in itself makes an individual less able to survive than his fellows or that this condition is always associated with other defects that do.

Lymphatic Leukemia. This disease is characterized by a great increase in the number of lymphocytes in the body. Any and many of the sites where lymphocytes are normally produced may be involved in the disease and produce more lymphocytes than usual. Other organs and tissues may become infiltrated by, and also may produce, lymphocytes. The number in the blood may become 10 to 20 times normal. The bone marrow may become so stuffed with lymphocytes filtered from the blood that other cells are literally crowded out of it and so there is a lack of granular leukocytes, red cells and platelets; this, of course, has many serious repercussions.

Lymphatic leukemia has been investigated extensively in mice. The members of certain pure strains of these, for example, those of the

AKR strain, almost all develop lymphatic leukemia and die from the disease. The thymus gland is often the site where leukemia begins in mice, and it has been shown that if the thymus gland is removed early in life, mice that ordinarily would develop leukemia do not do so. It has been known for several years that there was a higher incidence of leukemia in people who were exposed to substantial amounts of radiation than in those who were not exposed. It has been found that radiation increases the incidence of leukemia in mice of certain strains that do not ordinarily develop leukemia to any great extent. However, if the thymus gland is removed from the animals before they are radiated, leukemia does not develop, at least not nearly so often. But Kaplan, in some brilliant experiments, has shown that if a thymus gland from a non-radiated mouse is transplanted into a radiated mouse, leukemia will develop in the nonradiated thymus; this is an example of radiation having an indirect effect in inducing a malignant disease.

In recent years definite proof has come to hand that the spontaneous leukemia of AKR mice is caused by a virus. Gross has shown that cell-free extracts of leukemic tissue, if injected into newborn mice of a strain that ordinarily does not develop leukemia, will cause leukemia to develop in them as they grow older. Although the virus causation of some kinds of mouse leukemia is established, there is as yet no definite evidence that a virus is concerned in leukemia in man.

REFERENCES

LYMPHATIC TISSUE—GENERAL REFERENCES

Bloom, W.: Lymphatic tissue: lymphatic organs *in* Downey's Handbook of Hematology, p. 1427, New York, Hoeber, 1938.

Klemperer, Paul: The spleen *in* Downey's Handbook of Hematology, p. 1591, New York, Hoeber, 1938.

Krumbhaar, E. B.: Lymphatic tissue *in* Cowdry, E. V. (ed.): Problems of Ageing, p. 149, Baltimore, Williams & Wilkins, 1939.

Maximow, A. A.: The lymphocytes and plasma cells *in* Cowdry's Special Cytology, ed. 2, p. 603, New York, Hoeber, 1932.

Trowell, O. A.: The lymphocytes *in* Bourne, G. H., and Danielli, J. F. (eds.): International Review of Cytology, vol. 7, p. 235, New York, Acad. Press, 1958.

Weller, Carl Vernon: The hemolymph nodes *in* Downey's Handbook of Hematology, p. 1759, New York, Hoeber, 1938.

Yoffey, J. M., and Courtice, F. C.: Lymphatics, Lymph and Lymphoid Tissue, Cambridge, Mass., Harvard, 1956.

Yoffey, J. M., and Hanks, G. A.: Some problems of lymphocyte production, Ann. New York Acad. Sc. 73:47, 1958.

LYMPHATIC NODULES AND NODES—
SPECIAL REFERENCES

Andreasen, E., and Christensen, S.: The rate of mitotic activity in the lymphoid organs of the rat, Anat. Rec. 103:401, 1949.

Conway, E. A.: Cyclic changes in lymphatic nodules, Anat. Rec. 67:487, 1937.

Doan, C. A., and Wiseman, B. K.: The monocyte, monocytosis and monocytic leukosis, Ann. Int. Med. 8:383, 1934.

Dougherty, T. F.: Effects of hormones on lymphatic tissue, Physiol. Rev. 32:379, 1952.

Downey, H.: The structure and origin of the lymph sinuses of mammalian lymph nodes and their relations to endothelium and reticulum, Haematologica 3:31, 1922.

Farr, R. S.: Experiments on the fate of the lymphocyte, Anat. Rec. 109:515, 1951.

Gordon, A. S.: Some aspects of hormonal influences upon the leukocytes, Ann. New York Acad. Sc. 59:907, 1955.

Gross, L.: Mouse leukemia: an egg-borne virus disease (with a note on mouse salivary gland carcinoma), Acta haemat. 13:13, 1955.

Jordan, H. E.: The origin and fate of plasmacytes; a comparative histologic study of plasmacytes of normal lymph nodes and tumors of multiple myeloma, Anat. Rec. 119:325, 1954.

———: The significance of the lymphoid nodule, Am. J. Anat. 57:1, 1935.

Kindred, J. E.: Quantitative studies on lymphoid tissues, Ann. New York Acad. Sc. 59:746, 1955.

Scothorne, R. J., and McGregor, I. A.: Cellular changes in lymph nodes and spleen following skin homografting in the rabbit, J. Anat. 89:283, 1955.

FINE STRUCTURE (ELECTRON MICROSCOPY) OF
LYMPHATIC TISSUE

Bernhard, W., Hagenau, F., and Leplus, R.: Coupes ultrafines d'éléments sanguins et de ganglions lymphatiques étudiées au microscope électronique, Rev. hémat. 10:267, 1955.

Braunsteiner, H., Fellinger, K., and Pakesch, F.: Demonstration of a cytoplasmic structure in plasma cells, Blood 8:916, 1953.

Braunsteiner, H., and Pakesch, F.: Electron

microscopy and the functional significance of a new cellular structure in plasmocytes; a review, Blood *10*:650, 1955.

Palade, G.: The endoplasmic retieulum, J. Biophys. & Biochem. Cytol. *2*:85 (Supp.), 1956.

(*See* References on Lymphocytes and Monocytes in Chapter 8)

PLASMA CELLS AND ANTIBODY PRODUCTION
—SPECIAL REFERENCES

Attardi, G., Cohn, M., Horibata, K., and Lennox, E. S.: Symposium on the biology of cells modified by viruses or antigens. II On the analysis of antibody synthesis at the cellular level, Bacteriol. Rev. *23*:213-223, 1959.

Burnet, M.: The Clonal Selection Theory of Acquired Immunity, Nashville, Vanderbilt Univ. Press, 1959.

Bussard, A. D.: Biosynthesis of antibodies, facts and theories, Ann. Rev. Microbiol. *13*:279-296, 1959.

Ciba Foundation Symposium on the Cellular Aspects of Immunity, London, Churchill, 1960.

Cinader, B., and Dubert, J. M.: Specific inhibition of response to purified protein antigens, Proc. Roy. Soc., London ser. B *146*:18-33, 1956.

Coons, A. H.: Fluorescent antibody methods *in* Danielli, J. F. (ed.): General Cytochemical Methods, pp. 399-422, New York, Acad. Press, 1958.

————: The cytology of antibody formation, J. Cell. Comp. Physiol. *52*: Suppl. 1, 55-67, 1958.

Coons, A. H., Leduc, E. H., and Connolly, J. M.: Leukocytes involved in antibody formation, Ann. New York Acad. Sc. *59*:951, 1955.

————: Studies on antibody production: I. A method for the histochemical demonstration of specific antibody and its application to a study of the hyperimmune rabbit, J. Exper. Med. *102*:49, 1955.

Fagraeus, A.: Antibody production in relation to development of plasma cells; *in vivo* and *in vitro* experiments, Acta Med. scandinav. *130*: Suppl. *204*, 3-122, 1948.

Jerne, N. K.: The natural-selection theory of antibody formation, Proc. Nat. Acad. Sc. *41*:849-857, 1955.

Leduc, E. H., Coons, A. H., and Connolly, J. M.: Studies on antibody production: II. The primary and secondary responses in the popliteal lymph node of the rabbit, J. Exper. Med. *102*: 61, 1955.

Nossal, G. J. V.: Antibody production by single cells, Brit. J. Exper. Path. *39*:544-51, 1958.

Nossal, G. J. V., and Lederberg, J.: Antibody production by single cells, Nature *181*:1419-1420, 1958.

White, R. G.: Antibody production by single cells, Nature *182*:1383, 1958.

SPLEEN—SPECIAL REFERENCES

Barcroft, J.: Recent knowledge of the spleen, Lancet *1*:319, 1925.

Doggett, T. H.: The capillary system of the dog's spleen, Anat. Rec. *110*:65, 1951.

Foot, N. C.: The reticulum of the human spleen, Anat. Rec. *36*:79, 1927.

Knisely, M. H.: Spleen studies: I. Microscopic observations of the circulatory system of living unstimulated mammalian spleens, Anat. Rec. *65*:23, 1936.

————: Spleen studies: II. Microscopic observations of the circulatory system of living traumatized, and of dying spleens, Anat. Rec. *65*: 131, 1936.

Krumbhaar, E. B.: Function of the spleen, Physiol. Rev. *6*:160, 1926.

Kyes, Preston: The spleen *in* Cowdry's Special Cytology, ed. 2, p. 529, New York, Hoeber, 1932.

Lewis, O. J.: The blood vessels of the adult mammalian spleen, J. Anat. *91*:245, 1957.

————: The development of the circulation in the spleen of the foetal rabbit, J. Anat. *90*: 282, 1956.

MacKenzie, David W., Jr., Whipple, A. O., and Wintersteiner, M. P.: Studies on the microscopic anatomy and physiology of living transilluminating mammalian spleens, Am. J. Anat. *68*:397, 1941.

MacNeal, W. J.: The circulation of blood through the spleen pulp, Arch. Path. *7*:215, 1929.

McNee, J. W.: The spleen: its structure, functions and diseases (Lettsomian Lectures), Lancet *1*:951, 1009, 1063, 1931.

Mall, F. P.: On the circulation through the pulp of the dog's spleen, Am. J. Anat. *2*:315, 1903.

Peck, H. M., and Hoerr, N. L.: The effect of environmental temperature changes in the circulation of the mouse spleen, Anat. Rec. *109*: 479, 1951.

————: The intermediary circulation in the red pulp of the mouse spleen, Anat. Rec. *109*:447, 1951.

Robinson, W. L.: Some points on the mechanism of filtration by the spleen, Am. J. Path. *4*:309, 1928.

————: The vascular mechanism of the spleen, Am. J. Path. *2*:341, 1926.

————: The venous drainage of the cat spleen, Am. J. Path. *6*:19, 1930.

Solnitzky, Othmar: The Schweigger-Seidel sheath (ellipsoid) of the spleen, Anat. Rec. *69*:55, 1937.

Weiss, L.: A study of the structure of splenic sinuses in man and in the albino rat, with the light microscope and the electron microscope, J. Biophys. and Biochem. Cytol. 3:599, 1957.
————: An experimental study of the organization of the reticuloendothelial system in the red pulp of the spleen, J. Anat. 93:465, 1959.

THYMUS GLAND

Alapper, Clarence: Morphogenesis of the thymus, Am. J. Anat. 78:139, 1946.
Bell, E. T.: Tumors of the thymus in myasthenia gravis, J. Nerv. & Ment. Dis. 45:130, 1917.
Blalock, A., et al.: Treatment of myasthenia gravis by removal of thymus gland; preliminary report, J.A.M.A. 117:1529, 1941.
Eaton, L. M.: Myasthenia gravis: its treatment and relation to the thymus, Proc. Staff Meet., Mayo Clin. 17:81, 1942.
Feldman, J. D.: Endocrine control of lymphoid tissue, Anat. Rec. 110:17, 1951.
Kaplan, H. S., Carnes, W. H., Brown, M. B., and Hirsch, B. B.: Indirect induction of lymphomas in irradiated mice: I. Tumor incidence and morphology in mice bearing nonirradiated thymic grafts, Cancer Res. 16:422, 1956; II. Factor of irradiation of the host, ibid. 16:426, 1956; III. Role of the thymic graft, ibid. 16:429, 1956; IV. Genetic evidence of the origin of the tumor cells from the thymic grafts, ibid. 16:434, 1956.
Metcalf, D.: The thymic lymphocytosis stimulating factor and its relation to lymphatic leukemia, Ann. New York Acad. Sc. 73:113, 1958.
Norris, E. H.: The thymoma and thymic hyperplasia in myasthenia gravis with observations on general pathology, Am. J. Cancer 27:421, 1936.
Rowntree, L. G., Clark, J. H., and Hanson, A. M.: The biologic effects of thymus extract (Hanson), J.A.M.A. 103:1425, 1934.
————: Biologic effects of thymus extract (Hanson), Arch. Int. Med. 56:1, 1935.
Rowntree, L. G., Clark, J. H., Steinberg, A., Hanson, A. M., Einhorn, N. H., and Shannon, W. A.: Further studies on the thymus and pineal gland, Ann. Int. Med. 9:359, 1935.
Sainte-Marie, G.: Lymphocyte formation in the thymus of the rat, Proceed. Canad. Cancer Conf., vol. 3, p. 337, New York, Acad. Press, 1958.
Sainte-Marie, G., and Leblond, C. P.: Tentative pattern for removal of lymphocytes in cortex of the rat thymus, Proc. Soc. Exper. Biol. & Med. 97:263, 1958.
————: Origin and fate of cells in the medulla of the rat thymus, Proc. Soc. Exper. Biol. & Med. 98:909, 1958.
Smith, C.: Studies on the thymus of the mammal: VIII. Intrathymic lymphatic vessels, Anat. Rec. 122:173, 1955.
Smith, C., and Parkhurst, H. T.: A comparison with the staining of Hassall's corpuscles and the thick skin of the guinea pig, Anat. Rec. 103:649, 1949.

Chapter 19

Muscular Tissue

Each of the four primary tissues, as has been emphasized, represents a structural specialization for the performance of special functions. With a few exceptions (for example, the supporting function of connective tissue, performed by intercellular substance) the special functions performed by the different tissues are due to a high development of one or more of the general properties of protoplasm listed on page 53. Among these is the property of contractility. It is this property of protoplasm that is brought to a high state of development in muscular tissue. Another fundamental property of protoplasm, conductivity, is also well developed in muscular tissue, although not so highly as in nervous tissue.

Muscle *cells* are the contractile elements in muscular tissue. However, they are not commonly called cells but *fibers*. To a student who has just studied connective tissue and so become familiar with the nonliving fibers of intercellular substance, the designation of muscle cells as fibers may be confusing. It should be emphasized that muscle fibers and the fibers of intercellular substance are of fundamentally different natures; they are similar only in that they have threadlike forms. The shape of cells is often obviously adapted to their function (for example, the shape of the erythrocyte). It takes only a few seconds of reflection to realize that the shortening produced in any one diameter by a rounded cell contracting would be very limited. If, however, contraction occurs in the cytoplasm of a cell that is drawn out into a long threadlike structure (a fiber), it can effect a substantial reduction in the length of the cell. Nature, then, constructs muscle cells in the form of fibers so that their cytoplasmic contractions may be effective.

The kinetic energy and the heat that are obtained on the contraction of muscle are obtained from the potential chemical energy of food substances brought to the muscle cells by the blood stream. It follows, then, that any muscle exercised for any length of time requires an extremely good blood supply so that it may be furnished with a constant supply of fuel and oxygen. An extensive blood supply is also needed to dissipate the heat that is produced simultaneously with the kinetic energy and to take away the waste products of metabolism. As is usual, the blood vessels are carried in connective tissue; hence, connective tissue penetrates and extends throughout muscular tissue. Connective tissue is also needed in muscular tissue to form a harness, so that the pull exerted by muscle fibers may be applied usefully, and also to convey the nerves that supply the muscle fibers. Muscular tissue, then, is not composed entirely of muscle fibers; it is a mixture of muscle fibers and connective tissue.

Muscular tissue is often said to constitute the engines of the body. To pursue the analogy: anyone familiar with motor boats knows that it is not customary to install the same type of engine in a fast runabout as is required in a work boat. For the former, a relatively light type of engine capable of "turning up" a vast number of revolutions per minute might be chosen. Although such an engine might be built fairly sturdily, it could scarcely be expected to stand up if it were run at full capacity hour after hour and day after day without frequent opportunities for rehabilitation. However, such an engine could be expected to deliver its full power for short periods of time without straining it unduly. But if an engine is to be called upon to deliver full power day after day and hour after hour, such as may be needed for a work boat, a different type of engine is usually chosen, one that is heavier and turns more slowly and so does not develop as much horsepower per unit of weight, one that in general is designed to go on day after day with no trouble. The same kind of problem exists in connection with "powering" the different parts of the human body. For some actions, the equivalent of the high-speed light engine is required—for example, the actions of the muscles of a baseball pitcher who pitches only for a short time every few days. For other actions, such as moving the contents of the intestine along hour after hour, something more in the nature of the work boat engine is required. So, for this reason, the human body contains different kinds of muscular tissue. These will now be discussed.

CLASSIFICATION OF MUSCLE

Each of the different kinds of muscle in the body has several names. This is partly because muscle is classified on two different bases: a morphologic one and a functional one. First, if muscle fibers, under the microscope, exhibit a regular series of stripes or striations that cross the fibers at right angles, the muscle is said to be *striated* or *striped* muscle. If, however, muscle fibers exhibit no cross stripes or striations but only the longitudinal ones that all muscle fibers exhibit, they are said to be *smooth, nonstriated* or *nonstriped* muscle fibers. This classification of all muscle into striated and smooth is therefore made on a morphologic basis. However, muscle is also classified as to whether or not its action is controlled by the will, that is, on a functional basis. If any muscle can be controlled voluntarily, it is said to be *voluntary* muscle; however, if its actions are outside the control of the will, it is said to be *involuntary*. It so happens that most of the striated muscle of the body is under the control of the will, and almost all, if not all, of the smooth muscle is outside the control of the will. So it is usual to use the terms "striated" almost synonymously with voluntary, and "smooth" with involuntary. However, there is one important exception to this general rule. The muscle of the heart is striated, but it is not under the control of the will. Therefore, it is usually given a separate category and called *cardiac* muscle.

Striated or voluntary muscle is so often attached to one or more points on the skeleton that it is also called *skeletal* muscle.

A useful classification of muscle is as follows:

> Smooth involuntary
> Striated voluntary (skeletal)
> Striated involuntary (cardiac)

To complete the analogy about engines— the striated (voluntary) muscle of the body is comparable with the flexible, high-speed engines capable of developing great power per unit of weight, which should not be expected to run at full capacity all the time but only for moderate periods with intervals for rehabilitation. The smooth muscle of the body is more like the slow-speed, heavy-duty engine used in a work boat; it goes on day after day at much the same pace. Cardiac muscle has the virtues of smooth muscle in that it works on steadily day after day with no absolute rest, yet it, like the high-speed engine, is flexible and capable of responding to temporarily increased needs by working faster for limited periods of time without being damaged.

These 3 types of muscle will be considered in detail.

SMOOTH MUSCLE

Origin. Most smooth muscle develops from mesenchyme. This is accomplished by the differentiation of mesenchymal cells into smooth muscle fibers. The cytoplasm of each mesenchymal cell participating in this process becomes drawn out to form a long, tapering smooth muscle fiber. The nucleus of each also becomes elongated. In a few sites in the body in relation to glands (e.g., salivary, sweat, lacrimal), cells are found which have the appearance of smooth muscle cells but are developed from ectoderm. Such cells are called *myo-epithelial* cells.

Growth and Regeneration. The given amount of smooth muscle in certain parts of the body may increase in mass during postnatal life, even in adult life. Some of these increases are physiologic; for example, that which occurs in the wall of the uterus during pregnancy. Others are pathologic, such as the increase in the amount of smooth muscle that occurs in the arterioles of people suffering from hypertension. Therefore, it is of interest to inquire how a given mass of smooth muscle can increase in amount in adult life. There are three possibilities to be considered. (1) Under the stress of function, individual smooth muscle cells may become increased in size (hypertrophy). (2) Smooth muscle fibers are not very highly differentiated, so they can divide by mitosis. (3) Because they arise from mesenchymal cells, and because residual undifferentiated mesenchymal cells probably persist as such in many parts of the body, it is

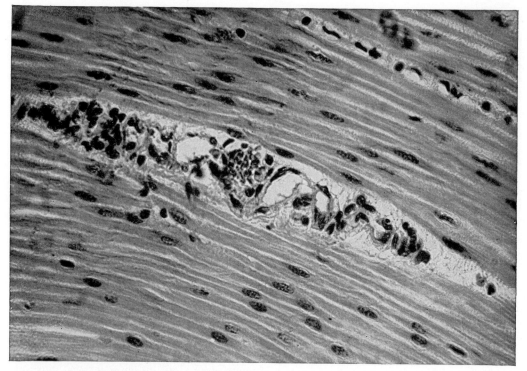

FIG. 253A. Medium-power photomicrograph of a portion of a section of the small intestine of a dog. The smooth muscle fibers in the wall of the intestine are cut longitudinally. In the middle part of the photograph the fibers are separated by some areolar tissue containing blood vessels and nerves. The remainder of the fibers are separated from one another only by slight amounts of intercellular substance, which shows up in the photograph as light lines.

by no means impossible that new smooth muscle fibers may arise as a result of the differentiation of residual undifferentiated mesenchymal cells, even in adult life.

Microscopic Structure. Smooth muscle fibers have an elongated, tapered form (Fig. 253A). Their size varies considerably according to their location. The smallest are those that encircle very small blood vessels (Fig. 333); these may be only about 20 μ in length. The largest are those that are encountered in the wall of the pregnant uterus; here they may be 0.5 mm. in length. However, the usual smooth muscle fiber is probably around 0.2 mm. long and at its widest part is somewhat wider than an erythrocyte.

The *cytoplasm* of smooth muscle cells (fibers) consists of two chief elements: myofibrils and sarcoplasm. *Myofibrils* are of the order of cytoplasmic organelles. They are threadlike structures less than 1 μ in width and are longitudinally disposed in the fiber.

They lie in the other and more fluid constituent of muscle cytoplasm, the *sarcoplasm.*

The myofibrils cannot be seen in every section. If they are not evident, the cytoplasm appears to be homogeneous. However, the fibrillar appearance, and hence the myofibrils of the cytoplasm, may be demonstrated in fresh tissue treated with acid.

The cytoplasm of muscle cells is characteristically pink or red in H and E sections. Sometimes empty spaces may be seen in it. These represent deposits of glycogen which have dissolved away in preparing the section, as can be established by fixing smooth muscle tissue in absolute alcohol and staining it by Best's carmine method. The significance of glycogen in muscle cells will become apparent when physiology is studied.

The *nucleus* of a smooth muscle fiber lies in its widest part (Figs. 253A, 253B), but, instead of being in the middle of the cell, it is situated somewhat eccentrically; this is

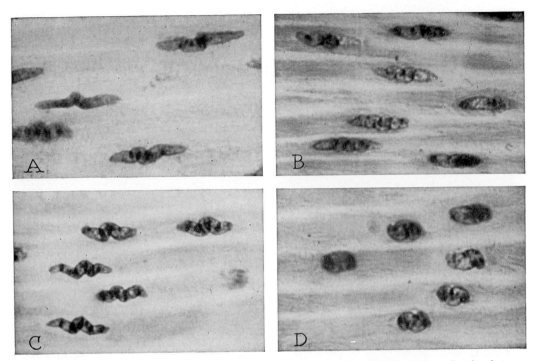

FIG. 253B. High-powered photomicrographs of smooth muscle of the intestine, showing how the elongated nuclei of the fibers are thrown into folds (pleats) when the fibers, on contraction, become shorter and thicker. In D they are folded so tightly that they appear, on superficial examination, to be ovoid.

seen to best advantage in cross sections (Fig. 254). The nucleus tends to possess a cylindrical form with either pointed or blunt, rounded ends. It contains fine chromatin granules; hence, it does not stain very intensely. It may contain several nucleoli. Often the nuclei of smooth muscle cells seen in longitudinal sections present a regularly wrinkled or pleated appearance. The rodlike nuclei become folded because they have to accommodate themselves to shorter spaces as fibers contract; hence, the degree to which their nuclei are folded (Fig. 253B) gives an indication of the extent to which fibers are contracted.

As smooth muscle fibers and connective tissue cells both arise from mesenchymal cells, it is not surprising that smooth muscle and connective tissue are intimately associated in the body. Smooth muscle cells may exist as single fibers surrounded by connective tissue, as in the skin (Fig. 536), but more often smooth muscle fibers are arranged together in bundles or sheets (Fig. 253A). In these, a little retic-

ular intercellular substance usually lies between the fibers that comprise the bundle or sheet (Fig. 253A). It seems likely that this is made by the smooth muscle fibers—another indication of their close relationship to connective tissue cells. Bundles or sheets of fibers are surrounded by connective tissue, often of a fairly elastic type (Fig. 254); however, the intercellular substance of this is made by the fibroblasts it contains. This connective tissue conveys capillaries and nerve fibers to the group of muscle fibers it surrounds (Fig. 253A, *center*).

Fine Structure. The cytoplasm of the smooth muscle cell contains longitudinally disposed myofilaments. These are arranged side by side to form a loose bundle. Within this bundle of myofilaments there are clefts for the nucleus, the mitochondria and other cytoplasmic components, for example, glycogen. The nucleus often contains one or two nucleoli in which the nucleonema may be obvious. Mark has described the uterine smooth muscle as arranged in a partial syncytium, and recently

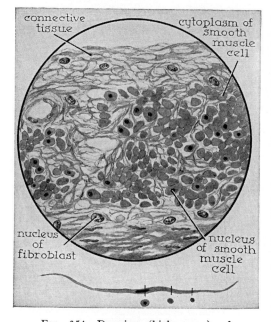

FIG. 254. Drawing (high-power) of a group of smooth muscle cells cut in cross section. Since smooth muscle fibers are elongated, cross sections cut through them seldom pass through their nuclei. Hence, most of the smooth muscle fibers seen in this illustration do not reveal nuclei. Those that are present are either centrally or eccentrically disposed. The single fiber illustrated in the lower part of the picture shows how cross sections through different parts of a fiber appear.

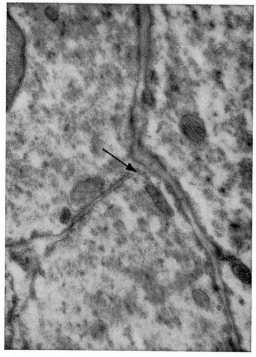

FIG. 255. Electron micrograph (× 27,000 as reproduced here) of a section of smooth muscle from the pylorus of a young rat. Note the protoplasmic bridge between two muscle cells (arrow). (Micrograph from J. C. Thaemert)

Thaemert has demonstrated protoplasmic anastomoses between smooth muscle cells in the gastrointestinal tract (Fig. 255). These anastomotic intercellular bridges obviously may play a role in the conduction of the impulse for contraction from one smooth muscle cell to another.

Function and Distribution. Although smooth muscle is used in certain sites for performing active contractions as, for example, in the wall of the intestine, where active contractions of smooth muscle force the intestinal content along its way, it is also used for maintaining a state of sustained contraction called *tonus*. In its employment for maintaining tonus, smooth muscle usually is disposed so as to encircle the lumen of a tube. In this situation the state of tonus of the encircling muscle regulates the diameter of the tube. The size

of arterioles depends to a great extent on the tonus of the encircling smooth muscle fibers in their walls, and this, it will be learned, is of great importance in regulating blood pressure. Not uncommonly (for example, in the intestine) smooth muscle is employed to serve both purposes: to maintain tonus constantly and to contract actively and inconstantly.

As various organs and structures are described, the distribution of smooth muscle in the body will become apparent. For the present it is enough to state that its chief role is to supply the viscera where either movement or the maintenance of tonus is needed.

Some Points About the Recognition of Smooth Muscle. In tissues in which smooth muscle and connective tissue are intimately mixed, it is sometimes difficult to tell them apart. The cytoplasm of the smooth muscle fibers (cells) may be confused with the collagen fibers of the connective tissue, and the

Fig. 256A. (*Top*) A very low-power photomicrograph of a portion of a section of human tongue. A bundle of striated muscle fibers may be seen horizontally disposed in the middle of the picture. Fat tissue is present on both sides of the bundle. A few obliquely cut fibers are present in the upper right-hand corner. The striated muscle fibers in the bundle may be seen to be multinucleated. (B, *Bottom*) Very high-powered photomicrograph of a longitudinal section of 2 striated muscle fibers (human) with a capillary between them.

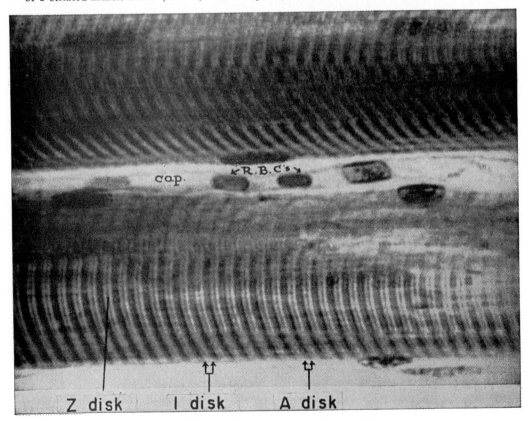

nuclei of smooth muscle cells with the nuclei of fibroblasts or other connective tissue cells.

The cytoplasm of smooth muscle fibers generally stains somewhat more darkly than collagen in H and E sections; it has a more "meaty" appearance. If cut longitudinally, the nuclei of smooth muscle fibers are longer and less ovoid (Fig. 253B) than the nuclei of young fibroblasts (Fig. 146). The nuclei of old fibroblasts, particularly in tendons, are often fairly long (Fig. 84), but if so, they tend to be thinner than the nuclei of smooth muscle fibers. Furthermore, the nuclei of smooth muscle fibers (if seen in longitudinal section) often exhibit a regularly wrinkled (snakefence) appearance (Fig. 253B).

Sometimes special staining is necessary to decide whether a given area of tissue is smooth muscle or collagen. Mallory's and Van Gieson's stains, which color collagen blue and red, respectively, are commonly used for this purpose.

STRIATED, SKELETAL OR VOLUNTARY MUSCLE

This constitutes what the layman calls the "muscles" with which man performs voluntary actions. It is capable of rapid powerful contraction (example, throwing a baseball) and also of maintaining prolonged states of partially sustained contraction—tonus (example, holding the head erect).

Like smooth muscle, the striated variety is made up of muscle fibers supported by connective tissue. However, the fibers are much larger than those of smooth muscle, measuring from 1 to 40 mm. in length and from 10 to 40 μ in width. A single nucleus is not sufficient for such an extensive mass of cytoplasm; hence, striated muscle fibers are multinucleated cells (Fig. 256A). The nuclei are of an elongated, ovoid shape, and in the striated muscles of man (but not in those of some animals), most of them are situated in the peripheral cytoplasm of the cylindrically shaped fibers (Fig. 265). The peripheral distribution of the nuclei constitutes an important criterion by which the student may distinguish striated from smooth and cardiac muscle, for in the latter two the nuclei have a more central position in the fiber (compare Fig. 265 with 254 and 269). The peripheral distribution of striated muscle fiber nuclei is seen to better

advantage in cross sections than in longitudinal sections, because a peripheral nucleus at the very top or bottom of a round fiber, on being viewed from above in a longitudinal section, will seem to be in its middle.

Another point of difference between smooth and striated fibers is that each striated fiber is enclosed by a thin, apparently structureless, membrane, called the *sarcolemma*, much as a sausage is covered with a skin. The sarcolemma is generally regarded as being formed by, and hence a part of, the muscle fiber rather than as a product of, and hence a part of, the connective tissue that surrounds the fiber. The sarcolemma cannot be seen in ordinary sections, not only because it is very thin and stains poorly, but also because it remains tightly adherent to the sides of the fiber. However, in fresh preparations, sometimes the sarcolemma can be seen in sites where the fibers are mechanically injured so that the cytoplasm, which seems to fracture more readily than the sarcolemma, is pulled apart.

The cytoplasm of striated muscle fibers is similar to that of smooth muscle fibers in that it consists of longitudinally disposed myofibrils contained in sarcoplasm. The longitudinal disposition of the myofibrils imparts a longitudinally striated appearance to striated muscle fibers (Fig. 258) as it does to smooth muscle fibers. But striated muscle fibers exhibit, in addition, a cross-striated appearance and in this respect they differ profoundly from smooth muscle fibers. It is to be emphasized that the term "striated muscle" is used only for muscle fibers that exhibit *cross striations* (Fig. 256B).

It should not be expected that every longitudinally cut striated muscle fiber seen in a section will clearly exhibit cross striations. For technical and other reasons they may not. But a search of different fields in a section, or of other sections, should reveal fibers that show cross striations clearly. The cross striations of longitudinally sectioned fibers appear as straight lines, but if the upper surface of a fiber is seen in a section, and that fiber does not lie exactly in a longitudinal plane, its cross striations will appear as crescents (Fig. 256B), as will the individual coins in a pile of coins if the edge of the pile is looked at obliquely.

When fibers showing good striations are

found and studied, the first impression one obtains is that the cross-striated appearance is due to the cytoplasm of the fiber consisting of alternating thin disks or bands (these two terms are used interchangeably) of light and dark material (Fig. 256B). With polarized light the disks that seem darker with the ordinary light microscope are anisotropic (birefringent) (Fig. 257) while those that are lighter are isotropic (Fig. 257). Accordingly, the darker disks are called A bands (A for anisotropic) or Q bands (Q for the German *Querscheibe*, which means transverse disk). The light transverse disks are called I bands (I for isotropic) or J bands (J is the German equivalent of I).

In good preparations each I band can be seen to be bisected by a thin dark disk or line; this is called the Z line or disk (Z for the German *Zwischenscheibe*, which means intermediate disk) (Fig. 256B).

It has been mentioned already that the fibers consist of longitudinally disposed myofibrils embedded in jellylike sarcoplasm. In most ordinary preparations stained with H and E the transverse disks that have been described (A, I and Z) appear to cross the whole fiber from one side to the other. But in excellent sections, and in fibers teased apart in solutions that more or less selectively dissolve the sarcoplasm, it can be seen with the light microscope that the transverse disks are properties of the myofibrils and that there are no A and I disks in the sarcoplasm which lies between the myofibrils. With the light microscope the Z disk appears to cross the sarcoplasm as well as the myofibrils, but with the E/M it can be shown that the Z disk likewise is limited to myofibrils (Fig. 258). The reasons for the transverse disks *seeming* to extend uninterruptedly across the whole fiber are (1) the myofibrils are very close together, with only a little sarcoplasm between them, and (2) the A, I and Z disks of adjacent myofibrils are each beside one another; this is often described by saying that the disks of adjacent myofibrils are *in register* with one another. Because of this and the fact that the myofibrils are close together, something of the nature of an optical illusion is created and the A, I and Z disks *seem* to extend uninterruptedly across a whole fiber.

In cross sections, the myofibrils of some

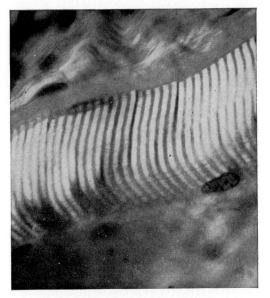

FIG. 257. High-power photomicrograph of a longitudinal section of a striated muscle fiber taken with crossed polaroid filters. The A bands are light, and the I bands are dark. (Preparation by P. M. Hartroft)

fibers are seen to be arranged more or less into bundles within the fiber. Sarcoplasm, of course, extends between each and every myofibril within each bundle, but there is more between bundles than between the myofibrils within a bundle. The thicker partitions of sarcoplasm between bundles more or less divide the fiber up into fields (each of which is a bundle of myofibrils), and these are sometimes termed *Cohnheim's fields*.

SARCOMERES

The portion of one myofibril between two Z disks is termed a *sarcomere*, and it is regarded as a unit of striated muscle structure (Fig. 258, *left side*). According to Huxley, sarcomeres in the striated muscles of frogs or rabbits are 2.3 μ in length. The A disk occupies 1.5 μ of the length of the sarcomere (Fig. 258, *left side*). Before considering the changes that occur in sarcomeres on contraction it should be mentioned that the midsection of an A band is less dense than the rest of it; this lighter disk that bisects the A band is generally termed the H disk (H for *heller* which means lighter) (Fig. 258, *left side*).

The Changes That Occur in Sarcomeres on Contraction. The description of the appearance of the transverse disks of the myofibrils given above refers to uncontracted muscle. As contraction occurs the sarcomeres become shorter and broader. Changes occur also in the cross banding; these will be described under "Fine Structure of Myofibrils."

THE FINE STRUCTURE OF THE CYTOPLASM OF STRIATED MUSCLE FIBERS

Figure 258 is a drawing illustrating a 3-dimensional view of a small block taken from a striated muscle fiber. The drawing was devised by Stanley Bennett and was based on his E/M studies of striated muscle, many of which were made in collaboration with Porter. It shows a surface view of 2 myofibrils on the right, and longitudinal sections of 2 on the left. Cross section views of myofibrils appear at the top. This illustration should be consulted frequently as the following section is read.

THE SARCOLEMMA

As has been noted already, the sarcolemma can be identified only with difficulty with the light microscope. It is too thin to be resolved as such by the instrument; its presence can be indicated only by its ability to diffract or scatter light; hence, it can be identified with the light microscope only if it is separated from the fiber. With the E/M Bennett has found the sarcolemma (Fig. 258, *right*) of fibers of the gracilis muscle of the mouse to be about 100 Å thick and to be composed of 2 membranes, each around 40 Å thick separated by a space about 20 Å thick.

SARCOPLASM

Long ago it was noticed that the sarcolemma had markings at sites where Z bands of myofibrils abutted on its inner surface, and it was thought that these represented the fastenings of Z disks which were then regarded as fibrous structures that ran across the whole muscle fiber. With the E/M Bennett and Porter recognized that these internal markings of the sarcolemma at sites of Z bands were actually sites where strands of a system of internal cytomembranes which lie in the sarcoplasm, which they term *sarcoplasmic reticulum,* were attached to the sarcolemma. This system of sarcoplasmic reticulum has been studied at length by Bennett and by Peachey and Porter. It consists of membranous tubules which in certain sites become expanded into vesicles. The outer aspects of the membranous tubules and vesicles are only sparsely studded with RNA granules.

The Sarcoplasmic Reticulum. In Chapter 4 it was pointed out that parts of the system of intracytoplasmic membranes were connected to the cell membrane, and that at least parts of the system probably developed as a result of invaginations of the cell membrane becoming pinched off in the cytoplasm. In a sense, therefore, parts of the system of membranes in the cytoplasm can be regarded *as extensions of the cell membrane into the cell.*

The sarcolemma is a membrane with very remarkable permeability and electrical properties. It acts to maintain a higher concentration of sodium and chloride ions outside than inside the fiber, and a higher concentration of potassium ions inside than outside the fiber. Furthermore, it seems to be able to maintain a potential difference of about 10 millivolts between the inside and the outside of the fiber. When a nerve impulse arrives at a motor nerve ending in a fiber (the nerve endings will be described presently) a wave of depolarization sweeps along the sarcolemma, and the fiber contracts. It always has been a mystery as to how the impulse for contraction could be conducted into the interior of the fiber quickly enough for all its parts to contract simultaneously. Ions could not diffuse into the fiber from the surface quickly enough to accomplish this end; hence, it seems most probable that the impulse for contraction is conducted into the fiber via the sarcoplasmic reticulum which could act similarly to the cell membrane (the sarcolemma) to which it is so closely related, by providing the means for a wave of depolarization to sweep into the fiber, and since strands of sarcoplasmic reticulum reach Z bands, to every sarcomere (Fig. 258, sarcoplasmic reticulum).

Mitochondria. The mitochondria of striated muscle fibers are sometimes termed sarcosomes. They lie in the sarcoplasm between myofibrils and beneath the sarcolemma; in the latter site they tend to congregate around nuclei. The myofibrils are often too close together to allow for mitochondria between

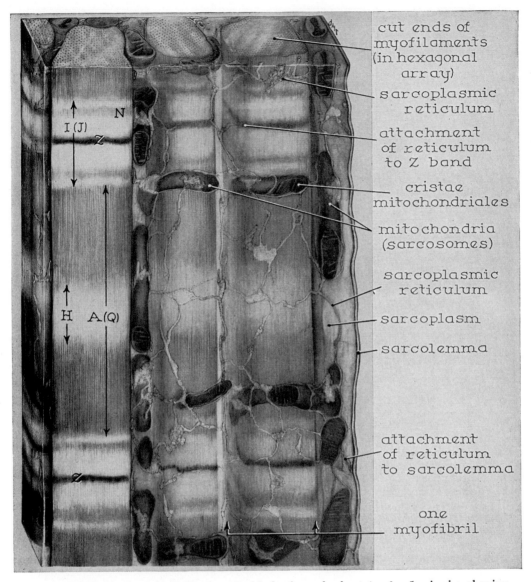

FIG. 258. Three-dimensional drawing of a block of muscle about 1 x 3 x 5 μ in size, showing detail revealed by the E/M. (Bennett, H. S.: J. Biophys. & Biochem. Cytol. (Supp.) 2:171, labeling added)

them, but in other instances they are separated from one another by about the width of mitochondria, and in these sites the mitochondria tend to be arranged in rows (Fig. 258). Generally, they are arranged with their long axes parallel with the fibers, but sometimes they are disposed so as to form angles with the long axes of fibers (Fig. 258). The mitochondria of striated muscle fibers are characterized by numerous and closely packed cristae (Fig.

258). Mitochondria are numerous close to motor nerve endings (Fig. 267).

The mitochondria and the sarcoplasmic reticulum lie in, and are components of, the sarcoplasm. The latter is a semifluid protein material containing what was named years ago the *myogen* of muscle fibers. Sometimes lipid inclusions are seen in the sarcoplasm where they may be mistaken for mitochondria. Glycogen is another inclusion that is com-

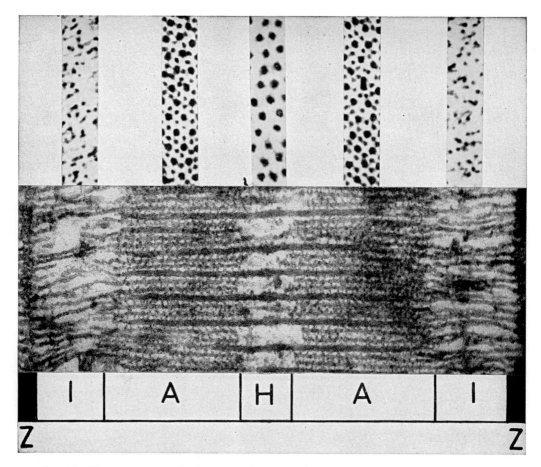

FIG. 259. Electron micrographs (× 150,000) of cross (above) and longitudinal (below) sections of relaxed striated muscle, taken from the rabbit psoas muscle. The thick (myosin) and the thin (actin) myofilaments are easily distinguished. Note that neither extends the full length of the sarcomere. Cross sections of the various bands are illustrated above. The cross bridges between the myosin and the actin filaments can be seen in the longitudinal sections. (Electron micrographs by Dr. H. E. Huxley)

monly present in sarcoplasm. It does not seem to have been identified as yet with the electron microscope, but light microscope studies have indicated that it occurs in granular form in the sarcoplasm close to the junctions of A and I bands of myofibrils.

THE FINE STRUCTURE OF MYOFIBRILS

Light microscopy showed clearly that muscle fibers are composed of myofibrils embedded in sarcoplasm. Furthermore, light microscopy suggested the existence of more delicate fibrils within the myofibril for, in 1888, Kolliker described myofibrils as containing still finer filaments within them. That the myofibrils were indeed made up of *myofilaments* was confirmed when it became possible to study sections of striated muscle with the E/M. The earlier studies with the E/M, although they disclosed myofilaments in the myofibrils, did not resolve them sufficiently well to make it obvious that in a relaxed fiber (1) the filaments do not extend from one end of a sarcomere to the other, and (2) there are two different types of myofilaments. Both of these latter facts have been established in recent years by Huxley and by Huxley and Hanson.

Proof that the sarcomere contains two types of filaments, and that neither type extends throughout the whole length of the sarcomere, came only from high resolution studies of both cross and longitudinal sections of myofibrils. From these studies it became apparent that the relative lack of density of I bands and H bands, noticed with the light microscope and the earlier studies with the E/M, was due to their each containing only one kind of myofilaments, and that the greater density of the A band was due to its containing both kinds of filaments, which interdigitated with each other (Figs. 259, 260A and B).

The two types of filaments differ in diameter, length, position and composition. The most convenient way to designate them is by their different diameters, so we shall term them the *fine* and the *coarse* filaments.

The fine ones in the rabbit psoas muscle, according to Huxley, are 50 Å in diameter and 2 microns in length. One end of each fine filament is attached to a Z disk. From the Z disks the fine filaments extend toward the middle of each adjacent sarcomere (Figs. 259, 260A and B) where they terminate in free ends before reaching the middle. The gap between the free ends of the fine filaments that extend inwardly from both of its ends accounts for the H bands (Figs. 259, 260A).

The coarse filaments, according to Huxley, are 100 Å in diameter and 1.5 microns in length. In relaxed muscle they are disposed longitudinally in the middle part of the sarcomere extending toward but not reaching each end of the sarcomere (Figs. 259, 260 A and B). In the middle of each sarcomere *only* coarse filaments are present, and this accounts for the H band (Figs. 259, 260A and B). However, proceeding from the H band toward both ends of the sarcomere, they interdigitate with the fine filaments which are extending from the Z bands toward, but not reaching, the middle. Since the coarse filaments do not reach the Z disks, there is a region on each side of each Z disk which has only fine filaments; this accounts for the I band and its relatively light density. The site where the coarse and the fine filaments interdigitate is

the A disk and the greater density of the myofibril in this site is, of course, due to its possessing both types of filaments; this is why the A band is dark when seen with the light microscope.

The Z band is a narrow band of dense material.

Cross sections cut through the I band of a relaxed fiber will reveal only the fine filaments (Fig. 259), and cross sections through the H band will reveal only the coarse filaments (Fig. 259). Of course, cross sections through the A band will reveal both coarse and fine filaments (Fig. 259).

Where the filaments interdigitate in the relaxed vertebrate muscle (the A band) the fine filaments are seen in a cross section to be arranged so as to form hexagons with a coarse filament in the center of each hexagon. The coarse filaments are arranged so as to form triangles, each of which has a fine filament in its center (Fig. 259 and Fig. 260A, *bottom diagram*). The bottom diagram in Figure 260A shows how a longitudinal section of a myofibril can be cut so as to show two fine filaments between each coarse one. It also shows how sections cut in a different plane would be very difficult to interpret and why the study of cross sections is so essential to revealing the true arrangements of the filaments.

Huxley has described also an intricate system of cross bridges between the coarse and the fine filaments. These project from the coarse filament at fairly regular intervals along their course and are arranged in a spiral. These bridges connect each thick filament at intervals to each of its three adjacent thin filaments in human muscle. They can be seen in Figure 259.

THE MECHANISM OF CONTRACTION

From the studies of Huxley it has become apparent that the contraction of a sarcomere (and hence of a muscle fiber) does not entail any significant shortening of either the coarse or the fine filaments. Contraction of the sarcomere is due to the fine filaments (which extend from each end of the sarcomere toward its middle) sliding further and further into the interstices between the coarse filaments (with which they interdigitate), pulling the Z disks to which they are attached with them, until at full contraction the free ends of the fine filaments meet each other in the middle of the sarcomere where they may even bulge against one another. Of course, this pulls the Z disks closer together and so shortens the sarcomeres.

Since the relative lack of density of the H zone in a relaxed myofibril is due to its containing only coarse filaments, it is obvious that in a contracted myofibril, in which the fine filaments slid into this area to meet one another, this area will then have both types of filaments and so will be as dense as the former A band. Likewise, the sliding of the fine filaments into the coarse ones pulls the Z bands so close to the free ends of the coarse filaments that the relative lack of density of the I bands disappears, for it too, as the fibril contracts, comes to contain both kinds of filaments.

From the foregoing it would seem that contraction is due to the fine and the coarse filaments suddenly coming to possess an increased attraction for each other, an attraction that is of a kind that results in one kind of filament sliding along the other so that the maximum attachment between their respective surface areas can be obtained. To inquire into the nature of the attraction that forms between the two types of filaments at contraction and the loss of the attraction that occurs on relaxation requires that the chemistry and the biochemistry of muscle be discussed briefly.

Three proteins have been isolated from muscle, myosin, actin and tropomyosin. Both chemical studies and interference microscopy have shown that the coarse filaments are composed of myosin. Furthermore, if myofibrils are treated so as to extract actin, the I bands

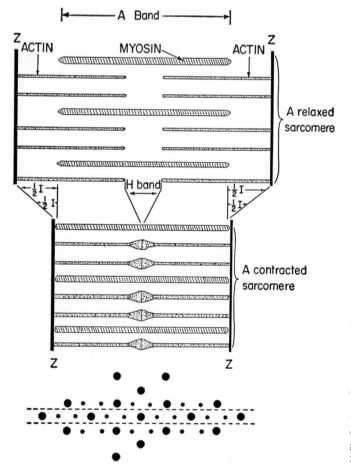

Fig. 260A. Diagram of part of one sarcomere of striated muscle to show how, in contraction, the thick and the thin myofilaments slide along each other with resulting shortening of the sarcomere and disappearance of the H and the I bands. The small diagram (below) illustrates a cross section through the A band. As indicated, a very thin longitudinal section, cut in the proper plane, will show two fine myofilaments between each pair of coarse ones. (Diagrams based on the sliding-filament hypothesis of H. E. Huxley)

(Continued on page 429)

of relaxed muscle are removed, which indicates that the fine filaments are composed of actin. It seems probable that the fine filaments also contain the tropomyosin of muscle.

Next, it has been shown that muscles derive their energy from the breakdown of adenosine triphosphate (ATP) to adenosine diphosphate (ADP). This reaction *releases* large amounts

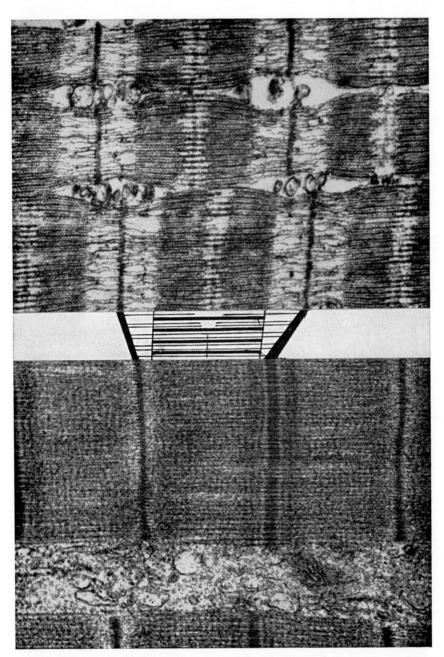

FIG. 260B. Electron micrographs (× 60,000) of longitudinal sections of relaxed (above) and a contracted (below) rabbit psoas muscle, illustrating the shortening of a sarcomere. Note the differences between the two micrographs as a result of the sliding that has occurred between thick and thin myofilaments. See also Figure 260A. (Assembled from illustrations by Huxley, H. E.: J. Biophys. & Biochem. Cytol. 3:631).

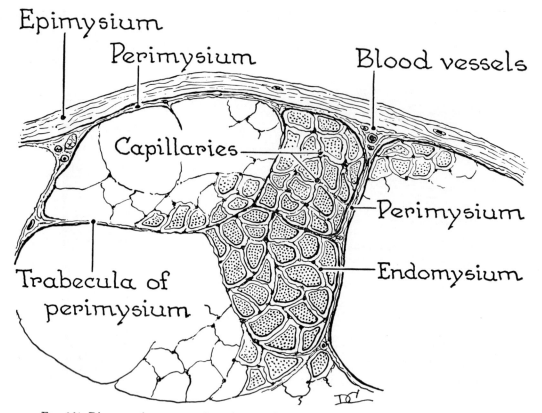

FIG. 261. Diagram of a cross section of a muscle. This shows the connective tissue epimysium that surrounds the muscle. The partitions of perimysium that divide the muscle into bundles and the delicate connective tissue endomysium that extends between the individual fibers in the bundles and carries the capillaries may also be seen.

of energy. Conversely, the resynthesis of ATP from ADP *requires* energy. This energy for the latter step is supplied by the breakdown of carbohydrates. Thus, the energy released in the breakdown of carbohydrates is stored in the form of ATP, which is, therefore, spoken of as a high-energy compound.

It has been known for a long time that actin would combine with myosin to form actomyosin, and some years ago it was shown that if artificially prepared threads of precipitated actomyosin were placed in a solution containing ATP they would contract. This finding seemed to suggest that energy donated by ATP could be utilized by actin and myosin that were already combined with one another and that it somehow led to a contraction of the combined proteins. More recently it has been shown that the action of ATP is not a direct one that induces a shortening of actin and myosin that are already combined, but

instead its presence leads to their dissociation, and this is what occurs when ATP is added to a solution of actomyosin—the actin and the myosin become dissociated. In the muscle fiber the action of ATP in dissociating the actin and the myosin filaments permits the muscle fiber to relax. Whenever the ATP is converted to ADP the actin and the myosin recombine, and this results in contraction. Therefore, the ATP has two actions: (1) its presence prevents actin and myosin from combining, and (2) the energy it gives off in being converted to ADP provides the energy for contraction. Hence, the energy for contraction in a relaxed muscle is stored in its ATP much in the same way that energy is stored in the spring of a cocked air rifle. When the trigger is pulled the potential energy of the spring is released. Similarly, when an impulse for contraction arrives at the muscle, ATP is broken down to ADP. This reaction

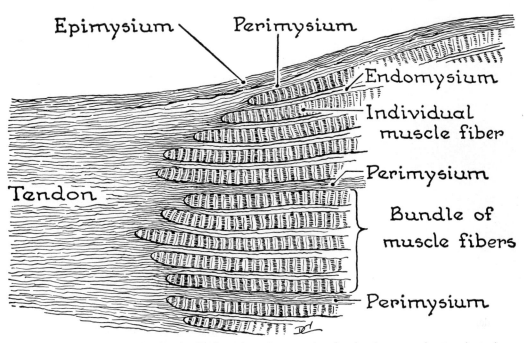

FIG. 262. Diagram of a longitudinal section of a muscle, showing how muscles terminate in tendons. The connective tissue of the epimysium, the perimysium and the endomysium is continuous with the connective tissue of the tendon. The sarcolemma covering each muscle fiber also is adherent to the connective tissue of the tendon.

is catalyzed by myosin, and the reaction provides the energy required for the myosin and actin filaments combining along their lengths.

Huxley has observed that when a muscle contracts, the extent of the sliding of the actin filaments along the myosin filaments is much greater than the distance between any two lateral projections on the myosin filaments, by which they are anchored to the actin filaments. Therefore, it is reasonable to suppose that during contraction, these lateral projections alternately disconnect and reconnect the myosin to new sites along the actin filament.

How Striated Muscles Are Harnessed

As noted previously, muscle *tissue* does not consist of muscle cells alone; it has a connective tissue component. This, as we shall see, serves several purposes. Further, different muscles contain different amounts of connective tissue. This fact has application for the cook as well as for the doctor. Since the collagen of connective tissue is much tougher than muscle fibers (which are protoplasm and hence tender), the toughness of any cut of meat depends largely on how great a compo-

nent of connective tissue the particular muscle from which it was taken contains. For example, the psoas major muscle (filet mignon) contains little.

Any given muscle may contain connective tissue, not only in its wrappings, but also in internal partitions of several different orders. First, the whole muscle is usually wrapped with a fairly substantial connective tissue sheath. This is termed the *epimysium* (upon the muscle) (Fig. 261). Second, if a whole muscle is cut in cross section and the cut surface viewed with the naked eye or under very low magnification, it will be seen that more or less longitudinally disposed partitions of connective tissue extend from the epimysium into the muscle to divide it into bundles (fasciculi). These bundles are of several different orders; for example, the whole muscle may be divided into a few big bundles, but with each of these being subdivided, by similar but thinner partitions of connective tissue, into smaller bundles, and so on. The connective tissue that divides a muscle into bundles of different orders constitutes its *perimysium,* so called because this tissue surrounds bundles of fibers (Fig. 261). Third, very delicate con-

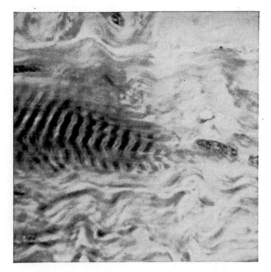

FIG. 263. Oil-immersion photomicrograph (taken with the phase microscope) of the termination of a striated muscle fiber in a tendon.

nective tissue extends from the perimysium surrounding each *bundle* of fibers into the interior of each bundle so as to penetrate between all its fibers. This constitutes the *endomysium* of the muscle and is not to be confused with the sarcolemma sheaths of the fibers, which are parts of the muscle fibers. The endomysium is seen to advantage in cross sections of muscle (Figs. 261 and 265). Here it appears as a delicate net carrying capillaries, in the interstices of which single sarcolemma-surrounded muscle fibers may be seen.

The connective tissue elements of a muscle, its epimysium, perimysium and endomysium, are all continuous with the connective tissue structures to which the muscle is attached and on which it exerts pull on contraction (Fig. 262). Such a structure may be tendon, aponeurosis, periosteum, dermis of skin, a raphe, or almost any other kind of dense connective tissue structure found in the body. The connective tissue elements of muscle, by being continuous with the connective tissue structures on which muscle pulls, have a function something like a harness. But this is not the only way muscles are attached to the connective tissue structures on which they pull. The sarcolemma covering of each rounded end of each muscle fiber that approaches a tendon or the periosteum or any other connective tis-

sue structure to which a muscle is attached blends firmly with it. Hence, the ends of the muscle fibers themselves, as well as the connective tissue elements of a muscle, are firmly attached to the connective tissue structures on which they pull. Several observers have thought that the myofibrils of the muscle fibers actually continue directly through the ends of the muscle fibers proper to merge insensibly with the collagen fibers of the tendon. However, this extreme view is not usually accepted. When observed with the phase microscope, the muscular fibers seem to end fairly abruptly (Fig. 263).

In the opinion of the author not enough attention is paid to certain physical factors which would operate to make it impossible for muscle fibers to pull themselves out of a tendon insertion. Muscle fibers that extend into a tendinous insertion (Figs. 262 and 263) would be comparable with fingers extending into a wet rubber glove, with no possibility of the fingers of the glove being peeled off so as to let air or fluid enter and substitute for the finger that was being withdrawn. In other words, for a muscle fiber to pull out of a tendon insertion would require the creation of a vacuum.

POSTNATAL GROWTH AND HYPERTROPHY OF MUSCLES

It is generally believed that the growth of muscles that occurs in postnatal life is due to the individual fibers of muscles becoming larger and not more numerous. It is also believed that the hypertrophy of muscles that can result from much exercise is due to the fibers becoming larger and not to their becoming increased in numbers.

REGENERATION OF STRIATED MUSCLE

A complete and informative investigation of the regeneration of striated muscle has been made recently by W. E. Le Gros Clark. He studied the process in rabbits in sections obtained from (1) pieces of muscle that were resected and then grafted back into place and left for different periods of time, (2) muscle that was destroyed by crushing and left to recover for varying periods of time and (3) muscle that was deprived of its blood supply and then left for different periods of time during which it became revascularized. His paper should be consulted for details; only a general account of his findings will be given here.

Muscle injured by ischemia or trauma shows no signs of regeneration for 2 days. During this time the fibers degenerate, and the area in which they are contained is invaded by neutrophils and macrophages; these assist in the breakdown and the removal of the dead material. During and after the third day proliferative changes are to be observed. The histologic picture in the damaged area is at first confused, because the fibroblasts and the endothelial cells (of the capillaries) of the endomysium proliferate and grow among the neutrophils and the macrophages. However, at the edges of the injured area, signs of muscle cell regeneration can be seen as early as the third day. This is manifested by new muscle protoplasm pushing out into the injured area from the still-living stumps of muscle fibers disposed at the edge of the injured area. In the rabbit this new protoplasm pushes ahead at the rate of from 1 to 1½ mm. per day. Meanwhile, in the injured area the neutrophils and the macrophages fade away, and the fibroblasts of the endomysium form new connective tissue tubes; these serve as guides for the muscle protoplasm that pushes into their open ends. If the sarcolemma of the muscle fibers has been lost, a new sarcolemma develops as the muscle protoplasm pushes into the endomysial tube. The capillaries of the endomysium regenerate so as to provide a blood supply for the ingrowing fibers. Some of the buds of muscle protoplasm that push into the damaged area may become separated from the fiber from which they originated; these become enclosed in sarcolemmal and endomysial sheaths to constitute *new fibers*. As a result of the formation of new fibers the regenerated muscle may have at first 50 per cent more fibers than it had originally; clearly, in the regeneration of striated muscle, new fibers can form. However, as time passes, the number of fibers in the regenerated muscle decreases again; some of the newly formed fibers do not persist. A whole muscle that is almost completely destroyed as a result of ischemia may, after revascularization and regeneration, once more develop an almost normal histologic constitution; this may entail

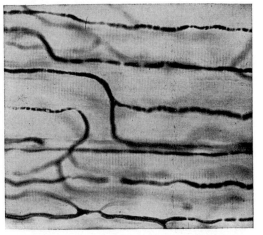

Fig. 264. Medium-power photomicrograph of a longitudinal section of striated muscle, the blood vessels of which were injected with India ink. The illustration shows how capillaries run between and parallel with the fibers in the endomysium. Compare with Figure 265. Some cross connections are also shown. (Preparation by W. S. Hartroft)

the disappearance of some of the connective tissue that forms in the repair process.

Le Gros Clark employed colchicine to study mitosis over a 10-hour period in regenerating muscle and found that although there were mitotic figures in the fibroblasts of the endomysium, there were no clear-cut ones in the nuclei of the muscle cells. Accordingly, he concludes that in the repair process the nuclei of striated muscle cells divide by amitosis. However, there are several reasons for not making a final decision about this latter matter until further evidence is at hand.

BLOOD VESSELS AND LYMPHATICS

As noted previously, striated muscle has a very rich blood supply. Arteries are carried from the epimysium by the perimysium into the substance of the muscle (Fig. 261). The arteries branch into arterioles and give off capillaries which are carried by the delicate endomysium. Most of the capillaries run parallel with the muscle fibers (Fig. 264), but side branches from them often run at right angles to the fibers. The capillary beds of striated muscle can be studied to advantage in cross sections where individual capillaries appear as

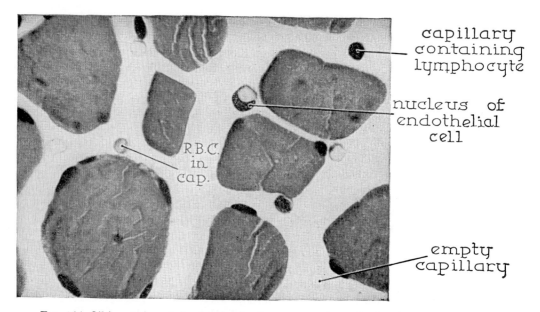

capillary containing lymphocyte

nucleus of endothelial cell

R.B.C. in cap.

empty capillary

FIG. 265. Oil-immersion photomicrograph of a cross section of striated muscle, showing the various appearances presented by capillaries in cross section. In some instances the line of section passes through a capillary at a site where a nucleus of an endothelial cell is present; if so, the nucleus appears as a blue crescent, as may be seen above. If a capillary is cut at a site where no nucleus is present, it appears as a thin cytoplasmic ring. Either red blood cells or leukocytes may be present in capillaries at the sites where they are sectioned.

delicate rings either empty or containing a red blood cell or a leukocyte (Fig. 265). A crescentic nucleus may be seen at one side of them; these are the nuclei of the endothelial cells comprising their walls (Fig. 265).

Although several capillaries usually abut on each muscle fiber, most of the exterior of each fiber is not in direct contact with capillaries. It has been assumed that a thin film of tissue fluid exists between the sarcolemma of the muscle fiber and the connective tissue endomysium that carries the capillaries and that this permits an interchange of dissolved substances between all points on the periphery of the fiber and the capillaries of the endomysium. However, it has been suggested recently that there may be a film of amorphous intercellular substance (a mucopolysaccharide) between the sarcolemma of the fiber and the endomysium. A gelled amorphous intercellular substance in this situation might facilitate diffusion.

It should be noted that the capillaries in striated muscle are much more numerous than

they are in smooth muscle, where relatively few capillaries between adjacent fibers may be seen (Fig. 253 A). The nutrition of smooth muscle depends to a considerable extent on the diffusion of substances through the fibers and the intercellular substance between them to and from capillaries in the tongues of connective tissue which penetrate the muscle (Fig. 253 A, *center*).

The lymphatics of striated muscle are confined almost entirely to its thicker connective tissue components, the perimysium and the epimysium. In this way it differs from cardiac muscle, which has lymphatics as well as capillaries in its endomysium.

THE EFFERENT INNERVATION OF STRIATED MUSCLE

Nerves are conducted into muscles by the connective tissue components of muscle. The number of muscle fibers supplied by a single motor nerve fiber varies greatly. In one of the extrinsic muscles of the eye, in which the greatest delicacy of movement is required, there is a separate nerve fiber for every muscle fiber. The other extreme is represented by muscles which are not required to perform delicate movements and in which one nerve fiber may branch and supply over 100 muscle fibers. A nerve fiber, together with all the muscle fibers it supplies, is described as a *motor unit*. If a single nerve fiber supplies many muscle fibers in a muscle, the latter do not, as might at first be expected, constitute a localized group of fibers; instead, the muscle fibers innervated by a single nerve fiber may have a considerable distribution throughout a muscle. This is important because a single muscle fiber, under the influence of a nervous stimulation, always contracts to its maximum capacity; this is spoken of as the *all or none law*. Accordingly, the ability of a muscle *as a whole* to contract with different degrees of intensity is dependent, not on the ability of individual muscle fibers to contract with different degrees of intensity—for they cannot—but on the fact that different *numbers* of the fibers in the muscle can be stimulated to contract under different conditions. Hence, if a weak contraction is required, only a small proportion of the fibers in the muscle are stimulated to contract. Under these conditions it is desirable for those that do contract to be representative of the muscle as a whole so that the contraction is general rather than local. And, since many fibers are supplied by a single nerve fiber, and since in minor contractions only a small proportion of the nerve fibers are stimulated, it is desirable that each fiber supply a group of fibers that extend fairly well throughout the length of the muscle—which they do—rather than a localized group.

Single nerve fibers from the terminal branches of peripheral nerves lead to striated muscle fibers. As a nerve fiber approaches a muscle fiber, its myelin sheath is lost. The endoneurium surrounding the nerve fiber appears to become continuous with the endomysium surrounding the muscle fiber. The axon, with its neurolemma, contacts the muscle fiber at a site along the muscle fiber where the sarcoplasm of the fiber forms a little moundlike protuberance. The sarcoplasm in this mound *under* the nerve ending is called the *sole* plasm, and it has more mitochondria and more nuclei than sarcoplasm in general. For

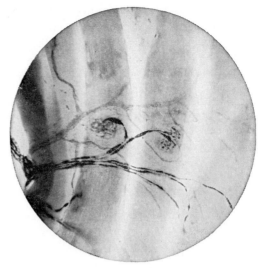

FIG. 266. High-power photomicrograph of a teased preparation of striated muscle fibers. The 2 that cross the middle of the field from top to bottom show motor endplates on their upper surfaces. The endplates and the nerve fibers that lead to them have been rendered dark by an impregnation technic.

many years it was commonly believed that the nerve fiber, before it branched into terminal arborizations, penetrated the sarcolemma and entered the substance of the sole plasm where it ended in many little treelike networks (arbor-trees, Fig. 266). The whole complex is called a motor end plate. Some observers in more recent years, from studies made with the light microscope, have doubted that the nerve fiber actually penetrated the sarcolemma of the muscle fiber. For example, Gutmann and Young, from studying the reinnervation of muscle fibers, concluded that nerve fibers ending in muscle were always separated from the sarcoplasm by a membrane. By means of vital staining Couteaux identified heavily stained membranous areas beneath nerve endings and considered these to be a continuation of the sarcolemma. Studies with the E/M by Palade and by Reger have shown definitely that the sarcolemma is not penetrated by nerve fibers but that it is continuous over the sole plasm where it, or one of its layers, becomes greatly thickened to form an irregularly grooved amorphous membranous structure (Fig. 267). The irregular ridges of amorphous membrane between adjacent grooves extend into the sole plasm (Fig. 267). The axolemma of the nerve fiber is in direct contact with this specialized region of sarcolemma, and the nerve fiber, close to the point of contact with the sarcolemma, contains many mitochondria and very numerous small vesicles (Fig. 267). The neurolemma (sheath of Schwann) of the nerve fiber probably terminates at the point where contact is made between axolemma and sarcolemma (Fig. 267).

CARDIAC MUSCLE

Until recently it was believed that cardiac muscle differed fundamentally from both smooth and striated muscle in that its fibers were not divided up into individual cells but instead were all joined together in such a way

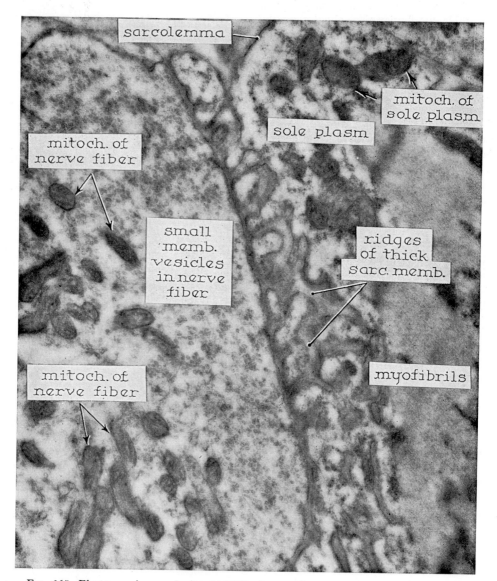

Fig. 267. Electron micrograph (× 34,000) of a section of a rat's diaphragm, showing part of a neuromuscular junction (motor end-plate). See text for description of the various components. (Preparation by G. Palade, labeling added)

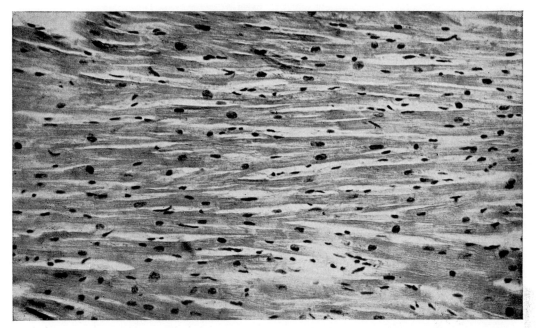

FIG. 268. Low-power photomicrograph of a longitudinal section of human cardiac muscle. Observe that the muscle fibers branch and anastomose and that the interstices so created are filled with light-staining connective tissue. This carries the blood and lymph capillaries and the nerves.

that they formed a huge protoplasmic network or syncytium (Fig. 268). In general, each muscle fiber in this network tends to be disposed in the same plane as its neighbors, and as a result the interstices of the network are slitlike, with the long axes of the slits being parallel with those of the fibers. The interstices contain the endomysium of cardiac muscle. This is of the nature of loose connective tissue and is abundantly supplied with capillaries which are thereby brought into close contact with the muscle fibers of the network. Moreover, the endomysium of cardiac muscle is provided with lymphatic capillaries as well as blood capillaries, and it also carries nerve fibers that end on the cardiac muscle cells.

The nuclei of cardiac muscle fibers tend to be disposed in the middle parts of the fibers (Fig. 269). They are usually ovoid in shape, but their ends, instead of being rounded, sometimes may be more or less squared (Fig. 268). They are pale.

The cytoplasm of cardiac muscle fibers contains myofibrils and sarcoplasm and shows cross striations similar to those described for striated muscle. The cross striations of cardiac muscle, although due to A and I disks, and Z lines similar to those of striated muscle, are not usually so distinct as those of striated muscle. In addition, cardiac muscle fibers are crossed every now and again by unique dark-stained bands called *intercalated disks* (intercalated means inserted). These disks which are more or less *inserted* between some sarcomeres are seen, with the light microscope, to be less than a sarcomere in thickness and to be present at the sites of Z bands (Fig. 270). Sometimes intercalated disks cross fibers in straight lines, but sometimes they cross fibers in a stepwise fashion (Fig. 270); this is due to the intercalated disks of different myofibrils of the fiber not being in register. There has been much speculation about their nature and function through the years. It was not until they were examined in thin sections with the E/M that their true nature was definitely established. With the E/M they were seen to be cell membranes of the cardiac muscle cells. Until this was discovered it was

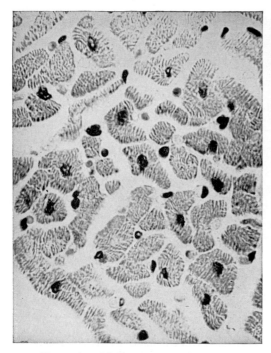

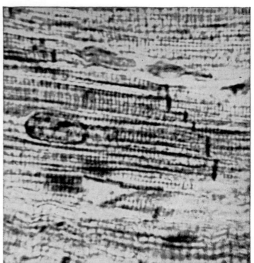

FIG. 270. High-power photomicrograph of a longitudinal section of cardiac muscle (dog) stained by Mallory's phosphotungstic hematoxylin method. This brings out the intercalated disks, which appear as dark lines crossing the fibers, sometimes in a steplike fashion.

FIG. 269. Medium-power photomicrograph of a cross section of human cardiac muscle. The connective tissue endomysium separating the individual fibers is too delicate and stains too faintly to be seen. Observe that the nuclei are present in the central parts of the fibers. The cytoplasm does not appear homogeneous because of the myofibrils in it.

generally assumed that cardiac muscle represented a syncytium; that there were no cell boundaries that extended across the fibers that branched and anastomosed. However, the E/M has shown that this assumption was erroneous, and that the sarcolemma of cardiac muscle fibers crosses them to separate them into segments which are individual cells, bounded along their sides and at each end with a cell membrane.

Fine Structure. As seen with the E/M the cell membranes of cardiac muscle cells, in passing across fibers at intercalated disks, pursue a zigzag course (Fig. 271). The membranes of the two cells that abut on each other at an intercalated disk are separated from each other by space of fairly constant width (Fig. 271) which contains light material. On the other hand, there is dense ma-

terial arranged along the cytoplasm side of each of the two cell membranes that abut on each other at intercalated disks (Fig. 271). This dense material is probably chiefly responsible for the staining reaction of the intercalated disks that is observed with the light microscope. Dense material is not uncommonly seen in a similar position in the cytoplasm of other kinds of cells that come into contact with one another as is shown in Figure 133.

Pigment. Beginning at the age of 10, granules of golden-yellow pigment tend to accumulate in the sarcoplasm at each end of the nuclei of cardiac muscle fibers. It seems probable that these granules represent a combination of pigments derived from the hemoglobin of blood. This pigment becomes very prominent in a condition termed "brown atrophy of the heart."

Growth. Many disease conditions require that the heart do more work. These lead to the heart becoming heavier and larger. Such a heart is said to be hypertrophied. There has been some question as to whether the increase in the amount of cardiac muscle in hypertrophy is brought about by an increase in the number or the size of its fibers. The studies of Karsner, Shapiro and Todd indicate that it is due to an increase in the size of the fibers and not in their number.

THE IMPULSE-CONDUCTING SYSTEM OF CARDIAC MUSCLE

This matter is considered in Chapter 21, which deals with the Circulatory System.

HOW TO DISTINGUISH BETWEEN SECTIONS OF THE 3 KINDS OF MUSCLE

In identifying sections of muscle on practical examination the student will find it helpful to examine the unknown section with particular reference to certain points:

1. The width of the fibers (smooth are narrowest; striated, widest; and cardiac, between).

2. The position of the nuclei in the fibers (in the periphery of striated, toward the middle of smooth and cardiac).

3. Whether the fibers branch and anastomose (cardiac).

4. Whether the fibers exhibit cross striations (striated, cardiac).

5. Whether intercalated disks are present (cardiac).

However, the use of these commonly listed criteria is not so simple as to render practice and experience unimportant. In ascertaining whether the nuclei of the fibers are in the middle or the peripheral parts of the fibers, the student must take care not to confuse the nuclei of the connective tissue endomysium with the nuclei of the muscle fibers themselves. Further, as has been explained, in longitudinal section, a peripheral nucleus of a striated muscle fiber may *seem* to be in the middle of the fiber. The position of the nuclei can be determined to better advantage if an area of the section can be found in which the muscle fibers are cut in cross section instead of longitudinally (compare Figs. 254, 265 and 269). However, with regard to point 3, the student should find a place on the section where the fibers are cut in longitudinal section. With regard to the fourth point, it should be recalled that cross striations are not always seen easily, and in particular they are often difficult to find quickly in sections of cardiac

Fig. 271. Electron micrograph ($\times$ 20,000 approximately) of a section of heart muscle, showing an intercalated disk. (Preparation by A. Muir)

muscle. They can be seen to better advantage if the light is cut down by lowering the condenser or by partly closing the diaphragm. Likewise, intercalated disks do not always show up well in sections, and they too can be seen to better advantage if the light is cut down. Furthermore, it should be remembered that positive evidence is better than negative evidence. For example, a student who sees nuclei disposed in the middle parts of fibers that clearly branch and anastomose and yet cannot see cross striations or intercalated disks, should place his trust in his positive evidence and diagnose cardiac muscle rather than smooth.

REFERENCES

Muscle—General References

Bennett, H. S.: The cytology of striped muscle *in* Palay, S. L. (ed.): The Henry Bunting Memorial Volume, New Haven, Yale Univ. Press, 1957.

Bourne, G. H. (ed.): The Structure and Function

of Muscle, vols. 1 and 2, New York, Acad. Press, 1960.

MUSCLE—SPECIAL REFERENCES

Beams, H. W., Evans, T. C., Janney, C. T., and Baker, W. W.: Electron microscope studies of the structure of cardiac muscle, Anat. Rec. 105:59, 1949.

Bennett, H. S.: An electron microscope study of sectioned breast muscle of the domestic fowl, Am. J. Anat. 93:61, 1953.

————: The microscopical investigation of biological materials with polarized light in Mc-Clung's Handbook of Microscopical Technique, ed. 3, pp. 591-677, Hoeber, New York, 1950.

————: The sarcoplasmic reticulum of striped muscle, J. Biophys. & Biochem. Cytol. 2:171 (Supp.), 1956.

Bennett, H. S., and Porter, K. R.: An electron microscope study of sectioned breast muscle of the domestic fowl, Am. J. Anat. 93:61-105, 1953.

Caesar, R., Edwards, G. A., and Ruska, H.: Architecture and nerve supply of mammalian smooth muscle tissue, J. Biophys. & Biochem. Cytol. 3:867, 1957.

Clark, W. E. Le Gros: An experimental study of the regeneration of mammalian striped muscle, J. Anat. 80:24, 1946.

Dempsey, E. B., Wislocki, G. B., and Singer, M.: Some observations on the chemical cytology of striated muscle, Anat. Rec. 96:221, 1946.

Edwards, G. A., Ruska, H., Santos, P. de S., and Vallejo-Freire, A.: Comparative cytophysiology of striated muscle with special reference to the role of the endoplasmic reticulum, J. Biophys. & Biochem. Cytol. 2:143 (Supp.), 1956.

Finck, H., Holtzer, H., and Marshall, J. M.: An immunochemical study of the distribution of myosin in glycerol extracted muscle, J. Biophys. & Biochem. Cytol. 2:175 (Supp.), 1956.

George, J. C., and Jyoti, D.: Histological features of the breast and leg muscles of bird and bat and their physiological and evolutionary significance, J. Animal Morphol. & Physiol. 2:1, 1955.

Gersh, I.: Improved histochemical methods for chloride, phosphate-carbonate and potassium applied to skeletal muscle, Anat. Rec. 70:311, 1938.

Goldstein, D. J.: Some histochemical observations of human striated muscle, Anat. Rec. 134:217, 1959.

Hanson, J., and Huxley, H. E.: The structural basis of contraction in striated muscle, Symposia Soc. Exper. Biol., no. 9, 228-264, 1955.

————: Structural basis of the cross-striations in muscle, Nature 172:530, 1953.

Hodge, A. J.: The fine structure of striated muscle: A comparison of insect flight muscle with vertebrate and invertebrate skeletal muscle, J. Biophys. & Biochem. Cytol. 2:131, (Supp.), 1956.

Hodge, A. J., Huxley, H. E., and Spiro, D.: Electron microscope studies on ultrathin sections of muscle, J. Exper. Med. 99:201-206, 1954.

Huxley, H. E.: The double array of filaments in cross-striated muscle, J. Biophys. & Biochem. Cytol. 3:631, 1957.

————: The contraction of muscle, Scientific Amer. 199:66, 1958.

Huxley, A. F., and Taylor, R. E.: Function of Krause's membrane, Nature 176:1068, 1955.

————: Muscular contraction. Endeavour 15:177, 1956.

Jones, W. M., and Barer, R.: Electron microscopy of the sarcolemma, Nature 161:1012, 1948.

Kisch, B.: Studies in comparative electron microscopy of the heart: II. Guinea pig and rat, Exper. Med. & Surg. 12:335, 1955.

Long, M. E.: The development of the muscle-tendon attachment in the rat, Am. J. Anat. 81:159, 1947.

Mark, J. S.: An electron microscope study of uterine smooth muscle, Anat. Rec. 125:473, 1956.

Muir, A. R.: An electron microscope study of the embryology of the intercalated disc in the heart of the rabbit, J. Biophys. & Biochem. Cytol. 3:193, 1957.

Peachey, L. D., and Porter, K. R.: Intercellular impulse conduction in muscle cells, Science 129:721, 1959.

Pease, D. C., and Baker, R. F.: The fine structure of mammalian skeletal muscle, Am. J. Anat. 84:175, 1949.

Perry, S. V.: Relation between chemical and contractile function and structure of the skeletal muscle cell, Physiol. Rev. 36:1, 1956.

Porter, K. R.: The myo-tendon junction in larval forms of Amblystoma punctatum, Anat. Rec. 118:342, 1954.

————: The sarcoplasmic reticulum in muscle cells of amblystoma larvae, J. Biophys. & Biochem. Cytol. 2:163 (Supp.), 1956.

Robertson, J. D.: Some features of the ultrastructure of reptilian skeletal muscle, J. Biophys. & Biochem. Cytol. 2:369, 1956.

Sjöstrand, F. S., and Andersson, E.: Electron microscopy of the intercalated discs of cardiac muscle tissue, Experientia 10:369-370, 1954.

————: The ultrastructure of the skeletal muscle myofilaments at various states of shortening, J. Ultrastr. Res. 1:74, 1957.

Sjöstrand, E. S., Andersson-Cedergren, E., and

Dewey, M. M.: The ultrastructure of the intercalated discs of frog, mouse, and guinea pig cardiac muscle, J. Ultrastr. Res. *1*:271, 1958.

Speidel, Carl Caskey: The fundamental transverse arrangement of cross striae in myofibrils of striated muscle, Anat. Rec. *100*:91, 1948.

Spiro, D.: The filamentous fine structure of striated muscle at different stages of shortening, Exper. Cell Res. *10*:562, 1956.

————: The ultrastructure of striated muscle at various sarcomere lengths, J. Biophys. & Biochem. Cytol. *2*:157 (Supp.), 1956.

Szent-Gyorgyi, A.: Chemistry of Muscular Contraction, ed. 2, New York, Acad. Press, 1951.

————: A study on muscle *in* Nature of Life, New York, Acad. Press, 1948.

Thaemert, J. C.: Intercellular bridges as protoplasmic anastomoses between smooth muscle cells, J. Biophys. & Biochem. Cytol. *6*:67, 1959.

Tower, S.: Atrophy and degeneration in skeletal muscle, Am. J. Anat. *56*:1, 1935.

van Breemen, V. L.: Intercalated discs in heart muscle studied with the electron microscope, Anat. Rec. *117*:49, 1953.

————: Myofibril development observed with the electron microscope, Anat. Rec. *113*:179, 1952.

Weinstein, H. J.: An electron microscope study of cardiac muscle, Exper. Cell. Res. *7*:130, 1954.

SPECIAL REFERENCES ON MOTOR NERVE ENDINGS IN MUSCLE

Beams, H. W., and Evans, T. C.: Electron micrographs of motor end-plates, Proc. Soc. Exper. Biol. & Med. *82*:344-346, 1953.

Couteaux, R.: Contribution a l'étude de la synapse myoneurale, Rev. Canad. Biol. *6*:563, 1947.

Gutmann, E., and Young, J. Z.: The reinnervation of muscle after various periods of atrophy, J. Anat. *78*:15, 1944.

Palade, G. E.: Electron microscope observations on interneuronal and neuromuscular synapses, Anat. Rec. *118*:335, 1954.

Reger, J. F.: Electron microscopy of the motor end-plate in intercostal muscle of the rat, Anat. Rec. *118*:334, 1954.

————: Electron microscopy of the motor end-plate in rat intercostal muscle, Anat. Rec. *122*:1, 1955.

Chapter 20

Nervous Tissue and
the Nervous System

PRELIMINARY CONSIDERATIONS

PROPERTIES OF NERVOUS TISSUE

Epithelial tissue, the first tissue we studied, was found to be structurally specialized to permit the superior expression of two of the basic properties of protoplasm: *absorption* and *secretion*. Nervous tissue, the fourth and last basic tissue we study, will be found to be structurally specialized for the superior—if not the exquisite—expression of two other basic properties of protoplasm, *irritability* and *conductivity*.

Irritability and Conductivity. Irritability is the basic property of protoplasm that enables a cell to respond to a stimulus. It should be emphasized that irritability is not a response, but that a cell must be irritable if it is to respond. For example, epithelial cells, on being stimulated, can *respond* by *secreting*, muscle cells by *contracting* and nerve cells by *conducting* waves of excitation over their whole extents. In order to respond to a stimulus, in any one of these three ways, a cell must first be irritable.

Some people are more irritable than others and become angry in response to stimuli that do not disturb their more placid companions. Similarly, some kinds of cells are more irritable than others; they are stimulated more easily to respond. It is in the cells of nervous tissue that irritability is most highly developed. Not only are nerve cells in general very sensitive to stimuli, but some kinds are specialized to respond to very special kinds of stimuli, for example, certain nerve cells in the eye respond to the stimulus of light.

The response elicited in nerve cells—no matter what kind of stimulus is responsible for it—*is always the same*; the cell conducts a wave of excitation (called a nervous impulse) over its whole extent. Since the cytoplasm of nerve cells commonly is drawn out into long threadlike extensions, called *nerve fibers*, which are sometimes several feet long,

therefore nerve cells are specialized *to conduct* nervous impulses over long distances. They are also specialized to transmit the impulses very rapidly; in nerve fibers impulses travel at speeds up to 100 meters per second.

ROLES OF NERVOUS TISSUE IN THE
BODY ECONOMY

With the foregoing paragraphs in mind, it is easy to understand the *basic* function of nervous tissue in the body. It is: (1) to serve as a tissue that is receptive to various types of stimuli that arise or are present either outside or inside the body and (2) on being stimulated, to conduct rapidly, and sometimes over great distances, nervous impulses to *muscle* and *gland* cells. Nervous impulses conducted to muscle cells make them contract; those conducted to gland cells make them secrete. Therefore, nervous impulses are the usual stimuli that evoke responses in muscle and gland cells.

Superimposed on this basic role of nervous tissue are others of a more complex nature. Environment provides so many stimuli that an individual literally would be in a chronic state of convulsion if all stimuli were immediately translated into responses. Therefore, there must be within nervous tissue some mechanism for more or less sorting out the nervous impulses that are set up by stimuli and for permitting only certain of these impulses to reach muscle and gland cells. There must also be a mechanism for permitting delayed responses to stimuli, for memory, for the initiation of voluntary activities, for consciousness and for the appreciation of different sensations—in short, for all those phenomena classed as higher nervous functions.

THE WAY NERVOUS TISSUE IS DISTRIBUTED
IN THE BODY TO PERFORM ITS BASIC
AND HIGHER FUNCTIONS

Nervous tissue extends into almost every part of the body. Yet every portion of nervous tissue in a body is connected to other portions, so that it is all welded together to form a great anatomic and functional unit termed the *nervous system*. However, nervous tissue is not equally apportioned to all parts of the body. In particular, there is a great depot of it which fills the skull as the *brain* and continues down the canal of the backbone as the *spinal cord* (Fig. 272). This great concentration of nervous tissue in the mid-line of the body—the brain and the spinal cord—constitutes what is known as the *central nervous system*, which hereafter we shall refer to as the C.N.S. The remainder of the nervous tissue of the body constitutes the other division of the system; this is known as the *peripheral nervous system*, which hereafter we shall refer to as the P.N.S. This part consists of cordlike nerves that extend out through foramina in the skull and the vertebral column, from the brain and the spinal cord, as cranial and spinal nerves, to reach almost all parts of the body (Fig. 272).

The higher functions of nervous tissue, of course, are dependent on the C.N.S. However, the basic function of nervous tissue is more dependent on the P.N.S. because it is responsible for conducting nervous impulses from sites of stimulation to the C.N.S. and then back again to muscles and glands. Nervous impulses always take this roundabout course. Those that arise, for example in the skin, are carried by the nerves of the P.N.S. into the C.N.S., where they are, so to speak, sorted out and evaluated. Only then are they sent out to muscles and glands again by way of the nerves of the P.N.S. The reason for their taking this seemingly roundabout route between sites of stimulation and muscles and glands is easily understood if a few of the factors that operated in the evolution of nervous systems are first reviewed; hence, we shall deal briefly with this matter next.

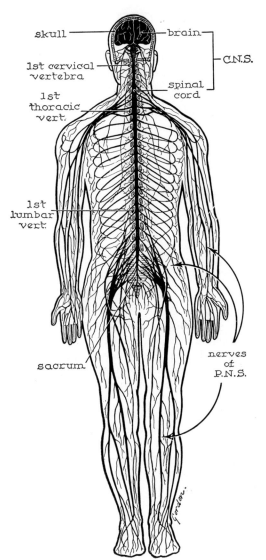

FIG. 272. Drawing to illustrate the position of the various parts of the nervous system in the body. Part of the brain is not shown so that the sites of certain cranial nerves could be indicated.

AN ACCOUNT (IN WHICH IMPORTANT NEW TERMS ARE INTRODUCED) OF SOME STEPS IN THE EVOLUTION OF NERVOUS TISSUE

Anyone whose activities are distributed over many fields of endeavor can scarcely expect to become expert in all; and so it is with cells.

Since the protoplasm of a unicellular organism, such as an ameba, must be competent with regard to all the properties of protoplasm, it could scarcely be expected to exhibit irritability, conductivity or contractility to a high degree; indeed, an ameba is a sluggish creature.

The advent of the multicellular organism made is practicable for cells to become spe-

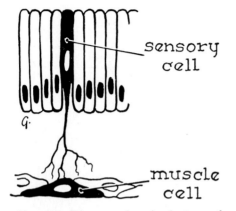

FIG. 273. Diagram of a simple type of receptor-effector system such as is seen in the tentacles of sea anemones. (Redrawn from Parker, G. H.: The Elementary Nervous System, Philadelphia, Lippincott)

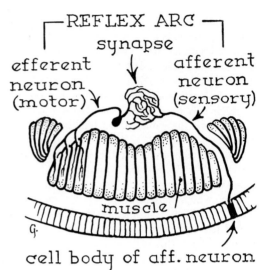

FIG. 274. Diagram of an afferent and efferent neuron arranged to constitute a reflex arc in the earthworm. (Redrawn from Parker, G. H.: The Elementary Nervous System, Philadelphia, Lippincott)

cialized. Muscle cells—specialized for contractility—probably appeared in the animal kingdom before nerve cells, because certain of the sponges, though vegetablelike in their general immobility, possess contractile cells around their pores. These are in direct contact with sea water, and, should it contain a noxious substance, the muscle cells are directly stimulated to contract and close the pores.

As multicellular organisms became more complex, muscle cells came to be more deeply located, hence not in direct contact with the external environment of the organism. This arrangement required that some sufficiently irritable cells of the organisms be exposed to surface stimulation and arranged so that they could conduct waves of excitation to the deeply situated muscle cells. One of the first arrangements of this sort to evolve is found in the tentacles of the sea anemone (Fig. 273). In this illustration one of the ectodermal cells (the black one) has differentiated into a *nerve cell* (labeled *sensory cell*), and although its cell body, which contains the nucleus of the cell, remains at the surface, its cytoplasm has extended in the form of a long threadlike process, called a *nerve fiber,* to a deeply disposed muscle cell. A combination of a nerve cell and a muscle cell such as this constitutes a simple *neuromuscular mechanism.* In such an arrangement the nerve cell bears much the same relationship to the muscle cell as does a detonator to an explosive shell. The term

"neuron" refers to a complete and single nerve cell, including its cell body, which contains the nucleus and one or more cytoplasmic extensions, called *processes*; some of these may be thick at first, but they all become thinned down to nerve fibers eventually. The processes are of only two kinds. The first kind are called *dendrons* (*dendron* = tree) or, more commonly, *dendrites,* because they branch like trees (Fig. 287). These carry nervous impulses toward the cell body. Most neurons have several dendrites. The second kind of process of a neuron is always single, and since it tends to be straight and long it is called an *axon* (*axon* = axis) (Fig. 287). The axon carries nervous impulses away from the cell body. The further evolution of nervous tissue hinged on the development of nervous pathways consisting of two or more neurons. In these pathways the processes of one neuron come into contact with either the cell body or a process of another. These points of contact with one another are termed *synapses.*

Synapses. The word synapse was derived from a Greek word which means *to clasp,* and as the tissues of two individuals who clasp hands are in contact, but not in continuity, so the cytoplasm of a neuron at a synapse is in contact but is not continuous with that of an-

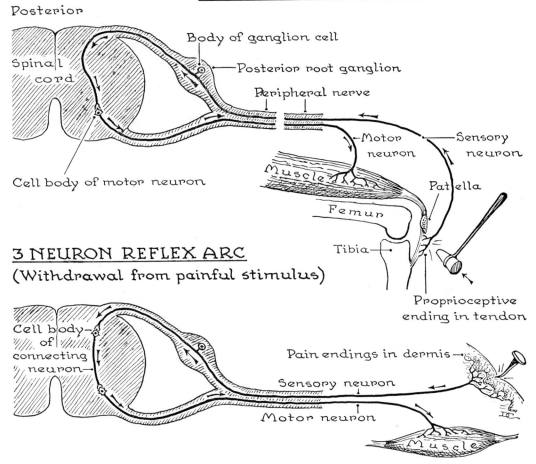

FIG. 275. Diagrams illustrating reflex arcs involving 2 and 3 neurons, respectively. Notice that the cell body of the afferent (sensory) neuron is situated in the posterior root ganglion outside the central nervous system.

other neuron. Synapses vary in form. In one common type, neurons come into contact with others solely through their fibers. In this arrangement the end of a fiber of one neuron approaches the end of a fiber of another neuron, and the ends of the respective fibers, at their point of contact, break out into filamentous little fingers which literally clasp each other (Fig. 274). In another common type, fibers from other neurons come into contact with the cell body of a given neuron; here the synaptic terminals of the fibers on the cell body are more like little feet than hands (Fig. 292); indeed, this type of terminal is called an *end-bulb* or *foot*. From histologic studies with the light microscope it was very difficult to establish whether synapses were points of contact or continuity between neurons. The E/M has shown clearly that these are merely points of contact, as will be described later. There is other evidence showing that synapses represent only points of contact; for example, (1) there is a slight delay as a nervous impulse passes over a synapse; (2) a synapse, unlike a nerve fiber, will transmit a nervous impulse in only one direction— it is said to be *dynamically polarized*; (3) synapses become fatigued more easily than nerve fibers; (4) they are more susceptible than nerve fibers to the action of certain drugs; (5) if the cell body of any given neuron is destroyed, all its fibers degenerate, but

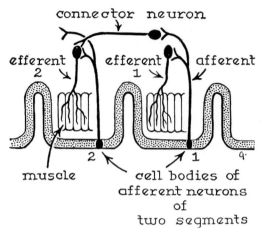

FIG. 276. Diagram of a portion of a theoretical segmented organism, showing how connector neurons permit correlation between segments.

the degeneration that spreads throughout the entire affected neuron stops at all its synapses.

The Reflex Arc—Afferent and Efferent Neurons. Arrangements of two or more neurons generally are required if a stimulus, received anywhere by an animal, is to evoke a response in a muscle or a gland. A simple example of a working arrangement of two neurons is to be seen in each segment of an earthworm (Fig. 274).

The first neuron, which has its cell body at the surface, sends a nerve fiber into the substance of the segment where the fiber terminates in synaptic connection with the fiber of a second neuron. The first neuron, because it carries a nervous impulse toward the more central part of the earthworm, is said to be an *afferent* (*affere* = to carry to) neuron. The second neuron in turn carries the impulse away from the deeper part of the organism to the muscle and is said to be an *efferent* (*effere* = to carry away) neuron (Fig. 274). The two neurons together constitute the very simplest form of a *reflex arc*. This term (derived from *reflectere* = to bend back, and from *arcus* = a bow or a curved line) aptly describes the arrangement, because the nervous impulse brought into the organism by means of the afferent neuron is *reflected* outwardly again by means of the efferent neuron.

Most Actions of Man Involve Reflex Arcs. The reader will soon be testing the reflexes of patients to learn if various parts of their nervous system are functioning properly. A common and important reflex tested is the knee jerk. This is done by having a patient cross his knees and relax; then the upper knee is given a sharp tap just below the patella, as is shown in Figure 275. The proper functioning of this reflex is indicated by the leg kicking forward smartly (but not too far) in response to the stimulus. Only two neurons are involved in this reflex. The cell body of the afferent neuron is contained in what is termed a posterior root ganglion (these structures will be described presently). From it, nerve fibers extend (1) in a peripheral nerve, to the ligament of the patella, and (2) into the spinal cord; in the cord the latter fiber synapses with the cell body of an efferent neuron, which sends a fiber, by means of a peripheral nerve, to the muscle fibers of the quadriceps femoris, as is shown in Figure 275. A slightly more complex reflex arc is shown in the second diagram in this illustration. However, most reflex arcs in the body are necessarily more complex than these, for reasons which will be explained in the following section.

Notice, as is shown in Figure 275, that both afferent and efferent fibers travel in the same peripheral nerve.

Segmented Animals and Connector Neurons. As evolution proceeded, larger animals appeared in the world. In becoming larger most animals became elongated. The mechanism for elongation generally depends on basic units of structure, called segments, becoming duplicated and reduplicated in the longitudinal axis of an animal. In lowly segmented organisms, such as the earthworm, the boundaries between segments are easily seen, and each segment retains a considerable amount of autonomy. Of particular interest to us is the fact that each segment contains an afferent and an efferent neuron and an individual unit of muscle to which the efferent neuron leads; hence, reflex activity is possible within each segment.

However, the evolution of the elongated segmented organism required the evolution of a new type of neuron, one that could provide nervous connections between segments and so permit the activities of the various segments to be regulated in the interests of the animal as a whole. Hence, segmented organisms have, in addition to afferent and efferent neurons, *intersegmental connector neurons*. In the diagram of a theoretical segmented animal (Fig. 276) it may be seen that these intersegmental connector neurons permit a stimulus received in one segment to cause a response in another. Intersegmental connector neurons *broaden the base of reflex arcs from one segment to many segments*.

In understanding the nerve supply of any part of the body it is of the greatest importance to remember that man is a segmented organism (Fig. 272). The spinal cord, as we shall see, contains intersegmental connector neurons; it is, in a sense, the outcome of the need for large numbers of connector neurons in an organism with many segments. Each of the spinal nerves that pass out from the spinal cord, one from each side, through the foramen between individual vertebrae, represents in man the afferent and the efferent neurons that are in the individual segments of the earthworm; the nerves that extend through each foramen contain many afferent and efferent neurons. Moreover, the afferent fibers in these nerves will be found to extend only to sites in the skin and other tissues that develop from that same segment. Likewise, the efferent fibers in each spinal nerve will be found to pass only to muscle fibers that develop from that same segment. During development, the muscle fibers that develop from any given segment only sometimes remain independent of those from other segments as, for example, occurs in the intercostal muscles; more commonly they fuse with muscle fibers from other segments to become parts of larger muscles that traverse many segments. Nevertheless, the fibers that develop from any segment retain their efferent innervation from that segment; hence, large muscles may have innervation from several segments.

The spinal nerves of man are named according to the vertebra (cervical, thoracic, lumbar and sacral) above or below (in the cervical regions above, in others below) which they pass to emerge into the body (Fig. 272). Since the arm develops from the 5th, 6th, 7th and 8th cervical and the 1st thoracic segments, the nerve supply of the arm is obtained from the spinal nerves that leave the vertebral column in this region (Fig. 272). The legs develop from the 2nd, 3rd, 4th and 5th lumbar and the

1st, 2nd and 3rd sacral segments; hence, they are innervated by spinal nerves that emerge from the spinal cord below each of these vertebrae, as may be seen in Figure 272.

Positions Assumed by the Cell Bodies of Afferent, Efferent and Connector Neurons. The study of animals representing different stages in the evolution of nervous tissue shows that the operation of the *tendency for the centralization of nervous tissue* gradually influenced the form and the position of nervous tissue in the body. The operation of this factor has led to as much nervous tissue as possible having a protected central position in the organism. How the operation of this tendency affected the position assumed in higher animals of afferent, efferent and connector neurons will now be described. For convenience we shall first describe its effects on connector neurons.

Connector Neurons. These neurons, as has been explained already, evolved so that the afferent and the efferent neurons of individual segments could be linked with those of others (Fig. 276). As evolution proceeded there came to be more and more of these connector neurons, with some running for only short distances and others for long distances. As more and more appeared they tended to become bundled together in the longitudinal axis of animals in a more or less central position to become the chief components, the *spinal cord*. In the head region the spinal cord is expanded, as it were, into the brain; this expansion, as will be explained presently, was due not only to a still greater increased number of connector neurons being required in this region but also to other factors. From the foregoing it is obvious that all connector neurons are contained in the C.N.S. However, in addition to these, the C.N.S. contains parts of both the afferent and the efferent neurons of each segment. The remaining parts of the afferent and the efferent neurons—and these, of course, are outside the C.N.S.—constitute the P.N.S. To explain which parts of the segmental afferent and efferent neurons are contained in the P.N.S. requires that we discuss the changes in position that took place in the cell bodies of these neurons as evolution continued.

Afferent Neurons. The first sensory cells to evolve had their cell bodies at the surface of the organism (Fig. 273), and the cell bodies

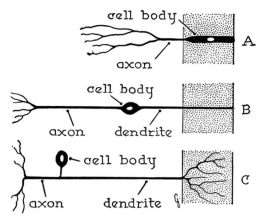

FIG. 277. Diagrams showing how the position of the cell body of afferent neurons changed as evolution proceeded. A is a sensory cell in a coelenterate, B is one in a mollusk and C is one from a vertebrate. (Redrawn from Parker, G. H.: The Elementary Nervous System, Philadelphia, Lippincott)

remained there in a few lower animals, for example, the earthworm, that have neurons, synapses and reflex arcs (Fig. 274). But the surface of an animal is not a suitable place for the cell bodies of afferent neurons, for in this position they are too easily injured and destroyed. The destruction of the *body* of a nerve cell is a very serious matter, because nerve cells seem to be too highly specialized to be able to undergo division; hence, if one is destroyed another cannot divide to provide a replacement for it. Although nerve cells cannot divide, they, in the P.N.S. (but not in the C.N.S.), can regenerate new fibers under suitable circumstances. Accordingly, in higher animals the expedient was adopted of having the cell bodies of the afferent neurons of the segments migrate inwardly so as to be out of harm's way, with the important provision, however, of their retaining connection with the surface by means of a fiber (Fig. 277). This is a much better arrangement than the original because fibers, injured at the surface, can be regenerated from the cell body, and by this means sensory function can be restored after surface injuries.

In some lower animals the cell bodies of afferent neurons migrated only a short distance inwardly (Fig. 277, *middle*), but in the higher animals they seem to have come as

close to the C.N.S. as they could without actually getting into the C.N.S. In this position the cell bodies of afferent neurons are housed in little nodules of nervous tissue called *ganglia* (a ganglion is a lump) (Fig. 275). The particular ganglia that house the cell bodies of those afferent neurons that enter the spinal cord from each segment of the body are termed *spinal ganglia* or *dorsal* or *posterior root ganglia*. There are two of them for each segment, and they are situated one on each side, close to the spinal cord, toward its posterior surface. (It is important at this time to examine Figs. 275 and 310, to see where these ganglia are situated.)

As has been noted already, some afferent neurons enter the brain by way of certain cranial nerves. The cell bodies of these afferent neurons also are situated in ganglia that are close to, but not actually inside, the brain. These are termed cranial ganglia. The term *cerebrospinal* ganglia refers to both groups. All the cell bodies of the afferent neurons that enter the C.N.S. from the body segments are housed in spinal or cranial ganglia.

The first afferent neurons to evolve were unipolar cells, having only one process which was an axon which passed inwardly from the surface (Fig. 273). When the cell body left the surface to migrate inwardly, the afferent neurons became bipolar cells, having a dendrite that passed out to the surface and brought impulses into the cell body and an axon which passed inwardly to conduct the impulse away from the cell body (Fig. 277). When the cell body migrated still farther inwardly and took up a position in a spinal or a cranial ganglion, it remained fundamentally a bipolar cell, with a dendrite leading into it and an axon leaving it, but the parts of the two processes close to the cell body seem to have swung around like the hands of a clock until they came together, as the hands of the clock do every hour, and then fused. As a result the bipolar cells become unipolar (Fig. 275). The single process of each, however, is short and soon branches into two, one of which extends to a sensory ending and the other into the spinal cord (Fig. 275). Functionally, the peripheral branch is a dendrite, and the second an axon, but since both processes have the histologic structure of axons, the peripheral processes of afferent neurons, although functionally dendrites, are commonly termed axons.

The axonal processes that enter the spinal cord from afferent neurons do so via the posterior roots of the cord (Fig. 275). On entering the cord they may synapse directly with efferent neurons, as is shown in Figure 275, or with connector neurons, or they may pass for short distances down the cord or for longer distances up the cord, before synapsing with efferent neurons of other segments or with connector neurons.

Efferent Neurons. The cell bodies of all efferent neurons, with the exception of certain of those of the autonomic nervous system, which will be described later, are all confined to the C.N.S. (Fig. 275).

Connector Neurons. The cell bodies of all connector neurons are, of course, confined to the C.N.S.

Neurobiotaxis. This term refers to a force that has operated through the period of evolution of nervous tissue and has acted to cause the cell bodies of efferent and connector neurons to move as close as possible to their chief sources of stimulation. Accordingly, the dendrites of efferent and connector neurons tend to be short and their axons long. This is not true of afferent neurons because in these the tendency for centralization is more potent than neurobiotaxis.

To sum up: The cell bodies of all afferent neurons are in spinal or cerebral ganglia outside the C.N.S. The cell bodies of all connector neurons, and all efferent neurons, except certain of those of the autonomic nervous system, are in the C.N.S.

Further Uses for the Terms "Afferent" and "Efferent." So far, these two terms have been used to indicate whether neurons carry impulses into or away from the C.N.S. The student should be warned that these terms are used in neuro-anatomy for a further purpose; connector neurons in the C.N.S. that bring impulses to some nerve station are said to be afferent with regard to that station, and those that carry impulses away from it are said to be efferent with regard to that station.

The Basis for Sensation. Perhaps the most extraordinary development in the evolution of nervous tissue was the advent of consciousness and the ability to experience different kinds of sensation. Man has many senses: touch, pressure, heat, cold, pain, sight, hear-

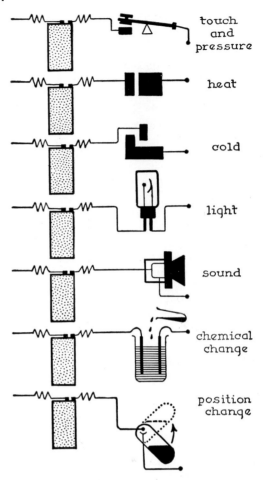

FIG. 278. Diagrams of pieces of apparatus which could be employed to complete an electrical circuit when subjected to the different kinds of stimuli listed on the right side.

ing, taste, position and movement. These sensations are experienced in the brain. However, the stimuli that give rise to these sensations do not reach the brain; only nervous impulses reach the brain. How can nervous impulses from different afferent neurons give rise to different sensations and make some of them, such as cold, seem as if they were being experienced in one's toes or fingers?

The passage of a nervous impulse along a nerve fiber has much in common with the passage of an electric current along a wire. Any amateur electrician could wire up a battery and an induction coil so that he can give himself a shock when he closes a switch.

Furthermore, switches can be obtained or made which could be said to be specialized with regard to different kinds of stimuli. For example, a telegraph key (Fig. 278, *top*) completes a circuit if it is touched or pressed; it is either a touch or pressure receptor, depending on how tightly its spring is adjusted. Contrivances can also be built which would complete a circuit if they were heated or cooled (Fig. 278). Indeed, it is possible to build or obtain electrical contrivances that will set up an electrical impulse in, and so complete, a circuit when they are exposed to any of the different kinds of stimuli that can stimulate the afferent neurons of man (Fig. 278).

Much the same kind of arrangement exists in the nervous system of man to enable him to discern various kinds of sensation. Instead of possessing instruments such as those illustrated in Figure 278, which set up electrical currents in different wires, man has sense organs and nerve endings which will be described in Chapter 29; they are selectively stimulated by different kinds of stimuli such as heat, light and sound, and are connected by chains of neurons to different parts of the brain. For example, the neuron chains that lead from the light-sensitive receptors in the eye pass to a special part of the brain. If this special part is stimulated electrically during an operation on the brain the patient experiences the sensation of light. Or, if it were possible to connect the neuron chains from the sound receptors to this part of the brain, the individual, on being subjected to what anyone else would say was a noise, would interpret it as light. Therefore, the basis for the understanding of different kinds of sensation depends on there being several different kinds of afferent receptors in the body, with each kind highly sensitive with regard to some particular kind of stimulus, and on these different kinds being "wired," so to speak, by means of afferent pathways, to different parts of the brain which, on receiving nervous impulses, give rise to different kinds of sensation.

Inherited and Conditioned Reflex Responses. It is a common analogy to liken the brain to a giant switchboard. Afferent pathways from all parts of the body lead to it, and efferent pathways lead from it to all parts of the body. Although connections exist between afferent and efferent neurons in the spinal cord, most afferent impulses that are set up in the body pass to the brain by means of afferent pathways before they activate efferent systems. Hence, it is in the brain—the giant switchboard—that circuits are set up between afferent and efferent systems. The number of different circuits available between afferent and efferent systems in this organ is enormous, and the same ones are not used to the same extent in all individuals. A sight that makes one woman laugh may make another cry. Why, in the first woman, should afferent impulses be directed over a circuit to efferent pathways that control the muscles employed in laughing, and in the second woman, to efferent pathways controlling the secretion of tears? In other words, what makes people behave differently to what would seem to be the same stimulus?

One fundamental factor in determining behavior is the fact that all higher animals are born with certain instinctive reflex responses. A puppy makes swimming motions as soon as he falls into the water. He inherits, in his brain, a preferential circuit between the afferent pathways that are activated by the stimulus of immersion and the efferent pathways that control the muscles of the legs. Another inherited reflex response possessed by puppies is that they will salivate if food is placed in their mouths.

By showing how further reflex responses could be superimposed on inherited instinctive ones, Pavlov, the famous Russian physiologist, showed that the only stimulus that would evoke salivation in a newborn puppy was the actual presence of food in its mouth. The afferent pathway activated in this instance would be a pathway leading from receptors in the mouth itself. In its brain, the puppy had inherited a preferred connection, as it were, between this afferent pathway and the efferent pathway that controls the salivary glands. Then Pavlov showed that the puppy, after being fed a few times, would salivate as soon as he smelled the food that was put before him. Obviously, this would require the use of a different afferent pathway from the first one employed—one from the nose rather than from the mouth. So there must be some connection in the brain between afferent pathways from the nose and the afferent

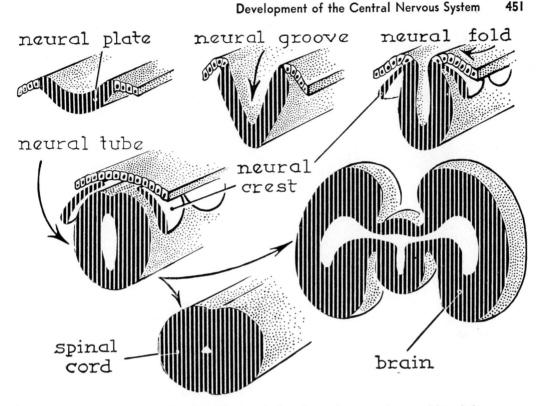

neural plate   neural groove   neural fold

neural tube

neural crest

spinal cord   brain

FIG. 279. Diagrams showing how the neural plate forms from ectoderm and how it becomes the neural groove and then the neural tube. The diagrams also show that the neural tube, in different sites, turns into the spinal cord and the brain respectively.

pathways from the mouth. The neurons by which such connections are made are termed *association neurons*. These permit the puppy to associate the taste of food with the smell of food, and once this association is built up the proper stimulus applied to the nose brings about the same reflex response as does food in the mouth. This new reflex response, which involves a different afferent pathway, and association neurons, Pavlov termed a *conditioned response*. He showed that the possibilities in conditioned responses are very considerable. A pup, for example, soon learns to salivate at the sight of food and can even be trained to salivate at the ringing of a bell, if a bell is rung every time it is fed. Then, by further conditioning procedures which need not be described here, the conditioned response to the ringing of the bell can be inhibited. Therefore, conditioning procedures are not only effective in broadening the base of our possible responses; they can also be used to broaden the base of our inhibitions. All in all, we are exposed to so many different associations in our lives that

it is not strange that all stimuli are not the same to all men and that what may attract one may repel another.

DEVELOPMENT OF THE CENTRAL NERVOUS SYSTEM

Formation of Neural Tube and Neural Crests. Soon after the 3 germ layers—ectoderm, mesoderm and endoderm—are distinguishable in the embryo, the ectoderm along the mid-line of the back, beginning in the mid-dorsal region, and then extending both forward and backward, becomes stratified to form a thickened band called the *neural plate* (Fig. 279). Almost as soon as it is formed, the neural plate becomes depressed along its midline to form the *neural groove* (Fig. 279) and elevated along its two edges to form two *neural folds* (Fig. 279). Near the crest of each fold, below the line along which the thickened ectoderm of the plate becomes continuous with the ordinary ectoderm of the back, some thickened ectoderm bulges laterally; these bulges,

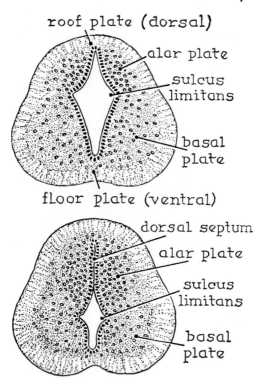

roof plate (dorsal)

alar plate

sulcus limitans

basal plate

floor plate (ventral)

dorsal septum

alar plate

sulcus limitans

basal plate

FIG. 280. Diagrams of cross sections of neural tube developing into spinal cord.

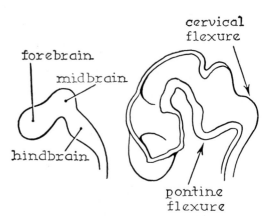

cervical flexure

forebrain

midbrain

hindbrain

pontine flexure

FIG. 281. Diagrams showing the early changes that occur as the neural tube in the head region begins to develop into a brain.

further on, how those of the neural crests give rise to most of the P.N.S.

MORPHOGENESIS OF THE SPINAL CORD

In order to form the spinal cord the walls of the neural tube thicken. The cellular proliferation that accounts for most of the thickening occurs in its lateral walls. The dorsal and the ventral walls of the tube are relatively passive, and they become known as the *roof plate* and the *floor plate*, respectively, of the tube. All sectors of the lateral walls do not thicken equally; actually, each lateral wall reveals two lines of thickening: one dorsal and the other ventral. The lumen extends out into the depression formed on each side between these two lines of thickening; this depression on each side is termed a *sulcus limitans* (Fig. 280). The two dorsal thickenings, seen in a cross section of a developing cord, resemble a pair of wings (Fig. 280, *top*) and are referred to as the *alar (ala = wing) plates* of the developing cord. The two ventral thickenings of the lateral walls form the *basal plates* of the developing cord. The unequal growth rate of the different parts of the wall of the tube makes the lumen diamond-shaped for a time (Fig. 280, *top*). Later, however, the edges of the part of the lumen that extends toward the roof plate fuse, and, as a result of this, a *dorsal septum* (Fig. 280, *bottom*) is formed. Eventually, the lumen of the neural tube is relatively very small and becomes

one on each side, constitute what are termed *neural crests*. Next, the edges of the two neural folds come together; this entails three fusions: (1) the edges of the thickened ectoderm of the neural groove fuse to convert the groove into a *neural tube* (Fig. 279); (2) the two neural crests fuse, but only temporarily, because they soon become separated again to appear as shown in Figure 279; and (3) as the tops of the two neural folds come together, the edges of the ordinary ectoderm, which extends up the lateral aspect of each fold to its top, meet and fuse with one another (Fig. 279). As this occurs the neural crests and the neural tube become detached from the ordinary ectoderm and sink into the mesoderm along the midline of the embryo, the back of which is covered thereafter with a continuous layer of ordinary ectoderm.

The cells of the neural tube and crests constitute the *neuro-ectoderm*. We shall now consider its further history and learn how the neuro-ectodermal cells of the neural tube develop into the C.N.S. and then, a few pages

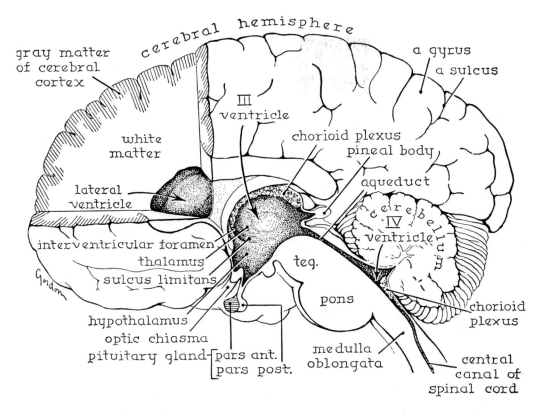

FIG. 282. A median sagittal section of the brain of man. A portion of the frontal lobe has been cut out (*upper left*) so as to disclose the lateral ventricle. What was originally the lumen of the neural tube is shown in dark stipple. In reading the text the student should begin at the right lower corner and follow the central canal of the cord into the various ventricles of the brain and visualize how the main parts of the brain have developed from the parts of the wall of the neural tube that originally surrounded the divisions of its lumen that later became ventricles.

known as the *central canal* of the cord; this can be seen in Figure 279 (*lower left*), and in Figure 285.

MORPHOGENSIS OF THE BRAIN

It seems almost incredible to anyone who examines a brain for the first time that an organ of such a complex appearance (Fig. 282) could have developed from something as simple as a neural tube. Probably two mechanisms are involved: (1) the dissimilar growth rates in different parts of the wall of the tube, and (2) an increasing state of compression in the long axis of the neural tube at its anterior end.

The first change seen as the anterior end of the tube begins to form a brain is that it develops three swellings separated by two con-strictions (Fig. 281). The swellings are called *vesicles* and are named the forebrain, the midbrain and the hindbrain, respectively (Fig. 281). Almost coincidentally a hairpin bend called the *cephalic flexure* occurs ventrally between the midbrain and the forebrain; this becomes so pronounced that the forebrain almost touches the hindbrain (Fig. 281). Following this, another kink, which is called the *pontine flexure,* occurs; this results in the hindbrain's bending acutely in a direction opposite (dorsal) to the cephalic flexure. Therefore, the primitive brain is "N"-shaped (Fig. 281).

We shall now describe some of the further changes that occur as the anterior part of the neural tube develops into a brain. We shall begin with the portion of the tube that becomes the hindbrain and work forward. If the student remembers that the brain develops from a tube, and that the various structures, which we shall now name and describe, represent *thickenings* or *bulgings* of the wall of the tube, it should be easily possible, from the following description, to obtain a general idea of the position and the nature of some of the more important parts of the brain that are illustrated in Figure 282. In order to keep oriented the student should understand that the lumen of the tube, which becomes the ventricles of the brain, is shown in dark stipple in Figure 282.

The Hindbrain. As already described, this is divided into two parts by the *pontine flexure*. If a rubber tube is bent or kinked upon itself, the region of the kink is no longer tubular but broad and flattened, and the lumen is distorted to a transverse slit. Thus, when the neural tube is bent at the pontine flexure, the lateral walls diverge, and the form described for the rubber tube is assumed. However, the thin roof plate stretches more than the floor of the tube, so it becomes a thin cover over the shallow, widened cavity of the neural tube with the alar and the basal plates forming the floor of the tube, which accordingly becomes *very thick* in the hindbrain (Fig. 282). The hindpart of the flexed tube is called the *medulla oblongata* (Fig. 282) because of its oblong-shaped cavity and is distinguishable from the cord, with which it is continuous, by its greater width, thicker floor and thinner roof.

The forepart of the hindbrain at first resembles the hindpart, but further development alters its appearance. As in the medulla oblongata, the alar and the basal plates form the floor for the lumen of the tube. The floor here becomes very thick and resembles a bridge and so is called the *pons* (*pons* = bridge) (Fig. 282). However, apart from this, the alar portions undergo rapid development and form two large lateral swellings on its forepart; these eventually meet and fuse medially and dorsally to constitute a large mass, the cerebellum (Fig. 282), which forms the roof over the lumen at this site. These two lateral swellings which fuse medially are termed the *cerebellar hemispheres* (Fig. 282). As noted, the alar and the basal plates at the flexure form the *pons,* which is to include a great bundle of fibers which *appear to bridge*

one cerebellar hemisphere to the other, around the ventral surface of this part of the hindbrain.

The lumen of the neural tube persists in the hindbrain as a flattened cavity called the *fourth ventricle* (Fig. 282). The thin roof plate, which covers it behind the cerebellum, is called the *posterior medullary vellum* (*vellum* = veil).

The Midbrain. Of the 3 divisions of the primitive brain, the midbrain alone retains a frank tubular structure, for the growth rate of the different parts of the wall of the tube is more equal here than elsewhere. During development its vesicular character is lost by the thickening of the alar and the basal plates, particularly the latter, which reduces the lumen to a small ductlike passage in the dorsal part of the midbrain. This passage, called the *aqueduct* (Fig. 282), connects the cavities of the forebrain and the hindbrain.

The medulla, the pons and the midbrain contain many important groups of cell bodies of neurons. These areas of frank gray matter are termed *nuclei*. Fiber tracts of white matter containing either ascending or descending fibers may synapse in these regions or pass through them uninterruptedly.

The Forebrain. The cephalic flexure that develops between midbrain and forebrain does not produce the rubber-tube effect that occurs in the instance of the pontine flexure. Here the neural tube is *relatively* constricted and conforms more readily to bending, without its lumen becoming flattened.

The forebrain undergoes so many changes, particularly in its forepart, that it is helpful to regard it as consisting of two portions. The hindpart of the forebrain gives rise to thickenings of the wall of the tube called the *thalamus,* the *hypothalamus* and the *subthalamus,* and the forepart to two huge thickened bulges, the *cerebral hemispheres* (Fig. 282).

In the hindpart of the forebrain the growth rate is less than the forepart. The alar and the basal parts retain their positions with the alar portion becoming the thalamus and the basal plate the hypothalamus and the subthalamus. The thalamus is concerned primarily with relaying afferent (particularly sensory) impulses from the lower levels of the brain and the cord to the higher centers

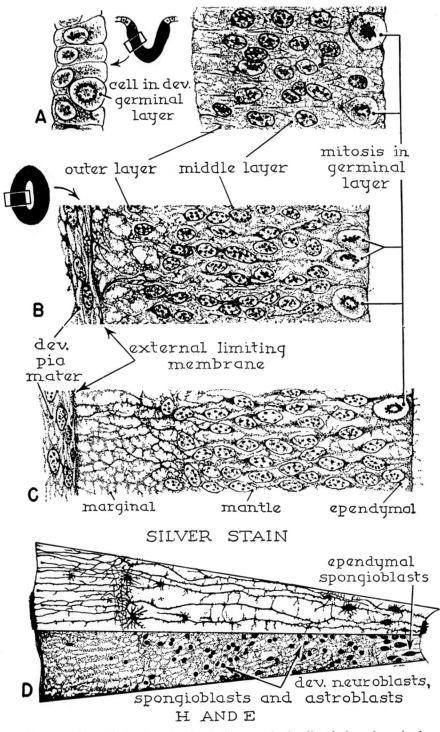

A cell in dev.
germinal
layer

mitosis in
germinal
layer

outer layer   middle layer

B

dev.
pia
mater

external limiting
membrane

C   marginal   mantle   ependymal

SILVER STAIN

ependymal
spongioblasts

D   dev. neuroblasts,
spongioblasts and astroblasts
H AND E

FIG. 283. (A, *left*) Section of a developing neural tube (just before closure) of a rabbit embryo. (A, *right*) Section of a developing neural tube of a pig embryo of 5 mm. (B) Section of a developing neural tube of a pig embryo of 7 mm. (C) Section of a developing neural tube of a pig embryo of 10 mm. (D) Section of a developing spinal cord of a pig embryo 55 mm. long. The upper part of this illustration shows the way the tissue appears when a silver technic is employed, and the lower part shows the way the same structure appears with H and E. (Modified from Haresty, Irving: Am. J. Anat. **3**:229)

of the cerebral hemispheres. The hypothalamus is concerned essentially with the automatic innervations of smooth muscles and glands; this matter will be described when the autonomic nervous system is considered.

The cavity of this part of the brain becomes a vertical slit and is known as the *third ventricle* (Fig. 282).

In the forepart of the forebrain, whereas the basal plates remain small, becoming the forepart of the hypothalamus, the alar plates undergo enormous development and form two huge evaginations called the *cerebral hemispheres* (Fig. 282). The cavities of these become the *lateral ventricles* (Fig. 282), which connect with the third ventricle through interventricular foramina (Fig. 282). In man the surface of the brain becomes greatly corrugated. The deeper grooves are termed *fissures,* and the shallower ones *sulci.* The latter separate *gyri* (Fig. 282).

HISTOGENESIS OF THE SPINAL CORD

Having considered briefly the changes that occur in the form of the neural tube as it develops into a spinal cord and a brain, we are now prepared to study the microscopic changes that occur in the walls of the tube which are responsible for the gross changes. In particular, we shall learn how the cells of the tube give rise to gray matter and to white matter, the differences between these two types of matter and why they come to be distributed differently in the spinal cord and the brain.

Before describing the details of histogenesis it may be helpful to point out that the cells of the wall of the neural tube in forming the spinal cord and the brain differentiate only along two main pathways to form either (1) *neurons* or (2) *neuroglia* (*glia* = glue) *cells* (Fig. 284). Neuroglia is a general term for the cells that provide internal support for the tissues of the C.N.S., and the few varieties of these will be named and described presently.

The Layers of the Walls of the Neural Tube. The thin wall of the newly formed neural tube becomes thicker because of the continued proliferation of the cells that abut on its lumen. Therefore, these cells are termed *germinal cells*

(Fig. 283) and they constitute what at first is called the *inner* or *germinal layer* of the tube (Fig. 283). The cells to which they give rise are pushed in to the *middle layer* of the wall of the tube where they become much longer than they are wide and radially arranged (Fig. 283). Moreover, many of these cells attain more cytoplasm at their outer than at their inner ends, and, as a consequence, a third and *outer layer* appears in the wall of the tube which is composed of the outer cytoplasmic ends of cells whose nuclei are the prominent feature of the middle layer (Fig. 283). The cytoplasm in this outer layer takes on a reticulated spongy appearance (Fig. 283) and this provides a basis for naming some of the cells of the tube *spongioblasts.*

DIFFERENTIATION OF THE INNER LAYER AND THE FORMATION OF THE EPENDYMA

As development proceeds, the germinal cells which comprise the inner layer of the wall of the tube develop long cytoplasmic processes that extend out to the periphery of the tube (Fig. 283) (*bottom*—silver stain). Their cell bodies, instead of being rounded as formerly, take on the appearance of columnar epithelial cells, and for a period these have cilia on their inner borders (Fig. 283). When they assume the appearance of columnar epithelial cells with long processes that extend out into the wall of the tube, they are known as *ependymal spongioblasts* instead of germinal cells. It is not clear as to why this name was chosen, because ependyma refers to an *outer garment,* whereas these cells actually form the lining of the tube. As development proceeds further, the ependymal spongioblasts become increasingly differentiated into ordinary ependymal cells. These form an epithelial lining for the central canal of the cord and the ventricles of the brain. Mature ependymal cells vary from columnar to flattened cuboidal types (Fig. 300). In some sites they are somewhat rounded.

DIFFERENTIATION IN THE MIDDLE LAYER AND THE FORMATION OF GRAY MATTER

As previously noted, cells produced as a result of mitosis in the germinal layer are

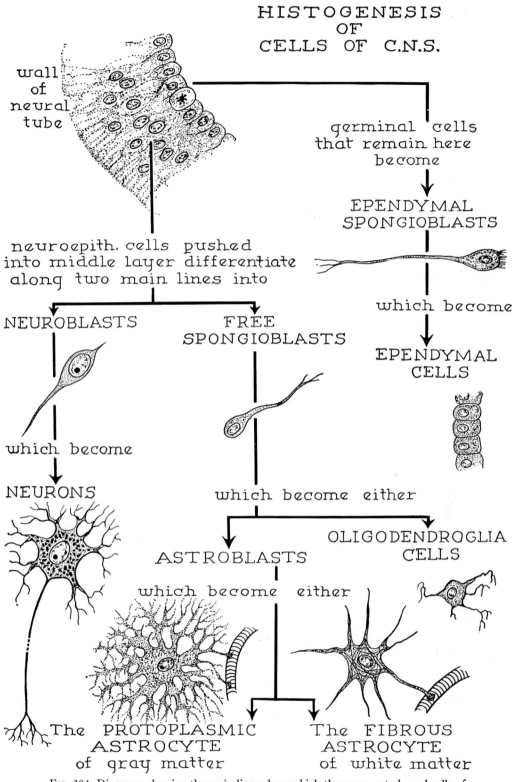

HISTOGENESIS
OF
CELLS OF C.N.S.

wall
of
neural
tube

germinal cells
that remain here
become

EPENDYMAL
SPONGIOBLASTS

neuroepith. cells pushed
into middle layer differentiate
along two main lines into

which become

NEUROBLASTS

FREE
SPONGIOBLASTS

EPENDYMAL
CELLS

which become

NEURONS

which become either

OLIGODENDROGLIA
CELLS

ASTROBLASTS

which become either

The PROTOPLASMIC
ASTROCYTE
of gray matter

The FIBROUS
ASTROCYTE
of white matter

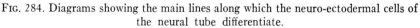

Fig. 284. Diagrams showing the main lines along which the neuro-ectodermal cells of
the neural tube differentiate.

GRAY AND WHITE MATTER OF SPINAL CORD

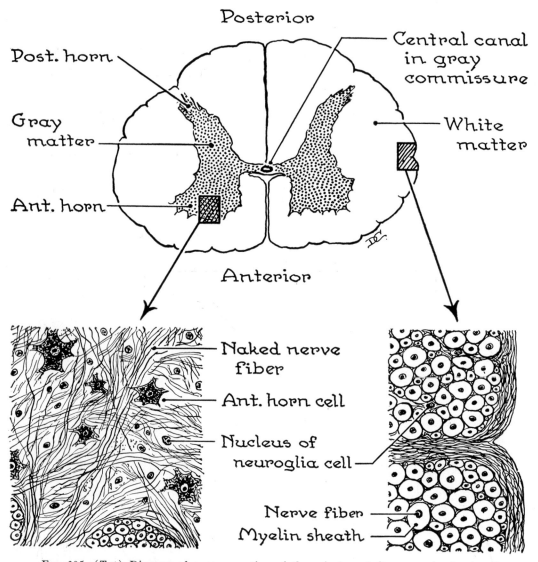

FIG. 285. (*Top*) Diagram of a cross section of the spinal cord (low-power), showing the distribution of gray and white matter in it. (*Bottom*) Two diagrams (high-power), showing the contents of the gray and the white matter, respectively.

pushed into the middle layer of the tube. Here, for a time, they all have a similar appearance, but as development proceeds they begin to differentiate along two main pathways. Most of them become neuroblasts and eventually nerve cells (Fig. 284, *left*). However, a minority become free spongioblasts (Fig. 284, *right*). These, as shown in Figure

284, differentiate along two sublines to form either astroblasts, which in turn form cells with so many radiating processes that they are star-shaped, and hence called *astrocytes* (*astron* = star), or *oligodendroglia*, which are small cells with few processes or branches (*oligos* = few; *dendron* = tree).

In giving rise to neuroblasts, the neuro-ectodermal cells of the middle layer develop larger nuclei than they do in giving rise to free spongioblasts. The middle layer soon comes to consist of neuroblasts and spongioblasts, which can be distinguished from each other by their nuclei. The neuroblasts become neurons, and the spongioblasts become astrocytes and oligodendroglia cells. This combination of neurons and supporting cells constitutes *gray matter*. Hence, the middle layer of the tube becomes the gray matter of the spinal cord. It does not form an even and continuous layer in the wall of the tube but becomes arranged in the form of a structure which roughly resembles an "H" when it is seen in cross section (Fig. 285). From its appearance in a single cross section, this H-shaped mass of gray matter is said to have two dorsal or posterior *horns* and two ventral or anterior horns (Fig. 285). Actually, the continuous horns are columns that extend up and down the cord. In some parts of the cord there is a lateral horn or column on each side as well (Figs. 301 and 302).

DIFFERENTIATION IN THE OUTER LAYER AND THE FORMATION OF WHITE MATTER

The axons that sprout from the neuroblasts of the developing posterior horns of gray matter and the axons that enter the dorsolateral aspect of the cord from the neuroblasts of the developing spinal ganglia pass into the outer layer of the developing cord, and in this layer they extend, mostly up, but some down, for considerable distances. Meanwhile, some of the neuroblasts that develop in the lower part of the brain also send axons down the outer layer of the developing cord. Furthermore, although most axons from anterior horn cells pass out of the cord as efferent fibers, a few pass down and up the cord to contribute also to the white matter. Therefore, the outer layer of the cord comes to contain vast numbers of axons which pass up and down the cord to comprise the afferent and the efferent pathways between different levels of the cord and the brain. However, the afferent and the efferent fibers are segregated from one another in different sectors of the cord. The fibers are subdivided further; for example, the fibers that carry impulses that give rise to the sensation of pain are bundled together on each side of the cord.

The outer layer of the part of the neural tube destined to become the spinal cord is invaded, not only by axons, but also by some free spongioblasts (from the developing middle layer) which differentiate into *fibrous astrocytes* and *oligodendroglia*. These two types of neuroglia cells fit into the crevices between the axons and send their processes out among them (Fig. 285). The oligodendroglia are sometimes arranged in rows between adjacent axons (Fig. 297).

Myelinization. As most copper telephone wires are covered with a coat of rubber insulation, so most axons in the outer layer of the developing cord become covered with white glistening fatty material called *myelin*. As myelinization occurs, the whole outer layer of the developing spinal cord becomes white; it is then said to be *white matter*. Therefore, white matter consists of myelinated fibers supported by fibrous astrocytes and oligodendroglia cells. White matter does not contain the cell bodies of neurons but only their fibers.

Myelin is a nonliving fatty material. It contains cholesterol, cerebroside and phospholipids, the most important phospholipid being sphingomyelin. Much of the lipid material is present in the form of lipid-protein complexes. Speidel's work indicates that myelin is synthesized in association with nerve fibers around which it is deposited and that it is formed primarily by the nerve fibers but with the collaboration of the neuroglia cells. Myelinization usually begins close to the cell body and advances along the axon toward its termination. Myelinization begins early in the 4th month and is not completed at birth; some fiber tracts become myelinated afterward. The total amount of myelin in the C.N.S. increases from birth to maturity; individual fibers become more heavily myelinated during the growth period. Myelin is not necessary for fibers to conduct nervous impulses but seems to be necessary for fibers to conduct nervous impulses sufficiently well to permit muscles to make delicate and precise movements.

Myelin is soluble in fat solvents; hence, when ordinary paraffin sections of the spinal cord are prepared, most of the myelin of the

myelinated
fibers
embedded in
neuroglial
web

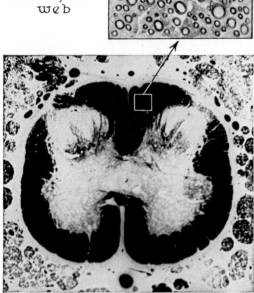

FIG. 286. (*Bottom*) Low-power photomicrograph of a cross section of spinal cord (sacral region) fixed in osmic acid. The white matter appears black. (*Top*) High-power drawing of a small area of white matter showing that the black material seen in the low-power illustration is the myelin of the sheaths of the nerve fibers. Observe that the fibers are of different calibers.

white matter dissolves away in the dehydrating and clearing agents. When such sections are stained, the sites where myelin was present appear as empty spaces (Fig. 285, *right*). However, there are special fixatives, most notably *osmic acid*, which fix myelin so that it does not dissolve away as paraffin sections are prepared. Osmic acid, in itself, colors myelin black, so that if a cross section of spinal cord, fixed in osmic acid, is examined under very low power, the white matter of the cord appears black (Fig. 286). If the white matter is examined under higher power the blackened myelin will be seen to be arranged in little rings around each nerve fiber (Fig. 286, *top*).

E/M investigations of the structure of myelin are described in connection with the P.N.S.

HISTOGENESIS OF NERVOUS TISSUE OF BRAIN

As has been explained already, different parts of the walls of the neural tube that forms the brain grow unequally so that the brain assumes a complex shape. Nevertheless, although there are certain points of difference that need not be described here, the histogenesis of the gray and the white matter of the brain is similar to that which occurs in the spinal cord. Gray matter forms from the cells of the middle layer of the tube, and white matter forms in the outer layer of the neural tube. Hence, in the medulla, the pons, the midbrain and in parts of the forebrain, gray matter develops in positions that are roughly comparable with those in which it develops in the spinal cord, and it becomes covered by the white matter that develops in the outer layer of the tube as it does in the cord. But in certain parts of the developing brain, neuroblasts from the middle layer of the neural tube migrate out through the outer layer of developing white matter to take up a position on the outside of the tube. Because of this phenomenon the cerebral and the cerebellar hemispheres come to possess a thin covering or *cortex* of gray matter (Fig. 282). Hence, in these two parts of the brain, gray matter exists not only deep to the white matter but superficial to it as well.

It should now be clear why the surface of the spinal cord is white and why the surface of the cerebral hemispheres is gray. It should be understood that white matter is white because of myelin and that it contains the bodies of no nerve cells but only neuroglia cells. All the bodies of the nerve cells of the C.N.S. are in gray matter. Furthermore, the reason for the tissue of the C.N.S. being so soft and jelly-like should now be apparent; it is because its supporting tissue is not ordinary connective tissue with tough intercellular substances such as collagen and elastin but only delicate ectodermal-derived cellular nerve glue—the neuroglia.

Having considered the histogenesis of the nervous tissue of the C.N.S., we shall now describe in some detail the histologic appearance of the different kinds of cells of which it is composed and then discuss briefly their arrangements in some of its representative parts.

THE CELLS OF THE NERVOUS TISSUE OF THE C.N.S.

NEURONS

Most neurons of the C.N.S. are said to be multipolar because they possess 3 or more processes. Multipolarity is gained by neurons having 2 or more dendrites; they never have more than one axon. However, axons may branch, as will be described, so one neuron can send impulses to many others.

Cell Bodies. The *cell body* is that part of the neuron that contains the nucleus; for this reason it is sometimes called the *perikaryon* (*peri* = around; *karyon* = nut or nucleus). The cell bodies of neurons vary from being small to large. The larger ones are among the largest cells in the body. The cell bodies of different kinds of neurons vary in shape; they may be round, oval, flattened ovoid or pyramidal.

Nuclei. The nucleus commonly has a central position, but in at least one type of neuron it is eccentrically disposed. Nuclei are generally large and spherical (Figs. 287 and 288). In small neurons the nucleus, though actually smaller, is larger in relation to the size of the cell body than it is in larger neurons. The nuclear membrane usually stains well with hematoxylin; nevertheless, it does not stand out sharply against the cytoplasm because this also stains well. The nucleus consists chiefly of pale-staining nuclear sap which causes it to resemble a vesicle (*vesica* = bladder); hence, the nuclei of neurons are sometimes said to be *vesicular* in type (Fig. 288). The chromatin granules are fine and dispersed (Fig. 287). One large nucleolus is commonly present, but there may be more. Since the nucleolus stands out so clearly against the pale nucleoplasm (Fig. 288), and since the nuclear membrane does not stand out sharply against the cytoplasm, the beginner is prone to confuse the nucleolus with the nucleus and the nucleoplasm with cytoplasm. The sex chromatin of neurons, illustrated in Figure 288, is described in Chapter 4.

Centrosomes can be demonstrated by spe-

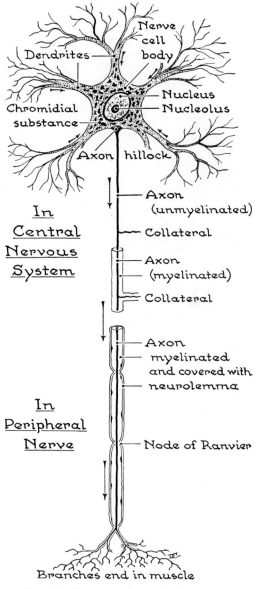

FIG. 287. Diagram of a multipolar neuron.

cial technics in the proliferating neuroblasts of embryonic tissue but only occasionally in the cell bodies of mature neurons. Since centrosomes are concerned in cell division their general absence in neurons may be of some significance with regard to the inability of neurons to divide.

Neurofibrils are very fine cytoplasmic fibrils which course through the cell body and are present also in the dendrites and the axons. In the cell body they are generally arranged

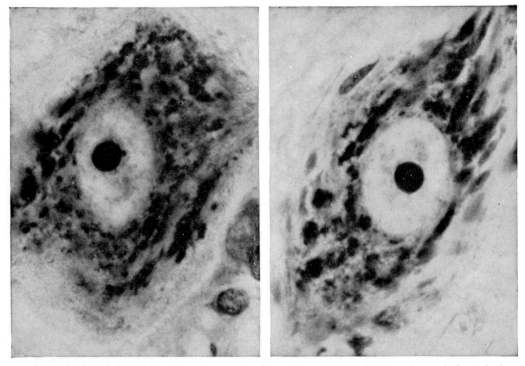

FIG. 288. Oil-immersion photomicrographs of anterior horn cells in sections of the spinal cord of the cat stained with cresyl violet. (*Left*) Picture taken from the cord of a female cat. (*Right*) From the cord of a male cat. Both pictures show chromidial substance to advantage. (Barr, M. L., Bertram, L. F., and Lindsay, H. A.: Anat. Rec. **107**:283)

in bundles which may interlace with one another. The course of the bundles determines, to some extent, the distribution of chromidial substance (to be discussed presently), for this is disposed in the interstices of the network of bundles of fibrils.

With the E/M, Palay and Palade have verified the existence of neurofibrils in nerve cells by finding fine, long threads of a diameter from about 60 to 100 Å arranged in a network fashion in the cytoplasm between Nissl bodies and Golgi material.

Nissl Bodies (Clumps of Chromidial Substances). Chromidial substance is a very prominent feature of the cytoplasm of nerve cells. Its distribution and appearance differ to some extent in different kinds of nerve cells, but, in general, in fixed material, stained with basic dyes, it appears in the form of irregular clumps, which may be small enough to be granules, in the sites in the cytoplasm which are probably the interstices of the network of bundles of neurofibrils (Figs. 287 and 288).

In honor of Franz Nissl, who studied this material intensively in the last century, the clumps of chromidial substance in the cytoplasm of nerve cells are often termed Nissl bodies. The studies instituted by Nissl have been continued; indeed, chromidial substance is perhaps the most studied feature of neurons. If the axon of a neuron is severed, what is known as an axon reaction occurs: the chromidial substance of the cell body tends to melt away temporarily (chromatolysis), and the nucleus moves to one side (Fig. 289). In view of the relatively recent work showing the relation of chromidial substance to protein synthesis, it seems probable that the chromidial substance of the cell body is concerned in the continued synthesis of new cytoplasm that Weiss and Hiscoe have shown occurs in the bodies of nerve cells, which, by passing into their axons, continuously renews them.

Nissl bodies (clumps of chromidial substance) seen with the E/M consist of aggregations of rough-surfaced flattened membranous vesicles with numerous RNA granules scattered between the adjacent flattened vesicles of which they are composed. Nissl bodies, as such, are not surrounded by any kind of limiting membrane but each consists of an aggregation of flattened membranous structures. The flattened vesicles in each Nissl body probably anastomose with one another. The arrangement of the flattened vesicles in Nissl bodies differs in different kinds of nerve cells. In large motor neurons the Nissl bodies are large, and the flattened vesicles in each are arranged more or less parallel with one another (Fig. 290). In other types of nerve cells the arrangement of the flattened vesicles is not so regular, and in some kinds of nerve cells the rough-surfaced vesicles are disposed in an irregular fashion in the cytoplasm. Palay and Palade should be read for details.

As has been emphasized previously, a high development of rough-surfaced membranous vesicles in the cytoplasm is usually associated with a considerable function on the part of the cell for producing some protein material for secretion (for example, as in the exocrine cells of the pancreas). Therefore, it is an unsolved problem as to why these structures should be so highly developed in nerve cells; the most probable reason would seem to be that the nerve cells, as was noted above, are continuously producing new cytoplasm that flows down their axons.

Mitochondria. The mitochondria show no unusual features and are disposed in the cytoplasm between Nissl bodies.

Golgi Apparatus. It was in the cell bodies of neurons that Golgi first demonstrated the network that bears his name. The location of the Golgi net varies in different kinds of nerve cells; not uncommonly it can be seen to surround the nucleus, lying closer to it than the cell surface, as is illustrated in Figure 291.

According to both Cajal and Penfield, the Golgi net breaks up after the axon of a cell is severed. Horning has shown that the Golgi nets of neurons break up in morphine poisoning.

The E/M shows that in addition to the rough-surfaced membranous vesicles, the cytoplasm of nerve cells contains many groups of smooth-surfaced flattened vesicles closely arranged in parallel array. These are the flattened vesicles of the Golgi apparatus, and aggregations of these are disposed in what seems to be a haphazard fashion in the cyto-

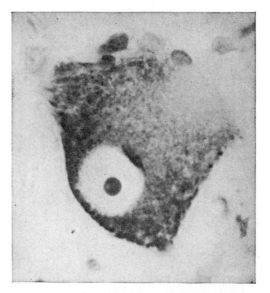

FIG. 289. High-power photomicrograph of a nerve cell, showing severe chromatolysis during axon reaction. The axon hillock of this cell is at the upper right, and the chromatolysis is typically most severe between the nucleus and the axon hillock. The nucleus has taken up an eccentric position, and a good "nuclear cap" is shown. (Barr, M. L., and Hamilton, J. D.: J. Comp. Neurol. **89**:93)

plasm. Small smooth-surfaced spherical vesicles are commonly associated with these.

Pigments. Two kinds of pigments may appear in nerve cells. The first, a golden *lipochrome* pigment (Fig. 82), appears during postnatal life, first in ganglion cells and later in cells of the C.N.S. Its amount increases with age. Its significance is not known. *Melanin* occurs in nerve cells in a few parts of the C.N.S., perhaps most notably in what is termed the *substantia nigra* (*niger* = black) —a landmark in the midbrain—that will be seen by the student when the brain is dissected. The significance of the presence of melanin in the bodies of some nerve cells of the C.N.S. is not known.

Dendrites extend from the various surfaces of multipolar neurons like branches from the trunk of a tree (Fig. 287). The dendrites themselves branch; hence, several different orders of branches that become smaller with branching are common. In their stouter parts, close to the cell body, the cytoplasm of den-

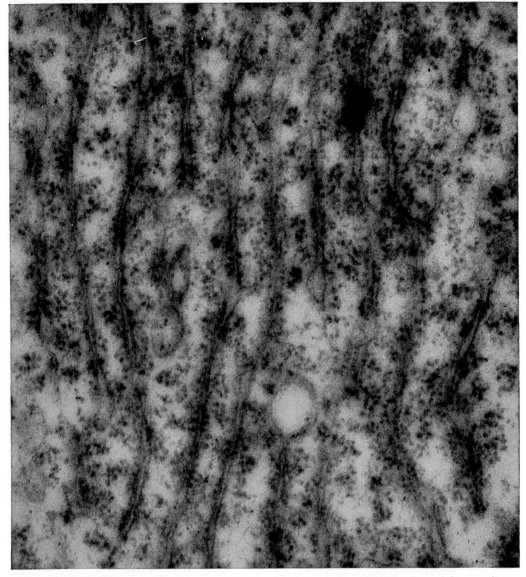

Fig. 290. Electron micrograph ($\times$ 85,000) of a section cut through the nucleus abducens of a rat. The field illustrated here is that of a Nissl body in a motor neuron. The illustration shows RNA granules to advantage; they are arranged along the flattened membranous vesicles (which appear in the illustration as double lines) and between adjacent flattened vesicles. The seemingly empty ovoid area below the center of the picture is the expanded end of a vesicle. (Palay, S., and Palade, G.: J. Biophysic. & Biochem. Cytol. I:69)

drites contains both chromidial substance and mitochondria. Neurofibrils probably extend into their finest branches. In special preparations impregnated with silver, little buds called *gemmules* (*gemmula* = a little bud), which take the form of little knobs or spines, can be seen to project from dendrites along their sides. Since dendrites branch so extensively, it is obvious that through them a nerve cell body can make contact with, and so receive impulses from, large numbers of other neurons.

Axons. In contrast with dendrites, only one axon extends from the cell body of even a multipolar neuron. It arises from a special part of the periphery of the cell body termed the *axon hillock* (Fig. 287). This area contains no chromidial substance, perhaps because neurofibrils converge through this area to enter the axon. Axons carry impulses away from the cell body. They vary from being part of a millimeter to several feet in length. The axons of different neurons vary in diameter from less than a micron to several microns. Each is of a constant diameter through-

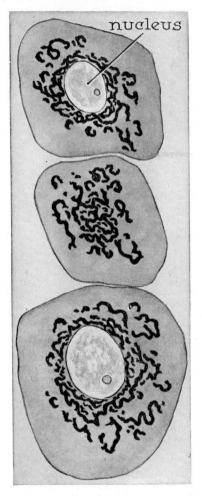

FIG. 291. Drawing of a section of a dorsal root ganglion of a mouse (high-power). The material was fixed in a ferric chloride-osmic acid mixture. This treatment results in the blackening of the Golgi network. A reference to Figure 8 will show why the middle cell seems to contain no nucleus. (Preparation by S. H. Bensley)

FIG. 292. Photograph of a model of the body of a nerve cell in the dorsal horn of the cat's spinal cord. The model as a whole was made by fitting together individual models made from serial sections and it shows the enormous number of nerve fibers that terminate as end-bulbs (end-feet) on the body of the nerve cell to effect synaptic relations with it. (Haggar, R. A., and Barr, M. L.: J. Comp. Neurol. **93**:17)

out its length. The larger ones conduct impulses more rapidly than the smaller ones. Axons may give off branches; these are termed *collaterals* (Fig. 287) because they come off the axon at right angles (laterally).

The axons that pass up and down the white matter of the cord, in the different afferent and efferent pathways, and those that extend through the white matter of the brain are myelinated. However, outside of their myelin sheaths they have no covering except that provided by the processes of fibrous astrocytes and oligodendroglia (Fig. 285). Unlike the axons of peripheral nerves, they are not covered with neurolemma sheaths, which will be

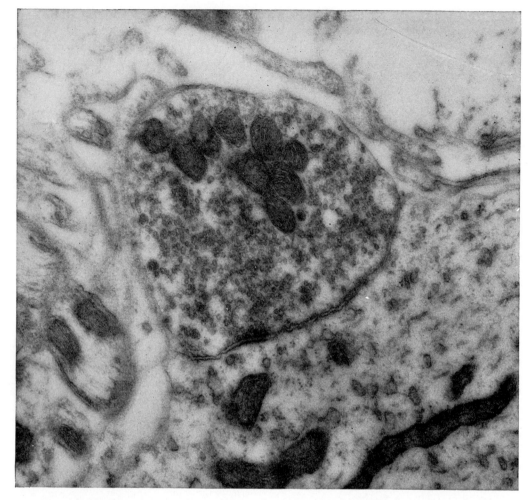

Fig. 293. Electron micrograph (× 57,000) of a section of the facial colliculus of a rat. The large central body seen in the picture is an end-foot which abuts on the surface of a neuron, the cytoplasm of which fills the right lower part of the picture. At the point of contact a dark double line is seen; one of the lines is the cell membrane of the end-foot and the other the cell membrane of the cell body of a neuron. The space between the 2 cell membranes is about 200 Å wide. Notice that the end-foot contains many mitochondria and very numerous neurovesicles. (Preparation by S. Palay)

described when peripheral nerves are considered. This fact is mentioned here because their lack of neurolemma sheaths is an important reason for axons of the C.N.S. not regenerating after they are severed or otherwise destroyed.

Types and Structure of Synapses in the C.N.S. Synapses were defined and some of their general characteristics were described early in this chapter. Their structure will now be considered in more detail.

The common type of synapse in the C.N.S. is one in which an axon from one neuron terminates on a dendrite or a cell body of an-other. In this type of termination, the axon, as it makes contact with the second neuron, becomes swollen into a little bulb that abuts on the cell body or the dendrite of the second neuron. The little swollen terminations of axons are called *end-bulbs, end-feet* or *boutons*. The reconstruction made by Haggar and Barr (Fig. 292) of the cell body of a neuron shows dramatically the vast number of axons that can come into synaptic association with another neuron in the C.N.S. by means of this type of termination.

The fine structure of synapses of this type

has been investigated extensively by Palay, one of whose illustrations is Figure 293. With the E/M, three very important features about end-feet are clearly apparent. First, there is an aggregation of mitochondria in them (Fig. 293). Some of these have longitudinally disposed cristae. The abundance of mitochondria in this site is probably related to the enzymatic activity and the ion transport concerned with the electrical phenomena that occur. Secondly, the cytoplasm of the end-foot contains innumerable tiny spherical vesicles from about 200 to 650 Å in diameter (Fig. 293). These *neurovesicles*, which are also seen in motor endplates (Fig. 267), are filled with a material that is denser than the cytoplasm outside them. These neurovesicles that are so densely aggregated at this site are probably concerned in the production and the liberation of the chemical agent involved in the transmission of nervous impulses across synapses; these chemical agents will be discussed later in this chapter. Thirdly, the E/M shows clearly that the membrane of the presynaptic neuron (that of the end-foot) and the membrane covering the body or dendrite of the cell body of the neuron on which the end-foot lies, are both continuous and separate entities. They are seen in Figure 293 as dark lines separated from each other by a light space of about 200 Å wide.

NEUROGLIA

A proper understanding of the function of neuroglia cells in providing internal support for the nervous tissue of the C.N.S. awaited the development of special histologic technics. Ordinary stains such as H and E give no intimation that these cells possess innumerable processes that permeate the substance of the nervous tissue of the C.N.S. and so bind it together and to the blood vessels that course through it. With ordinary stains only the nuclei of the neuroglia cells can be seen to advantage. However, the nuclei of neuroglia cells, as seen in ordinary sections, are of different sorts, suggesting that there are different kinds of neuroglia cells, and this concept is confirmed when the cells are studied by the special technics that will be described presently; they demonstrate their cytoplasmic outlines to better advantage than H and E.

In the past it has been customary to classify the neuroglia cells in postnatal nervous tissue into 3 groups: astrocytes, oligodendroglia and microglia. Recently, Smart and Leblond have utilized thymidine labeled with tritium to trace cell relationships in these cells in the brain of the mouse, and their studies suggest that there are 4 categories of cells in postnatal life, instead of 3, with the fourth type consisting of cells with small dark or medium-dark nuclei. Cells of this fourth type are probably the counterparts in postnatal life of the spongioblasts that give rise to astrocytes and oligodendroglia in fetal life.

Turnover of Cells in the Neuroglia Series. In their study of the mouse brain in postnatal life, Smart and Leblond showed that after a mouse was given labeled thymidine the label appears first in cells which have small dark or medium dark nuclei (Fig. 294). These cells are of the spongioblast type, and since they are the ones that take up the labeled thymidine they must be the ones in which DNA is being duplicated in preparation for division. Label does not appear in astrocytes or oligodendroglia until later and at a time when label is no longer available; this indicates that these latter cells do not take up label in preparation for division (for none is then available) but, instead, label appears in them because previously labeled spongioblasts have differentiated, in due course, into oligodendroglia or into astrocytes. Since labeled oligodendroglia are seen before labeled astrocytes make their appearance, it seems probable that oligodendroglia may sometimes differentiate into astrocytes.

Smart and Leblond consider from their findings that there must be a turnover of cells in the neuroglia series throughout life, even though this is relatively slow. It would seem that astrocytes grow old and die and that new ones are formed from oligodendroglia and spongioblasts. Oligodendroglia, which become astrocytes or die as oligodendroglia, are replaced by spongioblasts differentiating into oligodendroglia.

Since Smart and Leblond, by using labeled thymidine, were able to show that spongioblast type cells took up label, which would mean that their DNA was being duplicated, it could be assumed that these cells would divide. These investigators next used colchicine to see if they could not detect examples of

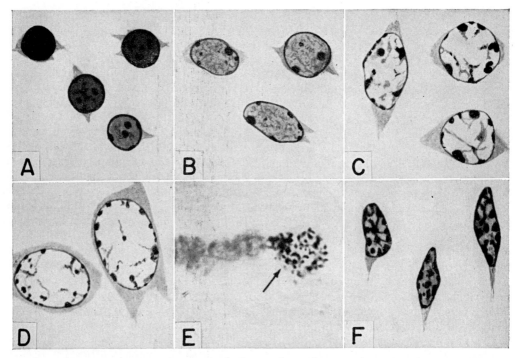

Fig. 294. All except E are drawings of cells seen in 3 micron sections of mouse brain stained with H and E. The drawings are at a magnification of 2,500. (A) Cells with dark round nuclei; these are probably spongioblasts. (B) Cells of the same general type with medium-dark nuclei. These are probably somewhat more differentiated than those seen in A. (C) Oligodendroglia. (D) Astrocytes. (E) Photomicrograph (× 1,300) of a radioautograph of a section of brain 7 days after labeled thymidine was injected into the animal. The astrocyte indicated by the arrow is heavily labeled. (F) Microglia. [Smart, I., and Leblond, C. P.: J. Comp. Neurol. (in press)]

these cells in the metaphase of mitosis. Their search in this respect was disappointing, for they could not find enough examples of cells of this type arrested in the metaphase of mitosis to account for the number of cell divisions that their studies with labeled thymidine indicated must take place. They lean to the view that the process of cell division in cells of the spongioblast type must be less obvious in some way than it is in the usual cell division. Indeed, if mitotic figures were as easy to detect in this type of cell as they are in most types they doubtless would have been observed before, and the concept of there being a turnover of cells of the neuroglia series would have come into existence long ago.

The Characteristics of the Nuclei of the Neuroglia Cells. *Astrocytes* have the largest nuclei. Generally, these are ovoid or round, and pale. The chromatin granules are fine, and sparse except at the nuclear membrane where many may adhere (Fig. 294 D). Nucleoli can be demonstrated in the nuclei of astrocytes, but they are generally not obvious in the ordinary preparation. An astrocyte labeled with thymidine as seen in a radioautograph is shown in Figure 294 E.

Oligodendroglia. The nuclei of these are the most common ones seen. Typically, an oligodendroglia nucleus is round or oval and somewhat smaller than the nucleus of an astrocyte. In routine sections the nucleus is dark-staining because its chromatin is closely packed. In very thin sections more detail can be seen in the nucleus, and in such sections coarse and fine granules can be seen to adhere to the nuclear membrane (Fig. 294 C). Here again nucleoli can be demonstrated but they are not prominent by any means in the usual section.

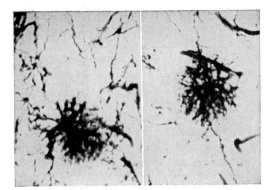

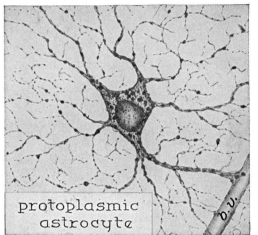

FIG. 295. Medium-power photomicrographs of 2 protoplasmic astrocytes in a Golgi preparation of the cerebral cortex of a dog. The heavy black line obliquely crossing the top of the picture on the right is a blood vessel, and the feet of the processes of the astrocyte are attached to it.

FIG. 296. A protoplasmic astrocyte. (Penfield, W.: Neuroglia and microglia; the interstitial tissue of the central nervous system *in* Cowdry's Special Cytology, ed. 2, New York, Hoeber)

Spongioblast-type Cells. The nuclei of these tend to be round, and they are of a smaller diameter than either the nuclei of astrocytes or oligodendroglia (Fig. 294 A and B). The chromatin is more closely packed than that of either astrocytes or oligodendroglia so that these nuclei generally are very dark staining. The medium dark ones are shown in Figure 294 B.

Microglia. These cells, although classed as one type of neuroglia cell, develop from mesenchyme and not from spongioblasts. Their nuclei are elongated and narrow (Fig. 294 F). The chromatin granules are spread more evenly through the nucleus than they are in oligodendroglia and astrocytes, where they tend to be associated with the nuclear membrane. A tail of cytoplasm from each end of the nucleus can commonly be seen in H and E sections.

Evolution of Silver-Impregnation Methods. If tissues are soaked in a weak solution of silver nitrate, the silver nitrate combines with some tissue ingredients more than with others. If tissues so treated are exposed to light, the silver is reduced and blackened; hence, the tissue ingredients with which it particularly combined are disclosed to advantage. However, silver nitrate by itself, was not a sufficiently good agent to permit the nature of nervous tissue of the C.N.S. to be elucidated. But, in 1872, a discovery was made which greatly enhanced the scope of its application.

At this time, an Italian anatomist, Camillo Golgi, was forced by economic circumstances to terminate temporarily his association with a proper laboratory and take a position as chief resident physician and surgeon in a hospital for incurable patients. Such was his zeal for anatomic research that he attempted to set up a histologic laboratory in the kitchen of his house where he could work evenings. He had little more than a microscope and a few simple instruments, and with these he made the discovery that revolutionized the study of nervous tissue.

Golgi had fixed some tissue of the C.N.S. in a solution of potassium bichromate and had left the tissue in this solution for a long time. He then soaked the tissue in silver nitrate, and a miracle occurred. Silver bichromate was deposited on only some of the cells in the tissue but not on most of them. Accordingly, the ones that were impregnated stood out against a clear background as if they had been mounted in a clear plastic for demonstration purposes. Curiously enough, this method does not impregnate parts of cells as erratically as it does cells in general; those cells that do become impregnated are generally well impregnated over their whole extent.

At first Golgi's discovery was not received enthusiastically by histologists in other countries. His method was considered freakish and

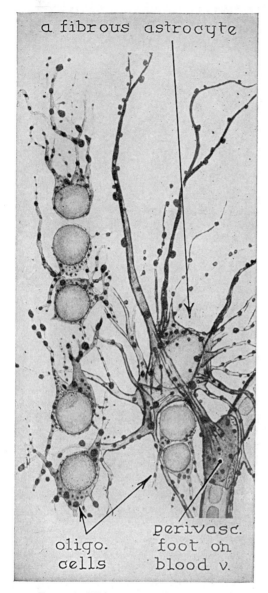

FIG. 297. White matter of the brain of a rabbit stained by Del Rio-Hortega's method for gliosomes. It shows a row of oligodendroglia cells on the left and a fibrous astrocyte on the right. (Modified from Penfield, W.: Brain 47:430)

these he systematically investigated the histology of nervous tissue. He was instrumental, among many other things, in providing histologic evidence for the individuality of neurons. Cajal published nearly 300 papers and many books on neurohistology, and much of what we know today about neurohistology can be traced to him. His great contributions to this field were acknowledged in 1906 by his being awarded, jointly with Golgi, the Nobel prize in Physiology and Medicine. Medical students will find inspiration and enjoyment in reading his *Recollections of My Life*. (This has been translated into English by E. Horne Craigie.)

The improvement and the use of silver and gold impregnation methods by Cajal and Del Rio-Hortega, who was one of his pupils, permitted neuroglia cells to be classified properly and their form and function clarified. Their nuclei, which appear to advantage with ordinary technics, have already been illustrated in Figure 234. Their morphology as shown by metallic impregnation methods will now be described.

Protoplasmic astrocytes, with few exceptions, are confined to gray matter. They have wavy branching cytoplasmic processes that extend out from all aspects of their cell bodies so that they resemble bushy shrubs (Figs. 295 and 296). Their processes often terminate on one or more small blood vessels in little structures called *perivascular feet* (Figs. 295 and 296). Since their processes extend through the nerve fibers of gray matter and are anchored to blood vessels, they not only hold the substance of gray matter together but also anchor it to the blood vessels that extend through it. Little granules, called *gliosomes* (Fig. 296), which may be the counterparts in astrocytes of the mitochondria of other cells, may be demonstrated in the cytoplasm of astrocytes.

Fibrous astrocytes, with few exceptions, are confined to white matter where their cell bodies are disposed between myelinated fibers and their processes run along and between myelinated fibers, binding them together and to blood vessels. Their processes are longer and straighter and do not branch so extensively as those of the protoplasmic variety (Fig. 297). Moreover, their processes, unlike those of protoplasmic astrocytes, contain fibers. Some have thought that at least the ends of these fibers were extracytoplasmic, but

unreliable. However, at that time, there was a young man in Spain who was destined to become the greatest neurohistologist of all time. Santiago Ramon y Cajal saw the great possibilities of Golgi's method, made improvements in it and, with his pupils, devised still further metallic impregnation methods. By means of

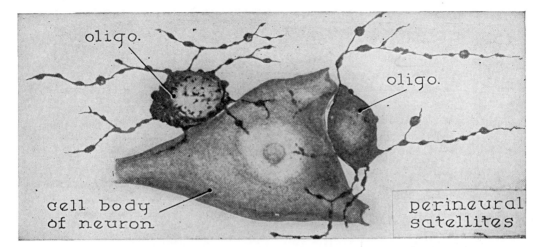

FIG. 298. The cell body of a neuron and 2 perineural satellites. (Penfield, W.)

now it is generally believed that the fibers are completely covered with cytoplasm. In favor of the latter view is the fact that gliosomes, which are composed of cytoplasmic constituents, can be demonstrated at and near the ends of the processes, even in the perivascular feet which clasp small blood vessels (Fig. 297).

Oligodendroglia exist in both gray and white matter. They were given their name by Del Rio-Hortega because, as has been explained before, they have fewer processes than astrocytes. They are also much smaller. Their processes contain no fibers and do not end in perivascular feet. Consequently, they do not function nearly so efficiently as astrocytes in holding nervous tissue together.

In the gray matter, they are commonly seen close to the cell bodies of neurons; here they are termed *perineural* satellites (Fig. 298). Their rounded-to-oval, fairly dark-staining nuclei (but not their cytoplasmic processes) can be recognized easily in H and E sections in this position (Fig. 305).

In the white matter, oligodendroglia are commonly distributed in rows between myelinated fibers (Fig. 297). Here their processes form very incomplete sheaths for myelinated fibers and assist the fibrous astrocytes in holding the white matter together.

They also are arranged close to blood vessels as *perivascular satellites,* both in gray and white matter.

Microglia. As noted before, the nuclei of

neuroglia cells appear to advantage in thin sections stained with ordinary stains such as H and E (Fig. 294 F). In this type of preparation, the nuclei of astrocytes and oligodendroglia cells are seen to have a regular outline. However, scattered among them are nuclei of about the same size as those of oligodendroglia cells, but they have irregular outlines. These are the nuclei of the cells that comprise what is termed the *microglia* or the *mesoglia* (Fig. 294 F). The nature of these cells long remained a mystery; it was not until 1920 that Del Rio-Hortega devised a metallic impregnation method that revealed their cell bodies and their processes clearly and showed that they neither formed fibers nor had perivascular feet.

Microglia cells are more common in gray than in white matter. In gray matter they are distributed as perineural satellites; of course, they are not so numerous in this position as oligodendroglia cells. They are also arranged on blood vessels as perivascular satellites (Fig. 299). In white matter they are distributed, but more sparingly than oligodendroglia cells, between myelinated fibers.

Del Rio-Hortega showed that microglia did not appear in the C.N.S. until blood vessels had begun to grow into it. As will be described presently, the brain and the cord become enveloped in a mesenchymal-derived sheath, the pia mater, and extensions from this sheath accompany blood vessels as they leave it to penetrate the brain. Microglia cells first appear as ameboid cells beneath the pia in certain

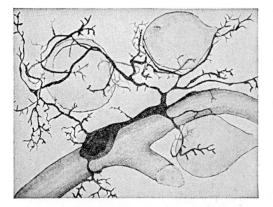

FIG. 299. Microglia perivascular satellite from cerebral cortex. (Modified from Penfield, W.: Brain *47*:430)

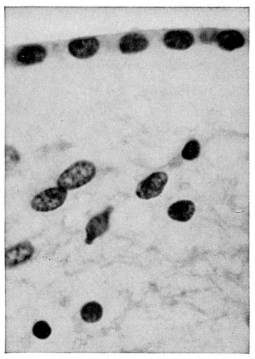

FIG. 300. High-power photomicrograph of an H and E section of brain, showing the ependyma lining the lateral ventricle.

regions and also in association with some of the blood vessels that pass into the substance of the C.N.S. The developing microglia cells are ameboid and migrate through the substance of the C.N.S. to take up various positions in it. From the evidence at hand it seems justifiable to consider that the microglia, in contrast with the other types of neuroglia, are mesenchymal-derived, probably from the developing pia mater. From their behavior after-brain injuries, in that they change their form and become large phagocytes, known as *compound granular corpuscles,* it seems probable that they are the counterparts of the macrophages of other parts of the body and that they are, therefore, members of the reticuloendothelial system.

Ependyma. The cells that line the lumen of the neural tube perform three more-or-less consecutive functions. At first their function is proliferative; they are the germinal cells that give rise to most of the cells that come to occupy the middle (mantle) layer of the wall of the tube and become neuroblasts and free spongioblasts. Their second function is supportive. As the wall of the neural tube thickens, the lining cells send out long processes that, for a time at least, reach the exterior of the tube and help to form the external limiting membrane that surrounds the tube (Fig. 283). At this time inner borders of the lining cells may be ciliated (Fig. 283), and they are called *ependymal spongioblasts.* Still later they gradually relinquish their supporting role and function chiefly in forming a

continuous epithelial lining, known as the ependyma, for the ventricles of the brain (Fig. 300). They also persist in the central canal of the spinal cord. In certain sites in the ventricles the ependyma is pushed inwardly by vascular tufts. These arrangements are called choroid plexuses, as will be explained presently. This matter is mentioned here only because the ependyma that comes to cover the capillaries of the choroid plexuses comes to be known as *choroid plexus epithelium* rather than as ependyma. Ependymal cells are classified as one type of neuroglial cells.

MICROSCOPIC STRUCTURE OF THE SPINAL CORD

General Considerations. The spinal cord is a cylindrical column but it is flattened noticeably in front, and less noticeably behind, so that a cross section of it is ovoid (Fig. 301).

The anterior horns of gray matter are broader and shorter than the posterior horns and do not approach the surface of the cord as closely as do the posterior horns (Fig. 301).

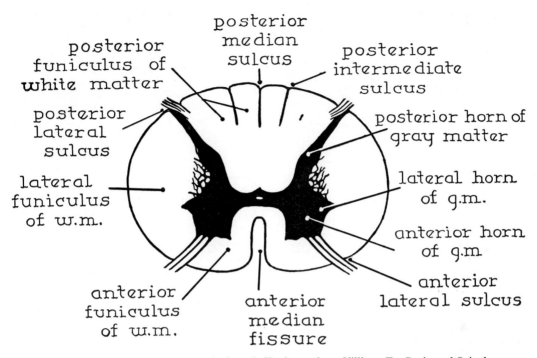

posterior
median
sulcus

posterior
funiculus of
white matter

posterior
intermediate
sulcus

posterior
lateral
sulcus

posterior horn of
gray matter

lateral
funiculus
of w.m.

lateral horn
of g.m.

anterior horn
of g.m

anterior
funiculus
of w.m.

anterior
median
fissure

anterior
lateral sulcus

FIG. 301. Cross section of the spinal cord. (Redrawn from Villiger, E.: Brain and Spinal Cord, Philadelphia, Lippincott)

In the thoracic and the first two or three lumbar segments of the cord a lateral horn of gray matter is also to be seen on each side of the cord (Figs. 301 and 302). The gray matter that forms the cross bar of the H is said to constitute a *commissure* (*commissure* = a joining together); that which lies in front of the central canal constitutes the *anterior commissure* of gray matter and that which lies behind the canal, the *posterior commissure* of gray matter. Immediately around the central canal there is a network of neuroglia cells that constitute what is termed the *central gelatinous substance*.

The white matter is divided up into funiculi (little cords) by longitudinal sulci (furrows) and a fissure. The posterior median sulcus (Fig. 301) overlies the dorsal median septum, the formation of which is illustrated in Figure 280. To each side of the posterior median sulcus on the posterior surface of the cord are two shallow sulci, termed separately the *posterior intermediate sulcus* and the *posterior lateral sulcus*. Between the posterior median sulcus and the posterior lateral sulcus on each side lies a *posterior funiculus* of white matter

(Fig. 301). Between the posterior lateral sulcus and the anterior lateral sulcus lies, on each side, a *lateral funiculus* of white matter, and between the two lateral sulci and the anterior median fissure lie the two *anterior funiculi* of white matter (Fig. 301).

Segmentation of the Cord. As has been noted already, man is a segmented organism, and each segment is represented by an individual vertebra. The afferent neurons that extend into the cord from any given body segment pass through the intervertebral foramen belonging to that segment and into the vertebral canal, where they extend to and enter the posterior horn of gray matter of the segment of the spinal cord that belongs to that body segment (Fig. 310). Likewise, the efferent fibers that extend out from anterior horns of gray matter of that same segment of the cord pass through the same intervertebral foramen to reach and innervate the muscles that belong to that particular body segment (Fig. 310). However, it so happens that during development the vertebral column elongates to a much greater extent than the spinal cord that is contained in its canal. This has two impor-

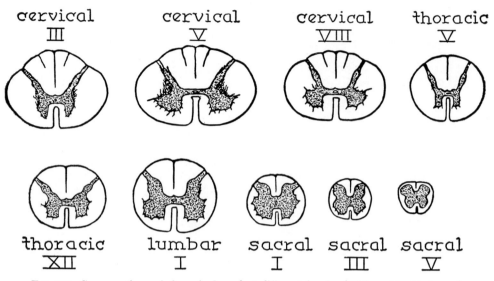

FIG. 302. Cross sections of the spinal cord at different levels. (Villiger, E.: Brain and Spinal Cord, Philadelphia, Lippincott)

tant effects. First, since the cord must remain connected to the brain, the lower end of the cord in the adult does not reach nearly to the lower end of the vertebral canal but only to the level of the 1st or the 2nd lumbar vertebra. Secondly, the various segments of the cord, which originally are in line with the body segments to which their afferent and efferent fibers are connected, gradually assume higher levels than their respective body segments; hence, the afferent and the efferent fibers that pass out from each segment of the cord to reach their respective body segments must pass down along the sides of the cord to reach their intervertebral canals. This condition, of course, becomes increasingly prominent as the caudal end of the cord is approached and accounts for the fact that although the caudal division of the vertebral canal does not contain any spinal cord, it does contain afferent and efferent fibers that are extending down from the lower segments of the cord to reach their proper intervertebral foramina.

Appearance at Different Levels. An expert can tell from the microscopic appearance of any given cross section of the spinal cord the approximate segmental level from which it was obtained. If a student learns a few general facts he, too, can demonstrate a certain amount of skill at making identifications.

The first fact to remember is that the amount of white matter in the cord thickens as the cord passes from lower to higher levels for the same reason that telephone cables from outlying districts become thicker as they approach a metropolis. The white matter consists chiefly of axons that are passing between the brain and the various levels of the cord. It is obvious then that in the sacral region—an outlying district, as it were—the white matter has to accommodate only those axons which are passing between the sacral portion of the cord and the brain, while in the cervical region—where the cable is nearing the metropolis—the white matter has to accommodate the axons that are passing between the brain and the cervical, the thoracic, the lumbar and the sacral levels, which, of course, requires that there be much more white matter here than in the sacral region. (See Fig. 302 and compare the appearance of cervical and sacral cross sections.)

Next, to continue our analogy, let us imagine that the cable from the outlying district, before reaching the metropolis, passes through two small cities. It is only to be expected that there would be substations in these cities with a corresponding local expansion of the wiring facilities. So it is with the cord; the two divisions of it which are concerned with the innervation of the arms and the legs —the counterparts of the two cities—are the cervical and the lumbar regions respectively, and the cord in both these sites is expanded into fusiform enlargements. Hence, cross sections of the cervical and the lumbar regions of the cord show its size to be greater in these sites than in others (Fig. 302). The enlargement in the cervical region has been shown by Donaldson and Davis to be due to both the gray matter and the white matter being increased, while the enlargement in the lumbar region is due entirely to an increase in the amount of gray matter in this site.

Another point that aids in identifying the site from which any given section of cord is taken is the fact that the lateral horns of gray matter are obvious only in the thoracic and the first two lumbar segments. There are, of course, other distinguishing features of cross sections of cord at different levels, but their explanation would require a more detailed description of the histology of the cord than is required here.

Some Features of the Gray Matter. The gray matter of the cord consists of the cell bodies of neurons, unmyelinated fibers, some myelinated fibers, protoplasmic astrocytes, oligodendroglia cells and some small blood vessels with a little connective tissue that accompanies them, including some microglia cells. The pale-blue background seen in an H and E section, and against which the cell bodies of neurons and the nuclei of neuroglia cells stand out, is a complex network of nerve fibers and the processes of neuroglia cells (Fig. 285).

The cell bodies of neurons are not distributed evenly in the gray matter of the cord but in aggregates, some of which are termed *nuclei*. These extend for varying distances up and down the cord in the gray matter. It is not necessary to describe here the positions occupied by these or the types of cell bodies seen in different ones. Only a few general remarks will be made about the types of cells in the different horns of gray matter.

The cell bodies in the anterior horn (Fig. 288) are the largest seen in the cord, and those of the posterior horn the smallest. Those of the lateral horns are of an intermediate size. The most notable cells in the anterior horns are those which are called *root cells,* which give rise to the axons that constitute the efferent fibers that extend out to the muscles of each segment. These neurons constitute the "final

common path" by which all neural activity which is to result in muscular action converges. They are generally referred to by the term *anterior horn cells*. They are large and multipolar with abundant chromidial substance in their cytoplasm (Fig. 288). These are the cells that are most likely to be affected by the virus that causes anterior poliomyelitis (infantile paralysis), and if they are destroyed the muscles which they normally innervate become paralyzed. There are other types of cells in the anterior horns as well; some have very short processes that terminate in the gray matter; others, called *column* or *tract cells,* send axons to other parts and levels of the cord.

The cells of the lateral columns give rise to axons which extend out to ganglia of the autonomic nervous system, as will be described later in connection with that system.

The neurons, the cell bodies of which are disposed in the posterior horns, are of the intrasegmental and the intersegmental types. Afferent fibers coming in from the body segments on entering the cord, as well as ascending and descending in white matter, enter the posterior horns of gray matter and make synaptic connections with them. By means of their axons they relay impulses received from the afferent neurons to various parts of the C.N.S.

Some Features of the White Matter. The general microscopic structure of the white matter of the cord has been described already. Before leaving this subject, however, it is pertinent to mention that the axons that pass up and down the cord and are related to different functions are not mixed together haphazardly but are segregated in a remarkable way. The axons of the efferent pathways are segregated in special sectors of the cord, as are the axons of the afferent pathways. Moreover, within these divisions there is further segregation; for example, the axons of neurons concerned in conveying impulses relating to touch and pressure sensation from all levels of the cord are bundled together in a special sector of the cord on each side, and those carrying impulses relating to pain are likewise isolated. Indeed, the segregation is so remarkable that if a nick is made in the white matter at some point around the circumference of the cord, the loss of muscle functions and/or sensory functions resulting from it can be accurately predicted.

Armed with full knowledge on this matter, the physician, from studying the particular kinds and sites of sensory and motor disturbance that follow an injury to, or disease of, the cord, can predict the particular site at which the cord is damaged; should an operation be required, he can indicate the site at which the cord should be exposed.

MICROSCOPIC STRUCTURE OF SOME PARTS OF THE BRAIN

The Gray Matter That Is Enclosed by White Matter. As has been noted already, the gray matter of the brain develops from the middle (mantle) layer of the neural tube, as it does in the spinal cord. As occurs in the spinal cord, much of it comes to be surrounded in some fashion by white matter. The great exceptions to this rule are, of course, the cerebral and the cerebellar cortices; and, as has been explained already, these are due to cells of the middle layer growing out through the outer layer of the developing neural tube in these sites to take up a position on the periphery of the tube. Except for the cortices, the gray matter that forms in the hindbrain, the midbrain and the forebrain is more or less buried in white matter, and it is comparable with the gray matter of the cord, though it is arranged somewhat differently. For example, it is not divided into posterior and anterior horns but rather is present as masses of various shapes and sizes which, however, are related either to sensory or motor functions, as are the horns of the cord. Moreover, it is generally not as pure as it is in the spinal cord; in many sites it is more or less obviously broken up by myelinated fibers; but it, like the gray matter of the spinal cord, consists essentially of the cell bodies of neurons, neuroglia cells, naked nerve fibers and in some instances, as has been mentioned above, myelinated fibers as well. In some sites there is so much white matter mixed with the gray that the mixture is called *reticular substance.*

Some of these masses of gray matter that are surrounded by white matter in the brain serve a similar function in relation to the cranial nerves that the posterior and the anterior horns of gray matter in the cord serve in relation to the spinal nerves. Consequently, afferent fibers in cranial nerves may terminate in association with neurons in sensory masses of gray matter; likewise, axons from motor masses of gray matter may extend out in cranial nerves that have efferent components. But the functions of these masses of gray matter in the brain are generally more complex than serving as the cranial counterparts of the anterior and the posterior horns of gray matter of the cord. In indicating some of their further functions it may be helpful to return to our analogy.

In likening the C.N.S. to a telephone system it is important to understand that there is one way in which its organization is different. In a telephone system the same wire can be used both for the reception and the sending of messages; in the nervous system two fibers, or more commonly, two chains of fibers, are generally necessary to serve these two functions, one of which is afferent and the other efferent.

The cerebral cortex, as we shall see, is the giant switchboard wherein are innumerable circuits by which afferent impulses can be redispatched on efferent pathways. We have already learned that inherited reflex patterns and conditioning are important factors in determining which of the innumerable circuits are used most extensively. We have also suggested that the white matter of the cord represents a trunk line that reaches out through the district served by the system. The gray matter at each level of the cord represents, as it were, a village exchange office, situated along the trunk line, with wires for both incoming and outgoing calls passing out into the particular body segment served by that local office. It has already been mentioned that two enlargements of the cord, the cervical and the lumbar, represent expansions of such local office facilities as are necessary for servicing the counterparts of two cities, the arms and the legs. As the trunk line—the white matter of the cord— passes toward the brain it becomes thicker because it must contain additional wires (fibers) from each community office along its way. If we traced any of the afferent fibers of the cord into the substance of the brain we should find that they would enter one of the masses of gray matter that are enclosed by white matter and there make synaptic connection with further neurons. This has the effect of enabling connections to be made with several further neurons and so widens the pathways

LAYERS OF CEREBRAL CORTEX

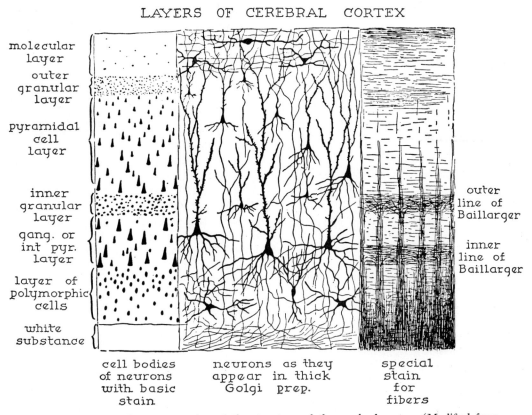

molecular
layer

outer
granular
layer

pyramidal
cell
layer

inner
granular
layer

gang. or
int pyr.
layer

layer of
polymorphic
cells

white
substance

outer
line of
Baillarger

inner
line of
Baillarger

cell bodies
of neurons
with basic
stain

neurons as they
appear in thick
Golgi prep.

special
stain
for
fibers

FIG. 303. Schematic representation of the structure of the cerebral cortex. (Modified from Villiger, E.: Brain and Spinal Cord, Philadelphia, Lippincott)

over which the afferent impulse may possibly spread thereafter.

To sum up: The gray matter that is surrounded by white matter in the brain serves, like that of the cord, as local exchanges for territories serviced by cranial nerves, for providing connections with other substations and, finally, in providing relay stations which, like the repeater stations on a long-distance telephone line, redispatch signals that are received from one direction along the next set of wires that lead to the next station. The last station, to which and from which messages are dispatched, is, of course, the cortical switchboard.

The Gray Matters That Covers White Matter. It will be recalled that the wall of the neural tube in the front part of both the hindbrain and the forebrain undergoes massive development to form the cerebellar and the cerebral hemispheres, respectively. Moreover, it will be recalled that as these are being formed, some of the cells of the middle (mantle) layer of the tube migrate through the outer (marginal) layer of the wall of the tube and take up a position and form gray matter on the surface of the developing hemispheres. It has already been mentioned that the gray matter covering the cerebral hemispheres provides the circuits by which innumerable connections are made between the afferent pathways which extend to it and the efferent pathways that lead away from it. It has also been explained that the stimulation of different parts of the cerebral cortex by different afferent pathways accounts for the interpretation of different kinds of sensation and its localization. We shall now consider very briefly the microscopic structure of the cerebral cortex.

The cerebral cortex is a layer of gray matter that varies from around 1.5 to 4 mm. in thickness and covers the white matter of the cerebral hemispheres (Figs. 282 and 303). The extensively convulated surface of the hemi-

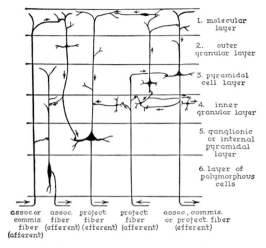

1. molecular
   layer

2. outer
   granular layer

3. pyramidal
   cell layer

4. inner
   granular layer

5. ganglionic
   or internal
   pyramidal
   layer

6. layer of
   polymorphous
   cells

assoc.or   assoc.   project.   project.   assoc., commis.
commis.   fiber   fiber   fiber   or project. fiber
fiber   (efferent) (efferent) (afferent) (efferent)
(afferent)

FIG. 304. Diagram showing some of the connections that are effected in the cortex between the fibers that lead to it and those that lead away from it.

spheres of man (Fig. 282) permits the gray matter to be much more extensive than it would be if the surfaces of the hemispheres were smooth, as they are in some animals. Sections cut through the cerebral cortex from different parts of the hemispheres show the same general plan of microscopic structure but also that the general plan is sufficiently modified in different cortical areas to imply that these different areas of the cortex perform somewhat different functions. The cortex, speaking generally, exhibits 6 layers (Fig. 303). The extent to which each of these 6 layers is developed differs in various areas, and since different areas have been shown to be related to somewhat different functions, some generalizations can be drawn about the relation of the cells of the various layers to particular functions. However, this matter is one for consideration in neuro-anatomy textbooks; here we shall describe only some of the characteristics of the 6 layers.

The outermost is called the *molecular layer* (Fig. 303). It contains relatively few cells and consists chiefly of fibers of underlying cells which run in many directions but generally parallel with the surface (Fig. 303, *right*). The second layer is called the *outer granular layer* because it contains many small nerve cells which give this layer a granular appearance when it is examined under low power

(Fig. 303). The third layer is called the *pyramidal cell layer* because of its content of the pyramidal-shaped cell bodies of neurons (Fig. 303). The fourth layer is termed the *inner granular layer* because it is "granulated" with small nerve cells (Fig. 303). The fifth layer is termed the *ganglionic* or *internal pyramidal layer*. The latter name describes its most prominent feature which is its content of pyramidal cell bodies. In one part of the cortex called the *motor area*, the pyramidal cells of this layer are huge; they are called *Betz cells*. The sixth and final layer is named the *layer of polymorphous cells* because the cells of this layer have many shapes. Of course, neuroglia cells are disposed in all 6 layers; the naming of the layers is based on their nerve cell and fiber content rather than on their neuroglia content.

Before commenting on some of the ways in which the neurons of the different layers of the cortex are connected, we shall describe the white matter which lies below the cortex. This consists of interlacing bundles of myelinated fibers which pass in almost all directions. Some of these fibers connect one part of the cortex to another part on the same side and, accordingly, are termed *association fibers*. Some connect cortical areas of one side with those of cortical areas of the other side and hence are known as *commissural fibers*. Still others, and these may be either afferent or efferent, connect the cortex with subcortical centers (areas of gray matter surrounded by white matter) and are termed *projection fibers*. The meaning of this term is clear with regard to afferent fibers because impulses dealing with, say a certain sensation, can be visualized as being projected from subcortical centers to certain parts of the cortex. Why the efferent fibers that lead away from the cortex to subcortical stations should be called projection fibers is not so clear.

Figure 304 shows some of the connections that exist in the cerebral cortex between the cells of its different layers and between them and the afferent association, commissural and projection fibers that lead into it (left and fourth from left). It also shows how the cell bodies of different layers in the cortex give rise to intracortical and extracortical association fibers and to commissural fibers (third from left) which pass to subcortical centers

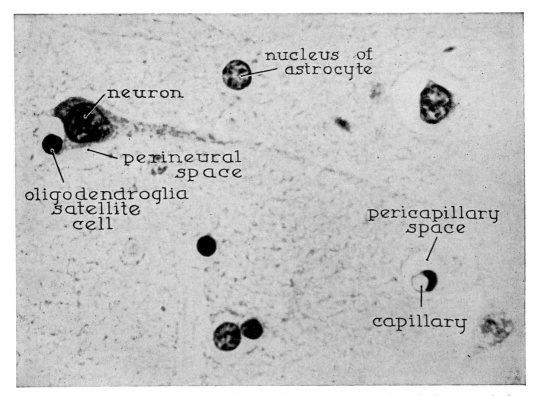

FIG. 305. High-power photomicrograph of a section of gray matter from the human cerebral cortex. The almost structureless-appearing background constituting most of the photograph can be studied to advantage only by means of special technics. It is probable that the perineural and the pericapillary spaces are the result of artefact.

of gray matter. It has been estimated that there are close to 10,000 million neurons in the cerebral cortex, and since one neuron may effect synaptic connection with several others the possibilities with regard to the number of pathways that are available here are indeed overwhelming.

It is to be understood that the most common type of histologic preparation—a thin section stained with H and E—reveals only a few features of cerebral cortex to advantage. Nevertheless, since such sections are used routinely, particularly for the detection of pathologic conditions, the student must be able to interpret them intelligently. Brief comment will now be made on what may be seen in one at moderately high magnification.

As may be seen in Figure 305, most of such a section consists of a pale-blue, almost structureless-appearing background. This is the so-called *neuropil* and it consists of a felt-work (*pilos* = felt) of naked nerve fibers and

the processes of neuroglia cells. Since these are distributed in all planes, they are, for the most part, cut in cross section or obliquely in a thin section; therefore, they appear as ill-defined dots that stain very lightly. In the aggregate these give the neuropil, as it is seen in a thin H and E section, a stippled appearance. It is obvious that in order to trace the direction of the fibers in the different layers of the cortex it would be necessary to use thick sections stained by methods which impregnate the fibers and show them as dark lines, as in Figure 303, *right*.

Nuclei, as might be expected, show up well in thin sections of cortex stained with H and E. Those of large neurons are recognized easily, and generally those of the 3 types of astrocytes can be distinguished also (Fig. 305). The student should see examples of the dark round nuclei of oligodendroglia cells close beside the cell bodies of neurons (Fig. 305, *left*) where the oligodendroglia cells are acting

blood vessels
in pia mater

mol.
layer

purk.
cell

gran.
layer

white matter

Fig. 306. Low-power photomicrograph of an H and E section of the cerebellum.

and pericapillary spaces (Fig. 305). It was generally believed in the past that these spaces were real and that they were filled with cerebrospinal fluid. The recent work of Woollam and Millen suggests that they are merely artefact spaces that do not exist in life and so do not contain cerebrospinal fluid.

Cerebellum. This (Fig. 282) consists of two *hemispheres* and a wormlike midportion, the *vermis.* Transverse fissures divide it into lobes. Each lobe consists of numerous transverse folds called *folia.*

Like the cerebrum, the cerebellum has a thin cortex of gray matter that overlies white matter. It also has a central mass of gray matter that is surrounded by white matter. However, the cerebellar cortex has only 3 layers (Fig. 306): (1) an outer molecular layer of few cells and many nonmedullated fibers, (2) an intermediate single layer of large flask-shaped cells, called *Purkinje cells,* and (3) an inner granular or nuclear layer that consists of the bodies of small nerve cells.

The Purkinje cells give rise to a few main dendrites (Fig. 306) which branch in a fanlike fashion through the molecular layer to the surface. The axons of the Purkinje cells arise from the opposite end of the cell to the dendrites and extend through the granular layer to enter the white matter of the folia and eventually reach the central mass of gray matter. Along their course the axons may give off collaterals that connect with other Purkinje cells.

The cells of the granular layer are small. Each has from 3 to 6 short dendrites that end in the granular layer and a long axon that ascends into the molecular layer where it divides and its branches run parallel with the surface. Therefore, the axons of these cells run at right angles through the dendritic arborizations of the Purkinje cells. Some larger cells also may be observed in the granular layer.

The stellate cells of the molecular layer are both superficial and deep; the latter are termed *basket cells.* The axons of these envelop Purkinje cells, whereas their dendrites ramify throughout the molecular layer.

Afferent cerebellar fibers of 2 types, mossy and climbing fibers, are seen in the cerebellum. The latter twine about the branches of the Purkinje cells. Mossy fibers synapse with dendrites of cells in the granular layer; climbing fibers twine about the dendrites of Purkinje

as perineural satellites. The cytoplasm of astrocytes is scarcely apparent in H and E sections, and no intimations are given of the processes of these cells that are revealed by special technics. However, the nuclei of astrocytes can be recognized by their size (Fig. 305), by the lack of cytoplasm around them (Fig. 305) and perhaps also by the fact that their nucleoli are very poorly developed as compared with neurons. Other things that may be seen in an H and E section are perineural

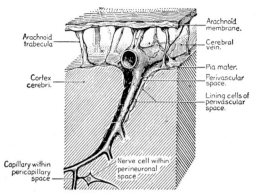

Arachnoid membrane.

Arachnoid trabecula

Cerebral vein.

Cortex cerebri.

Pia mater.

Perivascular space.

Lining cells of perivascular space.

Capillary within pericapillary space

Nerve cell within perineuronal space

FIG. 307. Schematic diagram to show the relations of the pia mater, the arachnoid, the blood vessels and the brain. (Weed, L. H.: Am. J. Anat. *31*:202)

cells like a vine climbing through the branches of a tree.

The cerebellum is related to the maintenance of equilibrium and to the co-ordination and the strength of muscular movements. Its connection with substations along afferent and efferent pathways in the brain is too complex a matter to discuss here.

THE MENINGES

The brain and the spinal cord are protected (1) by a bony encasement (the cranium and the vertebral column) and (2) by 3 connective tissue wrappings called the *meninges* (*meninx* = membrane) (Figs. 309 and 310). The innermost of these is applied directly to the surface of the brain and the cord and is called the *pia mater* (Figs. 307, 308, 309 and 310). The second and middle one is called the *arachnoid* (Figs. 307, 309 and 310), and the third and outermost one is called the *dura mater* (Figs. 309 and 310). In some sites this is adherent to the periosteum of the surrounding bone. The structure of these 3 membranes will now be considered in turn.

Pia Mater. As its name implies (*pia* = tender; *mater* = mother), this membrane that is applied directly to the surface of the brain is delicate. It consists of interlacing bundles of collagenic fibers but has some fine elastic networks in it as well. It is covered with a continuous membrane of flattened squamous cells which are morphologically similar to those of the mesothelial membranes of the great body cavities (Fig. 117). The substance of the

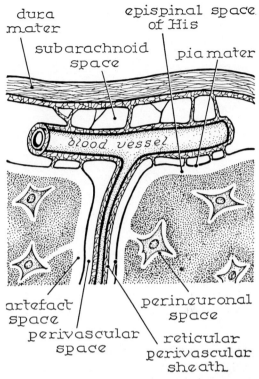

dura mater

subarachnoid space

epispinal space of His

pia mater

blood vessel

artefact space

perivascular space

perineuronal space

reticular perivascular sheath

FIG. 308. Diagram to illustrate the relations of the perivascular space. Note that the epispinal space of His is not a true space but is due to artefact. (Redrawn from Woollam, D. H. M., and Millen, J. W.: J. Anat. *89*:193)

membrane contains a few fibroblasts and macrophages and many blood vessels; these blood vessels are distributed by the pia mater over the surface of the brain (Fig. 308). From the pia mater these blood vessels penetrate into the substance of the brain. The pia mater dips into the brain substance with them to both line the spaces that conduct the vessels and to cover the vessels that are in the spaces. Between the piarachnoid that lines the spaces and that which covers the vessels there is a true *perivascular space*. This is found only in connection with the larger vessels; it does not extend as far as the capillaries, as was believed formerly. This true perivascular space communicates with the subarachnoid space and contains cerebrospinal fluid. Figure 307 depicts the older view which postulated that perivascular spaces communicate with little spaces in which the cell bodies of neurons lie,

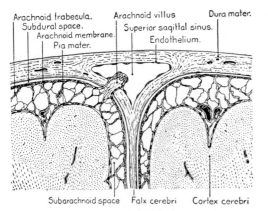

Arachnoid trabecula. Arachnoid villus   Dura mater.
Subdural space.   Superior sagittal sinus.
Arachnoid membrane.   Endothelium.
Pia mater.

Subarachnoid space   Falx cerebri   Cortex cerebri

FIG. 309. Schematic diagram to illustrate the meninges, the sagittal sinus and the arachnoid villus. The potential subdural space is shown of greater size than is normal. The subarachnoid space over the convolutions also is increased so as to illustrate the character of the subarachnoid mesh. (Weed, L. H.: Am. J. Anat. *31*: 203)

which are called *perineuronal spaces*. The investigations of Woollam and Millen have shown that the perineuronal space is an artefact, and, in addition, a space that is often seen between the pia and the brain substance (Fig. 308, *epispinal space of His*) is also an artefact. It is this latter artefact space that often seems to communicate with the artefact-induced perineuronal spaces (Fig. 308).

The Arachnoid. The middle membrane of the meninges is called the arachnoid because it is separated from—and at the same time joined to—the pia by a cobwebby (*arachnoid* = cobweb) network of trabeculae (Figs. 307, 308 and 309). The term arachnoid includes both the tissue that forms a continuous roof over the pia and the network of pillars which extend from the pia to the roof.

The pia and the arachnoid, because they are joined together, are sometimes described as a single membrane, the *piarachnoid*.

Both the membrane that is supported by the trabeculae and the trabeculae themselves are composed chiefly of delicate collagenic fibers together with some elastic fibers. Both the outer and inner surfaces of the membranous roof, and the trabeculae, are covered with a continuous lining of thin, flat lining cells that are similar to those that cover the pia. The space between the membranous roof of the arachnoid and the pia mater, that is, the

space through which the delicate arachnoid trabeculae extend, is filled with cerebrospinal fluid.

The surface of the brain is extraordinarily convoluted (Fig. 282). Whereas the pia extends down into the sulci and the fissures to cover the surface of the brain intimately, the membranous part of the arachnoid, except in the instance of some of the larger fissures, does not. Hence, over grooves there is more accommodation for cerebrospinal fluid than there is in other sites (Fig. 309, *not in the middle, but left and right*). Indeed, there are some sites where the brain surface is a considerable distance from the covering arachnoid, and, in these, there is accommodation for considerable amounts of cerebrospinal fluid. The precise location and nature of these will be learned in neuro-anatomy; they are termed *cisternae*.

Dura Mater. As its name implies (*dura* = hard, *mater* = mother), this outermost membrane is of a tough consistency and consists chiefly of dense, connective tissue (Fig. 309). The collagenic fibers tend to run longitudinally in the spinal dura but somewhat irregularly in the cranial dura. Elastic fibers are mixed with the collagenic to some extent. There are certain differences between the dura of the vertebral canal and that of the cranium. In the vertebral canal the dura consists of a relatively free dense connective tissue sheath. The potential space between its inner surface and the outer surface of the arachnoid is called the *subdural space* (Fig. 310) and it normally contains a slight amount of fluid which is *not* cerebrospinal fluid. The outer surface of the spinal dura abuts on the *epidural space* (Fig. 310), which is filled with loose areolar tissue containing a certain amount of fat and many veins. The internal periosteum of the vertebrae, which lines the vertebral canal, forms the outer limit of the epidural space.

In the vertebral canal, the dura, as has been pointed out, is separated from the periosteum lining the vertebral canal. In the cranium no such separation occurs, for in this region the membrane, which in the vertebral canal is called the dura, is fused with the internal periosteum of the bones of the cranium. This accounts for the cranial dura having 2 layers, its inner being the counterpart of what has been termed *dura* in the vertebral canal, and its outer, the internal periosteum of the bones

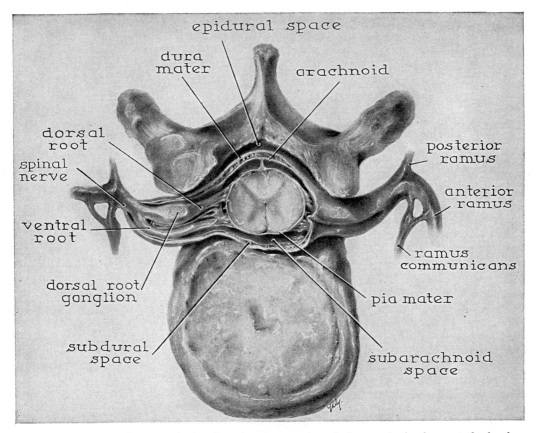

epidural space

dura mater

arachnoid

dorsal root

posterior ramus

spinal nerve

anterior ramus

ventral root

ramus communicans

dorsal root ganglion

pia mater

subdural space

subarachnoid space

Fig. 310. Semidiagrammatic drawing of a cross section of the vertebral column at the level of an intervertebral foramen. It shows the relations of the meninges to the spinal cord and the way the central nervous system is connected to the peripheral nervous system.

of the cranium. Since these 2 layers adhere to one another, the dura of the cranium is adherent to the bones of the skull. Furthermore, since its outer layer serves as the inner periosteum of the bones, its outer layer must contain many blood vessels. The inner layer is much less vascular than the outer layer. Although the outer and the inner layers of the cranial dura are continuous with one another over most of the brain, they are separated in a few specific sites. In these sites the inner layer of the dura extends deeply into fissures in the brain to form large partitions (Fig. 309, *middle*). Along the line from which the partition extends into the fissure a cavity may exist between the 2 layers of the dura. This is roughly triangular on cross section (Fig. 309) and is bordered on its base by the outer layer of the dura and on the other 2 sides by the inner layer, which sweeps from both sides of the fissure into it to form a partition

there (Fig. 309). These spaces between the layers of the dura which are disposed along the lines from which partitions originate are lined by endothelium and they constitute the *sinuses of the dura mater* (Fig. 309).

FORMATION, CIRCULATION AND ABSORPTION OF CEREBROSPINAL FLUID

The nervous tissue of the C.N.S. is soft and susceptible to injury. Accordingly, the brain and the cord are contained in bony cavities and are protected against shock by a fluid-filled cushion which encompasses them on all sides. This cushion is the piarachnoid, and all the interstices of its cobwebby structure are filled with a modified tissue fluid called *cerebrospinal fluid* (Figs. 307, 309 and 310). The fluid-filled piarachnoid completely surrounds the brain and the cord and functions as a hydraulic shock absorber for them as they are

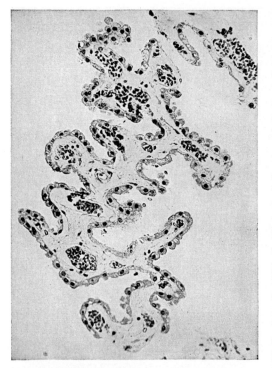

FIG. 311. High-power photomicrograph of a portion of a section cut from a human choroid plexus. (Section from Professor E. A. Linell)

the production of tissue fluid. However, the tissue fluid produced by the capillaries in them has to pass through a layer of cuboidal choroid plexus epithelium before it enters the cavity of a ventricle, and in passing through this epithelial membrane it is probably modified to some extent by the secretory activities of the epithelial cells. Accordingly, cerebrospinal fluid is spoken of as a modified tissue fluid.

Development of Choroid Plexuses. It has been noted already that the part of the wall of the neural tube that becomes the roof of the 3rd and the 4th ventricles becomes very thin; indeed, it comes to consist of no more than the single layer of cuboidal cells that comprise the ependyma plus the vascular piarachnoid which covers it. In these sites the piarachnoid, pushing the ependyma ahead of it, projects into the ventricles to form tufted structures called *choroid plexuses* (Fig. 282). A similar phenomenon occurs in the medial wall of the cerebral hemispheres along the line of attachment of the hemispheres to the hindpart (thalamus) of the forebrain; this accounts for the development of the choroid plexuses of the lateral ventricles. Thus, there are 4 choroid plexuses formed: one in the 4th, one in the 3rd and one in each of the lateral ventricles of the brain.

The choroid plexuses consist essentially of blood vessels, connective tissue remnants of the piarachnoid and a covering consisting of a single layer of cuboidal epithelium. As already noted, the tissue fluid produced by the capillaries is modified by the epithelium through which it passes to enter into the ventricles and become known as cerebrospinal fluid.

Microscopic Structure of Choroid Plexuses. The vascular arrangement of the plexuses is designed to expose as much of the capillary bed to epithelium as possible (Fig. 311). Thus the projections of the choroid plexuses are leaflike; these are said to be pedunculated if they resemble the leaves of a tree, or sessile or elongated if they resemble the leaves of a book. Secondary leaflike elevations may extend from the surface of primary leaves. A small artery or arteriole entering the attachment of a leaf usually extends to its free edge where it bifurcates, and thereafter its branches run an irregularly spiral or straight course along the edge in each direction. A capillary plexus extends from this into the body of the leaf

subjected to the bumps and the jars of everyday life. The fluid-filled membrane has another function as well; it helps to transmit and so disseminate over a wide area the impact of a localized blow on the skull which, if it were concentrated in a small area, might cause serious local damage to the underlying brain. The ventricles of the brain, which form a continuous passageway (Fig. 282), also are filled with cerebrospinal fluid. The fluid inside the brain is in communication with that outside the brain through the medium of 3 openings in the roof of the 4th ventricle. Normally, fluid flows through these openings from the interior of the brain to the exterior.

As will be described later, some cerebrospinal fluid is formed on the exterior of the brain, but most of it is formed in the ventricles by means of structures called *choroid plexuses*; as the thoughtful student will already suspect, they have a structure and a function somewhat similar to that of the glomeruli of the kidney. They are specialized structures for

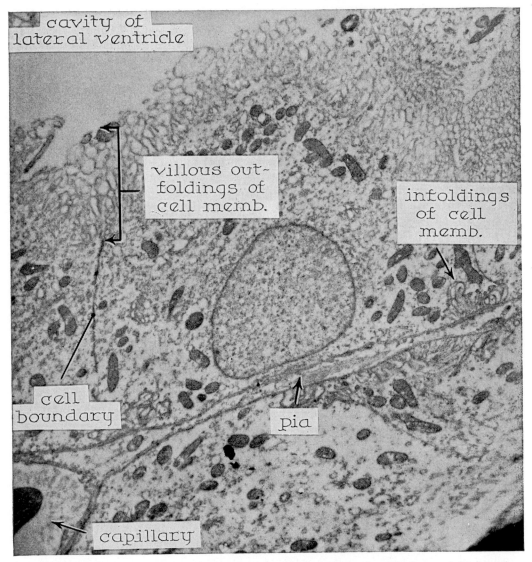

cavity of lateral ventricle

villous out-foldings of cell memb.

infoldings of cell memb.

cell boundary

pia

capillary

Fig. 312. Electron micrograph (× 7,000) of a section of the choroid plexus of the lateral ventricle of a rat. The free surface of the epithelial cell is greatly increased by numerous polypoid projections which extend into the cerebrospinal fluid. The basal surface of the cell is also increased by complicated infoldings. (Preparation by R. C. Buck)

where venules form and empty into a small vein that leaves the same way that the artery entered. The capillaries, becoming tortuous, produce elevations in the epithelium called *villi*, as may be seen in Figure 311, which is a section cut through a leaf and from which villi, containing large capillaries, project on either side.

As noted before, the epithelium that covers the leaves and the villi of the choroid plexuses develops from the inner layer of the wall of the neural tube and hence is the counterpart of, if not actual, ependyma. It is of the cuboidal type and is termed choroid plexus epithelium (Fig. 311). It rests on delicate connective tissue derived from the little pi-arachnoid that is pushed in ahead of the blood vessels.

With the E/M, the free surfaces of the epithelial cells of the choroid plexus are seen to be studded with microvilli, the free ends of which are often somewhat bulbous (Fig. 312, villous outfoldings). Furthermore, at sites where the basal borders of the cells turn toward the free surfaces to become the sides of the cell, the cell membrane of both the base of the cell and the sides of the cell extends into the cytoplasm to form many complex infoldings (Fig. 312, infoldings of cell membrane). It is assumed that the complex infoldings on the basal surface and sides of the cell and the outfoldings of the free surfaces of the cells are both designed to increase the surface area through which fluid can be taken up, transported and delivered from the cells.

The choroid plexuses of the lateral ventricles, as have been described by Hudson and Smith, go through many changes during development which modify their vascular pattern considerably. They point out that the degenerative changes that may be seen in these plexuses relatively early in life, before degenerative changes are general elsewhere, occur at the site of confluence of the large veins of the plexuses; this suggests that these changes have a vascular origin. The degenerative changes are manifested by calcium deposits (termed *concentric bodies*), which may be scattered or concentrated in masses and/or by cysts. Rarely, the latter may become large enough to almost fill a portion of a lateral ventricle.

Since the cerebrospinal fluid is liberated into the ventricles it is apparent that if the outflow through the roof of the 4th ventricle were blocked, the cerebrospinal fluid would accumulate in the ventricles and cause them to expand and so stretch the brain from within. Such a condition can occur as a result of disease or deformity and is called *internal hydrocephalus.*

The cerebrospinal fluid produced in the lateral ventricles must circulate through the interventricular foramina and, with that produced in the 3rd ventricle, pass through the cerebral aqueduct of the midbrain to the 4th ventricle and out through its roof into the subarachnoid space. Most of the cerebrospinal fluid in the piarachnoid spaces surrounding the brain and the cord is formed inside the brain. But not all of it is formed there. It will be recalled that vessels penetrate into the brain substance from its surface and that these

vessels lie in channels which are filled with tissue fluid which diffuses through their walls (Fig. 307). A certain amount of the tissue fluid formed in these sites makes its way back via these channels to the piarachnoid spaces on the surface of the brain to mix with, and become part of, the cerebrospinal fluid.

Since cerebrospinal fluid is formed more or less continuously, of course it must be absorbed continuously or a great increase in intracranial pressure would result. There must be some means whereby cerebrospinal fluid can be absorbed as fast as it is produced. This is accomplished chiefly by little structures known as arachnoid villi, which are buttonlike projections of the arachnoid into certain of the venous sinuses of the dura mater (Fig. 309). The more or less hollow cores of these arachnoid villi are filled with cerebrospinal fluid, which is separated from the blood in the sinus only by the cellular caps of the villi (Fig. 309). Cerebrospinal fluid diffuses through these to enter the venous blood of the sinus. The whole arrangement for the formation and the absorption of tissue fluid reminds one of the mechanisms by which tissue fluid is formed and absorbed in most parts of the body (Chap. 6). Presumably, the hydrostatic pressure in the capillaries of the choroid plexuses is fairly high (for capillaries); this could be inferred from the congested state that many of them exhibit. Tissue fluid, then, would be produced readily in choroid plexuses. On the other hand, the hydrostatic pressure in the venous sinus, into which the arachnoid villi project, is low, and in this site it might be expected that the greater osmotic pressure of the blood, imparted to it by its colloid content, would draw cerebrospinal fluid (which is normally of a low protein or colloid content) back into blood through the cells of the arachnoid villi. However, this arrangement differs from that ordinarily concerned in the absorption of tissue fluid because lymphatics are not provided in the central nervous system to draw off excess fluid. Some cerebrospinal fluid may be drained away in other ways than by the arachnoid villi, but these other mechanisms are not so important and will not be considered here.

Cerebrospinal fluid is clear and limpid. Like tissue fluid, it contains inorganic salts but very little protein. In its normal state it contains only a very few cells, and these are mostly lymphocytes. Its examination in suspected injuries or diseases of the central nervous system is of the greatest help in diagnosis. For example, finding blood in the cerebrospinal fluid may provide confirmation of a skull fracture involving a rupture of vessels from which blood has escaped. Or an increase in the number of cells in the cerebrospinal fluid may be of assistance in diagnosing certain inflammatory diseases of the nervous system or the meninges. Even the pressure under which the cerebrospinal fluid exists is often a great help in distinguishing between different types of pathologic conditions of the brain or the cord. However, a complete study of the cerebrospinal fluid is not usually made in histology but is reserved for the later and clinical years of the medical course.

THE PERIPHERAL NERVOUS SYSTEM

The P.N.S. consists of:

1. **Nerves.** These are branching cordlike structures that extend out from the brain as cranial nerves and from the cord as spinal nerves to reach almost every part of the body. These nerves, or *nerve trunks* as they are sometimes called, are like telephone cables that house many wires; each contains many wirelike nerve fibers—both afferent and efferent—which are distributed by means of the continued branching of the nerves to almost all parts of the body.

2. **Ganglia.** These little nodules contain the cell bodies of neurons. There are two general kinds of ganglia in the P.N.S. One kind contains the cell bodies of afferent, the other, of efferent neurons. The first kind is the cerebrospinal ganglia which has been described already (Fig. 275). These contain the cell bodies of the afferent neurons of the body segments. The second kind is the ganglia of the autonomic nervous system (soon to be described) which contain the cell bodies of efferent neurons.

3. **Nerve Endings and Organs of Special Sense.** A description of these is given in a separate chapter at the end of this book because these structures can be studied to better advantage after the organs and the structures in which many of them are distributed have been described.

The foregoing outline of the components of the P.N.S. provides a basis for completing our classification of nervous tissue as follows:

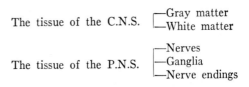

Nervous Tissue

The tissue of the C.N.S. ⎡—Gray matter
⎣—White matter

The tissue of the P.N.S. ⎡—Nerves
⎢—Ganglia
⎣—Nerve endings

THE DEVELOPMENT OF THE P.N.S.

The P.N.S. contains both afferent and efferent components, and these are developed from somewhat different sources. The development of the afferent components will be considered first.

The neural plate gives rise to two neural crests as well as to the neural tube. The neural crests are at first continuous strands of neuro-ectoderm that lie on the dorsolateral aspect of each side of the developing spinal cord (Fig. 279). Soon, however, each neural crest breaks up into a chain of nodules, and these are the forerunners of the posterior (dorsal) root ganglia of the spinal cord and their cranial counterparts (Fig. 313). Each segment of the cord has two: one on each side in a posterolateral position (Fig. 310).

The neuro-ectodermal cells of the developing posterior root ganglia differentiate along two main lines, as they do in the neural tube. Along one line of differentiation they form neuroblasts. These are at first bipolar cells, but as they differentiate into neurons their two processes, like the hands of a clock, move around their circumference toward each other until they meet and fuse; by this maneuver the bipolar neurons become unipolar neurons. However, their single process branches, with one branch, the axon, growing centrally along the line indicated with an arrow in Figure 313 to the dorsal root of the spinal cord; the other process, which is functionally a dendrite, grows peripherally and becomes enclosed with other fibers in a nerve trunk through which it extends to reach the tissue in which it is to provide a sensory ending (Fig. 313). The peripheral processes of these cells, while they are functionally dendrites in that they conduct impulses toward the cell bodies of the gan-

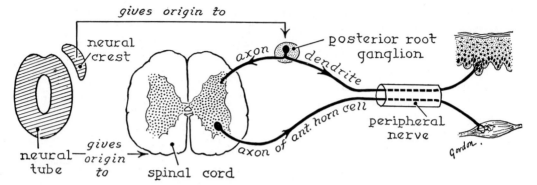

Fig. 313. Diagram illustrating the origin of the P.N.S. The neural crest gives rise to posterior root ganglion cells. Processes from these grow both outwardly and inwardly; hence, the neural crests give rise to the afferent components of the P.N.S. The efferent components of the P.N.S. develop from the neural tube by means of axons from anterior horn cells growing out from the developing spinal cord.

glion cells, have the histologic characteristics of axons. Accordingly, they are generally termed *axons*, but it is understood that physiologically they are dendrites.

The neuro-ectodermal cells of the developing spinal ganglia differentiate along a second pathway to form supporting cells. In differentiating along the second line they do not form true neuroglia, as they do in the neural tube, but certain other cells that are the counterparts of the neuroglia of the C.N.S. These cells are of 2 main types: *capsule* cells, which form capsules around the cell bodies of the ganglion cells (Fig. 314), and *neurolemma* or *sheath of Schwann cells* (Fig. 314), which form sheaths for the nerve fibers that extend from the ganglion cells, as will be described presently.

The efferent components of the P.N.S. arise from the middle layer of the neural tube (Fig. 313). Neuroblasts that develop in what is to become the anterior and lateral horns of gray matter sprout axons that extend out from the anterolateral surface of the spinal cord. These escape the confines of the C.N.S. by passing out through their proper intervertebral foramina (Fig. 310), and from there into nerve trunks along the line indicated by arrows in Figure 313 by which they are distributed to the structures that they innervate.

When we deal with the autonomic nervous system—and this part of the P.N.S. will be defined and described presently—we shall find that it consists of efferent neurons, and that

the cell bodies of some of these are in the brain and the cord, but the cell bodies of many others are scattered in autonomic (not posterior root) ganglia in various parts of the body. Therefore, the cell bodies that are in these ganglia represent the cell bodies of efferent neurons that are outside the confines of the C.N.S. They develop from neuro-ectodermal cells of the neural tube but they leave the tube and migrate outwardly early in development.

MICROSCOPIC STRUCTURE OF SPINAL GANGLIA

The bodies of the nerve cells of spinal ganglia usually are rounded. Many of them are large (Fig. 324) but some are small. Their nuclei, like those of the large multipolar neurons of the C.N.S., are large and pale and contain prominent nucleoli (Fig. 314). Their cytoplasm contains neurofibrils and chromidial substance; the latter is characteristically more dispersed than in anterior horn cells (Fig. 324). Accumulations of yellow-brown pigment may be present in the cytoplasm (Fig. 82). The significance of this is not known; perhaps it is a normal manifestation of aging. The rounded cell bodies of ganglion cells do not lie in direct contact with the connective tissue that surrounds them but are separated from it by a single layer of special flattened cells called *capsule* cells or amphicytes (Fig. 314). These cells are also termed *satellite* cells. They are derived from neuro-ectoderm and, although they are not classified as neuroglia cells, they bear a somewhat similar relation to the bodies of nerve cells of ganglia that neuroglial satellite cells bear to the cell bodies of neurons in the C.N.S.

The single process of each ganglion cell extends from its cell body, sometimes pursuing a devious course in the immediate vicinity of the cell body, to approach the main stream of fibers in the dorsal root. Somewhere between the cell body and the main stream of fibers the process divides into two branches. One of these branches passes into the spinal nerve to pass out to a receptor ending (Fig. 313). The other passes inwardly via the dorsal root to reach the posterior column of gray matter on that side of the cord (Fig. 313). Structually, both processes have the appearance of axons and most of them are myelinated. As noted before, the branch that extends to the receptor functions as a dendrite. The connective tissue in which the ganglion cells and their processes lie is the counterpart of the connective tissue sheaths of nerves; it will be described shortly.

MICROSCOPIC STRUCTURE OF PERIPHERAL NERVES

In the routine study of sections in a histology course, students often fail to identify peripheral nerves when they see them cut in cross, oblique and longitudinal sections. Somewhere, in almost every section taken from the body, a nerve sectioned in some plane or other is present. The student should become skilled in identifying them and should learn their structure well.

A peripheral nerve, encountered in gross dissection, has a cordlike structure. It is of a much firmer consistency than the nervous tissue of the C.N.S. because it contains collagen. Indeed, ordinary connective tissue, and not neuroglia, is the supporting tissue for peripheral nerves.

Histologic Structure of Nerve Fibers of Peripheral Nerves. All of the nerve fibers of the P.N.S. are covered with a thin delicate protoplasmic sheath termed the *neurolemma* (also spelled neurilemma) or *sheath of Schwann* (Figs. 315 and 317 A and B). The cells that comprise this sheath are derived from neuro-ectodermal cells that grow out along with the nerve fibers as they push out from the neural crests or the neural tube. In

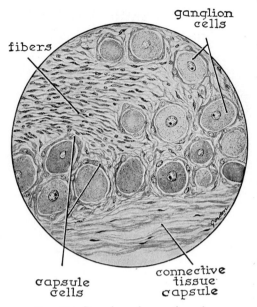

Fig. 314. Drawing of a portion of a section cut from a human spinal ganglion (high-power)

some nerve fibers the sheath of myelin between the nerve fiber and the neurolemma is of a substantial thickness (Figs. 315 and 317 A); hence, such fibers are termed *myelinated fibers*. Other fibers, and these tend to be smaller, are covered with only a trace of myelin; these are termed *nonmyelinated fibers*, and anywhere up to a dozen or more of these are enclosed by the cytoplasm of the same sheath of Schwann cell (Fig. 317 B).

The myelin of myelinated fibers is not continuous; it is interrupted periodically by constrictions (also called nodes) of Ranvier (Fig. 315).

The neurolemmal sheaths of the nerve fibers dip down in these constrictions but do not completely cover the nerve fibers. In these situations, as has been shown by Robertson, the nerve fiber is partially uncovered. There is one neurolemma cell between each two constrictions. Constrictions of Ranvier are present also in the C.N.S. as well as in peripheral nerves. In the C.N.S., the satellite cells, which have a similar morphologic relation to myelinated fibers as do Schwann cells in the P.N.S., dip down in the constrictions to partially cover the nerve fibers.

In peripheral nerves fixed with osmic acid, the myelin between constrictions of Ranvier is

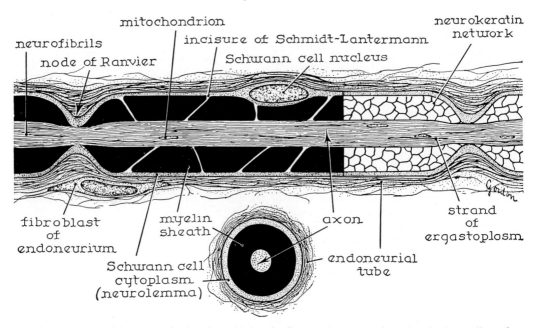

FIG. 315. Semidiagrammatic drawing of a longitudinal and cross section of a single myelinated nerve fiber and its endoneurial sheath. The left side of the upper drawing reveals what would be seen after fixation in osmium tetroxide, while the right side of the drawing represents what is seen after the fatty component of myelin has been dissolved away, as occurs with ordinary technics.

broken up by little incisures or clefts that extend down into it from the surface; these are termed the *clefts of Schmidt-Lantermann,* and the segments between them are termed *Schmidt-Lantermann segments* (Fig. 315, *left*).

Fine Structure. Hess and Lansing and, more recently, Robertson have studied the fine structure of nerve fibers in some detail. Mitochondria are present in axons and are usually elongated with their long axes parallel with the fiber. They have well-developed cristae. Tubular or vesicular components of the endoplasmic reticulum are seen, but the association of RNA granules with these membranes has not been described. Electron microscopy has clearly demonstrated the presence of fine filaments of 70 to 100 Å diameter in the axons. They appear to be more densely aggregated at the nodes where, in large fibers, the axon is relatively narrowed (Fig. 315). With the E/M, the presence of a thin membrane surrounding each fiber is clearly established. This is a typical cell membrane which lies in close association with the cell membrane of the Schwann cell. The paired membrane structure

so-formed (i.e., the cell membrane of the axon and that of the Schwann cell) is sometimes called the *axolemma.*

The Formation and the Fine Structure of Myelin Sheaths. A relatively early but exceedingly informative study of this matter with the E/M was made by Uzman (née Geren) and Schmitt, and from this study they suggested what is now generally termed the jellyroll hypothesis for explaining the formation of myelin sheaths. According to this hypothesis, which is now generally accepted, a Schwann cell embraces, and so far as possible encircles, an axon (Fig. 316 A, *left*). The axon then lies in a long trough in the Schwann cell. The Schwann cell then begins to rotate around the axon (Fig. 316 A, *center and right*). It should be noted here that the cell membrane of the Schwann cell is represented in this diagram (Fig. 316 A) as a single line. When the Schwann cell begins to wind around the axon, the cell membrane lining one side of the groove in which the axon lies comes into contact with the cell membrane that lines the other side of the groove (Fig. 316 A, *left and center*). These two membranes that come and

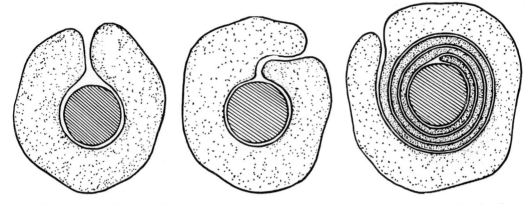

FIG. 316 A. Diagram illustrating the earlier stages of the formation of a myelin sheath according to the jelly-roll hypothesis. (Diagrams based on those of Geren, B. B., and Schmitt, F. O.: Symposium on the Fine Structure of Cells, p. 251, Groningen, Holland, Noordhoff, and diagrams supplied by Schmitt in a personal communication)

stay together are seen, as the cell continues to wind around the axon, as a series of rings made of double lines (Fig. 316 A, *right*). Between adjacent double rings there is at first cytoplasm (stippled in Fig 316 A). As the winding continues the cytoplasm is squeezed out, or lost in some other way. Accordingly, the myelin sheath evolves from 2-layered rings of cell membrane. To understand how a sheath made up of these rings of membrane becomes myelin, we no longer have to consider cytoplasm, for this is all squeezed out or lost; all that we have to consider is how a structure con-

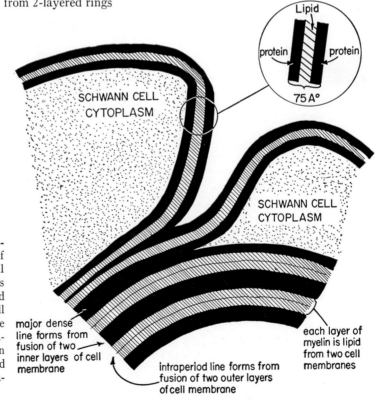

FIG. 316 B. Diagram illustrating the fine structure of cell membranes and how cell membranes of Schwann cells become myelin sheaths, and which parts of the cell membranes become the dense major and the intraperiod lines of the myelin sheaths. (Diagram based on descriptions and illustrations of J. D. Robertson)

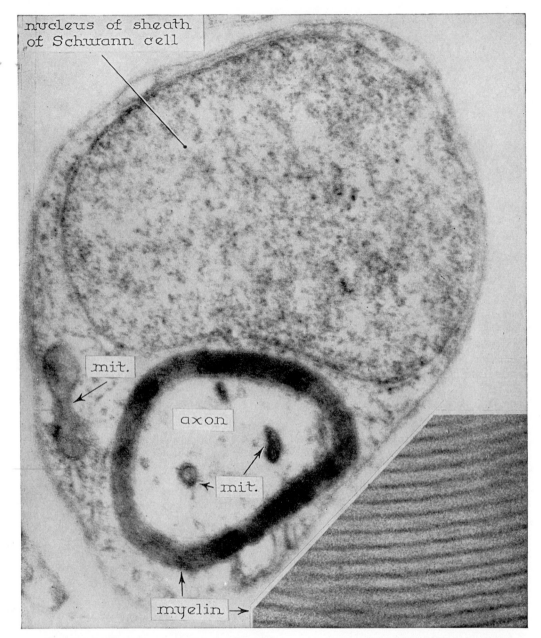

FIG. 317 A. Electron micrograph ($\times$ 44,000) of a cross section of a rat's sciatic nerve, showing a single myelinated fiber cut in cross section at the site of the nucleus of the sheath of Schwann cell. The inset ($\times$ 450,000) shows the lamellar structure of myelin that becomes apparent at very high magnification. The reason for the lamellar structure is to be explained by the way that myelin forms (see Fig. 316 A and B). (Preparation by R. Varvarande)

sisting of concentric rings, with each ring consisting of 2 cell membranes, takes on the appearance of myelin.

Under high resolution a fully formed myelin sheath reveals concentric dark rings that are each around 25 Å thick, separated from each other by rings of a lighter material about 100 Å thick. The dark repeating lines are termed the *major dense lines*, and these, and the lighter material separating them, can be seen

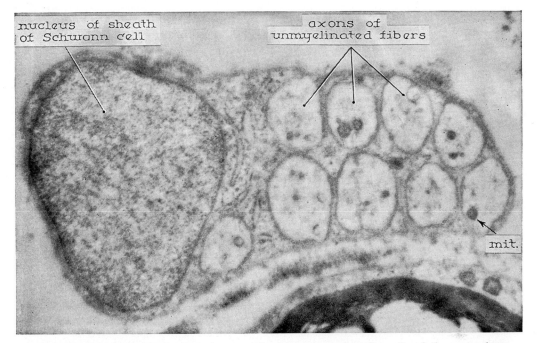

nucleus of sheath of Schwann cell

axons of unmyelinated fibers

mit.

FIG. 317 B. Electron micrograph ($\times$ 32,250) of a cross section of a rat's sciatic nerve, showing 9 nonmyelinated fibers running in the cytoplasm of the same sheath of Schwann cell. This is the usual arrangement. Nonmyelinated fibers do not each have their own sheath of Schwann as do the myelinated fibers; instead, several share a sheath of Schwann in common.

in the inset at the lower right of Figure 317 A. However, with special fixation, and even better resolution, a thinner dark line can be seen in the middle of each of the lighter layers; these fine lines that are halfway between the major dense lines are termed *intraperiod lines*. Some trace of these can be seen if the inset in Figure 317 A is inspected carefully. We shall now consider how this appearance can evolve from concentric layers of cell membranes.

In Figure 316 A, a cell membrane is illustrated as a single line, and this is the way it appears in most electron micrographs. To establish how cell membranes evolve into myelin, with its major dense lines and intraperiod lines, however, it was necessary to make studies with special fixatives and extremely high resolution as has been done by Robertson. Under the appropriate conditions a cell membrane appears as 2 dark lines with a light space between them (Figs. 90 and 316 B, *upper right*), the whole membrane being about 75 Å thick. Evidence suggests that the middle layer of the cell membrane (the light layer) contains lipid while the 2 dark layers which bound the membrane on each of its sides, contain protein. To follow the formation of myelin further, we must think from now on of each of the 2 cell membranes that come together, as the Schwann cell rotates, as *each* being a double line with light material which is probably lipid between each double line; they are represented this way in Figure 316 B.

As is shown in Figure 316 B, as the Schwann cell continues to encircle the nerve fiber, the outer lines of the 2 cell membranes come together and fuse (Fig. 316 B). The dark line so-formed becomes compressed to form the fine intraperiod line (Fig. 316 B). Next, as cytoplasm is squeezed away, the inner lines of the cell membranes that previously bordered this cytoplasm come together and fuse, and this forms the major dense line (Fig. 316 B). Therefore, the myelin that fills the space between two major dense lines is derived chiefly from the lipid that existed in the middle of one major dense line to the middle of the next, which is roughly the thickness of 2 cell membranes. Why the fusion of 2 outer layers of 2 cell membranes should result in only a thin dark (intraperiod) line and

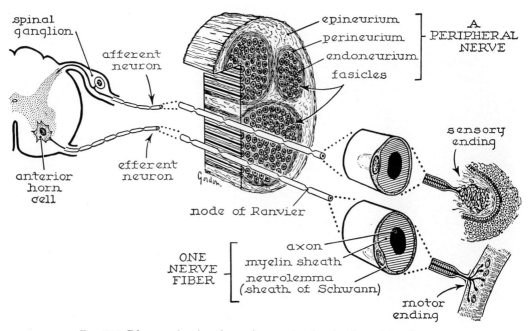

FIG. 318. Diagram showing the various parts of a sizable peripheral nerve.

the fusion of 2 inner layers of cell membrane in a heavy major dense line is not entirely clear.

Microscopic Structure of Peripheral Nerves. If a peripheral nerve is cut in cross section (Figs. 318 and 320), it will be seen to be more or less surrounded by a sheath of connective tissue. This wrapping, which is generally composed of loose connective tissue and extends around the whole nerve, is known as its epineurium (*epi* = upon). Inside this outer wrapping several bundles of nerve fibers may be seen, and each of these is also wrapped in a special dense and relatively strong sheath of connective tissue. These wrappings of bundles of nerve fibers are said to constitute the perineurium (*peri* = around) of the nerve (Figs. 318 and 320). Inside these bundles are the nerve fibers. These, each surrounded with its myelin sheath and neurolemma (Fig. 317 A), are each surrounded by tubes, the walls of which are composed of networks of delicate fibrils that are associated with some sticky amorphous intercellular substances. These tubes are termed *endoneurial* tubes (Fig. 315), and they are very important in nerve regeneration. The endoneurial tubes, each containing a nerve fiber, are packed in a delicate connective tissue medium that extends throughout the interior of each nerve bundle.

This connective tissue in which the ensheathed nerve fibers lie is known as endoneurium (*endo* = inside) (Fig. 318).

Large nerves consist of several fascicles of fibers. Each fascicle is surrounded with a dense sheath of perineurium (Fig. 318). Sunderland has shown that there is much communication between fascicles and that nerve fibers pass from one to another. Consequently, the relative size of the fascicles in a nerve changes continually along its course.

If small sections of a nerve are destroyed by trauma it is desirable to join the two stumps so that the fascicles in one are correctly apposed to those of the other. The fact that the size of fascicles changes so much along the course of a nerve makes this desirable end almost impossible to attain, because if a portion of a nerve is destroyed the fascicles in the two stumps will not match each other.

In order to join the two stumps of a nerve, a portion of which has been, for example, shot away, recourse may be taken to stretching the two parts of the nerve that are to be joined. Nerves can be stretched to some extent without damage to them (see Sunderland). This is probably due at least in part to the fact that nerve fibers do not pursue a straight course along a nerve but instead a zigzag course

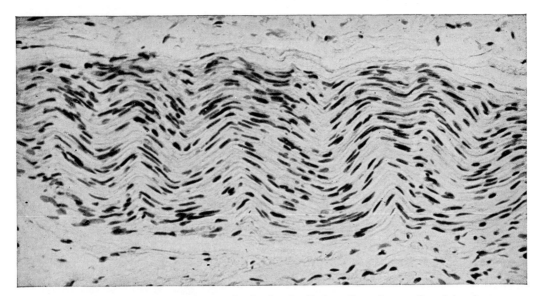

FIG. 319. High-power photomicrograph of a longitudinal section of a small peripheral nerve, showing the snake-fence appearance which is typical in longitudinal sections of nerves unless they are prevented from contracting.

(Fig. 319). Stretching a nerve (up to a point) merely straightens out the fibers and does not stretch them. The strong perineurial sheaths provide a limiting factor in stretching a nerve (for details on these points see Sunderland).

Small nerves are composed of only a single fascicle; this is surrounded by a perineurial sheath (Fig. 319).

The number of nerve fibers within a fascicle varies greatly, as does the diameter of the nerve fibers in the fascicle. Sunderland, Lavarack and Ray found, for example, that the lateral cutaneous nerve on the right side of one subject consisted of only one fascicle and that it contained 3,160 fibers. The same nerve on the left side consisted of 7 fascicles that contained a total of 10,178 fibers. They measured the diameters of the fibers in one fascicle

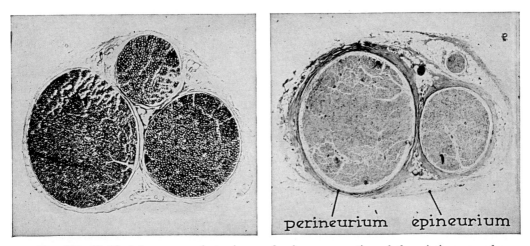

FIG. 320. (Left) A low-power photomicrograph of a cross section of the sciatic nerve of a dog; this was cut from material fixed in osmic acid. (Right) A photomicrograph, at the same magnification, of a cross section cut from material fixed in Zenker-formol solution and stained with H and E.

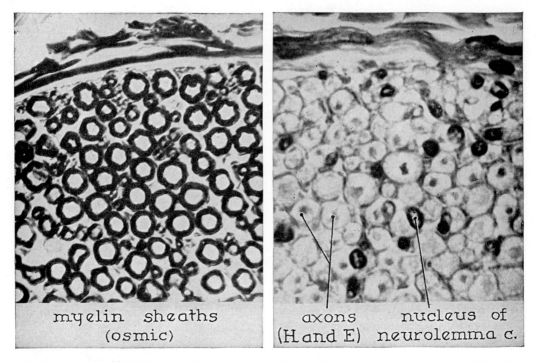

myelin sheaths
(osmic)

axons   nucleus of
(H and E) neurolemma c.

FIG. 321. (*Left*) High-power photomicrograph of a portion of a cross section of a peripheral nerve fixed in osmic acid. (*Right*) A similar preparation of a nerve fixed in formalin and stained with H and E.

that contained 1,242 fibers and found that around 60 per cent of these were less than 8 μ wide, 15 per cent were between 8 and 15 μ wide, 23 per cent were between 16 and 23 μ wide and 0.5 per cent were wider than 23 μ.

Lavarack, Sunderland and Ray have counted the number of fibers in nerves at different levels and have found more fibers in the distal parts of some nerves than at more proximal levels. The increased numbers of fibers is attributed to the branching of fibers within nerves.

The Blood Supply of Nerves. This matter has been investigated at length by Sunderland, whose papers should be read for details. It so happens in surgical procedures that nerves must sometimes be freed of their attachments for certain distances, and it is important to know whether or not this will interfere sufficiently with their blood supply to cause serious damage within them. Fortunately, nerves are supplied by a profusion of vessels that anastomose freely. The vessels are of several orders. There are longitudinally disposed

epineurial interfascicular, perineurial and intrafascicular arteries and arterioles. The endoneurium contains a capillary network. Nutrient arteries from vessels outside the nerve, and from longitudinally disposed vessels accompanying the nerve, pentrate the nerve frequently along its course to communicate with the neural vessels. The number of anastomoses between all these vessels is so great that nerves can be freed for considerable distances from their surrounding attachments; Sunderland states that in his experiments nerves sometimes were stripped from surrounding attachments for distances up to 15 cm., and yet when the nerve was cut at the distal end of the freed section, the nerve bled. Sunderland stresses the importance of preserving the superficial vessels that run along nerves when the nerves are being freed from adjacent structures, for these superficial vessels are important links in the system that provides such efficient anastomoses.

There are certain differences between the cross section appearance of nerves prepared differently. In preparing an ordinary paraffin section to be stained with H and E, the myelin surrounding the individual nerve fibers, unless it is treated with special mordants, will, because of its fatty nature, dissolve away in the dehydrating and clearing agents. This allows the nerve fiber to slip to one side of the tubular space that is left by the myelin dissolving away. Hence, ordinary H and E cross sections of nerves show the sites previously occupied by the myelin sheaths as little rounded spaces, mostly empty except for the nerve fiber, and this may be situated toward one side rather than in the center of the space (Fig. 321, *right*). At the exterior of the space, or bulging somewhat into it, the faint-staining neurolemma may be seen. The nuclei seen in the substance of a nerve bundle in an H and E preparation are those of the neurolemma or sheath of Schwann cells and those of the fibroblasts and macrophages of the endoneurium together with the nuclei of the cells of the blood vessels which lie in the endoneurium. However, in an osmic acid preparation the myelin surrounding the nerve fibers is not dissolved away but is preserved and blackened. Hence, the myelin sheaths of nerve fibers appear as blackened rings in this type of preparation (Fig. 321, *left*). However, the other elements of the nerve do not show up very well in the usual osmic acid preparation. Osmic acid preparations show very clearly that the fibers in a nerve are of different sizes.

In routine H and E preparations, nerves cut obliquely, or in planes approaching the longitudinal, have an appearance which is often substantially different from that which might be expected from their cross-section appearance. Instead of seeing rings, where myelin has dissolved away, one sees streaks. Moreover, the streaky appearance of obliquely and longitudinally sectioned nerves is accentuated by the long, thin, flat nuclei seen between the fibers; those are the nuclei of the neurolemma cells and the cells of the endoneurium (Fig. 319). The streaks do not run directly longitudinally but in a wavy snake-fence manner along it (Fig. 319).

Most peripheral nerves are of the mixed variety; they contain both afferent and efferent fibers. The endings of the afferent fibers are described in Chapter 29. All efferent fibers end either in or about muscle or gland cells. The ones that end in smooth muscle and glands are described later in this chapter in connection with the autonomic nervous system. The endings of efferent fibers in voluntary muscle were described in Chapter 19.

NERVE INJURIES AND THE DEGENERATION AND THE REGENERATION OF PERIPHERAL NERVES

Nerve injuries are of different orders of severity. Sunderland has made a useful classification that will be followed in part here.

First-Degree Injuries. Such injuries have been suffered by most of us. This type of injury is generally caused by pressure being applied to a nerve for a limited time; this probably acts by squeezing the blood vessels in the nerve to cause local anoxia of the axons sufficient to interfere with their function. However, it may be that pressure affects axons adversely in some more direct fashion. Sensory fibers are affected more readily by pressure than motor fibers, and different kinds of sensory fibers vary in their susceptibility. After the pressure is released, recovery of function of the affected fibers may occur in a matter of minutes, hours or weeks, depending on the severity of the injury. If recovery does not occur in a *few weeks* the injury must be regarded as more severe than a first-degree type, as will now be described.

Second-Degree Injuries. This kind is generally caused by prolonged and/or severe pressure being exerted on some part of the nerve. Nerves sometimes are injured purposefully in this fashion to bring about the temporary paralysis of some muscle or muscles whose actions are interfering with the rest and the recovery of some part of the body (for example, the nerves to one side of the diaphragm sometimes are crushed to put the lung on that side to rest).

The severe pressure required to bring about second-degree injuries to nerves causes the *death of the axons* of the nerve at the site where the pressure is applied. In this respect, the second-degree type of injury is fundamentally different from the first-degree type. When even a small segment of an axon dies the part of the axon distal to the injury also dies because it is separated from the cell body on which it depends for its existence. Accordingly, nerve function in a second-degree type of injury can be restored only by all parts of axons distal to the injury being regenerated. In a first-degree type of injury the axon is not destroyed; it is merely incapacitated temporarily and subsequently recovers its full health.

It has been mentioned already that the bodies of nerve cells continuously produce axoplasm. However, the crushing of an axon has repercussions in the cell body of that axon. It causes an axon reaction in that cell body; this involves a solution of the Nissl bodies (chromatolysis, Fig. 289), changes in the site of the nucleus and the sex chromatin and other effects. When the cell body recovers from the axon reaction it begins again to synthesize new axoplasm. This results in new axoplasm pushing into and through the site where the axon was crushed. To discuss its further fate we must consider certain other changes that result from the injury.

When the axons distal to the site of injury die, the myelin sheaths surrounding them also degenerate. The degeneration of the axon and its myelin sheath were first described by Waller, so the process often is termed wallerian degeneration. The degenerating myelin can be stained selectively, so it is possible to distinguish fibers that have been cut from those that have not been cut; this method is used experimentally to trace the course of certain nerve tracts in the C.N.S. The degenerating axon and myelin in the distal stumps of cut peripheral nerves attract macrophages from the endoneurium, and these phagocytose the degenerating material. It is believed that Schwann cells also become phagocytic and help rid the area of debris.

A second-degree type of injury, although it causes serious temporary repercussions in the axons, the myelin and the sheaths of Schwann cells distal to the injury, *does not interrupt the continuity of the endoneurial tubes at the site of injury.* Accordingly, when the cell bodies supplying the axons in the nerve recover and begin to send axoplasm into and through the site of the injury, the new axoplasm from each neuron pushes into the same endoneurial tube that formerly was occupied by the axon from that same neuron. Axoplasm generally extends down the endoneurial tubes at a rate of about 2 to 3 mm. per day, but the

rate is said to become slower as the new axoplasm approaches the terminations of the fibers. The new axoplasm becomes myelinated and covered with a sheath of Schwann similarly to the way it does in third-degree injuries, as will now be described.

Third-, Fourth- and Fifth-Degree Injuries. In third-degree injuries the endoneurial tubes do not retain continuity at the site of injury but fascicles do. In fourth-degree injuries the fascicles as well as tubes become disorganized, and in fifth-degree injuries the nerve trunk is severed. The last type of injury will now be considered in detail. If a peripheral nerve is cut, the muscular action in, and the reception of sensation from, the part of the body it supplies need not be lost forever. If the two cut ends of the nerve are brought together and fastened in place by sutures through their connective tissue wrappings, or held together by some other means, function, after a considerable period of time, may be restored to the part affected. How this is effected will now be considered. In discussing this matter we shall refer to the portion of the nerve between the spinal cord and the site of the cut as the proximal part or stump and the part between the cut and the termination of the nerve as the distal part or stump.

In the part of the nerve distal to the cut, the nerve fibers of afferent and efferent neurons are, of course, severed from their cell bodies, so they die and become necrotic. The disintegration of the axons takes only a short time, and in a few days only a little debris is left in the space that the living axon formerly occupied (Fig. 322). The myelin sheaths of these axons that are severed from their cell bodies also decompose (Fig. 322). The myelin breaks down rather more slowly than the material of the axon, but soon it becomes reduced to droplets (Fig. 322). The cells of the sheaths of Schwann proliferate and form cords that lie in the endoneurial tubes (Fig. 322). Macrophages from endoneurium phagocytose and digest the droplets of broken-down myelin and the remnants of the dead axons. After they phagocytose this debris, they move away. The fibroblasts of the endoneurium and the perineurium, particularly those close to the place where the nerve is cut, proliferate, but unless the site of the cut has become infected, they

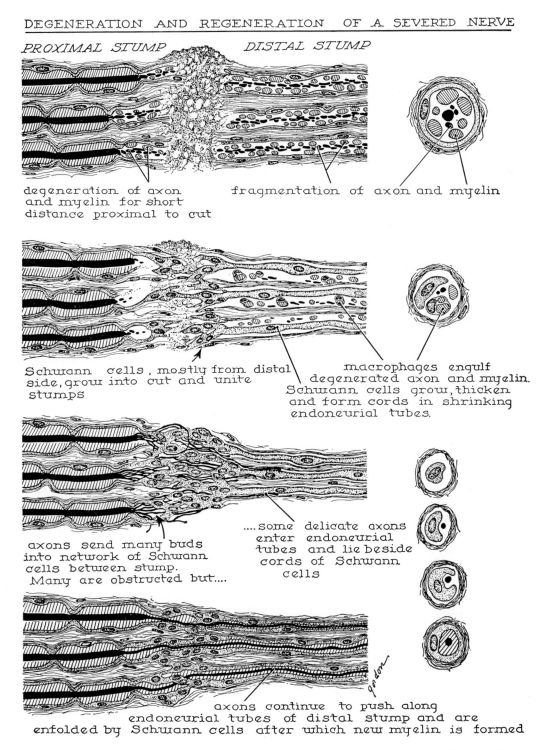

DEGENERATION AND REGENERATION OF A SEVERED NERVE

PROXIMAL STUMP   *DISTAL STUMP*

degeneration of axon
and myelin for short
distance proximal to cut

fragmentation of axon and myelin

Schwann cells, mostly from distal
side, grow into cut and unite
stumps

macrophages engulf
degenerated axon and myelin.
Schwann cells grow, thicken
and form cords in shrinking
endoneurial tubes.

axons send many buds
into network of Schwann
cells between stump.
Many are obstructed but....

....some delicate axons
enter endoneurial
tubes and lie beside
cords of Schwann
cells

axons continue to push along
endoneurial tubes of distal stump and are
enfolded by Schwann cells after which new myelin is formed

FIG. 322. Diagram showing the changes that occur in a nerve when it is severed and regenerates.

do not usually proliferate as rapidly as the cells of the sheath of Schwann, which at this site bulge from the cut ends of the endoneurial tubes of the distal stump, and also, but not so rapidly, from the endoneurial tubes of the proximal stump. The slitlike spaces between the proliferating sheath of Schwann cells offer a means for nerve fibers to grow across the gap into the distal stump (Fig. 322).

While all these changes are taking place in the portion of the nerve distal to the cut, changes also take place near the cut in that portion of the nerve which is still connected to the central nervous system. Near the cut the axons at first degenerate. As has been mentioned already, the sheath of Schwann cells proliferate and grow out into the gap and meet those from the distal stump. Thus, continuity is established across the cut by sheath of Schwann cells, and, as noted before, these cells have longitudinally disposed slits between them. The axons from the proximal portion of the severed nerve now start to push forward a little each day, and after a few days they reach the space where union has occurred between the two outgrowths of sheath of Schwann cells. The axons on growing into this mazelike arrangement often branch into many branches (Fig. 322), and the various branches push their way through such slits and spaces as are available, and before long many may manage to traverse the region of the cut and from then on grow along the tiny passageways that exist in the syncytium provided by the sheath of Schwann cells into the open ends of the endoneurial tubes of the distal stump: these, while they have become smaller, are still open. Under good conditions, the fibers grow down these tubes at a rate that has been variously estimated at from 1 to 4 mm. a day (Fig. 322 B). As they near the termination of the nerve they grow somewhat more slowly.

It is to be observed that no matter how carefully severed nerves are sutured together, it could scarcely be expected that the majority of axons that grow down it would ever find their proper paths. For example, a motor axon might invade an endoneurial tube that led it to an afferent ending, or an axon which formerly connected with a nerve ending designed to be stimulated by heat might, after repair, end up in a touch ending. It seems almost incred-

ible, under the circumstances, that efficient motor function and reasonably good sensation should ever return to a part of the body after the nerve supplying it has been severed. Nevertheless, good results often are obtained by the suturing of cut nerves. Perhaps one thing that helps is that the axons, on reaching the sheath of Schwann syncytium that forms at the site of the cut, branch into many branches. Hence, more axons actually may try to grow down the severed nerve than were present in the first place. Sometimes several enter one endoneurial tube; perhaps only the one that should be there survives.

In an endoneurial tube the new axon lies against a cord of Schwann cells (Fig. 322). The latter gradually enfold the axon, probably much as occurs in normal development (Fig. 322). New myelin then forms, probably as it does during development, and the cordlike Schwann cells once more assume their mature appearance.

It is obvious from the foregoing that the pathway across the cut and through which the axons can grow down into the severed portion of the nerve is provided by the sheath of Schwann cells which grow rapidly into the area of the cut from both the distal and the proximal portions of the severed nerve. However, should the cut become infected, with inflammation supervening, more fibroblasts from the endoneurium and the perineurium proliferate than is usual, with the result that a relatively impenetrable fibrous scar tends to form at the site of the cut. If this is extensive, it may comprise a complete obstruction. Scar tissue, then, is to be avoided if good regeneration is to be obtained.

Nerve Transplantation. In certain types of injuries—for example, gunshot wounds—a whole section of a nerve may be destroyed. Under these conditions, the two cut ends cannot be approximated, hence recourse may be taken to what is called *nerve grafting*. In this procedure a piece of some superficial nerve that is not essential is removed, and this is placed and sutured so as to fill the gap. On transplantation, the sheath of Schwann cells in a nerve graft appear to survive and proliferate. Hence, in this respect the graft acts very much like the distal fragment. However, even though its sheath of Schwann cells proliferate at both of its cut ends, to join with

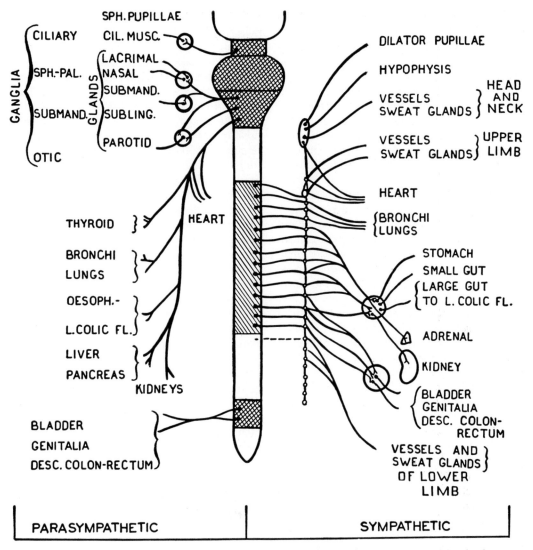

FIG. 323. Diagram of the autonomic nervous system. The parasympathetic division is shown on the left, and the sympathetic division on the right. (Slightly modified from Grant, J. C. B.: A Method of Anatomy, ed. 4, Baltimore, Williams & Wilkins)

the distal and the proximal fragments of the injured nerve, respectively, it is obvious that the use of a graft necessitates axons finding their way through two mazes rather than one. It is understandable, then, that the results from nerve grafting are not nearly so satisfactory as those that are obtained by joining the two cut ends of a nerve directly.

THE AUTONOMIC NERVOUS SYSTEM

To recapitulate: nervous tissue is structurally specialized to be excited selectively by different kinds of stimuli, originating both within and without the body, and to conduct nervous impulses rapidly to (1) the gland cells of epithelial tissue and (2) the muscle cells of muscular tissue.

It is to be observed further that only some of these responses are under the direct control of the conscious mind—those that occur in striated muscle. The control of all cardiac and smooth muscle, and all glandular secretion, is outside the direct influence of the conscious mind. However, these activities are controlled by reflex phenomena. Some of the afferent impulses concerned in these reflexes make their way into consciousness; for example, stimulation of the nerve endings in the taste buds of the mouth gives rise to the sensation of taste as well as initiating the response of salivation. But other afferent impulses (for example, those arising from the stimulation of nerve endings in the viscera) do not ordinarily appear even dimly in consciousness. Hence, we say that the function of smooth and cardiac muscle and glands is automatically controlled in the body because (1) many of the afferent impulses concerned in it give rise to no sensation in consciousness and (2) even though they do, the efferent control of the function of smooth and cardiac muscle and glands is not a function of consciousness.

The *efferent* neurons concerned in the innervation of the smooth and cardiac muscle and the glands of the body constitute the *autonomic nervous system*. It is to be kept in mind that this is not a segregated anatomic division of the nervous system because many of the neurons of which it is comprised are intermingled with neurons, both in peripheral nerves and in the central nervous system, that are concerned with consciously controlled activity. The term autonomic nervous system, then, is generally said to refer to a *functional* division of the nervous system rather than an anatomic one. It is not always easy to keep this distinction in mind because there are certain parts of the system that are anatomically distinct.

As explained before, although the activity in this system is reflex and therefore requires afferent neurons to pick up the stimuli which set its nervous impulses in motion, these afferent neurons are not considered to be part of the system. Hence, the term autonomic nervous system is limited only to efferent neurons—the efferent supply of the smooth and cardiac muscle and the glands of the body.

Next, cardiac muscle and most of the smooth muscle and glands of the body are doubly innervated by this system. This is accomplished by there being two divisions of the autonomic nervous system, with each division sending efferent neurons to most bits of muscle or gland that it innervates (Fig. 323) so that each has a double supply. Further, the efferent impulses arriving at muscle or gland by neurons of the two divisions tend to cause different physiologic effects. For example, the impulses arriving by way of the neurons of one division may lead to the contraction of a certain bit of smooth muscle, while those arriving at the same muscle by way of the neurons of the other division cause it to relax. The two divisions of the autonomic system are thus, at least to a considerable extent, functionally antagonistic to each other, with the responses in the muscle and the glands controlled by the system being more or less the result of a balance struck between the activities of the two divisions of the system.

The two divisions of the autonomic nervous systems are termed the *sympathetic* and the *parasympathetic* division, respectively, and as noted before, with certain exceptions, each division sends efferent fibers to each structure innervated by the autonomic system. Both divisions of the system arise in the C.N.S. but from different parts of it (Fig. 323). Hence, the neurons by which muscle and glands are innervated by the two systems travel along different routes. Moreover, in each system two efferent neurons are always required to join the C.N.S. with each gland or muscle innervated (Fig. 323). The cell body of the first neuron in each efferent chain in each system is situated in the C.N.S.; the cell body of the second in a ganglion. We shall now consider briefly the microscopic structure of the ganglia of the autonomic nervous system and then consider the two systems in more detail.

Autonomic Ganglia. The ganglia of the autonomic nervous system are generally similar to cerebrospinal ganglia in that both have connective tissue framework and contain ganglion nerve cells. However, there are certain differences. Whereas the nerve cells of cerebrospinal ganglia are unipolar, those of autonomic ganglia are multipolar, and since they give off many dendrites they have somewhat more irregular contours than those of cerebrospinal ganglia cells (Fig. 324). In general, the nerve cells of autonomic ganglia are smaller than those of cerebrospinal ganglia and not all of them are surrounded by capsules. Moreover, the nuclei are disposed eccentrically more often than those of cerebrospinal ganglia cells (Fig. 324). The terminal ganglia of the parasympathetic system may be very small (Fig. 408); indeed, sometimes a single ganglion cell may be encountered.

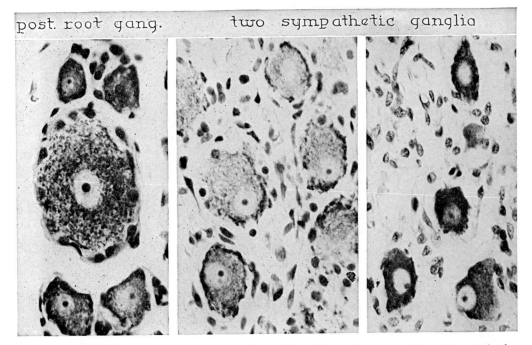

post. root gang.   two sympathetic ganglia

FIG. 324. High-power photomicrographs of ganglion cells as they appear in sections stained with cresyl blue. Observe the larger size of the dorsal root ganglion cell on the left and the eccentric distribution of the nuclei in some of the sympathetic ganglion cells.

The Sympathetic Division. In the thoracic, and upper part of the lumbar, portion of the spinal cord, a lateral, as well as an anterior and a posterior, column of gray matter is present (Fig. 302). The nerve cell bodies in these lateral columns of gray matter differ somewhat from those in the ventral columns; they are smaller, have fewer Nissl bodies and peripherally rather than centrally disposed nuclei. These cell bodies give rise to thin, lightly myelinated axons which leave the cord by way of the ventral roots to reach the spinal nerves (Figs. 325, 326 and 327) along which they extend to enter the ventral branches of these nerves. The axons extend along these ventral branches of the spinal nerves for only a short distance whereupon they leave them by way of little nerve trunks (Fig. 325) called *white rami communicantes* (*ramus* = branch; *communicans* = communicating, and white because the axons are myelinated). Before considering the course of these axons further, it is necessary first to describe the ganglia of the sympathetic division of the autonomic nervous system. According to their position these are called *paravertebral* or *prevertebral* ganglia.

The paravertebral ganglia are disposed in the form of chains, one on each side of the vertebral column, and are said to constitute two sympathetic *trunks* (Fig. 326). In the cervical region there are 3 ganglia in each; the superior, the middle and the inferior cervical ganglia, respectively. The middle cervical ganglia are not always present. In the thoracic region 10 or 11 ganglia are distributed along each side of the vertebral column (Fig. 323, *right*). In some instances, the first thoracic ganglion is fused with the inferior cervical; if so, the fused mass is termed the stellate ganglion. In the lumbar region 4 ganglia are present on each side, and in the sacral region 4 also are present on each side of the vertebral column. Nerve fibers extend between the ganglia in each chain. Since the position and the connections of these ganglia will be presented in detail in other courses, the student should not attempt to obtain anything but a general knowledge of them at this time (see Fig. 323, *right*).

The prevertebral ganglia constitute a group of ganglia that lie in front of the vertebral column and in closer association with the vis-

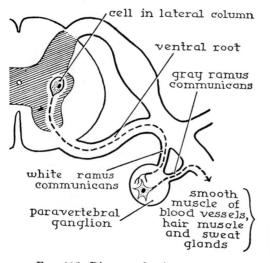

FIG. 325. Diagram showing one course taken by preganglionic and postganglionic fibers of the sympathetic division of the autonomic nervous system.

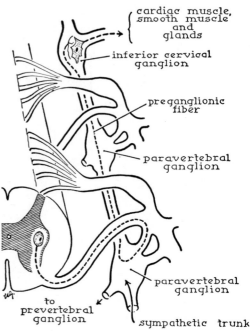

FIG. 326. Diagram showing a second course taken by preganglionic and postganglionic fibers of the sympathetic division of the autonomic nervous system.

cera than the paravertebral ganglia. There are 3 of them—the celiac ganglion, the superior mesenteric and the inferior mesenteric. An extension of the last may be present in the pelvis. These, too, will be learned about in detail in other courses, so the names need not be memorized here.

The axons from the bodies of nerve cells in the lateral column of the spinal cord, which we have traced to the white rami communicantes, end either in the paravertebral (Figs. 325 and 326) or the prevertebral (Fig. 327) ganglia. Therefore, they are all called preganglionic fibers. They reach one or the other of these ganglia by 3 different courses.

1. Some of them terminate in the paravertebral ganglion to which the white ramus from the adjacent spinal nerve extends (Fig. 325). In the paravertebral ganglion, the axon comes into synaptic relationship with the second neuron of the efferent chain, whose cell body is situated in the ganglion. This cell body of the second neuron of the chain sends out an axon, which is not myelinated and hence is gray in color, into a little nerve trunk (some may go directly) called the *gray ramus communicans* (Fig. 325), which conducts it back to the spinal nerve (Fig. 325), along which it travels to reach gland or muscle. Since this axon proceeds from a ganglion to nerve or muscle, it is called a *postganglionic* fiber.

2. Some of the axons from the bodies of nerve cells in the lateral column of gray matter in the spinal cord, on reaching adjacent paravertebral ganglia by way of the white rami, pass up or down along the sympathetic trunk to terminate in a paravertebral ganglion at some other level. Some, for example, travel up to the superior cervical ganglia (at which level, it is to be noted, no preganglionic fibers emerge from the cord) where they come into synaptic relationship with the second neurons of the efferent chains, whose cell bodies are situated in the ganglia (Fig. 326). The cell bodies of the second neurons send postganglionic fibers out to muscle and glands (Fig. 326, *top*).

3. Some axons from the bodies of nerve cells in the lateral column of gray matter of the spinal cord, after reaching the paravertebral ganglia by way of white rami communicantes, pass through the paravertebral ganglia concerned to proceed more or less directly to one of the prevertebral ganglia, where they come into synaptic relationship with the second neuron of the efferent chain, the cell body of which is situated in that particular preverte-

bral ganglion (Fig. 327). The cell body of the second neuron sends an axon, a postganglionic fiber, out to muscle or gland (the innervation of the medulla of the adrenal gland is different from the ordinary arrangement and will be described when this gland is considered later in this book).

The number of postganglionic fibers that emerge from a sympathetic ganglion is considerably greater than the number of preganglionic fibers that enter it. Preganglionic fibers, then, in ganglia must enter into synaptic relation with many different neurons whose cell bodies are situated in that ganglion. This arrangement allows ganglia to serve as instruments for broadening the stream of nervous impulses that enter them.

The Parasympathetic Division. Nerve fibers belonging to the parasympathetic division of the system also innervate most of the glands and muscles innervated by the sympathetic division, and, as noted before, the two systems are to some extent antagonistic to each other. Between each structure innervated by the parasympathetic division and the C.N.S., from which the parasympathetic division arises, a chain of two efferent neurons is always to be found.

The parasympathetic division has its origin from two widely separated parts of the C.N.S. The bodies of the nerve cells that give rise to one group of its preganglionic fibers are situated in nuclei of gray matter in the medulla and the midbrain, and the preganglionic fibers arising from these cell bodies make their way out of the C.N.S. by way of the 3rd, 7th, 9th and 10th cranial nerves (Fig. 323, *left*). The cell bodies from which the remainder of its preganglionic fibers arise are found in the lateral column of the sacral portion of the spinal cord, and they make their way out of the C.N.S. by way of the 2nd, 3rd and 4th sacral spinal nerves, which they soon leave by way of the visceral rami of these nerves (Fig. 323, *bottom, left*).

Since the preganglionic fibers of the parasympathetic division of the autonomic system emerge by way of cranial and sacral nerves from the C.N.S., the parasympathetic division is also termed the craniosacral division of the autonomic system (in contrast with the thoracicolumbar division).

The preganglionic fibers of the parasympathetic division are, in general, longer than

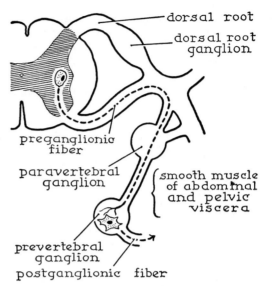

FIG. 327. Diagram showing a third course taken by preganglionic and postganglionic fibers of the sympathetic division of the autonomic nervous system.

those in the sympathetic division, and with certain exceptions, they proceed all the way to the muscle or the gland with whose innervation they are concerned. When they approach the gland or the muscle, they generally end in small ganglia that are closely associated, particularly in the viscera, with the gland or the muscle innervated. These are sometimes called *terminal ganglia,* and in them the preganglionic fibers come into synaptic relation with the second neurons, whose cell bodies are situated in the terminal ganglia and send axons, the postganglionic fibers, to the nerve endings in muscle or gland. The postganglionic axons are, then, generally short.

However, in the head region the ganglia of the parasympathetic division of the system are not within, or on the surface of, the gland or the muscle innervated, and in these instances the postganglionic fibers are correspondingly longer (Fig. 323, *top, left*).

NERVE ENDINGS IN THE AUTONOMIC
NERVOUS SYSTEM

The endings of the postganglionic fibers of the sympathetic and the parasympathetic systems in smooth or cardiac muscle or glands cannot be seen in H and E sections, although the terminal ganglia of the parasympathetic system show to advantage (Fig. 408). For the demonstration of the nerve endings of the fibers of the autonomic system in muscle or glands special technics are necessary. Silver impregnation methods or the treatment of fresh tissue by methylene blue are commonly employed to reveal them. Even with these special technics it is difficult to establish definitely how and where the fibers end. It is relatively easy to see that they form networks between muscle or gland cells. But it is not so easy to determine whether the terminal fibers actually possess free endings and whether these, when the technics reveal them, end outside or inside muscle or gland cells. General opinion is more disposed to consider that they end outside the cells than inside, but Boeke, to whom the student is referred for further information on this point, describes what appear to be authentic instances of fibers terminating inside smooth and cardiac muscle and gland cells.

Just how many fibers in a sheet of smooth muscle have separate nerve fibers ending on or in them is difficult to determine. Smooth muscle cells are packed closely together; furthermore, myofibrils may pass from one cell to another. Smooth muscle cells themselves can thus conduct waves of excitation for certain distances; hence, it would not be necessary for every cell in a sheath or bundle of smooth muscle to be innervated separately. Certainly, even the best technics do not suggest that many receive terminations of fibers; of course, this may be due to the best technics failing to reveal anything like a full proportion of the endings present.

Chemical Factors Involved in the Mediation of the Nervous Impulse

A nervous impulse arriving at nerve endings in either smooth or cardiac muscle fibers or gland cells evokes a response. The mechanism by which this is accomplished has been the subject of a series of interesting investigations which have yielded valuable information. These investigations and their results will be considered only briefly since this matter is dealt with in detail by the physiologist.

As will be explained in more detail later, the cells of the inner portions of the adrenal glands manufacture a hormone called *epinephrine*. This hormone has been obtained in a pure state, and nearly every physician keeps a bottle containing a weak solution of it in his office. An injection of only a very small amount of this hormone into a person or an experimental animal produces a great many effects. In general, these are almost identical with those that are obtained when the sympathetic division of the autonomic nervous system of that individual is stimulated.

In 1904, Elliott observed that injecting epinephrine into an animal would induce a response in gland or muscle even though the sympathetic nerves supplying that particular gland or muscle had been severed. This was enough to make him wonder if the stimulation of a sympathetic nerve does not normally produce an effect in the muscle or the gland because the nerve endings in the muscle or the gland, on being stimulated by the arrival of a nervous impulse, locally produce epinephrine, which thereupon evokes a response. Cannon, in particular, made many later investigations on this matter, and Elliott's suspicions were found to be justified. It was shown that the substance formed at the endings of sympathetic nerves when the nerves were stimulated was not precisely epinephrine but a very similarly acting substance which was called *sympathin*. Moreover, the work of Cannon and Rosenblueth suggests that there are two kinds of sympathin. One kind is formed at the endings of those sympathetic nerves that, on being stimulated, cause muscle to contract and the other kind at the endings of those sympathetic nerves that, on being stimulated, cause muscle to relax. These were termed sympathin E and sympathin I. It appears, then, that a response is evoked in muscle or gland when sympathetic nerves are stimulated because sympathin E (E for excitatory) or I (I for inhibitory) is formed at the nerve endings.

In the meantime, beginning about 1914, evidence accumulated, largely through the work of Dale, that a substance responsible for bringing about a response in gland or muscle forms at the endings of the nerves of the parasympathetic system when these nerves are stimulated. This substance formed at the nerve endings of parasympathetic nerves is called *acetylcholine*.

Responses in the muscle and the glands innervated by the autonomic nervous system, then, are evoked by the production of sympathin or acetylcholine. These are the *chemical mediators* of the nervous impulse.

As studies in this field continued, it became apparent that not all sympathetic nerve endings make sympathin. Some were found to make acetylcholine (for example, those ending in the sweat glands of the skin). Furthermore, it was found that the endings of preganglionic fibers of the sympathetic system make acetylcholine at the sites of their synaptic relation with postganglionic neurons in sympathetic ganglia, and that the formation of acetylcholine at these synapses by the preganglionic nerve endings is responsible for the postganglionic fibers becoming stimulated. Dale has suggested that sympathetic nerve fibers be classified as either *adrenergic* or *cholinergic* according to whether their nerve endings produce sympathin or acetylcholine. Whether any parasympathetic nerve endings make sympathin or not has not yet been established.

As studies continued in this field, it became established that chemical mediators of the nervous impulse were not confined to the autonomic nervous system, but that acetylcholine was released at motor end-plates in striated muscle and in synapses in the C.N.S. As matters now stand there is much theorizing about different aspects of the matter, but the following working hypothesis seems to have been established on good grounds.

When a nervous impulse reaches an endplate it causes a release of acetylcholine which previously was stored and inactive. From E/M studies it seems very probable that the acetylcholine is stored in neurovesicles (Fig. 267) which are very abundant in this region. The active acetylcholine causes a change in the permeability of the membranes that separate the termination of the axon from the sole plasm of the muscle cell, and this permits potassium ions to pass from the muscle and the sodium ions into the muscle. The change in permeability of the membrane is accompanied by a change in electrical potential along the sarcolemma, and this, as was suggested in the previous chapter, may reach all interior parts of the fiber via the sarcoplasmic reticulum (Fig. 258). The free acetylcholine that sets all the above machinery into motion is inactivated by the enzyme acetylcholinesterase in a matter of milliseconds, and the whole apparatus is then ready to respond to the arrival of another nervous impulse which probably causes the release and the activation of acetylcholine from certain others of the almost innumerable neurovesicles.

Much of the same sequence of events seems to occur at synapses in the C.N.S. The arrival of a nervous impulse at an end-foot probably liberates acetylcholine from the neurovesicles in the end-foot (Fig. 293). This acts to change the permeability of the membranes separating the end-foot from the cell body on which it lies, and it is also associated with a change in the electrical potential of the membranes. As a result of these actions, a nervous impulse is set up in the neuron on which the end-foot abuts.

REFERENCES

GENERAL REFERENCES ON NERVOUS TISSUE

Adrian, E. D.: The Mechanism of Nervous Action, London, Oxford, 1932.

Ariens Kappers, C. U., Huber, G. C., and Crosby, E. C.: The Comparative Anatomy of the Nervous System of Vertebrates, Including Man, vols. 1 and 2, New York, Macmillan, 1936.

de Rényi, G. S.: Architecture of the nerve cell *in* Cowdry's Special Cytology, ed. 2, p. 1371, New York, Hoeber, 1932.

Fulton, J. F.: Physiology of the Nervous System, New York, Macmillan, 1949.

Malone, E. F.: The general relation of histological character to function in mammalian neurons *in* Cowdry's Special Cytology, ed. 2, p. 1405, New York, Hoeber, 1932.

O'Leary, J. L.: Ageing in the nervous system *in* Lansing, A. I. (ed.): Cowdry's Problems of Ageing, ed. 3, p. 223, Baltimore, Williams & Wilkins, 1952.

Parker, G. H.: The Elementary Nervous System, Philadelphia, Lippincott, 1919.

Penfield, W.: Cytology and Cellular Pathology of the Nervous System, vols. 1, 2 and 3, New York, Hoeber, 1932.

————: Neuroglia and microglia *in* Cowdry's Special Cytology, ed. 2, p. 1447, New York, Hoeber, 1932.

Symposium: The submicroscopic organization and function of nerve cells, Exper. Cell Res. (Suppl.) 5:644, 1958.

(*See also* textbooks on neuro-anatomy and neurology)

SPECIAL REFERENCES ON THE FINE STRUCTURE (ELECTRON MICROSCOPY) OF ELEMENTS OF NERVOUS TISSUE

Causey, G., and Hoffman, H.: The relation between the Schwann cell and the axon in peripheral nerves, J. Anat. 90:1, 1956.

De Robertis, E., and Bennett, H. S.: Some features of fine structure of cytoplasm of cells in the earthworm nerve cord *in* Fine Structure of Cells, p. 261, New York, Interscience, 1955.

————: Some features of submicroscopic morphology of synapses in frog and earthworm, J. Biophys. & Biochem. Cytol. *1*:47, 1955.

————: A submicroscopic vesicular component in nerve satellite cells and Schwann cells, Anat. Rec. (Supp.) *118*:294, 1954.

————: Submicroscopic vesicular component in the synapse, Fed. Proc. *13*:35, 1954.

Estable, C., Reissi, M., and De Robertis, E.: Microscopic and submicroscopic structure of the synapsis in the ventral ganglion of the acoustic nerve, Exper. Cell Res. *6*:255, 1954.

Fernandez-Morán, H.: Observations on the structure of submicroscopic nerve fibers, Exper. Cell Res. *4*:480, 1953.

Fernandez-Morán, H., and Finean, J. B.: Electron microscope and low-angle x-ray defraction studies of the nerve myelin sheath, J. Biophys. & Biochem. Cytol. *3*:725, 1957.

Finean, J. B., Sjostrand, F. S., and Steinmann, E.: Submicroscopic organization of some layered lipoprotein structures (nerve myelin, retinal rods and chloroplasts), Exper. Cell Res. *5*:557, 1953.

Geren, B. B., and Raskind, J.: Development of the fine structure of the myelin sheath in sciatic nerves of chick embryos, Proc. Nat. Acad. Sc. *39*:880, 1953.

————: The formation from the Schwann cell surface of myelin in the peripheral nerves of chick embryos, Exper. Cell Res. *7*:558, 1954.

————: Structural studies of the formation of the myelin sheath in peripheral nerve fibers *in* Cellular Mechanisms in Differentiation and Growth, Princeton, N. J., Princeton Univ. Press, 1956.

Geren, B. B., and Schmitt, F. O.: Electron microscope studies of the Schwann cell and its constituents with particular reference to their relation to the axon *in* Fine Structure of Cells, p. 251, Groningen, Holland, Noordhoff, 1955.

————: The structure of the nerve sheath in relation to lipid and lipid-protein layers, J. Appl. Physics, *24*:1421, 1953.

————: The structure of the Schwann cell and its relation to the axon in certain invertebrate nerve fibers, Proc. Nat. Acad. Sc. *40*:863, 1954.

Gray, E. G.: Axo-somatic and axo-dendritic synapses of the cerebral cortex: an electron microscope study, J. Anat. *93*:420, 1959.

Haguenau, F., and Bernhard, W.: Aspect de la substance de Nissl au microscope électronique, Exper. Cell Res. *4*:496, 1953.

Hartman, J. F.: Electron microscopy of motor nerve cells following section of axones, Anat. Rec. *118*:19, 1954.

————: An electron optical study of sections of central nervous system, J. Comp. Neurol. *99*:201, 1953.

Hess, A.: The fine structure of young and old spinal ganglia, Anat. Rec. *123*:399, 1955.

Hess, A., and Lansing, A. I.: The fine structure of peripheral nerve fibers, Anat. Rec. *117*:175, 1953.

Luse, S. A.: Electron microscopic observations of the central nervous system, J. Biophys. & Biochem. Cytol. *2*:531, 1956.

Maxwell, D. S., and Pease, D. C.: Electron microscopy of the choroid plexus, Anat. Rec. *124*:331, 1956.

Palade, G. E., and Palay, S. L.: Electron microscope observations of interneuronal and neuromuscular synapses, Anat. Rec. *118*:335, 1954.

Palay, S. L.: Structure and function in the neuron *in* Korey, S. R., and Nurnberger, J. I. (eds.): Trends in Neurochemistry and Allied Fields, vol. 1, New York, Hoeber, 1955.

————: Synapses in the central nervous system, J. Biophys. & Biochem. Cytol. (Supp.) *2*:193, 1956.

Palay, S. L., and Palade, G. E.: The fine structure of neurons, J. Biophys. & Biochem. Cytol. *1*:69, 1955.

Pease, D. C., and Baker, R. F.: Electron microscopy of nervous tissue, Anat. Rec. *110*:505, 1951.

Pease, D. C., and Schultz, R. L.: Electron microscopy of rat cranial meninges, Am. J. Anat. *102*:301, 1958.

Robertson, J. D.: Ultrastructure of two invertebrate synapses, Proc. Soc. Exper. Biol. & Med. *82*:219, 1953.

————: The ultrastructure of adult vertebrate peripheral myelinated nerve fibers in relation to myelinogenesis, J. Biophys. & Biochem. Cytol. *1*:271, 1955.

————: The ultrastructure of a reptilian myoneural junction, J. Biophys. & Biochem. Cytol. *2*:381, 1956.

————: The ultrastructure of Schmidt-Lanterman clefts and related shearing defects of the myelin sheath, J. Biophys. & Biochem. Cytol. *4*:39, 1958.

————: Preliminary observations on the ultrastructure of nodes of Ranvier, Ztschr. Zellforsch. und mikroskop. Anat. *50*:553, 1959.

————: The ultrastructure of cell membranes and their derivatives, Biochemical Soc. Symposia, No. 16, p. 3, 1959.

————: Electron microscopy of the motor end-plate and the neuromuscular spindle, Am. J. Phys. Med. *39*:1, 1960.

————: The Molecular Biology of Cell Membranes *in* Nachmansohn, D. (ed.): Molecular Biology, New York, Acad. Press, 1960.

Schmitt, F. O., and Bear, R. S.: The ultrastructure of the nerve axon sheath, Biol. Rev. *14*:27, 1939.

Schultz, R. L., Maynard, E. A., and Pease, D. C.: Electron microscopy of neurons and neuroglia of cerebral cortex and corpus callosum, Am. J. Anat. *100*:369, 1957.

Van Breemen, V. L.: The structure of neuroglial cells as observed with the electron microscope, Anat. Rec. *118*:438, 1954.

Usman, B. G., and Nogueira-Graf, G.: Electron microscope studies of the formation of nodes of Ranvier in mouse sciatic nerves, J. Biophys. & Biochem. Cytol. *3*:589, 1957.

SPECIAL REFERENCES ON THE CENTRAL NERVOUS SYSTEM

Altschul, Rudolf: Lipofuscin distribution in the basal ganglia, J. Comp. Neurol. *78*:45, 1943.

Barr, M. L.: Axon reaction in motor neurons and its effect upon the end-bulbs of Held-Auerbach, Anat. Rec. *77*:367, 1940.

————: The morphology of neuroglial nuclei in the cat, according to sex, Exper. Cell Res. *2*: 288, 1951.

Barr, M. L.: and Bertram, E. G.: The behaviour of nuclear structures during depletion and restoration of Nissl material in motor neurons, J. Anat. *85*:171, 1951.

Barr, M. L., Bertram, L. F., and Lindsay, H. A.: The morphology of the nerve cell nucleus, according to sex, Anat. Rec. *107*:283, 1950.

Barr, M. L., and Hamilton, J. D.: A quantitative study of certain morphological changes in motor neurons during axon reaction, J. Comp. Neurol. *89*:93, 1948.

Bodian, D.: Further notes on the vertebrate synapse, J. Comp. Neurol. *73*:323, 1940.

————: A note on the nodes of Ranvier in the central nervous system, J. Comp. Neurol. *94*: 475, 1951.

————: The structure of the vertebrate synapse, J. Comp. Neurol. *68*:117, 1937.

Cameron, G.: Secretory activity on the chorioid plexus in tissue culture, Anat. Rec. *117*:115, 1953.

Costero, I., and Pomerat, C. M.: Cultivation of neurons from the adult human cerebral and cerebellar cortex, Am. J. Anat. *89*:405, 1951.

Donaldson, H. H., and Davis, D. J.: A description of charts showing the areas of the cross sections of the human spinal cord at the level of each spinal nerve, J. Comp. Neurol. *8*:19, 1903.

Elliott, H. C.: Studies on the motor cells of the spinal cord, Am. J. Anat. *70*:95, 1942.

Gersh, I., and Bodian, D.: Some chemical mechanisms in chromatolysis, J. Cell & Comp. Physiol. *21*:253, 1943.

Golgi, C.: Sur la structure des cellules nerveuses (1), Arch. ital. biol. *30*:60, 1898.

Haggar, R. A., and Barr, M. L.: Quantitative data on the size of synaptic end-bulbs in the cat's spinal cord; with a note on the preparation of cell models, J. Comp. Neurol. *93*:17, 1950.

Herrera, J. M.: Estudios sobre el problema de la genesis microglial: 1. La capacidad reaccional de la microglia en el encefalo post-mortem, Arch. méd. paname. *2*:3, 1953.

Hess, A., and Young, J. Z.: Nodes of Ranvier in the central nervous system, J. Physiol. *108*: 52P, 1949.

Hudson, A. J., and Smith, C. G.: The vascular pattern of the choroid plexus of the lateral ventricle, Anat. Rec. *112*:43, 1952.

McCulloch, W. S.: The functional organization of the cerebral cortex, Physiol. Rev. *24*:390, 1944.

Morrison, G. E., Jr., and Gibson, W. C.: The staining of synaptic terminals within the central nervous system by Rio-Hortega's double impregnation silver method, Science *117*:1, 1953.

Ortiz-Picon, J. M.: The neuroglia of the sensory ganglia, Anat. Rec. *121*:513, 1955.

Smart, I., and Leblond, C. P.: Evidence for division and transformations of neuroglia cells in the mouse brain, as derived from radioautography after injection of thymidine-H^3, J. Comp. Neurol. (in press).

Weed, L. H.: The cerebrospinal fluid, Physiol. Rev. *2*:171, 1922.

————: Certain anatomical and physiological aspects of the meninges and cerebrospinal fluid, Brain *58*:383, 1935.

————: Meninges and cerebrospinal fluid, J. Anat. *72*:181, 1938.

Windle, W., and Clark, S. L.: Observations on the histology of the synapse, J. Comp. Neurol. *46*:153, 1928.

Wislocki, G. B.: The cytology of the cerebrospinal pathway *in* Cowdry's Special Cytology, ed. 2, p. 1485, New York, Hoeber, 1932.

Woollam, D. H. M., and Millen, J. W.: The perivascular spaces of the mammalian central nervous system and their relation to the perineuronal and subarachnoid spaces, J. Anat. *89*: 193, 1955.

SPECIAL REFERENCES ON THE PERIPHERAL NERVOUS SYSTEM

Fernand, V. S. V., and Young, J. Z.: The sizes

of the nerve fibres of muscle nerves, Proc. Roy. Soc., London, B *139*:38, 1951.

Lavarack, J. O., Sunderland, S., and Ray, L. J.: The branching of nerve fibers in human cutaneous nerves, J. Comb. Neurol. *94*:293, 1949.

Peterson, E. R., and Murray, M. R.: Myelin sheath formation in cultures of avian spinal ganglia, Am. J. Anat. *96*:319, 1955.

Schmitt, F. O., Bear, F. S., and Palmer, K. J.: X-ray diffraction studies on the structure of the nerve myelin sheath, J. Cell. & Comp. Physiol. *18*:31, 1941.

Speidel, Carl C.: Adjustments of nerve endings, Harvey Lect. *18*:625, 1942.

————: Studies of living nerves: I. The movement of individual sheath cells and nerve sprouts, J. Exper. Zool. *61*:279, 1932.

————: Studies of living nerves: II. Activities of ameboid growth, cones, sheath cells and myeline segments, Am. J. Anat. *52*:1, 1933.

————: Studies of living nerves: III. Phenomena of nerve irritation and recovery, degeneration and repair, J. Comp. Neurol. *61*:1, 1935.

————: Studies of living nerves: VII. Growth adjustments of cutaneous terminal arborizations, J. Comp. Neurol. *76*:57, 1942.

Sunderland, S., and Lavarack, J. O.: The branching of nerve fibers, Acta anat. *17*:46, 1953.

Sunderland, S., Lavarack, J. O., and Ray, J. L.: The caliber of nerve fibers in human cutaneous nerves, J. Comp. Neurol. *91*:87, 1949.

Weiss, P., and Hiscoe, H. B.: Experiments on the mechanism of nerve growth, J. Exper. Zool. *107*:314, 1948.

Young, J. Z.: Growth and differentiation of nerve fibres, Symp. Soc. Exper. Biol. *2*:57, 1948.

————: The nature of neuroglandular contacts, J. Endocrinol. *6*:26, 1949.

Special References on Nerve Regeneration

Aitken, J. T.: Growth of nerve implants in voluntary muscle, J. Anat. *84*:38, 1950.

Aitken, J. T., Sharman, M., and Young, J. Z.: Maturation of regenerating nerve fibers with various peripheral connexions, J. Anat. *81*:1, 1947.

Bacsich, P., and Wyburn, G. M.: The effect of interference with the blood supply on the regeneration of peripheral nerves, J. Anat. *79*:74, 1945.

Bensley, S. H.: Cytological studies of the reaction of myelinated nerve fibers to section of the nerve, Anat. Rec. *90*:1, 1944.

Bueker, D., and Meyers, E.: The maturity of peripheral nerves at the time of injury as a factor in nerve regeneration, Anat. Rec. *109*:723, 1951.

Clark, E. R., and Clark, E. L.: Microscopic

studies on regeneration of medullated nerves in living mammal, Am. J. Anat. *81*:233, 1947.

Guth, L.: Regeneration in the mammalian peripheral nervous system, Physiol. Rev. *36*:441, 1956.

Gutmann, E., and Guttmann, L.: Factors affecting recovery of sensory function after nerve lesions, J. Neurol. & Psychiat. *5*:117, 1942.

Gutmann, E., Guttmann, L., Medawar, P. B., and Young, J. Z.: The rate of regeneration of nerve, J. Exper. Biol. *19*:14, 1942.

Gutmann, E., and Sanders, F. K.: Functional recovery following nerve grafts and other types of nerve bridge, Brain *65*:373, 1942.

————: Recovery of fibre numbers and diameters in the regeneration of peripheral nerves, J. Physiol. *101*:489, 1943.

Highet, W. B., and Sanders, F. K.: The effects of stretching nerves after suture, Brit. J. Surg. *30*:355, 1943.

Holmes, W., and Young, J. Z.: Nerve regeneration after immediate and delayed suture, J. Anat. *77*:63, 1942.

Ramon y Cajal, S.: Degeneration and Regeneration of the Nervous System, London, Oxford, 1928.

Sanders, F. K.: The repair of large gaps in the peripheral nerves, Brain *65*:281, 1942.

Sanders, F. K., and Young, J. Z.: The degeneration and re-innervation of grafted nerves, J. Anat. *76*:143, 1941.

Seddon, H. J.: Three types of nerve injury, Brain *66*:237, 1943.

————: War injuries of peripheral nerves, Brit. J. Surg. (War Surg., Supp. No. 2), p. 325, 1948.

Seddon, H. J., Medawar, P. B., and Smith, H.: Rate of regeneration of peripheral nerves in man, J. Physiol. *102*:191, 1943.

Sunderland, S.: The capacity of regenerating axons to bridge long gaps in nerves, J. Comp. Neurol. *99*:481, 1953.

————: Capacity of reinnervated muscles to function efficiently after prolonged denervation, Arch. Neurol. & Psychiat. *64*:755, 1950.

————: A classification of peripheral nerve injuries producing loss of function, Brain *74*:491, 1951.

————: Factors influencing the course of regeneration and the quality of the recovery after nerve suture, Brain *75*:19, 1952.

————: Rate of regeneration in human peripheral nerves, Arch. Neurol. & Psychiat. *58*:251, 1947.

————: Regeneration phenomena in human peripheral nerves *in* Weiss, P. (ed.): Genetic Neurology, p. 105, Chicago, Univ. Chicago Press, 1950.

Windle, W. F.: Regeneration of axons in the

vertebrate central nervous system, Physiol. Rev. *36*:427, 1956.

Young, J. Z.: The effect of delay on the success of nerve suture, Proc. Roy. Soc. Med. *37*:551, 1944.

————: Effects of use and disuse on nerve and muscle, Lancet *2*:109, 1946.

————: Factors influencing the regeneration of nerves, Advances Surg. *1*:165, 1949.

————: The functional repair of nervous tissue, Physiol. Rev. *22*:318, 1942.

————: Histology of peripheral nerve injuries *in* Cope, Z. (ed.): Medical History of the Second World War: Surgery, p. 534, London, Her Majesty's Stat. Off., 1953.

————: Structure, degeneration and repair of nerve fibers, Nature *156*:132, 1945.

Young, J. Z., Holmes, W., and Sanders, F. K.: Nerve regeneration—importance of the peripheral stump and the value of nerve grafts, Lancet *2*:128, 1940.

Special References on the Blood Supply of Nerves

Adams, W. E.: The blood supply of nerves, J. Anat. *76*:323, 1942.

Sunderland, S.: Blood supply of the nerves of the upper limb in man, Arch. Neurol. & Psychiat. *53*:91, 1945.

————: Blood supply of peripheral nerves, Arch. Neurol. & Psychiat. *54*:280, 1945.

————: Blood supply of the sciatic nerve and its popliteal divisions in man, Arch. Neurol. & Psychiat. *54*:283, 1945.

General References on the Autonomic Nervous System

Cannon, W. B.: Bodily Changes in Pain, Hunger, Fear and Rage, New York, Appleton, 1920.

————: The Wisdom of the Body, ed. 2, New York, Norton, 1939.

Cannon, Walter B., and Rosenblueth, Arturo: Autonomic Neuro-Effector Systems, New York, Macmillan, 1937.

Gaskell, W. H.: The Involuntary Nervous System, London, Longmans, 1920.

Kuntz, Albert: The Autonomic Nervous System, ed. 2, Philadelphia, Lea & Febiger, 1934.

————: The sympathetic nerve cells *in* Cowdry's Special Cytology, ed. 2, p. 1423, New York, Hoeber, 1932.

Pavlov, I. P.: Conditioned Reflexes, London, Oxford, 1927.

White, J. C.: The Autonomic Nervous System, New York, Macmillan, 1935.

Special References on the Autonomic Nervous System

Boeke, J.: Some observations on the structure and the innervation of smooth muscle fibers, J. Comp. Neurol. *56*:27, 1932.

————: The sympathetic endformation, its synaptology, the interstitial cells, the periterminal network, and its bearing on the neurone theory; discussion and critique, Acta anat. *8*:18, 1949.

Dale, H. H.: The transmission of nervous effects by acetylcholine, Harvey Lect. *32*:229, 1936-1937.

Hard, W. L., Peterson, A. C., and Fox, M. D.: Histochemical and quantitative studies on choline esterase distribution in cervical sympathetic ganglia, J. Neuropath. & Exper. Neurol. *10*:48, 1951.

Rosenblueth, A.: The transmission of sympathetic nerve impulses, Physiol. Rev. *17*:514, 1937.

PART FOUR

The Histology of the Systems

Chapter 21

The Circulatory System

When many different parts of the body collaborate with one another to carry out some specific function they are said to constitute a system. For example, the various tubes and hollow structures concerned in circulating the blood throughout the body are said to constitute the circulatory system. In the following chapters we shall deal briefly with the functions of those systems that lie within the scope of general histology and consider how the histologic structure of their different parts is related to the function of these parts and to the function of the system as a whole.

Certain parts of some systems are called *organs* (*organum* = instrument). However, not all the parts of each system are thus honored. Although there is no fixed rule about the matter, the term organ usually is reserved for the more impressive parts of a system in which some important function is segregated.

In discussing the microscopic structure of organs the terms stroma and parenchyma are commonly employed. *Stroma* (*stroma* = a mattress) refers to the supporting tissue in an organ and *parenchyma* (*parencheo* = I pour in, as into a mold) to the cells of the organ that perform the specific function of the organ. Many organs are glands; in these, epithelium constitutes the parenchyma, and connective tissue, the stroma.

General Function. In Chapter 6 it was explained that most of the cells of the body live in tissue fluid from which they obtain oxygen and food and into which they excrete their waste products. If there were no mechanism for constantly changing or freshening the tissue fluid of the body it would soon become depleted of food and oxygen and saturated with waste products. In most sites in the body the tissue fluid is kept fresh, not so much because it is changed rapidly, but because the substances dissolved in it always tend to come into equilibrium with those dissolved in the blood contained in the capillaries. The blood in the capillaries in any given part of the body supplied by the systemic circulation is al-

ways fresh because it is changed continuously. In these capillaries, blood that has recently passed through the lungs, where it has become charged with oxygen and rid of carbon dioxide, is continuously substituted for that which has lost oxygen to, and gained carbon dioxide from, the tissue fluid of the part. Moreover, in making the rounds of the circulatory system, a certain amount of blood is diverted through the kidneys, where waste products other than carbon dioxide are eliminated; this keeps the concentration of these waste products in the blood of the circulatory system as a whole at a low level. Likewise, part of the blood of the body passes through the intestine, where food can be absorbed. This food, because the blood circulates, is supplied to the tissue fluid of all parts of the body to replace that used by the cells it bathes. The chief function of the circulatory system, then, is to maintain the quantity and the quality of the tissue fluid in all parts of the body.

SOME MECHANICAL PROBLEMS INHERENT IN A CIRCULATORY SYSTEM

Heart and Arteries. The continuous circulation of a fluid in a closed circuit of tubes requires that a pump be inserted somewhere in the circuit. Indeed, since the circulatory system of the human body consists of two circuits, the pulmonary and the systemic, joined together in series, two pumps are required, one for each. The heart is a double pump; its right side circulates blood through the pulmonary circulation, and its left side through the systemic circulation. Although each of these pumps is different from the ordinary pump that the student has studied in his course in physics, such as is illustrated in Figure 328, each acts like the one-cylinder pump in the illustration because it delivers fluid in spurts and under considerable pressure. The tubes into which blood is delivered from the heart are called *arteries,* and their walls must be strong in order to withstand the

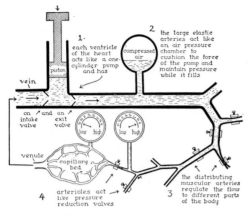

FIG. 328. Diagram illustrating the mechanical functions that must be performed by the different parts of the circulatory system. Begin at the upper left and proceed clockwise.

pressure that is generated in the heart and transmitted into them. Arteries deliver blood from the heart to the capillary beds of the body. Several problems arise in this connection. It is desirable for blood to flow evenly through capillary beds and not in spurts. This is a problem similar to that of a householder who has a one-cylinder pump connected to a well and wishes water delivered from his kitchen tap evenly instead of in spurts. He can achieve his wish by placing an air chamber on the pipe leading from the pump, as is shown in Figure 328, 2. This cushions the force of the pumping stroke, and, in addition, the air in the chamber, compressed by the pumping stroke, maintains the pressure in the circuit as a whole during the filling stroke of the pump. The same effect is accomplished in the human body by having the arteries that lead directly from the heart constructed chiefly of elastic tissue. These are termed *elastic* arteries. Blood delivered into them by the contracting heart both widens and lengthens them and thereby stretches the elastic tissue of their walls. Then, after the heart has finished contracting, its exhaust valves close, and the stretched walls of the elastic arteries passively contract to maintain pressure within the system for the short interval that elapses before the heart fills and contracts again.

The pressure within the arterial system, generated during the contraction of the heart, is called the *systolic* (*systole* = a contracting)

blood pressure, and it is slightly more than half as much again as the pressure which is maintained by the stretched elastic tissue of the arterial walls between the contractions of the heart; the latter is called the *diastolic* (*diastole* = dilatation) pressure.

It should be emphasized that the function of maintaining the pressure within the arterial system during diastole is performed chiefly by the largest arteries of the body; hence, these are the only ones that have walls consisting chiefly of elastin. The branches that arise from the largest arteries to deliver blood to the different parts of the body have a function different from that of the elastic arteries, and for this reason they have walls of a different character. Since different parts of the body, under different conditions of activity, require different amounts of blood, the arteries that supply them must be capable of having the size of their lumens regulated so that different amounts of blood can be delivered at different times. For example, the muscles in the right arm of a right-handed tennis player require more blood during a match than those of his left arm. For the size of these *distributing* arteries to be regulated by nervous control requires that their walls be made mostly of circularly disposed smooth muscle fibers (which are living and can respond to nervous stimuli) rather than of elastin (which is nonliving and can only contract passively), and, for this reason, distributing arteries are also called *muscular* arteries. The distributing arteries, then, variously regulate the flow of blood to different parts of the body according to the needs of these parts. In this way, they function like the valves on the pipes illustrated in Figure 328, 3.

Still other mechanical problems inherent in a circulatory system must be considered. A substantial pressure must be maintained within the system, otherwise blood would not be delivered in sufficient quantities to the various capillary beds of the body, particularly those of the brain, the supplying of which requires overcoming the force of gravity. However, the maintenance of a relatively high pressure within the arterial system must be accomplished in such a way that blood is delivered into capillary beds under greatly reduced pressure because the walls of capillaries must necessarily be thin (and therefore weak) to permit ready diffusion through them. A high pressure within the arterial system, and the delivery of blood into capillary beds under relatively low pressure, could be accomplished in a mechanical model by inserting pressure reduction valves between the ends of arteries and the capillary beds, as is shown in Figure 328, 4. The same effect is achieved in the human body by *arterioles*. These, as their name implies, are very small arteries, but they are of a special construction, having relatively narrow lumens and thick muscular walls. Since blood is of a certain viscosity, their narrow lumens offer considerable resistance to its flow, and this permits relatively high pressures to be built up behind them. The degree of pressure within the arterial system as a whole is regulated mainly by the degree of tonus of the smooth muscle cells in the walls of arterioles. If this becomes increased, hypertension (high blood pressure) results.

Since the capillary beds into which arterioles empty have a great capacity for blood, and since there is no obstacle interposed between these and the capacious venous system into which they drain, the effect of arterioles is much like that produced by a nozzle on a hose (containing water under high pressure) which permits water to be sprinkled gently on newly planted flowers. The arterioles, as it were, act as nozzles that spray blood gently into the capillary beds. Hence, arterioles act to maintain pressure in the arterial system as a whole and, in addition, permit blood to be delivered into capillary beds under relatively low pressure.

Capillaries. The formation and the absorption of tissue fluid by capillaries is considered at length in Chapter 6.

Veins. Capillaries empty into small veins (venules) which join with others to form larger veins, and so on. The blood from all the veins in the systemic circulation eventually drains into either the superior or the inferior vena cava and so into the right heart.

Blood enters venules from capillaries under a very low pressure. Indeed, the pressure in veins is so low that they do not require very thick walls. But, since the blood in them is under very low pressure, it travels relatively slowly. For this reason, veins require lumens much larger than those of arteries. Hence, in cross section, a vein always has a thinner wall

and a larger lumen than its arterial counterpart (Fig. 334).

The pressure in veins draining dependent parts of the body overcomes the force of gravity only with difficulty. To assist, most of these veins are provided with valves to prevent backflow. Valves also have other functions, which will be discussed presently. Since there is no need for veins to cushion the contraction of the ventricle, there are no venous counterparts of elastic arteries. And, since there is no need for a strong mechanism for narrowing their lumens against the force of arterial pressure, as is necessary in distributing arteries, there is no need for much smooth muscle in their walls. Collagen, then, is used more extensively in the walls of veins than in arteries.

Having considered some of the mechanical problems inherent in a circulatory system, we shall discuss the histologic features of its different parts in some detail.

THE MICROSCOPIC STRUCTURE OF ARTERIES

Introduction. The student should be particularly interested in arteries, for, in all probability, more of his future patients will die from arterial disease than from any other single cause. Arterial disease is the great enemy of those who pass middle life. The tissues of the body begin to deteriorate shortly after a man has reached the age of 40. Of all the tissues of the body, those that make up the walls of arteries commonly deteriorate the soonest.

The Problem of Nourishing Cells in the Walls of Arteries. Why should the tissues of the walls of arteries be the first to be so affected? There is some reason for this. The walls of arteries live, as it were, under constant tension; only death relieves them from having to withstand continually the pressure within the arterial system. This may assist in causing their relatively early deterioration. But it is probably not so important a factor as the fact that the arterial wall, stretched by pressure from within the artery, presents unique problems with regard to its nutrition.

The usual arrangement in the body for permitting any considerable mass of tissue to be supplied abundantly with oxygen and nourishment is to have it permeated with capillaries. Ordinarily, capillaries are supplied with blood

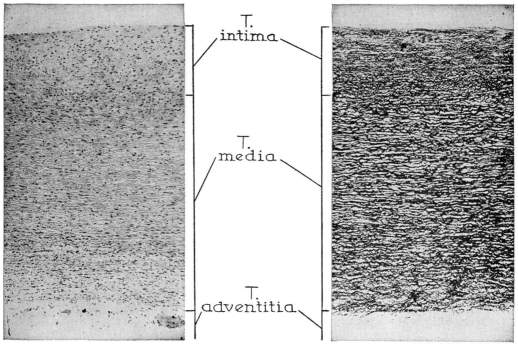

T. intima

T. media

T. adventitia

H and E

elastic tissue stain

FIG. 329. Low-power photomicrographs of 2 adjacent sections cut from the wall of the aorta; the elastic fibers and the laminae are stained specifically in the section on the right.

under relatively low pressure. If low-pressure capillary beds were present in the walls of arteries, it could be expected that they would be collapsed because the pressure transmitted into the wall of the artery from its lumen would be much greater than that in the capillaries. In any event, low-pressure capillaries are not present in the walls of arteries except in their outer layers; here they can remain open because the force of the pressure of the blood in the lumen of the artery is taken up by the inner and the middle layers of the artery walls. Lacking capillaries, cells in the inner and the greater part of the middle layers of the walls of arteries must be nourished by diffusion from (1) blood in the lumen and (2) blood in the capillaries in the outer part of the wall. Therefore, the situation in the inner layers of the wall is not unlike that which exists in hyalin cartilage where diffusion must occur over relatively long distances. It will be recalled that precipitation of materials in the gelled intercellular substance of cartilage can interfere with the nutrition of

its cells. It could be visualized that the deposition or accumulation of substances in artery walls likewise could interfere with the diffusion mechanism on which they are dependent and hence with the health of such cells as live in those layers of the wall.

The pressure within lymphatic capillaries is even less than that within blood capillaries; hence, patent lymphatic capillaries could not be expected to be present in those layers of the walls of arteries that bear the brunt of arterial pressure. It will be recalled that lymphatic capillaries, in addition to draining off that part of the tissue fluid that is not returned to blood capillaries, are responsible for keeping the tissue fluid free from the colloids that normally escape from blood capillaries to some extent in healthy, and more abundantly in damaged, tissue. It could be anticipated, then, that the tissue of arterial walls might not be able to rid itself of such colloidal materials as might gain entrance to, or be set free in, it as readily as the tissues in most parts of the body.

From the foregoing it might be expected that degeneration and necrosis might occur more readily in the tissues of arterial walls than in most sites in the body and, further, that arterial walls might be more likely to become the sites of accumulations of colloidal material of various sorts than the tissues of those parts of the body that have lymphatic capillaries to drain colloids away. Indeed, degeneration of, and accumulations in, the walls of arteries are two prominent features of what is termed *arteriosclerosis,* the general term employed to designate the condition in which arterial walls are variously deteriorated.

Coats of the Walls of Arteries. The walls of arteries generally are described as consisting of 3 coats or layers. The innermost is termed the *tunica intima;* the middle one, the *tunica media;* and the outermost one the *tunica adventitia.* The tunica media is the thickest of the 3. The structure of these 3 coats in elastic and distributing arteries and in arterioles will now be considered.

ELASTIC ARTERIES. The aorta and the innominate, the subclavian, the common carotid and the pulmonary arteries are grouped in this class. Since the aorta is the usual representative of the type studied by students, we shall consider the histologic structure of its wall in some detail.

Tunica Intima. The intima constitutes about one sixth of the thickness of the wall (Fig. 329). It is lined by a pavement of endothelial cells. The cytoplasm of these cannot be seen to advantage in sections, but their nuclei are apparent (Fig. 329, *left*). The endothelium rests on the "subendothelial layer" of the intima. This constitutes one fourth to one fifth of its total thickness and consists of fairly delicate elastic fibers that are disposed longitudinally and are immersed, along with some collagenic fibers, in amorphous intercellular substances (Fig. 329, *right*). The nuclei of a few cells may be seen in this layer (Fig. 329, *left*). They are mostly the pale-staining nuclei of fibroblasts, but the nuclei of macrophages also may be seen. The remainder of the intima is termed its *deep* or *external layer.* It consists of somewhat coarser elastic fibers embedded with collagenic fibers in an amorphous intercellular substance (Fig. 329, *right*). It has more cells than the subendothelial layer. Where it abuts on the tunica media its elastic fibers

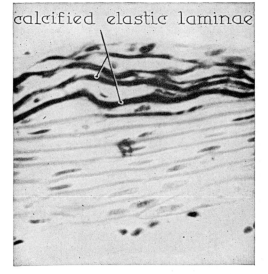

FIG. 330. High-power photomicrograph of a section of the wall of the aorta of a rat. The 4 inner elastic laminae are calcified; as a consequence, they stain a deep blue with hematoxylin. Calcification of the elastic laminae of arteries is one indication of arteriosclerosis.

are condensed to form a thick, fenestrated plate of elastic tissue (*fenestra* = window), called the *internal elastic lamina.* This is similar to the elastic laminae of the media and will be described presently.

Tunica Media. This coat constitutes the bulk of the wall and consists chiefly of concentrically arranged fenestrated laminae of elastic tissue similar to the internal elastic lamina of the intima. They appear as dark lines in Figure 329, *right,* and as lighter ones in Figure 329, *left.* The number of these varies with age. There are around 40 in the newborn and up to 70 in the adult. The laminae become thicker in adulthood than they are in childhood. Although they contain no mineral (Fig. 25) in the young aorta, they show a disposition to become calcified in certain types of arteriosclerosis (Fig. 330). Collagenic fibers, delicate elastic fibers and amorphous intercellular substance, probably of the sulfated mucopolysaccharide type, together with fibroblasts and smooth muscle fibers, fill the spaces between adjacent laminae. That the fibroblasts found here make more amorphous intercellular substance than those of ordinary connective tissue suggests that they have some of the

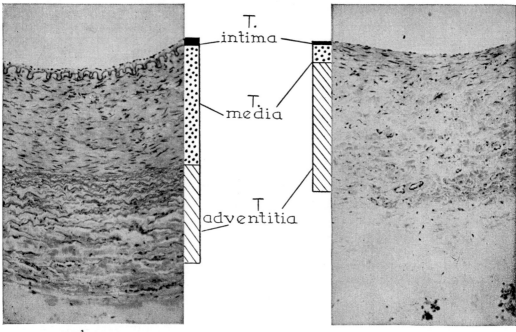

T. intima

T. media

T. adventitia

artery   vein

FIG. 331. (*Left*) A medium-power photomicrograph of a cross section of the wall of a distributing artery. (*Right*) A photomicrograph, taken at the same magnification, of a cross section of the wall of one of its two companion veins. Note the great disparity between the thickness of the media of the artery and the vein.

split internal elastic lamina

FIG. 332. High-power photomicrograph of a cross section of the wall of a distributing artery, showing a split internal elastic lamina.

properties of chondrocytes. This suggestion is supported by the fact that, under certain pathologic conditions, they sometimes form cartilage, or even bone, in these sites. The outermost lamina of the tunica media is termed the *external elastic lamina*.

Tunica Adventitia. This is thin in elastic arteries. It consists of irregularly arranged connective tissue which contains both collagenic and elastic fibers. Small blood vessels are present in it, and in suitable sections these may be followed into the outer parts of the tunica media. They are called the *vasa vasorum* (vessels of the vessels). They tend to become affected in the later stages of syphilis; hence, in this disease, parts of the adventitia and the tunica media may be denied a proper blood supply and so undergo necrosis.

DISTRIBUTING ARTERIES. Most arteries are of this type.

Tunica Intima. This is relatively thin. Its most prominent feature is a well-developed internal elastic lamina (Fig. 331, *left*). This consists of a single thick layer of elastic fibers (in the larger distributing arteries it forms a fenestrated plate) in youth, but it often splits into 2 layers in late adulthood (Fig. 332). It

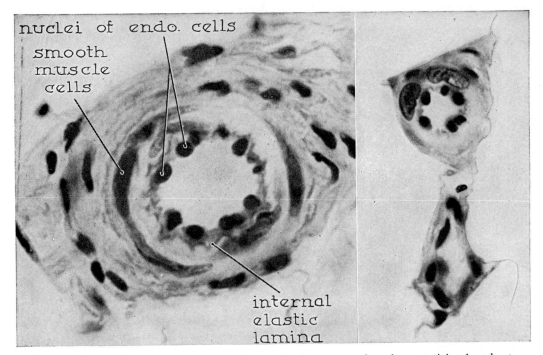

nuclei of endo. cells

smooth
muscle
cells

internal
elastic
lamina

FIG. 333. (*Left*) A high-power photomicrograph of a cross section of an arteriole of moderate size. (*Upper right*) A photomicrograph of a cross section of a small arteriole. Its companion venule shows below.

presents a wavy appearance in sections (Fig. 331, *left*), but it is not wavy in life, when it is stretched by the pressure within the vessel. Between the internal elastic lamina and the endothelium there is a very delicate layer of connective tissue.

Tunica Media. This is a fairly thick coat and consists chiefly of circularly disposed smooth muscle fibers held together to form a cohesive whole by reticular, collagenic and delicate elastic fibers (Figs. 331, *left,* and 334, *left*). The proportion of intercellular substance in relation to smooth muscle varies with the size of the vessel; hence, the media of a small vessel is mostly smooth muscle.

Tunica Adventitia. The thickness of this layer varies in distributing arteries but usually it is from one half to two thirds the thickness of the media (Fig. 331, *left*). It consists chiefly of elastic fibers but it also contains collagenic ones. The elastic fibers of the adventitia are condensed to form a noticeable external elastic lamina that is applied to, and continuous with, the outer border of the media. Vasa vasorum are present in the adventitia, particularly in the larger arteries.

Arterioles. Arteries with an over-all diameter of 100 μ or less generally are called *arterioles,* but some authors class considerably larger vessels as arterioles also. Cowdry has pointed out that the over-all diameter is not as important a criterion in determining whether any given vessels is an arteriole as is the thickness of the wall of the vessel in relation to its lumen. Kernohan, Anderson and Keith measured this relationship in a large number of arterioles in muscle tissue obtained from both normal people and from those suffering from hypertension (high blood pressure). They found that in the arterioles of normal people the ratio of the thickness of the wall of the vessel to the diameter of its lumen was 1:2, with variations from 1:1.7 to 1:2.7. They found that in hypertension the arterioles had thicker walls in relation to their lumens.

The walls of the larger arterioles have 3 coats (Fig. 333, *left*). The intima consists of endothelium applied directly, or with a trace of intervening connective tissue, to an internal elastic lamina. The media consists of circularly arranged smooth muscle fibers. In the larger arterioles some intimation of an external

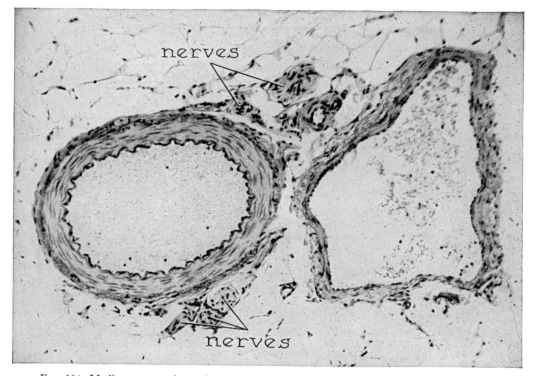

Fig. 334. Medium-power photomicrograph of a cross section of a distributing artery and its companion vein. Small nerves, cut in cross section, may be seen closely associated with the adventitia. Notice that the vein has a thinner wall and a larger lumen than the artery.

elastic lamina is present (Fig. 333, *left*). The adventitia may be as thick as the media, and it consists of a mixture of collagenic and elastic fibers.

As arterioles branch and become smaller, their walls become thinner, and their lumens smaller. The internal elastic lamina becomes very thin in the smaller arterioles (Fig. 333, *right*), and in the smallest it is absent. The smooth muscle cells of the media of a small arteriole are correspondingly small; if they were of usual length they would overlap each other in encircling the lumen (compare those on the left and the right sides of Fig. 333). In the smallest arterioles one or two smooth muscle cells constitute the media that is seen in a cross section (Fig. 333, *right*). The adventitia of small arterioles consists chiefly of collagenic fibers, and in the very small ones it is greatly reduced in amount.

A very small arteriole, with a lumen not much larger than a red blood cell and a wall consisting of only a layer of smooth muscle surrounded by a little connective tissue, is termed a *precapillary arteriole*.

NERVOUS CONTROL OF ARTERIES AND ARTERIAL PRESSURE

There are two problems to consider here: (1) the mechanism that regulates the flow of blood to different parts of the body according to their needs and (2) the control of the pressure within the system as a whole. We shall now discuss briefly these rather complex and somewhat interrelated problems in the order mentioned.

1. **Regulation of Flow to Different Parts According to Different Needs.** If cross sections of distributing arteries or arterioles are examined, bundles of, or even single, nerve fibers, cut either in cross section or obliquely, are seen in the adventitia (Fig. 334). Both nonmyelinated efferent fibers and myelinated afferent fibers are present in these. The efferent fibers in the nerves of most arteries are mostly sympathetic. Some, but probably not all, arteries have parasympathetic innervation as well. The nonmyelinated fibers end in association with the smooth muscle cells of the media. The myelinated afferent fibers end in

special sensory endings in the adventitia. The student will not be able to see the endings of these fibers unless special preparations are used.

VASOCONSTRICTOR NERVES. Most sympathetic fibers act to increase the tone of the smooth muscle of the arteries concerned and hence are vasoconstrictor in type. However, some sympathetic fibers are of the vasodilator type. Some years ago it was believed that the sympathetic fibers of the smaller arteries and arterioles reached their destination by traveling along the main distributing arteries and then along their branches. Accordingly, surgical attempts were made to relieve those unfortunate individuals who suffer from painful or otherwise harmful constrictions of the blood vessels of their extremities by stripping the adventitia off short segments of the main distributing arteries leading to the parts concerned. The operation is known as a "periarterial sympathectomy." However, it did not generally prove to have a permanent effect. Woollard has since shown that the sympathetic fibers in the adventitia of the main distributing arteries do not extend to the peripheral branches of the arteries. He found the latter to be innervated chiefly by sympathetic fibers derived from the peripheral nerves that travel to the part. Woollard's work provides an anatomic basis for explaining why the periarterial sympathectomy operation performed on main distributing arteries so often failed to relieve arteriolar spasm in the extremity supplied by the artery.

MECHANISMS OF VASODILATATION. Since it has not been established that all arteries are innervated by parasympathetic vasodilator fibers, and since the great majority of sympathetic fibers in the vessels of man are vasoconstrictors (the arteries supplying muscles have more sympathetic vasodilator fibers than most), the problem of how vasodilatation is obtained when it is necessary or desirable is somewhat complex.

Two mechanisms which do not depend on the presence of vasodilator fibers may be involved in bringing about vasodilatation. Before considering the first of these, it should be recalled that in the medulla of the brain there is a vasoconstrictor center which controls the impulses that pass out along the sympathetic nerves to the musculature of the arteries. Afferent impulses arising as a result of the stimulation of the afferent nerve endings in the adventitia of vessels, or in other sites, could, on being conducted into and up the cord to the vasoconstrictor center, inhibit it. Inhibition of the center would be reflected in diminished tone in the smooth muscle of the vessels innervated by it.

Secondly, the afferent fibers in the adventitia of peripheral vessels are branches of fibers from which other branches go to other sites, for example, to the skin. Therefore, there is a possibility that impulses arising from the stimulation of endings in sites such as skin might travel along the fiber until they reach the bifurcation at which the arterial branch of the fiber originates. Here they might be reflected back along the sensory fiber of the vessel antidromically (against the usual direction of the current of impulses) to reach the endings in the vessel wall and there, perhaps through chemical mediation, inhibit the encircling smooth muscle cells of the vessel. Such a reflex occurring within 2 branches of a single nerve fiber is called an *axon reflex*.

Some authors believe that impulses may reach the afferent endings in arteries antidromically from the cord to bring about vasodilatation.

2. **Nervous Control of the Pressure in the Arterial System as a Whole.** Under normal conditions, variations in the arterial pressure are due chiefly to variations in (1) the degree to which arterioles are contracted and (2) the output of blood by the heart. The innervation of arterioles has already been explained. The heart has both sympathetic and parasympathetic innervation, but the parasympathetic fibers exert the greater regulatory influence. They are derived from the vagus nerve and they act to depress heart action continuously. For example, if the vagus is paralyzed, the heart rate may double. It is obvious that if afferent impulses from any part of the body were directed to the centers in the brain that control the tonus of arterioles and the heart beat, they could, by reflex mechanisms, control arterial pressure within wide limits.

While it is probable that afferent impulses from many blood vessels, and from other sites, find their way to these centers and so affect blood pressure, there are a certain few sites in the vascular system where vessels are richly provided with nerve endings that are especially receptive to pressure changes. In other sites

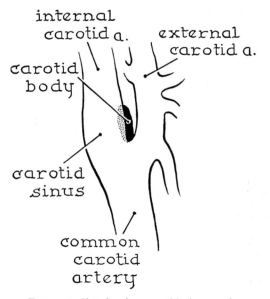

internal
carotid a.   external
              carotid a.

carotid
body

carotid
sinus

common
carotid
artery

FIG. 335. Sketch of a carotid sinus and a
carotid body.

there are complex nerve endings sensitive to changes in the chemical composition of the blood. The *carotid sinus* and the *carotid body* serve as excellent examples of such structures, and we shall consider their structure.

The carotid sinus is the name given to a slight dilatation of one of the carotid arteries near the bifurcation of the common carotid artery. Usually the site of dilatation is the internal carotid artery immediately above its point of origin (Fig. 335). In the dilated part the tunica media of the vessel is relatively thin, and the tunica adventitia is relatively thick. Many nerve endings of afferent fibers from the carotid branch of the glossopharyngeal nerve are present in the adventitia. Since the media is thin at this site, the adventitia must bear more of the brunt of withstanding the pressure within the vessel than is usual in arteries; hence, the nerve endings within it are readily stimulated by pressure changes. Nerve impulses set up by pressure changes within the sinus are conducted over nerve networks to the centers in the brain that control the heart and the arteries.

Recently, Green and Boss and Green have demonstrated that, in addition to the carotid sinus, there are other areas along the common carotid artery of the cat that have *baroceptor* (*baros* = weight) activity. Boss and Green

have studied the histology of these baroceptor areas and have found that basically it is similar to that of the carotid sinus. In each area myelinated fibers ramify in the adventitia of the vessel in fibrillar arrangement. Furthermore, there are structural alterations in the arterial wall in each site in that there is generally less muscle and sometimes less elastin in the media, and the collagenic fibers of the adventitia are in the form of finer fibers than usual, and these are intricately interwoven.

The carotid body is a small condensation of tissue on the wall of the internal carotid artery (Fig. 335). It has a structure similar to that of an endocrine gland in that it consists of cords and clumps of epithelial-like cells and is abundantly provided with sinusoidal capillaries. The epithelial-like cells are richly supplied with nerve endings. These seem to be stimulated by changes in the concentration of carbon dioxide or oxygen tension in the blood. Nerve impulses arising from these endings, as a result of chemical changes in the blood, are also conducted to the centers in the brain that control the heart and the arteries.

Small structures similar to the carotid body are also present in the arch of the aorta, in the pulmonary artery and at the origin of the right subclavian artery. Delicate pressure receptors are also present in the walls of the great veins close to the heart.

THE MICROSCOPIC STRUCTURE OF CAPILLARIES

To realize how capillary networks function, the student should examine living preparations, such as the web of the frog's foot, under the microscope, or at least see one of the motion pictures of capillary circulation. A visualization of capillary networks can also be gained from the study of thick, cleared sections of material in which the capillaries have been injected with a colored material (Fig. 264). Since capillaries are disposed in so many different planes in most tissues and since most of them pursue irregular courses, it is seldom that they are seen cut longitudinally in thin sections. Striated muscle is an exception, for in this tissue they parallel the muscle fibers; hence, longitudinal sections of striated muscle commonly reveal some capillaries cut in longitudinal section (Fig. 256 B). Contrariwise, the cross-section appearance of capil-

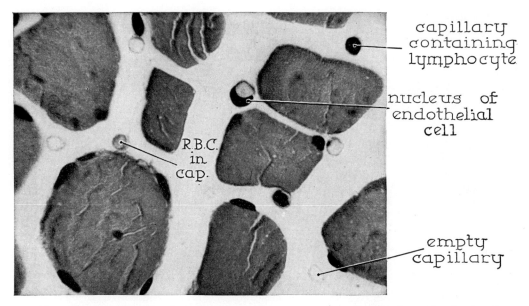

capillary
containing
lymphocyte

nucleus of
endothelial
cell

R.B.C.
in
cap.

empty
capillary

Fig. 336. Oil-immersion photomicrograph of a cross section of striated muscle, showing the various appearances presented by capillaries in cross section. In some instances the line of section passes through a capillary at a site where a nucleus of an endothelial cell is present; if so, the nucleus appears as a blue crescent, as may be seen above. If a capillary is cut at a site where no nucleus is present, it appears as a thin cytoplasmic ring. Either red blood cells or leukocytes may be present in capillaries at the sites where they are sectioned.

laries may be studied to great advantage in cross sections of striated muscle (Fig. 336). Such sections pass through most capillaries without passing through the nuclei of any of their endothelial cells; hence, these capillaries appear as cytoplasmic tubes (Fig. 336, *lower right*). However, in many instances, the nucleus of one of the endothelial cells making up a capillary wall will be cut, and, if so, it appears as a blue crescent partly encircling the lumen (Fig. 336, *slightly above center*). In cross section, some capillaries are seen to contain red blood cells (Fig. 336, *left of center*) and some, leukocytes (Fig. 336, *upper right*).

The Fine Structure of Capillaries. The fine structure of capillaries has been studied particularly by Palade, one of whose electron micrographs is Figure 337. The capillary in this illustration is cut in cross section. Two endothelial cells are required to encircle its lumen; the points where the cytoplasm of these come into contact are labeled in Figure 337 as *endothelial cell boundaries*. The lumen of the capillary contains fine granular material, which is probably precipitated blood pro-

tein, and dense round bodies, which are probably very small fat droplets that were present in blood. The inner and the outer cell membranes of the endothelial cells are clearly apparent as dark lines. Between the inner and the outer membranes of the endothelial cells that surround the lumen is the cytoplasm of the endothelial cells; this is characterized by the presence of very numerous small vesicles of about 400 Å in diameter. These are mostly aggregated along the outer and the inner cell membranes of the endothelial cells. Some of the vesicles that abut on the outer and the inner cell membrane can be seen on close inspection (with a magnifying glass) to open onto the surface on which they abut, like little goblet cells. Such vesicles are, in effect, invaginations of the endothelial cell membrane into the cytoplasm of the endothelial cells. There is evidence indicating that there is a transport of fluid across the endothelial cell cytoplasm by means of small vesicles forming on one surface (where they phagocytose fluid) and then moving across the thickness of the endothelial cell to the other surface where the fluid is discharged. The taking up of fluid by vesi-

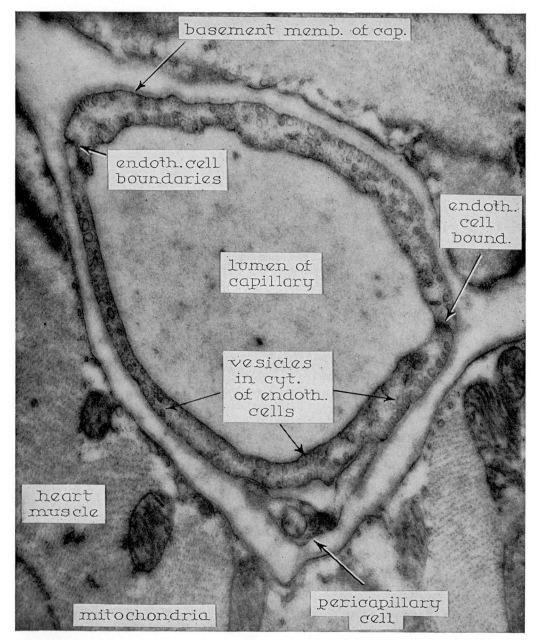

FIG. 337. Electron micrograph (× 57,000) of a section of heart muscle of a rat, showing a capillary cut in cross section and muscle fibers surrounding it. For further description see text. (Preparation by G. Palade, labeling added)

cles which transport it through cytoplasm is termed *pinocytosis* (*pinein* = to drink). How great a part this mechanism plays in the formation and the absorption of tissue fluid is not yet established.

The capillary as a whole is wrapped in a basement membrane which is only a fraction of the thickness of the endothelial cells. With the E/M it appears as a seemingly structure-less (amorphous) dark band that rings the capillary (Fig. 337, *upper right*). The basement membrane is separated from adjacent

Fig. 338. Scheme showing the relationship between arterioles, muscular capillaries or A-V bridges, true capillaries and venules. (Zweifach, B. W.: Anat. Rec. 73:478)

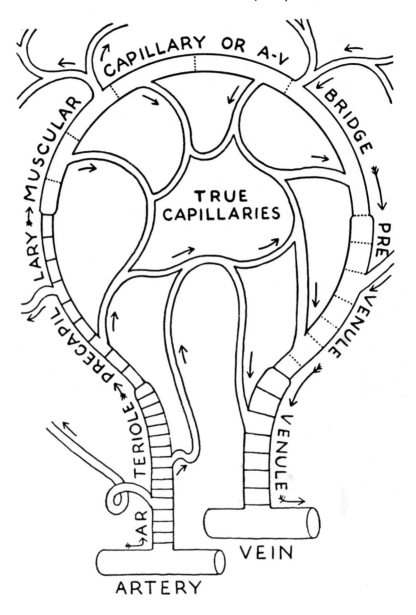

muscle fibers by a space that contains some amorphous material. A pericapillary cell may be seen at the lower border of the capillary.

The cytoplasm of endothelial cells contains mitochondria, but none are to be seen in this illustration.

CONTROL OF CAPILLARY CIRCULATION

The white face of fear and the blush of embarrassment provide evidence that capillary networks either may be closed off from or widely opened to the circulation by different emotional states. Moreover, it is obvious that the closing or the opening of capillary networks that occurs under these conditions is brought about through the influence of the autonomic nervous system, the functioning of which is so readily affected by emotional states. However, it is one matter to admit that the autonomic nervous system (under normal conditions as well as in emotional states) is a factor in controlling the extent to which capillary beds in different parts of the body are open to the circulation. It is another to decide just how this control is accomplished. Two possibilities must be considered: (1) that the endothelial cells of capillaries, or cells that more or less encircle capillaries, are innervated by sympathetic fibers and can respond to sympathetic stimulation by closing down the lumens of the capillaries concerned and (2) that capillaries are passive tubes and that the extent to which they are open depends entirely upon the state of tonus in the smooth muscle of the larger vessels supplying and draining them.

The devising, by Sandison in Clark's laboratory, of the transparent chamber which can be inserted permanently into the ear of a living rabbit, and into which capillaries will grow and so become available for direct microscopic study, considerably increased the possibilities for studying the mechanism of capillary contractility in mammals. Clark and Clark, in particular, have made many studies on this matter and they have not been able to give support to the idea that contractile cells surround capillaries. Such cells as they find disposed along the capillaries of mammals appear to be of a reasonably undifferentiated connective tissue type and are not contractile. However, these cells have the potentiality to become smooth muscle cells if the capillary concerned develops into an arteriole. Clark and Clark have come to the general conclusion that the control of capillary circulation is due to changes in the caliber of vessels that deliver blood into, and take blood away from, capillaries; in other words, that capillaries are passive tubes and that such cells as are usually associated with them are not contractile.

Zweifach has also made many studies on living capillaries and believes that much of the confusion surrounding this matter arises from the fact that there is no common definition of what constitutes a capillary. He believes that arrangements such as are shown in Figure 338, which is taken from one of his publications, exist. He believes that there are what might be termed "more direct" and "more indirect" paths through capillary beds. The more direct paths he calls *A-V bridges* (Fig. 338). They bear a superficial resemblance to capillaries, but have, scattered along their walls, thin muscular cells that represent a continuation of the musculature of arterioles. Zweifach finds, as might be expected, that the A-V bridges arise from arterioles and that most true capillaries arise from the A-V bridges (Fig. 338). Zweifach's belief seems to be that the A-V bridges are used when the traffic is light and so can pass easily through the peripheral circulation, but when the traffic becomes congested, because more blood is delivered into the A-V bridges than can conveniently be drained away in the venules, the side roads from the A-V bridges, the true capillaries, become more commonly used.

Since there is so little evidence to indicate that true (mammalian) capillaries are supplied with contractile cells, and since capillary endothelium, if it can contract on nervous stimulation, can do so only sluggishly, it would seem that the extent of capillary circulation is primarily a reflection of the hydrostatic pressures in the vessels with which they freely connect. The idea that there are alternate paths through capillary beds, with the shorter more direct ones (A-V bridges) equipped with some muscle cells, is a very attractive one. The state of tonus of the muscle cells of the bridges, the arterioles and the venules, which, in turn, is controlled by the sympathetic division of the autonomic nervous system, could then be visualized as indirectly controlling the extent to which blood would circulate through the relatively passive true capillaries.

ARTERIOVENOUS ANASTOMOSES

That arteriovenous anastomoses exist in many parts of the body, particularly in the distal parts of extremities, has been known for a very long time. Early evidence for their existence accumulated from two sources: (1) experiments in which particulate matter, too large to pass through capillaries, was injected into an artery and recovered from the corresponding vein and (2) histologic studies made on tissue, the vessels of which were injected with a colored material. However, comparatively little attention was paid to these important structures until some of the newer technics made their study possible in the living animal.

Grant first studied arteriovenous anastomoses in the living animal by subjecting carefully prepared rabbits' ears to direct microscopic observation by means of strong transmitted light. Grant and Bland later studied them in human skin and in the bird's foot. Clark and Clark, at almost the same time, studied them and their formation by means of transparent chambers inserted in rabbits' ears. Masson has described a special type of anastomoses seen in little organs in the skin called *glomi* (Fig. 366).

Arteriovenous anastomoses arise as side branches from arteries and arterioles and pursue either a tortuous or a fairly straight course to connect usually with the vein or the venule accompanying the arterial vessel from which they arise. Near the point where they empty into veins, their walls have the character of veins, and at their point of origin, their walls have the character of arteries but are slightly thicker. But, at the intermediate segment of transition, according to Grant, there is considerable muscular and adventitial thickening to be seen in the vessel. Moreover, this part of the anastomosis is particularly well supplied with nerve endings from the sympathetic division of the autonomic nervous system, and presumably it is more or less specialized to serve as a sphincter.

The dilatation of arteriovenous anastomoses in any part of the body permits a much greater amount of blood to pass through that part. It is obvious that arteriovenous anastomoses would serve a very important purpose in, for example, the tips of fingers or toes subjected to cold, because by their dilatation, they could permit greatly increased amounts of warm blood to pass through the extremities and so help maintain their temperature. It is very likely that arteriovenous anastomoses do serve a very important function in this way. Furthermore, it is not unlikely that they serve important functions in certain structures in the body that indulge in intermittent activities. Moreover, it is obvious that the dilatation of arteriovenous anastomoses in a normal body would have an effect in raising venous blood pressure and so aid the return of blood to the heart. Their closure under conditions of obstructed venous return similarly could help to diminish venous pressure. *Arteriovenous anastomoses are very different structures from A-V bridges, and to avoid confusion the latter are now commonly termed "preferred channels."*

VEINS

Venules. Blood is collected from capillaries by venules. These have a larger diameter than capillaries. The walls of the smaller venules

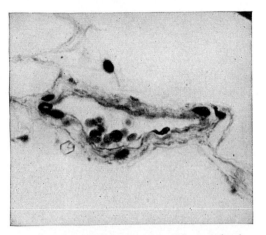

Fig. 339. High-power photomicrograph of a cross section of a venule. The wall consists chiefly of fibrous tissue lined by endothelium; one smooth muscle cell can be seen in the lower wall.

consist of endothelium supported externally by a little collagenic connective tissue (Fig. 339). Somewhat larger ones have smooth muscle fibers in their walls as well as collagenic fibers. Still larger ones, which perhaps are more properly called small veins, may have a continuous muscle coat. The muscle cells of venules and small veins are under nervous control; hence, these vessels are important factors in controlling the flow of blood in the peripheral circulation.

Veins of Medium Size. Their structure varies greatly. In general, their walls, like those of their corresponding arteries, consist of 3 tunics (Fig. 331, *right*). The intima consists of endothelium which rests either directly on a poorly defined internal elastic membrane (in which the fibers run longitudinally) or is separated from it by a slight amount of subendothelial collagenic connective tissue. The media is usually much thinner than that of a companion artery (Fig. 331). It consists chiefly of circularly disposed smooth muscle fibers. More collagenic fibers and fewer elastic fibers are mixed with them than in arteries. In some veins the innermost smooth muscle fibers of the media have a longitudinal course. In general, the media is much less muscular and hence thinner in veins that are protected, for example, by muscles or by the pressure of the abdominal contents, than in veins that are more exposed.

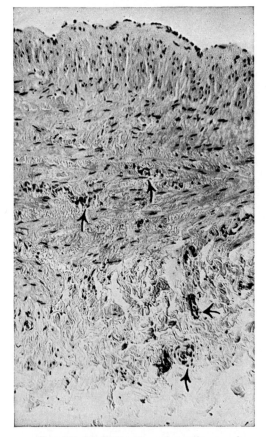

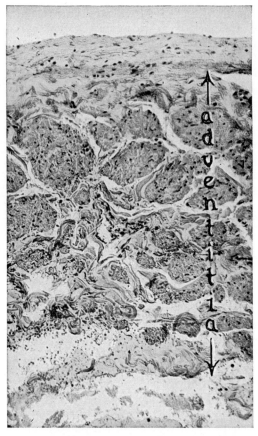

Fig. 340. Medium-power photomicrograph of the wall of the saphenous vein as it appears in a cross section. Note the inner layer of longitudinal muscle and note that the vasa vasorum, indicated by arrows, penetrate deeply into the media from the adventitia.

Fig. 341. Medium-power photomicrograph of the wall of the inferior vena cava, as seen in a cross section. Note the longitudinal muscle bundles in the adventitia.

The cerebral and the meningeal veins have almost no muscle in their walls. The adventitia of veins of medium size is often their thickest coat (Fig. 331, *right*). It usually consists chiefly of collagenic connective tissue.

The muscular media is well developed in the veins of the limbs, particularly in those of the lower ones. This is particularly true of the saphenous veins. Being superficial, these are not supported by the pressure of surrounding structures to the same extent as deeper veins. Furthermore, when a person stands erect, their walls must withstand the hydrostatic pressure generated by a long column of blood. For these two reasons their walls must be thicker than those of most veins. This is accomplished chiefly by a very sub-

stantial media. The innermost part of this consists chiefly of longitudinally disposed smooth muscle fibers associated with elastic fibers (Fig. 340) and the outermost and thicker part of circularly disposed smooth muscle fibers (Fig. 340).

Large Veins. The structure of different veins varies considerably. In general, the tunica intima resembles that of veins of medium size, but the subendothelial layer of connective tissue is thicker. In most of the largest veins there is little smooth muscle in the media. The adventitia is the thickest of the three coats, and it contains both collagenic and elastic fibers. In many instances, for example, the inferior vena cava, its innermost part contains bundles of longitudinally disposed smooth muscle fibers (Fig. 341).

Vasa Vasorum of Veins. Veins are supplied much more abundantly with vasa vasorum than arteries. Since veins contain poorly oxygenated blood, the cells of the walls of veins probably need more oxygen on occasions than can be obtained by diffusion from the lumen of the vessel. Vasa vasorum carrying arterial blood into the substance of the walls of veins supply this need. Furthermore, since the blood in veins is under low pressure, vasa vasorum can approach the intima of the walls of veins without necessarily being collapsed by the pressure within the vein. Hence, the vasa vasorum of veins penetrate much closer to the intima than do those of arteries. They are seen to advantage in the thick walls of the saphenous vein (Fig. 340).

Lymphatics. Since the walls of veins do not have to withstand great pressures, as do the walls of arteries, lymphatics, as well as vasa vasorum, can be present in a patent state within the substance of their walls. Indeed, the walls of veins are supplied much more abundantly with lymphatic capillaries than the walls of arteries. (This probably explains why tumors that spread by lymphatics invade the walls of veins but never the walls of arteries; see Fig. 427.) Lymphatic capillaries may approach the inner surfaces of the veins so closely that the tissue fluid that enters them to become lymph is probably a filtrate or a dialysate of the blood in the lumen of the vein itself.

Valves of Veins. Many veins are provided

SOME GENERAL DIFFERENCES BETWEEN DISTRIBUTING ARTERIES
AND THEIR COMPANION VEINS

ARTERIES	VEINS
Have a smaller over-all diameter and a smaller lumen.	Have a larger over-all diameter and a larger lumen.
Their walls are thicker because they must withstand pressure from the lumen.	Their walls are thinner because they have to withstand little pressure from the lumen.
The flow of blood is more rapid in them because the same amount of blood must pass through the narrower artery as passes through the wider vein.	The flow of blood is slower in them; the same amount of blood is handled as by companion arteries because of their larger lumens.
Their thicker walls do not collapse after death.	Their thinner walls collapse if blood drains out of them after death; hence, veins may appear as flattened structures in sections.
The oxygen content of blood in them is high.	The oxygen content of blood in them is low.
The inner parts of their walls contain no capillaries (low-pressure capillaries would be collapsed by the pressure from the lumen if they were present).	Low-pressure capillaries can be present and remain open in their walls because their walls do not have to withstand much pressure from their lumens.
No lymphatic capillaries are present in the inner layers of their walls for the same reason as above.	Lymphatic capillaries are present in the walls of veins.
The cells in the inner layers of their walls must be nourished by diffusion mechanisms that operate over long distances, from the blood in the lumen and from the vasa vasorum in the periphery.	The cells in their walls are nourished by diffusion mechanisms that operate only over short distances (from the vasa vasorum which permeate their walls and carry *arterial* blood).
The tunica intima is relatively thicker.	The tunica intima is relatively thinner.
The tunica media is muscular and considerably thicker.	The tunica media is generally a thin muscular layer.
The internal and the external elastic laminae are better developed.	The internal and the external elastic laminae are less well developed.
The tunica adventitia is about half the thickness of the media and has a high elastin content to assist in recoil during diastole.	The tunica adventitia is the thickest coat of the wall and is composed chiefly of collagen instead of elastin because no recoil effect is needed.
They have no valves.	Most of them have valves to prevent backflow.
Their structure is fairly constant.	Their structure is less constant—there are many variations related to particular positions, for example, saphenous veins.

with valves disposed so as to permit blood to flow toward the heart but not in the opposite direction. The valves of veins are of the flap (leaflet) type. Most valves have two leaflets, but some have only one. The leaflets are composed of folds of intima with some extra central reinforcements of connective tissue. Elastic fibers are disposed on the side of the valve that faces the lumen of the vessel.

Valves are especially abundant in the veins of the extremities, and they are generally absent from the veins of the thorax and the abdomen. Valves usually are placed immediately distal to sites where tributaries enter veins. Veins immediately proximal to the attachment of a valve are always dilated slightly to form a pouch or sinus. Hence, in distended superficial veins, localized swellings indicate the sites of valves.

The function of valves in veins is not completely understood. Obviously, valves must help to overcome the force of gravity by preventing backflow. But they may act in other ways. For example, valves in veins that are squeezed when surrounding muscles contract would enable the surrounding muscles to serve as pumps. Moreover, valves in such veins would prevent muscular contractions from creating back pressure on the capillary beds drained by the veins.

Varicose Veins. Superficial veins are relatively unsupported, and the force of gravity exerted through the blood within those below the heart is a more or less constant factor tending to cause their dilatation. Under conditions where there is obstruction to the return of blood from a part, or where the tissues of the walls of the veins are not as strong as usual, because of inheritance or disease, superficial veins gradually dilate. As dilatation proceeds, the valves become incompetent and, as a result, gravity exerts a still greater dilating force on their walls. Superficial veins that, under these conditions, become tortuous, irregular and wider than usual are called *varicose veins*.

THE TRANSPLANTATION OF BLOOD VESSELS

The transplantation of segments of blood vessels to bypass or replace segments of vessels that are malformed, diseased and weakened or occluded is now a relatively common

surgical operation. The discovery of anticoagulants, for example, heparin, had aided; these are commonly used locally to prevent agglutination and thrombosis from occurring at the sites where the new vessels are sutured to the old.

In the section on the transplantation of tissues, different kinds of transplants were described. A little thought is all that is required to realize that the use of autologous transplants of blood vessels would be very limited because there would be no source of autologous transplants for replacing any of the larger vessels of the body (except under certain circumstances when anastomoses are abundant). Some types or arterial defects can be repaired with autologous venous grafts, but the use of these is limited. Therefore, transplants of blood vessels must generally be of the homologous variety, and, as has already been explained, there is little use in hoping for the survival of cells in this type of transplant. Therefore, homologous transplants of blood vessels are effective because the intercellular substance in them survives for the time while new tissue is growing into them. Elastin is probably the most important in this respect, and it has been shown experimentally that it will remain intact for at least 6 to 9 months.

A homologous transplant is invaded by cells from the host site. These grow into its substance and form collagen. It is not believed that new elastin is formed in vessel transplants. The inner surfaces of the transplant become paved with a modified connective tissue. Discontinuous patches of cells appear along the interior of a transplant; hence, it is considered that endothelium does not grow from the host vessels to line it, but that cells from outside the transplant grow through its walls to reach its interior where they differentiate into a type of lining cell to substitute for endothelium.

Since no cell survival can be expected in homologous transplants they may be stored and treated in a variety of ways which might destroy any cells they contain. Homotransplants may be stored in the deep freeze or be frozen and dried or treated in other ways.

Synthetic materials, formed into the shapes of blood vessels, are now widely used as substitutes for homotransplants. These are made of materials that do not stir up a tissue re-action, furthermore, they are made so that they are porous; this permits cells from the host to grow into their substance and fill the interstices of it with cells and intercellular substance. Since they are porous, cells can grow through them to reach their lumens and line them with living tissue.

Heterologous transplants of blood vessels have been studied experimentally to some extent but are not used very commonly in practice.

HEART

Pericardial Cavity. The heart is a hollow muscular organ of four chambers. It is covered with a fibro-elastic connective-tissue membrane, which, in turn, is covered with a single layer of mesothelium. This mesothelial-covered, fibro-elastic membrane is termed the *epicardium* (*epi* = upon). The heart, so covered, is surrounded by another fibro-elastic membrane, the *pericardium*. This is lined with mesothelium. Between the pericardium and the epicardium is a potential space, the pericardial cavity, which, in health, contains up to 50 cc. of fluid. This fluid is so distributed that it amounts to no more than a film in most places. The epicardium is continuous at the base of the heart with the pericardium. Sometimes the epicardium is referred to as the *visceral layer of the pericardium,* and what we have just described as the pericardium as the *parietal layer of the pericardium.* The lubricating film of fluid between the mesothelial lining of the pericardium and the mesothelial covering of the epicardium permits the heart to move freely during contraction and relaxation. In certain diseases the amount of fluid in the pericardial cavity becomes greatly increased; in others, the epicardium becomes united by fibrous connective tissue to the pericardium. Both deviations from the normal greatly embarrass the action of the heart.

Epicardium. The character of the epicardium varies somewhat over different parts of the heart. Its more superficial layer consists of ordinary connective tissue. This is covered with mesothelium, and it contains some blood capillaries, lymphatic capillaries and some nerves. The deeper layer of the epicardium contains larger blood vessels and more fat and is continuous with the endomysium of the underlying cardiac muscle. Fat is particularly abundant along the course of the larger coronary vessels.

Myocardium. The muscular and thickest part of the wall of the heart lies deep to the epicardium. It is composed of cardiac muscle (this was described in Chap. 19). The arrangement of the various groups of fibers comprising the myocardium is considered in textbooks of gross anatomy.

Endocardium. This membrane forms a complete lining for the atrial and the ventricular cavities and covers all the structures that project into the heart (valves, chordae tendineae and papillary muscles). In general, the thickness of the endocardium varies inversely with the thickness of the myocardium it lines; for example, the endocardium in the atria is much thicker than that in the ventricles. The endocardium has 3 layers. The innermost consists of a delicate connective-tissue membrane lined with endothelium that is continuous with the lining of the blood vessels that leave the heart. The next (middle layer) is the thickest. It consists of dense connective tissue in which many elastic fibers are present, particularly in its inner part (Fig. 343). These commonly are disposed parallel with the surface, and in some sites where they are abundant, they alternate with layers of collagenic fibers. In the outer part of this layer some smooth muscle fibers may be present. The third and outermost layer of the endocardium consists of more irregularly arranged connective tissue. Fat may be present here. This layer contains blood vessels and cardiac muscle fibers of a special type (Purkinje fibers) (Fig. 348), to be described later. It is continuous with the endomysium of the myocardium.

Skeleton of the Heart. The aorta and the pulmonary artery arise from the left and the right ventricles, respectively. At its point of origin each is surrounded by a fibrous ring. The dense connective tissue of these rings is continuous either directly or indirectly, through the medium of a triangular mass of dense connective tissue with some cartilaginous qualities, the trigonum fibrosum, with the connective tissue of fibrous rings that surround the atrioventricular orifices. The fibrous rings surrounding the outlets of the atria and the ventricles prevent the outlets from becoming dilated when the muscular walls of the cham-

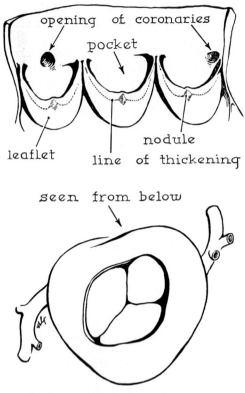

opening of coronaries

pocket

leaflet

nodule

line of thickening

seen from below

Fig. 342. (*Top*) The 3 leaflets of the aortic valve as they appear when the aorta is opened and spread out flat. (*Bottom*) The appearance of the closed valve as seen from below.

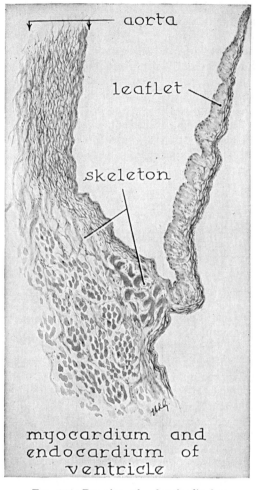

aorta

leaflet

skeleton

myocardium and endocardium of ventricle

Fig. 343. Drawing of a longitudinal section of the heart (low-power) cut through the site where the wall of the ventricle continues into the aorta. The section passes through an aortic valve leaflet. The tissue of the base of the leaflet merges into that of the skeleton of the heart.

bers contract and force their contents out through them. These fibrous structures, together with the fibrous (membranous) part of the interventricular septum, also provide a means for the insertion of the free ends of the fibers of the cardiac musculature. For this reason, these various fibrous structures sometimes are said to constitute the skeleton of the heart.

Valves of the Heart. Since each ventricle is of the nature of a one-cylinder pump, each requires an intake and an exhaust valve. The type of valve employed in the heart is the leaflet (flap) type (Figs. 342 and 343). The leaflets consist essentially of folds of endocardium. But, since 2 layers of endocardium would not be strong enough to withstand the pressures generated, each leaflet is reinforced with a flat sheet of dense connective tissue.

The intake valve of the right ventricle con-

sists of 3 leaflets and is called the *tricuspid valve*. Since cusp means a *point* and, in particular, as any mathematics student will recall, a point at which 2 curved lines meet tangentially, it is highly probable that the valve was so-named because the curved free margins of the 3 leaflets meet tangentially at 3 points on the circumference of the valve to form 3 cusps. Although, strictly speaking, the points of meeting of the free margins of the leaflets are the cusps, it has become common for those not mathematically inhibited to speak of the leaflets themselves as cusps. The intake valve of the left ventricle consists of only 2 leaflets; hence, its opening is 2-pointed, and it is called the *bicuspid valve*. The leaflets of both of the atrioventricular valves have a similar histologic structure. They are covered on both sides with endocardium and have a middle supporting layer of dense collagenic connective tissue. On the ventricular side of the layer of collagenic tissue there are numerous elastic fibers. A few are also present beneath the endothelium on the atrial side of the leaflet.

At the bases of the leaflets, the middle collagenic supporting flat plate becomes continuous with the dense connective tissue of the rings surrounding the orifices. Smooth muscle

fibers have been described at this site, and a sphincterlike action has been attributed to them. Capillaries may be present at the bases of the leaflets, where smooth muscle fibers are present, but capillaries do not extend into the valves proper in man. Such cells as are distributed throughout the dense connective tissue of the valves live in tissue fluid derived from the plasma of the blood that bathes the valves.

Tendinous cords of dense collagenic connective tissue (the chordae tendineae) covered by thin endocardium extend from the papillary muscles to connect with the ventricular surface of the middle collagenic supporting layer of each leaflet. It should be realized that the exhaust valves of the ventricles (the aortic and the pulmonary valves) open on ventricular

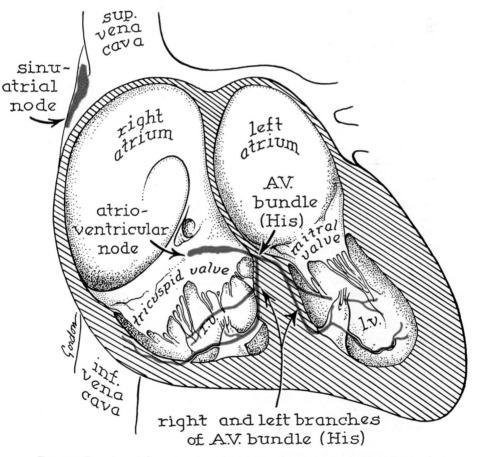

Fig. 344. Drawing of the cut surface (striped) and the interior of the heart, as seen from the front. The cut was made so as to expose and extend along, so far as was possible, the main parts of the impulse-conducting system, which is shown in red.

contraction and that only the closed intake (atrioventricular) valves must withstand the full pressure of ventricular contraction. There is a danger, then, that unless they were specially protected, they might, on strong ventricular contraction, behave like umbrellas on windy days and be blown inside out. The chordae tendineae and the papillary muscles from which they arise limit the extent to which the portions of the valves near their free margins can be "blown" toward the atria. (See Fig. 344).

The exhaust valve of the right ventricle is termed the *pulmonary semilunar valve* because of the shape of its leaflets. The exhaust valve of the left ventricle is termed the *aortic semilunar valve* and it too has 3 leaflets (Fig. 342). The leaflets of these valves are thinner than those of the atrioventricular valves. However, they are of the same general construction, being composed essentially of folds of endocardium reinforced with a middle layer of dense connective tissue; the folds of endocardium, at their bases, become continuous with the skeleton of the heart (Fig. 343). They have no chordae tendineae. The leaflets contain a considerable amount of elastic tissue on their ventricular sides (Fig. 343).

In a semilunar valve leaflet the dense middle layer becomes somewhat thickened along a line close to, and parallel with, its free margin, particularly near the middle of the leaflet. This is the line along which the leaflets touch one another when the valves close; hence, the tissue here must be relatively strong. Between this line of thickened tissue and their actual free margins, the leaflets are filmlike. The very pliable free margins permit a more perfect seal than could be obtained by stiffer tissue unless it were perfectly "machined."

For the free edges of 3 "patch" pockets bulging inwardly from the lining of a vessel toward its center to make a perfect seal requires that each leaflet, when the valve is closed, must have the appearance, when seen from below (except for having a curved base), of a triangle with its apex reaching the center of the vessel (Fig. 342). Furthermore, the sum of the angles of the apices of the 3 triangular leaflets of a closed valve must be 360°. At the apex of each leaflet, the thickening along the line close to the free margin, described in the previous paragraph, is accen-

tuated to form a nodule (Fig. 342). The free margin of a closed valve curves upward from both sides to a peak at this point; hence, this pointed portion of the free margin containing the nodule constitutes a true cusp (Fig. 342). However, as noted before, the whole leaflet is sometimes called a cusp.

Diseases affecting the valves of the heart may cause serious mechanical problems. In particular, in children suffering from rheumatic fever, the leaflets may become the seat of an inflammatory process. The healing of the leaflets often is associated with a considerable increase in their collagenic component; as a result, they may become stiffer and shorter or deformed in other ways. Leaflets sometimes become glued together with collagen. In any event, the end result is likely to be a valve that does not open or close properly. The student will see many examples of valves so affected in his clinical years.

IMPULSE-CONDUCTING SYSTEM OF THE HEART

In a cardiac cycle, the blood enters the right and the left atria from the venae cavae and the pulmonary veins, respectively. Part of this blood flows directly into the relaxed right and left ventricles, while the rest fills the atria. The two atria then contract simultaneously squeezing their contents into the partially filled ventricles to complete the filling process. Contraction of the ventricles then follows, which closes the atrioventricular valves and opens the aortic and the pulmonary valves through which their contents are discharged into the aorta and the pulmonary arteries, respectively. In the meantime, the atria are filling again.

The efficiency of the heart depends to a great degree on these different events following each other in orderly sequence. Unfortunately, in certain all too common diseases the orderly sequence of events is disturbed. For example, instead of a wave of contraction sweeping over the atria and later over the ventricles, the atria may begin to contract more or less independently of, and at different rates from, the ventricles. Or, the walls of the atria may only flutter instead of contracting properly. Indeed, there are far too many ways in which the normal order is disturbed to permit listing them here. But, since the student will

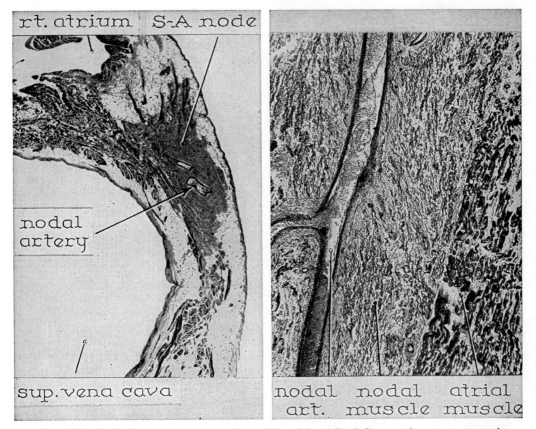

rt. atrium   S-A node

nodal
artery

sup. vena cava

nodal   nodal   atrial
art.   muscle   muscle

FIG. 345. (*Left*) Low-power cross section of the right wall of the superior vena cava at its junction with the right atrium, cutting through the sinu-atrial node. (*Right*) Low-power longitudinal section of the sinu-atrial node, showing the fine muscle fibers of the node, in contrast with the larger darker-staining atrial muscle. Note the nodal artery running through the center of the node. (Preparation by J. W. A. Duckworth)

soon be seeing examples of these conditions in the clinic, at this time he should become as familiar as possible with the mechanism that permits different events to be synchronized properly in the normal heart.

In Chapter 19 it was explained that two fundamental properties of protoplasm, contractility and conductivity, are brought to a high degree of development in muscular tissue. Therefore, a network of muscle fibers such as comprises cardiac muscle can readily conduct a wave of excitation. Long before the turn of the century, it was realized that the orderly sequence of contractions to be observed in the hearts of cold-blooded animals depended on a wave of excitation sweeping first along the muscular tissue of the atria and then along that of the ventricles. But the theory of mus-

cular conduction of the impulse for contraction could not be applied at that time to the hearts of mammals because these were thought to have a continuous connective-tissue partition between the atria and the ventricles. However, in 1893, the concept of there being a continuous fibrous partition between the atria and the ventricles was proved to be wrong when W. His, Jr., demonstrated that the partition in the human heart was pierced by a bundle of muscle which passes from the atrial septum to the upper border of the interventricular septum (Fig. 344). (Earlier in the same year, Kent had shown that the partition in the monkey heart was pierced by bundles of muscle fibers which were somewhat different from those of ordinary cardiac muscle.) The *atrioventricular* (A-V) bundle of muscle or,

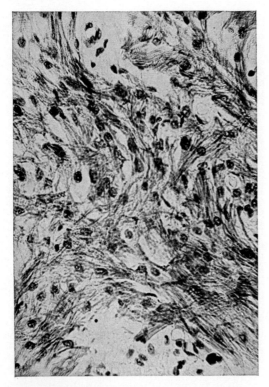

Fig. 346. Medium to high-power photomicrograph of a section of the A-V node stained with Hollande's chlorcarmine stain. The muscle cells have rather widely separated myofibrils and they are arranged in a complex branching network so that the myofibrils of one fiber are commonly seen to cross those of another at various angles. (Preparation by J. W. A. Duckworth)

as it is often called, the *bundle of His*, provides a means whereby each wave of contraction that sweeps over the atria can be conducted by muscular tissue to the ventricles to institute their contraction at precisely the time when they have been properly filled with blood by the contraction of the atria. It is obvious that the fibers in the A-V bundle would be specialized to conduct (at a special suitable rate) rather than to contract and, as we shall see presently, they have a different microscopic appearance from the fibers of ordinary cardiac muscle.

As additional investigations were made on the heart following the discoveries of His and Kent, it soon became apparent that there was further muscle tissue in the heart that was specialized primarily for conducting, and even some for initiating, the impulse for contraction. Indeed, it is now understood that the A-V bundle is only an important part of a whole system of fibers that are specialized for this purpose. These constitute what is termed the *impulse-conducting system of the heart,* and we shall now describe the various parts of this system and the microscopic structure of each representative division.

The Sinu-atrial (S-A) Node. This is a little mass of specialized cardiac muscle fibers that are contained in substantial amounts of dense fibro-elastic connective tissue. It is abundantly supplied with nerve fibers from both divisions of the autonomic nervous system. It lies in the right wall of the superior vena cava at the upper end of the sulcus terminalis (Figs. 344 and 345) and was first described, in 1907, by Keith and Flack, who considered that the impulse for the contraction of the heart arose in it. This concept soon received support because it was found, in 1910, that the S-A node was the first region to become electronegative when a wave of contraction developed in the heart of the dog. It is now often described as the *pacemaker* of the heart, and it is generally believed that here nervous impulses make their influence felt by affecting the rate at which impulses for contraction develop in the node to sweep over the heart thereafter.

Duckworth, in a recent and extensive study of the development and the histologic structure of the impulse-conducting system in man, has shown that the connective tissue content of the node becomes considerably increased immediately after birth and that at the same time the muscular elements in the node develop into their adult form. The adult nodal fibers are small cross-striated fusiform fibers about half the size of the ordinary atrial fibers which lie parallel with the long axis of the nodal artery as it descends through the center of the node. These fibers are embedded in a relatively large amount of collagen tissue which, unlike most dense connective tissue, contains many capillaries (Fig. 345, *right*). The presence of such large amounts of connective tissue between muscle fibers is histologic evidence to the effect that the purpose of the muscle fibers is not to contract but to conduct. Peripheral ganglia of the parasympathetic division of the autonomic system (of the vagus nerve) are present in close association with the node (Fig. 345, *left*), and, as has

ordinary cardiac
muscle fibers

the paler finer
fibers of the
A-V bundle

FIG. 347. Two high-power photomicrographs of the same magnification of adjacent areas in a section of the uppermost part of the interventricular septum of the heart of a human adult (Hollande's chlorcarmine stain). (*Left*) The muscle fibers are those of ordinary cardiac muscle. (*Right*) The muscle fibers of the A-V bundle; they may be seen to be both narrower and paler than those of ordinary cardiac muscle. The striations which they clearly exhibit in many instances cannot be seen in this illustration. (Preparation by J. W. A. Duckworth)

been noted already, the node is abundantly supplied with fibers from both divisions of the system. Parasympathetic stimulation slows the rate of the heart, while sympathetic stimulation increases it.

No pathways of special fibers have as yet been satisfactorily demonstrated in the walls of the atria; hence, it is assumed that the impulses that arise in the S-A node sweep through the ordinary muscle fibers of the atria to reach the next part of the impulse-conducting system which is the atrioventricular node. This will now be described.

The Atrioventricular (A-V) Node. This was discovered in 1906 by Tawara, and it consists of a little mass of specialized tissue that is disposed in the lower part of the interatrial septum immediately above the attachment of the septal cusp of the tricuspid valve; anteriorly, it is continuous with the A-V bundle (Fig. 344). Duckworth has shown that the

cells that give rise to the node in fetal life have, at first, very little cytoplasm as compared with those that are giving rise to ordinary cardiac muscle fibers; hence, areas of them are heavily nucleated and so appear to be dark staining. However, during the latter half of fetal life, the amount of cytoplasm in these cells gradually increases, but they never, even in adult life, come to contain such a dense concentration of myofibrils as that of ordinary cardiac muscle fibers.

In the node the muscle cells form curious branching networks (Fig. 346). The relatively scanty myofibrils of the cells appear to be separated more widely than in ordinary cardiac muscle fibers; hence, they are seen more often as distinct entities. The cells branch so extensively and in so many directions that the myofibrils of one cell are commonly seen to cross those of underlying or overlying cells at right angles (Fig. 346).

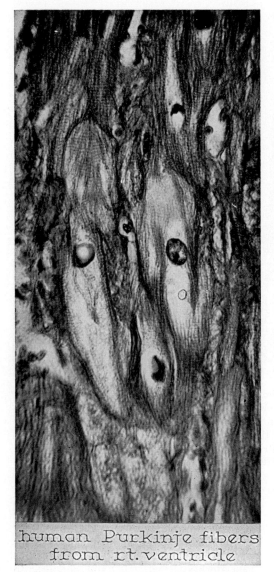

human Purkinje fibers
from rt. ventricle

Fig. 348. High-power longitudinal section of human Purkinje fibers from the right ventricle. Note their large size and that the myofibrils occupy the periphery of the cell. (Preparation by J. W. A. Duckworth)

The A-V Bundle. Duckworth finds that the fibers of the bundle, which are similar at birth to those in the A-V node, alter during the first year of life and become fine in caliber and fusiform in shape (Fig. 347). They become arranged parallel with one another with little connective tissue but with many capillaries between them. Many of the fibers are no wider than the capillaries. However, like the fibers of the S-A node, they anastomose freely.

In the human heart the two branches of the A-V bundle run about halfway down the two sides of the interventricular septum before their fibers enlarge to become continuous with what are called Purkinje fibers. These were first seen by Purkinje in 1845 in the subendocardial region in the ventricles of the ungulate heart. They resemble ordinary cardiac muscle fibers in that they have centrally disposed nuclei, cross striations and intercalated disks. However, they differ from ordinary cardiac muscle fibers in that they are generally wider, and also because the myofibrils in each fiber tend to be disposed around its periphery; this leaves the central core of each fiber relatively empty of myofibrils, and their place is taken by considerable amounts of glycogen. In H and E sections the glycogen is not seen as such; hence, the central part of each Purkinje fiber appears to be empty except where nuclei are present (Fig. 348).

The Purkinje fibers, which arise from the branches of the bundle, spread from the interventricular septum direct to the papillary muscles (Fig. 344), before passing on to the lateral walls of the ventricles, up which they spread as a subendocardial network. These fibers, which conduct the impulse for contraction much more rapidly than the ordinary heart muscle, thus ensure that the papillary muscles will take up the strain on the leaflets of the mitral and the tricuspid valves before the full force of the ventricular contraction is thrown against them.

Duckworth emphasizes that these various areas of specialized muscle that constitute the impulse-conducting system can be seen early in embryonic life to follow a different pattern of development from that of ordinary cardiac muscle, and that they do not become finally differentiated until after birth. Thereafter their fibers have different characteristics according to whether they are in the S-A node, the A-V node, the A-V bundle or the Purkinje network. The size, the rate of conduction and the glycogen content of the fibers of these different regions vary considerably. Therefore, it is wrong to refer to the specialized muscle of the heart as the Purkinje system when only a part of that system is made up of true Purkinje fibers.

Electrocardiograms. The passage of a wave

of excitation over either special or ordinary cardiac muscle fibers is associated with a changing electrical potential along the fiber. Essentially, the particular site over which the wave is passing at any given time is always negatively charged in relation to the parts of the fiber over which it has passed or which it has not yet reached. Hence, if a series of electrodes could be placed along the different parts of the conducting system and connected to different galvanometers, the passage of the impulse for contraction over the system could be followed by watching the galvanometers. Similarly, if electrodes are taken from the intact heart and connected to galvanometers, the passage of the impulse for contraction, plus the changing potentials due to waves of contraction occurring successively in different parts of the heart muscle on their reception of the impulse, could be followed by watching the galvanometers. Indeed, to obtain a great deal of information about the passage of the impulse for contraction over the heart and the successive activation of the muscle of different parts of it, it is not even necessary to connect electrodes to the heart. Since the body tissues that surround the heart contain electrolytes, they act as conductors; hence, if leads are taken off different parts of the body that are projections, as it were, of 3 widely separated points on the heart, they give somewhat similar information to leads taken directly from these 3 parts of the heart themselves. Commonly, 3 standard leads are taken. The first is from the left and the right hands; the second, from the right hand and the left foot; and the third, from the left hand and the left foot. Each lead is connected to a galvanometer that is so arranged as to permit the changes in the electrical potential occurring in the 3 leads, as the impulse for contraction passes over the heart and successively activates different parts of it, to be recorded on a photographic film in relation to the passage of time. Such a record is called an *electrocardiogram*, and the various waves present in a normal one are a record of the passage of the impulse over, and the activation of the muscle of, different parts of the heart. If any disease condition exists which interferes with the proper conduction of the impulse for contraction over the heart or the proper activation of its different parts, a deviation from the nor-

mal pattern of waves is apparent in the electrocardiogram. Hence, electrocardiography is of great importance in helping to diagnose certain types of cardiac disease.

THE LYMPHATIC DIVISION OF THE CIRCULATORY SYSTEM

Lymphatic Vessels. Lymphatic capillaries, from blind endings (Fig. 92), join together to form networks. The capillaries of these are generally at a greater diameter than blood capillaries, and the diameter of any given one varies more along its course than that of a blood capillary. Networks of lymphatic capillaries drain into somewhat larger lymphatic vessels. Both these and the larger lymphatic vessels into which they in turn drain are generally called *lymphatics*. The walls of the smallest of these—the kind into which the lymphatic capillaries empty—consist of a thin layer of connective tissue and an endothelial lining. When lymphatics become somewhere between one fifth and one half a millimeter in diameter, their walls show indications of being composed of 3 layers: an *intima,* a *media* and an *adventitia*. The 3 layers are not well defined in the walls of the smaller lymphatics (Fig. 349, *left*); however, they may be distinguished fairly clearly in the larger ones. The intima commonly contains elastic fibers. The media of the larger vessels consists chiefly of circularly and obliquely disposed smooth muscle fibers. The muscle fibers are supported by some connective tissue which contains elastic fibers. The adventitia is relatively well developed, particularly in the smaller vessels, and it contains smooth muscle fibers; these run both longitudinally and obliquely. Small blood vessels are present in the outer coats of lymphatics of a medium and a large size.

The lymphatics, which collect the lymph from the lymphatic capillaries and carry it to the larger lymphatic vessels that finally deliver it into the blood circulatory system, commonly pass through the tissue along with a vein and its companion artery. However, the lymphatic vessels do not show as much tendency to unite with one another to form a single large vessels as do small veins; hence, several lymphatics may be associated with a vein and its companion artery. The lymphatics, as they pass through the tissues, may unite with one

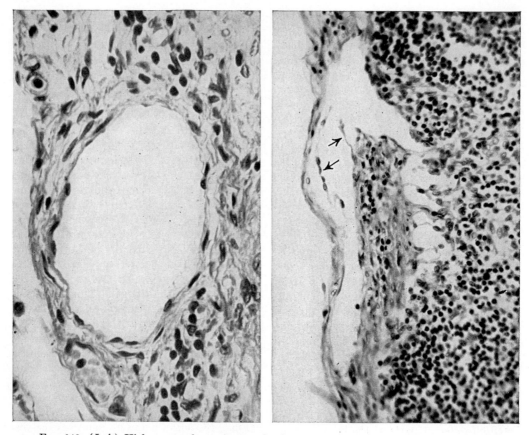

FIG. 349. (*Left*) High-power photomicrograph of a cross section of a small lymphatic vessel. The nuclei of a few smooth muscle fibers may be seen in its wall, but the layers of the wall are not clearly defined. (*Right*) High-power photomicrograph of an oblique section cut through the capsule of a lymph node and showing an afferent lymphatic vessel emptying into the subcapsular sinus. The 2 thin leaflets of a valve are indicated by arrows.

another but they also branch again and so remain numerous.

The lymphatic vessels that collect the lymph from the lymphatic capillaries, before they drain into the terminal vessels of the system, empty into lymph nodes that are disposed along their course (Fig. 237). This permits the lymph, as it percolates through the reticuloendothelial mesh of the node, to be filtered; also, lymphocytes can be added to it. Lymph that has passed through lymph nodes contains lymphocytes; this fact, together with the absence of erythrocytes in the lumens of lymphatics, may assist the student to distinguish lymphatics from veins in sections. Lymph that is brought to the convex border of a lymph node by a set of *afferent* vessels leaves the

concave border or hilus of the node in another set of efferent vessels (Fig. 237); these are the tributaries of the terminal vessels.

Lymphatic vessels, except the smallest ones, commonly, but not always, possess valves. These are more numerous and hence closer together than the valves of veins. Indeed, the valves of lymphatics may be so close together that a distended lymphatic appears to be beaded, because dilated sections between the numerous valves are so close together. The valves commonly have 2 leaflets; these consist of folds of intima, so they have delicate connective tissue plates in their middles and endothelial coverings (Fig. 349, *right*). The endothelial cells are said, like those of the valves of veins, to be orientated differently on the 2 surfaces of a leaflet, their long diameters being parallel with the stream on the side of the leaflet that faces the stream and at right angles to the stream on its sheltered side.

It is easy to understand how each segment of a lymphatic that is situated between 2 valves could act as a pump if (1) the wall of the lymphatic in that segment contracted or (2) that segment were squeezed because of compression developing outside the lymphatic. In frogs there are lymph hearts to propel lymph. It seems doubtful if lymph is propelled along the lymphatics of mammals by contractions of the smooth muscle in their walls. The compression of lymphatics occasioned by pulsating blood vessels in their vicinity, or by active or passive movements of the parts in which they are contained, may make lymphatic vessels serve as pumps to some extent and so aid in propelling lymph along them. This explains why massage may be employed to improve the lymphatic drainage of a part. It seems doubtful if there is very much lymph flow from normal tissues that are at rest. As we shall see when the intestine is studied, the lymphatics which drain it participate in the absorption of fat. After a fatty meal the lymph from the intestine is milky in color and is termed *chyle*.

The lymph that is collected in the body is finally returned to the blood stream by means of 2 main terminal vessels; the *thoracic duct* and the *right lymphatic duct* (the latter may be represented by several vessels). At its beginning in the abdomen, the thoracic duct is somewhat dilated to form what is termed the *cisterna chyli*, and from here it extends for about 18 inches before it opens into the left innominate vein in the angle of its junction with the internal jugular and left subclavian veins. Sometimes it is represented by several smaller vessels which open separately into the great veins. The right lymphatic duct or, more commonly, several representatives of the right lymphatic duct, enter the great veins on the right side at sites comparable with those at which the thoracic duct enters the great vessels on the left side. The tributaries that flow into the thoracic duct and the right lymphatic duct (or their representatives), respectively, are described in textbooks of gross anatomy; here it is enough to point out that the thoracic

duct receives all the lymph that forms in the abdomen; hence, it is much the larger vessel of the two.

REFERENCES

REFERENCES ON ARTERIES AND VEINS

Altschul, R.: Endothelium, Toronto, Macmillan, 1955.

Buck, R. C.: The fine structure of endothelium of large arteries, J. Biophys. & Biochem. Cytol. 4:187, 1958.

Clark, E. R., Clark, E. L., and Williams, R. G.: Microscopic observations in the living rabbit of the new growth of nerves and the establishment of nerve controlled contractions of newly formed arterioles, Am. J. Anat. 55:47, 1934.

Cowdry, E. V.: Structure and physiology of blood vessels *in* Arteriosclerosis, ed. by E. V. Cowdry, p. 53, New York, Macmillan, 1933.

Franklin, K. J.: A Monograph on Veins, Springfield, Ill., Thomas, 1937.

Kampmeier, O. F., and Birch, C. L. F.: The origin and development of venous valves, Am. J. Anat. 38:451, 1927.

Kernohan, J. W., Anderson, E. W., and Keith, N. M.: Arterioles in cases of hypertension, Arch. Int. Med. 44:395, 1929.

Reich, N. F.: Diseases of the Aorta, New York, Macmillan, 1949.

REFERENCES ON ARTERIOVENOUS ANASTOMOSES

Clark, E. R.: Arterio-venous anastomoses, Physiol. Rev. 18:229, 1938.

Clark, E. R., and Clark, E. L.: The new formation of arterio-venous anastomoses in the rabbit's ear, Am. J. Anat. 55:407, 1934.

————: Observations on living arterio-venous anastomoses as seen in transparent chambers introduced into the rabbit's ear, Am. J. Anat. 54:229, 1934.

Daniel, P. M., and Prichard, M. M. L.: Arterio-venous anastomoses in the external ear, Quart. J. Exper. Physiol. 41:107, 1956.

Grant, R. T.: Observations on direct communications between arteries and veins in the rabbit's ear, Heart 15:281, 1929-31.

Grant, R. T., and Bland, E. F.: Observations on the arterio-venous anastomoses in the human skin and in the bird's foot with special reference to the reaction to cold, Heart 15:385, 1929-31.

Prichard, M. M. L., and Daniel, P. M.: Arterio-venous anastomoses in the human external ear, J. Anat. 90:309, 1956.

————: Arterio-venous anastomoses in the tongue of the dog, J. Anat. 87:66, 1953.

————: Arterio-venous anastomoses in the tongue of the sheep and the goat, Am. J. Anat. *95*:203, 1954.

REFERENCES ON THE NERVOUS CONTROL OF ARTERIES AND VEINS INCLUDING BAROCEPTOR AREAS

Boss, J., and Green, J. H.: The histology of the common carotid baroceptor areas of the cat, Circulation Res. *4*:12, 1956.

Boyd, J. D.: Observations on the human carotid sinus and the nerve supply, Anat. Anz. *84*:386, 1937.

Burn, J. H.: Sympathetic vasodilator fibres Physiol. Rev. *18*:137, 1938.

Clark, W. E. LeGros: The innervation of blood vessels *in* Tissues of the Body, ed. 2, p. 200, Oxford, Clarendon, 1945.

De Castro, F.: Sur la structure et l'innervation du sinus carotidien, Trav. du Lab-de Recherch. biol. Madrid *25*:331, 1928.

Nonidez, J. F.: Identification of the receptor areas in the venae cavae and pulmonary veins which initiate cardiac acceleration (Bainbridge's reflex), Am. J. Anat. *61*:203, 1937.

Woollard, H. H.: The innervation of blood vessels, Heart *13*:319, 1926.

Woollard, H. H., and Phillips, R.: The distribution of sympathetic fibres in the extremities, J. Anat. *67*:18, 1932.

Woollard, H. H., and Weddell, G.: The composition and distribution of vascular nerves in the extremities, J. Anat. *69*:165, 1935.

REFERENCES ON CAPILLARIES AND THEIR CONTROL

Bensley, R. R., and Vimtrup, B.: On the nature of Rouget cells of capillaries, Anat. Rec. *39*:37, 1928.

Clark, E. R., and Clark, E. L.: Caliber changes in minute blood vessels observed in the living mammal, Am. J. Anat. *73*:215, 1943.

————: Microscopic observations on the extra endothelial cells of the living mammalian blood vessels, Am. J. Anat. *66*:1, 1940.

————: The relation of Rouget cells to capillary contraction, Am. J. Anat. *35*:265, 1925.

Florey, H. W., and Carleton, H. M.: Rouget cells and their function, Proc. Roy. Soc., London, s. B. *100*:23, 1926.

Krogh, A., and Vimtrup, B.: The capillaries *in* Cowdry's Special Cytology, ed. 2, p. 475, New York, Hoeber, 1932.

Nelemans, F. A.: Innervation of the smallest blood vessels, Am. J. Anat. *83*:43, 1948.

Sanders, A. G., Ebert, R. H., and Florey, H. W.: The mechanism of capillary contraction, Quart. J. Exper. Physiol. *30*:281, 1940.

Zweifach, B. W.: Character and distribution of blood capillaries, Anat. Rec. *73*:475, 1939.

————: The structure and reactions of the small blood vessels in amphibia, Am. J. Anat. *60*:473, 1937.

REFERENCES ON THE FINE STRUCTURE OF CAPILLARIES AND ON PINOCYTOSIS

Bennett, H. S.: The concepts of membrane flow and membrane vesiculation as mechanism for active transport and ion pumping, J. Biophys. & Biochem. Cytol. *2*:99, Supp. 1956.

Hibbs, R. G., Burch, G. E., and Phillips, J. H.: The fine structure of the small blood vessels of normal human dermis and subcutis, Am. Heart J. *56*:662, 1958.

Moore, D. H., and Ruska, H.: The fine structure of capillaries and small arteries, J. Biophys. & Biochem. Cytol. *3*:457, 1957.

Palade, G. E.: Fine structure of blood capillaries, J. Appl. Physics *24*:1424, 1953.

REFERENCES ON THE HEART AND ITS CONDUCTING SYSTEM

Bast, T. H., and Gardner, Weston D.: Wilhelm His, Jr., and the bundles of His, J. Hist. Med. & Allied Sc. *4*:170, 1949.

Blair, D. M., and Davies, F.: Observations on the conducting systems of the heart, J. Anat. *69*:303, 1935.

Davies, F., and Francis, E. T. B.: The conducting system of the vertebrate heart, Biol. Rev. *20-21*:173, 1946.

Duckworth, J. W. A.: The development of the sinu-atrial and atrio-ventricular nodes of the human heart, M.D. thesis, University of Edinburgh, 1952.

Gregg, O. E.: The coronary circulation, Physiol. Rev. *26*:28, 1946.

His, W., Jr.: Die Thätikeit des embryonalen Herzens, Arb. Med. Klin., Leipzig, 1893. Cited by Mall, F. P.: Am. J. Anat. *13*:278, 1912.

Kaylor, C. T., and Robb, J. S.: Observations on the differentiation and connexions of the specialised conducting tissue in the human heart, Anat. Rec. *97*:31, 1947.

Keith, A., and Flack, M.: The auriculoventricular bundle of the human heart, Lancet *2*:359, 1906.

Kent, S.: Researches on the structure of function of the mammalian heart, J. Physiol. *14*:233, 1893.

Kistin, A. D.: Observations on the anatomy of the atrio-ventricular bundle (bundle of His), and the question of other atrio-ventricular connexions in normal human hearts, Am. Heart J. *37*:848, 1949.

Lewis, T., Oppenheimer, B. S., and Oppenheimer,

A.: The site of origin of the mammalian heart beat; the pacemaker of the heart, Heart 2:147, 1910.

Mahaim, I.: Les maladies organiques du faisseau de His-Tawara, Paris, Masson, 1931.

Mall, F. P.: On the development of the human heart, Am. J. Anat. 13:249, 1912.

Purkinje, J. E.: Mikroskopisch-neurologische Beobachtungen, Arch. Anat. Physiol. 22:281, 1845.

Robb, J. S., Kaylor, C. T., and Turman, W. G.: A study of specialised heart tissue at various stages of development of the human heart, Am. J. Med. 5:324, 1948.

Sanabria, T.: Recherches sur la différenciation du tissue nodal et connecteur du coeur des mammifères, Arch. Biol. 47:1, 1936.

Shaner, R. F.: The development of the atrio-ventricular node, bundle of His and sino-atrial node in the calf, with a description of a third embryonic node-like structure, Anat. Rec. 44:85, 1929.

————: On the development of the nerves to the mammalian heart, Anat. Rec. 46:23, 1930.

————: On the muscular architecture of the vertebrate ventricle, J. Anat. 58:59, 1923.

Stotler, W. A., and McMahon, R. A.: The innervation and structure of the conductive system of the human heart, J. Comp. Neurol. 87:57, 1947.

Tawara, S.: Das Reizleitungssystem des Saugetierherzens, Jena, Fischer, 1906.

Walls, E. W.: The development of the specialized conducting system in the human heart, J. Anat. 81:93, 1947.

————: Dissection of the atrio-ventricular node and bundle in the human heart, J. Anat. 79:45, 1945.

Walmsley, T.: The heart, Quain's Elements of Anatomy, IV, 111:78, 1929.

Woollard, H. H.: The innervation of the heart, J. Anat. 60:345, 1926.

(For Fine Structure of Cardiac Muscle see references for Chap. 19)

Chapter 22

The Integumentary System

(The Skin and Its Appendages)

INTRODUCTION

The skin is a membrane with many protective functions. It presents a barrier to disease organisms. The skin is nearly waterproof; this enables a relatively fluid body to exist in dry air. It likewise permits a body to be immersed in fresh water without becoming swollen and in salt water without becoming shrunken. The skin, particularly when it becomes pigmented, protects the body from the harmful effects of too much light. However, it is not impervious to all substances, for certain chemicals can be absorbed through it into the blood stream. This may constitute an industrial hazard in certain trades (for example, in making certain kinds of explosives). But use may be made of this quality, for in treating certain diseases, some drugs may be administered by rubbing them on the skin, knowing that they will be absorbed.

The skin has other functions in addition to protective ones. It is important in regulating the temperature of the body. On hot days it facilitates heat loss and on cold days it acts as insulation. By sweating, the skin functions as an excretory organ. Vitamin D, the antirachitic vitamin, is made in skin exposed to ultraviolet light. Without vitamin D from other sources, children kept out of the sun develop rickets (p. 323). The skin contains nerve endings responsible for picking up stimuli that evoke many different types of sensation in consciousness (touch, pressure, heat, cold and pain). Hence, the skin is of the greatest importance in permitting man to adjust to his environment.

The peculiar importance of the skin in a physical examination should be realized by the student. No exploratory operations are necessary to see it; of all the important structures of the body, it alone is exposed so that it may be examined with the naked eye. Yet its appearance may reflect, just as truly as the appearance of deeply seated organs, the existence of a general disease. Its appearance often gives the doctor a more accurate estimate of a female patient's age than her own statement. The way hair is distributed helps in estimating inherent degrees of masculine and feminine personality components. The color of the skin may indicate a variety of conditions. Thus, it becomes yellow in jaundice, bronzed in certain glandular deficiencies, dry and hard in others and warm and moist in still others. Poisoning with silver may be revealed by the color of the skin. Cyanosis, already described, may give the skin a blue-gray appearance and so reflect impaired circulatory or respiratory functions. In vitamin A deficiencies, the skin of extensor surfaces may lose its hair and become rough, like sandpaper. In certain other vitamin deficiencies, the skin around the corners of the mouth may become cracked and scaly. Many infectious diseases that affect the whole body produce identifying rashes on the skin (for example, scarlet fever, measles, chickenpox, syphilis and others). The skin very commonly is affected when individuals are allergic (hypersensitive) to certain proteins and other substances, for example, some women develop rashes from certain kinds of face powder.

In addition to the involvement of the skin in conditions and diseases of a fairly general character, there are a whole host of skin diseases proper. The particular branch of medicine that deals with these and their treatment is called "dermatology."

Since the skin is the most exposed part of the body, it is peculiarly susceptible to various kinds of injuries. The treatment of cuts, abrasions, burns and frostbites are part of almost every doctor's life. So much skin is destroyed by accidents it is indeed fortunate that it can be grafted readily from one part of the body to another.

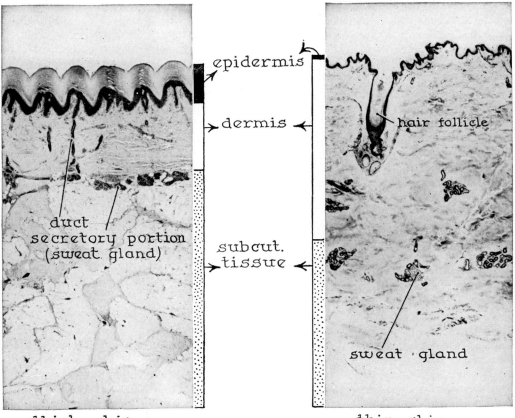

FIG. 350. Low-power photomicrographs, taken at the same magnification, of sections of thick and thin skin. The skin at the left was taken from the sole of the foot, and that on the right from the abdomen. Note that thick skin has a relatively thick epidermis that consists chiefly of keratin and that thin skin has a thin epidermis and a thick dermis.

GENERAL MICROSCOPIC STRUCTURE

The most important thing for the student to remember about skin is that it is a membrane consisting of *two* layers that are completely different in character and are derived from different germ layers. The outermost and thinner of these two layers, the *epidermis* (Fig. 350), is epithelial tissue and is derived from ectoderm. The innermost and thicker of the two layers, the *dermis* (Fig. 350), consists of dense connective tissue and is derived from mesoderm. These two layers are firmly cemented together to form a cohesive membrane —the skin—which varies in thickness from less than 0.5 mm. to 3 or even 4 mm. or more in different parts of the body. The skin rests on subcutaneous tissue which varies from areolar to adipose in character. This is the superficial fascia of gross anatomy. It is sometimes called the *hypodermis,* but it is not, like the epidermis, considered as part of the skin. Irregularly spaced bundles of collagenic fibers extend from the dermis into the subcutaneous tissue to provide anchorage for the skin (Fig. 350, *left*). The subcutaneous tissue permits the skin over most parts of the body a considerable latitude of movement.

That the skin consists of an outer, epithelial and an inner, connective-tissue layer has certain implications. For example, very thin shavings may be cut from the surface of the skin without causing bleeding. The reason for this is that the very thin shavings consist entirely of epidermis, and epithelial membranes, it will be recalled, contain no blood vessels. Bleeding does not occur until shavings are taken deeply enough to cut into the dermis, where capillaries are situated. Hence, the cells of the epidermis live in tissue fluid derived from the capillaries of the connective-tissue dermis (refer to Figs. 91 and 92).

It will be recalled that glands generally develop as a result of the epithelial cells of a covering or lining membrane invading the supporting connective tissue of the region (review Fig. 134). During embryonic development, cells of the developing epidermis invade the developing dermis to form simple coiled tubular *sweat* glands (Figs. 350, *left,* 352 and 354). Other cells from the developing epidermis also grow into the dermis, or even somewhat deeper, to form "glands" that will in a sense "secrete" hairs, the *hair follicles* (Fig. 356). Epithelial cells from the sides of developing hair follicles grow out into the adjacent dermis to form *sebaceous glands* (Fig. 356). Similarly, near the tips of the fingers and the toes, epidermal cells invade the dermis to form grooves that will produce nails (Fig. 369). Sweat glands, hair follicles, sebaceous glands and nails constitute what are termed the *appendages of the skin,* and all develop, more or less like glands, by the invasion of the covering epidermis into the dermis.

Skin is commonly classified as *thick* and *thin.* Thick skin is found on the palms of the hands and the soles of the feet; thin skin covers the remainder of the body. However, these terms tend to give false impressions, for they refer to the thickness of the epidermis rather than to the thickness of the skin as a whole (compare the left and the right sides of Fig. 350). The skin of the palms of the hands and the soles of the feet has a thick epidermis with a particularly thick layer of keratin on its outer surface (Fig. 350, *left*). The skin covering the remainder of the body, although it has a thick dermis in some sites, as on the back, has a relatively thin epidermis, and the outer keratinized layer of this is relatively thin (Fig. 350, *right*). The particular structure of thick and thin skin will now be described.

MICROSCOPIC STRUCTURE OF THICK SKIN

Surface Ridges and Grooves. In 1880, Henry Faulds, a Scottish medical missionary in Japan, published a note in *Nature* entitled "On the Skin Furrows of the Hand." He de-

scribed these as "forever-unchangeable" and pointed out that "finger marks" might be used for the scientific detection of criminals. Indeed, he reported some experience in this matter and described how some greasy finger marks had led to the identification of the individual who had been drinking their rectified spirits. This is the first reported instance of the use of fingerprints to detect a thief. From this beginning, fingerprinting has developed into a most useful tool in crime detection. More recently the dermal configurations have become a new area for medical research. For example, it has been shown that disturbances of fetal growth during the third and the fourth months of development may be permanently recorded in their patterns. Their study has also been proved useful with regard to deciding whether babies born at multiple births (twins, triplets, etc.) have their origin from the same or different ova.

Significance and Development of Surface Ridges and Grooves. If the palms of the hands (including the fingers) and the soles of the feet (including the toes) are examined with the naked eye or, better, with a magnifying glass, they are seen to be covered with ridges and grooves in a fashion reminiscent of a field plowed by the contour method. On the hands and the feet of the dark-skinned races the ridged area is clearly marked off by its lighter color.

Work by Cummins and others has shown that the ridges and the furrows develop during the third and the fourth fetal months. The pattern that then forms never changes afterward except to enlarge. The patterns are determined chiefly by hereditary factors, as is shown by the close similarity of those of one-egg twins and by the resemblances between those of the members of a family group. Racial differences are reflected in the patterns.

The patterns can be greatly modified by growth disturbances in the fetus during the third and/or the fourth months. This is strikingly shown in children that are born *mongoloid imbeciles* (this term originated because such children tend to have obliquely set eyes and certain other features that superficially resemble those of the Mongol race). Some 70 per cent of such children show combinations of patterns not seen in normal babies; hence, an analysis of the skin patterns

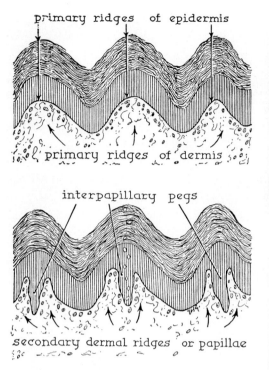

primary ridges of epidermis

primary ridges of dermis

interpapillary pegs

secondary dermal ridges or papillae

FIG. 351. Diagrams to show the relation between epidermal and dermal ridges. (*Top*) This diagram is not factual but is used to give the concept of a primary dermal ridge below each epidermal ridge. (*Bottom*) Actually, each primary dermal ridge is split into two secondary ridges as a result of the growth of the epidermis down into the primary ridge along its crest.

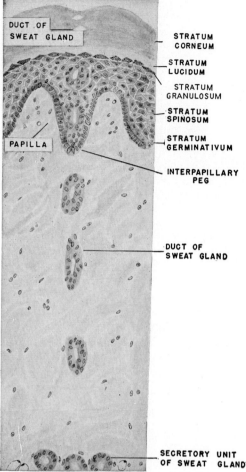

DUCT OF SWEAT GLAND

PAPILLA

STRATUM CORNEUM

STRATUM LUCIDUM

STRATUM GRANULOSUM

STRATUM SPINOSUM

STRATUM GERMINATIVUM

INTERPAPILLARY PEG

DUCT OF SWEAT GLAND

SECRETORY UNIT OF SWEAT GLAND

FIG. 352. Drawing of a section of thick skin (high-power) to illustrate the different layers of the epidermis, the way in which the duct of a sweat gland enters an interpapillary peg and how the wall of the duct thereafter is constituted by the cells of the different layers of the epidermis through which it passes. The thickness of the dermis is not in proportion; this was done to permit the secretory portion of the sweat gland to be shown.

of a newborn baby may give very important information as to whether or not it has been born an idiot, just as will the determination of the number of chromosomes in its somatic cells.

The epidermal ridges are due to the epidermis following the contours of underlying dermal ridges. These may be studied in sections of skin cut at right angles to them. Sections of skin, so cut, would be easier to interpret if they appeared as is illustrated in the upper drawing in Figure 351, which shows clear-cut *primary dermal ridges* underlying the epidermal ridges. However, actual sections of skin do not appear this way but as is shown in the lower picture in Figure 351. This latter and real appearance is due to the fact that ridges of epidermis grow down into the peak of each primary dermal ridge so that the pri-

mary dermal ridges are each split into two ridges. The latter, from the appearance they presented in single sections, were termed *papillae*, and, as a consequence, the epidermal downgrowth that lies between each pair is termed an *interpapillary peg*. (The structures termed papillae and interpapillary pegs are actually not cone-shaped papillae or pegs because they appear consistently in sections

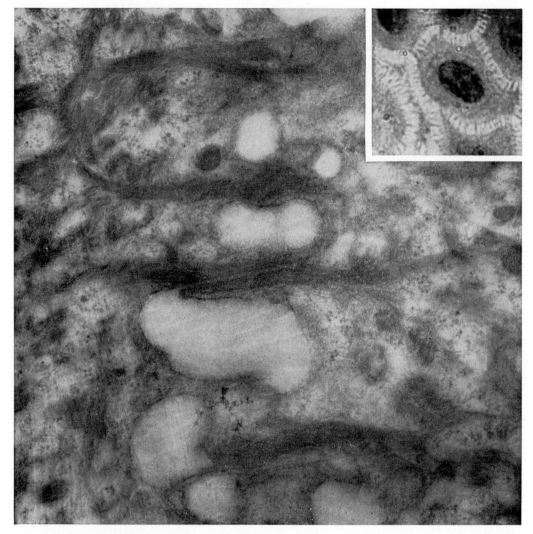

Fig. 353. Electron micrograph (× approximately 30,000 as reproduced here) of section of human epidermis showing 4 so-called intercellular bridges. The one nearest the center shows it to consist of 2 arms, one extending from one cell and the other from the other. The point of contact between the 2 attachment plaques appears as a narrow line of lighter density. Note how microfibrils pass from the base of each arm into the adjacent cytoplasm of the cells. (*Inset*) Oil-immersion photomicrograph of a section of thick epidermis showing the so-called intercellular bridges which give a prickly outline to the cells of the stratum spinosum.

(Fig. 350, *left*). If they were true papillae and pegs they would be seen only on those occasions when the plane of the section happened to pass through one. That they appear consistently proves that they are actually ridges; however, they are deficient occasionally along their courses.) As we shall see, the sweat glands of the skin open into the bottoms of the interpapillary pegs.

Epidermis. Since keratin is nonliving it cannot replace itself, and since it is continuously worn away or shed from the surface it must be continuously added to by means of the living cells beneath it turning into keratin. This requires that the living cells of the epidermis continuously proliferate to maintain their numbers. Storey and Leblond, by using colchicine and counting the mitotic figures in the epidermis, have shown that the living cells of plantar epidermis of rat are completely renewed every 19 days.

Many processes, then, are in more or less continual operation in the epidermis: (1) cell division in the deeper layers, (2) cells being pushed toward the surface as a result, (3) cells farthest from the dermis being transformed into keratin and (4) keratin desquamating from the surface. If these 4 processes are not synchronized properly—and in many skin diseases they are not—the character of the epidermis changes greatly.

Epidermis commonly is described as consisting of 5 layers or strata. The deepest of these abuts on the dermis. It consists of a layer of more or less columnar epithelial cells (Fig. 352). The borders of these are not distinct in the usual section, and the student must avoid thinking that their nuclei, which are distinct, are the cells themselves. This layer is called the *stratum germinativum* because it germinates new cells, which are pushed up into the next layer to be described.

The *stratum spinosum* or *prickle cell layer* is several cells thick (Fig. 352). The cells of this layer are of an irregular polyhedral shape. From appearances seen with the light microscope, such as the one illustrated in the inset at the upper right of Figure 353, inset, it was believed that tiny intracellular fibrils, called *tonofibrils,* passed from one cell to another, to hold the cells of this layer together. Between tonofibrils the cells were slightly separated from one another; this gave these cells a prickly outline (Fig. 353, *inset*). This fact was responsible for these cells being called prickle cells, and the layer in which they are present, the stratum spinosum. With the E/M, each of the so-called prickles or intercellular bridges is seen to consist of two arms that extend, one from the cell on one side, and one from the cell on the other, which hold tightly to each other (Fig. 353). The arms of cytoplasm that extend from the cell on each side to more or less grasp each other are covered with cell membrane and filled with a relatively dense material, and from this microfibrils extend off from the base of each arm into the adjacent cytoplasm (Fig. 353). The arms are called *attachment plaques,* and the surface of each that comes into contact with the surface of the other is probably ovoid in shape; but

each one generally appears more like an arm than a plaque because they are generally sectioned in a plane that crosses, rather than parallels, their greatest diameters. At the site where the plaque from one side is in contact with the plaque from the other, there is a light band along the length of the attachment, and it seems to be established that no tonofibrils extend across this from one cell into the other. The fine structure of these so-called intercellular bridges has been studied in detail by Odland, whose report should be consulted for details.

The *stratum granulosum* is from 2 to 4 cells thick and lies just outside the stratum spinosum (Fig. 352). Its cells are roughly diamond-shaped, and they are fitted together with the long axis of each paralleling the contour of the overlying ridge or groove. The deepest cells of this layer resemble the cells of the stratum spinosum except for their cytoplasm which contains granules that stain deeply with hematoxylin (Fig. 352). These are called *keratohyalin* granules. However, the more superficial cells of this layer are considerably modified. Their nuclei are either broken-up or dissolved, and the number of cytoplasmic granules is greatly increased. It is in the stratum granulosum that the cells of the epidermis die. The nature of the keratohyalin granules that form in them is not thoroughly understood, but they are concerned in some phase of the process by which soft keratin is formed. The student should not make the mistake of thinking of these granules as a pigment, or of the stratum granulosum as a pigmented layer. True pigments possess color in their natural state; keratohyalin granules become colored only when stained.

The next layer is not always seen to advantage. When visible it is thin and appears as a clear, bright, homogeneous line. For this reason it is called the *stratum lucidum* (Fig. 352). It is said to consist of eleidin, which is presumed to be a transformation product of the keratohyalin observed in the stratum granulosum.

The fifth and outermost layer of the epidermis is termed the *stratum corneum (corneus = horny)* (Figs. 350 and 352). Here the eleidin of the stratum lucidum has become transformed into keratin, and what were once living epithelial cells have become horny scales that adhere to one another tightly, except at the surface where they desquamate.

It is of interest to inquire briefly into the cause of the differentiation or, as some prefer to think of it, the degradation of living epidermal cells into horny scales of keratin. Dehydration is probably not an all-important factor, because the cells of malignant tumors that arise from the epidermis and invade deeply the underlying connective tissue still continue to form keratin in sites far removed from the air. Likewise, epidermis transplanted into the subcutaneous tissue continues to form keratin. Probably the reduction of the food and oxygen supply and the accumulation of waste products, occasioned by the distance keratinizing cells are from capillaries, play some part in determining the process, but there would seem to be a good measure of self-differentiation involved. In this connection it is of interest that certain other types of specialized epithelium in the body, ordinarily not keratinizing, become so under conditions of prolonged vitamin A deficiency. As we shall see, there are two kinds of keratin; however, we shall not discuss these until hair is considered.

Dermis. This has 2 layers which are not sharply separated from one another. The outer is by far the thinner of the two and is called the *papillary* layer because the papillae are a prominent part of it (Fig. 350). This layer extends only slightly below the bases of the papillae, where it merges more or less insensibly with the thicker *reticular* layer, which comprises the remainder of the dermis and is so-called because the collagenic fibers and bundles of fibers of which it is composed interlace with each other in a netlike manner.

Although both layers of the dermis consist of irregularly arranged fibrous tissue, the collagenic fibers in the papillary layer are not as coarse as those of the reticular layer; hence, the papillary layer has a finer and looser texture. Some elastic fibers are interwoven with the collagenic fibers in both layers.

The cells of the dermis of thick skin are mostly fibroblasts, and these are scattered about sparingly. A few macrophages are also present. Fat cells may be present singly but are more commonly found in groups. The cells associated with the blood vessels, the lymphatics and the nerves of the skin will be described separately.

Sweat Glands. These are simple tubular glands. They are particularly numerous in thick skin; it has been estimated that there are 3,000 per square inch in the palm of the hand. Each one consists of a secretory part and an excretory duct. The secretory part usually is situated immediately below the dermis, in the subcutaneous tissue. The secretory part of the tubule is coiled and twisted on itself; hence, in sections it appears as a little cluster of cross and oblique sections of tubes (Figs. 352 and 354). The secretory cells are cuboidal or columnar in type, and they may exhibit pigment and vacuoles in their cytoplasm. The lumen of the secretory part is wider than its wall is thick. Spindle-shaped cells, resembling smooth muscle cells, are disposed obliquely and longitudinally around the secretory portions of the tubules. These are commonly called *myo-epithelial cells*, and it is thought that their contractions may assist in expelling sweat. Immediately outside these flattened cells, connective tissue is condensed so as to form a sheath around the secretory portions of the glands.

After pursuing a tortuous course in a very limited area, the secretory portion of the gland changes into a duct which passes toward the surface. The epithelial cells lining the duct stain more deeply than those of the secretory cells, and ducts can be distinguished readily in sections (Fig. 354). The lumen of the duct is much smaller than that of the secretory part of the gland; this is unusual, for in most glands the lumens of ducts are much wider than the lumens of secretory units. Duct walls consist of a double layer of thin cuboidal epithelium. The ducts, which follow a somewhat spiral course through the dermis, enter the tips of the interpapillary pegs of epidermis that project down between the double rows of papillae (Fig. 352). The epithelium of the ducts at this site merges into that of the interpapillary pegs, and from this point on, the cells of the epidermis become the cells of the walls of the ducts. Ducts so constituted pursue a spiral course through the epidermis, and when the stratum corneum is reached, the spiral nature of their course becomes accentuated (Fig. 352). The ducts finally open on the

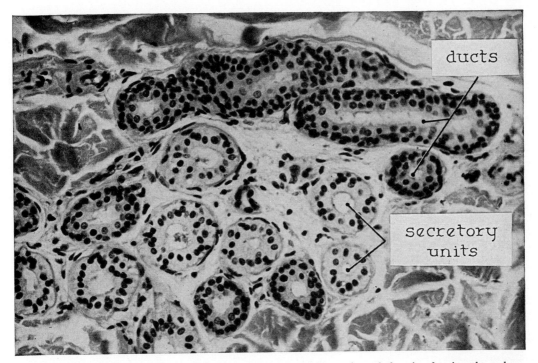

Fig. 354. High-power photomicrograph of an H and E section of dermis, showing the pale secretory units of sweat glands cut in cross section and the darker-staining ducts cut in both cross and oblique sections.

surfaces of the ridges; their openings are obvious in a good fingerprint.

The blood and nerve supply of sweat glands will be considered later.

MICROSCOPIC STRUCTURE OF THIN SKIN

Thin skin covers all of the body except the palms of the hands and the soles of the feet. As noted before, it should be understood that the adjective "thin" applies to the epidermis rather than to the skin as a whole. Actually, thin skin varies greatly in thickness in different parts of the body. These variations are due almost entirely to variations in the thickness of the dermis. The skin covering extensor surfaces is usually thicker than that covering flexor surfaces. The skin covering the eyelid is the thinnest in the body (0.5 mm. or less), and that covering the shoulders and the back is the thickest (up to 5 mm.) of the thin type. Figure 355 illustrates some specimens of thin skin obtained from different parts of the body.

Thin skin contains sweat glands (Fig. 350, *right*) but they are not so numerous as those in thick skin. Thin skin differs from thick in that it contains hair follicles. These are highly developed in the scalp and in certain other regions, but they are present in the thin skin over the whole body, with a few minor exceptions (e.g., glans penis). Moreover, the surface of thin skin is not thrown into ridges and grooves like that of thick skin.

Epidermis. This has fewer layers than that of thick skin. The stratum germinativum is similar to that of thick skin, but the stratum spinosum is thinner. The stratum granulosum does not form a distinct continuous layer, but numerous cells containing cytoplasmic granules are scattered along the line where this layer might be expected. No stratum lucidum is present, and the stratum corneum is relatively thin (Fig. 132).

Dermis. The surface this presents to the epidermis is considerably different from that presented by the dermis of thick skin. Instead of papillae distributed regularly in the form of double parallel rows, the sites of which are indicated by epidermal ridges, the papillae of the dermis of thin skin are distributed more

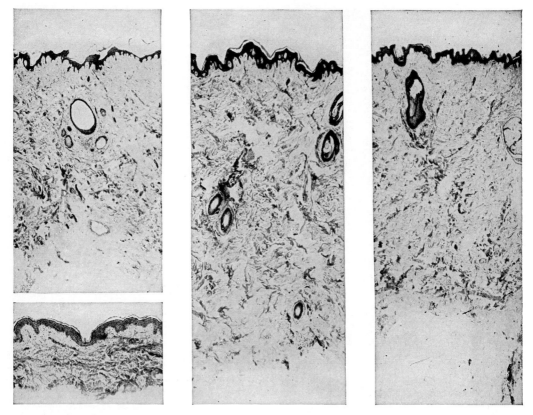

FIG. 355. The 3 large photomicrographs are all taken at the same magnification from sections of thin skin cut from different parts of the body. (*Left*) Skin from the inside of the leg. (*Center*) Skin from the abdomen which has been grafted to the wrist where it has been in position for some time. (*Right*) Skin from the lateral side of the thigh. (*Lower left*) Photomicrograph of a section cut from a split-skin graft that was cut at 18/1,000 of an inch in thickness. Notice that it contains a substantial content of dermis.

or less haphazardly, and their presence is not reflected by any unevenness of the epidermal surface above them. The pattern of the epidermal surface is caused chiefly by lines that tend to connect the slightly depressed openings of the hair follicles.

HAIR FOLLICLES

Development. Early in the third month of fetal life the epidermis begins to send downgrowths into the underlying dermis (Fig. 356, *I* and *II*). These develop first in the region of the eyebrows, the chin and the upper lip, but they are soon followed by others that develop in all parts of the body that later will be covered with thin skin. These epidermal downgrowths become hair follicles and give rise to hairs (Fig. 356, *III* and *IV*). By this means the fetus, at about the fifth or sixth month, has become covered with very delicate hairs. These constitute the *lanugo* (*lana* = wool) of the fetus. This coat of hair is shed before birth except in the region of the eyebrows, the eyelids and the scalp, where the hairs persist and become somewhat stronger. A few months after birth these hairs are shed and replaced by still coarser ones, while over the remainder of the body a new growth of hair occurs, and the body of the infant becomes covered with a downy coat called the *vellus* (fleece). At puberty, coarse hairs develop in the axilla and in the pubic region and, in males, on the face and to a lesser extent on other parts of the body. The coarse hairs of the scalp and the eyebrows and those that develop at puberty are termed *terminal hairs* to distinguish them from those of the lanugo and the vellus.

The human species, of course, is not very hairy. Most of the body is not covered with anything more than downlike vellus. Hair, then, is not a very important factor in keeping the body warm. It is, nevertheless, of the greatest importance that the skin of the human species should contain hair follicles. They, as we shall see, are instrumental in repairing epidermis injured by burns and abrasions, and they make split-skin grafting possible. We shall explain the reason for this presently.

The Two Kinds of Keratin in Hair Follicles and Hairs. From the work of Giroud, Bulliard and Leblond, Leblond, and Giroud and Leblond, it is apparent that there are two kinds of keratin. These, the *soft* and the *hard* types, can be distinguished by histologic means and they have different physical and chemical properties. Since both types are encountered in hair follicles we shall discuss the two types briefly so that their respective distribution in hair follicles can be described properly.

Soft keratin covers the skin as a whole; hard keratin is found only in certain of the skin appendages. The histologic changes that characterize the formation of soft keratin are

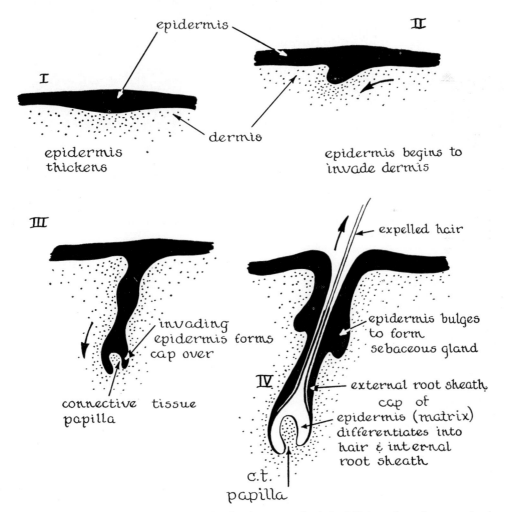

Fig. 356. Four sketches illustrating the development of a hair follicle and a sebaceous gland. (Redrawn and slightly modified from Addison: Piersol's Normal Histology, ed. 15, Philadelphia, Lippincott)

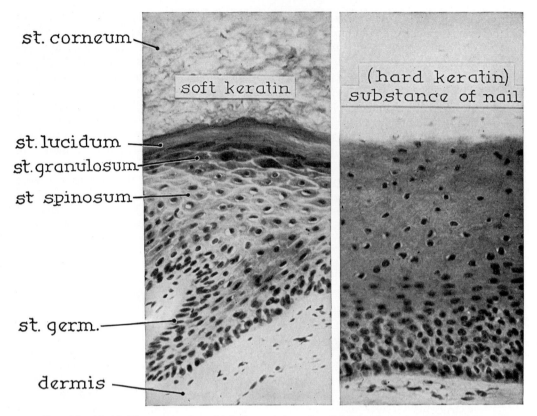

st. corneum

soft keratin

(hard keratin) substance of nail

st. lucidum
st. granulosum
st spinosum

st. germ.

dermis

FIG. 357. (*Left*) The process by which the soft keratin of thick skin is formed. Note keratohyalin granules in the stratum granulosum and that a stratum lucidum is present. (*Right*) The process by which the hard keratin of the nail is formed. Note the gradual transition of cells into nail substances with no stratum granulosum or lucidum and note that the hard keratin is more homogeneous than the soft.

seen most easily in thick skin (Fig. 357, *left*). The formation of soft keratin here, as everywhere else that it forms, is characterized by the epidermal cells that are becoming keratinized accumulating keratohyalin granules (or their counterparts) in their cytoplasm. Hence, an area where soft keratinization is occurring manifests a stratum granulosum or its counterpart. After this the cells become clear and glassy (stratum lucidum) before taking on the appearance which they characteristically present in the stratum corneum from which they continuously desquamate.

To sum up: Soft keratin is to be recognized histologically because in its formation the epidermal cells accumulate granules in their cytoplasm and because the keratinized squamous cells of which it is composed continuously desquamate from its surface (compare *left* and *right* of Fig. 357).

Hard keratin constitutes the nails and the cuticle and the cortex of the hairs of man as well as the feathers, the claws or the hooves of certain animals. Its formation is manifested histologically by the epidermal cells that form it not passing through a phase in which they demonstrate numerous granules of keratohyalin in their cytoplasm or by their forming a stratum lucidum; instead, in the formation of hard keratin there is a gradual transition from the living epidermal cells into keratin (Fig. 357, *right*). Physically, hard keratin appears to be solid, and it does not desquamate; hence, it is a more permanent material than soft keratin (nails and hair must be cut if they are not to grow too long). Chemically, hard keratin is relatively unreactive and contains more sulfur than the soft variety.

Structure of a Hair Follicle. A hair follicle, as noted before, results from the growth of cells of the epidermis into the dermis or into the subcutaneous tissue. Therefore, it is an

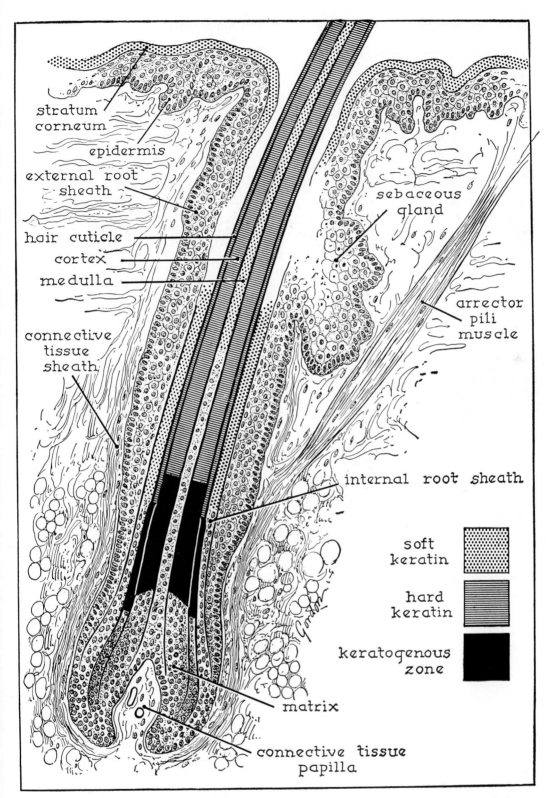

stratum
corneum

epidermis

external root
sheath

hair cuticle

cortex

medulla

connective
tissue
sheath

sebaceous
gland

arrector
pili
muscle

internal root sheath

soft
keratin

hard
keratin

keratogenous
zone

matrix

connective tissue
papilla

FIG. 358. Diagram of a hair follicle, showing the distribution of soft and hard keratin and the keratogenous zone in which hard keratin is produced. (Based on Leblond, C. P.: Ann. New York Acad. Sc. *53*:464)

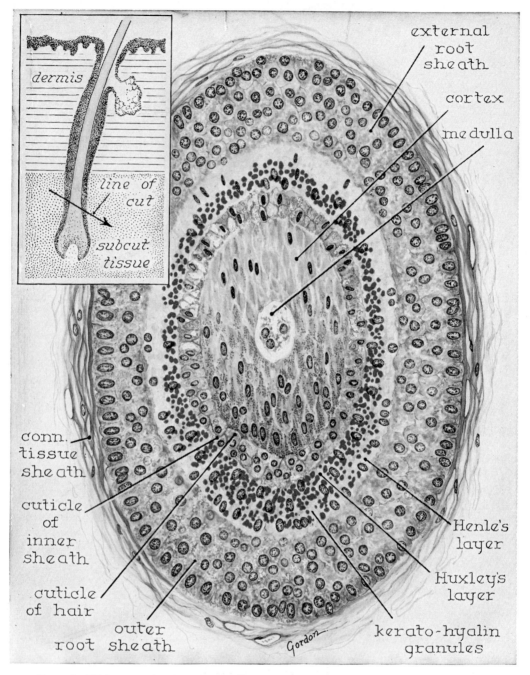

FIG. 359. High-power drawing of an oblique section cut through a hair follicle in the kera-togenous zone. The site and the plane of the section are shown in the inset at the upper left. (Hair follicles commonly extend into the subcutaneous tissue but usually not so far as the one shown in the inset.) Observe that the nuclei in both the internal root sheath and the hair are becoming pyknotic, and that red granules of trichohyalin (labeled kerato-hyalin) are present in the cells of the internal root sheath, thus indicating that it is forming soft keratin. No similar granules are to be seen in the cortex or the cuticle of the hair.

epithelial structure; indeed, it is much like a gland.

The deepest part of the epithelial downgrowth becomes a knobby cluster of cells and is called the *germinal matrix* of the hair follicle (Figs. 356 and 358) because, as we shall see, it germinates the hair. This cluster of epithelial cells (the germinal matrix) becomes fitted over a *papilla* of connective tissue (Figs. 356, *III* and 358) which brings capillaries, and hence a source of tissue fluid, into its central part.

The part of the epidermal downgrowth between the germinal matrix and the surface becomes canalized and thereafter is called the *external root sheath* of the hair follicle (Figs. 356, *III*; 358 and 359). Near the surface of the skin, the external root sheath exhibits all the layers of epidermis of thin skin. This, of course, is to be expected since the external sheath represents a downward continuation of the epidermis. Therefore, the external sheath near the surface of the skin is lined with soft keratin that is continuous at the mouth of the follicle with the soft keratin of the epidermis of the skin (Fig. 358). But deeper down the follicle, the external root sheath becomes thinner and does not exhibit some of the more superficial layers of the epidermis. At the bottom of the follicle, where the external root sheath surrounds, and becomes continuous with, the germinal matrix, the external root sheath consists of only the stratum germinativum of the epidermis (Fig. 358).

For a hair to form in a follicle, the cells of the germinal matrix must proliferate. This forces the uppermost cells of the germinal matrix up the external root sheath. As the cells are pushed up they get farther and farther away from the papilla which is their source of nourishment, and so they turn into keratin. Those that turn into the cuticle and the cortex of the hair, which are hard keratin, show no keratohyalin granules, but instead a keratogenous zone in which an even transition into keratin occurs (Figs. 358, 360). Hairs grow because of the continued proliferation of the epidermal cells of the germinal matrix and because of the successive conversion of these cells into keratin as they are forced up the follicle (Fig. 360).

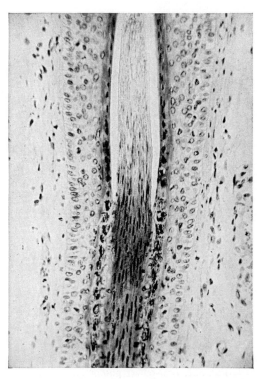

FIG. 360. Low-power photomicrograph of a longitudinal section of a hair follicle at the site where the cells from the matrix are losing their nuclei and becoming converted into keratin. The internal root sheath is thicker at the bottom of the figure than it is at the top.

However, the proliferating cells of the matrix form another structure in addition to a hair. This takes the form of a cellular tubular sheath which is pushed up around the hair to separate it from the external root sheath. This is called the *internal root sheath* (Figs. 358 and 359). It extends only part way up the follicle (Fig. 358). It is formed of soft keratin (Fig. 358); hence, granules of keratohyalin can be seen in its cells as they become keratinized. In this region the granules are generally called trichohyalin (*thrix* = hair, *hyalin* = glass) granules, and instead of being basophilic they stain a bright red (Fig. 359).

The inner root sheath has three layers: an inner layer of cuticle, a middle Huxley's layer and an outer Henle's layer (Fig. 359). The student may have difficulty distinguishing

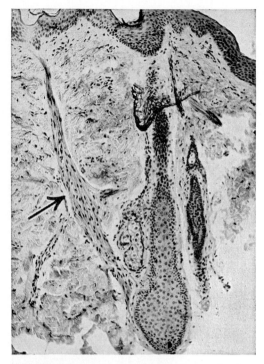

Fig. 361. Low-power photomicrograph of a section of thin skin at the site of an arrector pili muscle. The lumen and the upper part of the hair follicle do not show in this section. (Photomicrograph from Professor E. A. Linell)

these but he should recognize the internal root sheath by its content of acidophilic trichohyalin granules (Fig. 359).

As a hair follicle develops, cells from what will become the external root sheath of the upper third of the follicle grow out into the adjacent dermis and differentiate into sebaceous glands (Fig. 356, IV). When these are formed, their ducts open into the follicle at the site from which the outgrowth occurred; hence, the sebaceous glands empty into the upper third of the follicle, below its mouth (Fig. 358). This part of the follicle often is called the *neck*.

Most hair follicles slant somewhat from the perpendicular. Therefore, the angle between the hair follicle and the surface of the skin is acute on the one side and obtuse on the other. The sebaceous glands of a follicle usually are disposed on the side of the obtuse angle (Fig. 358).

The hair follicle, it should be understood,

is an epithelial structure. However, it is surrounded by a condensation of connective tissue which forms a *connective tissue sheath* about it (Figs. 358 and 359).

A little bundle of smooth muscle fibers, the *arrector pili* (erector of the hair), is attached to the connective-tissue sheath of the hair follicle (about halfway down the follicle or deeper) and passes slantingly upward to reach the papillary layer of the dermis a short distance away from the mouth of the hair follicle (Figs. 358 and 361). This muscle, like the sebaceous glands, is on the side of the follicle that makes an obtuse angle with the surface. This bundle of muscle makes a third side to a triangle, the other two sides of which are the follicle and the surface of the skin. The sebaceous glands are situated inside this triangle (Fig. 358). When the arrector pili muscle contracts, it not only pulls the whole hair follicle outward, but it also, by pulling on its deeper part from one side, makes the follicle more perpendicular (the hair "stands up"). Moreover, contraction of the muscle tends to "dimple in" the skin over the site of its attachment to the papillary layer of the dermis. The net result is a "goose flesh" appearance of, or "goose pimples" on, the skin. Moreover, the contraction of the muscle squeezes the sebaceous glands contained in the triangle previously described (Fig. 358), and this causes their oily secretion to be expressed into the neck of the follicle and onto the skin.

The arrectores pilorum, being smooth muscle, are innervated by the sympathetic nervous system. Cold is an important stimulus for setting off the reflex that leads to their contraction. The purpose of this reflex may be to express more oil onto the surface of the body from the sebaceous glands so that less evaporation, and hence less heat loss, can occur from the skin. Intense emotional states, as has been pointed out, tend to energize the body through the medium of the sympathetic nervous system, and these too cause the arrectores pilorum to contract. Fear can make one's hair "stand on end." Lower animals often "bristle with rage." This response is useful in the porcupine.

Some Points of Interest About Hair and Hair Growth

For the interested, further and very practical information about hair is given in *The Hair and Scalp* by Agnes Savill. The conference on "The Growth, Replacement and Types of Hair," held by the New York Academy of Sciences and published in the *Annals* of the Academy *53*:464-751, 1951, covers almost every scientific aspect of the subject.

Cyclic Activity of Hair Follicles. It is only natural that any individual who notices that hairs come out in his brush or comb should wonder if baldness is imminent. Reassurance is to be obtained from the knowledge that hair growth is cyclic. This is more obvious in animals that live in the far north than it is in man, for these northern animals commonly grow a new coat for each winter and lose it for each summer. The hair follicles of man also exhibit cyclic activity in that they alternate between growing and resting periods. During the growing phase of the cycle, the cells of the germinal matrix continue to proliferate and to differentiate and, as a result, the hair is continually elongated. However, the growing phase merges into a resting phase as the germinal matrix becomes inactive and atrophies. The root of the hair then becomes detached from its matrix and gradually moves up the follicle, gaining for a time a more or less secondary attachment to the external root sheath as the lower end of the hair approaches the neck of the follicle. Meanwhile, in the deeper part of the follicle, the epidermal external root sheath has retracted upwardly toward the surface. Finally, the hair comes out of the follicle. Either before or after this event, the deeper parts of the external root sheath grow downward again to cover either the old papilla, which becomes rejuvenated, or a new one. A new germinal matrix develops, and this leads to a new hair beginning to grow up the follicle again.

The cyclic activity of the hair follicles of man differs in two ways from that of animals that form and lose a coat of hair each year. First, the cycles are longer in man. The hairs of the scalp probably last from 2 to 6 years. Secondly, different, even adjacent, hair follicles in man tend to be in different phases of their cycles at any given time. For example, Trotter found that at a time when 45 per cent of the hair follicles of the leg were in their growing phase, 55 per cent were in their resting phase.

Common Baldness. Although anyone who finds a reasonable number of hairs on his brush or comb or in the water in which the hair is washed can be reassured to the effect that baldness is not impending, the male who experiences a profuse hair loss from the region of the temples and the posterior part of the vertex and shows little indication of their replacement cannot be so reassured. Baldness is very common in men. There have been several theories about its cause. Three factors, ranking in importance in the order mentioned, probably are concerned: heredity, male sex hormone and local disease of the scalp.

That baldness is very uncommon in women has suggested for long that male sex hormone might have something to do with its cause, and recently Hamilton has provided evidence to show that it has. His studies indicate that castration, and hence a lack of male sex hormone production in the male, tends to hold in check the hereditary tendency to develop baldness, and that the administration of male sex hormone to individuals deficient in it, permits a hereditary tendency toward baldness to become operative, with baldness resulting. In other words, the genetic factors which tend to cause baldness can be fully effective only if male sex hormone is present in the blood stream of the individual concerned. Although baldness is an obvious sign of male sex hormone activity, the compensating conclusion should not be drawn by balding men that they are necessarily more virile than those with good heads of hair. Male sex hormone does not cause baldness unless the hereditary disposition to develop baldness is present.

The Effect of Cutting on the Growth of Hair. Another question about hair, probably of more interest to women than to men, is whether or not shaving or otherwise cutting hairs encourages their growth. This has been the subject of much careful inquiry and has required long and painstaking experiments (see Trotter). The general conclusion from these experiments is that cutting or shaving hair has no effect on its growth. This is only logical, since the cellular activity responsible for the growth of a hair takes place in the matrix of the follicle, and it is difficult to understand how cutting the dead cornified end of a hair that projects from a follicle could influence the cellular activity in the matrix. Probably the reason for so many young women

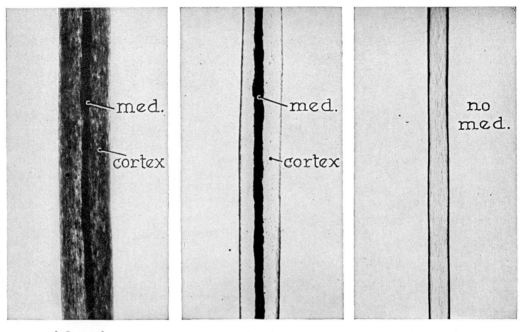

med.

cortex

med.

cortex

no
med.

black   white   blond

FIG. 362. High-power photomicrographs of 3 hairs. (*Left*) A black hair with pigment in both its medulla and cortex. (*Center*) A white hair; it is to be observed that although no pigment is present in its cortex, it has pigment in its medulla. This shows that it is the pigment in the cortex that gives color to hair. (*Right*) This hair is of the blond variety, and it has no medulla; the black along each of its sides is due to refraction.

asserting that shaving their legs caused the hairs on them to become coarser and to grow more vigorously is that they only began to think about such matters, and to shave their legs, when the hairs on them were automatically beginning to grow more vigorously because of hormonal changes.

Structure of Hair. The cross-section appearance and other features of hair vary in relation to race. In anthropology, three chief types of hair are recognized: straight, wavy and woolly. Straight hair is found in the members of the yellow or Mongol races, the Chinese, the Eskimos and the Indians of America. Straight hair is characteristically coarse and lank and is round in cross section. Wavy hair is found in a number of people, including Europeans, and woolly hair on nearly all the black races. A cross section of a wavy hair is oval and that of a woolly hair, elliptical or kidney-shaped.

A hair consists of a central medulla of soft keratin (Figs. 358 and 359) and a cuticle and a cortex of hard keratin (Figs. 358 and 359).

Many hairs contain no medulla (Fig. 362, *right*); hence, they consist entirely of a cuticle and a cortex of hard keratin.

The cuticle consists of very thin, flat, scale-like cells that are arranged on the surface of a hair like shingles on the side of a house, except that their free edges point upward instead of downward (Fig. 363). The free edges of these cells more or less interlock with the free edges of similar cells that line the internal root sheath and whose free edges point downward. The interlocking arrangement makes it difficult to pull out a hair without at least part of the internal root sheath coming with it.

The cortex consists of tapering cornified cells. It is the pigment in the cells of the cortex that gives color to hair (Fig. 362). This pigment may be present as finely distributed granules or in clumps. It is also thought that pigment may sometimes be in solution in the cortex (fluid pigment).

The medulla consists of a central core of cornified cells that are commonly separated from one another. Air or liquid may be present between the cells of the medulla.

Color of Hair. The color of hair depends upon the quantity and the quality of the pigment present in the cortex. If little or no pigment is present in this site the hair appears white even though it has a dark medulla (Fig. 362, *center*). White hairs mixed with pigmented hairs give what is commonly called gray hair (true gray hair is rare). The pigment responsible for black or brown hair is melanin. It is probable that the pigment of red hair is also of the melanin type but in a different stage of oxidation.

There is a widespread belief in unscientific circles that, as a result of an extraordinarily disturbing emotional experience, pigmented hair can "turn gray" overnight. History provides some well-known examples; for instance, Marie Antoinette's hair is supposed to have turned gray the night before her execution. However, one author, interested in this subject, suggests that the hair of anyone about to be executed is washed and hence that the overnight change in this instance was perhaps more apparent than real.

The melanin pigment responsible for the color of hair is formed in, and by, the living epithelial cells of the matrix of the follicle, and as these cells are pushed up the follicle to become dead and keratinized, the pigment that has formed in their cytoplasm is carried along with them. The pigment of hair is in, or mixed with, dead cells that are far removed from the cells of the living matrix of the follicle. It is very difficult to understand how any change in the living body could bring about a bleaching of the pigment of the dead hair. Hence, the usual scientific opinion on this matter is that while a change in the metabolism of the body can affect the nature of the hair that forms after the change occurs, it cannot affect the hair or the pigment already formed any more than it could affect the hair of a bald man's toupee.

However, scientists must always be prepared to face facts, and there are some facts that suggest that hair already formed can be affected and affected fairly quickly by changes in the metabolism of the body. As Szent-Györgyi points out, it is common knowledge that an illness quickly affects the state of the coat of a dog. Furthermore, although many of

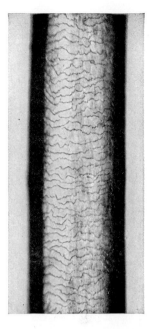

FIG. 363. Oil-immersion photomicrograph of the surface of a hair, showing its shinglelike cuticular scales.

the historic examples of hair turning gray overnight cannot be regarded as sufficient evidence for believing in the phenomenon, there are several fairly recent accounts written by competent observers which cannot be dismissed lightly. After all, as Szent-Györgyi points out, even though hairs are dead they are composed of protein which is in continuity with the proteins of living cells.

Keratin and Its Properties. The process by which the epithelial cells change into the hard keratin of the cuticle and the cortex of the hair is gradual (Fig. 360) and similar to that seen in the formation of the hard keratin of nails (Fig. 357, *right*). No keratohyalin granules are seen.

Keratin, like collagen and elastin, is a member of the albuminoid group of proteins and, like the others, is very resistant to chemical change. The hard type has a high content of sulfur.

Astbury investigated the structure of the keratin molecule by means of x-ray diffraction patterns. In addition to reporting these studies in journals, he has written, in Savill's book, a most readable account of the relation of these studies to an understanding of the elasticity and the behavior of hair. He describes keratin molecules as polypeptide chains, a hundred or more times as long as they are wide; hence, they may be thought of as *molecular threads*.

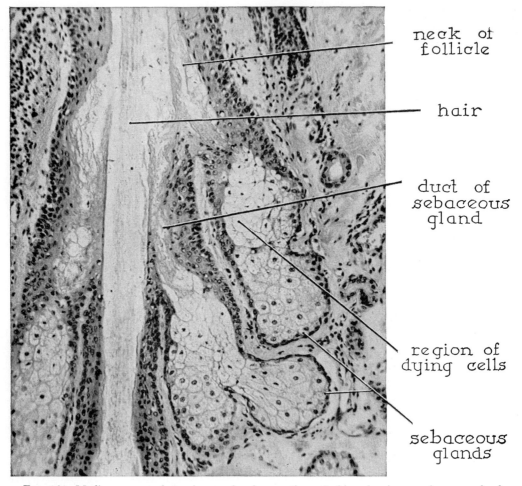

neck of
follicle

hair

duct of
sebaceous
gland

region of
dying cells

sebaceous
glands

Fig. 364. Medium-power photomicrograph of a section of skin, showing a sebaceous gland opening into a hair follicle.

Under normal conditions these molecular threads are not drawn out so that they are straight but instead they pursue a course much like that of an ant that crawls from one side of an accordion to the other; in other words, the molecular threads of keratin are "pleated." Obviously, if the pleats in the molecular threads could be straightened out, the threads would be much longer.

The molecular threads of keratin normally are arranged side by side and are held together by side chains. Long molecules held together in this fashion constitute a molecular grid. When a hair is dry, the molecules are held together in their pleated shapes by very strong forces; hence a dry hair resists stretching. But if a hair becomes wet, water molecules permeate between the long, pleated molecules and spread them apart to make the hair wider.

Moreover, the water molecules absorb some of the physical and chemical attracting forces that normally maintain the pleated state of the molecules of the grid. In this sense, wetting has the same effect on the pleats of the molecular fibers as it has on the pleats of a skirt or a kilt and allows them, if they are pulled, to come "out of press." Hence, a wet hair can be stretched considerably without its molecular fibers becoming broken; they merely become more or less unpleated. A wet hair can also be bent more easily than a dry hair. That is why wetting the hair allows it to be smoothed down.

Curling Hair. Years ago many women put their hair up in "curlers." The hair to be curled would be wet, pulled tightly around a little contrivance and left in this position for some hours. The steady strain so-induced seems to break down some of the molecular linkages, and new linkages more in line with the position in which the hair is held are formed. When the hair is released, these new linkages tend to hold the stretched molecules in their new position. However, these new linkages are unstable, and if the "curled" hair is washed in warm water, the curls all come out as the old pattern of linkages becomes re-established.

Permanent Waving. This is an improvement on the old methods of curling hair because heat makes the new cross-linkages that develop under the curling procedure more permanent; hence, when "permanently" waved hair is washed, the old pattern of cross-linkages does not return. In the "cold wave" type of procedure, chemicals are used to break down certain of the linkages in and between the keratin molecules, and then other chemicals are used to re-establish new permanent linkages that hold the molecules in the curled position.

SEBACEOUS GLANDS

During the development of a hair follicle, epithelial cells, generally from the region of its neck and on the side of the follicle that makes an obtuse angle with the skin, grow out into the adjacent dermis (Fig. 356, IV) to form little pear-shaped glands (Fig. 364). Usually, several form from each follicle. These open by very short but wide ducts (Fig. 364) into the neck of the follicle. These glands secrete a fatty material called *sebum*; this oils the hair and lubricates the surface of the skin. Sebum is said to possess some bactericidal properties. However, its chief function is probably that of acting as a natural "cold cream." It prevents undue evaporation from the stratum corneum in cold weather and so helps to conserve body heat. In hot weather, by keeping the stratum corneum oiled, it helps to keep it from becoming cracked and chapped when sweat is evaporating from it.

Sebaceous glands are holocrine glands (see Fig. 136). As noted before, each little gland is pear-shaped with its body being the secretory portion of the gland and its neck the duct. The body of the gland is surrounded by a basement membrane which is covered on its outer surface by a delicate connective tissue sheath. On the inner aspect of the basement membrane is the "stratum germinativum" or basal layer of the cells of the gland. This consists of thin, flat epithelial cells. On the inner aspect of this layer are cells that are derived from those of the basal layer but which are larger, more rounded and contain fat droplets (Fig. 136). Proceeding toward the central part of the gland, still larger cells containing more fat are seen. The nuclei of the cells in the central part of the gland are pyknotic or absent (Fig. 136). Some granules of keratohyalin are present in some of the cells. Toward the neck of the gland (its duct), the cells break down completely, and a blend of fat, keratohyalin granules, keratin and cellular debris is formed (Fig. 364). This is sebum.

For a sebaceous gland to secrete sebum, many processes must be in progress more or less simultaneously. These are: (1) the proliferation of the cells of the basal layer of the gland, (2) the pushing of the extra cells formed as a result of the proliferation toward the center of the gland, (3) the accumulation of fatty material in the cytoplasm of these cells as they move away from the basal layer and (4) the necrosis of these cells as they are pushed still farther toward the center of the gland (because they are so far removed from sources of nourishment), by the continuing proliferation and differentiation of cells behind them. As noted before, contraction of the arrector pili muscle can cause formed sebum to be expressed quickly from the gland into the hair follicle.

That sebaceous glands develop from hair follicles explains why no sebaceous glands are found in the skin that covers the soles of the feet or the palm of the hands. However, in a few sites in the body sebaceous glands develop without hair follicles (eyelids, papillae of breasts, labia minora and corners of lips near the red margins in some people). And in some sites, and in particular in the skin covering the nose, the sebaceous glands that develop from hair follicles become much more prominent than the hair follicle itself; the hair follicle in these sites is, as it were, a means to an end.

PIGMENTATION OF THE SKIN

The most important pigment in the skin is melanin. Its precise chemical constitution is not known, and it is likely that there are many melanins. These are widely distributed in

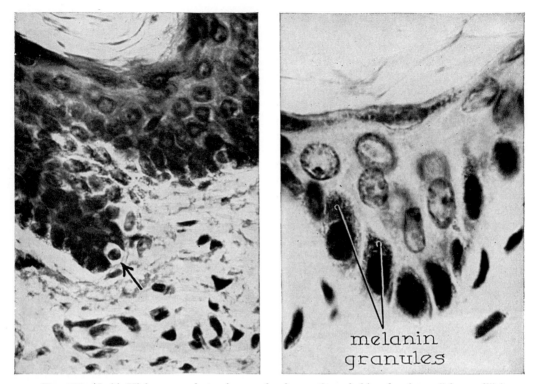

FIG. 365. (*Left*) High-power photomicrograph of a section of skin, showing a "clear cell" in the stratum germinativum. (*Right*) Oil-immersion photomicrograph of a section of pigmented skin, showing melanin granules in the cytoplasm of the cells of the stratum germinativum.

the animal kingdom and range from yellow, through brown, to black in color. In man, melanin occurs chiefly in the epidermis, particularly in the cells of the basal layers, where it tends to be disposed, as a student once wrote, on the sunny side of the nucleus (Fig. 365, *right*). Melanin occurs in the form of fine, brown to black granules but these commonly clump together if the pigment is abundant. The amount of melanin in the epidermis is responsible for the difference in the color of the skins of those of different races (black, brown, yellow and white). All have some melanin in their skins. An inherent inability in any individual of any race to produce melanin pigment results in an *albino* (*albus* = white).

Since the epidermis of white skin (unless tanned by the sun) contains relatively little melanin, it allows the color of the blood in those capillaries in the outer part of the dermis that are open to the circulation to show through it. If the blood in these capillary beds contains only a small amount of reduced

hemoglobin, the blood is red and this shows through the skin to give it a pink color. If a substantial amount of reduced hemoglobin is present in the blood in these vessels, a blue color is imparted to the skin (cyanosis).

Increased amounts of melanin appear in the epidermis of white skin when it is exposed to ultraviolet light. It is the ultraviolet light in sunlight that causes suntan to develop. Brunettes tan more readily than blonds. In some individuals the skin tans evenly. However, in some individuals melanin tends to form in little patches (freckles).

Melanin occurs in the cytoplasm of the cells of the skin as an inclusion. Cells containing melanin occur both in the epidermis and the dermis. Those that have made the pigment that they contain are called *melanoblasts* (these are almost entirely in the epidermis). Cells that contain melanin are not necessarily melanoblasts because they may have phagocytosed the pigment instead of having manufactured it. This is true of the cells of both the epidermis and the dermis.

Melanin tends to become distributed fairly evenly among the deeper cells of the epidermis; this is not because they are all melanoblasts but because the deeper cells take up melanin from the melanoblasts that are present among them. Cells of the dermis that phagocytose pigment are probably of the order of macrophages and are called *chromatophores* (*phoreo* = I carry). Melanoblasts that are actively engaged in the process of manufacturing melanin can be identified by the dopa reaction. If suitably prepared sections of skin are exposed to a properly buffered solution of dopa (dihydroxyphenylalanine), those cells that contain the enzyme *dopa oxidase* will act locally on the dopa of the solution to form black *dopa melanin*. Localized deposits of this black substance indicate the cells of the skin that contain dopa oxidase (the melanoblasts). The dopa melanin is distinguished from the natural melanin in chromatophores and inactive melanoblasts because it is black rather than golden-brown. Hence, the dopa reaction is very helpful in differentiating the cells that actually manufacture melanin pigments (melanoblasts) from those that only phagocytose it.

Pigmented skin tumors are very common in man. Most of these are benign, but occasionally they become malignant, and these are very dangerous indeed. The melanoblast is the cell at fault; hence, the pathologist is much interested in this cell. It is unfortunate that there should be so much uncertainty about its origin. Many different opinions have been held about this matter. Two views deserve consideration: (1) that the melanoblast is a modified cell of the basal layer of the epidermis and (2) that it has a neuro-ectodermal origin, perhaps from the cells of the sheath of Schwann (neurilemma cells) of nerve fibers that terminate in special endings in or about the dermal-epidermal junction. Masson's studies should be consulted regarding this latter theory.

Masson has described clear cells (Fig. 365) distributed along the deep border of the epidermis either between the ordinary cells of the stratum germinativum or between them and the dermis; these cells are similar to certain cells that are seen in pigmented skin tumors, and Masson believes that, on proper stimulation, they manufacture melanin pig-

ment (become melanoblasts). Becker has studied the matter in several pathologic conditions of the skin by means of an improved method for performing the dopa reaction and has found transitions between clear cells and branching epidermal melanoblasts which would suggest that the former give rise to the latter. Moreover, Becker was not able to find transitions between ordinary epidermal cells and the branched melanoblasts in the epidermis; therefore, he leans to the opinion that the melanoblasts of epidermis are derived from the clear cells whose origin Masson has traced to neuro-ectoderm.

Melanin-containing cells in the dermis are generally chromatophores. With one exception (the skin covering the sacral region), the melanoblasts of the skin are confined to the epidermis. In infants of the Mongol race, there may be so many melanoblasts deep in the dermis of the sacral region that they impart a blue color to the overlying surface. This is called the "Mongol spot." Melanoblasts are rarely found in this location in children of the white race. The skin of the ape appears blue because of melanin pigment deep in the dermis. There is a special kind of skin tumor that is blue for the same reason. The blue color imparted to skin by deeply buried melanin is not due to the fact that the melanin itself is of a different color from that in the epidermis but rather to the fact that it must be seen through a greater thickness of tissue.

How Melanin Is Produced. Since Bloch's discovery of the dopa reaction, general opinion has swung to the view that the production of melanin in skin is due to the action of the dopa-oxidase of the melanoblasts of the epidermis on some substrate like dopa which comes to the epidermis by way of the blood and the tissue fluid. However, one obstacle to the final adoption of this hypothesis has been the fact that no dopa or dopalike substance could be demonstrated in the body fluids of mammals. Therefore, an alternative theory continued to receive considerable consideration; namely, that melanin is formed from the amino acid tyrosine by means of the enzyme tyrosinase. But no tyrosinase can be demonstrated in skin. A solution to the whole problem is suggested by the following experiments:

Rothman showed that tyrosine disappears

from the blood if the skin is exposed to ultraviolet light and that the decrease in the concentration of tyrosine in the blood is proportional to the degree of pigmentation of skin that develops. This experiment strongly indicated tyrosine as the mother-substance of melanin, but, as noted before, no tyrosinase can be found in the skin to account for the local breakdown of tyrosine. Then, Arnow found that dopa was formed from tyrosine in the skin under the action of ultraviolet light. Rothman confirmed his findings but found that the reaction was too slow to explain the formation of melanin in skin. However, he found that suitable catalysts facilitated the reaction. It seems likely, then, that ultraviolet light and catalysts break down tyrosine in the skin to form a dopalike substance which is then converted to melanin by the dopa-oxidase of the melanoblasts. Certain vitamins and hormones affect the reaction concerned in the formation of melanin, and also the bleaching of melanin, in ways not yet thoroughly understood.

Function of Melanin. In the animal kingdom, melanin serves as a protective coloring. In man, the most logical function of melanin would seem to be that of protection from sunlight. Excessive sunlight can be harmful to the organism in several ways. It can cause burns and sunstroke. It can, in some mysterious way, probably by inducing mutations of cells in the epidermis, incite cancer. There is much more skin cancer in those peoples with white skins that are subjected to a great deal of sunlight than there is among either Negoes in the same environment or those individuals with white skins who live in regions where there is relatively little sunlight. Furthermore, it is possible that excessive sunlight can cause the production of too much vitamin D in the organism. Vitamin D is formed by the irradiation of certain derivatives of cholesterol by ultraviolet light. Cholesterol is one of the fatty materials in sebum, so it is likely that sebum is the source of the derivatives of cholesterol that become vitamin D on irradiation. It is known that extremely large doses of vitamin D can seriously damage the organism. Whether harmful amounts could ever be produced and absorbed from exposing the skin to too much sunlight is, of course, another matter. But the possibility exists.

That melanin protects against sunlight seems to be suggested by the fact that the skin of Negoes and the tanned skin of the white is more resistant to sunburn than ordinary white skin. That melanin protects against ultraviolet light and hence against the formation of vitamin D in the skin is suggested by the fact that when Negro children are brought up in northern regions, where there is less sun than there is in more southern regions and where the sunlight in winter contains little ultraviolet light, they develop rickets to a far greater extent than white children whose skins, as it were, are designed to absorb every bit of ultraviolet light possible. This fact suggests also that the site of vitamin D formation in the skin is below the level of the melanin in the epidermis. But it is difficult to draw final conclusions on all these matters. Ultraviolet light does not penetrate very deeply into the skin; further, there is evidence suggesting that at least part of the protection against sunlight that is afforded by the skin of the Negro is due to a relatively thick stratum corneum. This layer becomes thicker in the white also when the skin becomes tanned. Moreover, even skin in which little melanin forms acquires some degree of resistance to the effect of sunlight after frequent exposures. It is likely, then, that while melanin is important in protecting the body from too much sunlight, it is not the only means of protection available or commonly utilized.

Why exposure to ultraviolet light should increase the amount of pigment in skin has been the subject of much speculation through the years. It is possible that sunlight could increase pigmentation in three ways: (1) by increasing the number of melanoblasts (this could be a reaction to injury), (2) by increasing the activity or the production of dopa-oxidase in the melanoblasts and (3) by increasing the production of dopa from tyrosine. For a review of the biochemistry of melanin formation see Lerner and Fitzpatrick.

BLOOD SUPPLY OF THE SKIN

Arteries. There are several aspects to the knowledge of the blood supply of a part of the body. A surgeon must know where he will encounter blood vessels so that he will not inadvertently cut these and cause unnecessary bleeding. He must know how much he can depend on anastomoses to keep the tissues alive if he does cut certain vessels. He must know of the possible anomalies that may be encountered with regard to the blood vessels of the part. What should he know about the blood vessels of skin? He should know, for example, where to expect bleeding vessels when he makes an incision through the skin. He should know about the effectiveness of the anastomoses of the larger and the smaller vessels of the skin so that he will know how extensive an attachment he must leave when he cuts a flap of skin for a certain type of skin graft. He should know the planes of the chief beds of arteries and veins in the skin so that he can cut skin grafts with the least disturbance of the larger vessels. Then, in addition, he should know the sites of the capillary beds of the skin, for it is from these that a person with extensive burns can literally bleed to death into his own tissues. A knowledge of the blood supply of the skin, then, requires a knowledge of the disposition and the arrangements of vessels that can be seen with the naked eye and the sites of beds of vessels so small that they can be seen only with the microscope.

The largest arteries of the skin are arranged in the form of a flat network in the subcutaneous tissue, immediately below the dermis. This arterial network is called the *rete cutaneum*. It receives blood from branches of the larger arteries that run more deeply in the subcutaneous tissue. From the rete cutaneum, branches pass both inwardly and outwardly. Those that pass inwardly supply the adipose tissue of the more superficial parts of the subcutaneous tissue and the parts of such hair follicles as are disposed therein. Those that pass outwardly supply the skin. They generally pursue a curved course as they penetrate through the reticular layer of the dermis and they give off side branches to the hair follicles and to the sweat and sebaceous glands as they pass through it. On reaching the outer part of the reticular layer of the dermis, they form a second flat network, composed of smaller vessels, called the *rete subpapillare*. In the skin of the fingers and the toes, and in certain other sites, arteriovenous anastomoses are present in little bodies called *glomi* that are disposed deep in the dermis (Fig. 366).

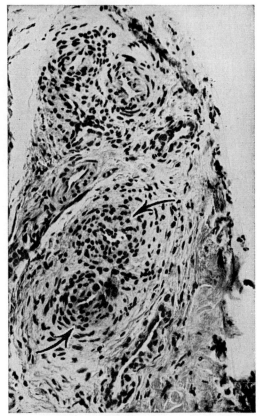

Fig. 366. Medium-power photomicrograph of a section of skin, showing a glomus. The thick-walled arterial vessel in the glomus (indicated by arrows) is coiled or convoluted; hence, cross sections of it appear in several sites.

Capillary Beds. It should be kept in mind that the dermis, since it consists chiefly of the relatively inert intercellular substance, collagen, does not require a very extensive capillary blood supply. Indeed, most of the dermis is very sparingly supplied with capillaries. As might be expected, the capillary beds of the skin are extensive only in that portion of the dermis that is in close association with epithelial cells that require abundant tissue fluid for their function and growth. The capillary beds of the skin, then, are confined to the connective tissue that (1) immediately underlies the epidermis, (2) surrounds the matrix of the hair follicles, (3) constitutes the papillae of hair follicles and (4) surrounds the sweat and sebaceous glands.

The first capillary bed mentioned **requires**

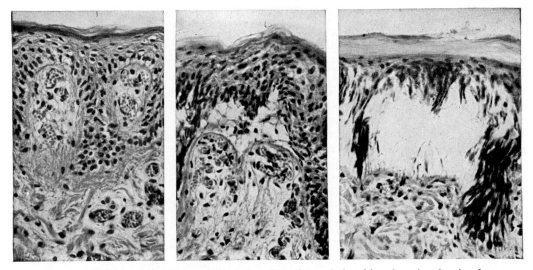

Fig. 367. Medium-power photomicrographs of sections of the skin of a pig, showing how a blister develops after a burn. (*Left*) Section taken from the skin 15 minutes after it suffered a light burn. Note that the capillaries in the dermal papillae, close to the epidermis, are dilated and congested with blood. (*Center*) Section taken 1 hour after the skin was burned lightly. The capillaries of the papillae are still dilated and congested, and, in addition, plasma has leaked from them and is accumulating between the dermis and the epidermis. (*Right*) Section taken 4 hours after the skin was burned lightly. It shows the epidermis lifted a considerable distance from the dermis by the plasma that has leaked from the injured capillaries of the dermis. (Ham, A. W.: Ann. Surg. *120*:692)

some further comment. Arterioles from the rete subpapillare pass toward the epidermis and give rise to capillaries that extend as loops up into the papillae. These efficiently supply tissue fluid to the basal cells of the epidermis. However, the capillary loops in the papillae are not the cause of the pink color of skin. This is due to flat networks of small thin-walled vessels (not the arterial plexus) in the deeper part of the papillary, and in the superficial part of the reticular, layers of the dermis. These flat networks constitute the *subpapillary plexuses* of the skin. Lewis has studied intensively the physiology of these vessels. It is generally conceded that most of them are independently contractile. It is questionable if these small vessels should be regarded as capillaries. The subpapillary plexuses are often described as venous plexuses. Probably they are best thought of as consisting of both capillaries and small venules, with most of the latter being sufficiently small to have walls thin enough to allow plasma to leak through them when they are injured. The capillaries in these plexuses are supplied by arterioles from the rete subpapillare. The small venules drain

into larger ones, which, in turn, drain into small veins. In general, the veins leave the skin with the arteries.

Function of the Superficial Capillaries and Venules. In man, heat generated in the body is lost directly through the skin. If the temperature of the air is lower than that of the body, the rate of heat loss can be increased or decreased by the degree to which the capillaries and the venules of the papillary and the subpapillary regions of the skin are open to the circulation. If the temperature of the air is close to, or higher than, that of the body, the *effect* of a low outside temperature can be achieved by the sweat glands pouring fluid onto the surface of the body, where it evaporates and so cools the outer part of the skin. Hence, blood circulating through the papillary and the subpapillary regions of skin from which sweat is evaporating is cooled, and by this mechanism heat can be lost from the body in hot weather. To keep down the temperature of an individual who performs violent muscular exercise on a very hot day and so generates a great deal of heat, both profuse sweating and dilatation of the superficial blood

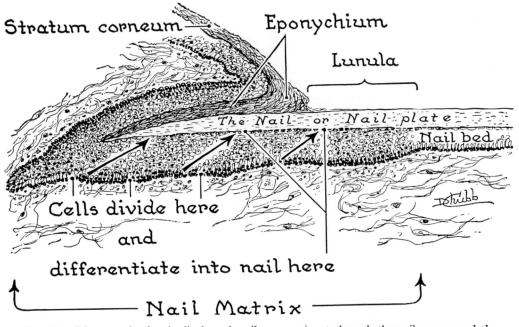

Fig. 370. Diagram of a longitudinal section (low-power) cut through the nail groove and the root of a growing nail.

the lower part of the matrix, the forming nail is pushed out of the groove and slowly slides along the dorsal surface of the digit toward its distal part. Although it slides slowly over the epidermis of the dorsal part of the digit, it remains firmly attached to it all the while. The epidermis over which it slides is called the *nail bed* (Fig. 370). It consists of only the deeper layers of the epidermis; the nail, as it were, serves as its stratum corneum. The skin of the dorsal surface of the digits is formed into a groove along each side of the nail (Fig. 371). With sufficient growth, the *free margin* of the nail will project beyond the distal end of the digit (Fig. 371).

The *body* of the nail is the part that shows. The part that is hidden in the nail groove is called the *root*. Seen from above, a crescent-shaped white area appears on the part of the body nearest the root. This is called the *lunule* (Fig. 371); it is seen to best advantage on the thumb and the first finger. It is usually absent from the little finger. The nail, except for the lunule, is pink because the blood in the capillaries of the dermis under the nail bed shows through. The lunule is white because the capillaries under it do not show through.

There are different theories to explain this. Some authorities think the lunule indicates the extent of the underlying matrix (Fig. 370). Since the matrix is thicker than the epidermis of the nail bed, capillaries beneath it would not show through it as well as they would through the epidermis of the nail bed. However, the region of the lunule cannot always be correlated with the site of the matrix in sections. Hence, some authors think

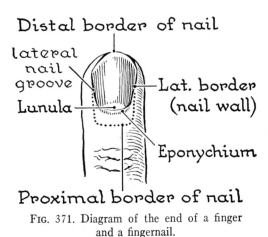

Fig. 371. Diagram of the end of a finger and a fingernail.

that its whiteness is due to the nail substance, when it is first formed, being more opaque than the more mature nail substance found over the bed.

At the proximal border of the nail, the stratum corneum of the epidermis of the skin of the dorsum of a finger or a toe projects over and is adherent to the nail. This, together with the stratum corneum of the epidermis that makes up the proximal and more superficial wall of the nail fold and is adherent to the proximal and outer surface of the nail root, constitutes the *eponychium* (*epi* = upon, *onyx* = nail) (Fig. 370) and it is soft keratin.

Infections in the region of the eponychium or along the lateral borders of the nail (Fig. 371) are not uncommon. Sometimes, in order to permit these infections to heal, it is necessary to remove the root of a nail. On being pulled out, the nail root will be seen to be shaped like the end of a curved chisel which does not extend into the nail groove as far as might be thought. Provided that the matrix is not destroyed, a new nail will grow out of the nail fold in due time. If the matrix is destroyed, a new nail will not form.

Sometimes, from wearing improper shoes, the curvature of toenails becomes accentuated, and they pierce the dermis along one of their lateral grooves (*a normal groove is shown in Fig. 371*). The condition is called an ingrown toenail. Sometimes it is necessary to cut away some matrix at one side of the nail groove to cure this condition. New nail will not grow from the region from which matrix is removed. Hence, the cutting away of matrix at one side of the nail groove results in the formation of a narrower nail, which, therefore, does not impinge on the skin at the bottom of the lateral groove, so the pierced skin at this point can heal.

The dermis beneath the epidermis of the nail bed is arranged in longitudinal grooves and ridges. In cross sections the ridges appear as papillae. The dermis in this site is very vascular. The ridges and the grooves of dermis present under the bed do not continue proximally under the matrix, but there are some papillae in this region.

On the average, nails grow about 0.5 mm. a week. Fingernails grow more rapidly than toenails, and both grow faster in summer than in winter. The rate of growth of nails is different at different ages. Nail growth may be disturbed when the body suffers from certain diseases. Even psychological upsets are said to be reflected sometimes by the pitting of nails. Certain hormone deficiencies and excesses affect the growth of nails; hence, the condition of the nails sometimes may help to indicate an endocrine gland disturbance.

SKIN GRAFTING

Skin may be grafted from one part of the body to another by two general methods. By one, the transplanted skin is never severed completely from its blood supply. By the second, the skin to be grafted is completely detached from its blood supply when it is transferred. This is called a *free graft*.

Shifting skin from one part of the body without ever severing it from a blood supply has led to the development of many ingenious operations by plastic surgeons. Without going into details, the general method, for example, by which skin from the arm can be transferred to the face, is as follows:

A flap of skin of the desired size is partly detached from the arm, and the wound so created is closed or covered with a free skin graft. If the flap has been cut properly, the blood vessels entering along its attached margin are sufficient to keep the whole flap alive. If the flap is protected (rolled up or otherwise treated), the blood vessels entering the flap from the attached margin respond to their increased duties by becoming larger and more numerous. After the flap is seen to have a satisfactory blood supply from its one attached margin, the arm is brought close to the site on the face where the new skin is needed and is fixed in this position. The free part of the flap then is sewed into the defect on the face. Blood vessels from the skin and the subcutaneous tissue of the face soon make connections with those in the flap. Soon the flap is being supplied by blood vessels from the site to which it has been transplanted. When the blood supply from this source becomes adequate, the original attachment of the flap to the skin of the arm, through which it has received blood up to this time, can be severed safely, and the repair of the facial defect can be completed.

The above-described method of skin grafting, though not necessarily using the arm as a source of skin, is employed particularly when reconstructions, such as the evolving of a new

Fɪɢ. 372. The upper 3 photographs illustrate how autogenous full-thickness skin grafts become vascularized. The bottom photograph shows that skin transplanted from one animal to another does not become vascularized. (These experiments were performed on pigs in collaboration with Dr. George Cloutier.) After death, the blood vessels of the animal on which the grafts had been made were injected with India ink in gelatin. In the photographs, the vessels containing black material are to be regarded as being open to the circulation. The striped band in each picture indicates the thickness of the graft. All the photographs are from thick sections that were cleared so that injected blood vessels could be seen readily.

The upper photograph illustrates an autogenous graft that was in position for 3 days. Blood is not yet circulating in its vessels; such black material as appears in the grafts is not the material injected into the blood vessels of the animal.

The second photograph illustrates an autogenous graft that was in position for 7 days, and the third photograph one that was in position for 10 days. Large vessels filled with the injection material are present in these. These vessels are too large to have grown into the grafts in such a short time; indeed, sections showed that they were the original vessels that were in the skin that was grafted. They have become connected by capillaries with vessels in the bed of the graft. It is probable that blood is passing into the graft through the veins of the graft.

The bottom photograph illustrates a graft taken from another animal (a homograft). Although it shows a great development of blood vessels immediately below it, no vessels have made any connections with those of the graft, which remains entirely bloodless.

external ear to replace one that has been shot away, are necessary or when particularly good cosmetic effects are desired. However, under most conditions where skin grafting is required, for example, the covering of a large area where the skin has been completely destroyed by a burn, *free* skin grafts, that is, grafts completely severed from their blood supply, are employed.

There are two kinds of free skin grafts: *split* grafts and *full-thickness* grafts. Although split grafts, which are thin shavings cut from the skin (Fig. 355, *lower left*), can be cut freehand, it is more common nowadays to cut

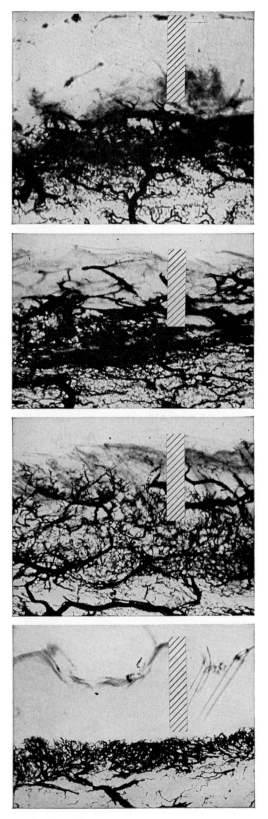

them with a dermatome, a special instrument which quickly cuts a thin, even layer of skin from a broad surface. It was widely believed in the past, and sometimes it is still taught, that a split graft consists chiefly of epidermis and that the surface from which it is cut (the donor site) is left with the deeper parts of the interpapillary pegs of epidermis intact, and that these subsequently provide foci from which epidermal cells can grow out and quickly cover the denuded surface. For some reason there is widespread misconception about the thickness of the epidermis of thin skin and it is highly unlikely that split-skin grafts are commonly cut this thin. Split-skin grafts usually include a fairly substantial amount of dermis as well as epidermis (Fig. 355, *lower left*). Epithelization of the donor sites is brought about by a growth of epithelial cells, not from remnants of interpapillary pegs, but chiefly from the external root sheaths of the hair follicles (Fig. 368). The sweat glands do not participate in the repair of epidermis nearly so energetically as the hair follicles. By this means, the surface of the donor site is soon covered with new epidermis, and, in the meantime, the underlying dermis, by means of the proliferation of fibroblasts and the formation of new intercellular substance, is quickly restored to its original thickness.

When a split graft is fastened in its new site and held in place with a little pressure, its constituent cells are kept alive by means of tissue fluid derived from the capillaries of the host tissue below. If the graft is thin, most of its cells can survive by this means until the graft becomes vascularized. Vascularization occurs when capillaries of the host make connections with capillaries of the graft (capillaries seem to be very adept at making such connections) and also by the growth of new capillaries from the host up into the graft.

In some instances, free grafts of the full-thickness variety are used. If the full thickness of the skin is removed from any site, no hair follicles are left to regenerate a new epidermal surface. For this reason, when a full-thickness graft is cut, the two edges of the donor site must be sewed together or, if this is not possible, it must, in turn, be covered with a split graft. However, many individuals are sufficiently plump to permit the suturing of the edges of the skin from which a full-thickness graft is removed.

Since full-thickness grafts are thicker than split grafts, it is somewhat more difficult for tissue fluid from the bed to which they are grafted to nourish them until they become vascularized. Vascularization of a free full-thickness graft is brought about by the abundant capillaries of the bed to which the graft is transplanted making connections with those in the graft. These connect with the larger vessels in the graft, so blood entering them soon flows again through the original blood vessels of the graft. The larger blood vessels of the graft begin to fill after 5 days and are fairly well filled, and hence functioning to some extent, by 7 days (Fig. 372, *second from top*).

Although skin may be grafted from one part of an individual to another, a graft taken from one individual and transplanted to another individual, with the exceptions described in Chapter 10, always dies and is cast off. In our experience an important reason for the failure of such a graft to "take" is that it does not become vascularized (Fig. 372, *bottom*).

REFERENCES

GENERAL REFERENCES INCLUDING FINE STRUCTURE

Clark, W. E., LeGros: The Tissues of the Body, ed. 4, p. 415, Oxford, Clarendon, 1958.
Hibbs, R. G., and Clark, W. H., Jr.: Electron microscope studies of the human epidermis, J. Biophys. & Biochem. Cytol. 6:71, 1959.
Montagna, W.: The Structure and Function of Skin, New York, Acad. Press, 1956.
Odland, G. F.: The fine structure of the interrelationship of cells in the human epidermis, J. Biophys. & Biochem. Cytol. 4:529, 1958.
Pease, D. C.: Electron microscopy of human skin, Am. J. Anat. 89:469, 1951.
Rothman, S.: Physiology and Biochemistry of the Skin, Chicago, Univ. Chicago Press, 1956.
Wilson, J. A.: The Chemistry of Leather Manufacture, ed. 2, vol. 1, New York, Chem. Catalog Co., 1928.

SPECIAL REFERENCES ON EPIDERMIS AND ITS APPENDAGES INCLUDING FINE STRUCTURE

Argyris, T. S.: Succinic dehydrogenase and esterase activities of mouse skin during regeneration and fetal development, Anat. Rec. 126:1, 1956.

Bertalanffy, F. D.: Mitotic activity and renewal rate of sebaceous gland cells in the rat, Anat. Rec. *129*:231, 1957.

Brody, I.: The keratinization of epidermal cells of normal guinea pig skin as revealed by electron microscopy, J. Ulstrastr. Res. *2*:482, 1959.

Bullough, W. S., and Ebling, F. J.: Cell replacement in the epidermis and sebaceous glands of the mouse, J. Anat. *86*:29, 1952.

Carruthers, C., and Suntzeff, V.: Biochemistry and physiology of epidermis, Physiol. Rev. *33*: 229, 1953.

Charles, A.: An electron microscopic study of the human axillary apocrine gland, J. Anat. *93*:226, 1959.

Cowdry, E. V.: The skin *in* Cowdry's Special Cytology, ed. 2, p. 1, New York, Hoeber, 1932.

Hibbs, R. G.: The fine structure of human exocrine sweat glands, Am. J. Anat. *103*:201, 1958.

Leuchtenberger, C., and Lund, H. Z.: The chemical nature of the so-called keratohyaline granules of the stratum granulosum of the skin, Exper. Cell Res. *2*:150, 1951.

Menefee, M. G.: Some fine structure changes occurring in the epidermis of embryo mice during differentiation, J. Ultrastr. Res. *1*:49, 1957.

Moore, K. L., Graham, M. A., and Barr, M. L.: The detection of chromosomal sex in hermaphrodites from a skin biopsy, Surg., Gynec. & Obst. *96*:641, 1953.

Odland, G. F.: The morphology of the attachment between the dermis and the epidermis, Anat. Rec. *108*:399, 1950.

————: The fine structure of the interrelationship of cells in the human epidermis, J. Biophys. & Biochem. Cytol. *4*:529, 1958.

Pelc, S. R.: The participation of the cell nucleus and its DNA in the formation of keratin, Exper. Cell Res. (Suppl.) *6*:97, 1958.

Porter, K. R.: Observations on the submicroscopic structure of animal epidermis, Anat. Rec. *118*:433, 1954.

Rogers, G. E.: Electron microscope observations on the structure of sebaceous glands, Exper. Cell Res. *13*:517, 1957.

————: Some aspects of the structure of the inner root sheath of hair follicles revealed by light and electron microscopy, Exper. Cell Res. *14*:378, 1958.

Storey, W. F., and Leblond, C. P.: Measurement of the rate of proliferation of epidermis and associated structures, Ann. New York Acad. Sc. *53*:537, 1951.

Swanbeck, G.: On the keratin fibrils of the skin. An x-ray small angle scattering study of the horny layer, J. Ultrastr. Res. *3*:51, 1959.

Takagi, S.: A study on the structure of the sudoriferous duct traversing the epidermis in man with fresh material by phase contrast microscopy, Jap. J. Physiol. *3*:65, 1952.

Wislocki, G. B., Fawcett, D. W., and Dempsey, E. W.: Staining of stratified squamous epithelium of mucous membranes and skin of man and monkey by the periodic acid-Schiff method, Anat. Rec. *110*:359, 1951.

SPECIAL REFERENCES ON FINGERPRINTS AND DERMIS

Cauna, N.: Nature and functions of the papillary ridges of the digital skin, Anat. Rec. *119*:449, 1954.

Cummins, H.: The topographic history of the volar pads (walking pads; tastballen) in the human embryo, Contrib. Embryol. *20*:103, 1929.

————: Dermatoglyphics: Significant patternings of the body surface, Yale J. Biol. & Med. *18*:551, 1946.

Cummins, Harold, and Midlo, Charles: Finger Prints, Palms and Soles, New York, Blakiston Division of McGraw-Hill, 1943.

Faulds, H.: On the skin-furrows of the hand, Nature *22*:605, 1880.

Henry, E. R.: Classification and Uses of Finger-prints, London, Darling, 1905.

Herschel, W. J.: Skin furrows of the hand, Nature *23*:76, 1880.

Wilton, G.: Fingerprints: History, Law and Romance, London, Hodge, 1938.

SPECIAL REFERENCES ON THE BLOOD SUPPLY TO SKIN

Burton, A. C.: The blood flow, temperature and color of the skin, Am. A. Adv. Sc., Publication No. 13, 1940.

Lewis, T.: The Blood Vessels of the Human Skin and Their Responses, London, Shaw, 1937.

SPECIAL REFERENCES ON HAIR AND KERATIN

Baker, Burton L.: The relationship of the adrenal, thyroid, and pituitary glands to the growth of hair, Ann. New York Acad. Sc. *53*:690, 1951.

Bear, Richard S., and Rugo, Henry J.: The results of x-ray diffraction studies on keratin fibers, Ann. New York Acad. Sc. *53*:627, 1951.

Birbeck, M. S. C., and Mercer, E. H.: The electron microscopy of the human hair follicle. I. Introduction and the hair cortex, J. Biophys. & Biochem. Cytol. *3*:203, 1957. II. The hair cuticle, J. Biophys. & Biochem. Cytol. *3*:215, 1957. III. The inner root sheath and trichohyaline, J. Biophys. & Biochem. Cytol. *3*:223, 1957.

Bissell, Grosvenor W.: Hirsutism, Ann. New York Acad. Sc. *53*:742, 1951.

Butcher, Earl O.: Development of the pilary system and the replacement of hair in mammals, Ann. New York Acad. Sc. *53*:508, 1951.

Charles, A.: Electron microscope observations on hardening in the hair follicle, Exper. Cell Res. *18*:138, 1959.

Chase, H. B.: Growth of the hair, Physiol. Rev. *34*:113, 1954.

Chase, H. B., Montagna, W., and Malone, J. D.: Changes in the skin in relation to the hair growth cycle, Anat. Rec. *116*:75, 1953.

Danforth, C. H.: Physiology of human hair, Physiol. Rev. *19*:94, 1939.

Duggins, O. H., and Trotter, M.: Age changes in head hair from birth to maturity: II. Medullation in hair of children, Am. J. Phys. Anthropol. *8*:399, 1950.

————: Changes in morphology of hair during childhood, Ann. New York Acad. Sc. *53*:569, 1951.

Forbes, T. F.: Sex hormones and hair changes in rats, Endocrinology *30*:465, 1942.

Garn, Stanley M.: Types and distribution of the hair in man, Ann. New York Acad. Sc. *53*:498, 1951.

Giroud, A., Bulliard, H., and Leblond, C. P.: Les deux types fondamentaux de kératinisation, Bull. d'hisol. appliq. à la Physiol. *11*:129, 1934.

Giroud, A., and Leblond, C. P.: The keratinization of epidermis and its derivatives, especially the hair, as shown by x-ray diffraction and histochemical studies, Ann. New York Acad. Sc. *53*:613, 1951.

Hamilton, J. B.: Male hormone stimulation is prerequisite and incitant in common baldness, Am. J. Anat. *71*:541, 1942.

————: Patterned loss of hair in man: types and incidence, Ann. New York Acad. Sc. *53*:708, 1951.

————: Quantitative measurement of a secondary sex character, axillary hair, Ann. New York Acad. Sc. *53*:585, 1951.

Hardy, M. H.: The development of mouse hair *in vitro* with some observations on pigmentation, J. Anat. *83*:364, 1949.

Herrington, L. P.: The role of the piliary system in mammals and its relation to the thermal environment, Ann. New York Acad. Sc. *53*:600, 1951.

Leblond, C. P.: Histological structure of hair, with a brief comparison to other epidermal appendages and epidermis itself, Ann. New York Acad. Sc. *53*:464, 1951.

Matoltsy, A. G.: A study of the medullary cells of the hair, Exper. Cell Res. *5*:98, 1953.

Myers, Raymond J., and Hamilton, James B.: Regeneration and rate of growth of hairs in man, Ann. New York Acad. Sc. *53*:562, 1951.

Noback, Charles R.: Morphology and phylogeny of hair, Ann. New York Acad. Sc. *53*:476, 1951.

Parnell, Jerome P.: Hair pattern and distribution in mammals, Ann. New York Acad. Sc. *53*:493, 1951.

Reynolds, Earle L.: The appearance of adult patterns of body hair in man, Ann. New York Acad. Sc. *53*:576, 1951.

Rogers, G. E.: Electron microscope observations on the glassy layer of the hair follicle, Exper. Cell Res. *13*:521, 1957.

————: Electron microscopy of wool, J. Ultrastr. Res. *2*:309, 1959.

Savill, A.: The Hair and Scalp, ed. 3, London, Arnold, 1944.

Trotter, M.: The hair *in* Cowdry's Special Cytology, ed. 2, p. 41, New York, Hoeber, 1932.

————: Hair growth and shaving, Anat. Rec. *37*:373, 1928.

————: The life cycles of hair in selected regions of the body, Am. J. Phys. Anthropol. *7*:427, 1924.

Whiteley, H. J.: Studies on hair growth in the rabbit, J. Anat. *92*:563, 1958.

SPECIAL REFERENCES ON PIGMENTATION

Arnow, L. E.: Acid-soluble pigments of red human hair, Biochem. J. *32*:1281, 1938.

————: Formation of dopa by the exposure of tyrosine solutions to ultraviolet radiations. J. Biol. Chem. *120*:151, 1937.

Becker, S. W.: Cutaneous melanoblasts as studied by the paraffin dopa technique, J. Invest. Dermat. *5*:463, 1952.

————: Melanin pigmentation, Arch. Dermat. & Syph. *16*:259, 1927.

Becker, S. W., Praver, L. L., and Thatcher, H.: An improved method for the dopa reaction, Arch. Dermat. & Syph. *31*:190, 1935.

Billingham, R. E., and Medawar, P. B.: Role of dendritic cells in the infective colour transformation of guinea pig's skin, Nature *160*:61, 1947.

Charles, A., and Ingram, J. T.: Electron microscope observations of the melanocyte of the human epidermis, J. Biophys. & Biochem. Cytol. *6*:41, 1959.

Clark, W. H., and Hibbs, R. G.: Electron microscope studies of the human epidermis. The clear cell of Mason (dentritic cell or melanocyte), J. Biophys. & Biochem. Cytol. *4*:679, 1958.

Edwards, E., and Duntley, S.: The pigments and color of living human skin, Am. J. Anat. *65*:1, 1939.

Gates, R. R., and Zimmermann, A. A.: Comparison of skin color with melanin content, J. Invest. Dermat. *21*:339, 1953.

Gordon, M., *et al.*: The Biology of the Melanomas, vol. 4, New York Acad. Sc., 1948.

Hamilton, J. B.: Influence of the endocrine status upon pigmentation in man and animals *in* The Biology of the Melanomas, Spec. Pub., New York Acad. Sc., vol. 4, p. 341, 1948.

Jacobsen, C. C.: Melanin: a review of the chemical aspects of the melanin problem, Arch. Path. *17*:141 & 391, 1934.

Jeghers, H.: Pigmentation of the skin, New England J. Med. *231*:88, 1944.

Laidlaw, G. F.: The dopa reaction in normal histology, Anat. Rec. *53*:399, 1932.

Lerner, Aaron B., and Fitzpatrick, Thomas B.: Biochemistry of melanin formation, Physiol. Rev. *30*:91, 1950.

Masson, P.: Melanoblasts et cellules de Langerhans, Soc. Derm. Paris, Réunion derm. de Strasbourg, p. 1112, 1935.

———: Pigment cells in man *in* The Biology of the Melanomas, Spec. Pub., New York Acad. Sc., vol. 4, p. 15, 1948.

Rothman, S.: Influence of ascorbic acid on oxidation of tyrosine by ultraviolet light, Proc. Soc. Exper. Biol. & Med. *45*:52, 1940.

———: Oxidation of tyrosine by ultra-violet light in its relation to human pigmentation, Proc. Soc. Exper. Biol. & Med. *44*:485, 1940.

Rothman, S., Krupa, H. F., and Smiljanic, H. M.: Inhibitory action of human epidermis on melanin formation, Proc. Soc. Exper. Biol. & Med. *62*:208, 1946.

SPECIAL REFERENCES ON BURNS AND SKIN REGENERATION AND GRAFTS

Bishop, G. H.: Regeneration after experimental removal of skin in man, Am. J. Anat. *76*:153, 1945.

Gillman, T., and Penn, J.: Studies on the repair of cutaneous wounds, Med. Proc. (South African) *2*:93, 1956.

Ham, A. W.: Experimental study of histopathology of burns, with particular reference to sites of fluid loss in burns of different depths, Ann. Surg. *120*:689, 1944.

———: Experimental study of tannic acid treatment of burns, with particular reference to its effect on local fluid loss and healing, Ann. Surg. *120*:698, 1944.

Harkins, H. N.: The Treatment of Burns, Springfield, Ill., Thomas, 1942.

Johnson, F. R., and McMinn, R. M. H.: The cytology of wound healing of body surfaces in mammals, Biol. Rev. *35*:364, 1960.

McGregor, I. A.: The regeneration of sympathetic activity in grafted skin as evidenced by sweating, Brit. J. Plastic Surg. *3*:12, 1950.

McMinn, R. M. H.: The cellular anatomy of experimental wound healing, Ann. Roy. Coll. Surgeons England *26*:245, 1960.

Scothorne, R. J., and Scothorne, A. W.: Histochemical studies on human skin autografts, J. Anat. *87*:22, 1953.

(See also references in Chapter 10 on Tissue Transplantation.)

Chapter 23

The Digestive System

INTRODUCTION

For practical purposes, the digestive system (Fig. 373) may be considered as consisting of: (1) a long muscular tube that begins at the lips and ends at the anus, at which two sites its epithelial lining becomes continuous with the skin; and (2) certain large glands situated outside the tube proper (salivary glands, liver, gallbladder and pancreas) that empty their secretions into the tube because they develop from its epithelial lining.

The first thing that a student should realize about the digestive tube is that the fluid and semifluid material in its lumen is as much outside the body as the water in which an ameba lives, and obtains its nourishment, is outside the ameba. Food must be absorbed from the lumen of the tube into the blood capillaries and the lymphatics of the wall of the tube before it can be said to have gained entrance into the body proper. However, most food taken in at the mouth is neither in a form suitable to be transported in the blood and the tissue fluid nor in a form suitable to be utilized by cells. For example, the carbohydrate of bread and potatoes is in the form of starch. Before this carbohydrate can be absorbed and used by cells it must be broken down to glucose. The process by which foods taken in at the mouth are converted into substances that may be safely absorbed and used by cells is known as *digestion*. Digestion occurs in the lumen of the digestive tube and is brought about by the food therein being acted upon by digestive juices that are secreted by the glands in the wall of the tube and by others situated outside the tube but emptying into it. The epithelial cells lining the tube are extremely selective in their absorptive functions; they absorb only the products of digestion. If they were not highly selective, and absorbed undigested substances, death would result.

The digestive tube consists of the mouth, the pharynx, the esophagus, the stomach, the small intestine and the large intestine (Fig. 373). These different parts of the tube serve somewhat different purposes. Before discussing the structure of each part in detail and how it relates to its function, we shall try to give a picture of the operation of the different parts of the tube by an analogy.

The operations that take place in the digestive tube are not unlike those that the biochemist performs when he wishes to extract a valuable material from some crude material. (1) He places the material in a mortar, adds some fluid to it, and then breaks up and mixes the mass with a pestle until it is fairly homogeneous. This operation corresponds roughly to what happens when food is taken into the mouth. Crude material here is ground with the teeth and mixed with saliva until it is brought to a reasonably homogeneous state. (2) The biochemist takes the homogeneous material from the mortar and puts it into a beaker, where he adds acid and enzymes and more fluid; he then stirs the mixture until the material is broken down into the simpler soluble compounds for which he is searching. This corresponds to what happens in the stomach and the first part of the small intestine. (3) The biochemist adds still more fluid to his mixture and puts it into a funnel provided with filter paper. The soluble simpler substances that have formed from the insoluble mass with which he began then pass through the filter paper into a separate container. This step is comparable with what happens in most of the small intestine. The simpler substances formed as a result of digestion are absorbed through the filtering inner lining of the intestine to enter the blood stream and the lymphatics. (4) The biochemist does not unduly prolong the filtration because the material he is filtering may become contaminated with bacteria, with the result that poisonous products may form. So, he discards the residue held in the filter paper before contaminating bacteria have an opportunity to flourish in it. This step is roughly comparable with what happens in the lower end of the small intestine, for there the residue in its lumen is ejected into the large

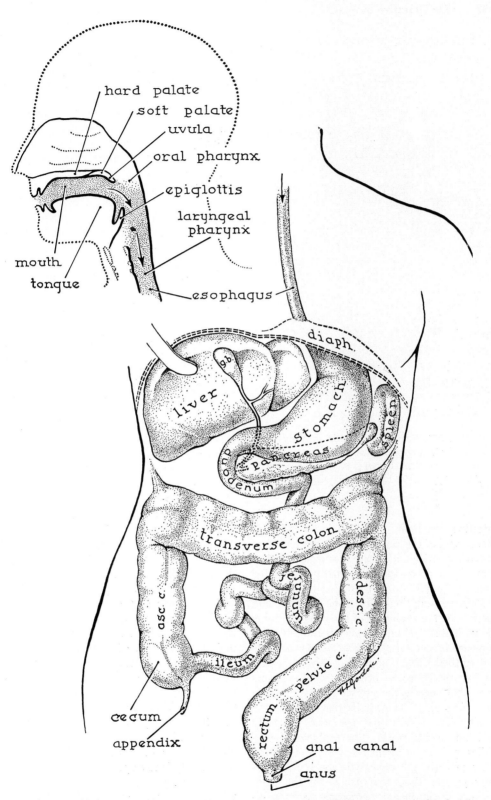

FIG. 373. Diagram of the parts of the digestive system. (Redrawn and modified from Grant, J. C. B.: A Method of Anatomy, ed. 4, Baltimore, Williams & Wilkins)

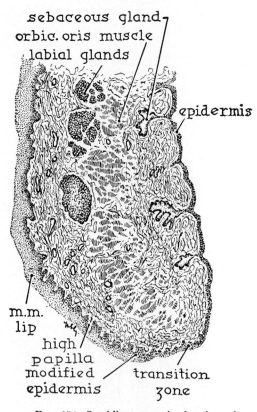

sebaceous gland
orbic. oris muscle
labial glands

epidermis

m.m.
lip
high
papilla
modified   transition
epidermis   zone

Fig. 374. Semidiagrammatic drawing of a sagittal section of a lip (low-power). (Redrawn from Huber: Piersol's Human Anatomy, ed. 9, Philadelphia, Lippincott)

intestine, the lining of which is not adapted for absorbing the products of digestion. Here bacteria flourish and so are a conspicuous feature of the feces that are finally eliminated from the body.

Before attempting to learn the structure and the function of each part of the digestive tube, the student should understand thoroughly what is meant by the term *mucous membrane*. The wet epithelial lining of the digestive tube and (as we shall see) of other internal passageways that open to the surface constitutes, like the epidermis of skin, a barrier between the community of cells that comprise the body and the outside world. The problem of providing protection along the vast, wet epithelial surface of the digestive tube is considerably greater than that faced by the skin, because the epithelial membrane over considerable distances must be thin enough to be absorptive. One of the chief agencies ensuring the integrity of this wet epithelial membrane is its lubrication with mucus. From one end to the other, the digestive tube is richly provided with either individual cells or with glands that produce mucus. Wet epithelial membranes thus equipped are termed mucous membranes. Actually, the term mucous membrane usually refers to something more than an epithelial membrane alone; it includes the underlying connective tissue that supports the epithelial membrane and is usually termed the *lamina propria* or *tunica propria* of the mucous membrane. In some instances mucous membranes contain some smooth muscle in their deepest parts; if present, this also is considered as part of the mucous membrane and is called the *muscularis mucosae* (muscle of the mucosa).

THE LIPS

The substance of the lips consists of striated muscle fibers and fibro-elastic connective tissue. The muscle tissue consists chiefly of the fibers of the orbicularis oris muscle and is distributed in the more central part of the lip (Fig. 374). The direction of the fibers and their attachments are discussed in textbooks of gross anatomy.

The outer surface of each lip is covered with skin that contains hair follicles, sebaceous glands and sweat glands (Fig. 374, *right*). The red, free margins of the lips are covered with a modified skin which represents a transition from skin to mucous membrane. The epithelium in this site is covered with a layer of dead cells, like that of the skin, but it is said that there is a high percentage of eleidin, which is relatively transparent, in it. The connective tissue papillae of the dermis beneath it are numerous, high and vascular (Fig. 374), and, as a result, the blood in their capillaries readily shows through the transparent epidermis to make the lips appear red. No sweat or sebaceous glands or hair follicles are present in the skin of the red, free margins of the lips. Since the epithelium is not heavily keratinized and is not provided with sebum, it must be wetted frequently with the tongue if its integrity is to be preserved. "Chapped" and "cracked" lips are common under conditions which favor evaporation. The high papillae bring many nerve endings as well as capillaries close to the surface of the red margins of the lips; for this reason, they are very sensitive.

As the skin of the red, free margin passes onto the inner surface of the lip it becomes transformed into mucous membrane. The epithelium of this is thicker than the epidermis covering the outer surface of the lip (Fig. 374, *left*) and is of the stratified squamous non-keratinizing type. However, some granules of keratohyalin may be found in the cells of the more superficial layers. High papillae of the connective tissue lamina propria (which, in mucous membranes, replaces the dermis of skin) extend into it. Small clusters of mucous glands, the labial glands, are embedded in the lamina propria (Fig. 374) and connect with the surface by means of little ducts.

THE CHEEKS

The mucous membrane lining the cheeks has a fairly thick layer of epithelium of the stratified squamous nonkeratinizing type. This is the kind of epithelium that is characteristically found on wet epithelial surfaces where there is considerable wear and tear and from which (ruminants excepted) little or no absorption occurs. The superficial cells are constantly being rubbed off the surface and replaced from below. This, of course, requires that the cells in the deeper layers of the epithelium divide rapidly enough to replace the cells worn away from the surface. If the ball of the finger is drawn across the inside of the cheek, many surface cells will be removed. If these are dabbed on a slide and stained with methylene blue, their flat bodies with their centrally disposed nuclei can be seen readily.

The lamina propria of the mucous membrane lining the cheek consists of fairly dense fibro-elastic tissue and extends into the epithelium in the form of high papillae. The deeper part of it merges into what is termed the *submucosa* of the lining of the cheek. This layer contains flat elastic fibers and many blood vessels. Strands of fibro-elastic tissue from the lamina propria penetrate through the fatty elastic submucosa to join with the fibro-elastic tissue associated with the muscle that underlies the submucosa and forms the chief substance of the wall of the cheek. These strands fasten the mucous membrane to the underlying muscle at intervals, with the result that when the jaws are closed, the relaxed

mucous membrane bulges inward in many small folds instead of in one large fold that would project inward so far that it would be an inconvenience and frequently would be bitten inadvertently.

There are small mucous glands, some of which have a few serous secretory demilunes, in the inner part of the cheek.

THE TONGUE

The tongue is composed chiefly of striated muscle, the fibers of which are grouped into bundles that interlace with one another and are disposed in 3 planes. Hence, if a longitudinal section is cut from the tongue, i.e., at right angles to the dorsal surface (a sagittal section), it will reveal both longitudinal and vertical muscle fibers cut longitudinally and horizontal fibers cut in cross section (Fig. 256 A). Such an arrangement of striated muscle fibers is so unique in the body that finding it in any given section permits that section to be identified as having been cut from the tongue.

The individual muscle fibers inside the bundles are each surrounded by endomysium which tends to be somewhat more substantial than that seen in most striated muscle. The endomysium brings capillaries close to the muscle fibers (Fig. 261). The fibro-elastic tissue between the muscle bundles can be thought of as constituting the perimysium. It contains the larger vessels and nerves and, in many sites, adipose tissue; in some parts of the tongue, glands are embedded in it.

Mucous Membranes. That covering the under surface of the tongue is thin and smooth. The lamina propria connects directly with the fibro-elastic tissue associated with the bundles of muscle. No true submucosa exists here.

The mucous membrane covering the dorsal surface of the tongue is of special interest (Fig. 375). Almost everyone can recall from his childhood being visited by a doctor and told to "put out his tongue" so that its dorsal surface might be examined. The dorsal surface of the tongue may give the physician information of two kinds. (1) If it is "coated" heavily it indicates that the general state of health of the individual, and perhaps particularly the operation of the digestive system, is not satisfactory. (2) Certain diseases, for example, scarlet fever and pernicious anemia,

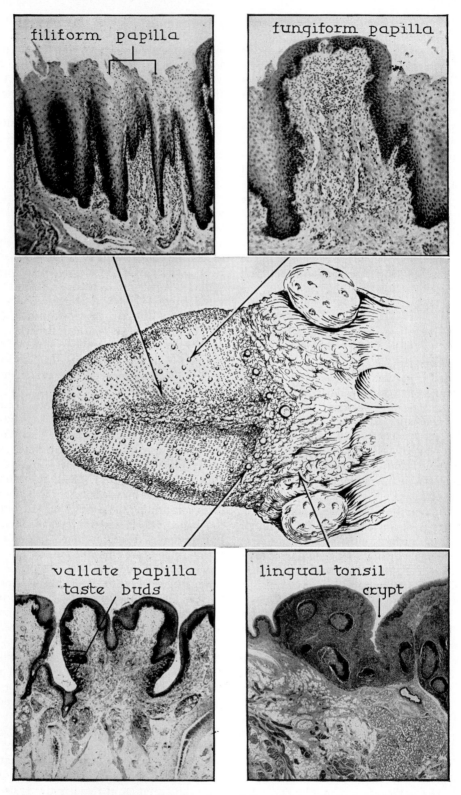

Fig. 375. Drawing of the dorsal surface of the tongue and photomicrographs of sections cut from its mucous membrane in 4 areas.

may cause certain specific alterations on the surface of the tongue, hence the detecting of these specific alterations may be a valuable help in making a diagnosis of one of these diseases.

The mucous membrane covering the dorsal surface of the tongue is divided into two parts: (1) that covering the anterior two thirds or oral part of the tongue (its body) and (2) that covering the posterior one third or pharyngeal part (its root). A V-shaped line, the sulcus terminalis, running across the tongue marks the border between these two parts (Fig. 375).

The mucous membrane covering the oral part of the tongue is very different from that covering the pharyngeal part. It is covered by little projections of the mucous membrane called *papillae.* There are three kinds of these in man—filiform, fungiform and vallate.

Filiform (*filum* = thread) **papillae** are relatively high, narrow, conical structures composed both of lamina propria and epithelium (Fig. 375, *upper left*). Each has a primary papilla of lamina propria from which secondary papillae of lamina propria extend toward the surface. The primary papilla is covered by a cap of epithelium which breaks up to form separate caps over each of the secondary papillae. Sometimes the epithelial caps over the secondary papillae break up into threads to justify the term filiform. The epithelium that caps the secondary papillae becomes very horny, but there is some question as to whether the surface cells become converted into true keratin in man. In some animals the horny filiform papillae make the dorsal surface of the tongue distinctly rasplike.

Filiform papillae are very numerous and are distributed in parallel rows across the tongue. Near the root these rows follow the V-shaped line that divides the body from the root of the tongue (Fig. 375).

Fungiform papillae are so-called because they project from the dorsal surface of the oral part of the tongue like little fungi which are narrower at their bases and have expanded smooth rounded tops (Fig. 375, *upper right*). They are not nearly as numerous as the filiform papillae among which they are scattered; they are somewhat more numerous at the tip of the tongue than elsewhere. Each has a central core of lamina propria which is termed

the *primary papilla,* and from this, secondary papillae of lamina propria project up into the covering epithelium. The epithelial surface does not follow the contours of the secondary papillae of lamina propria as it does in filiform papillae; hence, the secondary papillae of lamina propria bring capillaries very close to the surface of the epithelium. Since the covering epithelium is not keratinized, it is relatively translucent; this permits the blood vessels in the high secondary papillae to show through and, as a result, the fungiform papillae in life are red.

From 7 to 12 **vallate papillae** are distributed along the V-shaped line that separates the mucous membrane of the body of the tongue from that of the root (Fig. 375). The name (*vallum* = a rampart) suggests that each, like an ancient city, is surrounded by a rampart. Actually, each is like a turreted castle because it is surrounded by a moat or trench (Fig. 375, *lower left*). The moat that surrounds each is kept flooded, and so cleansed of debris, by glands disposed deep to the papilla but which empty by means of ducts into the bottom of the moat.

Each vallate papilla has a central primary papilla of lamina propria (Fig. 375, *lower left*). Secondary papillae of lamina propria extend up from this into the stratified nonkeratinizing epithelium that covers the whole papilla. Vallate papillae are narrower at their points of attachment than at their free surfaces, hence their shapes are not unlike those of papillae of the fungiform type.

Functions of Papillae. Animals in which filiform papillae are highly developed are capable of licking layers off solid and semisolid material with a sandpaperlike efficiency. Even though filiform papillae are not very highly developed in man, they permit children to lick ice cream satisfactorily. Such papillae contain nerve endings specialized for touch (tactile sense). Most fungiform papillae and all the vallate papillae contain taste buds in which there are special nerve endings which, on being stimulated, give rise to the nervous impulses that result in sensations of taste. Taste buds will be described in detail in a subsequent chapter.

Lingual Tonsil. No true papillae are present on the mucous membrane covering the root of the tongue. The small humps seen over this

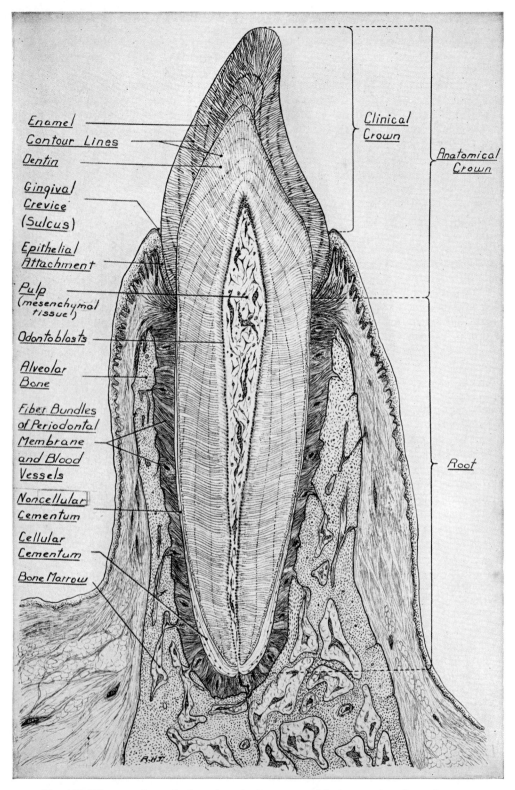

Enamel

Contour Lines

Dentin

Gingival
Crevice
(Sulcus)

Epithelial
Attachment

Pulp
(mesenchymal
tissue)

Odontoblasts

Alveolar
Bone

Fiber Bundles
of Periodontal
Membrane
and Blood
Vessels

Noncellular
Cementum

Cellular
Cementum

Bone Marrow

Clinical
Crown

Anatomical
Crown

Root

FIG. 376. Diagram of a sagittal section of a lower central incisor tooth and attachments.

part of the tongue are due to aggregations of lymphatic nodules in the lamina propria beneath the epithelium (Fig. 375, *lower right*). Such an arrangement, i.e., aggregations of lymphatic nodules in close association with stratified squamous epithelium, is generally called *tonsillar tissue*. That over the root of the tongue constitutes the *lingual tonsil*. Many of the lymphatic nodules in the lingual tonsil have germinal centers. Diffuse lymphatic tissue fills the spaces between them. Along with the lymphocytes there are many plasma cells. The stratified squamous nonkeratinizing epithelium that overlies the lymphatic tissue extends down into it in many sites to form wells or pits (Fig. 375, *lower right*). These are called *crypts* (*kryptos* = concealed). Lymphocytes migrate through the epithelium covering these patches of lymphatic tissue, but more particularly through the stratified epithelial walls of the crypts, to gain entrance to their lumens. The superficial epithelial cells from the linings of the crypts desquamate into the lumens of the crypts, with the result that the lumens of crypts may show accumulations of debris formed from lymphocytes and desquamated epithelial cells. Ducts from underlying mucous glands open into the bottoms of many crypts; this arrangement, when present, serves to keep the lumens washed out and hence free from debris. For this reason, infected crypts are not so common in the lingual tonsil as in tonsillar tissue in other sites where there are no underlying glands that open into the crypts.

THE TEETH

Introductory Description of an Adult Tooth and Its Attachments

In man the teeth function to reduce food that is taken into the mouth to small pieces and to mix it with saliva so that it is swallowed easily. They are arranged in two parabolic curves, one in the upper jaw and one in the lower. Each of these two curved rows of teeth constitutes a *dental arch*. The upper arch is slightly larger than the lower; hence, normally, the upper teeth slightly overlap the lower teeth.

The bulk of each tooth is made of a special type of calcified connective tissue called *dentin* (Fig. 376). Dentin generally is not exposed to the external environment of the tooth because it is covered with one or the other of two other calcified tissues. The dentin of that portion of the tooth that projects through the gums into the mouth is covered with a cap of very hard, calcified, epithelial-derived tissue called *enamel* (Fig. 376); this part of the tooth constitutes its *anatomic crown* (Fig. 376). The remainder of the tooth, the *anatomic root* (Fig. 376), is covered with a special calcified connective tissue called *cementum* (Fig. 376). There are two histologic types of cementum. That covering the coronal one half or one third of the root has no cells within its matrix and therefore is termed *noncellular cementum*. The rest of the cementum is called cellular cementum because it contains cells (cementocytes) within lacunae; the latter, like those of bone, have canaliculi extending from them. However, there are no haversian systems in cementum; normally, it is nonvascular as are all the other hard dental tissues. The junction between the crown and the root of the tooth is termed the *neck* or *cervix*, and the visible line of junction between enamel and cementum is termed the *cervical line*.

Within each tooth is a space that conforms to the general shape of the tooth; this is called the *pulp cavity* (Fig. 376). Its more expanded portion in the coronal part of the tooth is called the *pulp chamber*, and the narrowed part of the cavity that extends through the root is called the *pulp* or *root canal*. The pulp in the cavity consists of a mesenchymal-like connective tissue; this is what lay people call the "nerve" of the tooth because it is so sensitive. The pulp is well supplied with nerve fibers and small blood vessels. The sides of the pulp cavity are lined by modified connective tissue cells called *odontoblasts* (Fig. 376) whose function, as their name implies, is related to the production of dentin. The nerve and the blood supply of a tooth enters the pulp through a small hole (or holes) through the apex of the root called the *apical foramen* (Fig. 376, *not labeled*).

The lower teeth are set into a bony ridge that projects upward from the body of the mandible, and the upper ones into a bony ridge that projects downward from the body of the maxilla; these bony ridges are termed *alveolar processes*. In these processes are *sockets* (*alveoli*)—one for the root of each tooth. The teeth are suspended and held firmly in their alveoli by a connective tissue membrane called the *periodontal membrane* (Fig. 376). It consists chiefly of dense bundles of collagenic fibers running in various directions from the bone of the socket wall to the cementum that covers the root. The ends of the collagenic fibers are embedded in both the bone of the socket and the cementum of the tooth. The embedded fibers are called *Sharpey's fibers* (Fig. 389). The way in which Sharpey's fibers become embedded in bone and cementum will be explained later. The fibers are arranged so that when pressure is exerted on the biting surface of the tooth, the tooth, being suspended by them, will not be pressed farther into the narrowing socket (which could squeeze the blood vessels in the membrane), and at the same time the tooth is permitted some slight movement within its alveolus.

The mucous membrane of the mouth forms an external covering for the bone of the alveolar process; these coverings constitute the *gums*. That part of the gum tissue extending coronally beyond the crest of the alveolar process is the *gingiva* (Fig. 376).

The part of the tooth that extends into the mouth beyond the gingiva is called the *clinical crown* (as distinguished from the anatomic crown described previously). The clinical crown may or may not be identical with the anatomic crown of a tooth. Soon after the tooth erupts into the mouth, the gingiva is attached to the enamel somewhere along the anatomic crown, so the clinical crown is shorter than the anatomic crown. As eruption proceeds, there is a time when the gingiva is attached to the tooth at the cervical line; at this stage the clinical and the anatomic crowns are identical. As the gingiva recedes still farther, as generally occurs in older people, the gingiva is attached to cementum, so the clinical crown is longer than the anatomic crown.

A General Description of Dentitions in Man

Nature has provided for the maintenance of various tissues of the body by replacement and repair in different ways. For example, bone is more or less constantly renewed by the proliferation, the differentiation and the secretion of the cells that cover and line its surfaces. The deeper cells in epithelial membranes proliferate to maintain the thickness of these membranes as the surface cells are worn away. New secreting cells develop in most glands to keep the secreting complement normal. On the other hand, no new nerve and probably no new muscle cells develop during postnatal life.

The arrangement with regard to teeth is unique. Two separate sets of teeth, or *dentitions*, develop during life. The first or *primary* dentition serves during the period of childhood. The teeth that develop in this dentition are called the *deciduous* (*decidere* = to fall down), *baby* or *milk* teeth. The primary teeth are shed progressively and are replaced by the permanent teeth that are intended to last the individual for the remainder of his life.

There are 20 teeth in the primary dentition—10 in the upper and 10 in the lower jaw. The shape of these is not the same; each is modified for different functions related to mastication. The first 2 teeth on each side of the mid-line in the upper and the lower jaws are called *incisors* (*incidere* = to cut into). These are shaped like chisels and can cut into food. The 2 incisors immediately next to the mid-line are the *central* incisors, and those next to them are the *lateral* incisors. The next teeth in order proceeding back from the incisors are the *canine* or *cuspid* teeth; the free-biting surface of these has only a single *cusp* (conical projection). These teeth (particularly in lower animals) serve to grasp and tear or shred food. Next in line, traveling posteriorly in a child's mouth, are 2 *molar* teeth on each side, the first and the second molars. Each molar tooth is modified for grinding food; hence, its biting surfaces are wider and flatter than the other teeth and have 3 or more cusps projecting from them. Each of the molars has more than one root; the lowers have 2, and the uppers have 3.

As has been mentioned already, the upper arch is slightly larger than the lower; hence, the upper teeth slightly overlap the lower. In addition, since the upper incisors are wider than the lower ones, each upper tooth not only meets its counterpart in the lower jaw but also contacts the next tooth behind that one.

The first of the primary teeth to erupt are the lower incisors that appear in the mouths of infants at about the age of 6 months. The last of the primary dentition erupts at approximately 2 years. This set of teeth serves the child for the next 4 years or so, at which time the primary teeth begin to be shed and replaced by the permanent ones. In addition to replacing primary teeth, some of the permanent teeth erupt behind the last of the primary ones. This period of replacement of primary teeth extends over approximately 6 years, from about 6 through 12 years of age.

It should be realized that permanent teeth must be developing for some time prior to their eruption. Indeed, it takes several years (up to 12 for the upper cuspid) for a tooth to develop within a jaw. By the time a child is about 3 years of age, there are 48 teeth in the jaws that are either in function (the primary teeth) or in some stage of development. Figure 377 shows a dissected skull of a child of about 5½ years of age; the permanent teeth can be seen developing above and between the roots of the primary ones.

The permanent dentition consists of 32 teeth—16 in each jaw. Their shape is similar to the primary teeth but they are somewhat larger. The anterior or front teeth, as in the primary set, are the central and the lateral incisors and the cuspids. Immediately back of the cuspids are the 1st and the 2nd *bicuspids* or *premolars*, which are the teeth that occupy the spaces formerly occupied by the primary molars. Behind the bicuspids in each side of each jaw are 3 *molar* teeth. These are named the 1st, the 2nd and the 3rd molars; they have no predecessors in the primary dentition but erupt behind the last of the primary teeth in order. The 1st molar, or "6-year molar," erupts at about the age of 6 years. The 2nd molar erupts at about the age of 12 and is called the 12-year molar. The 3rd molar or "wisdom tooth" erupts considerably later, if it erupts at all. This tooth is subject to much variation in size and shape and all too frequently remains suppressed or impacted within the jaw. This may lead to disturbances later in life that can be relatively serious.

The Development of a Tooth

The following description will be limited to the development of a lower primary incisor because of the relative simplicity of its development and because it is one of the first teeth to begin development in the fetus. It should

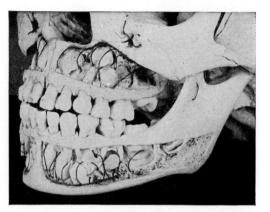

Fig. 377. Photograph of the jaws of a 5½-year-old child. The outer plates of bone have been removed from each jaw to show the roots of the primary teeth and the permanent teeth that are developing. (Preparation provided by K. J. Paynter)

be remembered that the other teeth develop in a similar manner in a regular chronologic sequence.

Early Development. To visualize the plane of section of the illustrations used to show the various stages of tooth development, the student should refer to the upper left sketch in Figure 378. This is a semidiagrammatic drawing of a sagittal section through the jaws and the tongue of an adult, cut in such a way as to permit the section to pass through both an upper and a lower incisor tooth. The remainder of the illustrations showing tooth development are all from within the rectangular area shown on this diagram.

To facilitate description, tooth development has been divided into various "stages" based primarily on the microscopic appearance of a tooth germ at various times during its growth. The student will realize, of course, that these "stages" pass from one to the next without interruption.

Teeth begin to develop early in embryonic life. At about 6 weeks after fertilization the first indication is apparent. At this time a section through the developing jaw would reveal a localized thickening of the basal cells of the oral ectoderm (Fig. 378, *upper right*). This thickening is apparent along the horseshoe-shaped line in a jaw, along which teeth will develop, and it has been called the *dental pri-*

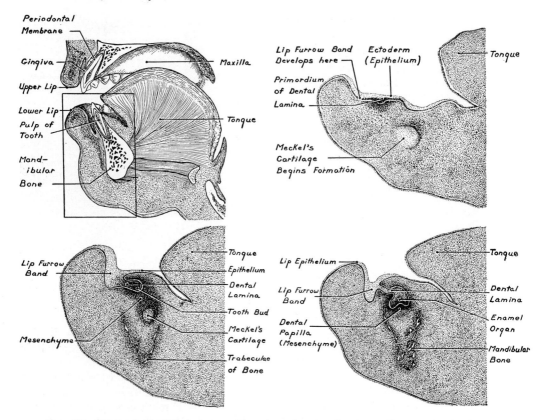

FIG. 378. (*Upper left*) This is to provide orientation for the succeeding figures. It shows the appearance of a sagittal section cut through the upper and the lower jaws of an adult in such a way as to pass through an upper and a lower incisor tooth. Note the rectangular area marked out by black lines. The appearance of this area, as seen in the developing embryo, is illustrated in the following figures. (*Upper right*) Diagram of a sagittal section of the developing lower jaw of an embryo at about the 6th week of development. The section passes through the area where a central incisor tooth will develop. (*Lower left*) Diagram of the same area in an embryo at about the end of the 7th week of development. The dental lamina has formed a tooth bud where the central incisor is to form. (*Lower right*) Diagram of the same area in an embryo toward the end of the 8th week. This illustrates the "cap" stage of development.

mordium (*primus* = first; *ordior* = to begin). From this an epithelial shelf called a *dental lamina* grows into the mesenchyme (Fig. 378). From each lamina little epithelial buds develop where each primary tooth will form; these buds give rise to the primary teeth and their successors. Also it can be observed (Fig. 378, *lower left*) that at about this same time another invagination of epithelium occurs in front of (labial to) the dental laminae; eventually, this will split so as to separate the lip from the remainder of the mouth by a groove.

During the first few days of development, the dental lamina tends to grow in a slanted direction down (or up) and lingually (toward the tongue). Next, increased proliferation occurs in the cells of the lamina to form an epithelial bulge at each place where a tooth will develop; each bulge is directed deeply. Each bulge is termed a *tooth bud*; one is shown in Figure 378, *lower left*.

As the tooth bud increases in size and penetrates deeper into the underlying mesenchyme, the lower surface of each becomes so indented that the lower concave surface of the bud comes close to the upper convex one. This makes the bud "cap-shaped." The "cap" stage of development is reached after about 2 weeks of development, and when it is reached the tooth bud is called the *enamel organ,* and

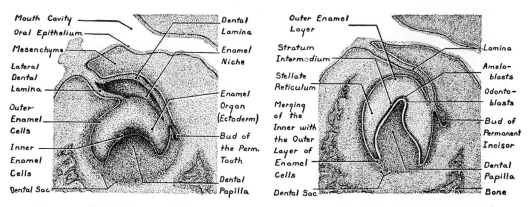

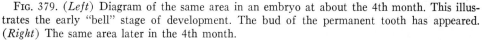

FIG. 379. (*Left*) Diagram of the same area in an embryo at about the 4th month. This illustrates the early "bell" stage of development. The bud of the permanent tooth has appeared. (*Right*) The same area later in the 4th month.

the little papilla of mesenchyme over which the cap fits is called the *dental papilla*.

During the next several weeks, the enamel organ increases in size, and the bone of the jaws grows up to enclose it partly (Figs. 378 and 379). By the 4th month the enamel organ has grown almost to full size. At this time it appears, when seen in sagittal section (Fig. 379), to have the form of a bell, so this is termed the "bell" stage of development. During this period, i.e., the 4th developmental month, considerable cellular differentiation and specialization occurs within the enamel organ, as will now be described.

During the bell stage, the line of junction between it and the mesenchymal papilla assumes the shape and the size of the future line of junction between the enamel and the dentin of the adult tooth (Fig. 380). By the 5th month of development, the dental lamina has been invaded and broken up by the surrounding mesenchyme, and the enamel organ loses any direct connection with the oral epithelium. Occasionally, some residual cells of the dental lamina may persist to give rise to cysts in later life.

At about this time the cells of the dental lamina, at the junction between the lamina and the enamel organ that formed from it, begin to proliferate; this results in a little bud of epithelial cells being formed on the lingual surface of the primary enamel organ. This is the bud of the *permanent tooth,* and later the succeeding permanent tooth will develop from it in this area (Fig. 379).

During this same stage of development, the

mesenchymal cells surrounding the enamel organ become differentiated and form collagenic fibers, and the whole developing tooth becomes surrounded by a discernible loose fibrous connective tissue capsule. This is called the *dental sac* (Fig. 379, *right*), and it gives rise to the periodontal membrane—that dense connective tissue membrane that suspends the tooth in its socket.

The mesenchymal papilla that becomes enclosed by the enamel organ consists of a delicate network of mesenchymal cells connected to one another by thin protoplasmic strands and separated from one another by an amorphous intercellular substance. This tissue becomes increasingly vascular as development proceeds. Increased vascularization is also apparent in the connective tissue of the dental sac, and the outer (convex) surface of the enamel organ changes from being smooth to wavy as capillaries press onto its surface (but do not enter it).

Cellular Differentiation Within the Enamel Organ and the Beginning of Hard Tissue Formation. Up to the end of the "cap" stage of development all of the cells of the enamel organ appear the same. Considerable differentiation and specialization among these cells occurs during the bell stage. First, the cells immediately adjacent to the tip of the dental papilla become tall and columnar. At first their nuclei are at their bases, next to the connective tissue of the papilla, but before secretory activity begins in these cells their nuclei move to their opposite ends. These cells are called *ameloblasts* (*amel* = enamel; *blastos*

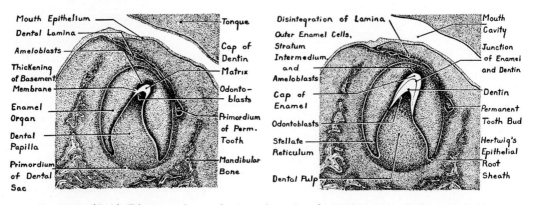

FIG. 380. (*Left*) Diagram of a sagittal section of a developing lower incisor tooth in an embryo between the 4th and the 5th months of development. This shows a cap of dentin at the tip of the papilla. (*Right*) The same area in the 5th month. Enamel, as well as dentin, has begun to form. The site where Hertwig's epithelial root sheath will form is indicated.

= germ) (Figs. 379 and 381), and they are responsible for the production of tooth enamel. The single layer of cells forming the outer boundary of the enamel organ is known as the *outer enamel epithelium*. Between it and the ameloblasts are two distinct cell layers. The inner one immediately adjacent to the ameloblast layer is one or two cells in thickness and is called the *stratum intermedium*; the other, forming the bulk of the organ, is called the *stellate reticulum*. In the latter region the cells assume a star shape and are connected to one another by long protoplasmic extensions (Fig. 381) similar to those of cells of mesenchyme.

While this differentiation is occurring in the enamel organ, some very important specialization also takes place in certain cells of the dental papilla. As was pointed out, the ameloblasts begin to differentiate at the tip of the developing cusp, or at the incisal edge of the tooth, and differentiation then proceeds down its sides, toward the base of the crown. As this occurs, the mesenchymal cells of the dental papilla immediately adjacent to the ameloblasts also become tall columnar cells; they are then known as *odontoblasts* (Fig. 380), for they will form dentin. The area where these two cellular transformations first appear in a tooth is termed its *growth center*. It is at this site that production of the hard tissues of the tooth first occurs. The actual mechanism of tissue production will be discussed in some detail below. It suffices to say here that the first tissue to appear is dentin; this is produced by odontoblasts at the tip of the

papilla. After a thin layer of this is deposited, the ameloblasts begin to produce the matrix of enamel on it.

It should be pointed out here that the formation of dentin and enamel differs from bone formation in that no formative cells are trapped within the matrix that they produce. There is no such thing as an "odontocyte" or an "amelocyte." Instead, the cells, as they produce the hard tissue matrix, retreat away from it—the ameloblasts outward, and the odontoblasts inward. Before discussing the formation of the hard tissues in more detail, the description of the development of the tooth as an organ will be completed.

Formation of the Root. During the "bell" stage of development of the enamel organ, the inner cells line up to assume the shape of the future line of junction between the enamel and the dentin of the adult tooth (Fig. 380, *right*). The deepest cells of the enamel organ differentiate to ameloblasts and produce enamel. But they also function to organize or induce the cells within the dental papilla to differentiate into odontoblasts. The inducing duties of these epithelial-derived cells seem to be all-important for the formation of odontoblasts and dentin. Since the roots of teeth, as well as their crowns, are largely composed of dentin, mesenchymal cells in the root region must be induced to become odontoblasts by epithelial cells of the enamel organ, even though the roots do not become covered with enamel. This is accomplished as follows:

After the formation of the hard tissues of

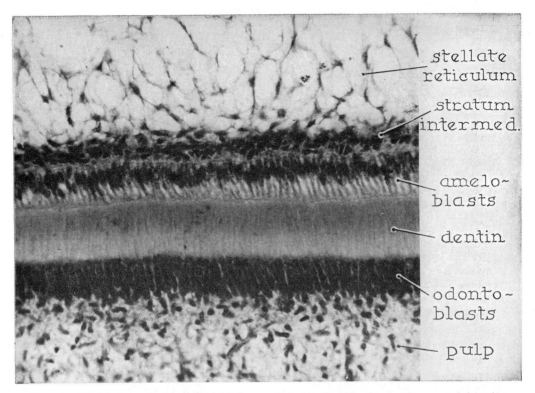

stellate
reticulum

stratum
intermed.

amelo-
blasts

dentin

odonto-
blasts

pulp

FIG. 381. High-power photomicrograph of a section cut through the dentino-enamel junction of a developing tooth shortly after dentin formation has begun.

the crown is well advanced, the epithelial cells around the base of the enamel organ begin to proliferate further. It should be realized that at this site (Fig. 380, *right*) the cells forming the inner layer of the enamel organ become continuous with those forming the outer layer, i.e., the ameloblast layer is continuous with the outer enamel epithelium. The cells at this line of junction—around the bottom of the "bell"—begin to proliferate and to migrate down into the underlying mesenchyme. Since the bottom of the bell is ring-shaped (if seen from below), the proliferating cells from the ring form a tube that surrounds further mesenchyme as it descends. The cells of the tube constitute *Hertwig's epithelial root sheath* (Fig. 382). As this sheath moves down it forms the pattern outlining the shape of the root of the tooth and it organizes the cells of the mesenchyme that it surrounds, which are immediately adjacent to it, to differentiate into odontoblasts. While the root is forming in this manner, the whole tooth is moving toward the oral cavity, and it erupts into the mouth be-

fore the root is fully formed. Indeed, most permanent teeth are in the mouth and in function for about 2 years before the end of the root is completely formed. As the epithelial root sheath approaches the end of the root it becomes narrower to form the typical conical shape of the apex (Fig. 383, *top*).

The root sheath grows downward by continued proliferation of the cells at its leading ring-shaped edge. The older part of it, toward the crown, having served its purpose, becomes detached from the root of the tooth, and the epithelial cells of it remain within the confines of the periodontal membrane surrounding the tooth. They may be observed histologically within the membrane at any age after the roots have formed. They are called the *epithelial rests of Malassez,* and under proper stimulus they may give rise to dental cysts at any time in life.

The root sheath separates from the formed root, and cells from the mesenchymal connective tissue of the dental sac deposit cementum on the outer surface of the dentin; this is laid

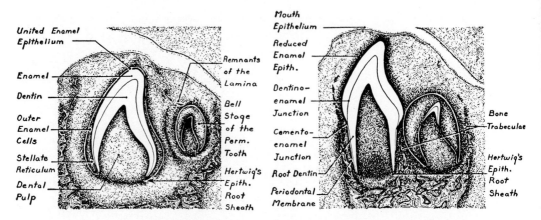

Fig. 382. (*Left*) Sagittal section of a developing lower incisor at about the time of birth. The development of the crown is almost completed. Hertwig's epithelial root sheath is beginning to develop. It should be noted that at this time the permanent tooth is developing in the same bony socket as the deciduous tooth. (*Right*) Diagram of the same area immediately before eruption. The crown is almost complete. The formation of the root is well advanced. Both dentin and enamel have appeared in the permanent tooth. Bone has formed to separate the two teeth, so the permanent tooth now has a separate socket.

down around the collagenic fibers of the membrane that the cells in this area are also forming.

While the primary tooth is developing and erupting into function, the tooth germ for its successor also is differentiating and laying down the substance of the permanent tooth (Figs. 382, *right,* and 383). As this occurs, the tooth moves toward the oral cavity. The root of the primary tooth begins to resorb (Fig. 383, *middle*), and by the time the permanent tooth is ready to erupt, the root of the primary tooth has been completely resorbed. The crown becomes detached from the gum tissue, and the tooth is shed to be replaced by its permanent successor (Fig. 383, *bottom*).

Some Further Details of the Formation and the Microscopic Structure of the Dental Tissues

In the foregoing section the way that teeth develop and take their places in the oral cavity has been described. In the following section the microscopic structure of the various tissues that form the dental organ will be described in more detail. Certain clinical observations, related to histology and thought to be of importance to the physician, will be included also.

The tissues with which we are concerned are both hard (calcified) and soft (uncalcified). They include dentin, enamel, cementum, dental pulp and periodontal membrane. With the exception of enamel, all are connective tissues.

1. Dentin

It will be recalled that after the enamel organ develops to a certain point, the epithelial cells lining its concave surface, adjacent to the dental papilla, become converted to tall columnar cells known as ameloblasts (Figs. 379, *right,* and 381). The presence of these cells apparently is necessary for the organization of cells within the dental papilla so that they are induced to develop into tall columnar cells called *odontoblasts* that play a leading part in the formation of dentin.

Odontoblasts begin to form dentin matrix very soon after they assume their typical form. At first they are separated from the ameloblasts by only a basement membrane. But soon a layer of intercellular substance is deposited by them; this separates them farther from the ameloblasts. The first intercellular substance to form is a complex of reticular fibers and an amorphous cementing material. The reticular fibers run in a characteristic corkscrew fashion through the odontoblast layer and parallel with the long axes of the cells of the layer until they reach the base-

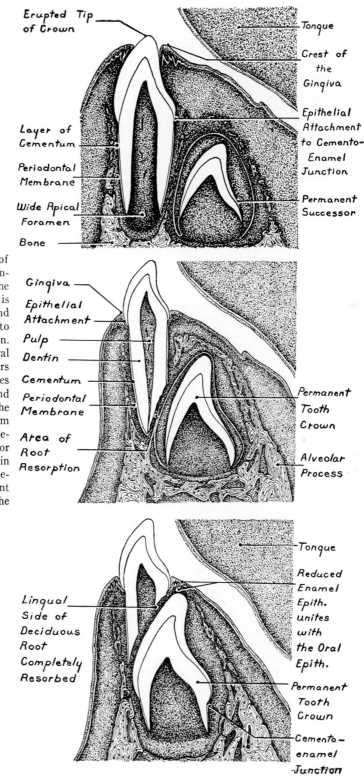

FIG. 383. (*Top*) Diagram of an erupting lower central incisor (6 to 12 months). The epithelium of the gingiva is attached to the enamel and continues down over it to the cemento-enamel junction. (*Center*) Diagram of a central lower incisor tooth 4 to 6 years after birth. The root becomes completed in the 2nd year, and its resorption begins after the 4th year. (*Bottom*) Diagram showing the shedding of a deciduous lower central incisor tooth. This usually occurs in the 7th year. The root has begun to form in the permanent tooth, which will erupt by the 8th year.

Labels (top): Erupted Tip of Crown; Tongue; Crest of the Gingiva; Epithelial Attachment to Cemento-Enamel Junction; Layer of Cementum; Periodontal Membrane; Wide Apical Foramen; Bone; Permanent Successor

Labels (center): Gingiva; Epithelial Attachment; Pulp; Dentin; Cementum; Periodontal Membrane; Area of Root Resorption; Permanent Tooth Crown; Alveolar Process

Labels (bottom): Tongue; Reduced Enamel Epith. unites with the Oral Epith.; Lingual Side of Deciduous Root Completely Resorbed; Permanent Tooth Crown; Cemento-enamel Junction

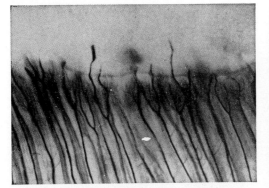

Fig. 384. The processes of odontoblasts lie in canals in the dentin. (Churchill, H. R.: Meyer's Histology and Histogenesis of the Human Teeth, Philadelphia, Lippincott)

ment membrane; here they spread out in a fanlike manner to run parallel with, and become continuous with, the basement membrane. These bundles of reticular fibers that may be seen as the first predentin forms are known as *Korff's fibers*. The fibers that form later (as the production of intercellular substance continues) are collagenic rather than reticular.

The intercellular substance that is formed by the odontoblasts is similar to, but not identical with, the intercellular substance of bone. There are certain chemical differences between the two. For example, bone has both a higher organic content (24-26% vs. 19-21%) and, as might be expected, contains more collagen (25% vs. 18% for dentin). However, the processes by which dentin is formed and calcified are similar to processes already described in connection with bone. We shall elaborate:

It will be recalled that a piece of bone can become larger only by means of the successive addition of new layers of bone to one or more of its surfaces (Fig. 165). This is also true of dentin, except that the growth of this material is even more limited because odontoblasts are present only along the inner or pulpal side of dentin in a tooth. Hence, any new layers of dentin that are produced can be added only to the pulpal surface of such dentin as is present already. Therefore, the addition of layers of dentin must encroach on the pulp.

It will be recalled also that osteoblasts are

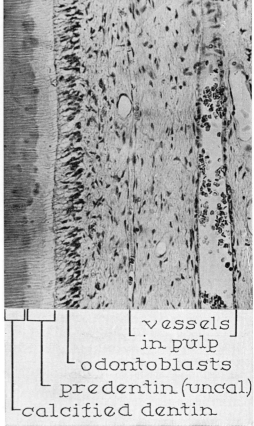

vessels in pulp
odontoblasts
predentin (uncal.)
calcified dentin

Fig. 385. High-power photomicrograph of a section of a child's tooth in which dentin was still forming. (Preparation by K. J. Paynter)

provided with cytoplasmic processes that act as molds when the organic intercellular substance is laid down around them; these are responsible for canaliculi (Fig. 163). Odontoblasts are provided also with processes about which organic intercellular substance is deposited. However, these processes do not extend in all directions from their cell bodies as do those of osteoblasts, but mostly outward to reach the basement membrane that lines the concavity of the enamel organ. Thus, when intercellular substance is deposited between the layer of odontoblasts and the basement membrane, the deposited intercellular substance surrounds these cytoplasmic processes which, therefore, come to lie in tiny canals called *dentinal tubules*. The odontoblastic processes do not retract but remain

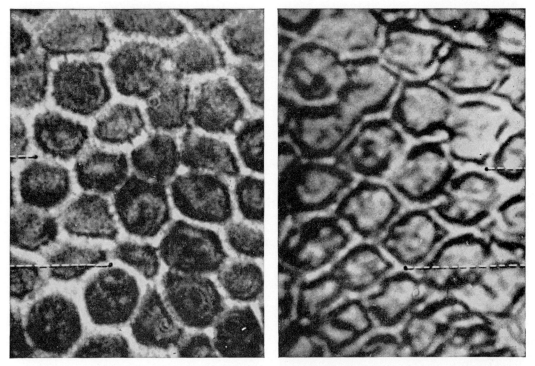

Fig. 386. (*Left*) This photomicrograph is from a cross section cut through ameloblasts; it shows the intercellular substance (indicated by leaders) between them. (*Right*) From a cross section of formed enamel, showing that interprismatic substance (indicated by leaders) has formed in the sites formerly occupied by intercellular substance. (Churchill, H. R.: Meyer's Histology and Histogenesis of the Human Teeth, Philadelphia, Lippincott)

within the tubules where they are called *Tomes' dentinal fibers* (Fig. 384). As more and more dentin is formed, the odontoblasts are displaced farther and farther away from the basement membrane that outlines the dentino-enamel junction. This requires that the dentinal processes, if they are to maintain a connection with the basement membrane, must become increasingly elongated, and that the dentinal tubules containing them must become increasingly elongated also.

It has been pointed out earlier in this text that two steps occur as bone is developing; the first is the manufacture of the organic intercellular substance, and the second is its calcification. For the formation of collagen in dentin see page 249. The calcification of the developing intercellular substance of dentin does not seem to take place as rapidly after its deposition as does the matrix of bone; hence, it is normal for the layer of most recently formed dentin in a growing tooth to be uncalcified for a short time. This

uncalcified layer of dentin is called *predentin*. The oldest dentin in a growing crown is that next to the basement membrane that separates it from enamel. The youngest dentin is that closest to the odontoblasts. Thus, in a growing tooth it is normal for the older calcified dentin to be separated from the odontoblasts by a layer of (uncalcified) *predentin* (Fig. 385).

It is probable that the mechanism of calcification in dentin is very similar to that which operates in cartilage and bone. Phosphatase is involved in the mechanism. It has been established that, although its distribution varies somewhat, depending on the stage of development of the tooth, alkaline phosphatase is present in substantial quantities in the odontogenic cells of the dental papilla during the period of elaboration and calcification of the hard tissue. The enzyme has been observed also to a lesser extent in the predentin and the dentinal tubules.

As most of us are well aware, teeth may be extremely sensitive to stimuli arising on a

FIG. 387. Low-power photomicrograph of a ground section of the enamel and a portion of the dentin of a tooth. The lines of Retzius may be seen curving from the left border upward and to the right. The irregular and slightly wavy structure that extends down from the surface at the upper right side and resembles an artefact is an enamel lamella. Enamel lamellae contain more interprismatic substance than ordinary enamel. Some dentin may be seen in the lower right corner. The tubules that extend from it into the enamel are called "enamel spindles."

dentin surface. The ability of dentin to be sensitive to stimuli is explained by the presence of the cytoplasmic processes of odontoblasts in the dentin, because nerve fibers have not been demonstrated in dentin except very close to the pulpal border. This sensitivity of dentin generally decreases with age; the decrease in sensitivity is related to a calcifica-tion of the dentinal tubules and their filling in with calcium salts.

2. Enamel

It has been pointed out that the presence of ameloblasts, differentiated from the inner enamel epithelium of the enamel organ, are necessary to bring about a differentiation of the cells of the mesenchymal dental papilla into odontoblasts. After the odontoblasts have produced the first thin layer of dentin, the ameloblasts (Fig. 381) are, in turn, induced to make enamel. Enamel then forms and covers the dentin, but only over the anatomic crown of the tooth (Figs. 380, *right,* and 382). It forms first as a relatively uncalcified matrix, which later calcifies.

Just prior to the laying down of enamel matrix, the basement membrane between the ameloblasts and the newly formed dentin thickens. This is thought to be due to the formation of a cuticlelike material by the ends of the ameloblasts that are in contact with the basement membrane. Next, the character of the cytoplasm of the ameloblasts undergoes changes; adjacent to the basement membrane, it first becomes granular and then later it becomes homogeneous as it produces the material of enamel. The process of the formation of enamel is a very complex one, and there are differences of opinion as to whether the homogeneous material should be considered as a secretion of ameloblasts or as a transformation of their cytoplasm. There is much chemical and histochemical evidence to indicate that a type of keratin is produced in the process and that this constitutes a part of the organic material that is formed. It should be recalled at this time that ameloblasts are epithelial cells.

Individual ameloblasts have 6 sides, as may be seen in cross sections, and are separated from one another by thin partitions of intercellular material (Fig. 386, *left*). The material of enamel is produced in the form of rods. The enamel matrix retains the shape of the cell; both are prismatic (Fig. 386, *right*). The transformed ends of the ameloblasts have been termed *Tomes' processes*; these are not to be confused with the Tomes' dentinal process described previously under dentin.

As enamel matrix is produced, the outer

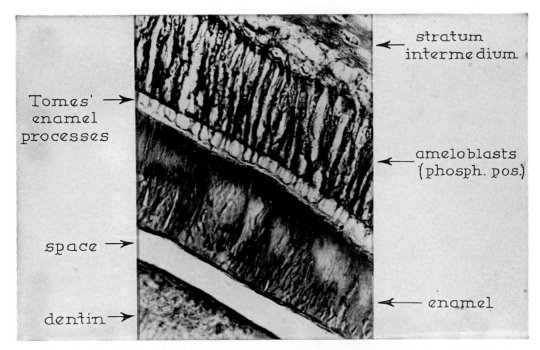

Tomes' enamel processes →

stratum intermedium →

ameloblasts (phosph. pos.) →

space →

enamel ←

dentin →

FIG. 388. Very high-power photomicrograph of a section from the cervical region of a 170-mm. pig canine tooth, decalcified by Kramer's and Shipley's method, and showing the cytoplasm of the ameloblasts to be phosphatase positive. (Bevelander, G., and Johnson, P. L.: Anat. Rec. *104*:125)

ends of ameloblasts migrate outwardly from their starting point—the basement membrane between them and the odontoblast layer. As they migrate they seem to do so rhythmically, i.e., they move in spurts—a certain distance each day; then they rest while preparing for the next day's work. This rhythmic production of matrix is manifest in ground undecalcified sections of adult teeth where it is indicated by lines visible in the enamel called the *striae of Retzius* (Fig. 387). Previously, it was thought that enamel matrix only partially calcified as it was produced and that it became fully calcified only after it was fully formed; the final step was termed *maturation*. Recent work using microradiography and the E/M indicates that calcification does not occur in two steps, but once it has begun it proceeds steadily to completion, proceeding from the dentino-enamel junction to the enamel surface (see Frank and Sognnaes).

Fully formed and calcified enamel is a very highly calcified material (approximately 95% inorganic) constructed of long hexagonal rods

tied together with an interrod calcified cementing substance. Enamel is relatively inert; it has no cells in association with it because the ameloblasts are lost after they form all the enamel and the tooth erupts. Thus, enamel is completely incapable of repair if it is injured by decay, fracture or other means. However, there is a fairly rapid exchange of certain ions between enamel and saliva.

Phosphatase has been demonstrated in the nuclei and the cytoplasm of ameloblasts before enamel matrix formation takes place, and a high concentration of phosphatase is maintained both before and during elaboration of the matrix (Fig. 388). The enzyme gradually disappears from the cells when calcification of the matrix is complete.

3. Cementum

Some cells of the mesenchyme of the dental sac in close proximity to the side of the developing root differentiate and become similar to osteoblasts. Here they are associated with the laying down of another special nonvascular

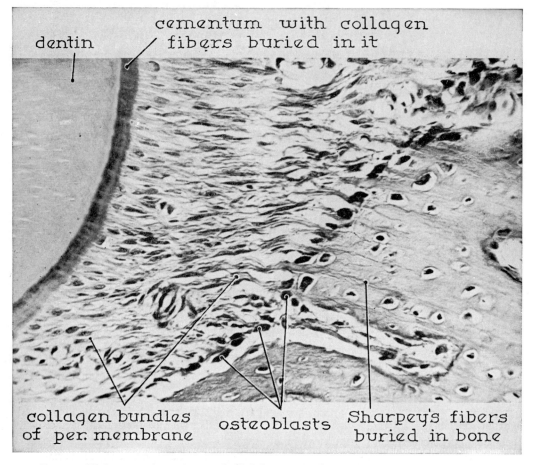

dentin

cementum with collagen fibers buried in it

collagen bundles of per. membrane

osteoblasts

Sharpey's fibers buried in bone

FIG. 389. High-power photomicrograph (lightly retouched) of a portion of a decalcified section of a tooth of a rat, showing how the collagenic fibers of the periodontal membrane continue into both the cementum and the bone to anchor the tooth firmly in its alveolus. (Section supplied by W. J. Linghorne)

calcified connective tissue called *cementum,* which buries in its substance the ends of the fibers of the periodontal membrane and so attaches them to the tooth (Fig. 389).

Cementum in the upper one third to one half the length of the root is noncellular (Fig. 389); the remainder has cells within its matrix. These cells are called *cementocytes* and they, like osteocytes, reside in small spaces within the calcified matrix called *lacunae* and communicate with their source of nutrition through canaliculi.

Under certain circumstances cementum may be subject to resorption, although this does not occur with the same ease or frequency as it does in bone. This fact is utilized clinically during the process of moving teeth slowly from one position to another in the jaw. Such treatment is indicated when teeth are badly aligned. Pressure on the tooth, when sustained long enough, brings about a resorption of bone in front of the tooth as it moves, and a deposition of bone occurs behind it. The cementum, on the other hand, does not resorb under such circumstances.

Cementum, like bone, can increase in amount only by additions to its surface.

THE STUDY OF THE MINERALIZATION OF GROWING TEETH AND BONES BY THE RADIOAUTOGRAPHIC TECHNIC

Leblond, Belanger, Greulich and others, using the radioautographic technic, have studied the development and the subsequent calcification of the matrix of the various hard tissues of the body. Animals have been injected with various radioactive materials, including sulfur, carbon, calcium and phosphorus, and then sacrificed at various time intervals following the injection. Then radioautographs have been made either by fluid coating the slide with emulsion or by preparing "inverted" autographs of the preparations.

These investigators have found that in the case of enamel there is a clear-cut distinction between the deposition of organic matrix and of minerals. The formation of the components of the matrix is indicated by the deposition of radioactive sulfur and carbon, and this occurs considerably in advance of the deposition of calcium and phosphorus. It was found that the labeled sulfur and carbon disappeared from the matrix at the site of, and at the time of, the appearance of labeled calcium and phosphorus. In the case of dentin (and presumably also of bone) the matrix is elaborated in two steps. First, predentin is formed incorporating radioactive carbon; this probably is in the forming collagen. Radioactive sulfur enters into the formation of sulfated mucopolysaccharides. This complete matrix takes up calcium and phosphorus (Fig. 390).

4. Periodontal Membrane

As the root of the tooth forms and cementum is deposited on its surface, the periodontal membrane develops from the mesenchyme of the dental sac that surrounds the tooth during development and fills the space between it and the bone of the alveolar process. This tissue comes to consist of heavy bundles of collagenic fibers arranged in the form of a suspensory ligament between the root of the tooth and the bony wall of its socket (Fig. 376). The fiber bundles are embedded at the one end in the bone of the wall of the alveolus and at the other end in the cementum covering the root (Fig. 376). At both ends the parts of the fibers that actually are embedded in hard tissue are called *Sharpey's fibers* (Fig. 389).

How Sharpey's Fibers Become Attached to Bone and Cementum. It is most important for the student to understand clearly how collagenic fibers become embedded into either bone or cementum to become Sharpey's fibers. The fibers do not grow into the bone or the cementum. It should be understood that the cells of the developing periodontal membrane have the ability to produce not only collagenic fibers but also the organic matrix of both bone and

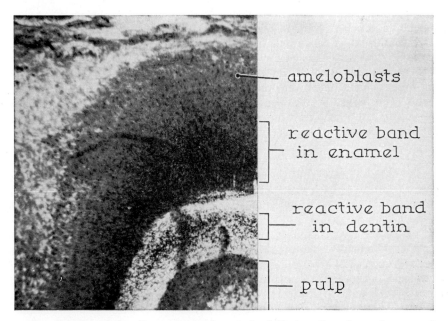

Fig. 390. Inverted radioautograph of an undecalcified section of a molar cusp of an 8-day-old hamster that was injected with radiophosphorus 4 days previously. (Preparation from L. F. Bélanger and C. P. Leblond)

cementum. At the bone border the cells of the membrane produce collagenic fibers and also the other elements of bone matrix; the latter materials are laid down around the bundles of collagenic fibers which, thereby, are embedded in bone matrix that becomes calcified and is cemented to the bone. The same phenomenon occurs at the tooth side of the membrane; here the cells of the developing periodontal membrane make collagenic fibers and also the other components of cementum. The latter materials are laid down around the fibers so as to embed them in a material that becomes calcified and is firmly cemented to the dentin. It is important to realize that *cementum must be formed* if the collagenic fibers of the membrane are to be attached firmly to the tooth. Hence, if fibers become detached from the cementum, as occurs in some kinds of periodontal disease, they cannot be reattached firmly unless new cementum is formed.

The fibers of the periodontal membrane are generally a little longer than the shortest distance between the side of the tooth and the wall of the socket (Fig. 376). This arrangement allows for a certain limited movement of a tooth within its alveolus. In addition to having a suspensory function, the periodontal membrane has other functions. Both the osteoblasts lining the bony wall of the socket and the cementoblasts associated with the side of the root are considered as cells of the membrane; hence, it has osteogenic and cementogenic functions. The blood capillaries within it form the only source of nutritive supply to cementocytes. The nerves of the membrane supply the teeth with their very important and remarkably sensitive tactile sense.

5. The Epithelial Attachment and Periodontal Disease

The gingiva surrounds each tooth like a collar, and under normal conditions the inner surface of the collar is attached tightly to the tooth. If the tooth and its surrounding gingiva are sectioned longitudinally, the gingiva appears to extend up each side of the tooth as a narrow triangle, the apex of which is termed the *gingival crest* (Fig. 376). The side of the triangle next to the tooth is covered with epithelium. This epithelium, as it extends down from the crest, is at first not adherent to the tooth; hence, there is a crevice between it and the tooth surface; this is called the *gingival crevice or sulcus* (this rings the tooth) (Fig. 376). At the bottom of the sulcus the epithelium of the gingiva becomes adherent to the tooth. In erupting teeth the epithelium, from here to the bottom of the anatomic crown, is attached to enamel. However, the epithelium extends a little below the enamel and is attached to the cementum of the root (Fig. 376). The attachment of the epithelium to the enamel is not nearly as strong as its attachment to the cementum because there is nothing on the surface of the enamel (except a little cuticle that is left over from the enamel organ) to which the epithelium can become firmly attached. However, the cementum in this region has been shown by Paynter to develop more or less like a basement membrane (it is P.A.S. positive), so it provides the same means for a firm attachment of epithelium as does the material of basement membranes elsewhere.

It is obvious that the gingival sulcus would provide a site where debris might accumulate. Since there is calcium in saliva it is not surprising that calcified material, called *tartar or calculus,* accumulates in the gingival sulcus, and expanding accumulations of this tend to separate the epithelial attachment from the tooth. Once the epithelial seal around the tooth is broken it is obvious that bacteria could gain entrance to the connective tissue of the gingivae. Therefore, the gingival crevice is a danger zone.

For the reasons given above, or for other reasons (perhaps systemic factors) which are not yet understood, the epithelium of the gingivae may become separated from the cementum, and what are called *pockets* may develop down the sides of a tooth. Pockets commonly separate the cementum-covered root from the fibers of the periodontal membrane, and this, of course, loosens the tooth. The gingival epithelium generally grows down the outer side of pockets so that the pockets are bordered on their outer aspects by epithelium and on their inner aspects by cementum-covered dentin. The pockets become infected. Unfortunately, the type of periodontal disease produced by the above described means is common in individuals in the middle and the older age groups; indeed, its prevalence in this age group is responsible for the loss of more teeth than any other condition. More research into the cause and the treatment of periodontal disease is badly needed.

6. The Dental Pulp and Dental Caries

The life of the tooth depends on the health of the dental pulp. The health of the dental pulp is threatened all too commonly by the development of dental caries, so before discussing the pulp in detail a few remarks will be made about this condition which is probably the most common of all diseases.

Dental caries causes cavities to develop on exposed tooth surfaces. The disease begins on the outer surface of the enamel, commonly in tiny pits or crevices, or between adjacent teeth—areas where food debris is not readily washed away by saliva or the toothbrush. The food in these tiny areas acts as a substrate for the metabolism of bacteria, which are abundant in the mouth. It is generally believed that the bacterial action leads to the formation of acid products which locally decalcify and destroy enamel. Cavities that thus develop tend to be progressive, for they retain food debris which continues to be acted on by bacteria. Unless such cavities are treated, sooner or later they will reach the dentin and continue to extend through it to reach the pulp of the tooth. When they near the pulp they are prone to cause inflammation of the pulp, and, as will be explained below, this can cause its death.

A developing cavity causes no pain when it is confined to the enamel. When it reaches the dentin it may or may not give rise to increased sensitivity of the tooth; the increased sensitivity may be related to certain foods, for example, sweet materials. The presence of cavities is best determined by regular dental inspections. To treat them, all the surrounding affected enamel and dentin must be drilled away or otherwise removed. Then the cavity is shaped so that it will retain a filling. Fillings must be used because there are no cells on the outer aspects of the tooth to make new enamel and dentin.

Dental pulp is a connective tissue derived from the mesenchyme of the dental papilla (Fig. 380, *left*), and it occupies the pulp chambers and the root canals of teeth (Fig. 376). It is a soft tissue which retains its mesenchymal appearance throughout life (Fig. 385). The bulk of its cells appear stellate in sections, being connected to one another by long cytoplasmic processes. Pulp is very vascular; the main vessels enter and leave it through the apical foramina. However, the pulpal vessels, even the large ones, have very thin walls (Fig. 385). This, of course, renders this tissue very susceptible to changes in pressure because the walls of the pulp chamber cannot expand. A fairly mild inflammatory edema often can lead to compression of the blood vessels and hence to the necrosis and death of the pulp. Following pulp death, sometimes the pulp can be removed surgically and the space it occupied filled with an inert sealing material. Such a tooth constitutes what is commonly called a "dead" tooth.

The pulp is richly supplied with nerves, and nerve endings have been observed in close association with the odontoblast layer between the pulp and the dentin. Some authors have reported finding nerves actually entering the dentinal tubules, but, as was mentioned above, there is no indication that they proceed more than a very short distance within the tubules.

It was explained before that any new dentin that is added to the walls of the tooth must be deposited on the surface of already existing dentin, and only on the surface abutting on the pulp, because this is the only place where odontoblasts exist. Dentin normally is produced throughout life, and under certain conditions it may form rapidly (for example, under a cavity), but under the latter conditions the dentin is of a more irregular character and is designated as *secondary dentin*. Dentin deposition leads to a gradual reduction in the size of the pulp chamber and the canals throughout life; hence, in older people the pulp is generally much reduced in size. Its character also changes in that it becomes more fibrous and less cellular.

The continuously growing incisor of the rat has provided a valuable experimental tool in dental research. Schour in particular has exploited this to great advantage.

THE SALIVARY GLANDS

Introduction. Three large paired glands—the parotid, the submandibular (submaxillary) and the sublingual—are usually considered as constituting the salivary glands. However, the secretions of numerous smaller glands, previously described as being scattered throughout

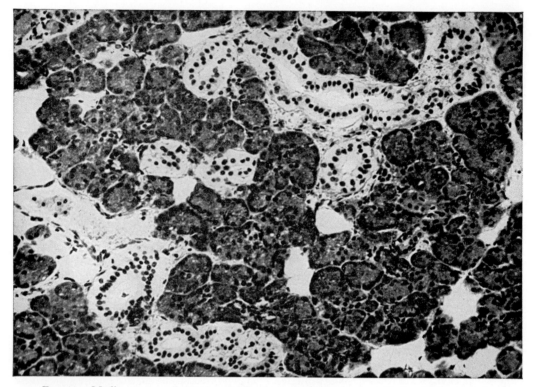

Fig. 391. Medium-power photomicrograph of a section of the parotid gland. The cytoplasm of the cells of the many ducts is light, and that of the cells of the secretory units, dark. The empty spaces represent fat, and a vein may be seen at the left.

the buccal mucosa, also contribute toward the saliva. Since these smaller glands have been described already, the following will deal only with the 3 large paired glands. These, like the liver and the pancreas, are situated outside the digestive tract proper. Their secretions are conveyed to the oral cavity through individual ducts.

Saliva and Its Functions. The mixed secretions of all the salivary glands are called *saliva*. Essentially fluid, it usually contains some cellular and bacterial debris and leukocytes. In man, the volume of saliva secreted in 24 hours varies from 1,000 to 1,500 cc. It may range from being thin and watery to viscous in consistency. Its composition varies with the type of stimulus that initiates its secretion. It is 99.5 per cent water. The remainder is made up of salts, gases and organic material. Two enzymes (*ptyalin* or *salivary amylase*, and *maltase*) and mucin make up part of the organic material.

Saliva has several functions: (1) It provides for the lubrication and the moistening of the buccal mucosa and the lips, thus aiding articulation. This function must be carried on continuously because of the evaporation and the swallowing of saliva, and the providing of a more or less steady supply of saliva for this purpose is probably the chief function of the buccal glands. (2) It provides a means whereby the mouth may be washed clear of cellular and food debris which otherwise might provide an excellent culture medium for bacteria. (3) Probably the most important function of saliva is to moisten food and transform it to a semisolid or liquid mass so that it may be swallowed easily. It may be noted here that animals such as the cow, which live on a fairly dry diet, may secrete up to 60 liters of saliva daily. Moreover, moistening the food allows it to be tasted. Taste buds are stimulated chemically, and substances that stimulate them must be in solution. (4) The role of the salivary enzymes in the digestion of food is questionable. Amylase breaks down starch to maltose in an alkaline or slightly acid medium. The food is retained in the mouth for much too short a time for any significant digestion to occur there, and when food reaches the stomach, the acid reaction therein, it might be thought, would inhibit any further amylase activity. But it has been shown that some of the starches that are consumed near the end of a meal may be broken down to maltose in the stomach because, being in the innermost part of the gastric contents, they are protected for a time from the gastric juice liberated from the stomach lining. (5) Some heavy metals and other inorganic and organic substances may be excreted in part in the saliva. (6) The secretion or lack of secretion of saliva indirectly aids in the control of water balance in the body. When too much fluid has been lost, the tissues, including the salivary glands, become dehydrated; this results in decreased secretion, hence, in a drying of the oral mucosa which, in turn, gives rise to a sensation of thirst. (7) It also acts as a buffer.

The Parotid Glands. These are the largest of the 3 pairs of salivary glands proper. Each lies packed in the space between the mastoid process and the ramus of the mandible. It overflows onto the face below the zygomatic arch, and from this process of the gland, its duct (Stensen's), running parallel with and immediately below the arch, plunges through the buccinator muscle to open into the vestibule of the mouth opposite the 2nd upper molar tooth.

The gland is enclosed in a well-defined fibrous connective tissue capsule and is a compound tubulo-alveolar gland of the serous type. The microscopic details of the secretory units of such glands have been described in Chapter 12. In addition to the usual features to be seen in a gland of this type, it is specially characterized by many and prominent intralobular ducts (Fig. 391). Accumulations of fat cells in the connective tissue septa are also characteristic of this gland.

The Submandibular Glands (Submaxillary). These lie in contact with the inner surface of the body of the mandible, and their main ducts (Wharton's) open into the floor of the oral cavity beside each other, anterior to the tongue and behind the lower incisor tooth. They are compound alveolar or tubulo-alveolar glands. Although of the mixed type, the majority of their secretory units are of the serous variety. Mucous units are usually capped by serous demilunes (see Chap. 12 for a description and illustrations of mixed glands). Like the parotid glands, the submandibular glands have well-defined capsules and fairly prominent duct systems.

The Sublingual Glands. Unlike the other salivary glands, the sublingual glands are not so definitely encapsulated. They lie well forward, near the mid-line, below the mucous membrane of the floor of the mouth, and their secretions empty by several ducts (Rivinus) that open along a line behind the openings of Wharton's ducts. They are compound tubulo-alveolar glands of the mixed type, but differ from the submandibular gland in that the majority of their alveoli are of the mucous type. Their microscopic appearance is different in different parts of the gland. In some areas only mucus-secreting units and mucous units with serous demilunes may be found. The connective tissue septa are usually more prominent than they are in the parotid or the submandibular glands.

Control of Salivary Secretion. No hormone appears to have any effect on salivary secretion. Ordinarily, salivary secretion is controlled by nervous reflexes. Briefly, the efferent or secretory fibers to the salivary glands are derived from the cranial outflow of the parasympathetic system and the thoracic outflow of the sympathetic system. The parasympathetic preganglionic fibers to the submandibular and the sublingual glands run in the chorda tympani to the submaxillary ganglion, whence postganglionic fibers pass to the glands. The fibers ramify about serous units and supply vasodilator fibers to the vessels. The post-ganglionic sympathetic fibers are derived from the superior cervical ganglion and end in the secretory cells and in the walls of the blood vessels. The preganglionic parasympathetic fibers to the parotid gland travel by a devious route to the otic ganglion, from which postganglionic fibers arise. The sympathetic supply is the same as for the other salivary glands. There are many afferent pathways that may be concerned in salivary reflexes. The stimulus that evokes secretion reflexly may be mechanical or chemical. For example, the presence of food (or even pebbles or dry powders in the mouth) stimulates the ordinary sensory

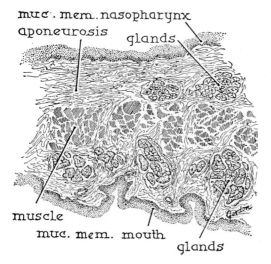

muc. mem. nasopharynx
aponeurosis   glands

muscle
muc. mem. mouth
glands

FIG. 392. Drawing of a section of the soft palate. (Redrawn and modified from Huber: Piersol's Human Anatomy, ed. 9, Philadelphia, Lippincott)

nerve endings and causes salivary secretion. The taste buds are receptive to chemical stimulation. Stimulation of many sensory nerves other than those of the oral cavity may initiate a salivary reflex, provided that the reflex has been conditioned (see p. 450). The amount and the composition of the saliva depends on the nature of the stimulus that initiates the reflex and on whether sympathetic or parasympathetic fibers are predominantly involved in the efferent path. It has been shown that sympathetic stimulation of the submandibular gland gives rise to a thick, viscous, mucous secretion; parasympathetic stimulation gives rise to a copious, thin, serous secretion.

THE HARD PALATE

It is desirable that the mouth (Fig. 373) should possess a strong roof so that the anterior part of the tongue, which is the part of the tongue that can move most freely, can bring force to bear against it in the process of mixing and swallowing food. It is also desirable that the mucous membrane lining the roof of the mouth in this site should be firmly fixed to the strong roof so that forceful movements of the tongue do not dislodge it, and that its epithelium should be capable of withstanding wear and tear. These desirable struc-

tural characteristics are realized by there being a bony roof over the mouth which is lined on its under surface by a mucous membrane, the lamina propria of which is continuous with the periosteum of the bone above, and the epithelium of which is of the stratified squamous keratinizing variety.

Laterally, the mucous membrane is not so evenly adherent to the bony roof and is connected to it by strong bundles of connective tissue. Fat cells are disposed between these anteriorly, and glands, posteriorly.

In the median line is a ridge of bone to which the epithelium is attached by a very thin lamina propria. This ridge is called the *raphe*. Rugae with connective tissue cores radiate out from this laterally. They are more prominent in early life than thereafter.

THE SOFT PALATE

The soft palate continues posteriorly from the hard palate (Fig. 373). Its functions are different from those of the hard palate. It does not have to bear the thrust of the tongue. It must be movable so that in the act of swallowing it can be drawn upward so as to close off the nasopharynx and so prevent food from being forced up into the nose. This requires that it contain muscle. It must be reasonably strong, and this requires that it contain connective tissue which is disposed in it as an aponeurosis.

The soft palate projects backward into the pharynx from the hard palate (Fig. 373). Hence, the mucous membrane on its upper surface forms part of the lining of the nasopharynx, and the mucous membrane on its lower surface forms part of the lining of the the oral pharynx. From above downward it exhibits the following layers (Fig. 392); (1) stratified squamous or pseudostratified ciliated columnar epithelium; (2) a lamina propria which contains a few glands and, near the hard palate, has the form of a strong aponeurosis; (3) a muscular layer (posteriorly); (4) a thick lamina propria containing many glands; and (5) stratified squamous nonkeratinizing epithelium.

THE PHARYNX

The pharynx is a somewhat conical-shaped chamber that serves as a passageway for both the respiratory and the digestive systems.

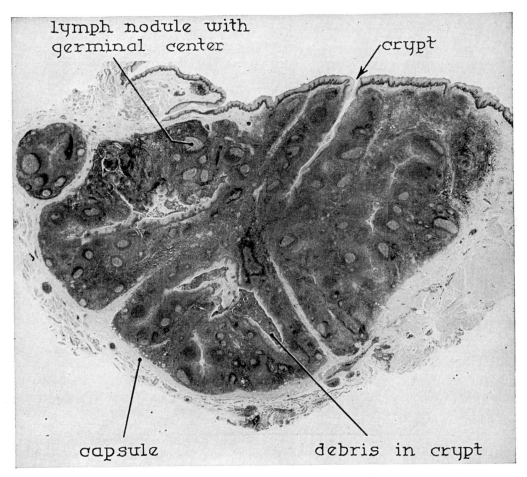

FIG. 393. Very low-power photomicrograph of a section of palatine tonsil.

Under conditions of nose breathing it conducts air between the nasal cavities and the larynx and to the eustachian tubes (Fig. 431). It also conducts food from the mouth to the esophagus, with which its apex is continuous (Fig. 373). But, since it is common to both systems, it permits an individual whose nasal passages are obstructed to breathe through his mouth or, when his mouth is immobilized for surgical reasons, to be fed with a tube through his nose.

The pharynx is divided into 3 parts. The *nasopharynx* lies above the level of the soft palate (Fig. 373). The posterior limit of the mouth is indicated by the glossopalatine arches, and the part of the pharynx behind these is the *oral pharynx* (Fig. 373). The *laryngeal pharynx* is the part that continues from the oral pharynx, from below the level

of the hyoid bone, into the esophagus (Fig. 373).

The pharynx is lined with epithelium. This varies in the different parts in accordance with their various functions. Where there is wear and tear, such as that occasioned by food passing over a part or by parts rubbing together, the stratified squamous nonkeratinizing type of epithelium is found. Where the lining epithelium comes into contact only with air, the pseudostratified columnar ciliated type is present. Stratified columnar epithelium is found in some sites, particularly in the transition zones between the other 2 types.

The lining of epithelium rests on a fairly dense connective tissue membrane which contains elastic as well as collagenic fibers. At the side of this farthest from the epithelium there is usually a stout layer of elastic fibers. Out-

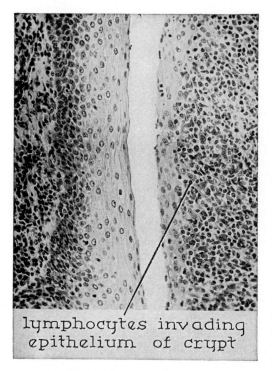

lymphocytes invading
epithelium of crypt

Fig. 394. High-power photomicrograph of a section of palatine tonsil, showing lymphocytes migrating through the epithelial lining of a crypt.

side this again is striated muscle—the longitudinal and the constrictor muscles of the pharynx—and outside the muscle there is another fibrous layer that connects the pharynx to adjacent structures.

Glands are present deep to the epithelium of some parts of the pharynx, particularly near the openings of the eustachian tubes. In some instances the glands extend into the muscle coat.

THE PALATINE TONSILS

These ovoid masses of lymphatic tissue are embedded in, and hence thicken, the lamina propria of the mucous membrane that extends between the glossopalatine and the pharyngopalatine arches. The epithelium here is of the stratified squamous nonkeratinizing type and dips into the underlying lymphatic tissue to form 10 to 20 little glandlike pits (*primary crypts*) in each palatine tonsil (Fig. 393). The stratified squamous epithelium lining the primary crypts may extend out into the adjacent lymphatic tissue to form secondary crypts. Either primary or secondary crypts may ex-

tend deeply enough to reach the outer limits of the tonsil.

The lymphatic tissue in the tonsil is mostly arranged close to the epithelium; it lies directly deep to the covering epithelium and extends down along the sides of the crypts. It consists of primary nodules, with or without germinal centers, that may be so close together that they melt into one another or they may be separated by loose lymphatic tissue. In addition to lymphocytes there are many plasma cells in this tissue.

The tonsillar tissue disposed near the beginnings of the digestive tube and the respiratory system would seem to be designed to function as outposts, on the watch for infective agents against which antibodies should be made as soon as possible. However, this is a hazardous occupation, and often the infective agents conquer the outposts and become so well established in the tonsils that the latter must be removed.

Primary nodules may be very close to the epithelium of the crypts. Many lymphocytes formed in the tonsil leave it by migrating through the crypt epithelium (Fig. 394). Lymphocytes may so infiltrate the epithelium that it becomes very difficult to establish its deep border. The lymphocytes that escape form degenerate bodies in the saliva called *salivary corpuscles*.

Glands are associated with the palatine tonsils, but their ducts open beside it and not into its crypts; hence, the crypts are not flushed out as they are in the lingual tonsil, and debris can accumulate in them and dispose them to infection.

GENERAL PLAN OF THE GASTROINTESTINAL TRACT

A good understanding of the general plan on which the digestive tube is constructed is of assistance in learning the microscopic structure of the various parts of it which are now to be considered. Therefore, the general plan will be described in some detail before the particulars about different parts of the tract are given.

The wall of the gastrointestinal tube consists of 4 main layers (see Fig. 395, *lower right*): the mucous membrane, the submucosa, the muscularis externa and the serosa. The relation of the structure to the function of these 4 layers will now be described.

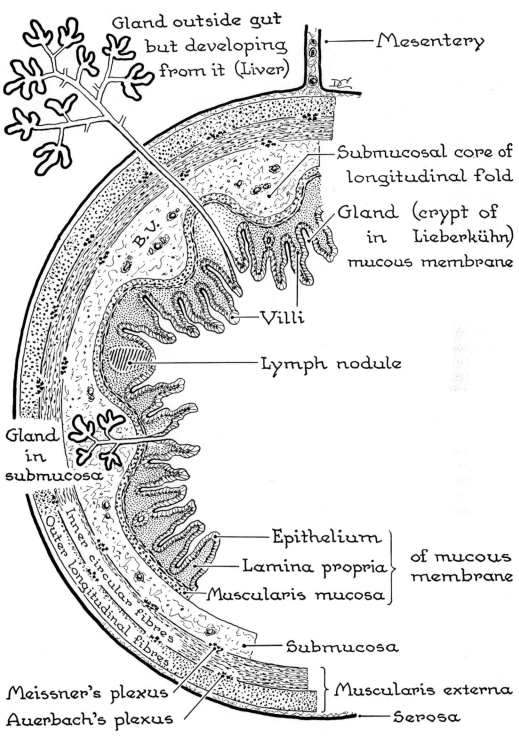

Gland outside gut but developing from it (Liver)

Mesentery

Submucosal core of longitudinal fold

Gland (crypt of Lieberkühn) in mucous membrane

B.V.

Villi

Lymph nodule

Gland in submucosa

Inner circular fibres
Outer longitudinal fibres

Epithelium
Lamina propria } of mucous membrane
Muscularis mucosa

Submucosa

Meissner's plexus
Auerbach's plexus

} Muscularis externa
Serosa

FIG. 395. The general plan of the gastrointestinal tract.

Mucous Membrane. This consists of 3 layers: an *epithelial lining*, a supporting *lamina propria* and a thin, usually double, layer of smooth muscle, the *muscularis mucosae* (Fig. 395).

EPITHELIUM. The type of epithelium varies in relation to the function of the part of the tube it lines. In some sites it is primarily protective, in others it is absorptive, and in still others, secretory. In most of the gastrointestinal tract the surface-lining epithelial cells are unable to provide all the secretions that are needed. To supplement the secretions supplied by surface-lining cells, vast numbers of glands are present. The commonest ones are short and extend outwardly only to the muscularis mucosae; therefore, they are wholly contained in the lamina propria of the mucous membrane (Fig. 395, labeled "gland in mucous membrane"). *The student, then, must expect to find the lamina propria of the mucous membrane of most parts of the gastrointestinal tract riddled with glands; indeed, in many parts the thin films of lamina propria between glands can scarcely be seen.* The second position occupied by glands that develop from the lining cells, to supplement their secretions, is the submucosa (Fig. 395, *middle left*). Glands in this position are found only in the esophagus and the duodenum. The third site occupied by glands that arise from the lining of the gastrointestinal tract is outside the tract altogether. The salivary glands, the liver and the pancreas are of this sort (Fig. 395, *upper left*). Since they all arise from the lining of the alimentary tract, they all drain into it by ducts which proclaim the sites of their origins.

LAMINA PROPRIA. This layer consists of connective tissue that is difficult to classify. In some sites it closely resembles areolar tissue; in others, it is frankly lymphatic tissue; and in still others, it is what probably is best described as areolar tissue with lymphatic tendencies.

The functions of the lamina propria are numerous. In order to support the epithelium and to connect it with the muscularis mucosae, it contains collagenic, reticular and, in some sites, elastic fibers. The reasons why so much of the lamina propria has lymphatic properties are probably not yet known. The frank lymphatic tissue with which it is sprinkled is of the nonencapsulated type and hence typical of lymphatic tissue that is commonly disposed under wet epithelial surfaces, presumably for the purpose of filtering tissue fluid in that vicinity. In this way it could act as a second line of defense against bacteria or other disease organisms that gain entrance to the tissues by invading the epithelial membrane, which, to be absorptive, must be relatively thin in much of the gastrointestinal tract. It could

function in this respect by virtue of the engulfment, by its phagocytic cells, of bacteria or other foreign materials or by the manufacture of antibodies by its plasma cells.

The fact that lymphocytes are produced in great numbers in the lamina propria of the digestive tube and make their way through the lining epithelium to enter the lumen suggests that lymphocytes play some nutritive function in connection with the maintenance of the lining epithelium; possibilities in this connection were described in Chapter 8.

The lamina propria carries both blood and lymphatic capillaries close to the epithelial surface, particularly in the little fingerlike villi that project into the lumen from the small intestine (Fig. 395). Consequently, the products resulting from the digestion of carbohydrates, proteins and fats do not have to diffuse any great distance through the tissue fluid of the lamina propria in order to gain entrance to either type of capillary.

In villi (Fig. 395) particularly, smooth muscle fibers are present in, and are a constituent of, the lamina propria. These permit villi to sway from side to side and to shorten and lengthen. The latter movement may have a milking effect and so help to force lymph along their lymphatics.

MUSCULARIS MUCOSAE. This, the third and outermost layer of the mucous membrane, consists generally of 2 thin layers of smooth muscle fibers together with varying amounts of elastic tissue. In the inner layer of muscle the fibers are circularly disposed, and in the outer, longitudinally (Fig. 395). The muscularis mucosae probably permits localized movements of the mucous membrane. Increased tonus of the circular fibers would tend to throw the mucous membrane into circular folds. The muscularis mucosae also could be visualized as acting on occasion to relieve the pressure on the veins in the submucosa caused by the tonus of the muscularis externa.

Submucosa. This coat connects the mucous membrane to the muscularis externa. It consists of a loose pliable type of connective tissue. It houses the plexuses of larger blood vessels (Fig. 395). The elastic fibers of these impart an elastic quality to the coat as a whole. This is augmented, particularly in the upper part of the gastrointestinal tract, by a considerable number of elastic fibers distrib-

the *pyloric antrum and canal*; these lead to the *exit* or *pylorus* (= gate).

If an empty, contracted stomach is opened, its mucous membrane is seen to be thrown into branching folds, most of which are disposed longitudinally. These are termed *rugae*. The cores of these consist of submucosa (Fig. 399, *top*). When the stomach is full, the rugae are almost completely "ironed out."

General Microscopic Features. The wall of the stomach is composed of the 4 layers described in the general plan of the alimentary tract. The mucous membrane of the stomach is relatively thick and contains millions of little simple tubular glands. In some sites the muscularis mucosae has 3 layers instead of the 2 described in the plan. There are no glands in the submucosa except in the pyloric part adjacent to the duodenum. The muscularis externa consists of 3 instead of 2 layers. The fibers of the innermost layer are disposed obliquely; those of the middle coat, circularly; and those of the outermost coat, longitudinally. A serosa is present.

It has been noted already that the gastric mucosa of the empty stomach is thrown into folds called rugae; these are substantial ridges easily seen on gross inspection or in sections with a very low-power objective (Fig. 399).

If the gastric mucosa is examined with reasonably high magnification it is seen to be studded with tiny little openings through which the gastric juice wells up when the stomach is actively secreting. These little openings are the openings of what are termed *gastric pits* or *foveolae*. The pits descend through the gastric mucosa to reach the glands which, therefore, open into the pits. The glands produce the secretion, deliver it into the bottoms of the pits, and the pits conduct it to the surface. There is not universal agreement about the shape of the pits. Sometimes they are depicted as having a tubular form and sometimes as being crevices. Probably both kinds exist, with the percentage varying in relation to species, but it is also probable that many crevices are interpreted as tubules, because a section that cuts across a crevice makes it appear as a longitudinal section of a tubule. Unless tubules were arranged in perfect rows it would be impossible to see so many in a single section as appear in Figure 399; the appearance shown here could result only

from roughly parallel crevices being sectioned at right angles to their long diameters. The lamina propria between the bottoms of the pits and the muscularis mucosae is literally packed with simple tubular glands that open into the bottoms of the pits. In their deepest parts these glands reach or almost reach the muscularis mucosae. There are so many glands in the zone between the bottoms of the crevices and pits and the muscularis mucosae that the student may have difficulty in thinking of this zone as lamina propria. And, indeed, the tissue of the lamina propria itself is so broken up by the glands that it can be seen only as thin films between them (Fig. 399, *lower right*).

The inner surface of the stomach is lined by simple columnar epithelium (Fig. 399, *middle right*). This extends down to line the pits, and also into the isthmus, which is the region where gland becomes pit. The character of the surface epithelial cells will now be described.

Surface Epithelium. The chief function of the surface epithelium is to provide protection. In order to do this, its cells are tall and all alike; the fact that they are all alike enables the student to distinguish at a glance a section of stomach from a section of small or large intestine. (In the small and the large intestines goblet cells alternate with nonmucus-producing absorptive cells; this has a very different appearance from the lining cells of the stomach.) The surface epithelial cells form a membrane that, although it is only one cell thick, is fairly substantial. These cells also provide an indirect type of protection by producing the mucus which characteristically coats the lining of the stomach. They are unusual mucus-producing cells, however, for they do not have the usual shape of goblet cells (Fig. 399, *middle right*), and the mucigen granules in their cytoplasm stain only with certain of the mucus stains. As might be supposed, there is probably a fairly high rate of mortality among these surface cells, and they regenerate from those cells of the isthmus and deeper parts of pits, the cells of which seem to be somewhat less specialized in that they contain less mucigen than the cells that are more exposed.

Why the surface epithelial cells are not digested by the juices that well up into the pits and the crevices from the glands of the

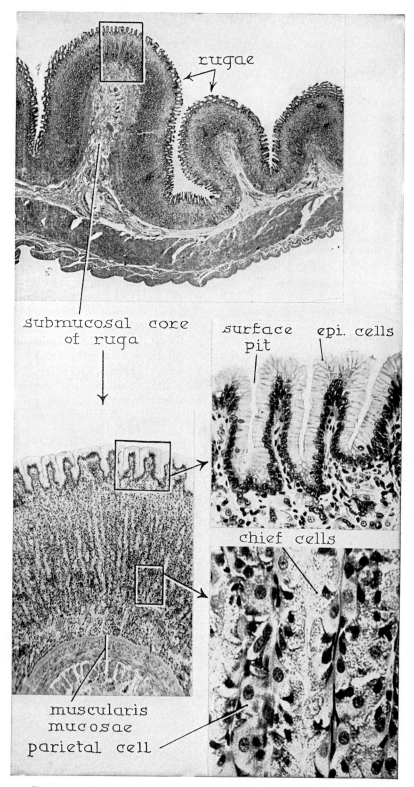

rugae

submucosal core
of ruga

surface
pit

epi. cells

chief cells

muscularis
mucosae

parietal cell

FIG. 399. Photomicrographs, taken at various magnifications, of a
section of the body of the stomach of a cat.

lamina propria in some parts of the stomach is not understood. Obviously, the protection against being digested, possessed by these cells, is a vital property, for they become digested immediately after death. Sections of stomach obtained from autopsies characteristically fail to demonstrate the surface epithelial cells to advantage since they have become digested during the interval between death and autopsy.

Ulcers of the mucous membrane are not uncommon. These sometimes extend into the other coats in the wall; they may even cause perforations. One might expect that if any surface epithelial cells were ever destroyed, the digestive juices present in the stomach would prevent healing. Yet wounds of the stomach under proper conditions heal rapidly; hence, the wall may be cut and sutured at operations with every confidence that the surface epithelium will regenerate and spread over the affected part to become a continuous membrane once more.

Glands of the Lamina Propria of the Cardia. The glands in the lamina propria in the area immediately surrounding the entrance of the esophagus into the stomach are somewhat different from those in the remainder of the organ. They are either simple or compound tubular glands composed of cells with pale cytoplasm. They secrete mucus and perhaps some enzymes. They are of little practical importance.

Glands of the Mucous Membrane of the Fundus and Body. These glands produce nearly all the enzymes and hydrochloric acid secreted in the stomach; they also produce some of the mucus. In the body of the stomach the pits are shallower than they are in the pyloric region and they extend into the mucous membrane for only about a quarter to a third of its thickness (Fig. 399, *lower left*). Therefore, the glands that extend from the bottoms of the pits to the muscularis mucosae are two to three times as long as the pits and the crevices are deep. The glands are straight except near the muscularis mucosae where they may be bent (Fig. 400). Since they are straight, they may be seen as reasonably complete longitudinal sections of tubules if sections are cut at right angles to the surface epithelium (Fig. 399, *lower left*).

According to Stevens and Leblond, each tubular gland of the body of the stomach con-

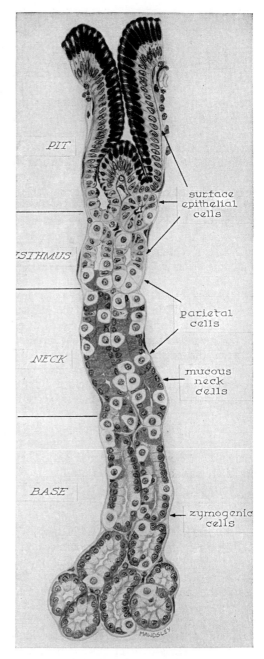

FIG. 400. Drawing of a section of the body of the stomach of a monkey, stained by the P.A.S. method and by hematoxylin. (Preparation by C. P. Leblond)

sists of 3 parts or segments. The deepest part is the *base* (Fig. 400), the middle part is the *neck* (Fig. 400), and the upper part is the *isthmus* (Fig. 400). The isthmus is continuous with a pit. It should be understood that pits are not parts of glands; they are merely little wells and crevices sunk from the surface and lined by surface epithelial cells.

The gastric juice is secreted by the glands. The glands contain 4 kinds of secretory cells, but these are not evenly distributed in the different segments, as will now be described. The 4 types of cells can be demonstrated to advantage in sections stained by the P.A.S. method and hematoxylin, as has been shown by Stevens and Leblond.

The isthmus, according to these investigators, contains 2 types of cells, surface epithelial cells and parietal cells. The surface epithelial cells along the sides of pits have a considerable apical content of mucus that is represented as black in Figure 400. In the deepest parts of the pits the amount of mucus in the apical parts of the cell is considerably less (Fig. 400), and in the isthmus the surface epithelial cells demonstrate only a few granules of mucus in their apical parts. Scattered between the surface epithelial cells of the isthmus are large *parietal cells* that have relatively clear cytoplasm when stained by the P.A.S. method and hematoxylin. In good H and E preparations the cytoplasm of these cells is pink (Fig. 399). The parietal cells, as seen in a section, vary from being rounded to triangular in shape (Figs. 399 and 400). Their nuclei are dark and generally centrally placed.

The neck of a gland is made up chiefly of cells that were first described by Bensley as *mucous neck cells*. These are very difficult to identify in H and E sections. With the P.A.S. method the cytoplasm of the mucous neck cells is seen to be literally stuffed with pink mucus (dark in Fig. 400) and to have a foamy appearance. The nuclei of these cells are generally pressed against their bases, where they often have a more or less triangular shape (Fig. 400). Parietal cells are scattered as individuals between groups of mucous neck cells in this part of the gland (Fig. 400).

The base or body of a gland is made up mostly of *zymogenic (chief) cells*. These have accumulations of chromidial substance near their bases. The cytoplasm between their nuclei and their free surfaces appears differently with different fixatives and stains. In an ordinary H and E preparation it appears vacuolated and reticular (Fig. 399) because the secretion granules it contains are not well fixed or stained. The P.A.S. and hematoxylin method demonstrates a similar appearance in it (Fig. 400). Parietal cells are sprinkled among the zymogenic cells. Not uncommonly a parietal cell will be seen with one of its three sides applied closely to the basement membrane of the gland and with two of its angles extending between the bases of adjacent chief cells and the basement membrane (Fig. 399). The apex of such a cell projects between the sides of the two chief cells that border it but not far enough to reach the lumen proper. The secretion from such a parietal cell then must pass between the two chief cells that almost cover it to reach the lumen proper of the gland. Parietal cells have centrally disposed, rounded nuclei and decidedly acidophilic cytoplasm. Hence, in H and E sections, they stand out as red cells among the paler chief cells. Under special conditions, secretory canaliculi may be seen in their cytoplasm. These open on the side of the cell closest to the lumen of the gland.

The zymogenic (chief) cells produce the enzymes of the gastric secretion, and the parietal cells produce the hydrochloric acid. The other types of cells produce only mucus.

FINE STRUCTURE

All 4 types of cells described above have been studied with E/M and described by different authors. Since these studies have often been made on different species, some of the inconsistencies in the various reports are probably due to this fact.

Parietal Cells. Under the E/M the parietal cell is characterized by the presence of a branching canaliculus which extends into it from its apex and by which it delivers its secretion into the lumen of the gastric gland (Fig. 401 A). In addition to intracellular canaliculi there are intercellular canaliculi between adjacent parietal cells. A unique feature of the canaliculi, particularly the intracellular kind, is the tremendous number of microvilli which project into them (Fig. 401 A). The intracellular canaliculus takes up a considerable amount of space in a parietal cell and so encroaches on the cytoplasm, and the cytoplasm that remains is literally stuffed with mitochondria. Other components of the cytoplasm are present, but the striking feature of the cytoplasm is the abundance of mitochondria and the vast system of microvilli

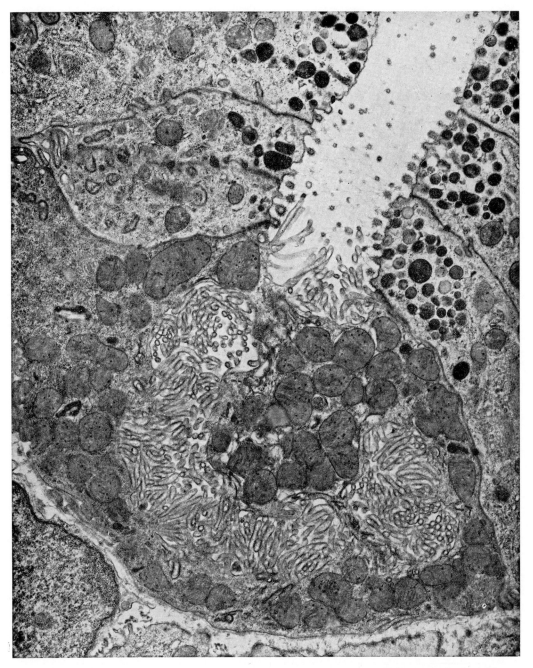

Fig. 401. (A) Electron micrograph (× 9,500) of the bottom of a gastric gland of a bat. The clear area is the lumen of the gastric gland, lined on each side by mucous cells. Only the apical portions of these are shown. They contain many mucous granules and have short microvilli projecting into the lumen of the gland. The cell at the base of the gastric gland is a parietal cell. Its cytoplasm contains many round to ovoid mitochondria. Extending into this cell from the lumen of the gastric gland is a large C-shaped passageway which is an intracellular canaliculus. This does not appear empty, as might be expected, because it is filled with numerous microvilli projecting into it. These microvilli are cut in all planes, and more microvilli project from the surface of the parietal cell into the lumen of the gastric gland. (Preparation by Dr. S. Ito, Dr. R. J. Winchester and Dr. D. W. Fawcett)

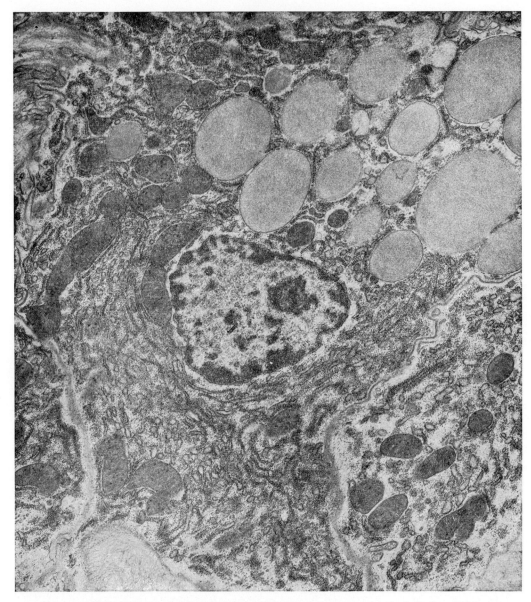

FIG. 401. (B) Electron micrograph (× 14,000) of part of a zymogenic (chief) cell from the stomach of a bat showing nucleus, large secretory granules, granular endoplasmic reticulum and mitochondria. (Dr. S. Ito, Dr. R. J. Winchester and Dr. D. W. Fawcett)

which project into the intracellular canaliculi. The cytoplasm does not reveal any secretion granules. Therefore, the E/M appearance of the cell would not indicate that HCl is secreted in the form of a protein complex, as has been suggested in the past, because if it were one might expect to see many rough-surfaced vesicles of endoplasmic reticulum con-

taining the protein secretory product. The intracellular canaliculi and the vast number of microvilli suggest that a vast area of cell membrane is involved in the secretion of HCl. Bradford and Davies, using a variety of dyes, have shown that there is sometimes a very low pH in the canaliculi in the parietal cells of frogs; their work suggests that HCl is secreted into the canaliculi as free acid. References to their work are given for those who wish to study this matter further.

Zymogen Cells. These cells are characterized by an abundance of rough-surfaced vesicles and cisternae of endoplasmic reticulum (Fig. 401 B). These are probably concerned in the formation of the many secretion granules that are also seen in these cells (Fig. 401 B). Short microvilli are present on the apical surfaces of these cells.

Mucous Neck Cells and Surface Epithelial Cells. Both of these cell types show many mucigen droplets, particularly near the end through which the secretion is delivered. The cells at the upper right in Figure 401 A are probably mucous neck cells; they have short microvilli on their free surfaces. Surface epithelial cells are similar but probably do not generally have so many secretory droplets in their cytoplasm.

Renewal of Cells of the Gastric Mucosa. Stevens and Leblond, using their colchicine method, found that only the two mucus-containing types of cells showed any significant mitotic activity. They found that the surface epithelial cells are maintained by divisions of these cells occurring in the isthmus (where they contain less mucus). They estimated that 5.87 per cent of the surface epithelial cells enter mitosis every 4 hours. The mucous neck cells were found to divide less often; only 2.59 per cent enter mitosis every 4 hours. From the foregoing observations it would appear that the surface epithelium in the stomach is renewed (in the rat) every 3 days, and that this is done by cells in the isthmus dividing, and the new cells formed here push up the sides of the crypts and then over the surface to replace those that are constantly being lost by desquamation.

Glands of the Pylorus. The pits and the crevices in the pyloric portion of the stomach are deeper than those in the body and the fundus. Furthermore, the glands that open into the pits and the crevices are much shorter than those in the body and the fundus. Hence, there is a considerable difference between the ratio of the depth of the crevices and the pits to the depth of the glands in the pyloric portion of the stomach and that in the body and fundus (compare Figs. 399 and 402). This point should enable the student to distinguish

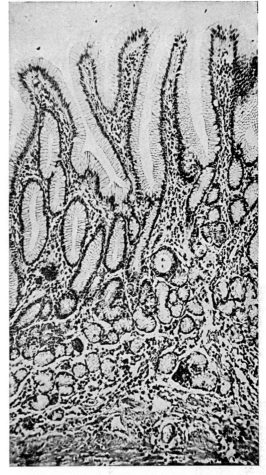

FIG. 402. Low-power photomicrograph of a section of the mucous membrane of the pyloric portion of the stomach of a man.

readily sections of pylorus from those of body and fundus. Another point of difference between the glands of the two regions is that the pyloric glands are coiled; hence, they never are seen in longitudinal section (the glands of the body and the fundus are, if sections are cut perpendicular to the surface). Still another point of difference is that the pyloric glands, except near the pyloric sphincter and the body where a few parietal cells may be seen, consist of only one type of cell. In H and E sections, the cytoplasm of these cells is pale, but with special stains it may be shown to contain mucigen. The nuclei are more or less flattened and pressed against the bases of the cells (Fig. 402). The lumens of the glands are wider than those of the glands in the body and the fundus.

Many observers have commented on the similarity between the cells of the pyloric glands and the mucous neck cells of the glands of the body and the fundus. They have the same function, for the pyloric glands do not produce enzymes but only mucus.

At the pylorus, the circularly disposed smooth muscle fibers of the middle coat of the muscularis externa of the stomach are increased so as to form a thick bundle which encircles the exit of the stomach. This is called the *pyloric sphincter*. The stout band of muscle of which it is composed bulges the submucosa and the mucous membrane inwardly so that these are thrown into a circular fold. The chief ingredient of the core of this fold, it should be noted, is the thickened middle coat of the muscularis externa. This fold differs from most folds in the alimentary tract, which have cores of only submucosa.

Peristaltic movements begin near the middle of the stomach and spread down to the pylorus. The pyloric sphincter automatically opens to permit such food as is sufficiently fluid and digested to enter the small intestine. At the same time it holds back solid undigested food. The precise way its operations are controlled is too complex a matter to discuss here.

Control of the Secretion of Gastric Juice. There is some difference between the secretion of gastric juice in experimental animals and its secretion in man. In dogs, the surface of the resting stomach is coated with mucus; gastric juice wells up from the glands to flood the surface only when a meal is in prospect or is consumed. However, in man, Carlson has shown that there is a more or less continuous secretion of gastric juice, varying from 10 to 60 cc. per hour. This is augmented when food is about to be eaten or is eaten. Several factors are concerned in augmenting the secretion. Psychic factors, as shown by Pavlov, play an important part and so justify the imaginative cook. Psychic factors must operate through a nervous control of secretion by the vagus nerve. Certain foods, when they reach the stomach, have the ability to stimulate secretion further. These foods stimulate secretion even if the nerves to the stomach are cut. Hence, if they stimulate secretion by means of a reflex initiated in the mucosa of the stomach, the reflex concerned must have something

of the nature of a local one. Then, in addition to certain foods stimulating secretion, the breakdown products of a wide variety of foods also have this property, particularly when the breakdown products reach the small intestine, where they act on its mucosa possibly to make a substance that circulates by the blood stream to reach the gastric glands. Accordingly, the gastric glands are said to secrete through 3 phases: (1) the cephalic (psychic factors), (2) the gastric, where consumed food either directly or indirectly stimulates the mucosa to induce secretion, and (3) the intestinal, where the breakdown products of digestion, and the gastric juice itself, reach and affect the intestinal mucosa to make it produce something that circulates by the blood stream to stimulate further the gastric glands.

THE SMALL INTESTINE

Relation of General Structure to Functions. The small intestine is about 20 feet long. Its first 10 to 12 inches constitute the *duodenum* (Fig. 373). This, except for its first inch or so, is relatively fixed in position, not being suspended by a mesentery. It pursues a horseshoe-shaped course around the head of the pancreas to become continuous with the *jejunum*, which constitutes the next two fifths of the small intestine (Fig. 373). The last three fifths is termed the *ileum* (Fig. 373). In general, the small intestine tends to become narrower throughout its course.

The small intestine has two chief functions: (1) completing the digestion of food delivered into it by the stomach and (2) selectively absorbing the final products of digestion into its blood and lymph vessels. In addition, it also makes some hormones.

The structure of the small intestine is specialized with regard to both its digestive and its absorptive functions. It will be more convenient to describe how its structure is specialized for absorption before describing how its structure is specialized for digestion.

To perform its absorptive function efficiently, the small intestine requires a vast epithelial surface, since it is through the epithelium of the mucous membrane that absorption occurs. The great length of the small intestine helps considerably in providing such a surface, but this is not enough, and provision is made in 3 other ways for increasing the absorptive surface still further.

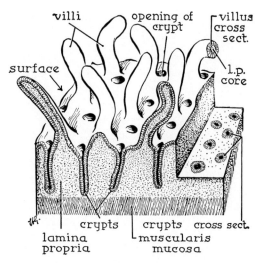

FIG. 404. Three-dimensional drawing of the lining of the small intestine. Observe that villi are fingerlike processes, with cores of lamina propria that extend into the lumen. Note also that crypts of Lieberkühn are glands that dip down into the lamina propria. Observe particularly the difference in the cross-section appearance of villi and crypts.

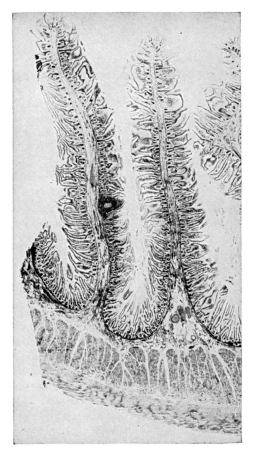

FIG. 403. Low-power photomicrograph of a longitudinal section of the wall of the jejunum of a dog, showing 2 plicae circulares cut in cross section. The plicae are studded with irregular villi.

1. Beginning about an inch beyond the pylorus, the mucous membrane is thrown into circularly or spirally disposed folds called the *plicae circulares* or *valves of Kerkring*. These folds are generally crescentic and extend from one half to two thirds of the way around the lumen. However, single folds may extend all the way around the intestine or even form a spiral of 2 or 3 turns; the highest ones project into the lumen for about a third of an inch. They all have cores of submucosa, are not ironed out if the intestine is full and, at first, are large and very close together (Fig. 403). In the upper part of the jejunum they become smaller and farther apart. In the middle or lower end of the ileum they disappear.

2. The surface of the mucous membrane over the folds and between the folds is studded with tiny leaf, tongue or fingerlike projections that range from ½ to 1 mm. or more in height. These are called the *intestinal villi* (Fig. 404). Since they are projections of mucous membrane, they have cores of lamina propria. The muscularis mucosae and the submucosa do not extend into them as they do into the plicae circulares. The plicae could be likened to the ridges that cover a rough country and the villi to the trees that grow from the surface of both the ridges and the valleys between them (Fig. 403).

The villi of the duodenum are broader than those elsewhere, and many examples of leaflike ones can be found in this region. In the upper part of the jejunum, the villi, in general, are said to be tongue-shaped. Farther down the jejunum they become longer and finger-shaped. There are fewer of them in the ileum, and those present tend to be narrower still. Villi, as will become apparent when their structure is described in detail presently, are highly specialized little absorptive organs.

3. The absorptive surface is made still greater by the microvilli that are present on

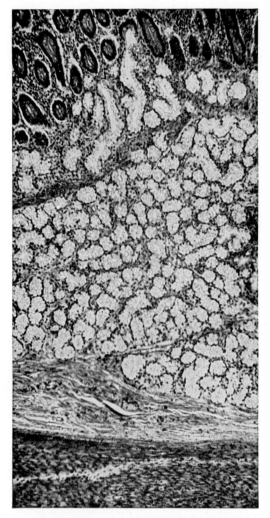

Fig. 405. Low-power photomicrograph of a section of the wall of the duodenum, showing Brunner's glands in the submucosa. The muscularis mucosae may be seen passing to the right and upward from above the middle of the left side. In the middle of the upper part of the figure, a gland of Brunner may be seen emptying into a crypt of Lieberkühn. The muscularis externa is seen at the bottom of the picture.

the free surfaces of the absorptive cells (Fig. 123).

In order to perform its other chief function (completing the digestion of food received from the stomach), the small intestine requires large supplies of digestive enzymes and considerable quantities of mucus to protect its epithelial lining from injury. The digestive enzymes are provided by glands; mucus is provided both by proper glands and by innumerable goblet cells that are intermingled with other cells along the mucous membrane. The glands that provide the digestive juices and the mucus necessary for the function of the small intestine are distributed in 3 general sites: (1) outside the intestine, but connected with it by ducts, (2) in the submucosa and (3) in the lamina propria.

The microscopic structure of the pancreas and the liver, the two glands that are situated outside the small intestine and deliver their secretions into it, will be considered later. Here we are concerned only with the effect of their secretions on the digestive process. Their ducts, usually conjoined, open into the duodenum about 3 inches from the pylorus (Fig. 373). The secretion of the pancreas, delivered into the duodenum at this site, is alkaline (and so helps neutralize the acid stomach contents), and it contains enzymes concerned in the digestion of proteins, carbohydrates and fats; several enzymes that effect different steps in protein digestion probably are elaborated. The enzymes are not active until they reach the intestine, where some agency renders them potent. In their totality they can break down proteins to amino acids; it is in this form that proteins are absorbed. The pancreatic juice also contains enzymes that break down starches to sugars. Some sugars, for example, maltose, must be acted on further by enzymes secreted by glands in the lamina propria and must be converted to monosaccharides before they are absorbed. The pancreatic juice also contains lipolytic enzymes that both emulsify fat and break down its structure. The effect of these enzymes is facilitated by the presence of bile, the secretion of the liver.

The second group of glands to consider are those situated in the submucosa. Glands are found in this position only in the duodenum. These are compound tubular in type and are called the *glands of Brunner* (Fig. 405). Their precise distribution varies considerably. They may extend into the pylorus for a short distance. Generally, they are most numerous in the first part of the duodenum and become less numerous and finally disappear in its more distal parts. Nevertheless, they have been observed on occasion in the first part of the jejunum.

The secretory portions of Brunner's glands

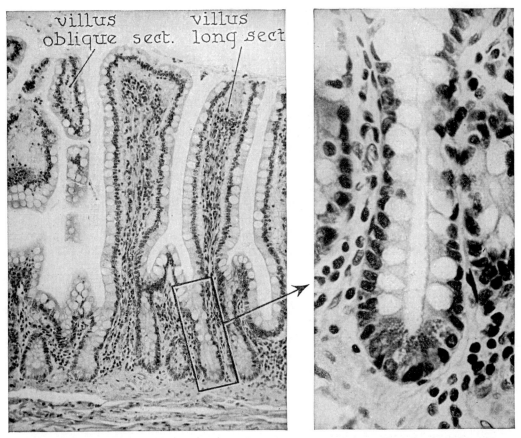

Fig. 406. (*Left*) Low-power photomicrograph of a section of the wall of the small intestine of a child, showing villi in longitudinal and cross section and crypts of Lieberkühn. (*Right*) High-power photomicrograph of a crypt of Lieberkühn, showing goblet cells along its sides and some Paneth cells with cytoplasmic granules at its deepest part.

are sufficiently expanded to have a somewhat alveolar appearance. The secretory portions are chiefly confined to the submucosa. The excretory ducts lead through the muscularis mucosae to empty into the crypts of Lieberkühn, to be described shortly. The muscularis mucosae does not always constitute a well-defined structure over them, for often it is so split up by glandular elements that it appears as a network of smooth muscle fibers whose interstices are filled with glandular elements.

The secretory cells are columnar and resemble those of the pyloric glands. Their nuclei are dark and flattened toward the bases of the cells. The cytoplasm is pale and finely granular in H and E sections (Fig. 405), but, with suitable stains, can be shown to contain mucigen.

There has been much discussion as to whether these glands produce proteolytic enzymes. The matter is complicated by the difficulty of obtaining pure extracts and by the fact that the glands of some experimental animals have different cellular components from those of man. There is some evidence to suggest that the secretion has some ability to activate other secretions concerned in protein digestion. But it has not been shown definitely that the Brunner's glands of man themselves produce a proteolytic enzyme. The glands are obviously useful in producing extra mucus at the site where the pancreatic enzymes are emptied into the intestine.

The third set of glands to consider are those of the mucous membrane itself. These are called *crypts of Lieberkühn* and they dip down from the surface between villi to reach almost to the muscularis mucosae (Fig. 395). Their openings on the surface of the intestine may be seen between the villi (Fig. 404). If the villi are likened to trees growing on ridges (plicae circulares), the crypts of Lieberkühn could be thought of as little wells that have been dug between each pair of trees. To avoid confusion, the student should realize that the villi project into the lumen from the mucous membrane of the small intestine and that the crypts of Lieberkühn extend down from the surface into the mucous membrane (Fig. 404). In all probability, cells in the crypts of Lieberkühn secrete many enzymes. They secrete a complement of proteolytic ones, particularly erepsin, which acts in the later stages of protein digestion to produce amino acids. They secrete enzymes that affect carbohydrates, in particular enzymes that convert disaccharides into monosaccharides. Furthermore, they secrete a special enzyme that acts on the nucleic acid of nucleoproteins.

The pancreas and the liver supply almost no mucus to the small intestine. Mucus is provided by the glands of Brunner and by innumerable goblets cells present both in the crypts of Lieberkühn and among the absorptive epithelial cells that cover the villi and otherwise line the interior of the intestine (Fig. 406).

Some Details Concerning the Structure of the Mucous Membrane

Epithelium. It will be recalled that the surface epithelial cells of the stomach, although not typical goblet cells, all secrete mucus and are all alike. The cells of the epithelial membrane lining the small intestine do not all secrete mucus and are not all alike. Most of them are tall columnar in type, with each having a striated free border (Figs. 121, 122, and 123); these are primarily absorptive in function and they do not secrete mucus. However, true goblet cells that do secrete mucus are distributed among them (Figs. 121, 122 and 123). Hence, there is a division of labor among the epithelial lining cells of the small intestine.

The epithelium lining the glands that dip down into the mucous membrane (the crypts of Lieberkühn) varies at different depths. At the bottoms of the glands there are columnar cells that are narrower at their apices than at their bases. Their nuclei are disposed close to the basement membrane, and the cytoplasm between the nucleus and the apex of each contains eosinophilic granules (Figs. 406, *right*,

and 407 A). These are the as yet mysterious Paneth cells, mysterious because no confirmed function has yet been established for them. The intestine is so long, and the crypts of Lieberkühn so numerous, that the total number of Paneth cells in the body must be tremendous. Relatively recently it has been shown that Paneth cells are one of the few kinds in the body to contain demonstrable amounts of zinc; the significance of this is not yet understood. Somewhat higher in the crypts, the cells are of a low columnar type and most of them appear to be the forerunners of the goblet and absorptive cells seen on the surface, which, being subject to much wear and tear, need constant replacement. Some must be secretory. Mitotic figures are extraordinarily abundant here (Fig. 407 B). Leblond and Stevens, by using colchicine, have shown that the epithelial cells of the duodenum are replaced every 1.57 days, and those of the ileum every 1.35 days.

Disposed among the cells lining the crypts and those covering the villi are cells that are usually termed *argentaffine* or *enterochromaffine* cells because of the affinity of their cytoplasmic granules for silver and chromium salts. Two of these cells are seldom found together; almost invariably they are disposed in a solitary fashion between the other cells of the region. Figure 407 A illustrates an unusual grouping of them. Their shape varies in relation to their position. On the villi they are columnar, but in the crypts they tend to be triangular (Fig. 407 A). Moreover, in the crypts, their apices tend to be withdrawn slightly from the surface and their bases may crowd between the bases of adjacent cells and the basement membrane. Their position in this respect is reminiscent of that of parietal cells in the glands of the stomach. Their nuclei are round and may be disposed toward either end of the cell, although most commonly the nucleus is in the basal end of the cell but not far from its center. Their fine structure is illustrated in Figure 407 C.

Argentaffine (enterochromaffine) cells have been demonstrated in all parts of the alimentary tract, from the esophagus to the anus, but they are more numerous in the small intestine, and for this reason they are described here. They have also been seen in the bile and the pancreatic ducts and in other sites. Similar

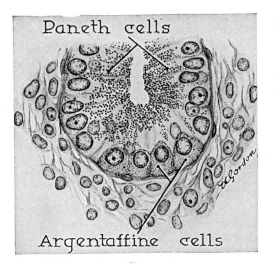

FIG. 407. (A) Drawing of the bottom of a crypt of Lieberkühn (high-power). Both Paneth and argentaffine cells may be seen. It is unusual for argentaffine cells to be grouped together as they are in this section.

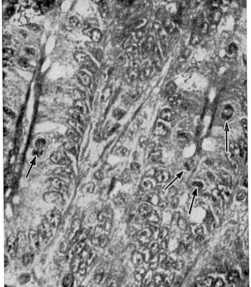

FIG. 407. (B) High-power photomicrograph of section of small intestine of a rat showing many mitotic figures in cells of crypts. Cells are produced here to replace those lost at the tips of the villi.

(perhaps identical) cells have been described in other layers of the intestine. Curious little tumors (carcinoid), not uncommon in the appendix, have been traced to cells of this or a similar type. The precise origin of these cells is not clear. It has long been suspected that they develop from neuro-ectoderm and that they might produce some secretion affecting the autonomic nervous system. Relatively recently it has been established that they produce *serotonin*; the actions of this were described in connection with platelets.

Lamina Propria. The cores of villi are composed of lamina propria. In this particular site it consists of a loose connective tissue which has many of the attributes of lymphatic tissue. Its chief supporting element is a network of reticular fibers that extends throughout its substance and, at the sides and the tip, unites with the basement membrane under the surface epithelium. Branching cells with pale cytoplasm are irregularly scattered over the fibers in the reticular net. These are generally thought to be reticular cells, and probably both the undifferentiated and the reticuloendothelial types are represented. In the meshes of the network, lymphocytes are common and are probably of local origin (Fig. 406). Plasma cells are sometimes fairly abundant. Eosinophils that have migrated from the capillaries

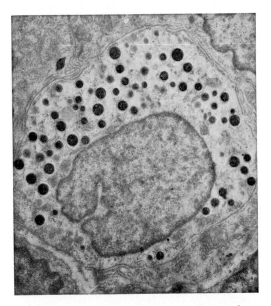

FIG. 407. (C) Electron micrograph ($\times$ 8,000) of an argentaffine cell from the stomach of a bat. The cytoplasm shows dense granules each of which is surrounded by a membrane. (Dr. S. Ito, Dr. R. J. Winchester and Dr. D. W. Fawcett)

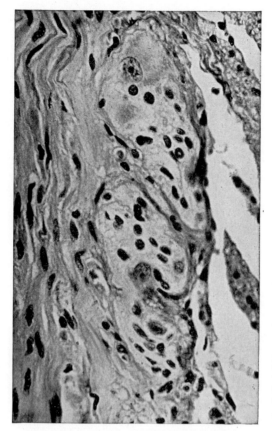

Fig. 408. High-power photomicrograph of a section of the small intestine of a child, showing a portion of Auerbach's plexus between the two layers of the muscularis externa. Note the large ganglion cell at the top. Its cytoplasm lies mostly above and to the right of its nucleus.

of the villus are also sometimes seen in the reticular net. Furthermore, smooth muscle fibers with their long axes parallel with that of the villus are characteristically disposed in its central part, usually around a single, large, lymphatic capillary that begins near the tip of the villus; this lymphatic capillary is usually termed the *lacteal* of the villus.

A single arterial twig from the submucosa usually penetrates the muscularis mucosae below each villus and ascends into it for some distance and then breaks up into a capillary network. The capillaries approach the epithelial cells very closely. Separate arterial twigs break up into capillary nets surrounding the crypts of Lieberkühn. Nerve fibers from Meissner's plexus in the submucosa likewise

penetrate the muscularis mucosae to ascend into each villus. Here they break up into networks that are said to extend throughout all its substances. Frank nodules of lymphatic tissue are not uncommon in the lamina propria of any part of the digestive tract but they are relatively more numerous in the small intestine, particularly in the ileum. They appear either singly, as "solitary" nodules, or in such close association with others that "confluent" masses are formed. The possible function of lymphatic tissue in the lamina propria was discussed in the general plan.

Solitary lymphatic nodules may be present almost anywhere in the lamina propria in the small intestine. They range from ½ to 3 mm. in width. The smaller ones are entirely confined to the lamina propria, but the larger ones may bulge through the muscularis mucosae into the submucosa. The epithelium over them and the other tissues about them are usually infiltrated with lymphocytes derived from these nodules. When nodules are numerous they tend to become confluent. The larger confluent masses have an elongated oval shape and are confined to the side of the intestine opposite the mesenteric attachment. They vary from 1 to 12 cm. in length and from 1 to 2½ cm. in width. They are called *Peyer's patches* after their discoverer. There are usually 20 to 30 of them, but more have been observed in young subjects. They are confined mostly to the lower part of the ileum, where they are largest, but they are also present in the upper part of the ileum and the lower part of the jejunum; they have even been observed in the lower part of the duodenum. Villi are usually absent over them. They were perhaps of more interest when typhoid fever was a prevalent disease, for in this condition they exhibit a profound inflammatory reaction and are common sites of ulceration, hemorrhage and even of perforation. Like the lymphatic tissue as a whole, both the solitary and the confluent nodules become less prominent as an individual ages. In old age, Peyer's patches disappear almost completely.

The *muscularis mucosae* and the *submucosa* of the small intestine require no description other than that given in the general plan.

The *muscularis externa* of the small intestine exhibits no special features, but sections of the small intestine provide a good opportunity for the student to see and examine the ganglion cells and the nerve fibers of Auerbach's plexus which is to be seen between the two muscle layers (Fig. 408).

Absorption from the Small Intestine. Precise evidence regarding the particular cells that absorb the products of digestion and how they accomplish this function is difficult to obtain. However, it seems logical to suppose that in health most absorption is performed by the villi and, in particular, by the columnar cells which the E/M has shown to be covered with microvilli (Fig. 123).

In our present state of knowledge, the laws of diffusion and osmosis cannot be applied to explain all aspects of intestinal absorption. As yet, obscure vital activities of the epithelial lining cells must be postulated to account for the selective action of the absorptive cells as well as for their ability to remove substances from sites of low concentration and to deliver them into sites of higher concentration.

Under normal conditions, carbohydrates are absorbed (as monosaccharides) through the absorptive epithelial cells and into the blood capillaries that are so close to them in the lamina propria. Proteins are absorbed as amino acids by the same route. Until recently, it was generally believed that fats were broken down in the lumen of the intestine to fatty acids and glycerol and absorbed as such by the epithelial lining cells, and that the fat droplets that reappeared in the cytoplasm between the striated border and the nucleus of the absorptive cells indicated a resynthesis of the fat in this site. More recently, Frazer has provided evidence showing that all fat is not split to the point where free glycerol is liberated from it before it is absorbed. This requires that some be absorbed as an emulsion. That this actually occurs has been proved recently by E/M studies made by Palay and Karlin. They fed rats a fatty meal and then studied sections of the jejunum, taken at different times afterward, with the E/M. They found that small fat droplets, between 300 and 500 Å in diameter, appeared between the microvilli 20 minutes after the animals had been fed. Moreover, at this time some droplets were found in the cytoplasm close to the bases of the microvilli. From ½ to 1 hour after the feeding, the fat droplets were seen deeper in the cytoplasm, and each could be shown to be surrounded by a membrane (this would seem to suggest that the mechanism operating here is similar to that already described for phagocytosis by macrophages and pinocytosis by endothelial cells). The fat droplets did not reach the basal parts of the absorptive cells but instead seemed to migrate to and through the sides of the cells so that dense clusters of droplets came to lie between the borders of adjacent absorptive cells. From here the droplets seemed to pass through the basement membrane and so gained entrance to the lamina propria and its lymphatics.

The lymphatics that drain the intestine contain considerable amounts of emulsified fat after a fatty meal; this creamy lymph is termed *chyle*.

THE LARGE INTESTINE

Parts. The large intestine consists of the cecum, the vermiform appendix, the ascending, transverse, descending and pelvic colons, and the rectum (including the anal canal). It terminates at the anus (Fig. 373).

Function. The unabsorbed contents of the small intestine are emptied into the cecum in a fluid state. By the time the contents reach the descending colon they have acquired the consistency of feces. Absorption of water by the mucous membrane is an important function of the large intestine.

Although a great deal of mucus is present in the alkaline secretion of the large intestine, no enzymes of importance are secreted with it. Nevertheless, some digestion occurs in the lumen. Part of this is due to enzymes derived from the small intestine remaining active in the material delivered into the large intestine, and part is to be explained by the putrefactive bacteria that thrive in its lumen, breaking down cellulose, which, if consumed in the diet, survives to reach the large intestine because no enzymes that attack it are liberated by the intestine of man.

Many years ago, Metchnikoff (mentioned in connection with phagocytes) decided, for various reasons, that many of the ills of man were due to the absorption from the large intestine of the products of bacterial putrefaction. His ideas were responsible for a great number of people regularly consuming cultures of bacteria designed to supplant the putrefactive ones that normally flourish in the large

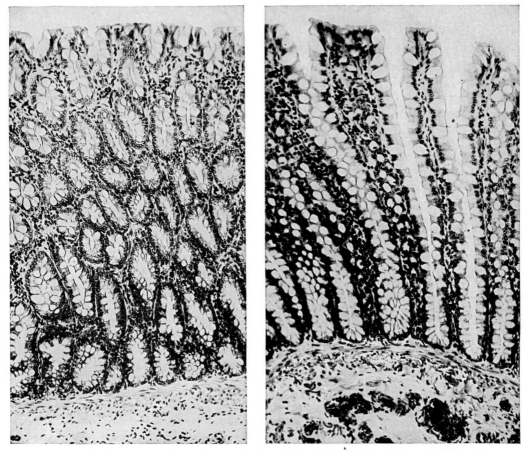

Fig. 409. Medium-power photomicrograph of sections of the wall of the large intestine, showing the mucous membrane. At the left, the crypts of Lieberkühn are cut in oblique section, and at the right, in longitudinal section. They are seen to extend down to the muscularis mucosae.

bowel. Undoubtedly, poisonous materials *do* form in this location but they are probably not absorbed in sufficient quantities by healthy individuals to exert an adverse effect, particularly since special detoxifying mechanisms exist to deal with many of them. Furthermore, it has recently become apparent that some of the products of bacterial putrefaction are helpful, if not essential, to the organism. Vitamin K, spoken of in connection with the clotting of blood, is a product of the putrefactive process, as are certain members of the B complex.

Feces consist of bacteria, products of bacterial putrefaction, such undigested material as survives passage through the large intestine, cellular debris from the lining of the intestine, mucus and a few other substances.

Histologic Structure. The mucous membrane of the large intestine differs from that of the small intestine in many respects. It has no villi in postnatal life. It is thicker; hence, the crypts of Lieberkühn are deeper (Fig. 409). The crypts contain no Paneth cells (except in the young), but they have more goblet cells than are present in the small intestine. The surface epithelial cells have striated borders like those of the small intestine, and some goblet cells are interspersed between them. The crypts of Lieberkühn are distributed over the whole inner surface of the large bowel except in the lower end of the anal canal. The stratified squamous epithelium of the skin, though not keratinized in this particular site, extends into the anal canal for about 2 cm. and there becomes continuous with the columnar epithelium above. At the anus itself, the stratified squamous epithelium becomes keratinized. In the skin round the anus, but not immediately adjacent to it, circumanal glands are present. These are of the branched tubular type and are to be regarded as enlarged and otherwise modified sweat glands; sebaceous glands are also present in this area.

In the anal canal, the mucous membrane is thrown into a series of longitudinal folds known as the *rectal columns* or *columns of Morgagni*. Below, adjacent columns are connected by folds. This arrangement produces a series of so-called anal valves, each of which somewhat resembles the leaflet of an aortic semilunar valve. The concavities of the pockets so formed are called *rectal sinuses*.

The muscularis mucosae continues only to the region of the longitudinal folds and in them it breaks up into bundles and finally disappears. Hence, there is not the same demarcation between lamina propria and submucosa in this region as in other parts of the tract. The merging lamina propria and submucosa contain many convolutions of small veins. A very common condition, *internal hemorrhoids,* is the result of the dilatation of these veins so that they bulge the mucous membrane inwardly and encroach on the lumen of the anal canal. External hemorrhoids result from the dilatation of veins in the skin at, and close to, the anus.

Muscularis Externa. In the large intestine, this layer differs somewhat from its arrangement in other parts of the tract. Beginning in the cecum, the longitudinally disposed fibers of the outer coat, though present to a certain extent over the whole circumference of the bowel, are for the most part collected into three flat bands, the *teniae coli*. These are not as long as the intestine along which they are disposed; hence, they are responsible for gathering the wall of this part of the bowel into sacculations or haustra (Fig. 373). If the teniae are cut or stripped away, the bowel immediately elongates and the sacculations disappear. The three teniae extend from the cecum to the rectum, where they spread out and fuse to some extent so as to form a muscle coat that is thicker on the anterior and the posterior aspects of the rectum than on its sides. The anterior and the posterior aggregates of longitudinally disposed smooth muscle are somewhat shorter than the rectum itself, and this results in a type of sacculation in this region; this causes the underlying wall of the rectum to bulge inwardly to form two transverse shelves, one from the right and a smaller one from the left, called the *plicae transversae* of the rectum. These help to support the weight of the rectal contents and so make the work of the anal sphincter less arduous.

The circularly disposed smooth muscle fibers of the inner coat of the muscularis externa form a thicker coat between sacculations than they do over the sacculations. In the anal canal they are increased to form a sphincter muscle, the internal sphincter of the anus.

Serosa. Along the colon and the upper part of the rectum, the serous coat leaves the surface of the intestine at irregular intervals to form little peritoneal sacs that enclose fat. These peritoneal redundancies hang from the external surface of the bowel and are termed *appendices epiploicae*. In some sites they contain only areolar tissue.

Vermiform Appendix. This wormlike appendage of the cecum (Fig. 373) is the seat of so much disease that it merits a separate description. Developmentally, it is the lower, blind end of the cecum that has failed to enlarge as rapidly as the remainder and, as a result, it appears as a diverticulum arising from the cecum an inch or less below the entrance of the ileum. In many lower animals it is larger than it is in man and so provides a good-sized pouch off the main track of the intestine where cellulose can be subjected to prolonged digestion. In man it is too short and has too narrow a lumen to serve a similar function. Indeed, its form is commonly so bent and twisted that there is grave danger of bacterial activity destroying not only the contents of the lumen but also the lining of the organ itself. As a result, organisms sometimes gain entrance to the tissues of its wall and lead to its infection. For this reason, surgical removal of the infected organ is one of the commonest abdominal operations.

The appendix usually is studied microscopically by means of cross sections (Fig. 410). In preparations of this sort, the lumen of the appendix of a young person often has a some-

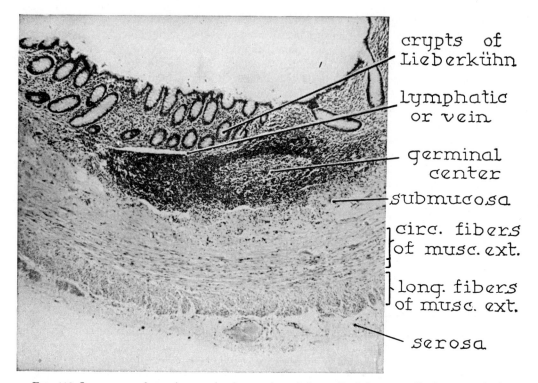

crypts of
Lieberkühn

lymphatic
or vein

germinal
center

submucosa

circ. fibers
of musc. ext.

long. fibers
of musc. ext.

serosa

Fig. 410. Low-power photomicrograph of a portion of the wall of the appendix (cross section).

what three-horned instead of a circular appearance. In adults, it is usually rounder, and in advancing years, it may be obliterated by connective tissue's replacing the mucous membrane as well as filling the lumen.

The epithelium of the mucous membrane is similar to that of the large intestine (Fig. 410). However, the lamina propria contains much more lymphatic tissue; indeed, confluent lymphatic nodules may completely surround the lumen, though the amount diminishes with age. The muscularis mucosae is not well developed and may be missing in some areas. A few eosinophils are normal constituents of the lamina propria but, if present in the submucosa, are considered as being of some significance in indicating a chronic inflammatory condition of the organ. Neutrophils in any numbers in the lamina propria or any other layer (Fig. 156) indicate an acute inflammatory lesion (acute appendicitis). The muscularis externa shows no deviation from the general plan found in the intestine, and the longitudinal fibers form a complete coat. The appendix has a rudimentary mesentery.

THE PANCREAS

Introduction. The pancreas is a large and important gland. It lies in the abdomen with its head resting in the concavity of the duodenum and with its body extending toward the spleen, which its tail touches (Fig. 373). Grossly, a fresh pancreas is white with a pink tinge. With the naked eye its surface appears lobulated; it lacks a sufficiently substantial capsule to obscure the structure beneath it.

The pancreas is both an exocrine and an endocrine gland. The bulk of its cells are concerned with producing its exocrine secretion. This is collected and delivered by a duct system into the second part of the duodenum. The functions of the pancreatic secretion in digestion have already been described. The endocrine secretion of the pancreas is made by little clumps of cells, richly supplied with capillaries, that are scattered throughout its substance, and so surrounded by exocrine glandular tissue. Hence, these little endocrine units are appropriately termed *islets* and are named after Langerhans who described them.

The known hormone produced by the *islets of Langerhans* is called *insulin* (*insula* = an island). The insufficient production of this hormone leads to the development of diabetes mellitus, a disease that will be described when the islets of Langerhans are discussed in detail in the chapter dealing with endocrine glands.

Development. The development of exocrine and endocrine glands is illustrated in Figure 134. The development of the pancreas offers examples of both the processes illustrated therein. Two diverticula (a ventral and a dorsal) arise from the epithelial (endodermal) lining of the developing duodenum and grow out and branch into mesoderm. Most of the pancreas (the tail, the body and the upper part of the head) arises from the dorsal outgrowth, while the lower part of the head arises from the ventral diverticulum. In some animals the fact that the pancreas arises from two different outgrowths is emphasized by the proximal parts of the outgrowths persisting to form two main ducts, each of which opens into the duodenum and drains the part of the pancreas originating from the particular outgrowth with which that duct is associated. However, in man, although two ducts persist in the majority of individuals, the dorsal and the ventral outgrowths fuse in such a fashion that the proximal part of the duct developing in the ventral outgrowth becomes continuous with the duct developing in the dorsal outgrowth, with the result that most of the secretion made by the part of the pancreas developing from the dorsal outgrowth actually comes to be conveyed, on the last part of its passage, into the duodenum by the duct that developed from the ventral outgrowth. This main duct, made up of parts of both embryonic ones, is known as the *pancreatic duct* (of Wirsung). The proximal part of the duct that develops from the dorsal outgrowth persists in the majority of individuals to form the accessory pancreatic duct (of Santorini).

The terminal portions of the two branching duct systems develop into exocrine secretory units. Although tending to be tubular in shape, these are sufficiently fat and rounded to resemble grapes hanging on stems, hence they are called *acini* (*acinus* = grape).

Some clumps of cells that arise from the developing duct system fail to develop a lumen. In many instances, though by no means always, these become completely detached from the duct system proper to become the islets of Langerhans—the endocrine units that are scattered through the pancreas. Moreover, there is reason to believe that some of the branches of the developing duct system fail to develop lumens or, if they do, that their lumens make no connection with those of the duct system proper. By this means, an ill-defined network of cords or tubules of cells comes to be disposed irregularly through the substance of the pancreas in addition to the functional duct system. The cells of this network are relatively undifferentiated, and under certain circumstances they appear to give rise to new endocrine cells. This is the probable origin of those islet cells that are sometimes seen scattered singly among the acini.

MICROSCOPIC STRUCTURE

It is not easy for the beginner to become oriented when sections of pancreas are first examined with the microscope. In order to facilitate orientation, the following account is so written that one feature of the tissue at a time may be identified and studied with the microscope.

Capsule. Most sections of the pancreas are cut at right angles to its surface, so, by looking around the periphery of a section with a low-power objective, the student should be able to find a capsule on one side. Here it will be seen that the connective tissue capsule that separates the pancreatic tissue from adjacent structures is remarkably thin; indeed, it scarcely merits being called a capsule. The pancreas, then, is poorly protected.

Septa. If the section as a whole is next studied by moving it about on the stage while it is examined with the low-power objective, it will be observed that partitions (septa) of connective tissue extend in from the capsule to divide it into lobules. These septa, like the capsule, are very thin (Fig. 411). Furthermore, separation commonly occurs along them when pancreatic tissue is fixed. Consequently, the lobules commonly are clearly indicated because they are separated from one another by fissures of the nature of artefacts.

The septa of the pancreas are so thin it might be concluded that the pancreas is as

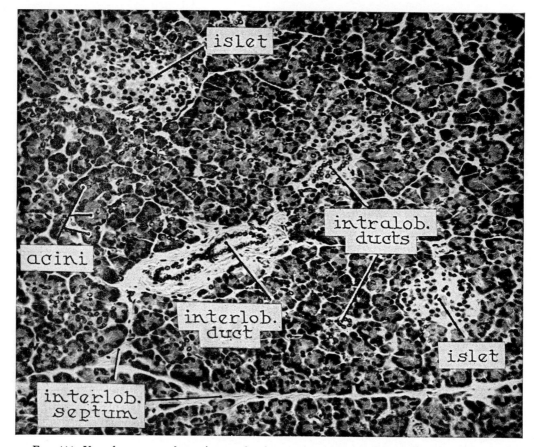

FIG. 411. Very low-power photomicrograph of a section of the pancreas, showing 2 islets, a large interlobular duct and smaller intralobular ducts, many acini and an interlobular septum.

poorly provided with internal support as it is with a protective covering. But this is not the universal rule throughout the pancreas, for considerable condensations of dense connective tissue are often present around the main duct of the organ and its more immediate branches (Fig. 411).

Acini. The tissue comprising the substance of the lobules should be examined next. Most of this consists of secretory units, the *pancreatic acini* (Fig. 411). These are packed together in a most irregular way with only a little reticular tissue between them, so that a microtome knife, in cutting a section of pancreas, cuts acini in almost every conceivable plane. Most, of course, are cut in oblique section. In many sections of pancreas the acini do not stand out at all clearly as individual structures. The student, then, may have difficulty in deciding just what constitutes an

acinus. It may be helpful to realize that under the high-power objective an acinus is approximately a tenth of the field in width. And, since the nuclei of the secretory cells that make up the acinus lie toward their bases, the nuclei in a single acinus tend to be arranged so as to form a rough ring of nuclei in its outer part (Fig. 412). Individual acini would be easier to recognize if their central parts were always free of nuclei (the ring of peripheral nuclei could then be observed more easily), but they are not; this is because the ducts that lead from acini do not always begin from their ends but sometimes from their central part. A duct may be more or less invaginated into the lumen of the acinus. The duct cells that are in this position are termed *centro-acinar* cells (Fig. 412).

The sides of the more or less pyramidal cells that are packed together to form acini

are so close together that cell boundaries between individual cells are not always distinct
(Fig. 412). The apices of the cells of an acinus
do not quite come together in the central part
of each acinus; hence, a very small lumen is
present in this site (Fig. 58). The cytoplasm
between the nucleus and the apex of each
secretory cell contains acidophilic zymogen
granules which may be seen easily by partly
closing the condenser diaphragm (Fig. 412).
The nuclei are rounded and lie toward, but
not against, the bases of the cells. They exhibit prominent nucleoli, which are commonly
more acidophilic than those of most cells. The
cytoplasm between the nuclei and the bases of
the cells, as well as that on each side of the
nuclei, is commonly basophilic because of its
content of chromidial substance (Fig. 412).
This is probably an example of a cell which
is synthesizing a great deal of protein (the
zymogen granules which are secreted, day by
day, are protein) having accumulations of
ribonucleic acid in its cytoplasm. In the bases
of the cells, the chromidial substance may
present a striated appearance because mitochondria are disposed in this region in a plane
parallel with the long axis of the cell.

Fine Structure of Acinar Cells. The fine
structure of the secretory cells and the formation of zymogen granules is described in Chapter 4 and illustrated in Figures 65 and 73.

A delicate, reticular connective tissue fills
the space between individual acini and brings
capillaries close to the bases of the secretory
cells. Nerve fibers are also conducted in this
reticular connective tissue.

Islets of Langerhans. If enough lobules are
inspected with the low-power objective, pale
areas, considerably larger than cross or oblique
sections of acini, will be seen (Fig. 411). These
areas are *islets of Langerhans* and contain
cords and irregular clumps of cells and capillaries. Red blood cells are present in the capillaries commonly enough for the capillaries to
appear, even with the low-power objective, as
pink or red streaks. However, with only the
low-power objective, a beginner may confuse
an islet with a duct or a little patch of connective tissue. With the high-power objective,
the usual islet is a third to a half or more of
the field in width and its characteristic structure of cords and clumps of cells separated by
capillaries can be seen clearly. Islets are *not*

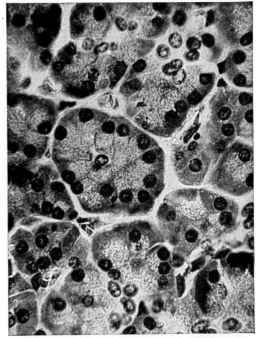

Fig. 412. High-power photomicrograph
of a section of the pancreas, showing an
acinus with the nucleus of a centro-acinar
cell appearing in its center.

encapsulated and so are separated from acinar
tissue by only a film of reticular tissue. Internal support in islets is provided by reticular
fibers that are associated with capillaries. But
there is not much connective tissue in islets;
otherwise, the secretion of the cells would have
difficulty gaining entrance to capillaries.

Since the pancreas is a large organ and since
the percentage and the size of the islets is not
constant in all its parts, any estimate of the
relative amount of islet tissue made from a
single section of any given pancreas has little
more authority than a guess. A rough idea
may be gained by the sampling method; that
is, studying unselected sections cut from a
dozen or so different parts of the organ. The
total number of islets and the total extent of
islet tissue can be determined by cutting a
whole pancreas into serial sections of known
thickness and measuring the area of islets seen
in each and every section. This, of course, is
an enormous task. Bensley, many years ago,
described a much simpler method of determining the number of islets present in a pancreas. He perfused the blood vessels of the

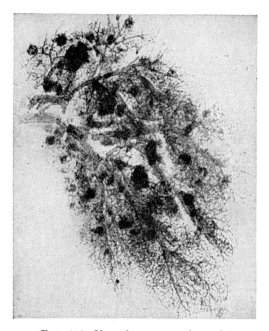

Fig. 413. Very low-power photomicrograph of a piece of a guinea pig's pancreas perfused with Janus green. The blood vessels subsequently were injected with carmine gelatin. The islets appear as dark patches, and the reticulated appearance of the background is due to the injected blood vessels. (Preparation of S. H. Bensley)

fresh organ with dilute solutions of either neutral red or Janus green. Both these supravital dyes stain the pancreas diffusely, but they stain the cells of the islets more or less specifically. Furthermore, as reduction occurs on standing, the dyes fade from the acinar tissue so that the islets stand out as either red or blue areas, depending on the dye used (Fig. 413). Pancreas so prepared is cut into little pieces that can be mounted on slides, and a group of observers can soon count the number of islets in all the pieces and so determine the number of islets in the pancreas. Haist and Pugh devised a more elaborate technic based on the same staining principles; this permits them to estimate not only the number of islets in a pancreas but also the total volume of islet tissue.

The different types of cells in islets and their appearance in different physiologic states will be described in the chapter on endocrine glands.

Ducts. Before describing the appearance of ducts seen in a section of pancreas under low-power magnification, a few words about their general arrangement are in order. The main duct of the pancreas, the duct of Wirsung, is enveloped by connective tissue and serves more or less as a "backbone" for the organ through which it runs. From this, side branches emerge regularly at angles, so that the duct system, stripped clean of other tissues, resembles a herring bone. The side branches of the main duct run between lobules and hence are interlobular ducts. These branch to give rise to intralobular ducts which enter the substance of lobules. Intralobular ducts are not nearly so prominent in the pancreas as they are in salivary glands. A relative absence of clean-cut intralobular ducts is then an important criterion by which the student can quickly distinguish a section of pancreas from that of parotid gland. The presence of islets of Langerhans in the lobules is, of course, another, but, in some preparations, considerable study is needed before islets can be identified with certainty.

The larger of the relatively few intralobular ducts can be seen, under low power, to be ensheathed by dense connective tissue derived from the septa from which they emerge (Fig. 411). The intralobular ducts give rise to very small ducts lined with flattened epithelium. These small ducts lead to the acini and are called *intercalated* (*intercalare* = to insert) *ducts* because they are inserted between the secretory units and the intralobular ducts proper. As noted before, the intercalated ducts often extend into the central part of acini to be known as centro-acinar cells (Fig. 412).

The lumen of the main duct may be as much as 2½ mm. wide. It is lined by columnar epithelium. Goblet cells may be interspersed between the ordinary columnar cells. Near the duodenum, small mucous glands may be associated with the main duct. The interlobular ducts are lined by low columnar epithelium. In the intralobular ducts, the epithelium is low columnar to cuboidal, and in the intercalated ducts, flattened cuboidal.

CONTROL OF EXOCRINE SECRETION

Since the pancreatic juice contains so many important enzymes needed to carry on the further digestion of food that has passed through the stomach, the need for some mechanism to regulate pancreatic secretion in accordance with deliveries of food into the duodenum from the stomach is obvious. Such a mechanism exists in the form of a hormone called *secretin*. It is made by the mucosa of the duodenum when the acid contents of the stomach are delivered into it. This hormone circulates by the blood stream to the capillaries that surround pancreatic acini and there acts in some fashion to stimulate the secretory activity of the acinar cells. When enough alkaline pancreatic juice has been delivered into the duodenum to neutralize the acid chyme contained therein, the formation of secretin by the duodenal mucosa stops, and this in turn results in a cessation of pancreatic secretion. But when further acid chyme reaches the duodenal mucosa, more pancreatic secretion is delivered into the duodenum. By this mechanism a sufficient quantity of pancreatic juice to ensure further digestion is delivered automatically into the duodenum each time a fresh supply of chyme is received from the stomach.

Stimulation with secretin, particularly if it is prolonged, leads to some diminution in the number of granules in the acinar cells, but its effects are chiefly manifested by its stimulating the secretion of the nonenzymatic ingredients of pancreatic juice. Another hormone, *pancreozymin*, made by the duodenal mucosa, recently has been shown to be much more effective than secretin in stimulating the secretion of enzyme-rich pancreatic juice. Stimulation of the vagus nerve also causes the same effect. On the other hand, in starvation, when no appreciable amount of acid chyme is delivered into the duodenum and hence little secretin is made, the acinar cells accumulate granules.

THE LIVER

For the convenience of those students who have not yet studied the gross anatomy of the liver, some of its features, important with regard to understanding its microscopic structure, will be described.

Some Gross Features. The liver is the largest organ in the body, weighing, in the adult, about 3 pounds. It is an epithelial gland that performs both exocrine and endocrine functions. Its exocrine secretion is bile.

The liver is reddish brown in color. Most of it lies on the right side of the body with its upper convex surface fitting the undersurface of the dome-shaped diaphragm (Fig. 373). It consists of two main lobes, the right and the left, and the right is much the larger of the two (Fig. 373). The inferior surface of the liver is exposed in Figure 373 and shows the impressions of the several organs with which it normally comes into contact (parts of the alimentary tract and the right kidney which are separated from it in Fig. 373), so its inferior surface is often called its visceral surface. The visceral surface exhibits a short deep transverse fissure called the *porta* (door) of the liver (not shown in Fig. 373).

The liver is covered with a connective tissue capsule (of Glisson). At the porta, the trunk of a tree of connective tissue, which is continuous with the capsule, grows up, as it were, into the substance of the liver. In the substance of the liver the tree branches so extensively that no part of the liver substance is ever farther than a millimeter or two from one or, more generally, several of its branches.

The branching connective tissue tree provides internal support for the liver. It also performs another function, that of providing a means whereby branches of the portal vein (which brings food-laden blood to the liver from the intestine), the hepatic artery and the bile duct, as well as the lymphatic vessels, can reach all parts of the liver. At the porta the portal vein and the hepatic artery both *enter* the trunk of the connective tissue tree, and thereafter each of the vessels branches with every branching of the tree. Likewise, the lymphatic vessels and the bile ducts have branches in every branch of the tree. The main lymphatic vessels and the two main bile ducts, one from the right lobe and one from the left, *leave* the liver at the porta. The two main bile ducts soon join to form a single duct (Fig. 373). This is joined by the cystic duct from the gallbladder, and the common bile duct carries bile to the duodenum (Fig. 373).

Since the portal vein, the hepatic artery, the lymphatics and the bile ducts all branch along with the branching of the connective tissue tree, each branch of the tree that is seen in sections of human liver (and the branches are very numerous) reveals the presence of at least 4 vessels: a branch of the portal vein, a branch of the hepatic artery, a bile duct and one or more lymphatics (Fig. 417, *right*).

Venous blood is brought to the liver by the portal vein, and arterial blood by the hepatic artery. Blood is drained away from the liver by hepatic veins. These do not travel in the branches of the connective tissue tree; their tributaries (called sublobular veins) and they themselves pursue lonely courses through the substance of the liver (where they are associated with only a little connective tissue) and empty into the vena cava as it comes into close contact with the back of the liver.

Development. The liver originates from the entodermal epithelium of the developing duodenum; the epithelium here first bulges outwardly to form what is termed the *hepatic diverticulum*. One branch of this forms the cystic duct and the gallbladder. The epithelial cells of another part grow in the form of projections into the splanchnic mesoderm and split it up. Branches from the veins which will become the portal vein grow into the area where the epithelium is splitting up the mesoderm, and the spaces between the developing epithelial projections become richly vascularized. At this time, sections of the developing liver reveal irregular cords of epithelial cells separated by vascular spaces which will be sinusoids. The cords that are seen in sections probably would prove, to some extent at least, to be sheets or plates if they could be seen in 3 dimensions. The whole mass grows rapidly. The mesoderm provides a capsule for the organ and also the tree of connective tissue that forms in the interior of the organ.

In the development of exocrine glands the terminal outgrowths become secretory units, and the epithelial cells that connect these with the site from which the gland originates form the ducts (Fig. 134). The cordlike epithelial outgrowths that become secretory units of the liver invade very vascular connective tissue with the result that they are separated from one another by sinusoids which have only a little intercellular substance in their walls. (The liver, in this sense, has a fairly typical *endocrine* gland structure.) But the epithelial cells that connect the developing secretory units with the site of origin of the liver (the duodenum) do not disappear as commonly occurs in the formation of endocrine glands; they remain to form the system of bile ducts that afterward drain the secretion of the liver to the duodenum. So, although secretory units

of the liver exhibit an endocrine gland arrangement and perform endocrine functions, they actually secrete into ducts so that it is an exocrine gland as well. The exocrine and the endocrine functions of the liver are performed by the same cells—those that comprise the cord and the platelike secretory units.

SOME PRELIMINARY HISTOPHYSIOLOGIC CONSIDERATIONS

Exocrine Function. The liver secretes 500 to 600 cc. of bile each 24 hours. The bile of man is a yellow to yellow-brown fluid. Its coloring matter is *bilirubin*, which is a bile pigment. Bilirubin is easily oxidized to biliverdin, which is a green pigment. In some animals (birds) there is normally a large amount of biliverdin in bile so that it is green, as anyone who has "cleaned" a bird knows. The formation of bilirubin will be explained presently. Bile contains, in addition to pigment, bile salts, lipoids, lecithin and minute amounts of other substances, some of which are waste products of metabolism. Some of the substances present in bile—for example, bile salts, which facilitate the digestion of fat—are useful substances; hence, bile can be considered a secretion. But since bile also contains waste products it is also, in part, an excretion.

As has already been noted, the liver is both an exocrine and an endocrine gland. Most endocrine glands secrete hormones, as will be explained fully in Chapter 26. However, it should be understood that a gland does not have to secrete hormones to be termed an endocrine gland; a gland is endocrine if it secretes any useful substance into the blood stream. The liver, as we shall see, is termed an endocrine gland, not because it secretes hormones into the blood stream, but because it secretes sugar into the blood stream. But before discussing its endocrine function, we shall comment briefly on the interesting fact that the liver does indeed secrete hormones, but in a most unusual way; it secretes hormones that come to it by way of the blood stream from other endocrine glands into its *exocrine* secretion.

Relation of Liver to Steroid Hormones. The sex hormones and the hormones secreted by the adrenal cortex are compounds of a type called *steroids*. These compounds are all built around what is termed the *cyclopentenophen-*

anthrene (chemical) nucleus. Cholesterol and bile salts, both of which are present in bile, are also built around this nucleus. Therefore, the fact that the liver secretes cholesterol and bile salts might very well arouse the suspicion that it also secretes steroid hormones as they come to it by way of the circulation from the sex glands and the adrenal cortex. Indeed, that it does has been established. It has been shown, for example, that there is what is termed an enterohepatic (*enteron* = intestine; *hepar* = liver) circulation of female sex hormone; this means that a part of the female sex hormone that is present in the blood that passes through the livers of females is secreted into the bile and then when this reaches the small intestine a part of the hormone is reabsorbed into the blood stream. It has been shown also that a certain percentage of male hormone injected into dogs appears in the bile, so it is probable that there is an enterohepatic circulation of this also. Certain adrenal cortical hormones have also been shown to be secreted into bile. Bile salts stimulate the secretion of bile. In addition, in our laboratory, Mosbaugh and the author have shown that cortisone (an adrenal cortical hormone) injected into chick embryos stimulates the premature secretion of bile. From all the above it seems clear that the liver and the phenomenon of bile secretion are concerned in an important way with the metabolism of steroids, and that it at least secretes the steroid endocrine secretions produced by other glands in its exocrine secretion. It is probable that some portion of the steroid hormones undergo some metabolic changes as they pass through the liver, and the possibility of the liver's being capable of changing one steroid hormone into another should be considered. The possibility of the body's being unable to reabsorb steroid hormones secreted into bile should be considered as a possible cause of hormone deficiency. Moreover, it is known that liver damage can cause excessive amounts of certain steroid hormones to accumulate in the blood stream. Obviously, the liver is of the greatest importance in connection with steroid hormones and their fate, and steroids are of great importance in affecting bile secretion.

Endocrine Function. Although bile aids digestion and has other functions as well, the exocrine function of the liver alone is not sufficient to justify the huge size of the liver. It might be assumed, then, that the endocrine functions of the liver are of great importance. This is true; the liver secretes into the blood stream foodstuffs that are needed by other cells. As we shall see, the liver is bound up with what is called the *intermediary metabolism* of the body, and this will now be described briefly.

The foodstuffs that are absorbed from the small intestine, either directly into the blood stream through capillaries or indirectly by means of lymphatics, are utilized by the cells of the body for their energy requirements and for the synthesis of such new protoplasm and intercellular substance as are required. The reactions which proceed to permit these ends to be attained constitute what is generally termed the intermediary metabolism of the body. The liver dominates intermediary metabolism. Its cells carry out certain steps in certain reactions which the other cells of the body are not equipped to perform. But its most important role is a regulatory one. In this connection, its position in the circulatory system is significant. All the food-laden blood returning from the small intestine is carried by the portal vein to the liver, and the arrangements therein are such that this blood must percolate slowly along channels where it comes into close contact with many liver cells before it is permitted to enter the general circulatory system. This arrangement permits the liver to function as a great receiving depot and storehouse.

The regulatory function of the liver is exemplified by the way it acts to control the level of sugar in the blood. Sugar is as essential for life as oxygen, and it is consumed continuously. If the blood sugar level falls to too low a level, death will result. Moreover, the presence of large amounts of sugar in the blood is harmful. Hence, there is a great need for a regulatory mechanism whereby a fairly constant normal level of blood sugar is maintained, and in most individuals this must be done under conditions of a variable carbohydrate intake in the diet. The parenchymal cells of the liver perform this regulatory function. Provided that sufficient amounts of the hormone insulin (to be described in Chap. 26) are available, the ingestion of a great deal of carbohydrate by an individual does not materially raise the blood sugar level because excess absorbed glucose that flows into the liver from the intestine through the portal vein is taken into the parenchymal cells of the liver and stored as glycogen (Fig. 79). If there is more than can be handled this way, it is converted into fat in the fat depots. Thereafter the carbohydrate is liberated from the liver cells into the blood stream as glucose, at a rate sufficient to maintain the blood sugar level between meals. Under conditions of starvation it might be thought that the stores of glycogen in the liver would become exhausted rapidly. As this tends to occur, a second mechanism is brought into action—the manufacture of glycogen and glucose from protein. Adrenal cortical hormones play a part in bringing about this reaction in which the liver cells are also vitally concerned. By this second mechanism, the liver, in co-operation with other tissues, can maintain a blood sugar level that is compatible with life even though no carbohydrate or even any other food is consumed for considerable periods of time. Eventually, of course, in starvation, the protein stores of the body—which for all practical purposes consist of the living protoplasm of cells—are exhausted, and death results.

The Lobules of the Liver

Definition. The term lobule means little lobe, so to learn its meaning we shall have to inquire into the meaning of *lobe*. This term seems to have been used first in anatomy to describe any projecting rounded part of a structure, for example, the lobe of the ear (its rounded lowermost part). When the term lobe came to be used in connection with glandular organs it was employed to designate any part that projected from the main mass of an organ or was separated from other parts of the organ by fissures, septa or indentations. The term lobule was used to designate smaller divisions that were detected within lobes which could be seen to be separated from each other by smaller fissures, septa or indentations. Hence, the primary concept of a lobule would seem to be that of its being a portion of a lobe that is separated off from other portions by some kind of *obvious* boundary.

With the advent of the microscope, lobules of *exocrine* glandular tissue were seen to be divisions of glandular tissue in which a group of closely adjacent secretory units drain into a common duct or set of ducts. So a second definition for lobules came into being—they are small divisions of an organ and are constituted of groups of closely adjacent secretory units that drain into a common duct or set of ducts. This second definition proved to be useful, for, as we shall see, it enables lobules to be identified in the kidney even though they are not separated from one another by fissures, septa or indentations. However, it must be remembered that this was not the primary definition of the term; so if in any organ there are (1) areas of tissue that are separated from one another by septa but do not represent groups of closely adjacent secretory units that drain into a common duct or set of ducts, and (2) areas of closely adjacent secretory units that drain into a common duct but are not the areas that are separated from one another by septa, there should be no question as to which should be termed the lobule. In any instance of conflict, lobules should be defined according to the primary meaning of the word, hence as divisions of tissue that are separated from one another by septa.

As the apprehensive student has already concluded, there is a conflict about what should be called a liver lobule. Most of the conflict is due to the pig. The liver of this animal exhibits small divisions of tissue that are separated from one another by septa (Fig. 414). There is no question about the correctness of calling these areas lobules. However, these lobules do not represent adjacent units of secretory units that drain into a common duct, for the secretory units of each, as we shall see, drain into several *different* ducts that are disposed in the interlobular septa, and each receives secretion from secretory units of two or more adjacent lobules.

In the liver of man there are no interlobular septa. Therefore, the question arises as to whether the liver lobule in man should be considered to be (1) the counterpart of the area in the pig which is enclosed by septa, or (2) a group of adjacent secretory units that drain into a common duct. The *classic* liver lobule (hepatic lobule) of man is the counterpart of the area that in the liver of the pig is enclosed by septa. However, there have been, and are, many authorities on the liver who think that the liver lobule of man should be defined as

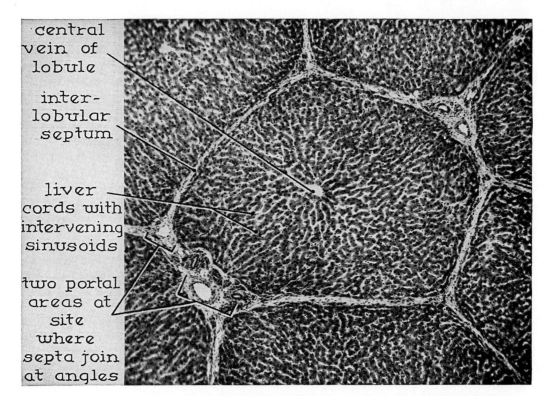

central vein of lobule

inter-lobular septum

liver cords with intervening sinusoids

two portal areas at site where septa join at angles

Fig. 414. Low-power photomicrograph of an H and E section of the liver of the pig, illustrating the classic hexagonal lobule.

the group of secretory units that drain into a common duct. They reason that if this latter view were adopted it would make easier the understanding of certain pathologic conditions of the liver. We shall discuss this matter further when we deal with the liver of man, but before doing so we shall consider the lobule of the liver of the pig.

The Liver Lobule of the Pig. If a section of pig liver is examined with the low-power objective, an area such as that illustrated in Figure 414 will soon be seen. This figure shows a cross section of a hepatic lobule with parts of 6 other lobules ranged round its periphery. The lobules are separated from one another by interlobular septa of connective tissue. The lobules in cross section generally reveal 5 or 6 sides. They are about 1 mm. in width and 2 mm. in length.

The already described branching tree of connective tissue that extends into the substance of the liver from the porta and carries the branches of the portal vein, the hepatic artery, the bile duct and the lymphatic vessels to all

parts of the liver is expanded in the pig, so that its terminal twigs give rise to broad leaves of connective tissue that connect the twigs and so ensheath each lobule; the leaves are the interlobular septa. Since branches of the portal vein, the hepatic artery, the bile duct and the lymphatic vessels are all carried in the branching tree of connective tissue, representatives of these 4 tubes are brought via the interlobular septa to the periphery of each lobule at several different points. Usually 4 tubes—vein, artery, duct and lymphatic—run close together in the connective tissue. Groups of 4 tubes are commonly seen in the septa at, or close to, the sites at which the septa exhibit angles. Such sites seen in cross section each reveal 4 different tubes, and each group of 4 tubes, are commonly seen in the septa at, or close to, the sites at which the septa exhibit angles. Such sites seen in cross section each reveal 4 different tubes, and each group of 4 tubes, together with the connective tissue that immediately surrounds the group, constitutes what is termed a *portal radicle, canal* or *area*

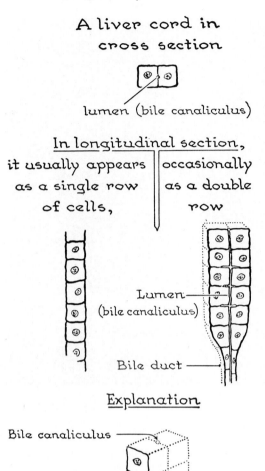

A liver cord in cross section

lumen (bile canaliculus)

In longitudinal section, it usually appears as a single row of cells,   occasionally as a double row

Lumen (bile canaliculus)

Bile duct

Explanation

Bile canaliculus

FIG. 415. Three-dimensional illustration showing why liver cords may appear as single rows of cells, and the sites of canaliculi.

ery of the lobule, and they carry this blood from the periphery to the center of the lobule where they empty it into the *central vein* of the lobule. This runs longitudinally along the central axis of the lobule and drains into sublobular veins which are the tributaries of the hepatic veins.

Having established that blood flows through sinusoids between liver cords from the periphery of the lobule to its center, we can next investigate where bile is secreted and the direction in which it flows in the lobule. A consideration of this question requires that we briefly analyze the structure of liver cords.

It has been observed already in this book that many things studied in histology were originally named by the 2-dimensional appearance that they presented in section when they were first seen, and that their original names, which we continue to use, are not suitable for many of these structures when they are visualized in 3 dimensions. Liver cords are an example. We shall comment on this matter in more detail when we describe the liver of man; for the time being it is enough to say that liver cords are not single rows of liver cells as their name might imply. Liver cords are *secretory units,* and secretory units of exocrine glands always have lumens around which the secretory cells are arranged. The very smallest liver cord must be at least 2 cells thick so that a tiny lumen can exist between the 2 rows of cells that comprise it. Therefore, if liver cords *appear* in a section to be only 1 cell thick, it is because a double row, or a row of several cells arranged in a plate, has been sectioned at right angles to its wider surface. Figure 415 illustrates how a double row of liver cells (and the same principle would apply to a plate made up of several rows of cells) could be sectioned so that it would appear to be only 1 cell thick. We conclude then that the so-called liver cords are always at least 2 cells thick, and they always contain a lumen that exists between the adjacent surfaces of the 2 rows. These lumens are very small; actually, they are tiny crevices (Fig. 415) and are termed *bile canaliculi* because the liver cells secrete bile into them. The branching platelike liver cords, with their tiny lumens (bile canaliculi), extend from the center of the lobule toward its periphery, and

(Fig. 417). There are usually as many portal radicles in the periphery of a lobule as there are sites where any 2 of the 5 or 6 sides of the lobule make angles with one another.

The substance of the liver lobule consists of branching cords of epithelial cells (dark in Fig. 414) that radiate out from the center of the lobule to its periphery. Between these *liver cords* are light spaces (Fig. 414); these are the *sinusoids* of the liver. The sinusoids receive blood from the branches of the portal vein and the hepatic artery that are in the periph-

Bile in canaliculus flows on toward
bile duct

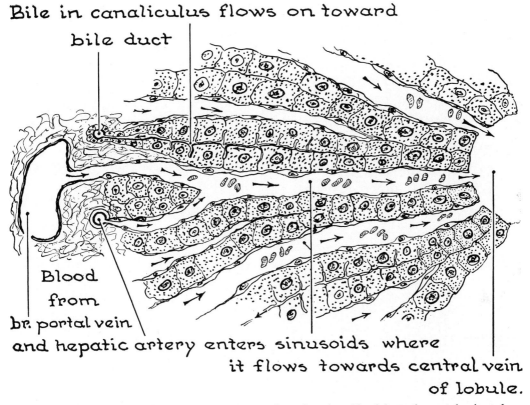

Blood
from
br. portal vein
and hepatic artery enters sinusoids where
it flows towards central vein
of lobule.

Fig. 416. Drawing (at high-power magnification) to show how blood from the portal vein and the hepatic artery (*left*) flows into sinusoids, lined by reticuloendothelium, that lie between liver cords, and empties into the central vein (*right*). The way that bile travels in the opposite direction in canaliculi to empty into bile ducts in portal areas is also shown.

their canaliculi eventually empty at or near the periphery of the lobule into little branches of the bile ducts that project briefly from portal areas into the substance of the lobule. Hence, bile flows deviously through the canaliculi of the branching cords from the central part of the lobule toward its periphery. Figure 416 shows diagrammatically how bile and blood flow through the lobule in opposite directions and without coming into contact with each other.

The Lobule of the Liver of Man. It has been explained already that a branching tree of connective tissue extends into the substance of the liver from the porta, and that each branch of the tree carries 4 tubes. In the pig the smaller branches sprout broad thin leaves of connective tissue which join the branches together, and the areas so enclosed are called *lobules.* In man the branches of the tree do not sprout leaves of connective tissue; hence, the branches (called portal radicles or canals) are isolated from one another in the substance of the liver. Since the tube-containing branches are generally cut in cross or oblique section, they commonly appear in sections as tiny islands of connective tissue, each of which contains 4 tubes. Each of these islands is generally called a *portal radicle or area* (Fig. 417, *right*).

The classic lobule of the liver of man is the counterpart of the lobule that is outlined by connective tissue in the liver of the pig. Hence, to visualize the classic lobule in the liver of man (where it is not outlined by septa) the observer first finds a central vein (Fig. 417, *left*). This is the center of the lobule. The periphery of the lobule is established by finding the 5 or 6 portal areas that generally lie nearest the central vein. These portal areas are

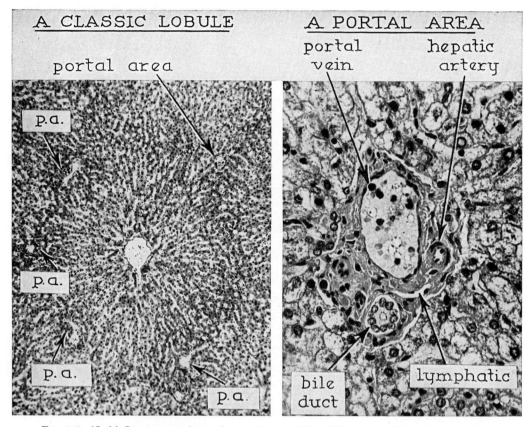

Fig. 417. (*Left*) Low-power photomicrograph of an H and E section of human liver, showing a classic lobule. (*Right*) High-power photomicrograph of a portal area, showing connective tissue and a branch of the portal vein, the hepatic artery and a bile duct and a lymphatic.

then connected together with an imaginary continuous line so that the central vein lies in the center of a pentagon or a hexagon (or roughly polyhedral) figure. If a continuous line were drawn through the 5 portal areas indicated in Figure 417, *left*, it would outline a pentagonal lobule which would have a central vein in its center. As will be discussed later, it is very difficult to find a perfect example.

Portal Areas (*Radicles*). As the trunk of a tree is larger than any of its branches, and the main branches are larger than the next order of branches, and so on, the size of portal areas varies in relation to whether they represent sections cut through major, intermediate or small branches of the connective tissue tree. When sections pass through the tree at sites where branching is occurring, the portal areas that appear may show double the number of tubes. The larger portal areas may show both

large and small portal veins and both arteries and arterioles. The larger vessels seen under these circumstances are carrying blood to distant portions of the liver, and the smaller ones are branches from them that are designed to supply the surrounding parenchyma. The branches of the portal vein are the largest tubes seen in portal areas, and they exhibit the typical microscopic structure of veins except that they are not commonly collapsed because they are contained in fairly solid connective tissue (Fig. 417, *right*). The arteries and the arterioles have a typical structure. The bile duct can be recognized easily by its *cuboidal* or *columnar epithelial* lining; it is a typical duct (Fig. 417, *right*). The lymphatics appear as spaces lined with endothelium; they are often slitlike, as is shown in Figure 417, *right*.

The Alternate (Portal) Lobule. It has been explained that lobules of exocrine glands can be defined in two different ways. However, if

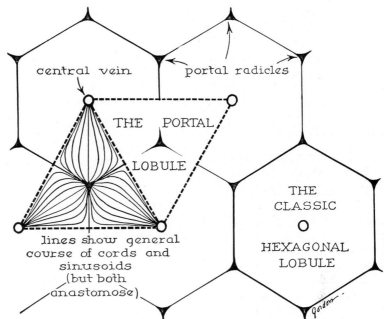

FIG. 418. Diagram of cross-section views of classic and portal lobules. Nodal points are not labeled but are present where the borders of portal and classic lobules bisect each other. Those interested will notice that this diagram differs from Mall's diagram of lobules (Fig. 1 of Mall's paper) but that it is in accord with his Figures 47 and 48, which were tracings of injected material, and his finding that there are twice as many portal radicles as central veins in the liver.

there are areas of parenchyma that are separated from one another by fibrous septa in any exocrine gland they should be called lobules, whether they fit the second definition of lobule or not, because the primary definition of the words refers to divisions of tissue that obviously project or are separated from other divisions. Therefore, there is no question about what should be termed a liver lobule in the pig. However, there are no fibrous partitions in the liver of man to separate lobules; accordingly, the question arises as to whether the lobule of the liver of man should be defined as (1) the counterpart of the area that is enclosed by partitions in the pig (Figs. 417, *left*, and 418) (and this is the classic lobule of the liver of man), or (2) the area containing a group of adjacent secretory units (liver cords) that empty into a common duct (Fig. 418, portal lobule). The latter has been designated a *portal* lobule to distinguish it from the classic *hepatic* lobule.

It is obvious that the center of the classic lobule is a central vein (Fig. 418). The periphery of a classic lobule in man is established by joining surrounding portal areas with a continuous imaginary line (Figs. 417, *left*, and 418). It is likewise obvious that the center of the portal lobule is the portal area because this contains the bile duct into which the sur-

rounding adjacent secretory units (liver cords) empty their exocrine secretion (Fig. 418). Moreover, it is obvious that since bile from secretory units drains into bile ducts of portal areas from all points of the compass, the secretory units that contribute this bile would be disposed, generally, in the 3 classic lobules which surround each portal area (Fig. 418).

It has been claimed that in the seal, portal lobules are sometimes surrounded by septa, but Arey has shown that this is a misconception probably arising out of a misinterpretation of some early studies.

If classic lobules are roughly hexagonal and portal lobules roughly triangular, as is shown in Figure 418, twice as many portal lobules as classic lobules would be present in the liver. (An elementary exercise in geometry will show that the triangle outlining the portal lobule in Figure 418 is half as large as the hexagon outlining the classic lobule. It is assumed that both kinds of lobules would have the same average length.)

It seems probable that the liver of man is similar to that of the dog in that the classic lobule is generally believed to be hexagonal. However, it should be pointed out that there is no assurance that this (2-to-1) ratio of portal to central veins is to be found in all types of experimental animals. A few diagrams will easily show that if, in any animal, there were only 4 sides to a classic lobule, portal lobules would be as numerous as classic lobules and roughly of the same size and shape, although they would occupy different territories. It is important, then, in interpreting liver lesions in experimental animals to know the ratio between the number of portal radicles and central veins in the liver of that particular animal.

PROBLEMS ASSOCIATED WITH THE INTERPRETATION OF SECTIONS OF LIVER

The classic lobule of the liver of man is commonly depicted as a hexagon, a little longer than it is wide, with a central vein running through its center, parallel with its long axis. Moreover, 6 portal radicles are commonly pictured as running along the sides of the lobule, with one close to each of the 6 angles around its periphery. The 6 portal radicles are generally illustrated as running parallel with the long axis of the lobule, hence, as being parallel with the central vein.

The ideal, described above, is seldom realized for several reasons. Liver lobules are not stacked on their sides in an orderly array in the liver but are fitted together in a bewildering fashion. Hence, any portal radicle between lobules, while it may be parallel with a lobule on one of its sides, may be disposed at various angles to the 2 lobules on its other sides. Any student who examines a few sections of liver soon realizes how difficult it is to find a cross section of a hexagonal lobule that has a central vein in its center and 6 portal radicles cut in cross section at the 6 points around its periphery; indeed, such a picture is very unusual. The matter is complicated further by the fact that the vessels in portal radicles give off branches at various angles; such branches would not run parallel with the long axis of the stem vessels or to the lobule and would not be cut transversely in cross sections of lobules. In view of the foregoing, it can be understood that attempts to interpret single sections of livers that have been subjected to circulatory disturbance are hazardous. It can be assumed that the parenchyma around each central vein that is seen probably had the poorest blood supply of any part of the lobule. But from such topography of a lobule as can be seen in a single section, it is very difficult to know about the nearness of an arterial blood supply to any other parts of the lobule that are seen, because arterial vessels, running roughly in the plane of the section, may have been present immediately below or above any site that is examined.

The Liver Acinus or the Structural and Functional Hepatic Unit. The problems involved in trying to relate liver damage to the relative blood supplies of the different parts of lobules that can be recognized in single sections have stimulated the search for some smaller functional unit of liver tissue, the backbone of which would be its blood supply. Rappaport has described such a unit; he terms it the *liver acinus*. To understand his concept it is helpful to realize first that in sections of liver it is very difficult to find cross sections of hexagonal lobules that have 6 well-defined triangular portal areas at the 6 points of their compass; indeed, it is most unusual to find a perfect example. Rappaport suggests that the observer is much more likely to find only 2, 3, or 4 well-defined triangular portal areas around the hexagon. He explains this by saying that if there are, for example, 3 portal areas distributed around the 6 points of the compass, the 3 represent main conducting branches of the hepatic artery, the portal vein and the bile duct (these are represented as triangles in Fig. 419). Rappaport believes that distributing terminal branches extend out from these 3 main sets of vessels more or less at right angles to them, toward angular points around the hexagon where well-defined portal areas are "missing" (labeled M in Fig. 419). Since these smaller terminal vessels grow out in a tridimensional way, and roughly at right angles from the main vessels, they are not cut transversely in cross sections of lobules. However, they are sometimes cut obliquely because they pursue irregular courses. Therefore, oblique sections through these vessels, which are sheathed by scanty connective tissue, from which no other vessels branch out, have not a triangular but rather an oval appearance. On their arched and irregular course toward the points of the compass where triangular portal areas are "missing" (Fig. 419, M), they may be cut repeatedly or not at all by the same plane of section and thus bring about the appearance of too many or of "missing" portal radicles around one central vein. Thus the impression we get of the hexagonal field is due to a prevailingly tridimensional budding, in a limited space, of terminal bile ductules and associated vessels growing out from 3 neighboring portal radicles (Fig. 419, I, II, III). In their course approximating the "missing" portal areas or corners of an imaginary hexagon, the terminal portal and arterial branches, in association with the terminal bile ductules, form the backbones of small and irregularly shaped clumps of hepatic parenchyma. The sinusoids of these acinar clumps are supplied by twiglike arborizations of the terminal vessels, while the secretory product of the same area, the bile, is carried away by the accompanying bile ductule. Thus these little clumps show structural and functional unity. There is a dependence of the parenchymal cells on their blood supply and a zonal interrelationship between them (Fig. 419, Zones 1, 2, 3). If the acini were arranged regularly, each acinus, as is shown in Figure 419, would encompass sectors of 2 classic lobules, and each portal lobule would contain halves of 3 acini. However, it should be realized that there would be many consecutive acini hanging on the main vessels that run along the corners of the imaginary hexagonal lobule, and that they would be of irregular shapes and sizes, for the latter would depend upon the course and the size of the vessels and the bile ductule in the acini. Rappaport believes that the interpretation of liver damage is much more meaningful if this concept is used. His several recent publications are listed in the bibliography for further information on the structure of the acinus and its relation to the interpretation of certain pathologic conditions of the liver.

The Parenchyma of the Liver

The parenchyma of the liver consists of glandular epithelium that develops from endoderm. This includes the bile ducts and the epithelial cells that make up the so-called liver cords which secrete bile into their canaliculi and also perform endocrine functions. The reticuloendothelial cells that line the sinusoids are not generally regarded as being part of the parenchyma because they belong to the connective tissue stroma of the organ. Although the cells of the bile ducts are part of the parenchyma, the term *parenchymal cell* is usually used to refer to the epithelial cells of

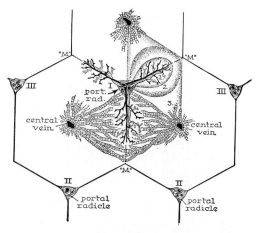

Fig. 419. Diagram illustrating the liver acinus and how its cells are arranged in 3 zones around its blood supply. A liver acinus occupies adjacent sectors of 2 neighboring hexagonal fields. The central veins of the latter, with which the acinus interdigitates perpendicularly, are situated at its periphery farthest from its afferent vessels. Its backbone is formed by terminal branches of the hepatic artery, the portal vein and the bile ductule (the latter is not shown in the drawing) branching out (downward) from the portal radicle labeled I. Another pair of terminal vessels growing out from the same radicle supplies the acinar parenchyma at the upper right. In this acinus, zones 1, 2 and 3, respectively, represent areas supplied with blood of first, second and third quality with regard to oxygen and nutrients. These zones center about the terminal afferent vascular branches and extend toward the portal radicle from which these branches originate. The central veins, the drainage centers of several acini, are situated in their peripheral circulatory zones labeled 3. The outcropping of vascular and biliary channels from the triangular portal radicles I, II and III, when it occurs regularly, gives the illusion of an outlined hexagonal field. "M" denotes the points where, according to the description of the classic hexagonal lobule, one would expect to find other triangular portal radicles.

the liver cords; these cells are also called *hepatic* cells.

It has been stated that liver "cords" are secretory units; hence, even if they appear in sections to be only 1 cell thick, they must always be at least 2 cells thick or 2 cells wide

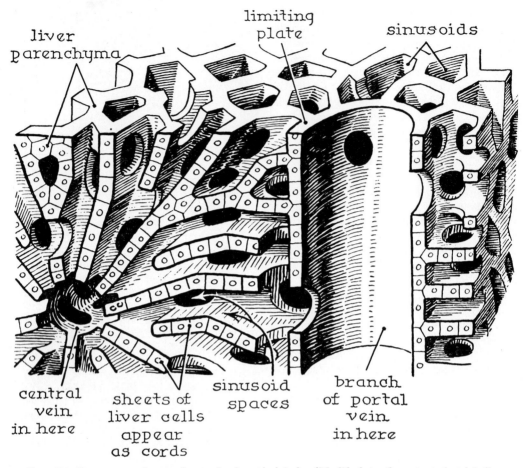

liver parenchyma

limiting plate

sinusoids

central vein in here

sheets of liver cells appear as cords

sinusoid spaces

branch of portal vein in here

FIG. 420. Stereogram of a quadrant of a hepatic lobule. (Modified, to the extent that labeling was added, from Elias, H.: Am. J. Anat. *85*:379)

so that the 2 adjacent rows of cells can enclose a bile canaliculus between them (Fig. 415). Elias, who for years has been interested in visualizing structure in 3 dimensions, made several studies of the arrangement of the parenchyma within the liver lobule. He visualizes the parenchyma of the human liver as being arranged in the form of perforated anastomosing plates (Fig. 420). These enclose spaces in which sinusoids are present (Fig. 420), and the sinusoids communicate with each other through the perforations in the plates (Fig. 420). It might be thought, if the liver cells were arranged in plates, that a fortuitously cut section occasionally would pass through a plate parallel with its broad surface; hence, that broad solid sheets of cells might be seen sometimes in liver sections. The reasons for this appearance not being seen are:

(1) the plates are not flat but curved or bent; hence, any given section, no matter how it is cut, can pass through only a small portion of one plate; and (2) the plates are perforated so extensively to permit communication between the sinusoids they enclose that even if a plate is cut parallel with its broad surface, the many perforations in it make it appear as if it consisted of anastomosing cords.

Elias describes the portal areas as being surrounded by a limiting plate of liver parenchymal cells that are somewhat smaller than those found in the remainder of the parenchyma. This plate is termed the *limiting plate* (Fig. 420), and it is perforated by blood vessels and by branches from the bile ducts. The canaliculi in it are continuous with those in the remainder of the liver parenchyma.

The site and the manner of terminations of

the hepatic arteries of the portal areas in the sinusoids in the liver of man are somewhat controversial. Knisely, Bloch and Warner have made an elaborate study of the circulation in the lobule of the frog liver in the living animal. They believe that there are contractile arteriovenous anastomoses between the hepatic artery and the portal vein in the portal radicles (these, when open, would permit arterial blood to enter sinusoids through the portal vein inlets). They believe that almost every sinusoid is supplied by a separate end branch from both the portal veins and the hepatic artery, and that each sinusoid has a sphincter that controls the flow of portal blood into it at the periphery of the lobule, and another sphincter that controls the flow out of it into the central vein. They have shown that, because of all these various contractile structures, there can be great variations in the total flow of blood through the different lobules of the same liver, and also that the kind of blood that flows through lobules can vary greatly with regard to the proportions of arterial and venous blood it contains. Their paper should be read for details.

The circulation of blood through the liver is necessarily complex because its sinusoids receive blood from the portal vein under low pressure and blood from the hepatic artery under higher pressure. It could be visualized that if the sphincters on the arterial and the venous outlets were both wide open, the arterial blood would exert considerable back-pressure on the portal vein and even force blood backward in it. It could also be visualized that if, in a part of the liver, the sphincters on the venous inlets of the portal vein were closed and those on the arterioles open, the blood in the sinusoids in this part of the liver would be flushed toward the central veins of the lobules without any particular back-pressure being exerted on the portal vein. Hence, some degree of intermittency of arterial and venous flow in different parts of the liver would seem to be required for its proper function.

The Cytology and the Fine Structure of the Parenchymal Cells

Liver cells have a polygonal shape, and, as has already been described, are fitted together to form cords and plates. Low- and high-power views of liver sections are illustrated in Figures 31 and 32.

Nuclei. The nuclei are round to ovoid (Figs. 32 and 80). It is not unusual to find binucleated cells in the liver, and some cells may have more than two nuclei (Fig. 43). Polyploid nuclei are common (Fig. 42). Mitotic figures are very uncommon in the normal liver but appear in great numbers if part of the liver is removed, for the liver regenerates very quickly (Fig. 33).

The nucleoli of liver cells have been described in Chapter 4 and are illustrated in Figures 52 and 80.

Cytoplasm. With the light microscope and H and E sections, the cytoplasm reveals granules and flakes of chromidial substance. In the healthy liver these are separated by cytoplasm, which, during life, contains glycogen. With the E/M, the flakes of chromidial substance are seen to be composed of groups of flattened rough-surfaced membranous vesicles (Fig. 80). Fawcett has made an intensive study of liver cells with the E/M. He has confirmed previous observations to the effect that the chromidial substance becomes reduced in amount after starvation and that it reforms after feeding is resumed. Fawcett has described the reformation of membranous vesicles and tubules as occurring in the vicinity of cell membrane where they, at first, have smooth surfaces. Later they accumulate RNA granules.

Accumulations of glycogen in the cytoplasm have a mottled grayish appearance in electron micrographs (Fig. 80). Mitochondria and flattened rough-surfaced membranous vesicles tend to remain in association with one another as glycogen accumulates; hence, little areas containing mitochondria and flattened vesicles become separated from one another by areas of glycogen (Fig. 80) as the latter accumulates.

Mitochondria. The mitochondria of normal liver cells are described in Chapter 4 (Figs. 61 and 63), where information about their numbers per cell also is given. After starvation, the mitochondria of liver cells appear to swell, as if they had imbibed water (Fig. 421). However, their seeming enlargement under these conditions may not be real but due to their becoming shorter and more rounded.

Peribiliary Bodies (Lysosomes). Small

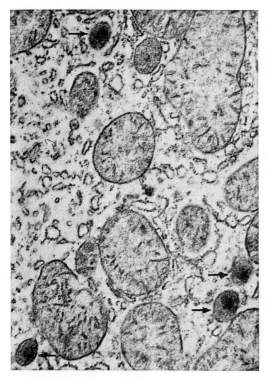

FIG. 421. Electron micrograph ($\times$ 24,000) of a section of the liver of a rat that was starved for 4 days. Note that the mitochondria appear swollen. Bodies smaller and denser than mitochondria, which are probably lysosomes, are marked with small arrows. Numerous small rough-surfaced vesicles are also present. (Preparation by R. Varvarande)

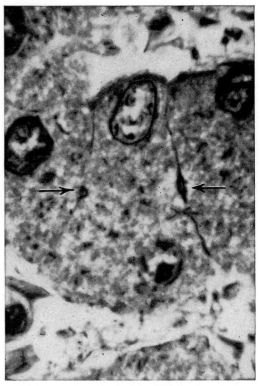

FIG. 422. Oil-immersion photomicrograph taken with the phase microscope of an H and E section of a liver cord, showing 2 bile canaliculi indicated by arrows.

bodies that are different from mitochondria in their morphology and enzymatic properties have been identified in liver cells with the E/M. They are smaller and denser than mitochondria, averaging about 0.4 μ in diameter (Fig. 421). Each is enveloped by a single membrane, and they have no cristae (Fig. 421). Small ill-defined regions of increased density may be seen within some of them (Fig. 421). According to Palade these bodies are usually seen near bile canaliculi, and he terms them *peribiliary bodies*. They probably correspond to the lysosomes that de Duve, Novikoff and others have isolated from rat liver by differential centrifugation. Lysosomes are rich in acid phosphatase.

Golgi Apparatus. Seen with the E/M, the Golgi apparatus has the usual assortment of flattened smooth-surfaced membranous vesicles, small rounded vesicles and vacuoles as elsewhere. In liver cells the Golgi apparatus is commonly situated close to a bile canaliculus, but it may be close to a nucleus.

The fine structure of liver tumor cells has been described by Howatson and the author.

Bile Canaliculi and Their Connections With Bile Ducts. Bile canaliculi can be demonstrated by different methods. Sometimes they can be seen in H and E sections, as in Figure 422; however, their visualization without special treatment probably depends on their being distended. Gomori showed that histochemical methods for phosphatase revealed them; this is because phosphatase is secreted into bile. Bile canaliculi can be injected with opaque materials through the bile ducts and studied in cleared thick and thin sections.

It has been questioned whether canaliculi are structures or spaces—clefts between contiguous liver cells. The former view was sup-

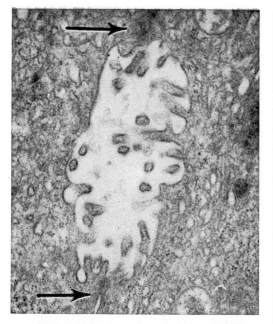

FIG. 423. Electron micrograph (× 32,000) of a section of a rat's liver, showing a bile canaliculus between 2 parenchymal cells. The arrows indicate desmosomes which are arranged to form terminal bars on each side of a bile canaliculus. (Preparation by R. Varvarande)

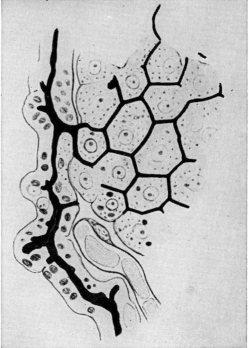

FIG. 424. Biliary network in a hepatic lamina of a dog, draining into an intralobular duct. Golgi preparation. (Elias, H.: Am. J. Anat. *85*:379)

ported by studies in which liver cells were partially digested; the procedure used left behind what seemed to be a system of tiny cuticular tubules. However, studies with the E/M have shown clearly that the bile canaliculi are not tubes with walls of their own but merely spaces between the membranes of contiguous liver cells.

It has been pointed out already that contiguous liver cells are separated from one another by a space which contains no dense material and is about 100—150 Å wide. At sites of bile canaliculi, the membranes of contiguous cells separate from each other much farther (Fig. 423). At the sites where the cell membranes begin to diverge from one another there are desmosomes arranged in a row as in terminal bars (these sites are indicated by arrows in Fig. 423); hence, contiguous liver cells are joined more tightly to one another at the edges of bile canaliculi than elsewhere.

The parts of the cell surfaces that form the lining for bile canaliculi extend out into the lumina of canaliculi in the form of microvilli (Fig. 423).

The bile canaliculi within the anastomosing perforated plates of parenchyma form a most complicated branching network. At the periphery of the lobule they drain into short branches which extend out from the bile ducts of the portal areas into the periphery of the lobule (Fig. 424). Elias says that these short branches have no ends, that they either form loops or anastomose with other ducts of the same type, and that slightly enlarged bile canaliculi, each of which drains bile from different plates, empty laterally into them.

The Border Between Parenchymal and Lining Cells of Sinusoids. Fawcett has studied the border between parenchymal cells and the lining cells of sinusoids. He finds that the surface of parenchymal cells that face the lining cells may have many short processes of the general form of microvilli but are of irregular shapes. In sites where these are present, the lining cells of the sinusoids rest on them;

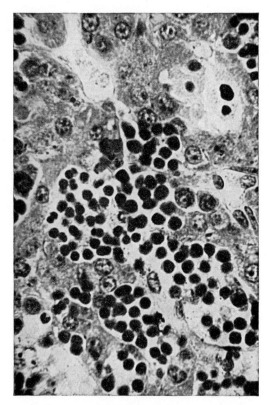

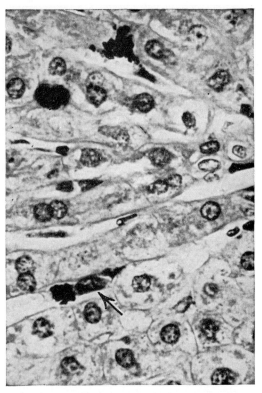

FIG. 425. High-power photomicrograph of a section of fetal pig liver, showing hemopoiesis in the sinusoids. The cells with the dark nuclei are mostly proerythroblasts and erythroblasts.

FIG. 426. High-power photomicrograph of a section of the liver of a rabbit that was previously injected intravenously with India ink. The arrow points to the nucleus of a reticuloendothelial cell that has phagocytosed India ink, which may be seen in its cytoplasm both to the left and the right of its nucleus. Two large masses of India ink in the cytoplasm of the R.E. cells may be seen in the upper part of the picture.

hence, they are not closely applied to the parenchymal cells. This may account for the fact that a space (the space of Disse) between the lining cells and the parenchymal cells is sometimes seen with the light microscope.

Fawcett, in his most comprehensive and instructive investigation of the fine structure of liver cells, also found that the lining cells of the sinusoids do not always form a continuous membrane—that there are some bare areas among the course of sinusoids where blood is in direct contact with parenchymal cells. It is possible, of course, that gaps in the lining cell membrane may be due to fixation artefact, but several observations from light microscopy have been recorded which would support the view to the effect that the sinusoidal lining is not always continuous.

A network of reticular fibers can be demonstrated by suitable methods between the lining and the parenchymal cells.

THE STROMA OF THE LIVER

The stroma of the liver consists of that part of it which is formed by connective tissue. It includes: (1) the capsule, (2) the branching tree of connective tissue that extends into it from the porta and carries the portal vein and other tubes to the periphery of each of the classic lobules and (3) the hemopoietic tissue that covers the cords and the plates of parenchymal cells and so lines the sinusoids. It is to be understood that this hemopoietic tissue, which in postnatal life is mostly reticuloendothelium, consists of both intercellular substances and cells; the former are chiefly reticular fibers, and they support both the parenchymal cells and the reticuloendothelial cells.

As has been noted before, the liver, during a certain period of fetal life, functions as a hemopoietic organ (Fig. 425). Occasionally, it resumes this function in postnatal life. It might be expected, then, that the liver is provided with the same basic cellular components as are present in other hemopoietic tissues. Like them, it contains primitive reticular cells that have the capacity to differentiate along two general lines: (1) into reticuloendothelial (phagocytic) cells and (2) into free, rounded stem cells. Although, in prenatal life, differentiation proceeds along both lines, in postnatal life it is commonly restricted to the first line. Consequently, the lining of sinusoids in postnatal life is composed of primitive reticular cells, true phagocytic reticuloendothelial cells and cells in different stages of differentiation between these two types. The primitive cells are flatter and have darker nuclei than the more highly differentiated phagocytic cells. These latter tend to have larger, paler nuclei and more abundant cytoplasm, which, in sections, may project into the lumen of a sinusoid in a fashion to give the cell a starlike appearance. Because of their shape, and because they were first described by von Kupffer, the phagocytic reticuloendothelial cells disposed along the sinusoids are often termed the *stellate cells of von Kupffer* (Fig. 426). However, it is to be kept in mind that not all the cells disposed along sinusoids are phagocytic; many of them are primitive cells that, while not phagocytic, have the capacity to differentiate into phagocytic cells (or into free, rounded stem cells) if the need arises.

Because of pathologic change and/or artefact, the continuous lining of the sinusoids may be separated from the liver cords that they line by the *space of Disse* (Fig. 32). It is improbable that this space contains lymphatic capillaries or that it connects with lymphatics in the portal areas. The R.E. cells make the reticular fibers that bind the sinusoid wall to the parenchyma.

Most of the old worn-out red blood cells in the circulatory system are phagocytosed in the spleen, the bone marrow and the liver. Hence, the reticuloendothelial cells of these organs produce most of the bilirubin (bile pigment) that is formed in the body (*see the end of Chapter 4 for a discussion of pigments formed from hemoglobin*). The bilirubin formed in all these sites eventually is excreted by the parenchymal cells of the liver into the bile canaliculi and thereafter is carried by the bile ducts into the intestine. The bilirubin formed in the spleen and the bone marrow is brought to the liver sinusoids by the blood stream and diffuses through their walls to enter the parenchymal cells. That formed by the Kupffer cells of the liver sinusoids can pass directly into adjacent parenchymal cells. In the parenchymal cells, the bilirubin is probably modified slightly before it is excreted into the canaliculi.

As a result of disease, the tissues and the fluids of the body may contain abnormal amounts of bile pigment. When this occurs an individual is said to be *jaundiced* (*jaune* = yellow) because his skin becomes yellow. Jaundice may arise from the bile ducts' being obstructed so that the bile pigment excreted by the parenchymal cells cannot reach the intestine and, as a consequence, is absorbed into lymph and blood capillaries. On the other hand, a high content of bilirubin in the blood can be produced, at least theoretically, by the reticuloendothelial cells of the body phagocytosing red blood cells at such a rapid rate (usually because the latter are imperfect) that the parenchymal cells of the liver cannot effectively excrete all the bilirubin brought to them. In the first instance, the increased bilirubin in the blood stream would be of a sort that had passed through the parenchymal cells of the liver. In the second instance, the increased bilirubin in the blood stream would be of a sort that had not yet passed through the parenchymal cells of the liver. The type of bilirubin present in the blood in jaundice (whether it has as yet passed through the parenchymal cells of the liver) can be distinguished by a chemical test known as the *van den Bergh reaction*. It should be kept in mind that combined types of jaundice, in which both kinds of bilirubin are increased in the blood, can occur.

The reticuloendothelial cells of the liver sinusoids, like those of the spleen and the bone marrow, can be demonstrated very effectively in the experimental animal by the procedure of vital staining. Dilute solutions of certain relatively nontoxic colloidal dyes with negatively charged particles (for example, trypan blue), or certain metals prepared in colloidal form (for example, colloidal silver), or sus-

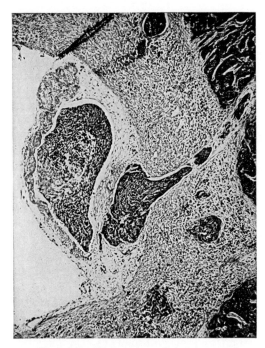

FIG. 427. High-power photomicrograph of a section of the wall of a portal vein being invaded from the right by cancer cells. These are dark in color and extend toward the lumen of the vein (which is at the left) by traversing the lymphatics that are present in the wall of the vein. (Photomicrograph by Dr. William Boyd)

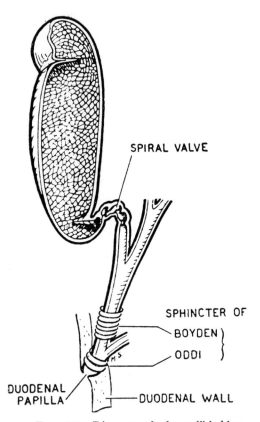

FIG. 428. Diagram of the gallbladder (showing its corrugated inner surface), the cystic duct, the bile duct and the sphincters of Boyden and Oddi. (Grant, J. C. B.: A Method of Anatomy, ed. 4, Baltimore, Williams & Wilkins)

pensions of fine particles in water (for example, India ink) are employed for this purpose. If an experimental animal is given an intravenous injection of any of these substances each day for a period of days, the cytoplasm of its reticuloendothelial cells becomes engorged with the colloidal particles which the reticuloendothelial cells seemingly strive to remove from the circulation (Fig. 426).

The reticuloendothelial cells of the spleen, the bone marrow and the liver, together with the macrophages of the connective tissues of the body and the microglia (mesoderm derived cells in the central nervous system which have macrophagelike potentialities), are often described as together constituting the reticuloendothelial system. Some prefer to call the reticuloendothelial lining cells of the sinusoids of the spleen, the liver and the bone marrow *fixed macrophages* and to call the whole system the *macrophage system*.

The reticuloendothelial system performs the normal function of ridding the body of old worn-out red blood cells, platelets and such other debris as results from physiologic processes. It is also of the greatest importance in combating certain kinds of bacteria, parasitic protozoa and other kinds of infective agents that may gain entrance to the body.

Lymphatics. The liver produces a great deal of lymph, and there has been controversy about where it is formed. Some experimenters, by injecting the lymphatics of the liver, claim to have traced the material injected to lymph capillaries or to the spaces of Disse between the hemopoietic tissue lining the sinusoids and the cords of parenchymal cells. But other experimenters have failed to demonstrate lymphatics in this site and believe that positive results are due to the use of too high injection pressures which tear the tissue and so permit the injected material to pass into regions where no lymphatics exist.

Even if there were lymphatics in the sites that some claim, it is difficult to understand how they could remain open and drain lymph away. In the connective tissue of the body, provision is made to keep lymphatics open even if the hydrostatic pressure of the tissue fluid is increased (Chap. 6). But, if there were lymphatic capillaries between the films of hemopoietic tissue lining the sinusoids and the liver cords, it might be expected that they would be collapsed by the hydrostatic pressure of the blood within the sinusoids. Further, the hydrostatic pressure within the sinusoids is greater at the periphery of lobules than in their central parts—even when the liver is congested due to back pressure from the heart —*otherwise blood would not flow from the periphery of the lobule toward its center*. If there were lymphatics between the hemopoietic tissue lining the sinusoids and the liver cords, the lymph in them—in order to leave the lobule—would have to flow from an area of low hydrostatic pressure to one of high. There are reasons, then, for thinking that, even if there were lymphatic capillaries in the liver lobule, they would not function.

Such lymphatics as have been demonstrated with certainty in the liver are confined to the connective tissue of the capsule and the tree of connective tissue that carries the branches of the portal vein, the hepatic artery and the bile duct to the sides of each lobule and also to the sparse connective tissue associated with the hepatic veins. It might be thought that little lymph would form in this connective tissue, which is by no means abundantly supplied with capillaries. But there is reason to believe that lymph spaces and lymph capillaries exist in the walls of the veins of the liver, even in their inner layers. In the spread of cancer, cords of malignant cells (which characteristically grow along lymphatics) can sometimes be seen growing from the outside of veins in the liver into their walls to reach almost to their endothelial linings (Fig. 427). As was pointed out in Chapter 21, the hydrostatic pressure within the walls of veins is such that patent lymphatic capillaries can exist even in the inner parts of their walls. There is, then, some reason for believing that a part of the large quantity of lymph that arises in the liver originates in the walls of branches of the portal vein.

Bile Ducts. In examining any section of liver, the student will observe that the bile ducts seen in different portal areas are of different sizes. Generally, small bile ducts will be seen to be associated with relatively small arteries and veins and large ones with relatively large vessels. Furthermore, when the tubes are small the amount of connective tissue surrounding them is considerably less than that which surrounds groups of larger tubes. The size of any bile duct, and portal radicle in which it is contained, depends on the order of branch that is cut in the section.

The finer bile ducts, the end twigs, which receive the bile from the canaliculi through short side branches (Fig. 424), have walls of low cuboidal epithelium. The larger ones, seen in portal areas, have walls of columnar epithelium. Within the liver, bile ducts of increasing orders of size join with one another to form eventually two main hepatic ducts which, leaving the liver at the site of the porta (the transverse fissure), unite to form the hepatic duct. The extrahepatic ducts require more support than the intrahepatic ones that are embedded in the connective tissue of the portal areas. This is provided by dense connective tissue and smooth muscle arranged so as to surround the epithelial-lined lumen of the tube.

When bile ducts are large enough to be lined by columnar epithelium, fat droplets within the cytoplasm of their lining cells are not uncommon. In the larger intrahepatic bile ducts, and in the extrahepatic ones, tubuloalveolar glands are present in a much-folded mucous membrane.

THE GALLBLADDER

A side branch (the cystic duct) extends from the hepatic duct to a somewhat elongated pear-shaped sac, the gallbladder (Figs. 373 and 428). The gallbladder is lined by a mucous membrane which is thrown into so many folds when the bladder is contracted (Fig. 428) that a student, on seeing a section of the wall of the organ, might think its mucosa was beset by glands (Fig. 429). Actually, there are no glands in the mucosa of the gallbladder except near its neck, and if the organ is distended, most (but not all) of its mucosal folds disappear.

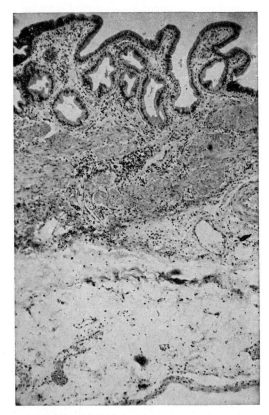

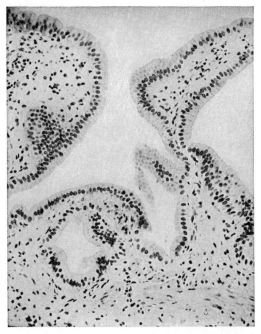

FIG. 430. High-power photomicrograph of H and E section of gallbladder showing the mucosal surface.

FIG. 429. Low-power photomicrograph of H and E section of human gallbladder.

The epithelium of the mucous membrane of the gallbladder is high columnar (Fig. 430). Each cell in the membrane resembles the one beside it; in this respect it resembles the epithelium of the stomach (Fig. 430). But the cells themselves are not like those lining the stomach. They resemble more closely the absorptive cells of the small intestine and, like them, are provided with microvilli. Secretory granules have been described in the more superficial parts of the cytoplasm of the cells, but the primary function of the lining cells is absorptive rather than secretory.

The epithelium rests on an areolar lamina propria (Fig. 429). There is no muscularis mucosae in the gallbladder; hence, the mucous membrane rests on a skimpy layer of smooth muscle comparable in position, but not in thickness, with the muscularis externa of the intestine (Fig. 429). Some of the smooth muscle fibers of which the muscularis externa is composed run circularly and longitudinally, but most run obliquely. Many elastic fibers are present in the connective tissue which fills the interstices between the smooth muscle bundles of this coat.

Outside the muscle coat is a well-developed perimuscular or subserosal coat (Fig. 429). This consists of areolar tissue, and it may contain groups of fat cells. It conveys arteries, veins, lymphatics and nerves to the organ. Along the side of the gallbladder that is attached to the liver, the connective tissue of its perimuscular coat (which here cannot be termed properly its subserosal coat) is continuous with the connective tissue of the liver.

The neck of the gallbladder is twisted in such a fashion that its mucosa is thrown into a spiral fold (Fig. 428). Somewhat similar crescentic folds of mucosa are present in the lining of the cystic duct. More muscle appears in the wall of the gallbladder at its neck, and in the wall of the cystic duct, than is present in the remainder of the gallbladder.

The Bile Duct and the Sphincter of Oddi. The duct that extends from the point of junction of the cystic and the hepatic ducts to the duodenum was, in the past, generally termed the *common bile duct*. In recent years there has been a tendency to omit the qualifying "common" from the term. This duct penetrates the outer coats of the duodenum close to the point of entry of the pancreatic duct. Part way through the duodenal wall the two ducts fuse, and the lumen of the fused duct is sufficiently expanded to be called an *ampulla* (*ampulla* = flask), the *ampulla of Vater*. The ampulla pursues an oblique course through the inner layers of the duodenal wall to open on the summit of a papilla that projects into the duodenal lumen, the *duodenal papilla*.

In the past, the muscle associated with the ampulla and the ends of the two ducts that enter the ampulla were said to constitute, collectively, the *sphincter of Oddi*. More recently, the development, the amount, the arrangement and the control of this muscle has been studied in detail by Boyden and his associates, whose papers (listed at the end of this chapter) should be consulted for full details. Briefly, these investigators have found that this muscle develops from mesenchyme independently and hence is not part of the muscle of the intestinal wall proper. That which develops around the preampullary part of the bile duct becomes strong and serves as a sphincter at the outlet of the bile duct; this may be called the *sphincter of Boyden* (Fig. 428). The muscle that develops around the ampulla itself and around the preampullary part of the pancreatic duct is not substantial enough to exert a very potent sphincteric action, except in a minority of individuals. The closure of the strong sphincter of Boyden, surrounding the preampullary part of the bile duct, prevents the secretion of the liver from entering the intestine, and, as a result, bile formed during its closure is by-passed, by way of the cystic duct, to the gallbladder, where it is stored and concentrated. There are also smooth muscle fibers disposed parallel with the preampullary parts of the bile and pancreatic ducts; their contraction shortens (and presumably broadens) the ducts so as to encourage flow through them.

Functions of the Gallbladder. The gallbladder stores and concentrates bile. Concentration is effected by the absorption of water and inorganic salts through the epithelium into the vessels of the lamina propria of its mucosa. This results in bile in the gallbladder coming to have an increased content of bile pigment, bile salts and cholesterol. Radiopaque substances of such a nature that they are excreted by the liver and so appear in the bile may be given to individuals. If the gallbladder is concentrating normally, these become sufficiently concentrated in the gallbladder to allow that organ to be outlined by x-rays. In this way, gallbladder function can be tested in the clinic. The reaction of bile becomes somewhat altered in the gallbladder; the absorption of the inorganic salts from it somehow results in its becoming less alkaline.

Both nervous and hormonal mechanisms are probably concerned in causing the gallbladder to empty. The feeding of fat is particularly effective in causing the gallbladder to empty. Boyden has shown that if the blood of a recently fed animal is injected into the veins of another animal, such blood will cause the gallbladder of its recipient to empty. It is probable that a hormone is made by the intestinal mucosa under the influence of digesting food, and that this travels to the gallbladder by the blood stream to cause its contraction. Ivy and Oldberg have suggested "cholecystokinin" as a name for this hormone.

The muscle of the wall of the gallbladder is so thin that many investigators have doubted if its contraction could be an important factor in emptying it. However, considerable experimental work provides little ground for these doubts.

REFERENCES

SPECIAL REFERENCES ON THE ORAL CAVITY
AND THE SALIVARY GLANDS

Dewey, M. M.: A histochemical and biochemical study of the parotid gland in normal and hypophysectomized rats, Am. J. Anat. *102*:243, 1958.

Gairns, F. W.: The sensory nerve endings of the human palate, Quart. J. Exper. Physiol. *40*:40, 1955.

Jacoby, F., and Leeson, C. R.: The post-natal development of the rat submaxillary gland, J. Anat. *93*:201, 1959.

James, J.: Epithelium and lymphocyte in the development of the palatine tonsil, Acta anat. *27*:222, 1955.

Leeson, C. R., and Jacoby, F.: An electron microscopic study of the rat submaxillary gland during its postnatal development and in the adult, J. Anat. *93*:287, 1959.

Orban, B.: Atlas of Oral Histology and Embryology, St. Louis, Mosby, ed. 2, 1960.

Scott, B. L., and Pease, D. C.: Electron microscopy of the salivary and lacrimal glands of the rat, Am. J. Anat. *104*:115, 1959.

Stormont, D. L.: The salivary glands *in* Cowdry's Special Cytology, ed. 2, p. 151, New York, Hoeber, 1932.

SPECIAL REFERENCES ON TEETH

Bélanger, L. F.: Autoradiographic and histochemical observations on the mineralization of teeth in rats and hamsters of various ages, Anat. Rec. *114*:529, 1952.

——: Autoradiographic studies of the formation of the organic matrix of cartilage, bone and the tissues of teeth *in* Wolstenholme, G. E. W., and O'Connor, C. M. (eds.): Ciba Foundation Symposium on Bone Structure and Metabolism, p. 75, London, Churchill, 1956.

——: A method for routine detection of radiophosphates and other radioactive compounds in tissues: the inverted autograph, Anat. Rec. *107*:149, 1950.

Bélanger, L. F., and Leblond, C. P.: Mineralization of the growing tooth as shown by radiophosphorus autographs, Proc. Soc. Exper. Biol. & Med. *73*:390, 1950.

Bélanger, L. F., Lotz, W. E., Visek, W. J., and Comar, C. L.: Autoradiographic visualization with Ca^{45} of normal growth of the incisor of pigs and the effect of fluorine feeding, Anat. Rec. *119*:53, 1954.

Bevelander, G., and Johnson, P. L.: Alkaline phosphatase in amelogenesis, Anat. Rec. *104*:125, 1949.

Bodecker, C. F.: Fundamentals of Dental Histology and Embryology, Including Clinical Applications, ed. 4, New York, Columbia, 1944.

Churchill, H. R.: Meyer's Normal Histology and Histogenesis of the Human Teeth and Associated Parts, Philadelphia, Lippincott, 1935.

Frank, R. M., and Sognnaes, R. F.: Electron microscopy of matrix formation and calcification in rat enamel, Arch. Oral Biol. *1*:339, 1960.

Fullmer, H. M.: Observations on the development of oxytalan fibers in the periodontium of man, J. Dent. Res. *38*:510, 1959.

Glasstone, S.: The development of tooth germs on the chick chorio-allantois, J. Anat. *88*:392, 1954.

Gustafson, G.: The structure of the human dental enamel, Odontologisk Tidskrift. (Supp.), p. 53, 1945.

Hals, E.: Fluorescence Microscopy of Developing and Adult Teeth; Supplemented by Investigations with Ordinary, Polarizing and Phase-Contrast Microscope, Oslo, Norwegian Acad. Press, 1953.

Jit, I.: The development of the unstriped musculature of the gall-bladder and the cystic duct, J. Anat. Soc. (India) *8*:15, 1959.

Kronfeld, R.: Histopathology of the Teeth and Their Surrounding Structures, ed. 4, Philadelphia, Lea & Febiger, 1955.

Kumamoto, Y., and Leblond, C. P.: Radioautographic study of mineralization of growing teeth with labelled calcium, J. Dent. Res. *35*:147, 1956.

——: Visualization of C^{14} in the tooth matrix after administration of labeled hexoses, J. Dent. Res. *37*:147, 1958.

Leblond, C. P., Bélanger, L. F., and Greulich, R. C.: Formation of bones and teeth as visualized by radioautography, Ann. New York Acad. Sc. *60*:629, 1955.

Lorber, M.: A study of the histochemical reaction of the dental cementum in alveolar bones, Anat. Rec. *111*:129, 1951.

McLean, F. C., and Urist, M. R.: Bone; An Introduction to the Physiology of Skeletal Tissue (The Scientist's Library), Chicago, Univ. Chicago Press, 1955.

Nuckolls, J., Saunders, J. B. de C. M., and Frisbie, H. E.: Amelogenesis: a further study of the development of Tomes' process and the enamel rod matrix in the molar and incisor teeth of the rat, J. Am. Coll. Dent. *10*:241, 1943.

Orban, B.: Oral Histology and Embryology, ed. 4, St. Louis, Mosby, 1957.

Orban, B., Sicher, H., and Weinmann, J. P.: Amelogenesis, J. Am. Coll. Dent. *10*:13, 1943.

Sasso, W. S., and Castro, N. M.: Histochemical study of amelogenesis and dentinogenesis, Oral Surg., Oral Med. and Oral Path. *10*:1323, 1957.

Schour, I.: Recent advances in oral histology, Internat. Dent. J. *2*:10, 1951.

——: The teeth *in* Cowdry's Special Cytology, ed. 2, p. 67, New York, Hoeber, 1932.

——: Oral histology and embryology *in* Noyes, F. (ed.): Oral Histology and Embryology, ed. 8, Philadelphia, Lea & Febiger, 1960.

Schour, I., and Massler, M.: Studies in tooth development; the growth pattern of human teeth, J. Am. Dent. A. *27*:1778; *27*:1918, 1940.

Scott, D. B.: The electron microscopy of enamel and dentin, Ann. New York Acad. Sc. *60*:575, 1955.

Shroff, F. R., Williamson, K. I., Bertaud, W. S., and Hall, D. M.: Further electron microscope studies of dentine, Oral Surg., Oral Med. & Oral Path. *9*:432, 1956.

Sognnaes, R. F.: Microstructure and histochemical characteristics of the mineralized tissues, Ann. New York Acad. Sc. *60*:545, 1955.

Stack, M. V.: The chemical nature of the organic matrix of bone, dentin, and enamel, Ann. New York Acad. Sc. *60*:585, 1955.

Symons, N. B. B.: The cells of the odontoblast, ameloblast, and internal enamel epithelial layers, Brit. Dent. J. *98*:273, 1955.

————: Ribonucleic acid-alkaline phosphatase distribution in the developing teeth of the rat, J. Anat. *90*:117, 1956.

Szabó, G.: Studies on the cultivation of teeth *in vitro*, J. Anat. *88*:31, 1954.

Watson, M. L., and Avery, J. K.: The development of the hamster lower incisor as observed by electron microscopy, Am. J. Anat. *95*:109, 1954.

Weinmann, J. P., and Sicher, H.: Bone and Bones, ed. 2, St. Louis, Mosby, 1955.

Wislocki, G. B., Singer, M., and Waldo, C. M.: Some histochemical reactions of mucopolysaccharides, glycogen, lipids and other substances in teeth, Anat. Rec. *101*:487, 1948.

Wislocki, G. B., and Sognnaes, R. F.: Histochemical reactions of normal teeth, Am. J. Anat. *87*:239, 1950.

Special References on the Stomach

Bensley, R. R.: The gastric glands *in* Cowdry's Special Cytology, ed. 2, p. 197, New York, Hoeber, 1932.

Berger, E. H.: The distribution of parietal cells in the stomach; a histotopographic study, Am. J. Anat. *54*:87, 1934.

Bowie, D. J.: The distribution of the chief or pepsin forming cells in the gastric mucosa of the cat, Anat. Rec. *78*:9, 1940.

Bowie, D. J., and Vineberg, A. M.: The selective action of histamine and the effect of prolonged vagal stimulation on the cells of the gastric glands in the dog, Quart. J. Exper. Physiol. *25*:247, 1935.

Bradford, N. M., and Davies, R. E.: Site of hydrochloric acid production in stomach as determined by indicators, Biochem. J. *46*:414, 1950.

Challice, C. E., Bullivant, S., and Scott, D. B.: The fine structure of some cytoplasmic inclusions of oxyntic cells, Exper. Cell Res. *13*:488, 1957.

Crane, E. E., Davies, R. E., and Longmuir, N. M.: Relations between hydrochloric acid secretion and electrical phenomena in frog gastric mucosa, Biochem. J. *43*:321, 336, 1948.

Davenport, H. W.: Gastric carbonic anhydrase in dogs, Am. J. Physiol. *128*:725, 1939-40.

————: In Memoriam: The carbonic anhydrase

theory of gastric acid secretion, Gastroenterology *7*:374, 1946.

Davenport, H. W., and Fisher, R. B.: Carbonic anhydrase in the gastro-intestinal mucosa, J. Physiol. *94*:16, 1938-39.

————: The mechanism of the secretion of acid by the gastric mucosa, Am. J. Physiol. *131*:165, 1940-41.

Davies, R. E.: Hydrochloric acid production by isolated gastric mucosa, Biochem. J. *42*:609, 621, 1948. (Appendix by Davies, R. E., and Roughton, F. J. A.)

Davies, R. E., and Longmuir, N. M.: Production of ulcers in isolated frog gastric mucosa, Biochem. J. *42*:621, 1948.

Davies, R. E., and Ogston, A. G.: On mechanism of secretion of ions by gastric mucosa and by other tissues, Biochem. J. *46*:324, 1950.

Ferguson, A. N.: A cytological study of the regeneration of the gastric glands following experimental removal of large areas of the mucosa, Am. J. Anat. *42*:403, 1928.

Grant, R.: Rate of replacement of the surface epithelial cells of the gastric mucosa, Anat. Rec. *91*:175, 1945.

Hally, A. D.: The fine structure of the gastric parietal cell in the mouse, J. Anat. *93*:217, 1959.

Helander, H., and Ekholm, R.: Ultrastructure of epithelial cells in the fundus glands of the mouse gastric mucosa, J. Ultrastr. Res. *3*:74, 1958.

Hunt, J. N.: Gastric emptying and secretion in man, Physiol. Rev. *39*:491, 1959.

Hunt, T. E.: Regeneration of the gastric mucosa in the rat, Anat. Rec. *131*:193, 1958.

Patterson, W. B., and Stetten, De Witt, Jr.: A study of gastric HCl formation, Science *109*:256, 1949.

Sharples, W.: A note on the relatively high number of argentaffin cells in the mucosa of the human stomach, Anat. Rec. *91*:237, 1945.

Stevens, C. E., and Leblond, C. P.: Renewal of the mucous cells in the gastric mucosa of the rat, Anat. Rec. *115*:231, 1953.

Thomas, J. E.: Mechanics and regulation of gastric emptying, Physiol. Rev. *37*:453, 1957.

Special References on the Intestine

Baker, J. R.: The free border of the intestinal epithelial cells of the vertebrates, Quart. J. Micros. Sc. *84*:73, 1942.

Clark, S. L., Jr.: The ingestion of proteins and colloidal materials by columnar absorptive cells of the small intestine in suckling rats and mice, J. Biophys. & Biochem. Cytol. *5*:41, 1959.

Dalton, A. J.: Electron micrography of epithelial

cells of the gastro-intestinal tract and pancreas, Am. J. Anat. *87*:109, 1951.

Dalton, A. J., Kahler, H., and Lloyd, B. J.: The structure of the free surface of a series of epithelial cell types in the mouse as revealed by the electron microscope, Anat. Rec. *111*:67, 1951.

Dalton, A. J., Kahler, H., Striebich, M. J., and Lloyd, B.: Finer structure of hepatic, intestinal and renal cells of the mouse as revealed by the electron microscope, J. Nat. Cancer Inst. *11*: 439, 1950.

Florey, H. W., Wright, R. D., and Jennings, M. A.: The secretions of the intestines, Physiol. Rev. *21*:36, 1941.

Frazer, A. C.: Differentiation in absorption of olive oil and oleic acid in the rat, J. Physiol. *102*:306, 1943.

————: Lipolysis and fat absorption, J. Physiol. *102*:329, 1943.

Frazer, A. C., Schulman, J. H., and Stewart, H. C.: Emulsification of fat in the intestine of the rat and its relationship to absorption, J. Physiol. *103*:306, 1944.

Fredricsson, B., and Wirsen, C.: In vivo effect of colchicine on alkaline phosphatase of rat intestinal epithelium, Exper. Cell Res. *10*:749, 1956.

George, W. C.: The digestion and absorption of fat in lamellibranchs, Biol. Bull. *102*:118, 1952.

Granger, B., and Baker, R. F.: Electron microscope investigation of the striated border of intestinal epithelium, Anat. Rec. *107*:423, 1950.

Grossman, M. I.: The glands of Brunner, Physiol. Rev. *38*:675, 1958.

Hally, A. D.: The fine structure of the Paneth cell, J. Anat. *92*:268, 1958.

Hancox, N. M.: Alkaline phosphatase in the normal and explanted embryonic duodenum, Acta anat. *21*:18, 1954.

Irwin, D. A.: The anatomy of Auerbach's plexus, Am. J. Anat. *49*:141, 1931.

Kirkman, H.: The anal canal of the rhesus monkey with emphasis upon a description of bipolar, argyrophile cells in the zona columnaris, Am. J. Anat. *88*:177, 1951.

Landboe-Christensen, E.: The Duodenal Glands of Brunner in Man: Their Distribution and Quantity; An Anatomical Study, London, Oxford, 1944.

Leblond, C. P., and Messier, B.: Renewal of chief cells and goblet cells in the —H^3 into mice, Anat. Rec. *132*:247, 1958.

Leblond, C. P., and Stevens, C. E.: The constant renewal of the intestinal epithelium in the albino rat, Anat. Rec. *100*:357, 1948.

McMinn, R. M. H.: The rate of renewal of intestinal epithelium in the cat, J. Anat. *88*:527, 1954.

McMinn, R. M. H., and Mitchell, J. E.: The formation of villi following artificial lesions of the mucosa in the small intestine of the cat, J. Anat. *88*:99, 1954.

Palay, S. L., and Karlin, L.: Absorption of fat by jejunal epithelium in the rat, Anat. Rec. *124*: 343, 1956.

————: An electron microscopic study of the intestinal villus, I. The fasting animal, J. Biophys. & Biochem. Cytol. *5*:363, 1959.

Puchtler, H., and Leblond, C. P.: Histochemical analysis of cell membranes and associated structures as seen in the intestinal epithelium, Am. J. Anat. *102*:1, 1958.

Richardson, K. C.: Electron microscopic observations on Auerbach's plexus in the rabbit, with special reference to the problem of smooth muscle innervation, Am. J. Anat. *103*:99, 1958.

Salton, A. J.: Electron micrography of epithelial cells of the gastro-intestinal tract and pancreas, Am. J. Anat. *89*:109, 1951.

Verzár, F.: The absorption of fat, Am. J. Physiol. *90*:545, 1929.

Zetterqvist, H.: The Ultrastructural Organization of the Columnar Absorbing Cells of the Mouse Jejunum, Stockholm, Karolinska Institutet, Aktiebolaget Godvil, 1956.

Special References on the Pancreas

Bensley, R. R.: Structure and relationships of the islets of Langerhans, Harvey Lect. *10*:250, 1915.

————: Studies on the pancreas of the guinea pig, Am. J. Anat. *12*:297, 1911.

Ekholm, R., and Edlund, Y.: Ultrastructure of the human exocrine pancreas, J. Ultrastr. Res. *2*:453, 1959.

Haist, R. E., and Pugh, E. J.: Volume measurement of the islets of Langerhans and the effects of age and fasting, Am. J. Physiol. *152*:36, 1948.

Kuntz, A.: Effects of stimulation of the nerves of the pancreas on its exocrine secretory activity (abstr.), Anat. Rec. *100*:55, 1948.

Munger, B. L.: A phase and electron microscopic study of cellular differentiation in pancreatic acinar cells of the mouse, Am. J. Anat. *103*:1, 1958.

Opie, E. L.: Cytology of the pancreas *in* Cowdry's Special Cytology, ed. 2, p. 373, New York, Hoeber, 1932.

Saguchi, S.: Cytological Studies, No. 8, Kanazawa, Japan, Kanazawa Med. Coll., 1949.

Siekevitz, P., and Palade, G. E.: A cytochemical study on the pancreas of the guinea pig. II. Functional variations in the enzymatic activity of microsomes, J. Biophys. & Biochem. Cytol. *4*:309, 1958.

(*See also* References for Pancreas under Endocrines)

SPECIAL REFERENCES ON THE LIVER
AND THE GALLBLADDER

Arey, I. B.: On the presence of the so-called portal lobules in the seal's liver, Anat. Rec. 51:315, 1932.

Bernick, S., Hyman, C., and Paldino, R. L.: Histological studies on the sex difference in intrahepatic distribution of thorotrast and T-1824 in rabbits, Anat. Rec. 126:213, 1956.

Bollman, J. L.: Studies of hepatic lymphatics in Tr. of 9th Conf. on Liver Injury, p. 91, New York, Macy, 1950.

Boyden, E. A.: An analysis of the reaction of the human gallbladder to food, Anat. Rec. 40:147, 1928.

————: The sphincter of Oddi in man and certain representative mammals, Surgery 1:25, 1937.

Dalton, A. J., Kahler, H., Striebich, M. J., and Lloyd, B. J.: Fine structure of hepatic intestinal and renal cells of the mouse as revealed by the electron microscope, J. Nat. Cancer Inst. 11:439, 1950.

Deane, H. W.: The basophilic bodies in hepatic cells, Am. J. Anat. 78:227, 1946.

————: A cytochemical survey of phosphatases in mammalian liver, pancreas and salivary glands, Am. J. Anat. 80:321, 1947.

Dorfman, R. I.: The metabolism of androgens, Rec. Adv. Horm. Res. 2:179, 1948.

Elias, H.: Morphology of the stellate cells of Kupffer, Quart. J. Chicago M. Sch. 13:13, 1952.

————: A re-examination of the structure of the mammalian liver: I. Parenchymal architecture, Am. J. Anat. 84:311, 1949.

————: A re-examination of the structure of the mammalian liver, Am. J. Anat. 85:379, 1949.

Elias, H., and Petty, D.: Gross anatomy of the blood vessels and ducts within the human liver, Am. J. Anat. 90:59, 1952.

Elias, H., and Sokol, A.: Dependence of the lobular architecture of the liver on the portohepatic blood pressure gradient, Anat. Rec. 115:71, 1953.

Fawcett, D. W.: Observation on the cytology and electron microscopy of hepatic cells, J. Nat. Cancer Inst. 15:1475, 1955.

Gomori, G.: The distribution of phosphatase in normal organs and tissues, J. Cell. & Comp. Physiol. 17:71, 1941.

Hard, W. L., and Hawkins, R. K.: The role of the bile capillaries in the secretion of phosphatase by the rabbit liver, Anat. Rec. 106:395, 1950.

Hartroft, W. S.: Accumulation of fat in liver cells in lipodiastaemata preceding experimental dietary cirrhosis, Anat. Rec. 106:61, 1950.

————: The escape of lipid from fatty cysts in experimental dietary cirrhosis in Tr. of 9th Conf., p. 109, New York, Macy, 1950.

Howatson, A. F., and Ham, A. W.: Electron microscope study of sections of two rat liver tumors, Cancer Res. 15:62, 1955.

Irwin, J. W., and Macdonald, J., III: Microscopic observations of the intrahepatic circulation of living guinea pigs, Anat. Rec. 117:1, 1953.

Jaffé, R. H., and Berman, S. L.: The relation between Kupffer cells and liver cells, Arch. Path. 5:1020, 1928.

Janes, R. G., and McEnery, W. B.: Hepatic lipids in normal and in diabetic rats as demonstrated by cytochemical methods, Anat. Rec. 103:151, 1949.

Knisely, M. H.: The structure and mechanical functioning of the living liver lobules of frogs and rhesus monkeys (abstr.), Proc. Inst. Med. Chicago 16:286, 1947.

Knisely, M. H., Bloch, E. H., and Warner, L.: Selective phagocytosis: I. Microscopic observations concerning the regulation of the blood flow through the liver and other organs and the mechanism and rate of phagocytic removal of particles from the blood. Det. Kong. Dans. Videnskab. Selskab, Biol. Skr. 7:1, 1948.

Lazarow, A.: Particulate glycogen: A submicroscopic component of the guinea pig liver cell; its significance in glycogen storage and the regulation of the blood sugar, Anat. Rec. 84:31, 1942.

Lee, F. C.: On the lymph vessels of the liver, Contrib. Embryol. 74:65, 1925.

Mall, F. P.: A study of the structural unit of the liver, Am. J. Anat. 5:227, 1906.

Mosbaugh, M. M., and Ham, A. W.: Stimulation of bile secretion in chick embryos by cortisone, Nature 168:789, 1951.

Novikoff, A. B., Beaufay, H., and de Duve, C.: Electron microscopy of lysosome-rich fractions from rat liver, J. Biophys. & Biochem. Cytol. 2:179 (Supp.), 1956.

Palade, G. E., and Siekevitz, P.: Liver microsomes, an integrated morphological and biochemical study, J. Biophys. & Biochem. Cytol. 2:171, 1956.

Paschkis, K. E., Cantarow, A., Walkling, A. A., Pearlman, W. H., Rakoff, A. E., and Boyle, D.: Secretion and excretion of carbohydrate-active adrenal compounds (oxysteroids), Fed. Proc. 7:90, 1948.

Paschkis, K. E., and Rakoff, A. E.: Some aspects of the physiology of estrogenic hormones, Rec. Prog. Horm. Res. 5:115, 1950.

Popper, H.: Correlation of hepatic function and structure based on liver biopsy studies *in* Tr. of 9th Conf., p. 9, New York, Macy, 1950.

Ralph, P. H.: The surface structure of the gallbladder and intestinal epithelium of man and monkey, Anat. Rec. *108*:217, 1950.

Rappaport, A. M.: Anatomic considerations *in* Schiff, L.: Diseases of the Liver, Philadelphia, Lippincott, 1956.

————: The structural and functional acinar unit of the liver; some histopathological considerations (Monograph), Internat. Symp. Hepatitis Frontiers, Boston, Little, 1957.

————: The structural and functional unit in the human liver (liver acinus), Anat. Rec. *130*:673, 1958.

Rappaport, A. M., Borowy, Z. J., Lougheed, W. M., and Lotto, W. N.: Subdivision of hexagonal liver lobules into a structural and functional unit; role in hepatic physiology and pathology, Anat. Rec. *119*:11, 1954.

Rappaport, A. M., and Hiraki, G. Y.: The anatomical pattern of lesions in the liver, Acta anat. *32*:126, 1958.

————: Histopathologic changes in the structural and functional unit of the human liver, Acta anat. *32*:240, 1958.

Rich, A. R.: The formation of bile pigment, Physiol. Rev. *5*:182, 1925.

Wakim, K. G., and Mann, F. C.: The intrahepatic circulation of blood, Anat. Rec. *82*:233, 1942.

(*See also* references for Chap. 4)

Chapter 24

The Respiratory System

INTRODUCTION

It is obvious that the blood which leaves the capillaries of the systemic circulatory system with a diminished oxygen and an increased carbon dioxide content should be provided, at some point on the rounds of the circulatory system, with an opportunity of ridding itself of carbon dioxide and taking on a fresh charge of oxygen. This opportunity is provided in the pulmonary circuit as blood passes through the lungs. The latter are two large organs, spongy because they contain innumerable little pockets of air. They are also provided with a vast number of capillaries which abut on the air pockets. Hence, in passing through these organs, carbon dioxide diffuses from the blood in the lung capillaries into the air pockets, and oxygen from the air pockets diffuses into the blood in the lung capillaries. This, of course, would soon cause the air in the pockets to become highly charged with carbon dioxide and depleted of oxygen if there were no provision for constantly changing the air in the pockets. The latter action is accomplished by respiratory movements: inspiration, by which act fresh air is drawn into the lungs; and expiration, by which vitiated air is expelled from the lungs.

Since the microscopic structure of the lung is commonly studied before the student has learned the gross anatomy of the thoracic cavity and the precise nature of respiratory movements, and since a proper understanding of the microscopic structure of the lung depends on some knowledge of how its volume is regularly altered by these movements, at this time we shall give an elementary description of respiratory movements and their effects on the lungs.

Respiratory Movements and Their Effects. The lungs are contained in the thorax (Fig. 431). The thorax has a cagelike framework composed of the vertebral column, the ribs, the costal cartilages and the sternum. The bottom of the cage is a dome-shaped musculotendinous sheet, the diaphragm. The ribs are

disposed in such planes, and articulate with the vertebral column and the sternum at such angles, that the contraction of the muscles attached to them makes the thoracic cage both deeper in its anteroposterior diameter and wider. Moreover, contraction of the diaphragm (and relaxation of the muscles of the abdominal wall, which permits the diaphragm to descend) elongates the cage. Hence, by the contraction and the relaxation of muscles, the thoracic cage can be made larger by becoming deeper, wider and longer.

The two lungs fill two large compartments in

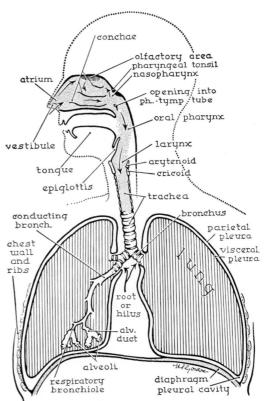

FIG. 431. Diagram of the parts of the respiratory system. (Redrawn and slightly modified from Grant, J. C. B.: A Method of Anatomy, ed. 4, Baltimore, Williams & Wilkins)

663

the thoracic cavity. Each compartment is lined with a fibro-elastic membrane, the *parietal pleura* (Fig. 431), which is provided with an internal layer of squamous mesothelial cells. Likewise, each lung is covered with a similar membrane, the *visceral pleura* (Fig. 431), the outermost layer of which consists of squamous mesothelial cells. A film of fluid is present between the two layers of the pleura; this has lubricating value and allows the visceral pleura covering the lungs—hence, the lungs themselves—to slide along the parietal pleura that lines the cavities during respiratory movements.

Except at its hilus, where a bronchus and blood vessels enter it (Fig. 431), each lung, because of the slippery pleural surfaces, is freely movable within its cavity. Around its point of attachment at the hilus, the visceral pleura covering each lung becomes continuous with the parietal pleural lining each cavity (Fig. 431). The space between the two layers of pleura contains, as was noted before, only a film of fluid; hence, it is only a *potential space* or *cavity*. Under certain abnormal conditions the amount of fluid becomes increased; this converts the potential cavity into a real one. The potential or real space between the two layers of pleura is known as the *pleural cavity*. It should be understood that, although a lung occupies a cavity in the thorax, it does not lie in the pleural cavity but outside it, just as the intestines occupy the abdominal cavity but lie outside the peritoneal cavity.

With these few points in mind we are in a position to discuss how respiratory movements change the air in the lungs. Everyone knows that opening a bellows draws air into it. Furthermore, one cannot open an airtight bellows if its spout is plugged. One cannot pull up the plunger of a large pump if its intake valve does not open. Likewise, the muscular movements involved in performing an inspiratory movement can be effective in enlarging the thoracic cage only if something (air, fluid or viscus) can be drawn into the cage to permit its expansion. Inspiratory movements are not powerful enough to create any significant degree of vacuum in the thoracic cage. If they were, sometimes they might accomplish the same result that was witnessed when, in the 17th century, Guericke first created a vacuum by exhausting the air from a large copper

sphere with a strong, small pump. After prolonged pumping, the sphere suddenly collapsed, with what was said to be a great noise, inspiring terror in all who watched.

Normally the thoracic cage can be enlarged by inspiratory movements only to the extent to which air and blood can be drawn into it. Air, under normal conditions, is drawn only into the lungs, but extra blood is drawn both into the vessels of the lungs and into those outside the lungs but inside the thorax. The reason for air not being drawn into any other part of the thoracic cavity except the lungs is that there is no opening to the surface from these other parts of the thorax through which it can be drawn. If an opening is provided, for example, a deep knife wound in the chest, air may be drawn into parts of the thorax other than the lungs.

Some Fundamental Features of Lungs. The lungs consist essentially of: (1) the spongy respiratory tissue in which gaseous exchange occurs between blood and air and (2) a branching system of air tubes called *bronchioles* and *bronchi* which "pipe" air into and from the pockets and passageways of the spongy respiratory tissue. The main bronchus from each lung connects with the trachea (Fig. 431), and this, in turn, by means of the larynx, the nasopharynx and the nose (or the mouth if need be), connects with the outside air. Hence, on an inspiratory act, air is drawn through the nose, down the trachea, into the bronchial tree to its end branches and from there into the passageways and the pockets of the foamy, capillary-rich respiratory tissue, where, and only where, gaseous exchange occurs (Fig. 431, *alveoli*).

Before briefly considering the mechanism of expiration it is necessary to point out that the lungs would not fill the cavities in which they lie unless they were considerably stretched in all directions. A large amount of elastin is present in the visceral pleura that covers them, in the walls between the air pockets and in the bronchial tree. Since the lungs fill their respective cavities when they first develop in embryonic life, and since there is no easy way for fluid to be drawn into the pleural cavity during fetal life, the lungs are gradually stretched as the cavities containing them increase in size. The same process continues in the growing period of postnatal life. As a result, the elastic tissue of the lungs, under normal conditions, is always stretched, and the lung is always trying, as it were, to collapse and retract to the one point where it is attached (its root or hilus). Hence, if a hollow needle is inserted through the chest wall into the pleural cavity (between the parietal and the visceral layers of pleura), air immediately rushes through it into the pleural cavity, which increases in size as the lung retracts toward the hilus. This procedure is sometimes used to put a lung at rest in the treatment of tuberculosis. Such a state of affairs is called a *pneumothorax*. In certain diseases the fluid in the pleural cavity becomes greatly increased in amount. This, too, permits the lung to retract. This condition is known as a *hydrothorax*.

Since the elastic tissue of the lungs is normally stretched, it is scarcely necessary for an individual at rest to indulge in muscular movements to allow such air as is drawn into the lungs on inspiration to escape. The elastic recoil of the lungs is enough, or almost enough, to expel the air out through the bronchial tree and draw in the sides and the bottom of the thoracic cage. But the elastic recoil of the lungs is not sufficient to expel large quantities of air as quickly as is necessary when one engages in violent exercise. Expiration is facilitated under such conditions, and probably to some extent in quiet breathing, by contractions of the abdominal muscles, which force the abdominal viscera against the undersurface of the diaphragm and so push it up into the thorax.

The system of cavities and tubes that conduct air from outside the body to all parts of the lungs constitutes the *conducting portion* of the respiratory system, and the pockets and the passageways of the respiratory tissue of the lung—the only sites where gaseous interchange occurs—are said to constitute the true *respiratory portion* of the system. The conducting part of the system consists of the nose, the nasopharynx, the larynx, the trachea, the bronchi and the bronchioles (Fig. 431). It is to be noted that some of these structures lie outside the lung, and others (some bronchi and all the bronchioles) within it. It should be realized that those parts of the conducting system that lie without the lung must be provided with reasonably rigid walls; otherwise, a strong inspiratory act might collapse them, as suck-

ing a soft drink through a wet straw (dry straws have rigid walls) collapses the straw. Rigidity is provided by cartilage or bone. Moreover, it should be kept in mind that the conducting part of the respiratory system performs functions other than conducting air to and from the lungs. The mucous membrane lining the conducting passageways strains, washes, warms or cools, as the case may be, and humidifies the air that passes along it toward the respiratory portion of the system. In other words, the conducting portion of the respiratory system is an excellent air-conditioning unit. Its different parts and their microscopic structure will now be described.

THE NASAL CAVITIES

The nose contains two nasal cavities, one on each side, separated from one another by the nasal septum. Each cavity opens in front by a *naris* or *nostril* and behind into the *nasopharynx* (Fig. 431).

Bone and, to a lesser extent, cartilage and, to a small degree, dense connective tissue provide rigidity to the walls, the floor and the roof of the nasal cavities and so prevent their collapse on inspiration.

Each nasal cavity is divided into two parts: (1) a *vestibule,* the widened part of the passageway encountered just behind the naris, and (2) the remainder of the cavity, called its *respiratory portion*.

The epidermis of the skin covering the nose extends into each naris to line the front part of each vestibule. It is provided with many large hair follicles together with some sebaceous and sweat glands. The hairs are intended to strain coarse particles from air that is drawn through the nostrils. Farther back in the vestibule, the stratified squamous epithelium is not keratinized, and, still farther back, the epithelium becomes pseudostratified ciliated columnar with goblet cells. This type of epithelium lines the remainder of each nasal cavity.

The mucous membrane lining the respiratory portion of the nasal cavities is sometimes called the *schneiderian membrane* after the anatomist who first described it carefully. Typically, it consists of pseudostratified columnar ciliated epithelium with goblet cells and a lamina propria that contains both mucous and serous glands, which is adherent to the periosteum of the bone, or the perichondrium of the cartilage, beneath it. For this reason, the mucous membrane in this region is sometimes termed a *mucoperiosteum* or a *mucoperichondrium*.

The surface of the epithelium is normally covered with mucus provided by its goblet cells and by the glands of its lamina propria. Probably over a pint of fluid is produced by the nasal mucous membrane each day. The mucus, together with the particles of dust and dirt that are picked up by it, is moved backward through the nasopharynx to the oral pharynx by means of the cilia with which the epithelial lining cells, excepting the goblet cells, are provided. Each cell has between 15 and 20 cilia that are about 7 μ in height and are anchored in the cytoplasm by rootlets. The drainage of the nose depends to a great extent on orderly ciliary action, and a loss of cilia from trauma or disease can interfere with the proper drainage of the nose.

The lamina propria contains both collagenic and elastic fibers. In some sites, and evidently by no means regularly, the lamina propria forms a well-developed basement membrane with elastic properties. Lymphocytes, plasma cells, macrophages and even granular leukocytes may be seen in the lamina propria. In general, it is a very vascular membrane, and in cold weather it helps warm the air that is to be drawn into the lungs. In some sites lymphatic nodules appear; these are most numerous near the entrance to the nasopharynx.

The character of the mucous membrane of the respiratory portion of the nose differs from the typical in two sites. That lining the upper parts of the sides and the roof of the posterior part of each cavity constitutes the organ of smell (the olfactory organ), and its special microscopic structure will be described in the chapter dealing with the system of sensory receptors (Chap. 29). The other site in which the mucous membrane is not typical will be dealt with now.

Three plates of bone, arranged one above the other like shelves, are disposed along the lateral wall of each nasal cavity. However, they are not flat like useful shelves; they are more like unsupported metal shelves which have had to bear too much weight, for they all curve downward. Since their curved form makes them look something like shells, they

are called the *superior,* the *middle* and the *inferior conchae* (*concha* is Latin for shell), respectively (Figs. 431 and 432). They are also often referred to as the *superior,* the *middle* and the *inferior turbinate* (*turbinatus* = scroll-like) bones.

Although the mucous membrane of the nasal cavities is typically vascular, containing many arteries, capillaries and veins, that of the lamina propria of the mucosa covering the middle and the inferior conchae has, in addition, a large number of venouslike structures which, under normal conditions, are collapsed. However, under certain circumstances, they can become distended with blood (Fig. 432), and this so increases the thickness of the mucosa that in some individuals it encroaches on the airway to such an extent that nose breathing is made difficult.

The term *erectile tissue* is usually used to designate any tissue that contains a large number of endothelial-lined cavities which, although they are on the circuit of the blood stream, are usually collapsed and become distended with blood, to increase greatly the size of the tissue in which they lie, only as a result of special nervous stimulation. Most of the substance of the male copulatory organ, the penis, is erectile tissue; this accounts for the changes in the size and the consistency of this organ that can occur under conditions of erotic stimulation. The lamina propria of the nasal mucosa of the conchae is not as typically erectile tissue as that present in the penis, and some observers consider that it is not true erectile tissue at all. Perhaps it is better described as possessing a great many thin-walled veins along which smooth muscle fibers are both circularly and longitudinally disposed (Fig. 432, *right*). Nevertheless, it reacts like erectile tissue in that it can rapidly become turgid with blood. A further indication of its similarity to erectile tissue (which otherwise is limited to the genital systems of the male and the female) is that in certain individuals the mucosa covering the conchae is affected by erotic stimuli. Mackenzie, many years ago, wrote a most interesting and learned article about this relationship. From individuals encountered in his own practice he obtained many examples of erotic stimulation being associated with sneezing, with engorgement of the nasal mucosa covering the conchae and even with bleeding from this area; indeed, he even quotes one 16th century report of a youth who sneezed whenever he saw a pretty girl. It is difficult to understand the purpose served by having the erectile tissue of the nose linked nervously with that of the genital systems. The relationship probably hinges somehow on the fact that sex stimulation is so very dependent on the sense of smell in a large part of the animal kingdom. That a relationship exists between the erectile or pseudoerectile tissue of the nose and that of the genital system not only enlarges the number of possible factors that may be concerned in nasal congestions but also provides a basis for attempting to treat some atrophic states of the nasal mucosa with sex hormones.

PARANASAL AIR SINUSES OF THE NOSE

The air *sinuses* (*sinus* = bay or hollow) are spaces in bones. There are 4 associated with each nasal cavity. They are named after the bones in which they are contained and hence are called the *frontal*, the *ethmoidal*, the *sphenoidal* and the *maxillary* sinuses, respectively. The maxillary sinus is the largest and is sometimes called the *antrum* (*antron* = a cavity) *of Highmore*.

The 4 sinuses on each side all communicate with the nasal cavity of that side. They are all lined by mucous membrane continuous with that lining the nasal cavity. The ciliated epithelium in the sinuses is not so thick as that in the nasal cavity itself, and it does not contain nearly so many goblet cells. A basement membrane is not present. The lamina propria is relatively thin and is continuous with the periosteum of the underlying bone. It consists chiefly of collagenic fibers and contains eosinophils, plasma cells and many lym-

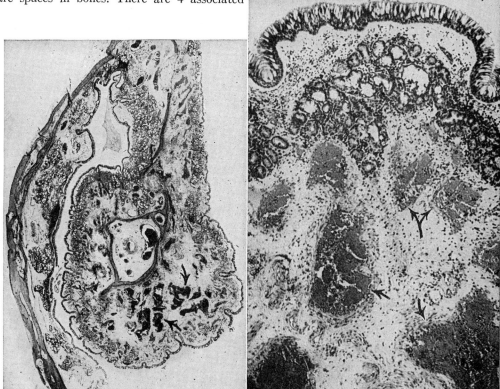

Fig. 432. (*Left*) Very low-power photomicrograph of a cross section of a concha. Thin bone may be seen in its central part. The blood in the venous spaces is dark. (*Right*) Medium-power photomicrograph of a section of the mucous membrane covering a concha. Glands may be seen in the upper region, and large venous spaces distended with blood may be seen in the lower part of the figure.

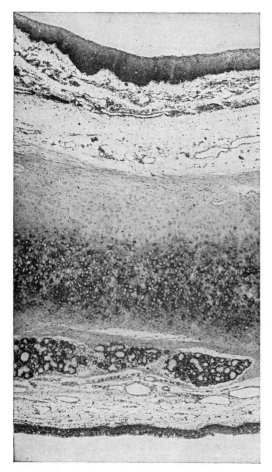

Fig. 433. Low-power photomicrograph of a section cut across the epiglottis. The anterior surface is above; the posterior below.

phocytes in addition to fibroblasts. It has relatively few glands embedded in it.

The openings by which the sinuses communicate with the nasal cavities are not so large as to prevent their becoming closed if the mucosa at and around the opening becomes inflamed or sufficiently swollen for other reasons. Normally, the mucus formed in sinuses is moved to the nasal cavities by ciliary action. If the openings of the sinuses become obstructed, the sinuses may fill with mucus or, under conditions of infection, with pus. Drugs which have an adrenalinlike action and cause contraction of the blood vessels of the part are often used locally to lessen the congestion about the openings of inflamed sinuses and so permit them to drain. Sometimes new open-

ings must be made surgically to permit them to drain properly.

THE PHARYNGEAL TONSIL

This consists of an unpaired median mass of lymphatic tissue in the lamina propria of the mucous membrane lining the dorsal wall of the nasopharynx (Fig. 431). A child who has an enlarged pharyngeal tonsil is said to have *adenoids* (*aden* = gland) because the enlarged lymphatic follicles of the tonsil give it a glandlike appearance. Adenoids may obstruct the respiratory passageway and lead to persistent mouth breathing. The muscular actions entailed in keeping the mouth always open, by changing the normal lines of force to which the bones of the developing face are subjected, may prevent the bones of the face from developing as they otherwise would, and the effect produced is usually unfortunate. For this reason, and also for the reason that an enlarged pharyngeal tonsil is usually more or less persistently infected, the removal of adenoids is a relatively common operation.

The pharyngeal tonsil resembles the palatine tonsil in microscopic structure except that: (1) it is more diffuse, (2) its covering epithelium dips down into it as folds rather than crypts, and (3) its epithelium may be pseudostratified, at least in some areas, instead of stratified squamous nonkeratinizing.

THE LARYNX

The larynx is the segment of the respiratory tube that connects the pharynx with the trachea (Fig. 431). Its walls are kept from collapsing on inspiration by a number of cartilages that are contained in its wall which are connected together with connective tissue membranes. Muscles that act on the cartilages are present both outside them (the extrinsic muscles of the larynx) and between them and the mucous membrane (the intrinsic muscles of the larynx). The larynx has many functions. It plays the most important part in phonation; however, this is phylogenetically a late development. A more fundamental function of the larynx is that of preventing anything but air from gaining entrance to the lower respiratory passages. It is said to be the watchdog for the lung, and if, in spite of its efforts, anything but air enters it, a cough reflex is set in motion immediately. It is of interest in this connection to note that some individuals who apparently have died from drowning are found at autopsy to have very little water in their lungs; they probably die from asphyxiation caused by laryngeal spasm induced by water gaining entrance to, and irritating, this organ.

The apex of a flaplike structure, the *epiglottis*, whose free portion projects upward and slightly backward, is attached anteriorly to constitute the uppermost part of the larynx (Fig. 431). In days past it was thought that the free part of this structure flapped down over the entrance of the larynx when food was swallowed and in this way kept food and fluid from gaining entrance to the larynx. Although this view has some modern supporters, it is now generally thought that the epiglottis plays a more subsidiary and passive role in keeping food and fluid out of the larynx during the act of swallowing and that the main factor responsible for this latter effect is the larynx being brought upward and forward in the act of swallowing so that the upper end of its tubular part is pressed against the posterior aspect of the epiglottis, under the root of the tongue. Individuals who have had the epiglottis removed for one cause or another can still swallow without food entering the larynx.

A plate of elastic cartilage (Fig. 433) forms an internal support for the epiglottis. The perichondrium of this is continuous with the lamina propria of the mucous membrane which covers both its surfaces. The epithelium of the mucous membrane varies in relation to the function of the different parts of the epiglottis. On the anterior surface, where the epiglottis comes into contact with the root of the tongue in the act of swallowing, the epithelium is of the stratified squamous nonkeratinizing type (Fig. 433) that is so well-adapted to cover wet surfaces subjected to wear and tear. The epithelium covering the upper part of the posterior surface comes into contact with things being swallowed and so is subjected to considerable wear and tear. It, too, is of the stratified squamous nonkeratinizing type. Taste buds are occasionally present in it. However, the epithelium covering the lower part of the posterior surface does not come into contact with food, and, since it constitutes the lining of part of the respiratory tube, it is lined with

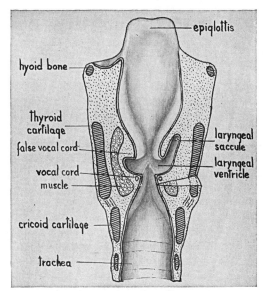

FIG. 434. Drawing of the anterior half of a coronally sectioned larynx as seen from behind. The cut is farther forward at the upper right side of the illustration so that the saccule is disclosed. (Redrawn and modified from Schaeffer, E. A.: Textbook of Microscopic Anatomy, published as Vol. 2, Part I of Quain's Elements of Anatomy, ed. 11, New York, Longmans)

pseudostratified columnar ciliated epithelium with goblet cells (Fig. 433, *bottom*). The cilia beat toward the pharynx and wash mucus and particles picked up by the mucus in that direction. Mucous glands with some serous secretory units are present in the lamina propria under the posterior surface. They are said to be present also under the anterior surface. Glands are more numerous toward the attached margin of the epiglottis.

The lumen of the larynx is narrowed and made more or less slitlike (the slit being directed in an anteroposterior direction) in two sites by folds of mucous membrane that projects into the lumen from each side. The upper pair of folds constitute the false vocal cords (Fig. 434). The second pair of folds lie below the first pair, and their cordlike free margins constitute the true vocal cords (Fig. 434). The opening between the two vocal cords is termed the *rima glottidis*. It is slitlike when the vocal cords are close together but somewhat triangular in shape, with the apex of the triangle being directed forward, when the vocal

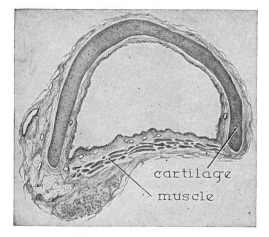

Fig. 435. Drawing of a cross section of the trachea of an adult (very low-power).

cords are farther apart. The expansion of the lumen of the larynx between the two sets of folds is called the *sinus* or *ventricle* of the larynx (Fig. 434). Anteriorly the sinus of each side is prolonged upward. Each cul-de-sac, so formed, is called the *laryngeal saccule* (Fig. 434). The cores of the folds that comprise the false vocal cords are composed chiefly of a somewhat loose lamina propria which contains glands. The cores of the second and lower pair of folds consist of connective tissue and muscle. The cores of the vocal cords themselves (the parts of the folds nearest their free edges) consist of connective tissue that is composed chiefly of elastic fibers. The aperture between the true vocal cords, and the tension under which the cords exist, is affected both by muscle fibers that act on the cords directly and by muscle fibers that affect the cords indirectly by shifting the tissues to which they are anchored.

The epithelium of the mucous membrane of the larynx varies in relation to the functions performed by its different parts. That covering the true vocal cords, which are subjected to considerable wear and tear, is of the stratified squamous nonkeratinizing type. All the epithelium lining the larynx below the true vocal cords is of the pseudostratified columnar ciliated type with goblet cells. Most of that lining the larynx above the true vocal cords is also of this type, although patches of stratified squamous nonkeratinizing epithelium may

be present in some sites. The cilia beat toward the pharynx. Except over the true vocal cords the lamina propria of the mucous membrane contains mucous glands. Lymph nodules occur in the lamina propria of the mucous membrane. They are more numerous along the lateral and dorsal wall in the region of the ventricle and the false vocal cords.

THE TRACHEA

The trachea is a tube continuous with the larynx above and ending below by dividing into two primary bronchi which pass toward the right and the left lungs, respectively (Fig. 431).

The trachea is prevented from collapsing by about 20 U- or horseshoe-shaped cartilages that are set in its wall one above the other so that each almost encircles the lumen. The open ends of these incomplete cartilaginous rings are directed backward (Fig. 435), and the gap between the two ends of each ring is bridged by connective tissue and smooth muscle (Fig. 435).

If a *longitudinal section* is cut from the wall of the trachea, the cartilaginous rings that encircle its wall are cut in *cross section*. The cross-section appearance of each ring is roughly ovoid (Fig. 436) with a greatest supero-inferior diameter of 3 or 4 mm. and a greatest mediolateral diameter of 1 mm. or thereabouts. The inner surface of each ring is convex, and its outer surface relatively flat (Fig. 436). The space between adjacent rings is considerably less than the supero-inferior diameters of the rings themselves and is filled with dense connective tissue which is continuous with that of the perichondrium of each ring (Fig. 436). The bundles of collagenic fibers which make up this connective tissue are woven in such a way that some degree of elasticity is imparted to the tracheal wall. Some elastic fibers, distributed among the bundles of collagenic fibers, also may be of some importance in this respect.

The trachea is lined wtih a mucous membrane. The fine structure of this is the subject of a recent extensive monograph by Rhodin and Dalhamn, some of whose findings were described in Chapter 11. The membrane consists of pseudostratified ciliated columnar epithelium with goblet cells (Fig. 128). The lamina propria on which the epithelium rests

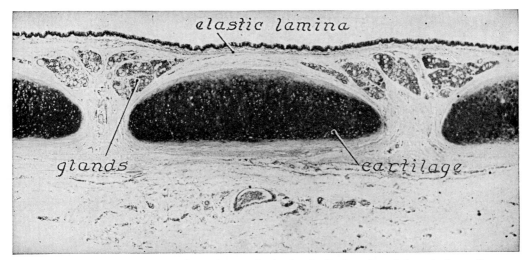

Fig. 436. Very low-power photomicrograph of a longitudinal section of the anterior wall of the trachea of an adult.

is condensed to form a moderately distinct basement membrane. The remainder of the lamina propria contains a fairly high proportion of elastic fibers. A tendency toward a lymphatic character is indicated by the presence in the membrane of cells of the lymphocyte series and occasional true nodules. The deep border of the lamina propria is marked by a dense lamina or membrane of elastin (Fig. 436). The tissue just outside this is termed *submucosa*. The secretory portions of many mucous glands, with some serous secretory units, are embedded in the submucosa. In longitudinal sections of the trachea the secretory portions of these glands are seen to be disposed chiefly in the submucosa that fills in the triangular spaces between adjacent cartilages (Fig. 436). The ducts from these glands pierce the elastic lamina of the lamina propria to empty on the inner surface of the trachea. Some secretory units may be present also in the lamina propria.

The posterior wall of the trachea is composed of interlacing bundles of smooth muscle fibers, arranged chiefly in the transverse plane and knitted together by connective tissue (Fig. 435). The inner surface of the posterior wall of the trachea is lined with a mucous membrane similar to that lining the remainder of its wall. The secretory units of glands are present in the mucous membrane, outside the mucous membrane in the interstices between the bundles of smooth muscle, and even outside the smooth muscle, in the connective tissue of the outer layers of the wall.

THE BRONCHIAL TREE

The trachea ends by dividing into 2 branches, the 2 primary bronchi, which pass to the roots of the lungs (Fig. 431). The microscopic structure of the walls of these is the same as that of the wall of the trachea.

Usually the right lung is made up of 3 lobes and the left lung of 2. Each primary bronchus, in a sense, continues into the lower lobe of the particular lung to which it passes. The right primary bronchus, before doing so, gives off 2 branches to supply the middle and the upper lobes, respectively, of that lung. Likewise, the left primary bronchus, before continuing into the lower lobe of the left lung, gives off a branch to supply the upper lobe of that lung. At the hilus of each lung the primary bronchus and its main branches become closely associated with the arteries which also enter the lung at this site and the veins and lymphatics which leave the lung, and all these tubular structures become invested in dense connective tissue. This complex of tubes invested in dense connective tissue is termed the *root* of the lung.

As stated above, a large bronchus enters each of the lobes of the two lungs. Within the lobes these branch to give rise to progressively smaller bronchi. The manner in which the first branchings occur to supply different parts of

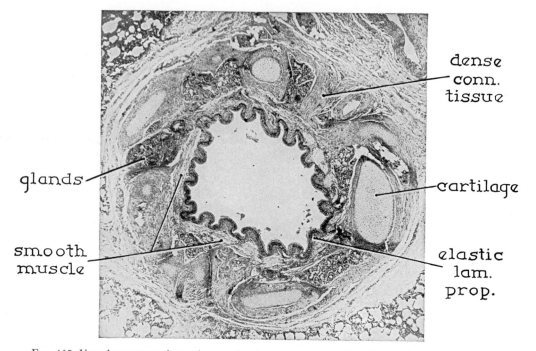

dense
conn.
tissue

glands

cartilage

smooth
muscle

elastic
lam.
prop.

FIG. 437. Very low-power photomicrograph of a cross section of an intrapulmonary bronchus.

the different lobes of the lung is a matter of considerable interest, particularly with regard to the surgical treatment of certain diseases of the lung. Although there is some variation, certain parts or areas of each lobe tend to be supplied by certain main branches of the bronchus that enters the lobe. These parts or areas represent units of lung structure that may be dealt with surgically and are of a smaller order of size than whole lobes. The pattern and the bronchial connections of these constitute a matter too specialized to discuss here.

Microscopic Structure of Intrapulmonary Bronchi. Although the bronchi that are within the lung have a microscopic structure similar to that of the trachea and the extrapulmonary portions of the 2 primary bronchi, they are somewhat different in a few respects which will now be described.

1. The U- or horseshoe-shaped cartilages of the trachea and the extrapulmonary parts of the primary bronchi are replaced in the intrapulmonary bronchi by cartilage plates of a most irregular shape. In a cross section of an intrapulmonary bronchus these appear as crescents (Fig. 437), and the impression is given that several are required to encircle the tube.

But, as Miller has pointed out, this appearance is deceptive, for he found from reconstructions that what seemed to be several cartilages in a single section are only the various prolongations of a single large cartilage of irregular shape. In many instances he found the irregular cartilages to encircle the lumen completely. Since cartilages are disposed around all parts of the walls of these bronchi, the latter are not flattened on one surface like the trachea and the extrapulmonary bronchi. At sites of branchings Miller found that special saddle-shaped cartilages were often present to support the 2 branches at the site where they make an acute angle with one another. The spaces between different cartilages and parts of the same cartilage which would otherwise be weak spots in the bronchial wall are filled with collagenic connective tissue which is continuous with the perichondrium of the cartilages concerned.

2. The smooth muscle which is present only in the posterior part of the trachea and the extrapulmonary bronchi comes, in the intrapulmonary bronchi, to constitute a layer which completely encircles the lumen. This layer of muscle lies between the mucous membrane and

the cartilages (Fig. 437). It does not appear as a complete layer in every section because it is composed of 2 sets of smooth muscle fibers that wind down the bronchial tree in a left and a right spiral, respectively. The arrangement of muscle can be roughly demonstrated by winding 2 shoelaces down a broomstick in fairly close spirals, one clockwise and the other counterclockwise.

3. The contraction of this muscle after death, and perhaps to some extent during life, throws the mucous membrane into the longitudinal folds that are characteristic of intrapulmonary bronchi seen in cross sections (Fig. 437).

4. The elastic lamina that marks the outer limit of the mucous membrane of the trachea is not present as such in the intrapulmonary bronchi but instead is represented by a diffuse network of elastic fibers throughout the whole lamina propria (Fig. 437). This facilitates its being thrown into longitudinal folds.

The intrapulmonary bronchi are lined with ciliated pseudostratified columnar epithelium, and the secretion of the goblet cells disposed in this membrane is augmented by that of glands. The secretory portions of these are disposed, for the most part, outside the muscular layer (Fig. 437), particularly in sites where there are intervals between cartilages.

Both lymph nodes and individual nodules are scattered along the bronchi in the outermost fibrous parts of their walls.

Method of Branching. In general, the branching that occurs in the bronchial tree is of the *dichotomous* (*dichotomia* = a cutting in two) variety, with the total cross-sectional area of the lumens of each 2 branches that arise being greater than the cross-sectional area of the lumen of the parent tube. This fact has implications with regard to the relative speeds at which air travels in the smaller and the larger branches of the bronchial tree. Since the same amount of air (per unit of time) can only pass through a parent tube as can pass through its 2 branches (which have a greater total cross-sectional area) if it moves faster in the parent tube, it follows that air moves slowest in the smallest tubes of the bronchial tree and fastest in the largest. Keeping this in mind is of importance in interpreting the breath sounds heard with a stethoscope.

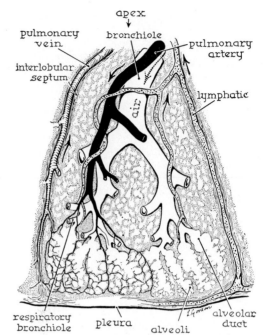

FIG. 438. Diagram of a lobule of the lung with its base abutting on the pleura. The size of the bronchioles and the air passages, as well as that of the blood vessels and the lymphatics, is out of proportion. To make it easier to follow the course of the blood vessels and the lymphatics, the former have been omitted from the right side, and the latter from the left side.

The continued branching of the bronchial tree results in the formation of successively narrower bronchi. The smaller ones differ in structure from the larger ones, chiefly because their cartilages are not so large and do not extend around their walls so completely. Branches of less than 1 mm. in diameter are usually termed *bronchioles* and these have no cartilages in their walls. Engel has recently criticized the use of diameter as a criterion for distinguishing bronchi from bronchioles. He suggests that the deciding factor should be position rather than size. He regards those tubes that run in the connective tissue root of the lung, and in the extensions of connective tissue which radiate from the root into the lung, as bronchi. Bronchi, in other words, would be comparable with the interlobular, or perhaps what might be termed the *extralobular,* ducts of glands that run in connective tissue. Bronchioles, Engel considers, are tubes

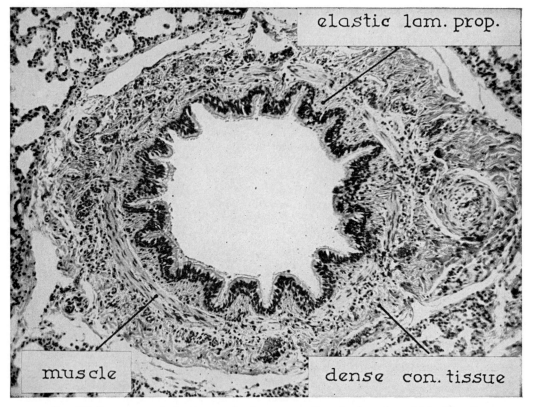

elastic lam. prop.

muscle

dense con. tissue

FIG. 439. Low-power photomicrograph of a cross section of a large bronchiole (Engel's bronchiolus) in the lung of a child.

which leave the connective tissue skeleton of the lung to enter the substance of the respiratory tissue. In other words, bronchioles are comparable with the intralobular ducts of glands. However, as is true of intralobular ducts, some connective tissue from the septa extends along bronchioles to provide the larger ones particularly with support (Fig. 439).

Lung Lobules. Likening bronchioles to intralobular ducts is helpful because each of the bronchioles that arises from the branching of the smaller bronchi enters what is called a *secondary lobule* of the lung to course thereafter, like an intralobular duct, through, and branch within, the substance of a lobule. Before discussing how the bronchioles connect with the air spaces where an interchange of gases between blood and air occurs, we shall discuss the structure of secondary lobules in more detail. (The units of structure that logically would be called the lobules of the lung are generally called secondary lobules because certain authorities of the past de-

scribed smaller ill-defined units of lung structure, which we shall not describe, as primary lobules. The latter term is falling into disuse; hence, the term lobule is now often used without any qualifying adjective to refer to the unit of structure that we are describing as the secondary lobule, which for all practical purposes is *the* lobule of the lung.)

Secondary lobules, like pyramids, have apices and bases (Fig. 438). But here their resemblance to pyramids usually ends, for lobules are very irregular in shape. They vary greatly in size; their bases vary from somewhat less than 1 cm. to 2 or more cm. in diameter, and their height varies even more. Before considering how they are arranged within lobes, it may be helpful to recall that a bronchus "grows" from the root of the lung toward the central part of a lobe, and even beyond this point, branching as it grows. The smaller branches of the tree mostly point outwardly toward the periphery of the lobe, but a considerable number of the smaller branches point not outwardly, but inwardly, toward the central part of the lobe. The secondary lobules are so arranged that their apices receive these bronchioles (Fig. 438). This means that the bases of some lobules face the periphery of the lobe and those of others face its interior. The bases of many of the former type are applied directly to the pleura (Fig. 438), where their outlines can be seen when the pleural surface is viewed in full face, as polygonal areas.

In some animals, for example, the pig, the secondary lobules are completely separated from each other by interlobular septa of dense connective tissue. This is continuous with the connective tissue of the visceral pleural at the base of the lobule (Fig. 451) and with the dense connective tissue that ensheathes the bronchi at the apex of the lobule. However, in other animals, for example, the rabbit, the secondary lobules are not separated from one another by septa. In man the septa tend to be complete, but such observations as we have made from large sections cut parallel with the pleural surface suggest that they may be defective in various sites.

Microscopic Structures of Bronchioles. A bronchiole on entering a lobule gives rise to many branches, and these extend in a treelike fashion to all parts of the lobule. Since bronchioles, like intralobular ducts, lie within the substance of lobules, they are attached on all sides to the elastic spongework of tissue that contains the air spaces where gaseous exchange occurs (Fig. 439). There is, then, no tendency for them to collapse on inspiratory movements; indeed, on an inspiratory movement they are "pulled on," all around their circumference, as the elastic fibers of the respiratory spongework are stretched. Hence, there is no need for the walls of the bronchioles to be protected against collapsing on inspiratory movements by cartilaginous rings or plates, and they have none in their walls. They differ from bronchi also in not having any glands in their walls; perhaps they are so close to the respiratory spaces that secretions delivered into them from glands might be sucked into the respiratory spaces. Moreover, their epithelial lining is not as thick as that of bronchi. In the larger branches it is ciliated columnar, and in the final branches, nonciliated and high cuboidal in type. To sum up, the walls of

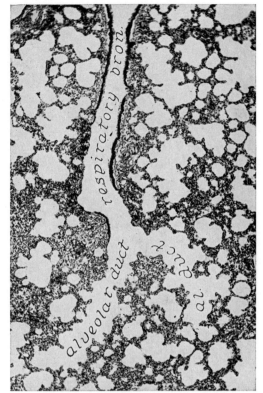

FIG. 440. Very low-power photomicrograph of a section of the lung of a very young child. A respiratory bronchiole is cut longitudinally and may be seen to be opening into 2 alveolar ducts.

bronchioles consist of epithelium that rests on a thin elastic lamina propria, and this layer, in turn, is surrounded by the muscular coat previously described for bronchi (Fig. 439). The muscle is supported by connective tissue.

The final branches of the bronchioles within a lobule are termed *respiratory bronchioles*. Toward their terminations they flare out, something like the horns of trumpets.

Before describing the tissue in which gaseous exchange occurs, it is perhaps helpful to emphasize that the bronchial tree (including the bronchioles) constitutes a set of tubes whose primary function is to deliver air from the trachea to all parts of the spongework of respiratory tissue that makes up the great part of each lobule. It is also helpful, in understanding the minute structure of the lung, to emphasize that bronchi and bronchioles are structures in themselves—tubes, each with a

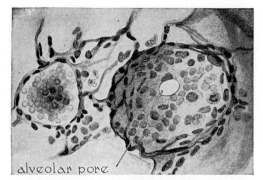

FIG. 441. Drawing of a thick section (high-power) of the lung of the rabbit. A venule shows at the left, and the floor of an alveolus is to be seen on the right. The blood cells in the floor are in capillaries. At one site, the floor of the alveolus exhibits a defect, and alveolar pore.

wall of its own. The respiratory bronchioles open into spaces in a spongework of respiratory tissue where the gaseous exchange occurs.

THE MICROSCOPIC STRUCTURE OF RESPIRATORY TISSUE

The spaces in the respiratory spongework are of different orders. Those into which the tubular respiratory bronchioles open are like long hallways and are called *alveolar ducts* (Figs. 438 and 440). These, in turn, branch; this enables each respiratory bronchiole to supply several hallways. Rooms open into the hallways not only along their sides but also from their floors and ceilings. The "rooms" are termed *alveoli* (Fig. 440). The frame of the "open doorway" between alveolar ducts and alveoli contains some smooth muscle fibers; this belongs to the alveolar duct rather than to the alveolus into which the duct opens. The alveolar ducts along their course, and particularly near their ends, may also open into rotundalike spaces which, in turn, open into individual alveoli. The rotundalike spaces in the spongework are termed *alveolar sacs*. Alveoli, then, are arranged along both the alveolar ducts themselves and around the rotundalike alveolar sacs.

As has been noted before, the elastic fibers of the spongework of the lung necessarily are stretched to enable a lung to fill the cavity in which it lies. Hence, when the pleural cavities are opened at autopsy the lungs collapse

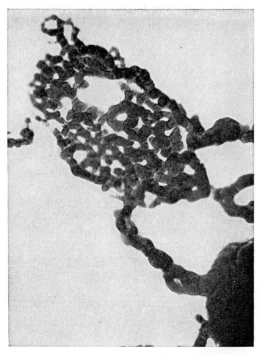

FIG. 442. High-power photomicrograph of a thick section of a lung, the blood vessels of which were injected with an opaque material. The figure shows the floor of an alveolus (an interalveolar partition in full face), and the injected capillaries may be seen to form an extensive and close mesh.

toward their roots. Sections cut from collapsed lungs do not give a representative picture of the structure of the respiratory spongework during life, for, when a lung collapses, the spaces in the spongework become smaller, and the partitions between the spaces become thicker. A better impression of the structure of the lung during life can be obtained from the study of sections cut from lungs that have been redistended to their original size immediately after death by injecting fixative through a cannula into a stem bronchus and subsequently tying off the bronchus so that the lung cannot collapse again.

Alveolar Walls or Septa vs. Interalveolar Walls or Septa. Most of the partitions seen in the spongework of the lung separate adjacent alveoli from one another. Some partitions, of course, separate the passageways of alveolar ducts from alveolar spaces that are just outside the duct but communicate with some other duct. In general, all of these partitions are called *alveolar septa* or *alveolar walls*. However, it should be understood clearly that the word alveolus has two meanings: it can be used to depict either *a little space* or *a little vessel* (structure). In the instance of the postnatal lung, the word is used to depict a space. The structure that is termed an alveolar wall contains many components and is actually an interalveolar wall or septum; it lies between two alveoli. In this way there is a distinction between bronchioles and alveoli. Bronchioles are structures with walls of their own; alveoli are spaces with walls between them, and the wall that lies between any two alveolar spaces is common to both. Accordingly, alveoli do not have walls of their own (except very thin epithelium), so the whole wall that lies between two alveoli should be termed an *interalveolar wall* or an *interalveolar septum*.

THE STRUCTURE OF INTERALVEOLAR WALLS OR SEPTA

The Use of Thick Sections. In thin sections of distended lungs, interalveolar partitions are always cut in cross or oblique sections (Fig. 444). The reason for this is that, in distended lungs, interalveolar partitions are as thin as the sections themselves, and, since they are never perfectly flat (as sections are), it is impossible for a whole alveolar partition to be present in a thin section so that its full face may be examined. To see an interalveolar partition in full face it is necessary to cut sections of lung that are about as thick as the diameter of alveoli. In such sections, sites may be found where the top of one alveolus has been sliced off, together with the bottom of the alveolus immediately below it. One may then look down into an alveolus as one looks into a cup to inspect its bottom (Fig. 441). In this instance the bottom of the cup is the interalveolar partition between the alveolus into which one is looking and the alveolus immediately below it.

The Capillaries of the Walls. It is not easy to identify the various cells and structures in interalveolar walls seen this way. Many nuclei are seen; the various cells that contain these will be described presently. The extent of the capillary network in an interalveolar septum can scarcely be realized unless thick sections of lungs, the blood vessels of which have been injected with opaque material, are studied.

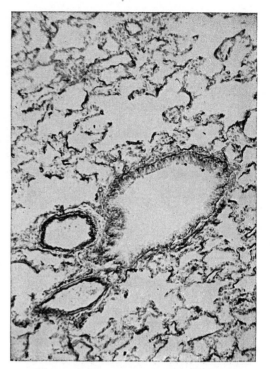

FIG. 443. Low-power photomicrograph of a section of rabbit lung stained with orcein to demonstrate elastic fibers. The elastic fibers appear as black lines and may be seen in the wall of the bronchiole, in the arteries, in the interalveolar partitions and along the alveolar ducts.

Interalveolar walls seen in full face in such preparations show the networks in the interalveolar walls to be of a very close mesh (Fig. 442).

Alveolar Pores. Some interalveolar partitions studied in full face in thick sections will be seen to be defective. The defects appear as little round or oval holes termed *alveolar pores* (Fig. 441). These have been studied extensively by Macklin. Where they are present they permit air to pass from one alveolus to another. Although some argue that pores are always the result of a previous disease process, they are so abundant in the interalveolar partitions of so many different kinds of animals that the view that considers them all to be pathologic defects seems unlikely.

How Interalveolar Walls Are Supported. The capillary networks of which interalveolar walls are chiefly composed have little tensile strength. If they were not supported in some

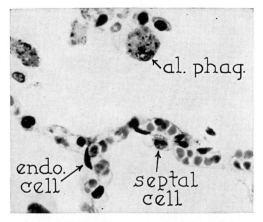

FIG. 444. High-power photomicrograph of a section of adult lung, showing an interalveolar partition cut in cross section. The capillaries of this lung were congested; hence, they are wider and contain more red blood cells than is normal. A septal cell and an alveolar phagocyte may be seen.

fashion, individual alveoli might become so overexpanded with air that the capillaries would be ruptured. However, such support as is provided for interalveolar walls cannot be too rigid, lest it interfere with their normal expansion. The matter seems to have been solved by interalveolar walls having two kinds of support, *basic* and *intimate*. The basic support consists of a skeleton of elastic fibers (Fig. 443). These are coarse and too infrequent to provide an intimate support for the many capillaries and cells in the walls; however, they do provide a backbone that would resist this overexpansion. In addition to the occasional fibers that course along in walls, there are, according to Short, elastic fibers around the free margins of alveoli (where they open into alveolar sacs or ducts), in the form of rings that encircle alveolar ducts.

As noted above, the occasional elastic fibers that run in interalveolar walls provide a backbone for them but no intimate support for the capillaries and the cells within the wall. Intimate support is provided for these by delicate fibrils of the reticular or the collagenic variety and by basement membranes, as will now be described.

New Concepts. Our concepts of the microscopic structure of interalveolar walls has changed considerably in the past few years; this is due to research along two different lines. First, studies with the E/M, particularly those of Low, have shown clearly that alveoli are lined with a continuous layer of epithelium which, except in sites where nuclei are present, is so thin that it would not be clearly visible in ordinary sections examined with the light microscope (Figs. 445 and 446). Secondly, the use of the P.A.S. technic has made it possible, as has been shown so clearly by Leblond and Bertalanffy and their associates, to demonstrate the existence and the distribution of the basement membranes that underlie the epithelium and cover the capillaries in interalveolar walls (Fig. 445). From the evidence gained from these two lines of investigation it has become apparent that air in alveoli is separated from blood in the capillaries by: (1) the cytoplasm of the epithelial cells that line alveoli; (2) the basement membrane of the epithelium, which in some sites blends with the third component; (3) the basement membrane that covers the endothelium of the capillaries; and (4) the cytoplasm of the endothelial cells of capillaries. In some sites there are tissue spaces that contain fine fibrils between 2 and 3 (Fig. 446).

Since the light microscope did not uniformly reveal a continuous lining of thin epithelium in alveolar walls, and since a proper demonstration of the basement membranes in the walls awaited the development of the P.A.S. technic, there was substantial, but by no means universal, opinion in the past to the effect that blood was separated from air in the lung only by the endothelium of the capillaries and perhaps by a little delicate connective tissue associated with the capillaries.

The Cells of Interalveolar Walls. The nuclei that are visible in alveolar walls are those of several types of cells. The largest number appear as flattened or bent ovoids with fairly condensed chromatin; these are the nuclei of the endothelial cells of the capillaries and the epithelial cells that line alveoli (Figs. 444, 445 and 446). The two kinds are similar in appearance, but the latter type can be distinguished from the former, according to Bertalanffy and Leblond, in P.A.S. preparations, because they are outside the basement membrane that underlies the epithelium (Fig. 445).

FIG. 445. Schematic drawing of a thin section of 2 alveoli. In order to illustrate the modern concept of lung structure, the alveolar walls, the lining epithelium and the basement membranes all have been represented as being thicker, in relation to the size of the alveolar spaces, than they are. (Drawing based on illustrations provided by F. Bertalanffy and C. P. Leblond)

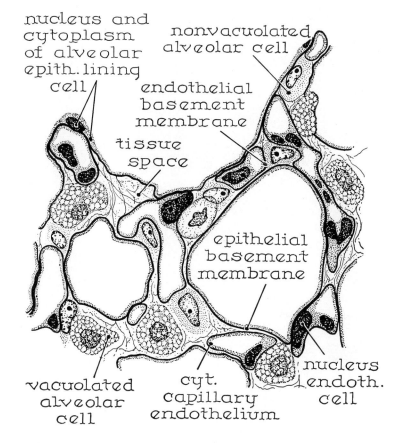

Alveolar (Septal) Cells. The second most common kind of nuclei (about 30%, according to Bertalanffy and Leblond) are those of *alveolar (septal)* cells. The nuclei of these are ovoid but are somewhat larger, and they do not have as condensed chromatin as those of the first type discussed. The cytoplasm may be vacuolated because it contains numerous lipoid droplets or it may be of an even texture; hence, two types of alveolar or septal cells are described, the vacuolated and the nonvacuolated varieties (Fig. 445). Transitions are also seen. Alveolar cells of either types may be in alveolar walls, along the sides of alveolar walls or free in the alveoli. Both kinds are phagocytic, and, in general, the alveolar cells behave very much as do the macrophages of other parts of the body. The evidence suggests that new ones are formed in and along alveolar walls by the mitosis of pre-existing alveolar cells. Bertalanffy and Leblond, using the colchicine technic, estimated that the entire stock of alveolar cells in the lung is replaced about

once a week. It has been suggested that alveolar cells may be concerned with maintaining the film of alveolar fluid that coats the inner surfaces of alveoli. Their obvious and pronounced function is that of serving as phagocytes so that any dust particles or other types of debris that gain entrance to alveolar spaces can be removed (Figs. 83 and 444). They are motile. Born in or along the sides of alveolar walls (those born in the walls would have to break through the epithelial basement membrane), they move up along the air passages to reach bronchioles where their further progress is aided by the cilia. Once alveolar cells become free of their attachments to alveolar walls they are generally termed *alveolar phagocytes* (Figs. 83 and 444). When lungs are congested with blood, because of an incompetent heart, blood often escapes into alveolar spaces where the alveolar phagocytes engulf the erythrocytes and form iron pigment from the hemoglobin they contain. The pigment-containing cells are commonly coughed up in

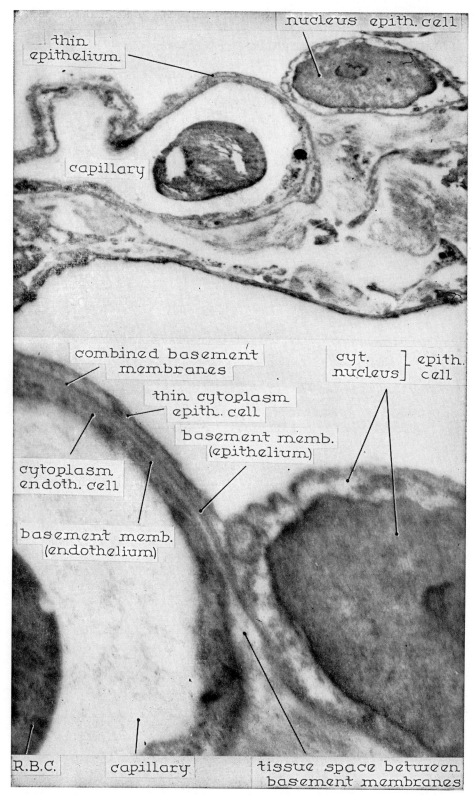

FIG. 446. Two electron micrographs (× 11,000, *top*; × 40,000, *bottom*) of the same area of a section of human lung. (Low, F. N.: Anat. Rec. *117*:241, with labeling added)

large numbers under these conditions, and they give positive histochemical tests for iron. Such cells are called *heart failure cells.*

The origin of the alveolar (septal) cells is not certain. There are two main views about the matter. According to one school of thought, they are descendants of the epithelial cells that grow into mesenchyme to outline the bronchial tree and the alveoli of the lung. According to this view, they are members of the same family of cells as those that are flattened and line the alveoli. According to the other school of thought, they are of mesenchymal origin— macrophages that arise from the mesenchymal component of developing lung. According to this latter view, they could have their numbers supplemented readily by monocytes coming to the lung by way of the blood stream.

A third type of nucleus seen in interalveolar walls is that of leukocytes that are in the blood in the capillaries. Occasional leukocytes escape into other parts of the wall under normal conditions. In infections of the lung, for example, in lobar pneumonia, alveolar spaces may be packed solidly with fibrin and neutrophils.

The Fine Structure of Interalveolar Walls. The nuclei of the epithelial lining cells are surrounded by a relatively narrow rim of cytoplasm (Fig. 446). From the nuclear region the cytoplasm spreads out as a thin sheet to form a cytoplasmic lining for the alveolar wall (Fig. 446, *middle left*). Low estimates that the thickness of this sheet is approximately 0.2 μ in the rabbit, the guinea pig, the dog and in man. In the rat it is only about 0.1 μ thick. In the mouse the sheet is thinner still. Karrer, in particular, has studied the endothelium with the E/M; in the mouse it averages about 0.15 μ in thickness, but in some sites it may become as thin as 0.01 μ. In Figure 446 (man) it is seen to be slightly thicker than the epithelium. The identification of the basement membranes of the epithelial and the endothelial cells in electron micrographs is somewhat difficult. They are only about 0.05 to 0.1 μ in thickness. According to Low, their electron density, when they are osmicated, is even, and their outlines are sharp (Fig. 446). Karrer describes the basement membranes of the lung as consisting of a rather homogeneous material of low electron density. A problem is created in interpreting what is seen in electron micrographs because at some sites the basement membrane of the epithelium and that of the endothelium approach one another and in all probability fuse to become a single homogeneous membrane (Fig. 446 combined basement membranes). However, at other sites, they diverge from one another to enclose tissue spaces (Fig. 446, tissue space between basement membranes). The tissue spaces contain fine fibrils of the collagenic or the reticular variety. If the tissue space labeled in Figure 446 is followed to the left it will be seen that it becomes so greatly thinned that the basement membrane of the epithelium is separated from that of the endothelium by a film of tissue that could only contain very fine fibrils. It could be argued that such thin films of tissue between basement membranes were actually parts of the basement membrane, but it seems preferable to consider them as parts of the fibrillar tissue that offers intimate support for the elements in alveolar walls, which becomes expanded in some sites and thinned in others and disappears altogether when the basement membranes of endothelium and epithelium come into direct contact (Fig. 446, combined basement membranes).

Karrer has studied the alveolar cells with the E/M and finds that one type has microvilli extending from its free surfaces.

THE DEVELOPMENT OF THE LUNGS

The lungs develop like exocrine glands. The outgrowth responsible for them arises from the epithelium of the anterior wall of the foregut. The epithelial outgrowth first assumes the form of a longitudinal bulge but this, before long, becomes pinched off from the foregut except at its cephalic end. The tube formed as a result of the pinching-off process is the forerunner of the larynx and the trachea. Its caudal end is closed, but cell proliferation at this site soon results in two hollow epithelial bulges forking out from it, one being directed toward the left, and the other to the right. These bulges are commonly termed the lung buds, but they are better termed the *primary bronchial buds* because they are the forerunners of the 2 primary bronchi.

The 2 primary bronchial buds, because of the continued proliferation of cells in their ends and walls, advance toward the sites at which lungs will develop. Bulges appear on these advancing tubes; these subsequently grow and elongate to give rise to the second-

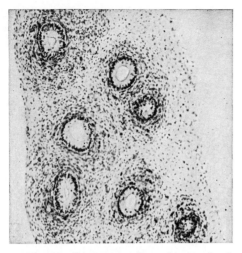

FIG. 447. Low-power photomicrograph of a section of the lung of a pig embryo in an early stage of development. Epithelial tubules (future bronchi) are growing and branching into the mesenchyme. (Ham, A. W., and Baldwin, K. W.: Anat. Rec. *81*:377)

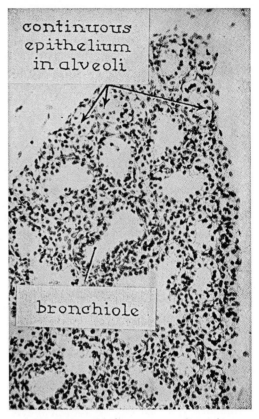

FIG. 448. Medium-power photomicrograph of a section of the lung of a pig embryo about halfway through prenatal development. Notice that the developing bronchioles have given rise to epithelial alveoli, which are structures comparable with the secretory alveoli or glands.

ary bronchi. These, in turn, usually by pairs of bulges which appear at their blind ends, continue to branch and grow to give rise to the smaller bronchi (Fig. 447). The branching then becomes more irregular but continues to give rise to the forerunners of bronchioles.

Although it simplifies matters to say that the growing, branching, hollow epithelial tree that develops originally from the epithelium of the foregut gives rise to the bronchi and the bronchioles of the lungs and that these are comparable with the interlobular and intralobular ducts of exocrine glands, this is not the whole truth, for the epithelial outgrowth gives rise to only the epithelial lining and the glands of the bronchi and the bronchioles. The connective tissue and the smooth muscle of the walls of the bronchi and the bronchioles, and the cartilages of the bronchi, develop from the mesenchyme that is invaded by the growing, branching, hollow epithelial tree. The mesenchyme, as it is invaded, becomes condensed around the epithelial tubes (Fig. 447) and there differentiates into the connective tissue constituents of their walls.

In the development of exocrine glands, secretory units sprout from the ends of the branching duct system. A comparable phenomenon occurs in the developing lung in the 5th

month of development. The epithelium of what at this time are the terminal branches of the bronchial tree extends out into the mesenchyme to form epithelial structures comparable with alveolar ducts and alveoli. The soft cellular mesenchyme around these hollow epithelial outgrowths does not immediately (although it may, much later in development) become condensed to make these outgrowths into bronchioles; hence, these outgrowths are comparable with the epithelial secretory units that develop from the terminal portions of the developing duct systems of exocrine glands (Fig. 448).

That the lung attains a stage of development, sometimes during the 5th month, when it is clearly glandlike, possessing a branching

FIG. 449. (*Top*) Low-power photomicrograph of a section of the lung of a pig about two thirds of the way through prenatal development. It is not gland-like, and the alveoli are angular. (*Center*) Photomicrograph of a section of the lung of a pig killed 3 hours after birth. The alveoli are larger. (*Bottom*) Photomicrograph of another area of a section of the lung of a pig killed 3 hours after birth. The alveoli here are greatly expanded. (Ham, A. W., and Baldwin, K. W.: Anat. Rec. *81*:377)

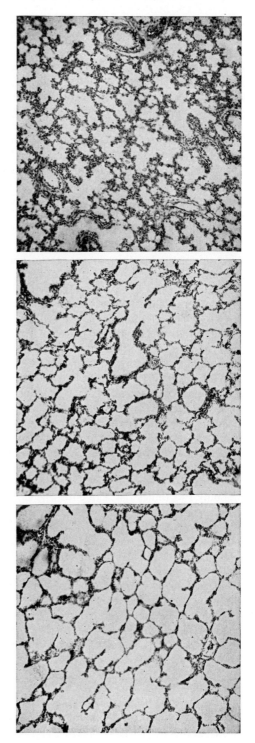

duct system (the bronchial tree), the terminal branches of which connect with epithelial structures that are the equivalent of secretory units (alveolar ducts and alveoli), is generally accepted (Fig. 448). However, there has been a difference of opinion as to whether the lung remains glandlike throughout the remainder of prenatal development. What might be termed the classic view on this matter holds that the developing lung retains its glandlike character until the time of birth; that is, until the time of birth, the alveoli of the fetal lung are *rounded* hollow epithelial structures, being made of cuboidal to columnar epithelial cells firmly attached to one another. According to this view, the glandlike nature of the lung disappears only when respiratory movements begin after birth. When the thorax is expanded by inspiratory movements, the air drawn into the alveoli greatly expands them. Their epithelial walls, according to this view, consequently become greatly stretched and thinned so that what was cuboidal to columnar epithelium before birth becomes a simple squamous type afterward. However, according to the classic view, the thin epithelial membrane that results from the stretching process is a continuous one and so provides a complete epithelial lining for alveolar walls.

However, many investigations of lung development made with the light microscope yielded results at variance with the classic view. Perhaps the first point of importance to discuss is whether or not the lung remains glandlike throughout development. If glandlike refers to the alveoli remaining rounded, like secretory units, until the time of birth, the lung does not remain glandlike, for in the later stages of development the alveoli become angular, taking on the appearance that they have in postnatal life (Fig. 449, *top*). This fact has medicolegal implications, as will be described soon.

Fetal Respiratory Movements and Their Possible Effects on Lung Structure. It is interesting to question whether or not the change in the appearance of the fetal lung that occurs about two thirds of the way through pregnancy, which is reflected in the alveoli becoming angular and, in general, assuming an appearance similar to the one that they reveal in the postnatal lung (Fig. 449), is due to, or is facilitated by, fetal respiratory movements. Before considering this question it must be admitted that there is some question as to whether respiratory movements of any consequence occur in the fetus. This matter has been investigated many ways, but particularly by injecting dyes and x-ray opaque substances into amniotic fluid and then ascertaining whether or not these subsequently are sucked into the lungs of the fetus concerned. Windle thinks that inspiratory movements of a magnitude necessary for this do not occur under normal conditions but only when asphyxia is brought about by the experimental procedure or by other means. However, Davis and Potter have provided additional evidence to the effect that inspiratory movements powerful enough to ensure a circulation of amniotic fluid through the developing lungs normally occur in fetal life.

It should be understood that the thoracic cage can become larger in prenatal or postnatal life only if something can enter it to let it enlarge. For all practical purposes only two things can enter the thoracic cage in postnatal life to permit it to enlarge with inspiratory movements—air and blood. In prenatal life the only two things that can enter the cage to let it expand with fetal inspiratory movements are amniotic fluid and blood. Therefore, it is obvious that inspiratory movements in fetal life would draw amniotic fluid into alveolar ducts and alveoli, and so would let them expand, and blood into the capillaries of interalveolar walls to let them expand. It seems not improbable that inspiratory movements in fetal life assist in opening up alveoli so that they become angular rather than round, and that the movements also play a part in filling and expanding the capillary bed of the lungs, which may stimulate its growth, for it develops very rapidly in the interalveolar walls as the lung changes its character.

According to the more modern concept of the development of the lung, birth is not such an important milestone as it is according to the classic view. According to the newer view, the developing lung ceases to be glandlike, not at birth, but approximately two thirds of the way through fetal life (Fig. 449, *top*). At this time it goes through most of the preparations for birth so that a baby born prematurely has a chance of living.

A fetus of 7 months is generally said to be *viable*; that is, it is capable of living by means of breathing air if it should be born. The great development of the capillary beds of the interalveolar walls that begins around two thirds of the way through fetal life is an obvious factor in permitting the fetus to attain this state.

Some Medicolegal Aspects. It has been observed already that it is sometimes of great importance to know whether a baby has breathed air after it was born, for it then would be considered as having been born alive. If a newborn baby has breathed air and subsequently dies, its lungs, when removed at autopsy, will not sink if they are placed in a pan of water, because the air they contain makes them lighter than water. If a baby has not breathed air, its lungs will sink. This test is probably much more reliable than that afforded by microscopic examination. There has been much confusion about this because certain of those who subscribe to the classic view of the development of the lung may argue that a departure from the glandlike appearance is an indication that air has been breathed. Certainly, if sections of a fetal lung show it to be glandlike throughout, it can be assumed with much justification that the fetus concerned never breathed air. But, if a lung is not glandlike but instead, opened-up, as in Figure 499, *top*, it cannot be assumed that the fetus concerned has breathed air because such an appearance can be caused presumably by the fetus "breathing" amniotic fluid in fetal life. The medicolegal significance of interpretations of sections of lungs of the newborn with reference to whether the infants concerned breathed air or not has been thoroughly investigated and discussed by Shapiro in the light of the newer knowledge of lung development.

Is There Continuous or Discontinuous Epithelium in the Fetal Lung? Many of the studies made with the light microscope over the past 2 decades provided evidence for considering that the epithelial lining of the alveolar ducts and the alveoli of the fetal lung becomes discontinuous at about the time when the alveoli become angular and the capillary beds in interalveolar walls develop greatly (for references on this view see Stewart, Palmer, Barnard and Day, Clements, Ham and Baldwin and Loosli). The more or less simultaneous separation of the epithelial lining cells and the growth of capillaries were visualized by the adherents of this view as resulting in the capillaries bulging nakedly into the air spaces; indeed, the appearances seen with the light microscope suggest that this actually occurs (Fig. 450, *cap.*). Since Low has shown so convincingly that the alveoli of the postnatal lung are lined with a continuous epithelium membrane, too thin to be resolved properly with the light microscope, the question has arisen as to whether or not the apparently naked capillaries that bulge from interalveolar walls in fetal life are always covered with attenuated epithelium too thin to be observed with the light microscope. It is obvious that E/M studies of developing lungs will be required to settle this point. In the meantime, two views could be entertained: (1) that when the capillaries bulge from the wall they are at first naked and subsequently become covered as sheets of epithelial cytoplasm glide over them, or (2) that when they bulge from the walls they push a thin epithelial membrane ahead of them.

It should be noted here that Bensley and Groff, several years ago, used special technics for fresh preparations of developing lung tissue and found evidence indicating that the epithelium remained continuous and became thinned. Recently, Krahl has made further investigations with the light microscope and finds evidence that the epithelium in the mouse remains continuous and becomes thinned. Moreover, Krahl has extensively reviewed evidence from many fields and considers that the lining epithelium remains continuous throughout development and that it becomes greatly thinned as alveoli expand. Krahl also points out the importance of proper fixation for lung studies, and he shows that separation of epithelial cells in fetal lungs can be caused by improper fixation.

Changes at Birth. According to the newer view of the development of the lung, it is assumed that since the future air spaces of the fetal lung are filled with fluid at the time of

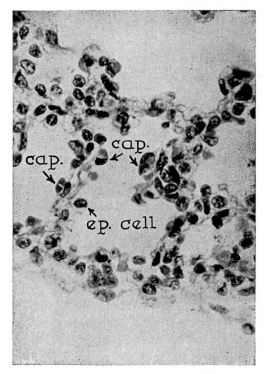

Fig. 450. High-power photomicrograph of a section of the lung of a pig about two thirds of the way through prenatal development. Observe that capillaries are bulging through the separating epithelial cells of the alveoli to abut directly on the future air spaces.

birth, these spaces must be expanded further if air is to be taken into the lungs after birth. Their greater expansion after birth (Fig. 449, *center, bottom*) is brought about by the greatly intensified respiratory movements that occur when a baby is born. It is of interest that these inspiratory movements, which are intensified over those that occur in intrauterine existence, not only draw air into the lungs but also more blood. This may explain why a newborn baby will increase its weight by several ounces if the umbilical cord is not cut too soon after a baby is born. Every effort is made by the doctor who delivers a baby to remove all the fluid that he can from the upper respiratory tract and so assist its displacement by air. However, it is questionable if all the fluid in the air spaces of the lung is drained away through the upper respiratory tract after birth; perhaps much of it is absorbed.

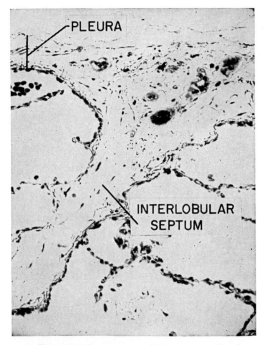

PLEURA

INTERLOBULAR
SEPTUM

Fig. 451. Low-power photomicrograph of a section of the human adult lung showing the pleura at the top and the interlobular septum extending down from the pleura into the substance of the lung.

The Respiratory Portion of the Lung and the Problem of Interstitial Emphysema.

Occasionally, when an individual breaks a rib and the broken end of the rib punctures lung tissue, air from the lung infiltrates the injured tissue of the chest wall. As the process continues, bubbles of air may continue to permeate the injured tissues and even spread from the site of injury throughout the body; indeed, there have been instances where incisions have had to be made to let the accumulating air out of a part of the body far removed from the lungs. The ease with which bubbles of air that gain entrance to tissue can spread was taken advantage of in an old form of torture. A small slit was cut in the skin of the victim and a straw inserted through it into the loose areolar tissue. The torturer then would blow through the straw, and if he blew long enough the whole body of the victim would become more or less inflated. In modern times, compressed air, delivered through a needle into the subcutaneous tissues of animals

that are to be skinned, is sometimes used to facilitate the process. All in all, air that gains entrance to tissue tends to spread through it for considerable distances. The condition is known as *interstitial* or *surgical emphysema* (*physema* = a blowing).

It might be thought that air would gain entrance into the substance of interalveolar walls under many circumstances because the attenuated epithelium that lines these walls would not be a very substantial barrier. Air probably does gain entrance to the thicker alveolar walls, and the bubbles that form in the thicker walls as a result of this probably become lined with epithelium to become new alveoli. It might be asked why air that does gain entrance to interalveolar walls does not spread into other parts of the body or enter lymphatics and gain entrance to the circulatory system where it could cause air embolism. The reason it does not is (1) there are no lymphatics in interalveolar walls, and (2) air that gains entrance to any interalveolar wall cannot make its way out of the lung because air in the respiratory portion of the lung is confined there by a complete limiting membrane of dense connective tissue. These confining membranes of dense connective tissue develop, as was pointed out by the author and Baldwin, from the noncellular mesenchyme of the fetal lung. They consist of the pleura and the interlobular septa (Fig. 451) and the outer wrappings of the branches of the bronchial tree and the branches of the veins and the arteries that enter lobules. For air to escape from the respiratory portion of the lung into the root of the lung would require its infiltrating through this dense membrane that is firmly wrapped around the vessels at the root of the lung.

Growth. A way that new alveoli could form in postnatal life has been described in the preceding paragraph. In the later stages of prenatal life, as well as in the earlier stages of postnatal life, new generations of bronchioles, as well as new alveoli, develop in the lung. It is believed that new bronchioles develop as a result of the epithelium of respiratory bronchioles growing down alveolar ducts, after which the mesenchymal-derived connective tissue around the duct becomes increased and differentiates into the other constituents of a bronchiolar wall. It is believed that the fact that alveoli commonly open from the sides of respiratory bronchioles is evidence that the bronchiole concerned was once an alveolar duct which became converted into a respiratory bronchiole.

BLOOD SUPPLY OF THE LUNG

Blood from the right ventricle is delivered, by the pulmonary artery and its branches, to the capillary beds of the respiratory tissue of the lung to be oxygenated there. Oxygenated blood is collected from the capillary beds of the lung by the branches of the pulmonary vein and delivered to the left atrium of the heart. It is to be kept in mind that, in the instance of the pulmonary circulation, the arteries carry what is ordinarily called venous blood, and the veins, arterial.

The pulmonary artery to each lung enters it at its root and within the lung it branches along with the bronchial tree so that each branch of the bronchial tree is accompanied by a branch of the pulmonary artery. The small branches that reach the respiratory bronchioles break up into terminal branches which deliver blood into the capillary beds of the alveolar ducts, the alveolar sacs and the alveoli (Fig. 438, *left*).

Blood from the capillary beds of the respiratory tissue of the lungs is collected by the smallest branches of the pulmonary vein. These begin within the substance of lobules and in this region are supported by thin connective tissue sheaths. Supported in this fashion, they travel to, and enter, interlobular septa, where they empty into interlobular veins (Fig. 438, *left*). These in turn are conducted by the septa to the site where the apices of the lobules concerned meet. Here the veins come into close association with branches of the bronchial tree. From this point to the root of the lung, the veins follow the bronchi. In other words, except within lobules, the branches of the pulmonary artery and the pulmonary vein follow the branches of the bronchial tree, but within lobules, only the arteries follow the bronchioles.

Oxygenated blood is supplied to parts of the lung by the bronchial arteries. These also travel in close association with the bronchial tree and supply the capillary beds of its walls. They also supply the lymph nodes that are scattered along the bronchial tree. Moreover,

branches of the bronchial arteries travel out along the interlobular septa and supply oxygenated blood to the capillaries of the visceral pleura.

LYMPHATICS OF THE LUNG

General principles are easier to remember than details. It could be said that there is a rough general principle about the distribution of lymphatics in the lung: they are confined to the relatively dense connective tissue structures that prevent the spread of any air leakage that might occur into the delicate walls of alveoli. Hence, they are present in the visceral pleura, in the interlobular septa and in the dense connective tissue wrappings of the bronchioles, the bronchi, the arteries and the veins (Fig. 438, *right*). They are not present in the interalveolar partitions. However, Miller has described lymphatics in the tissue bordering the alveolar ducts. Lymphatic capillaries in alveolar walls might very well constitute a hazard, as has been explained already.

It is customary to describe the lung as having a superficial and a deep set of lymphatics. The superficial ones are contained in the visceral pleura (Fig. 438, *bottom*). In city dwellers these are usually blackened by carbon particles which have become incorporated into their walls. The larger ones follow the lines where interlobular septa join the pleura; hence, the bases of those lobules which are projected onto the pleura are usually outlined by dark lines. Smaller lymphatics in the pleura form a pattern of closer mesh than those which surround the bases of lobules. The pleural lymphatics join up with one another to form vessels that are conducted by the pleura to reach and empty into the lymph nodes at the hilus of the lung.

The deep set consists of 3 groups: (1) those in the outer layers of the walls of bronchioles and bronchi (Fig. 438); (2) those that accompany the branches of the pulmonary artery (Fig. 438)—these anastomose with those in the branches of the bronchial tree; and (3) those that run in the interlobular septa, particularly in association with the interlobular veins (Figs. 438, *right*). All 3 groups drain toward lymph nodes at the hilus of the lung.

The lymphatics of the interlobular septa (which belong to the deep set) communicate with those of the pleura (which belong to the superficial set) at sites where interlobular septa join the visceral pleura (Fig. 438, *lower right corner*). It has been taught for years, largely because of Miller's influence, that the lymphatics of the interlobular septa have valves that are disposed close to the pleura (Fig. 438, *lower right corner*) and that these valves prevent lymph from the pleural lymphatics from draining into the lymphatics of the septa. In other words, it has been generally conceded that although lymph could pass from the lymphatics of the interlobular septa outwardly into the pleural lymphatics, because of the direction of the valves it could not pass the other way, hence that lymph in the pleural lymphatics, to reach the hilus of the lung, would have to pass by way of the pleural lymphatics over the whole surface of a lobe to reach the hilus. Recently, however, Simer has shown that this older view is fallacious, and that the valves that were generally believed to prevent flow from the pleural lymphatics into the lymphatics of the interlobular septa (Fig. 438, *lower right corner*) are: (1) not always present, (2) if present, often poorly developed, and (3) do not always point toward the pleura. Simer showed that Inda ink injected into the pleural lymphatics does not usually pursue a course around the periphery of the lobe in order to reach the hilus, but instead passes into the lymphatics of the interlobular septa and from there into the lymphatic vessels associated with the bronchial tree and its vessels and so it takes a direct rather than a roundabout course to the hilus of the lung.

EFFECTS OF RESPIRATORY MOVEMENTS ON LUNG STRUCTURE

The descent and the expansion of the lungs on inspiration require that the bronchial tree be elastic. Macklin has shown that bronchi become longer and wider on inspiration. The root of the lung also descends on inspiration. Recoil from these movements is accomplished chiefly by the already described elastic tissue of the tracheobronchial tree. Macklin's papers should be consulted for details of this and the recoil mechanism.

It is probable that the expansion of the respiratory tissue itself, that occurs on inspira-

tion, is due more to the elongation and the dilatation of alveolar ducts than it is to expansion of alveoli.

INNERVATION OF THE SMOOTH MUSCLE OF THE BRONCHI AND THE BRONCHIOLES

Fibers from both divisions of the autonomic nervous system pass to the bronchial tree. The parasympathetic supply is brought by branches of the vagus nerve. Stimulation of the efferent fibers causes the bronchiolar musculature to contract. Stimulation of the fibers of sympathetic nerves causes the bronchiolar musculature to relax. In the condition known as asthma, the smooth muscle of the smaller bronchioles contracts, and the mucous membrane of the affected tubes swells. This narrows the passages by which air can enter or leave alveolar ducts and makes breathing exceedingly difficult. Adrenalin, or a similarly acting substance, is often given to relax the bronchiolar musculature and so widen the lumens of the bronchioles of an individual suffering an attack. It is of interest that it is more difficult for an individual with asthma to expel air from his lungs than it is to draw it in; this is because inspiratory movements tend to expand such tubes as lie within lobules and so enlarge their lumens, while powerful expiratory movements, such as occur in asthma, tend, if air cannot be forced out freely through the bronchial tree, to compress such tubes as lie within lobules and so make their lumens still narrower.

REFERENCES

GENERAL REFERENCES ON THE LUNG

Engel, S.: The Child's Lung, London, Arnold, 1947.

Krahl, V. E.: Microscopic anatomy of the lungs, Am. Rev. Respir. Dis. *80*:24, 1959.

Miller, W. S.: The Lung, Springfield, Ill., Thomas, 1937.

SPECIAL REFERENCES ON THE UPPER RESPIRATORY TRACT AND THE BRONCHIAL TREE

Arey, L. B.: On the development, morphology and interpretation of a system of cryptanalogues in the pharyngeal tonsil, Am. J. Anat. *80*:203, 1947.

Burnham, H. H.: An anatomical investigation of blood vessels of the lateral nasal wall and their relation to turbinates and sinuses, J. Laryng. & Otol. *50*:569, 1935.

Jackson, C., and Jackson, C. L.: Diseases and Injuries of the Larynx, ed. 2, New York, Macmillan, 1942.

Karrer, H. E.: The fine structure of connective tissue in the tunica propria of bronchioles, J. Ultrastr. Res. *2*:96, 1958.

Lucas, A. M.: The nasal cavity and direction of fluid by ciliary movement in Macacus rhesus (Desm.), Am. J. Anat. *50*:141, 1932.

Mackenzie, J. N.: The physiological and pathological relations between the nose and the sexual apparatus of man, Johns Hopkins Hosp. Bull. *9*:10, 1898.

Macklin, C. C.: Bronchial length changes and other movements, Tubercle *14*:16 & 69, 1932.

———: The dynamic bronchial tree, Am. Rev. Tuberc. *25*:363, 1932.

———: The mechanics and dynamics of the human lungs and bronchi, M. Rec. *143*:89, 1936.

———: The musculature of the bronchi and lungs, Physiol. Rev. *9*:1, 1929.

Rhodin, J., and Dalhamn, T.: Electron microscopy of the tracheal ciliated mucosa in rat, Ztschr. Zellforsch. *44*:345, 1956.

Schaeffer, J. P.: The mucous membrane of the nasal cavity and the paranasal sinuses *in* Cowdry's Special Cytology, ed. 2, p. 105, New York, Hoeber, 1932.

SPECIAL REFERENCES ON THE MICROSCOPIC STRUCTURE OF THE RESPIRATORY PORTION OF THE LUNG, INCLUDING REFERENCES ON FINE STRUCTURE

Bensley, R. D., and Bensley, S. H.: Studies of the lining of the pulmonary alveolus of normal lungs of adult animals, Anat. Rec. *64*:41, 1935.

Bertalanffy, F. D., Glegg, R. E., and Eidinger, D.: Chemical confirmation of the abundance of reticulin in the lung, Canad. M. A. J. *70*:196 & 220, 1954.

Bertalanffy, F. D., and Leblond, C. P.: The continuous renewal of the two types of alveolar cells in the lung of the rat, Anat. Rec. *115*:515, 1953.

———: Structure of respiratory tissue, Lancet *2*:1365, 1955.

Bremer, J. L.: Evidence of an epithelial lining in the labyrinth of the avian lung, Anat. Rec. *73*:497, 1939.

Brettschneider, H.: Electron mikroskopische Untersuchungen an der Nasenschleimhaut, Anat. Anz. *105*:194, 1958.

Hartroft, W. S., and Macklin, C. C.: The size of the human lung alveoli expressed as diameters of selected alveolar outlines as seen in specially prepared 25 micron microsections, Tr. Roy. Soc. Canada, Sec. V (Biol. Sc.) *38*:63, 1944.

Hesse, F. E., and Loosli, C. G.: The lining of the alveoli in mice, rats, dogs and frogs following acute pulmonary edema produced by antu poisoning, Anat. Rec. *105*:299, 1949.

Josselyn, L. E.: The nature of the pulmonary alveolar lining, Anat. Rec. *62*:147, 1935.

Karrer, H. E.: The ultrastructure of mouse lung, J. Biophys. & Biochem. Cytol. *2*:241, 1956.

———: The ultrastructure of mouse lung, J. Biophys. & Biochem. Cytol. (Supp.) *2*:287, 1956.

———: The ultrastructure of mouse lung: the alveolar macrophage, J. Biophys. & Biochem. Cytol. *4*:693, 1958.

———: The experimental production of pulmonary emphysema, Am. Rev. Respir. Dis. *80*: 158, 1959.

Krahl, V. E.: Current concept of the finer structure of the lung, A.M.A. Arch. Int. Med. *96*: 342, 1955.

———: The respiratory portions of the lung, Bull. School Med. Univ. Maryland *40*:101, 1955.

Leblond, C. P., and Bertalanffy, F. D.: Reticulin membranes of the framework of the alveolar lung, tissue in the albino rat, Canad. M. A. J. *65*:263, 1951.

Loosli, C. G.: The rabbit's lung after phrenectomy and pneumothorax, Anat. Rec. *62*:381, 1935.

———: The structure of the respiratory portion of the mammalian lung with notes on the lining of the frog lung, Am. J. Anat. *62*:375, 1938.

Loosli, C., Adams, W. E., and Thornton, T. M., Jr.: The histology of the dog's lung following an experimental collapse with special reference to the nature of the alveolar lining, Anat. Rec. *105*:697, 1949.

Low, F. N.: Electron microscopy of the rat lung, Anat. Rec. *113*:437, 1952.

———: The electron microscopy of sectioned lung tissue after varied duration of fixation in buffered osmium tetroxide, Anat. Rec. *120*: 827, 1954.

———: The pulmonary alveolar epithelium of laboratory mammals and man, Anat. Rec. *117*: 241, 1953.

Low, F. N., and Sampaio, M. M.: The pulmonary alveolar epithelium as an entodermal derivative, Anat. Rec. *127*:51, 1957.

Macklin, C. C.: Pulmonic alveolar epithelium; report of a round table conference, J. Thoracic Surg. *6*:82, 1936.

Miller, W. S.: The epithelium of the lower respiratory tract *in* Cowdry's Special Cytology, ed. 2, p. 131, New York, Hoeber, 1932.

Ogawa, C.: The finer ramifications of the human lung, Am. J. Anat. *27*:333, 1920.

Rose, S. B.: The finer structure of the lung, Arch. Path. *6*:36, 1928.

Ross, I. S.: Pulmonary epithelium and proliferative reactions in the lungs; a study of the cellular response in lungs after intratracheal injections of toxic and nontoxic foreign substances, Arch. Path. *27*:478, 1939.

Swigart, R. H., and Kane, D. J.: Electron microscopic observations of pulmonary alveoli, Anat. Rec. *112*:93, 1952.

Woodside, G. L., and Dalton, A. J.: The ultrastructure of lung tissue from newborn and embryo mice, J. Ultrastr. Res. *2*:28, 1958.

SPECIAL REFERENCES ON THE DEVELOPMENT AND GROWTH OF THE LUNG

Barnard, W. G., and Day, T. D.: The development of the terminal air passages of the human lung, J. Path. & Bact. *45*:67, 1937.

Bensley, S. H., and Groff, M. B.: Changes in the alveolar epithelium of the rat at birth, Anat. Rec. *64*:27, 1935.

Clements, L. P.: Embryonic development of the respiratory portion of the pig's lung, Anat. Rec. *70*:575, 1938.

Cooper, E. R. A.: A histological investigation of the development and structure of the human lung, J. Path. & Bact. *47*:105, 1938.

Flint, J. M.: The development of the lungs, Am. J. Anat. *6*:1, 1906.

Ham, A. W., and Baldwin, K. W.: A histological study of the development of the lung with particular reference to the nature of the alveoli, Anat. Rec. *81*:363, 1941.

Krahl, V. E.: The respiratory portions of the lung, Bull. School Med. Univ. Maryland *40*: 101, 1955.

Loosli, C. G., and Potter, E. L.: Pre- and postnatal development of the respiratory portion of the human lung, Am. Rev. Respir. Dis. *80*:5, 1959.

Palmer, D. M.: Early developmental stages of the human lung, Ohio J. Sc. *36*:69, 1936.

———: The lung of a human foetus of 170 mm. C. R. length, Am. J. Anat. *58*:59, 1936.

Shapiro, H. A.: The limited value of microscopy of lung tissue in the diagnosis of live and stillbirth, Clin. Proc. *6*:149, 1947.

Short, R. H. D.: Alveolar epithelium in relation to growth of the lung, Phil. Tr. Roy. Soc. London *235*:35, 1950.

Stewart, F. W.: An histogenic study of the respiratory epithelium, Anat. Rec. *25*:181, 1923.

Willson, H. G.: Postnatal development of the lung, Am. J. Anat. *41*:97, 1928.

SPECIAL REFERENCES ON FETAL RESPIRATORY MOVEMENT AND FETAL CIRCULATION

Barcroft, J.: Fetal circulation and respiration, Physiol. Rev. *16*:103, 1936.

Davis, M. E., and Potter, E. L.: Intrauterine respiration of the human fetus, J.A.M.A. *131*: 1194, 1946.

Potter, E. L., and Bohlender, G. P.: Intrauterine respiration in relation to development of the fetal lung, Am. J. Obst. & Gynec. *42*:14, 1941.

Reynolds, S. R. M.: The fetal and neonatal pulmonary vasculature in the guinea pig in relation to hemodynamic changes at birth, Am. J. Anat. *98*:97, 1956.

Windle, W. F.: Physiology of the Fetus, Philadelphia, Saunders, 1940.

SPECIAL REFERENCES ON ALVEOLAR PORES

Loosli, C. G.: Interalveolar communications in normal and in pathologic mammalian lungs, Arch. Path. *24*:743, 1937.

Macklin, C. C.: Alveolar pores and their significance in the human lung, Arch. Path. *21*:202, 1936.

———: Pulmonic alveolar vents, J. Anat. *69*: 188, 1935.

———: Pulmonic interlobular air passages, Tr. Roy. Soc. Canada, Sec. V (Biol. Sc.) *28*:37, 1934.

SPECIAL REFERENCES ON ALVEOLAR (SEPTAL) CELLS AND ALVEOLAR PHAGOCYTES

Bertalanffy, F. D., and Leblond, C. P.: The continuous renewal of the two types of alveolar cells in the lung of the rat, Anat. Rec. *115*: 515, 1953.

Bremer, J. L.: Postnatal development of alveoli in mammalian lungs in relation to the problem of the alveolar phagocyte, Contrib. Embryol. *25*:83, 1935.

Clements, L. P.: On the origin and relations of the pulmonary macrophages, Anat. Rec. *78*: 429, 1940.

Macklin, C. C.: Residual epithelial cells on the pulmonary alveolar walls of mammals, Tr. Roy. Soc. Canada, Sec. V (Biol. Sc.) *40*:93, 1946.

Sampaio, M. M.: The use of thorotrast for the electron microscopic study of phagocytosis, Anat. Rec. *124*:501, 1956.

SPECIAL REFERENCES ON SURGICAL EMPHYSEMA AND THE LUNGS

Macklin, C. C.: The pattern of interstitial emphysema induced in the excised lung of the calf by overinflation, Tr. Roy. Soc. Canada, Sec. V *34*:69, 1940.

———: Pneumothorax with massive collapse from experimental overinflation of the lung substance, Canad. M. A. J. *36*:414, 1937.

———: Spontaneous mediastinal emphysema; a review and comment, M. Rec. *150*:5, 1939.

Macklin, C. C., and Macklin, M. T.: Pulmonic interstitial emphysema and its sequelae: an anatomical interpretation *in* Essays in Biology in Honor of Herbert M. Evans, Berkeley, Univ. California Press, 1943.

SPECIAL REFERENCES ON THE LYMPHATICS AND BLOOD VESSELS OF THE LUNG AND LUNG FLUID

Macklin, C. C.: Lung fluid, alveolar dust drift, and initial lesions of disease in the lungs, Canad. M. A. J. *72*:664, 1955.

———: Pulmonary sumps, dust accumulations, alveolar fluid and lymph vessels, Acta. anat. *23*:1, 1955.

———: Terminal pulmonary venules in mammalian lungs, Tr. Roy. Soc. Canada, Sec. V *39*: 105, 1945.

Miller, W. S.: The lymphatics and the lymph flow in the human lung, Am. Rev. Tuberc. *3*:193, 1919.

Simer, P. H.: Drainage of pleural lymphatics, Anat. Rec. *113*:269, 1952.

Tobin, C. E.: Lymphatics of the pulmonary alveoli, Anat. Rec. *120*:625, 1954.

(*See also* Flint, J. M., p. 690)

Chapter 25

The Urinary System

SOME GENERAL CONSIDERATIONS

The combustion of coal results both in the production of energy and the formation of waste products. Some of the latter are gaseous and go up the chimney, but some are not so easily disposed of and remain in a furnace as ashes. Likewise, the metabolism of food by the cells of the body produces not only energy but also many waste products. These substances seep from cells through tissue fluid and into the blood stream. From there an important waste product, carbon dioxide, goes up the chimney, as it were, by being eliminated from the lungs. Some of the others, particularly those that result from the metabolism of proteins, are not disposed of so easily; indeed, to eliminate these the body is equipped with two similar and specially constructed organs of substantial size—the kidneys—through which more than one fifth of the total blood of the body circulates every minute.

In the kidneys, waste products are eliminated continuously from blood and are concentrated in a fluid called *urine,* which is carried away from each kidney by a tube called a *ureter.* The ureter from each kidney leads to the *urinary bladder;* here urine can accumulate so as to be evacuated from the body periodically and at will through another, and single, tube, the *urethra.* The two kidneys, the two ureters, the urinary bladder and the urethra comprise the *urinary system.*

However, it should be emphasized that the kidneys perform other functions of very great importance in addition to that of ridding the body of the waste products of metabolism. For example, they can vary the amount of water that is lost from the body in urine. Hence, the kidneys play a very important part in regulating the *fluid balance* of the body. Likewise, the kidneys can vary the amounts and the kinds of electrolytes that are eliminated from the body in urine; thus they assist in maintaining a proper *salt balance* in blood and tissue fluid. The kidneys, in addition to eliminating waste products, act in many ways to maintain a fluid environment in the body which is suitable for the life of body cells. In maintaining this environment it should be understood that the kidneys act not only to *eliminate* waste and superfluous materials from the blood stream but also to *conserve* fluid and/or dissolved materials that are needed to maintain a proper state of affairs in the blood stream.

It should be obvious from the foregoing that kidney function is indispensable. However, the fact that over a fifth of the total blood of the body circulates through the kidneys every minute exposes them widely to injury should poisons or toxins be present in the blood. Fortunately, these organs possess a considerable measure of reserve so that a certain amount of impairment of function can be tolerated by the body. Since the kidneys perform so many different functions, kidney disease may be reflected by a lessened ability to perform any of their several functions as well as usual. Therefore, its diagnosis may require considerable study, and its proper management must be based on a sound knowledge of the microscopic structure of these organs and how their different parts perform their various functions in health and disease.

THE BASIC MECHANISMS OF EXCRETORY TUBULES

Before attempting to learn the microscopic structure of the kidney, the student will find it helpful to know something about the simpler excretory organs of certain lower animals.

In simpler organisms, in which blood circulatory systems are not highly developed, tissue fluid is the dominant fluid. In it the waste products of metabolism tend to accumulate, and from it they must be excreted. A relatively simple mechanism for accomplishing this effect is present in the earthworm. Its segments are provided with tubules, both ends of which are open. One end of each tubule opens into the interior of the worm and the other onto its exterior. Tissue fluid enters the open internal end of each tubule and

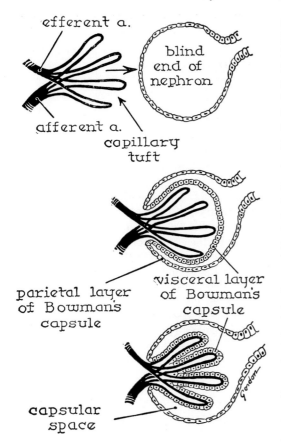

efferent a.

blind
end of
nephron

afferent a.

capillary
tuft

parietal layer
of Bowman's
capsule

visceral layer
of Bowman's
capsule

capsular
space

FIG. 452. Diagrams to show how capillary loops between afferent and efferent vessels are invaginated into the blind end of the excretory tubule. The visceral layer of Bowman's capsule at first covers the group of capillary loops as a whole; later it covers each loop (*lower picture*) and finally it almost completely surrounds the outgoing and the incoming arms of each loop (not shown here).

passes slowly along it to be eliminated at the exterior of the worm.

However, the tubules are not short and straight but long and coiled. Therefore, it takes some time for tissue fluid to pass along them. This provides an opportunity for the tissue fluid to be altered as it passes along the tubule by the epithelial cells lining the tubule either (1) *absorbing* certain valuable constituents of the fluid back into the organism or (2) *excreting* further things into the fluid in the tubule. It might be anticipated, then, that the fluid that finally emerges from the tubule onto the surface of the organism (and this, for all practical purposes, is urine) contains fewer valuable constituents than the tissue fluid that enters the tubule and also that it contains waste products in greater concentration. We shall see that in man, as in the earthworm, urine is *tissue fluid* that has been *modified* in the above-described fashion by passing along a tubule.

Evolution of the Glomerulus. As organisms became more complex the blood circulatory system became of increasing importance in distributing oxygen and food to cells in different parts of the body and in carrying away their waste products. This required some mechanism by which waste products could be removed from the blood more or less continuously. To accomplish this effect the excretory tubule was retained, but at one point along its course a cluster of thin-walled blood vessels was brought close to its wall, and the epithelial wall of the tubule at that site was bulged out to surround, more or less, the cluster of blood vessels. Under these circumstances, tissue fluid that is exuded by the blood vessels in the cluster has only to pass through the thinned wall of the tubule that bulges around the vessels to enter the lumen of the tubule. A little cluster of blood vessels of this sort is called a *glomerulus* (*glomus* = a skein), and the tissue fluid they exude into the tubule is called *glomerular filtrate*. Glomeruli greatly increase the amount of tissue fluid that can be delivered into excretory tubules.

THE NEPHRONS OF HIGHER ANIMALS AND HOW THEY FUNCTION

The arrangement of glomeruli being disposed along the sides of tubules was retained in only a few species. As evolution proceeded the innermost end of the tubule became closed; a glomerulus of capillaries was invaginated into it at this site (Fig. 452). The epithelial cells of the tubules at their blind ends, where the glomeruli of capillaries are invaginated, are very thin, so that at this site the lumen of a capillary is separated from the lumen of the excretory tubule by only two layers of living cells: the endothelium of the capillary wall and the thin squamous epithelium of the wall of the tubule (Fig. 452). An excretory tubule complete with a glomerulus invaginated into its blind end is termed a *nephron,* and there are over a million of these in each kidney of man.

Tissue fluid is formed only at the arterial ends of most capillaries in the body and resorbed at their venous ends (Fig. 92). The reasons for this are fully explained in Chapter 6. If the drainage of capillaries is impeded, as occurs, for example, in venous obstruction, tissue fluid is formed along the whole length of the capillary (Fig. 94). In most places in the body, extra tissue fluid produced this way results in edema. Arrangements are made in glomeruli so that the capillaries of glomeruli normally operate under conditions comparable with a certain amount of venous obstruction; hence, they produce tissue fluid along their whole lengths. This, of course, does not cause edema, because the tissue fluid, instead of accumulating in tissue spaces, as it would anywhere else in the body, enters the lumens of nephrons as glomerular filtrate.

The arrangement made in a glomerulus, so that its capillaries produce tissue fluid along their whole lengths, is that of having them drain, not into a wide unobstructed venule but into an arteriole. Since glomerular capillaries are supplied by an arteriole and also drained by an arteriole they represent, as it were, a tuft of capillaries interposed along the course of an arteriole. The arteriole that supplies the glomerular capillaries is termed the *afferent arteriole* of the glomerulus, and the arteriole into which the glomerular capillaries empty is termed the *efferent arteriole* of the glomerulus (Fig. 452). Since the lumen of the efferent arteriole is not much larger than that of the afferent one (as would be the case if the efferent vessel were a venule), a certain amount of resistance is offered to the free passage of blood from glomerular capillaries, enough to maintain a sufficiently high hydrostatic pressure throughout their whole lengths to permit them to exude tissue fluid along their whole lengths. The tonus of the muscle in the walls of the efferent arteriole can change so as to vary the amount of resistance it offers.

According to Allen, from the 1,700 liters of blood that passes along the glomerular capillaries of the two kidneys every 24 hours, 170 liters of tissue fluid (glomerular filtrate) is formed. It follows, then, that every 24 hours 170 liters of glomerular filtrate is emptied into the tubular portions of nephrons. As this passes along the nephrons approximately 169 liters of it is resorbed back into the blood stream so that only about 1 liter emerges from the ends of the nephrons each 24 hours to constitute the daily output of urine. Obviously, there must be as efficient a mechanism for the *tubular resorption* of fluid as there is in glomeruli for its production. A basic factor in the mechanism of resorption will now be considered.

The tubular portions of nephrons lie in a rich capillary bed (Fig. 470). This bed, as will be explained in detail later, is supplied almost entirely by the efferent arterioles of glomeruli. Hence, the blood that supplies the capillaries in which the tubular portions of nephrons lie has passed through glomerular capillaries where it has lost approximately 10 per cent of its fluid and crystalloid content, and, as a result, its colloid (protein) content has become relatively increased. Since the blood in the beds that surround the tubules drains into venules, which offer no substantial resistance to its flow, it is comparable with the blood in the venous ends of ordinary capillaries in that it has an increased osmotic pressure and is under a low hydrostatic pressure. Under these circumstances, the osmotic pressure becomes the dominant factor and acts to draw fluid back from the lumens of the tubules into the capillaries.

To sum up the foregoing: The nephron—an epithelial tubule with a glomerulus of capillaries invaginated into its blind end—is the structural and functional unit of the kidney. The blood supply of its different parts is arranged so that so far as the production of tissue fluid is concerned, the capillaries of glomeruli function along their whole lengths as do only the arterial ends of capillaries in most parts of the body, and, so far as the resorption of tissue fluid is concerned, the capillaries that surround the tubular portions of the nephrons are arranged so that they function along their whole lengths as do only the venous ends of the capillaries in most parts of the body. However, it must not be thought that the relatively low hydrostatic and high osmotic pressure of the blood in the capillary beds that surround the tubular portions of nephrons are the only factors con-

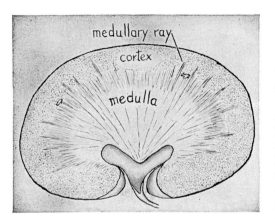

FIG. 453. Drawing of the cut surface of a split kidney of a rabbit. Notice that medullary rays appear to be extensions of the striated medulla into the granular cortex.

THE UNILOBAR (UNIPYRAMIDAL) KIDNEY

The gross and the microscopic anatomy of the multilobar kidney of man is a sufficiently difficult topic to justify its being approached by a somewhat circuitous route if that makes the understanding of its structure easier. It so happens that the kidneys of rats, rabbits and certain other animals consist of only a single lobe, and the structure of such a kidney is much simpler to discuss than the structure of a multilobar kidney. Accordingly, we shall first describe the gross and the microscopic structures of a unilobar kidney and then afterward the gross and the microscopic appearances of the multilobar kidney of man. In order to avoid undue repetition, the description of the microscopic anatomy of the unilobar kidney will be confined to what can be seen with the low-power objective. Such details of the microscopic anatomy of the kidney as are seen to best advantage with the high-power and the oil-immersion objectives will be reserved for the discussion of the multilobar kidney of man, as will a discussion of the blood supply of the organ. However, the student should note that the kidney lobule is something that is best investigated with the low-power objective; hence, it will be considered in detail in connection with the unilobar kidney rather than with the multilobar kidney. The concept of the kidney lobule should be learned from, and reviewed in, the section dealing with the unilobar kidney.

Some Gross Features. The kidney of the rabbit or the rat is shaped like a Lima bean; hence, if one is laid flat on a table and viewed from above, it is seen to have an extensive convex and a smaller concave border (Fig. 453). Considerable fat is generally present in its concavity or *hilus,* and a tube, the *ureter,* together with the renal artery and vein and a surrounding plexus of fine nerves, extend into the kidney through the fat at this site.

If a kidney from a rabbit or a rat is laid flat on a table and then cut in half by keeping the blade of a knife parallel with the surface of the table, the cut surface, when viewed with the naked eye, shows the kidney aside from its covering connective tissue *capsule* to consist of two chief parts. The first is called the *cortex,* and it consists of a broad red-brown granular

cerned in the resorptive process. If they were, the wall of the tubule would be required to perform no function other than serving as a selective dialyzing membrane, and for this purpose alone it would need to be no more than a thin membrane. As we shall see, only a part of each nephron has a wall thin enough to suggest that its only function is that of serving as a selective dialyzing membrane. Over most of the length of the nephron, its wall, though only one cell thick, is composed of cells of substantial thickness, a fact that suggests that these cells do additional vital work, the larger part of which is concerned with the absorption of valuable materials from the lumen of the nephron, and the smaller part, with the excretion of certain substances against a diffusion gradient into the lumen of the nephron.

The various specialized resorptive and excretory functions performed by the tubular portion of the nephron are not performed with equal facility along its whole length. The tubular portion of each nephron exhibits three consecutive segments which exhibit somewhat different structural features and perform somewhat different functions. These are termed the *proximal convoluted segment,* the *loop of Henle* and the *distal convoluted segment,* respectively. Their particular structure and functions will be described in some detail somewhat later when the nephron of the human kidney is considered.

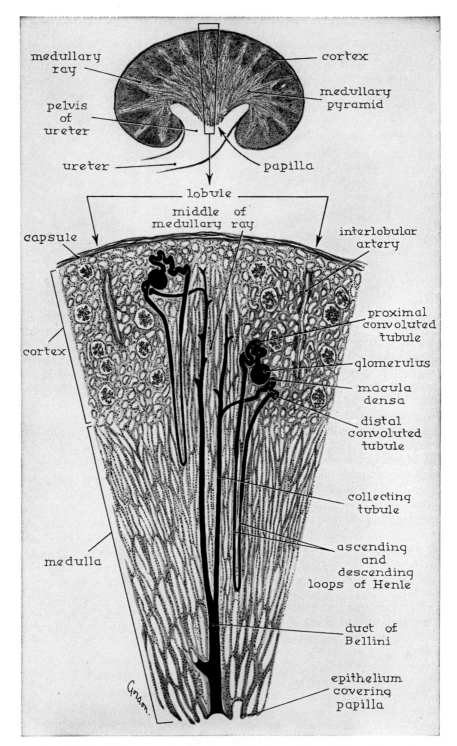

FIG. 454. Semidiagrammatic drawings of sections of a unilobar kidney. Two complete nephrons (in black) have been inserted into the drawings so that their course in the kidney may be followed. Of course, complete nephrons cannot be seen in any single section.

layer of tissue that lies immediately beneath, and follows the contours of, the convex border of the organ (Fig. 453). The remainder of the kidney is shaped like a broad pyramid. The base of this is convex rather than flat and is fitted against the concave inner border of the cortex (Fig. 454). The apex of the pyramid points downward in Figure 453 and juts into the concavity or hilus of the kidney (Fig. 454). In contrast with the darker and granular cortex, the cut surface of the medulla is lighter and has a striated appearance, with the striations fanning out from the apex of the pyramid to all parts of its broad base (Figs. 453 and 454).

A pyramid of medullary substance, together with the cap of cortical substance that covers its base, constitutes a *lobe* of kidney tissue, and there is only one of these in the kidney of the rat or the rabbit. We shall now consider how nephrons are disposed in the lobes of kidneys; this will show why the cut surface of the cortex has a granular appearance and why the cut surface of the medulla has a striated appearance. It will also reveal the way in which kidney lobes are divided up into lobules.

Disposition of Nephrons. Most nephrons are so long that they can fit into a kidney only by pursuing a devious course in its substance.

All nephrons begin in the cortex; hence, *glomeruli are all confined to the cortex* (Fig. 454). The segment of the nephron that leads off from a glomerulus has fairly thick walls and pursues a very looped and tortuous course in the cortical tissue close to the glomerulus. This part of the nephron, for obvious reasons, is called the proximal convoluted segment or tubule (Fig. 454). In its next segment the nephron turns toward the medulla and pursues a straight course into it (Fig. 454). After having descended a certain distance into the medulla it loops back and follows a fairly straight course back to the glomerulus again. (Some nephrons whose glomeruli are in the outer part of the cortex loop back before they actually reach the medulla; compare the two in Fig. 454.) The segment of the nephron that loops down into or toward the medulla and back again is termed the *loop of Henle*. Each loop has a descending limb and an ascending limb. In the lower part of the descending limb, the epithelial wall which, up to this time, has been relatively thick, becomes very thin and

then, in the ascending limb, it becomes thick again (Fig. 454).

The ascending limb of the loop of Henle on reaching the glomerulus of the nephron curves in to touch its root between the site of entry of the afferent arteriole and the site of exit of the efferent arteriole. The portion of the wall of the tubule that comes into contact with the glomerular root becomes heavily nucleated and constitutes a thick spot known as the *macula densa* (Fig. 454).

The segment of the nephron that continues on from the macula densa is known as the *distal convoluted tubule*. It pursues a mildly tortuous course in the neighboring cortical tissue (Fig. 454). It then becomes continuous with a little side branch of one of the members of a branching system of long straight *collecting tubules* that extend from the cortex down through the medulla to open through its tip which is called the *papilla* of the pyramid (Fig. 454).

Collecting Tubules. The collecting tubules are not parts of nephrons, although they may possibly absorb some water. They do not otherwise modify the fluid that flows along their lumens. In general, then, they merely convey fluid from the nephrons into the pelvis and the ureter, thus bearing a relation to nephrons similar to that which ducts bear to secretory units of glands. Indeed, they have a different developmental origin from that of nephrons. A nephron develops from mesodermal cells which become organized into a tubule; this later becomes associated with blood capillaries that are forming a renal corpuscle in the kidney cortex. On each side of the body, a tube grows up from the developing bladder into the developing kidney where it branches. This tube becomes the ureter and the pelvis of the kidney, and each of its many branches becomes a collecting tubule which later connects with a nephron in such a way that the lumens of the two become continuous.

Why the Cortex Is Granular and the Medulla Striated. The cortex contains all the glomeruli and all the convoluted parts of the tubules; these constitute most of the bulk of the cortex (Fig. 454). If a slice is cut through a kidney, the proximal and distal convoluted tubules, being tortuous, are cut in cross and oblique section. Seen in the gross, tubules cut in this way, as well as the glomeruli scattered among them, appear to be granular.

The parts of nephrons in the medulla are the loops of Henle and the collecting tubules (Fig. 454). These run fairly straight courses so, if the medulla is sliced roughly parallel with them, it has a striated appearance with the striations fanning out from the apex of the medullary pyramid toward the base of the pyramid which, as has been noted before, fits into the concave border of the cortex.

The Connection between the Ureter and the Kidney. In a fresh unilobar kidney the ureter is seen to extend out from the kidney through the fat at its hilus (Fig. 453). If this tube is traced back up into the fat of the pelvis of the kidney it will be seen to become expanded to form a cap which fits over the papilla of the pyramid (Fig. 454). This expanded end of the ureter is called its *pelvis* (basin). Urine formed by nephrons passes into collecting tubules which carry it out through the papilla of the pyramid, and here it is collected by the caplike basin portion of the ureter. Urine here can only enter the lumen of the expanded end of the ureter because the epithelium that lines it is continuous with that covering the papilla of the pyramid, and this, in turn, is continuous with that lining the collecting tubules (Fig. 454). The papilla is so riddled with the collecting tubules that pass through it that it is called the *area cribrosa* (*cribrum* = a sieve). Smooth muscle has been described in the wall of the pelvis of the ureter, and it has been suggested that its contraction may exert a milking influence on the papilla and so squeeze urine out of the collecting tubules into the pelvis.

LOBULES AND MEDULLARY RAYS

One of the commonest mistakes made in studying the kidney is that of confusing lobes with lobules. Therefore, this matter will be dealt with at some length.

A *lobe* of kidney tissue is a medullary pyramid with its cap of cortical tissue (Fig. 454). Accordingly, a unipyramidal kidney is a unilobar kidney. Each kidney of man consists of a dozen or more lobes; each of these lobes in itself greatly resembles a whole unipyramidal kidney.

A *lobule* of kidney tissue, like a lobule of liver tissue, is not a clearly outlined structure. In trying to locate a portal lobule in the liver

(not a classic lobule) the student first identifies a portal area. This gives a landmark for the center of a lobule and so enables the periphery of the lobule to be visualized. The same procedure is used in identifying kidney lobules (kidney lobules are comparable with portal lobules in the liver, see p. 640). The student looks first for a landmark which marks the middle of the lobule. After this is found the periphery of the lobule can be roughly visualized, at least in the mind. The landmarks looked for, which form the central cores of kidney lobules, are structures termed *medullary rays,* and these will now be described.

The cortex of a freshly cut kidney has been said to be granular. But it is not *evenly* granular because *raylike* extensions of the light-colored striated medullary substance project up into it at intervals from the base of the medullary pyramid (Figs. 453 and 454). These raylike extensions of medullary substance that are *projected* into the cortex are termed *medullary rays,* and the student must take care to remember that these are not, as their name might be thought to imply, in the medulla but in the cortex.

In order to explain medullary rays it is necessary to amplify somewhat the description already given of the disposition of nephrons in the kidney. It has been explained previously that a proximal convoluted tubule leads off from a glomerulus and then after pursuing a tortuous course in the vicinity of the glomerulus it dips down toward the medulla as the descending limb of a loop of Henle. It then returns to the cortex as an ascending limb of the loop of Henle and after touching the glomerulus again at the macula densa becomes the distal convoluted tubule which pursues a tortuous course and empties, together with many other nephrons, into a *common collecting tubule* which, in turn, descends into and through the medulla to open through the papilla of the pyramid into the pelvis of the ureter. *Many nephrons drain into each collecting tubule* (Fig. 454).

The core of a lobule is a medullary ray, and the core of a medullary ray is the branched collecting tubule into which the distal convoluted segments of the many nephrons that surround it empty. The branched collecting tubule, in the kidney cortex, is the counterpart of a branched *intralobular* duct of an exocrine gland. In addition to a branched collecting tubule, a medullary ray contains the descending and the ascending limbs of the loops of Henle of the nephrons that, in the cortex, empty into the branched collecting tubule that the ray contains. The medullary ray, plus the surrounding glomeruli and proximal and distal convoluted tubules of the nephrons that empty into its branched collecting tubule, constitutes a *lobule* of kidney tissue (Fig. 454). It has been observed already that these lobules, like those of human liver, are not clearly delineated. However, when we study the blood supply of the cortex we shall find that interlobular arteries ascend into the cortex roughly between lobules, and these are seen occasionally in sections where they serve as landmarks to indicate the margins of lobules (Fig. 454).

The narrowest part of a medullary ray is the part that most closely approaches the capsule of the kidney. This is because medullary rays in the outer part of the cortex contain, in addition to relatively narrow collecting tubules,

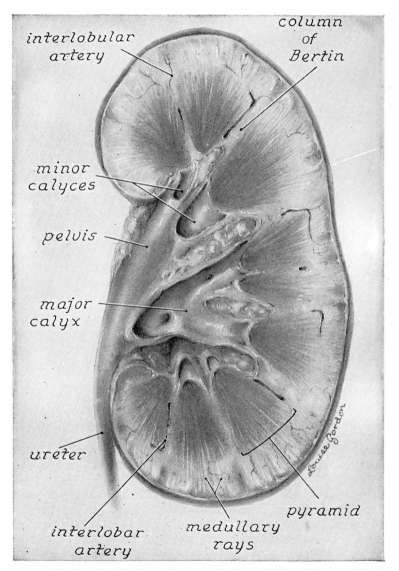

Fig. 455. Drawing of the cut surface of a human kidney. The granular cortex is streaked with medullary rays.

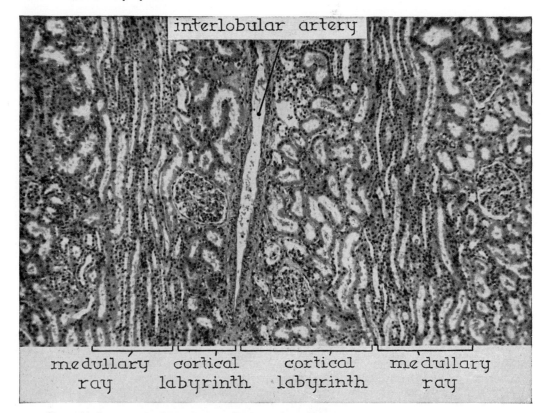

interlobular artery

medullary ray   cortical labyrinth   cortical labyrinth   medullary ray

Fig. 456. Low-power photomicrograph of an H and E section of a human kidney showing 2 lobules separated by an interlobular artery. The 2 medullary rays that form the central cores for the 2 lobules are each surrounded by the glomeruli and convoluted tubules of the nephrons that empty into the collecting ducts of the ray; these comprise what is termed the cortical labyrinth.

only the descending and the ascending limbs of loops of Henle of the nephrons whose glomeruli are in the outermost zone of the cortex. But as medullary rays descend in the cortex toward the medulla, they are added to by the descending and the ascending limbs of loops of Henle of the nephrons whose glomeruli are in the deeper parts of the cortex, and this, of course, makes the rays broader (Fig. 454).

A medullary ray, on entering the medulla, is no longer called a ray, because it does not stand out like a ray against a background of a different character; the substance of the medullary continuation of the ray is the same as that of medullary substance in general (Fig. 454). This leads to students visualizing kidney lobules as purely cortical structures. However, it should be remembered that the bundle of tubules that enters the medulla from each

medullary ray, even though its limits can no longer be identified, is as much a part of the lobule as the bundle that projects into the cortex as the medullary ray. In other words, kidney lobules have medullary as well as cortical components.

THE MULTIPYRAMIDAL OR MULTILOBAR KIDNEY OF MAN

Some General Features. The kidney of man contains from 6 to 18 lobes—individual pyramids of medullary tissue capped by cortical tissue. These are arranged within the kidney so that the tip of each pyramid points toward the pelvis (Fig. 455) of the ureter. In fetal, and for at least part of the first year of postnatal, life the lobes are sufficiently distinct for their limits to be seen on the surface of the kidney. This condition occasionally persists into adult life and accounts for what is termed *fetal lobulation.* This term is not apt because *lobes,* not *lobules,* are demarcated. Normally, however, as growth continues, the surface distinctions between lobes is lost in early childhood, and the cortical tissue that covers each pyramid comes to merge smoothly into that which covers adjacent ones. However, a lobed appearance is retained in the medulla, for although some pyramids fuse during development and come to have a common papilla, many remain separated and provide the basis for a multilobar structure. Individual medullary pyramids, curiously enough, are separated from one another *by partitions of cortical substance* that extend down between them from the cortex proper. When a kidney is sliced, these partitions of typical cortical substance between pyramids appear as columns and are called the *columns of Bertin* (columni Bertini) (Fig. 455).

Medullary rays extend from the base of each pyramid of medullary tissue into cortical substance as they do in unipyramidal kidneys to form the cores of lobules (Figs. 454, 455 and 456). In sections of cortex a ray is seen to be surrounded by cortical substance composed of the convoluted tubules and glomeruli of the nephrons that empty into its branched collecting tubule (Fig. 456). Since convoluted tubules pursue such tortuous courses, the cortical substance of lobules that surrounds the medullary rays is termed the *labyrinth* (*labyrinthos* = a maze) of the cortex (Fig. 456), to distinguish it from the substance of the ray.

Since the multilobar kidney has many medullary pyramids, each of which elaborates urine through its papilla, the pelvis of the ureter of the multilobar kidney is more complex than that of the unipyramidal organ. The ureter, on approaching the hilus of a multilobar kidney, becomes expanded into a pelvis as it does in the instance of a unipyramidal kidney. But, since there are many papilla from which urine must be collected, the pelvis of the ureter of the multilobar kidney divides into several large primary branches. Each of these, in turn, branches into a set of smaller tubes so that a separate tube (with an open end) is provided to fit over the papilla of each pyramid. Since these tubular branches from the pelvis fit over the individual papillae like cups they are termed *calyces* (*kalyx* = the

cup of a flower). Each one that fits over a papilla is termed a *minor calyx* (Fig. 455), and the main (primary) branches of the pelvis, from which the minor calyces arise, are termed *major calyces* (Fig. 455). Each papilla is, as it were, pushed for a short distance into the open end of its calyx. Of course, it cannot be pushed into the open end of the tubular calyx for any great distance because of its pyramidal shape (the tip of a sharpened pencil can be pushed into the open end of a glass tube for only a short distance). The walls of the open end of a calyx come into contact with the sides of the papilla a short distance up from its tip, and here the tissues of the wall of the calyx become continuous with those of the papilla. In particular, the epithelium that lines the calyx loops back to become the covering of the papilla.

THE NEPHRON OF THE KIDNEY OF MAN: ITS PARTS AND THEIR FUNCTIONS

Some General Features

Knowledge about the parts and the courses of nephrons was worked out, not by making reconstructions of nephrons from serial sections of kidneys which would be an almost impossible task, but by the method of maceration and dissection. This was employed around the turn of the century by both Huber and Peter, and our knowledge of the morphology and the course of the normal nephron stems from this work. More recently, Jean Oliver, by employing maceration and dissection, combined with staining technics, has investigated nephrons in many types of diseased kidneys and kidneys altered by experimental procedures and so has made an enormous contribution to an understanding of the pathology of this organ.

The nephrons of the kidney of man are similar to those of the unilobar kidney, the general features of which have been mentioned. However, in describing the nephrons of the kidney of man, we shall give considerably more detail than was presented in our preliminary description of nephrons of the unilobar kidney. It should be understood that most of this description applies to the nephrons of unilobar kidneys as well as to those of the kidney of man.

Nephrons of the kidney of man are said to be of an average length of from 50 to 55 mm. Those nephrons that begin from glomeruli situated in the zone of cortex that is close to the medulla (the juxtamedullary glomeruli) have longer loops of Henle than those nephrons that begin from glomeruli nearer the exterior of the kidney. There are probably about 1,300,000 nephrons in each kidney; some estimates run as high as 4,000,000. Allen gives the total length of all the tubules of both kidneys as approximately 75 miles. The nephron of the kidney of man consists of 4 chief parts: (1) the malpighian or renal corpuscle which contains the glomerulus, (2) the proximal convoluted tubule, (3) the loop of Henle and (4) the distal convoluted tubule (Fig. 457). The microscopic structure of each of these parts of the nephron will now be described and related, so far as is practicable, to its particular function.

The Microscopic Structure of the Malpighian or Renal Corpuscle

Definition and Development. A glomerulus, as has been noted, is a tuft of capillaries supplied by an afferent arteriole and drained by an efferent arteriole—an arrangement admirably suited for the production of tissue fluid. When, during development, a glomerulus is invaginated into the blind end of an epithelial tubule (Fig. 452), the structure that comes into existence is known as a *malpighian* or *renal corpuscle*. This structure is composed of capillary networks plus the epithelium they push ahead of them which comes to cover them, plus the expanded blind end of the epithelial tubule into which the epithelial-covered capillary networks are pushed. The epithelium that is pushed ahead of the capillaries at first covers the tuft of capillaries as a whole (Fig. 452) and is known as the *visceral layer of Bowman's capsule* or, more commonly, as the *glomerular epithelium*. As development proceeds, the epithelium becomes apposed to all the individual capillaries in the network so that they will be completely covered with basement membranes, as will be explained in detail later. The epithelium of the bulged end of the nephron, into which the epithelial-covered glomerulus is invaginated, is known as the *parietal layer of Bowman's capsule* or, more commonly, as the *capsular epithelium*

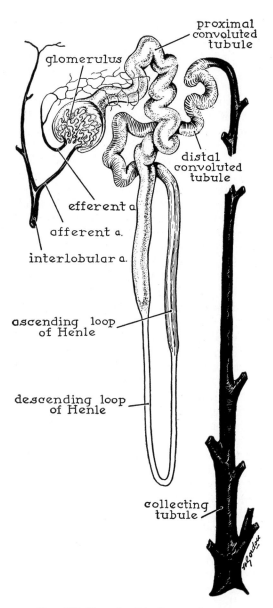

FIG. 457. To make this diagram less complex, the ascending limb of the loop of Henle is not shown in its normal relation to the vascular pole of the glomerulus; actually it should return to the glomerulus and fit into its vascular pole to form a macula densa before continuing on as the distal convoluted tubule.

(Fig. 460). It is continuous with the glomerular epithelium. The lumen of the tubule, the spaces between the epithelial-covered capillaries and the parietal layer of Bowman's cap-

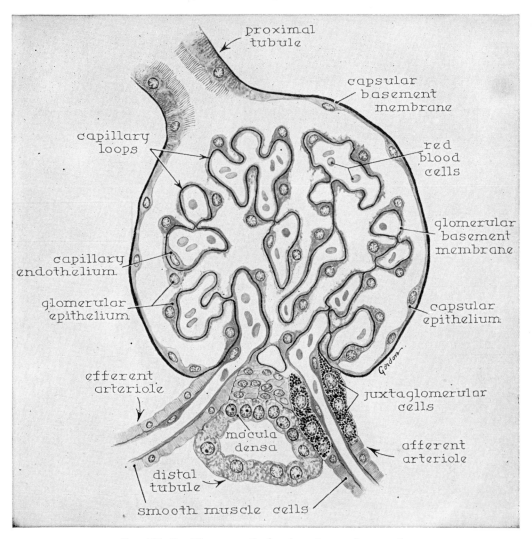

FIG. 458. Semidiagrammatic drawing of a renal corpuscle.

sule, constitutes *Bowman's* or the *capsular space* (Fig. 460).

Renal corpuscles range from around 150 to 250 μ in diameter. They are oval rather than spherical. The juxtamedullary corpuscles are generally larger than those nearer the capsule, probably because the juxtamedullary ones are the first to form during development and hence are the oldest.

Course and Character of the Larger Glomerular Blood Vessels. The over-all diameter of the afferent arteriole of a glomerulus is generally about twice that of the efferent arteriole. However, the lumen of the afferent arteriole of most glomeruli probably is not much larger than that of the efferent one during life, because R. D. Bensley found that in preparations fixed by injection while under pressure, they were of about the same size. Indeed, more recently, Trueta and his associates have shown that the lumens of the efferent arterioles of the juxtamedullary glomeruli may even be wider than those of the afferent arterioles. Since the over-all diameter of the afferent arterioles is so much greater than that of the efferent arterioles, it is obvious that afferent arterioles must have thicker walls than those of efferent arterioles. Since the adventitia and the intima of afferent arterioles is poorly developed, it is obvious that the great difference

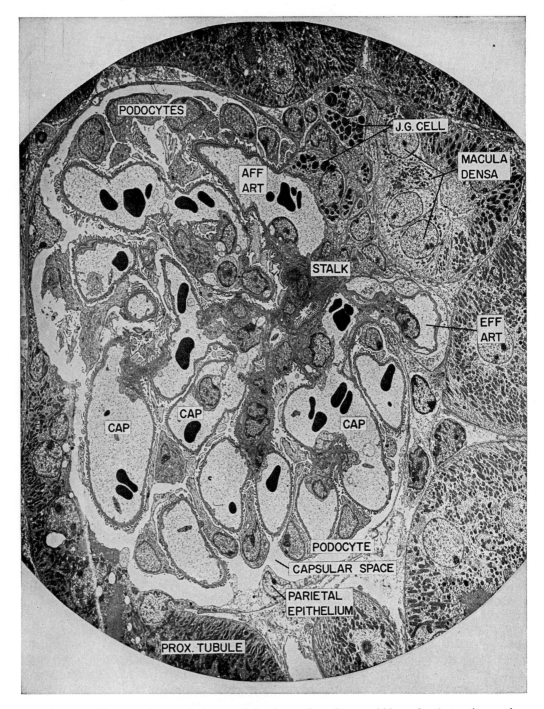

FIG. 459. Electron micrograph ($\times$ 2,200) is of a section of mouse kidney showing entire renal corpuscle. The vascular pole with afferent and efferent arterioles is in the upper right corner, and the urinary pole is in the lower left corner. The macula densa is wedged in between afferent and efferent arterioles, and JG cells are associated with the afferent arteriole. Numerous glomerular capillaries are sectioned, each being lined by endothelium and covered with small foot processes (pedicels) which are cytoplasmic extensions of the visceral epithelial cells or podocytes. The glomerular stalk contains some mesangial cells. (Preparation by Dr. J. Rhodin)

in the thickness of the walls of the two vessels is due to the afferent arteriole's having a more substantial muscular media. The muscular media of the efferent vessel is not well developed, but Bensley has provided definite evidence of contractile cells in the wall of this vessel.

Glomerular Root, Vascular Pole and Macula Densa. Afferent and efferent arterioles generally pursue curved diverging courses as they respectively enter and leave glomeruli close to one another (Figs. 458 and 459). This site is termed the *vascular pole* or the *root* of the glomerulus. It has been mentioned that the ascending limb of the loop of Henle of each nephron returns to the glomerulus of that nephron, and before it continues on as the distal convoluted tubule it bends in between the afferent and the efferent arterioles at the vascular pole so that its wall, on one side, comes into close contact with the root of the glomerulus and also with the wall of the afferent arteriole (Figs. 458 and 459). The epithelial cells of the wall of the nephron, where it touches the root of the glomerulus and the afferent vessel, as has been mentioned before, exhibit a concentration of nuclei (Figs. 458 and 459). This relatively heavily nucleated portion of the wall of the nephron constitutes a structure, far from being sharply defined, termed the *macula densa* (thick spot). Between it and the glomerulus proper, in the concavity between the afferent and the efferent arterioles, is a curious little aggregation of small cells with pale nuclei (Fig. 458). There is as yet no certainty about their nature, function or nomenclature.

The Juxtaglomerular Complex. The cells of the media of the afferent arterioles of glomeruli, in the region of the glomerular root, are distinctly different from ordinary smooth muscle cells. Their nuclei, instead of being elongated, are rounded, and their cytoplasm, instead of containing myofibrils, or as many as usual, contains granules (Figs. 458 and 459). Moreover, the shape of these cells resembles that of epithelial cells. They are often termed epithelioid cells but more commonly today they are termed JG (juxtaglomerular) cells. They have been found in many species and under many different conditions by different investigators. However, it should be understood that their granules are not visible with many of the usual histologic technics.

The granules can be demonstrated with the P.A.S. technic. However, the best method for their demonstration is the one evolved by Wilson working with the Hartrofts and is a modification of Bowie's neutral stain that has been commonly used for the demonstration of beta granules in the islets of Langerhans.

There are several peculiarities about the position of the JG cells. (1) They are to be found only in the walls of afferent arterioles and not in the walls of the efferent ones. (2) The internal elastic lamina of the afferent arteriole disappears at the site where they are present; therefore, they are in very close contact with the endothelium lining the afferent arteriole and hence with the blood in its lumen. (3) They are in very close contact with the macula densa (Figs. 458 and 459), which, as has been described, nestles into the depression between the afferent and the efferent arterioles of the glomerulus. (4) McManus has shown that the basement membrane which otherwise surrounds the nephron throughout its whole length, which will be described presently, is absent at the macula densa; hence, the JG cells come into intimate contact with the cells of the distal convoluted tubule at this site. Finally, McManus has also shown that the Golgi network, which in the cell of a nephron generally is situated between its nucleus and the lumen, is situated, in the cells of the macula densa, between the nucleus and the outer border of most of its cells; in fact, on the side of the cell that faces the JG cells. Unfortunately, the reasons for these structural arrangements are not yet clear, and the problem remains, for the most part, a fascinating riddle yet to be solved. Some of the lines along which this riddle is being investigated will now be mentioned.

The student doubtless understands that a condition termed *high blood pressure* or *hypertension* is by no means uncommon in individuals who have passed the prime of life and that it may also occur, but less commonly, in younger people. Hypertension is due to the arterioles of the body becoming constricted; this raises the pressure within the arterial system. This, of course, puts more work upon the heart, which therefore tends to become hypertrophied. The arteriolar constriction may be due, at least for a time, to increased tonus or hypertrophy of the muscle cells of the arteriolar walls, with the cells of the wall remaining healthy. But in all too many instances the cells of the arteriolar walls become diseased, and deposits of abnormal materials accumulate in and beside them; these encroach on the lumens of the vessels and narrow them further. This type of hypertension is almost always associated with kidney disease; indeed, the relation between kidney disease and hypertension has been so noticeable through the years that each has been suggested as the cause of the other.

In 1939, Goldblatt made a brilliant discovery in this field; he showed that if the arterial blood supply of the kidneys was not entirely cut off, but only diminished, the blood pressure of an animal would rise. Moreover, he showed that this was due to the kidneys' liberating into the blood, under these ischemic conditions, a substance called *renin*. In the blood stream renin acts on another substance, *hypertensinogen* (also called *reninactivator*), to convert it to *hypertensin* (also called *angiotonin*), the substance which acts to raise the blood pressure. Renin can be extracted from kidneys; indeed, it was demonstrated in 1898, many years before Goldblatt's discovery.

It is only natural that it should have been suspected that the JG cells make renin, and that the granules in them (Figs. 458 and 459) are either renin or its precursor. Goormaghtigh, in Belgium, was the first to suggest that the JG cells make a hypertensive substance. Dunihue, in America, also found indications of hypertrophy of the JG apparatus in animals made hypertensive. However, Dunihue made a further and very important observation to the effect that the JG apparatus becomes more heavily granulated when the adrenal glands are removed. The Hartrofts have studied the apparatus extensively in rats under a variety of conditions and have made the striking observation that the JG cells both proliferate and become more heavily granulated when the sodium chloride intake of an animal is restricted and that they contain fewer granules if rats are given extra sodium chloride. Since the adrenal cortex, through some of its hormones, controls sodium metabolism, the Hartrofts' findings are in accord with Dunihue's findings that the JG apparatus becomes more heavily granulated in adrenalectomized animals.

There now are three types of evidence that JG cells elaborate renin. Pitcock, Hartroft and Newmark recently showed that there was a correlation between the amount of renin in the kidneys of sodium-deficient rats and the degree of granulation of the JG cells. Secondly, Bing and Kazimierczak, using microdissection technics, have demonstrated that the concentration of renin is highest in the region of the JG cells. The third type of evidence for secretion of renin by JG cells has been obtained by Edelman and Hartroft, using the immunofluorescence technic. Antiserum to renin prepared in the dog was coupled with a fluorescent dye and then used to locate renin in kidney sections. This showed that the fluorescent antibody attached itself chiefly to the JG cells. Therefore, the present-day evidence suggests that the JG cells elaborate renin and that, in addition to its pressor effect, renin stimulates the zona glomerulosa of the adrenal cortex to increase the secretion of aldosterone. As has already been noted, sodium depletion causes the JG cells to produce renin. Under the E/M JG granules are osmophilic and spherical to oval in shape. They can be distinguished readily from the mitochondria of the JG cells (Fig. 459).

The Microscopic Structure of Glomeruli

Glomerular Capillaries and Glomerular Lobules. Through the years there have been different views held about the arrangements in which capillaries are disposed in glomeruli. One view that has had a considerable impact on kidney literature stemmed from the work of Vimtrup. According to him, an afferent arteriole, on entering a glomerulus, branches into from 2 to 4, or even more, primary branches; these either give rise to further branches that give off capillaries or they give off capillaries immediately. Each of the up to 50 capillaries formed in this way is visualized as pursuing a somewhat tortuous course before and as it loops back to join a primary branch of the efferent vessel. According to this view, capillaries in the glomeruli do *not* branch.

However, Vimtrup's views were not accepted by all, and some investigators, through the years, recorded examples of branching capillaries. Hall reinvestigated this matter by injecting glomerular vessels with latex and then macerating the tissue so that the injected material in the vessels could be dissected and examined under the light microscope. Hall's studies show that each afferent arteriole branches into a few main (basal) branches; each of these basal branches supplies a "lobule" of the glomerulus. Hall does not consider that anastomoses between lobules are common but anastomoses are common between the capillaries in any given lobule. The basal vessel in each lobule is thought to give rise to two or more major capillaries which act as preferred channels (probably somewhat similar to the A-V bridges in Fig. 388) and these follow a looped course, to return and empty into basal branches of the efferent system. Hall believes that capillaries are given off along the course of the preferred channels and that they anastomose with one another and with other preferred channels in the same lobule.

This concept of the glomerular vessels being disposed in lobules is in keeping with what is seen under the microscope (Fig. 460). Boyer, by reconstruction of injected glomeruli, has found that Vimtrup's concept of nonanastomosing capillary loops is no longer tenable. The glomerulus is composed of a capillary network comparable with all other capillary beds in the body. However, Boyer believes that there are some anastomoses between the structures that others would call lobules. This view has been confirmed recently by Lewis, and by Baringer.

The Internal Support of Capillary Nets and Lobules: The Question of a Mesangium. When it was believed that capillaries were arranged in nonbranching loops, there was a widespread but not universal view to the effect that each loop, like a loop of intestine, had a mesentery of connective tissue of some sort; this mesenterylike structure that was visualized was termed the *mesangium*. Those who believe in a mesangium could likewise visualize films of connective tissue supporting the loops of communicating or preferred channels and the capillary nets between them in lobules. Although there are certain pathologic conditions of the glomerulus which can be interpreted more easily if the existence of a mesangium is assumed, there is as yet little basis for believing that there is a connective tissue mesangium supporting the capillaries of normal glomeruli except perhaps close to their roots. (See Fig. 459, Stalk.) Hall made an intensive study of the glomerulus with the E/M and found no

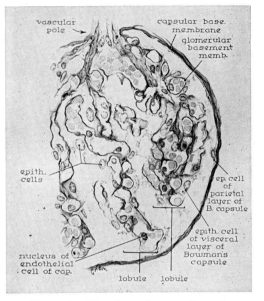

FIG. 460. Drawing of a portion of a renal corpuscle as seen under oil-immersion in a section of human kidney stained by the P.A.S. method and by hematoxylin. Three lobules are to be seen hanging from the vascular pole. Note that the glomerular basement membrane surrounds each capillary in the lobules.

evidence of connective tissue or of collagenic fibrils among the glomerular capillaries. He found that, excluding blood cells in the capillaries, all the cells that are seen in glomeruli are either the endothelial cells of the capillaries or the epithelial cells of the visceral layer of Bowman's capsule. Elias, in a recent comprehensive article on the renal glomerulus, is most emphatic about the nonexistence of a connective tissue mesangium. His reconstructions have verified Hall's observations.

The Covering Layers of Glomerular Capillaries: An Exercise in 3-Dimensional Visualization. Basement membranes were described in Chapters 5 and 13. It will be recalled that they consist of a homogeneous amorphous material that is P.A.S. positive and that they are commonly interposed between epithelial membranes and the connective tissue on which the epithelium lies and from which it is nourished; the latter fact attests to the permeability of basement membranes.

Basement membranes are present in renal corpuscles exactly where they might be expected; they are interposed between the epithelial membranes and the mesenchymal-derived structures (capillaries develop from mesenchyme) that are covered or lined by the epithelial membranes. First, there is a substantial basement membrane between the parietal layer of Bowman's capsule and the stroma of the kidney cortex (Fig. 460). Secondly, there is a thinner basement membrane between the epithelial cells of the visceral layer of Bowman's capsule and the capillaries that they cover. The P.A.S. method, which has been used to such advantage by McManus in studying the kidney, reveals these basement membranes both beautifully and clearly (Figs. 460 and 464).

Perhaps the most significant finding to take into account in attempting to visualize the arrangements of glomerular capillaries in 3 dimensions is the fact that *every capillary appearing in a cross, an oblique or an almost longitudinal section is seen in a good P.A.S. preparation to be completely surrounded with a basement membrane* (Fig. 460). At first thought it might be assumed that these basement membranes are produced by the endothelial cells of the capillaries. But capillaries in other parts of the kidney are *not* covered with basement membranes that are readily demonstrated by the P.A.S. method. Furthermore, pronounced basement membranes *are* found around all the epithelial tubules of the cortex of the kidney, between their epithelial walls and the connective tissue stroma in which they lie (Fig. 464). Therefore, the basement membranes in the kidney seem to be disposed where there is interaction between epithelium and mesenchymal-derived tissue (connective tissue stroma or capillaries). This leads to the conclusion that the basement membranes seen around the capillaries in glomerular lobules must have formed under the influence of epithelial cells, and this leads to the further conclusion that the epithelial cells of the visceral layer of Bowman's capsule therefore must thoroughly permeate all the interstices that exist in the capillary networks of glomerular lobules to come into intimate contact with all capillaries.

The visceral layer of Bowman's capsule not only covers lobules as entities but in doing so it pushes into every cleft and space in the lobules and from all sides of the lobule so that in the middle of the lobule prongs of epithelium from one surface meet prongs that have pushed in from other surfaces. Everywhere throughout the lobule the epithelial cells apply themselves to the surfaces of capillaries to provide them with basement membranes (Fig. 460). Each capillary becomes covered with a basement membrane, one side of which may be produced by one epithelial cell and the other by another epithelial cell. Since there is no evidence for a connective tissue mesangium in the lobule, it would seem that the chief support of the capillary nets is provided by the extensive system of basement membranes and that epithelial cells might be expected to be found everywhere throughout lobules tucked here and there in the interstices between capillaries. It might be suggested that the mesangium of glomerular capillaries is composed of basement membranes.

Since the basement membranes surround capillaries it is easy to distinguish endothelial from epithelial cells in a P.A.S. preparation; the endothelial cells are contained within the variously shaped rings of basement membrane, and the epithelial cells are outside the rings of basement membrane (Figs. 458 and 460).

The Surface Area of Glomerular Capillaries. The total surface area of the capillaries of a glomerulus has been both estimated and measured. The latter procedure requires the use of enlarged replicas of serial sections cut through a glomerulus and is so laborious and fraught with difficulties that few have attempted it. Book, when he was an associate of the author, and two of whose preparations are shown in Figure 9, injected the blood vessels of a kidney of a child of 6 and made replicas of each section cut through one glomerulus. On these replicas he measured the capillary surfaces. Allowing for certain corrections, he calculated the capillaries of the glomerulus to have a surface area of 0.3813 sq. mm. More recently, Kirkman and Stowell have measured painstakingly the capillary surface area of several rat glomeruli and find that it averages 0.19 sq. mm. They suggest that Book's illustrations indicate that the injection distorted the capillary loops to some extent and that injected material is not suitable for this type of study. However, they state that his figure is the most reliable one available for the

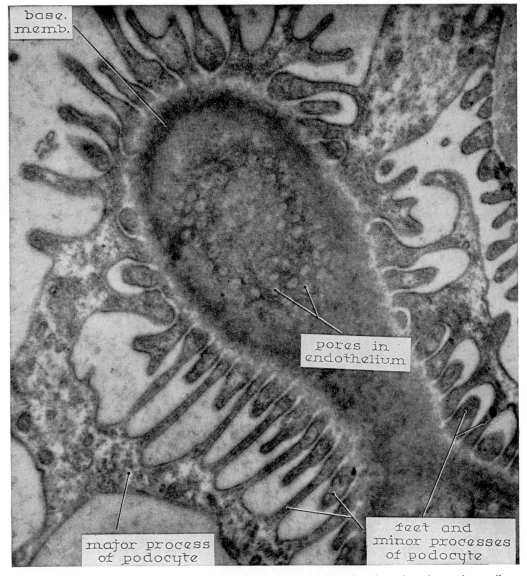

base. memb.

pores in endothelium

major process of podocyte

feet and minor processes of podocyte

FIG. 461. Electron micrograph ($\times$ 40,000) of a tangential section through a glomerular capillary, showing pores in the endothelium as well as the interdigitating processes and the feet of podocytes. (Pease, D. C.: J. Histochem. *3*:295, with labeling added)

human glomerulus. Rat glomeruli are smaller than human glomeruli; hence, there is surprisingly good agreement between Book's findings and those of Kirkman and Stowell. Since it has been estimated that there are well over a million glomeruli in each human kidney, it seems probable that the total filtration surface of all the glomeruli of both kidneys is well over a square meter.

It has been estimated that the glomerular capillaries of all the renal corpuscles of the two kidneys produce from 170 to 200 liters of tissue fluid each 24 hours. As this fluid moves along through proximal convoluted tubules, loops of Henle and distal convoluted tubules, about 99 per cent of it is resorbed through the walls of the tubules back into the blood stream. After considering the fine structure of the glomerulus we shall consider the structures of these parts of the nephron where resorption occurs and how their structure is related to their functions.

THE FINE STRUCTURE OF THE GLOMERULUS

The study of kidney glomeruli with the E/M has been particularly rewarding. Two major findings of morphologic and physiologic interest have been made: one relates to the character of the endothelium of the capillaries and the other to the nature of epithelial cells of the visceral layer of Bowman's capsule. These findings will now be described.

The Fenestrated Endothelium of Glomerular Capillaries. The presence of nuclei in the endothelial cells of capillaries causes the cells to bulge into the lumen where nuclei are present (Fig. 463, *upper right*). Around the periphery of each bulged area the cytoplasm of an endothelial cell quickly attenuates (Fig. 463, *upper right*) and spreads out in a thin film to make up the remainder and major part of the wall of the capillary; hence, except

where nuclei are present the capillary walls consist of only thin films of cytoplasm. From early studies with the E/M, made before thin sectioning technics were well developed, it became apparent that this endothelium is different from that of capillaries in most parts of the body in that it is riddled with pores (Figs. 461, 462 and 463). It was suspected for a time that the pores seen with the E/M might be fixation artefacts, but from the persistent studies of Hall and subsequent studies by Pease and others it has become generally accepted that the pores are real and exist during life. The pores, although they are regularly arranged and close together, are not all of precisely the same size but measure on an average of around 0.1 μ in diameter. There is some evidence to indicate that their size varies somewhat in relation to the fixation procedures that are employed.

The Epithelial Cells of the Visceral Layer of Bowman's Capsule: the Podocytes. Al-

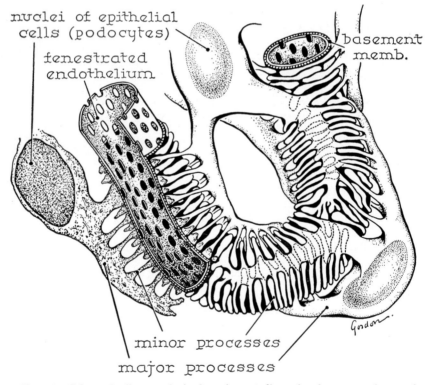

FIG. 462. Schematic diagram devised to give a 3-dimensional concept of part of a capillary loop in a glomerulus with its covering of podocytes and its fenestrated endothelium. At the upper left, part of a podocyte and part of a capillary have been cut away. (Based on electron micrographs from D. C. Pease and a diagram *in* Pease, D. C.: J. Histochem. *3*:295)

though some histologists who have studied the kidney through the years with the light microscope have suggested that the epithelial cells that comprise the visceral layer of Bowman's capsule are of an unusual form, having many processes which are attached to the basement membranes that overlie the capillaries, not much attention was paid to their views, and there was a general belief that these cells are squamous in type and that they form a continuous covering for the capillaries. With the E/M it has become evident that this view is incorrect on both counts, for the cells are not squamous in type, and they do not provide a continuous covering for the capillaries. They have a most unusual form and, for reasons that will soon become apparent, are now generally termed *podocytes*.

The main cell body of a podocyte (which contains its nucleus) is separated from the capillary over which it lies by a *subpodocytic space* that is filled with glomerular filtrate (Figs. 459 and 463). Numerous arms of cytoplasm, which we shall call *major processes,* extend from the cell body (Figs. 462 and 463); these tend to run roughly parallel with the long axis or the circumference of the capillary, and they too tend to be separated from the capillary by spaces (Figs. 462 and 463). From the major processes, delicate minor processes extend in orderly array to the capillary (Figs. 461 and 462) where they terminate in *feet*; the soles of these are planted firmly on the basement membranes of the capillary (they are probably set in a cement substance) and follow its curvature (Figs. 462 and 463). It is because of these feet that the cells are called podocytes. The minor processes and feet from different major processes interdigitate with one another as they approach and come into contact with the capillary (Figs. 461 and 462). The minor processes and feet that interdigitate with one another may be derived from two or more major processes of the same podocyte or from the major processes of two or more podocytes (Fig. 462). Such evidence as is available suggests that one podocyte can send processes to two capillaries, although generally their processes probably all go to one.

As may be seen in Figures 461, 462 and 463, the interdigitating feet do not come into contact with one another; there are tiny clefts between them. This means, of course, that the

capillaries do not have a continuous epithelial covering and that it would not be necessary for glomerular filtrate to pass through the epithelial feet in order to enter the glomerular space.

Since the endothelium is fenestrated, and since there are clefts between epithelial feet, neither the endothelium nor the epithelium could serve as dialyzing membranes. This means that the basement membrane is *the* dialyzing membrane in glomeruli; it constitutes the only intact membrane between the blood and the glomerular filtrate. It should be mentioned here that Pease believes that both the inner and the outer surfaces of the basement membrane are coated with a cement substance (Figs. 461 and 462) to hold the endothelium and the epithelial feet, respectively, in place. Pease suggests that swollen feet could hinder glomerular filtration and that podocytes may have elastic or contractile powers.

THE PROXIMAL CONVOLUTED TUBULE

The proximal convoluted segment of the renal tubule or, as it is more commonly termed, the proximal convoluted tubule, is about 14 mm. in length and has an over-all diameter of about 60 μ. The first part of it, which leads off from the glomerulus, is sufficiently narrow and straight in some species to constitute a neck for the tubule. But, in man, this portion of the tubule differs so little from the remainder of the tubule that it does not merit a separate name or description. Proximal convoluted tubules pursue looped and tortuous courses in the immediate vicinity of the renal corpuscles from which they originate (Fig. 457). They then enter medullary rays (Fig. 456) and descend in these as the upper parts of descending limbs of loops of Henle. The descending limbs enter the medulla and extend into it for different distances before looping back as ascending limbs (Fig. 454). Aside from becoming straight, the character of the proximal convoluted tubule does not change materially as it becomes the first part of the descending loop of Henle. It is only after it has descended for some distance that the character of the tubule changes. Therefore, there is a segment of the descending loop of Henle which, though straight, has the same character and presumably performs the same

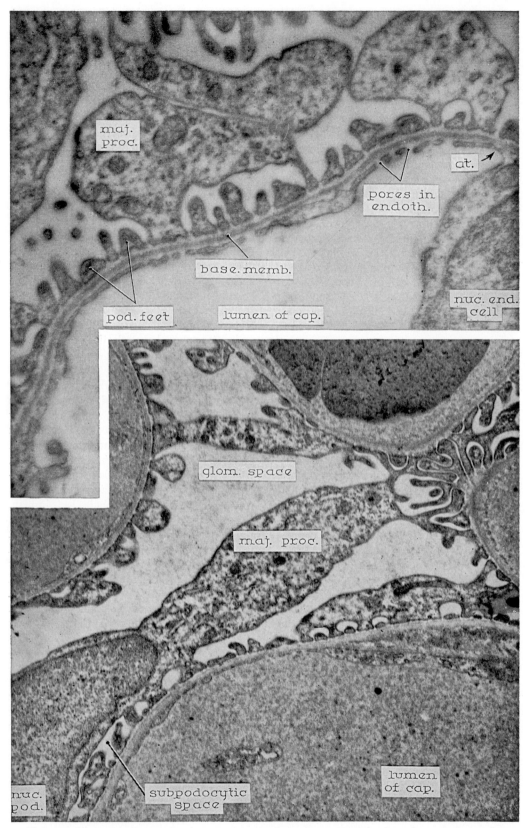

FIG. 463. Electron micrographs (*top*, × 30,000; *bottom*, × 22,000) of sections of glomerular capillaries and podocytes. (Pease, D. C.: J. Histochem. *3*:295, with labeling added)

function as the proximal convoluted tubule proper. This upper segment of the descending loop should be considered as part of the proximal convoluted tubule even though it is not convoluted.

In identifying and studying proximal convoluted tubules in sections of kidney cortex, a few points should be kept in mind. (1) For the most part they present themselves in such a preparation as oblique sections cut through curved tubes (Fig. 464). Reference to Figures 10 and 11 may assist the student in understanding why they appear as they do. (2) Oblique and cross sections of proximal convoluted tubules are the most common sight in a section of kidney cortex; hence, the kind of tubule that is seen most often is the proximal convoluted tubule (Fig. 464). (3) The cells of proximal convoluted tubules become altered very rapidly as a result of postmortem degeneration; consequently, many of the features of them that are described for their appearance in well-fixed material cannot be seen in the usual H and E section obtained from autopsy material. (4) Even if the cells of the proximal convoluted tubules are altered as a result of postmortem degeneration, their cytoplasm is generally more acidophilic than that of other tubules; accordingly, proximal convoluted tubules are not only the most numerous tubules seen in an H and E section of kidney cortex; they are also the pinkest (Fig. 464).

The cells of the walls of proximal convoluted tubules are broader at their bases, which lie against a basement membrane, than at their free margins, which abut on the lumen. These cells are often described as being truncated in the sense that they resemble pyramids that have had their apices cut off. The boundaries between adjacent cells cannot be seen to advantage because the edges of any two cells that touch each other are serrated with the projections from the edge of one fitting into the notches of the other. In tissue fixed immediately after death and suitably stained, the appearance of proximal convoluted tubules varies between two extremes. At one the epithelium is low, and the lumen wide and round; at the other the epithelium is high, and the lumen small and triangular. These two extreme appearances, as well as intermediate ones, are to be explained by two factors: (1) the state of functional activity of the epithelial cells of the tubule, and (2) the degree to which the lumen of the tubule is distended by glomerular filtrate; the latter is affected by whether or not the glomerulus of the nephron is producing much or little filtrate. It is believed that the low epithelium and the wide round lumen is associated with the production of much filtrate.

The nuclei of the cells of proximal convoluted tubules are disposed toward the bases of the cells. They are large and spherical and demonstrate nucleoli (Fig. 464).

Proximal convoluted tubules are ensheathed in a substantial basement membrane which is beautifully demonstrated by the P.A.S. technic (Fig. 464).

Fine Structure. The fine structure of the proximal convoluted tubules has been investigated by many workers, notably Rhodin and Pease.

The cell surfaces that face the lumen are covered with thin microvilli about 1 μ long, which in many respects are similar to those of the lining cells of the small intestine (Figs. 465, *top*, and 466, *top*). However, there is one way in which these microvilli differ from those of the intestine; there appears to be a sort of matrix that fills in the spaces between them. Accordingly, in electron micrographs of cross sections of microvilli, the matrix between individual microvilli may appear as prominent as the microvilli themselves, and this appearance may suggest that the microvilli, instead of being fingerlike structure that project into the lumen from the cell surface, are actually pits, lined with cell membrane, that project inwardly into the cytoplasm from the free surface of the cell. This view was suggested in the past to explain the E/M appearance of the brush border of the proximal convoluted tubule, but general opinion now holds the concept that the brush border consists of countless microvilli with some sort of jellylike matrix between them. Between the bases of adjacent microvilli the cell membrane sometimes extends down into the cytoplasm. The channels so formed may connect with vesicles. The number of microvilli is enormous, and obviously they increase the surface area greatly. In man, the total surface of the brush border of the proximal tubules of both kidneys is about 50 to 60 square meters and, as Fawcett has observed, the existence of such an enormous absorbing area goes a long way to explain the extraordinary capacity of the nephron for concentrating the glomerular filtrate.

At the base of a cell, the cell membrane shows many infoldings into the cytoplasm (Fig. 466, *bottom*). These infoldings or inflections are also seen in the distal convoluted tubule where they are more highly developed. They more or less divide the basal part of the cytoplasm into compartments which contain the characteristic long, large mitochondria of these cells. This system of infoldings of the cell membrane increases the surface through which fluid and dissolved materials can be resorbed by capillaries. Such resorption is known to require energy, and the close association of many mitochondria is a guarantee of a perfect enzymatic supply for the process. Ruska, Moore and Weinstock have studied this association of mitochondria and infoldings of the cell membrane and regard it as a functional unit for passing fluid resorbed from the lumen into the capillaries at the base of a tubule.

The basement membrane at the base of the cells is seen to advantage with the E/M; it can be seen at the lower right in the bottom picture in Figure 466.

Function. The proximal convoluted tubules probably resorb more than two thirds of the water of the glomerular filtrate that passes by them. Part of this absorption is facilitated by the fact that the blood in the capillaries that are disposed between them is rich in colloid (protein) and is under a low hydrostatic pressure. But some of the selective absorption that occurs here is against an osmotic gradient and so requires that the cells perform special absorptive work. For example, in a healthy person all the sugar in glomerular filtrate is resorbed in the proximal convoluted tubules. The presence of the enzyme phosphatase, which may be demonstrated in proximal convoluted tubules in kidney sections by a histochemical technic, is probably related to the resorption of sugar by these cells. In addition to sugar, the proximal convoluted tubules resorb part of the sodium chloride and the phosphates present in glomerular filtrate and several other substances. Their cells have been shown to contain many enzymes which are concerned in the resorptive phenomena in which they engage.

Cortical Capillaries. Fluid and dissolved substances resorbed from the proximal (or distal) convoluted tubules must pass through the basement membranes that surround these tubules to gain access to the capillaries which are disposed in beds around the tubules. Pease has shown that the endothelium of the capillaries that lie between tubules in the kidney cortex is like that of the glomerular capillaries, fenestrated. However, the pores are somewhat smaller. Only patches of fenestrated capillaries occur in the medulla.

The cells of the proximal convoluted tubules can also perform excretory functions. Evidence has accumulated to establish the excretory capacity of tubular cells from several sources and procedures: (1) species whose kidneys have tubules but no glomeruli, (2) species in which the glomeruli and the tubules of the kidney have a different blood supply and so permit the glomeruli to be put out of action by experimental procedures, (3) by lowering the blood pressure of animals in whose kidneys the glomeruli and the tubules have a common blood supply below the point at which glomeruli continue to produce tissue fluid, and (4) from the study of tubules in tissue culture. But while it is admitted that proximal convoluted tubules can indulge in excretory as well as resorptive functions, the modern physiologic view places much more emphasis on the latter than on the former.

Loop of Henle

Loops of Henle are either short or long. The majority of those nephrons, the glomeruli of which are in the outer part of the cortex, have short loops that do not extend for any great distance into the medulla; perhaps this is because they were the last nephrons to develop, and their loops had to accommodate themselves to such space as was available. The nephrons that arise from glomeruli near the medulla have long loops that extend well down into the medulla.

The first part of the descending loop is the straight continuation of the proximal convoluted tubule (Fig. 457). As this passes down into the medulla—a short distance in the instance of tubules that arise from glomeruli in the outer part of the cortex, and a greater distance in the instance of tubules that arise from glomeruli near the medulla—its lumen rather abruptly becomes narrower, and the cells of its walls squamous (Fig. 457). After this change has occurred the tubule is known as the *thin segment* of the descending limb of the loop of Henle. The thin segments of nephrons that arise from juxtamedullary glomeruli are much longer than those that arise from glomeruli in the outer part of the cortex (Fig. 454).

The appearance of this part of the nephron is so similar to that of a capillary that the student may not be able to distinguish easily these tubules in the medulla from the capillaries that run between them (Fig. 467). It may be of help to understand that the tubules are wider than capillaries, but they may be partly collapsed. In general, the nuclei of the epithelial cells of the tubules bulge into the lumen of the tubule somewhat more than the nuclei of the endothelial cells of the capillaries. The nuclei of the squamous cells of the tubules are somewhat closer together than the nuclei of the endothelial cells of capillaries. Red blood cells in the capillaries may also be helpful toward identifying them, but artefact may lead to red blood cells being present in the tubules. The distinction between tubules and capillaries is to be made more easily if the blood vessels are injected with colored injection mass, as is shown in Figure 467.

In the instance of long loops, the first portion of the ascending limb may be similar to the thin portion of the descending limb. But this soon gives way, in the ascending limb, to a wider tubule with thicker walls; this is known as the *thick segment* of the ascending arm (Fig. 457). The character of the thick segment is very similar to that of the distal convoluted tubule, which will soon be described. In the instance of nephrons with short loops of Henle, the epithelium may change from the thin to that of the thick type, even before the nephron has looped back to begin its ascending arm.

Function. The cells of the wall of the thin loops of Henle are not thick enough to permit their being visualized as performing as much *selective resorptive work* as the cells of the walls of either the proximal or the distal tubules. The histologic appearance of these cells would suggest that their chief functions might be that of serving as semipermeable membranes for osmotic phenomena. We have already described how the increased colloid content of blood in the capillaries, which lie between the tubules in the medulla, contributes to the return of fluid from the tubules to the blood stream. It might be thought that since the walls of this part of the tubule are so thin that a great percentage of water might be returned in this part of the loop. However, it is not believed that nearly so much water is returned here as in the proximal tubule; this could be partly explained by the fact that even though the loops here have thin walls the fluid within them has already become more concentrated than tissue fluid by having passed through the proximal tubule. Nevertheless, Trueta and his associates have stressed recently the function of this part of the tubule in returning water.

Crane points out that only animals with loops of Henle in their kidneys can secrete urine that is hypertonic to blood. Therefore, it would appear both that fluid is absorbed and electrolytes are concentrated in the thin loops. It would seem reasonable to expect that the increased electrolyte content in tubular fluid here is related to the fact that the colloids of blood are relatively concentrated in the capillaries that run between the tubules.

THE DISTAL CONVOLUTED TUBULE

As has been described already, the thick segment of the ascending loop of Henle returns to the glomerular root of the glomerulus from which the nephron has its origin, and there the part of its wall which comes into contact with the glomerular root becomes heavily nucleated and forms a thick spot, the *macula densa* (Figs. 458 and 459).

Some authorities define the distal convoluted tubule as only that part of the nephron which extends from the macula densa to a collecting tubule. However, more authorities classify the thick ascending arm of the loop of Henle as part of it. Distal convoluted tubules differ from proximal convoluted tubules in several respects which are listed below.

1. They are not so long; hence, cross and oblique sections of them are not seen nearly so often in a section of kidney cortex (Fig. 464).

2. Their cross-section diameters are generally not quite as great, but since the cells of

their walls are generally lower their lumens tend to be larger (Fig. 464).

3. The cells of their walls are smaller in all directions; hence a cross section through a distal tubule reveals many more nuclei than similar sections of proximal convoluted tubules (Fig. 464).

4. The cells of their walls have no brush or striated borders on their free surfaces, and their cytoplasm is not nearly so acidophilic (Fig. 464).

Like proximal convoluted tubules, the distal ones have a pronounced basement membrane encircling them (Fig. 464).

Fine Structure. The cell surfaces that face the lumen show only a few minor villous projections (Fig. 465, *bottom tubule*). The basal parts of the cells show very highly developed infoldings of the cell membrane which are even more highly developed than those seen at the bases of proximal convoluted cells and illustrated in the bottom picture of Figure 466; these more or less divide this portion of the cytoplasm into compartments which contain large long mitochondria. RNA granules are not nearly so numerous as in the cells of the proximal convoluted tubules.

Function. By the time glomerular filtrate has reached the distal convoluted tubules it has lost an estimated 85 per cent of its water content. Since 99 per cent is resorbed before the fluid reaches the collecting tubules, there remains about 14 per cent to be resorbed in the distal convoluted tubules. There is opinion to the effect that it is in the distal convoluted tubule that the antidiuretic hormone of the posterior lobe of the pituitary gland (to be described in Chap. 26) exerts its function. If this hormone is not present in the blood stream, the distal convoluted tubules do not, according to this theory, resorb their full complement of water; hence, the urinary output is greatly increased. Moreover, the distal convoluted tubules resorb the remainder of the sodium and the chloride that is to be resorbed as well as the remaining water.

Other Features of the Kidney

Collecting Tubules. These are not to be thought of as parts of nephrons, even though they may possibly absorb a little water. They comprise a series of drainage ducts into which

urine is delivered by distal convoluted tubules and conducted to medullary papillae where it is emptied into the calyces of the ureter (Figs. 454 and 457).

The collecting tubules form a branched system. The largest ones are known as the *ducts of Bellini*. These are easily seen in the apical part of a medullary pyramid where they empty through its papilla. They are large ducts with wide lumens and thick walls composed of pale-staining, high columnar cells with a thin cuticle on their free border. In contrast with the different parts of the renal tubules, the borders between the cells that make up the walls of the ducts of Bellini and the smaller collecting tubules that empty into them are distinct in the ordinary section (Fig. 468). The pale cytoplasm of these cells is illustrated in Figure 464. With the E/M, the cells of the collecting tubules have been found to have only moderately deep infoldings of the cell membrane from the base of the cell.

In the medulla, the ducts of Bellini branch at very acute angles (Fig. 454). Several generations of branches arise to provide a sufficient number of collecting ducts to supply each medullary ray in the kidney. In the rays, the ducts give off side branches. There each pursue a short arched course before becoming continuous with the termination of a distal convoluted tubule (Fig. 457).

Although each nephron is provided with an individual arched collecting tubule, several arched tubules empty into a single straight collecting tubule. Hence, there are not nearly so many straight collecting tubules as nephrons in the kidney

Casts. A cast is a structure formed by the solidification of material that is poured into a mold. In connection with the kidney, the term is used to describe coagulated material, usually protein, that is seen sometimes in the lumens of the more distal parts of nephrons and in collecting tubules. Casts are not seen in the strictly normal kidney. But material obtained at autopsy and used for teaching kidney histology may not always be strictly normal; hence, some casts may be seen in the lumens of the tubules in it. There are many types of casts, but generally they form as a result of some kind of protein material gaining entrance to the lumens of nephrons, and then as the material becomes more concentrated, as resorption of fluid occurs along the length of the nephron, the material coagulates. The fact that enough protein gains entrance to the lumens of nephrons to form casts indicates altered kidney function. Under normal circumstances, either no protein or, as some believe, a very little escapes into the glomerular filtrate. Even if the latter view is true, the amount is so limited that it is all resorbed by the tubules and does not accumulate to form casts. As it is being resorbed it may appear in the form of hyalin droplets in the cells of the proximal convoluted tubules.

The Connective Tissue of the Kidney. The kidney is covered with a thin translucent *capsule* that consists of fibrous connective tissue; the intercellular substance in it is chiefly collagen, but a few elastic fibers may be present. In health the capsule is smooth and glistening and can be stripped easily from the cortex. In some kinds of kidney disease fibrous connective tissue forms in the parenchyma of the cortex and extends out to the capsule to bind it firmly to the organ. Under these conditions the capsule cannot be stripped readily from the organ, and this fact is noted at autopsy as an indication that the kidney has become diseased.

The basement membranes that surround the tubules are supported on their outer surfaces by delicate reticular fibers. As already noted, the latter do not extend into the glomeruli except perhaps for a short distance into their roots. More substantial fibrous types of intercellular substance may be found in association with the larger vessels of the kidney. But, all in all, the fibrous connective tissue of the kidney parenchyma, except between the ducts of Bellini in the papilla, where there is some loose connective tissue, is extraordinarily scanty, a fact which suggests that there is a great amount of osmotic activity requiring that only substances through which diffusion can occur (amorphous types of intercellular substances) be present between the tubules and the capillaries. Increased fibrous tissue in the kidney is a manifestation of past disease and in itself acts as a cause of disease because it obstructs the diffusion and the filtration phenomena that normally ensue between capillaries and nephrons in the organ.

THE CIRCULATION OF BLOOD THROUGH THE KIDNEY

Each kidney is supplied by a renal artery. These are relatively large vessels that arise from the aorta, so each kidney receives large amounts of blood delivered under a high pressure.

Interlobar Arteries. On reaching the hilus of a kidney the renal artery divides, usually into three branches. Two of these (the anterior branches) commonly pass toward the concavity of the kidney in front of the pelvis of the ureter, and one (the posterior branch), behind it. Before entering the substance of the organ both the anterior and the posterior branches of the main vessel branch further. As a result of this branching, separate vessels are provided to penetrate the substance of the kidney between each pair of adjacent pyramids (Fig. 469). In addition, vessels are provided to extend up the outside border of the pyramids at the two poles of the kidney (Fig. 469). Since the pyramids represent lobes, the branches that ascend into the kidney substance between the medullary pyramids are called *interlobar arteries*. It is of interest that an interlobar artery does not ascend in the middle of a column of Bertin but at one of its sides, close to one of the pyramids that bounds the column (Fig. 469). The interlobar arteries, as they ascend in columns of Bertin, give off *small* branches to supply the perirenal fat, but the glomeruli in the columns of Bertin are supplied by branches from the next two types of artery to be described.

Arcuate Arteries. Some of the interlobar arteries break up into main branches as they ascend in the columns of Bertin, but most of them do so only when they have almost reached the corticomedullary border. Here their branches are given off at wide angles, nearly at right angles, and in all directions in this plane. These main branches, into which the interlobar arteries break up, arch over the bases of the medullary pyramids and are called *arcuate* (*arcuatus* = arched) arteries. Actually, the group of arcuate arteries that arise from each interlobar artery should be compared with a single stone in a stone arch; the name arcuate was given to these vessels because *together* they form an arch. But as there is no continuity between the stones in a stone arch, there is no continuity between the arcuate arteries that arise from any given interlobar artery and those that arise from any other. Hence, there are no anastomoses between interlobar arteries through arcuate arteries (Fig. 469). Accordingly, if an interlobar artery becomes plugged with a thrombus, a pyramidal-shaped segment of kidney tissue dies (the area supplied by the arcuate arteries from that particular interlobar artery).

Interlobular Arteries. The arcuate arteries give off branches that ascend into the cortex (Fig. 469). These vessels run between lobules and are termed interlobular arteries (Figs. 469 and 470). They mark the boundaries between lobules and so alternate with the medullary rays that form the central cores of lobules (Fig. 456).

The interlobular arteries give off branches at wide angles on every side. Since these immediately enter the substance of surrounding lobules (the cortical labyrinth), they are called *intralobular arteries* (Fig. 470). These give rise to the afferent vessels of glomeruli. However, the terminal branches of the interlobular arteries continue on to the capsule to supply its capillary bed.

How the Capillary Beds of Cortex and Medulla Are Supplied. The efferent arterioles of glomeruli in different parts of the cortex deliver blood into different capillary beds. As may be seen in Figure 470, which is based on the study of Morison, the efferent arterioles from glomeruli in the outer part of the cortex (Fig. 470) empty their blood into the capillary beds that surround the proximal and the distal convoluted tubules in the cortex. Those from glomeruli somewhat deeper in the cortex (Fig. 470) contribute to the capillary bed of the cortex but also to long straight capillarylike vessels that descend into the medulla and are called *arteriolae rectae spuriae* (false straight arterioles) for reasons that will become obvious later. The efferent vessels from the deepest glomeruli in the cortex, some of which are below the level of the arcuate arteries, deliver most or all of their blood into the arteriolae rectae spuriae (Fig. 470).

The return of the blood from the capillary beds of the cortex and the medulla is illustrated on the right side of Figure 470. In general, the veins correspond to the arteries already described. It is to be noted that at the surface of the kidney little veins arise from the capillary beds of the capsule and the superficial part of the cortex to pass in a converging fashion to interlobular veins. Since these end branches radiate out in a starlike fashion from the ends of the interlobular veins, they are called *stellate veins* (Fig. 470).

Since the arteriolae rectae spuriae, which supply the capillary beds of the medulla, are all supplied by the efferent vessels of glomeruli in the deeper part of the cortex (Fig. 470), it follows that all the blood that is delivered into the capillary beds of the medulla, like that which is delivered into the capillary beds of the cortex, has passed immediately beforehand through glomeruli and consequently has an increased protein content. This fact is of considerable significance to an understanding of kidney function, as has been explained already. However, that it is a fact has been contested from time to time. It has been claimed by some who have investigated the circulation of blood through the medulla that arterioles arise directly from the arcuate and the interlobular arteries to pass directly to the capillary beds of the medulla. To distinguish these from the arteriolae rectae spuriae (the false straight arterioles) they are called the *arteriolae rectae verae* (true straight arterioles). If these exist it would mean that the medulla was supplied with blood that had not passed through glomeruli. Most modern students of this matter do not believe that enough of these exist to be of any functional significance. Hartroft's study shows how some vessels, apparently of this nature, could arise through the fusion of the afferent and the efferent arterioles of the juxtamedullary glomeruli that undergo a physiologic atrophy during the growth of the kidney. Moreover, MacCallum's study shows how estimates of the number of arteriolae rectae verae present in normal kidneys might be overestimated because of their being investigated in kidneys that have been injured throughout life by disease. He has shown that the capillaries of glomeruli that are affected by certain disease processes tend to atrophy and disappear, and at the same time a more or less direct connection becomes established between their afferent and efferent vessels. Unless an observer looked very carefully, he might fail to see these atrophied glomeruli—and there are some, according to MacCallum, even in apparently normal kidneys (Hartroft's physiologic atrophy?)—and so the observer might conclude that what is really an afferent arteriole joined to an efferent arteriole at the site of a defunct glomerulus is an arteriole that has extended from an interlobular artery directly to the capillary bed of the medulla without there being a glomerulus inserted along its course. Therefore, general opinion is to the effect that for all practical purposes the blood in the capillary beds of the medulla has passed through glomeruli and has an increased colloid content over that of blood elsewhere and that this would be effective in withdrawing fluid from nephrons back into blood by osmotic phenomena.

It is possible that a small amount of blood that has not passed through glomeruli may be delivered to the capillary beds of the cortex by means of branches of afferent arterioles that have long been described as emptying into these beds. Such a branch of an afferent arteriole is known as a *Ludwig's arteriole.*

The Two Circulatory Pathways Through the Kidney. During World War II, attention was focused on the study of those unfortunate individuals who were partly buried by rubble when buildings collapsed from bombing. It was found that an individual whose legs had been crushed by a great weight but not necessarily irreparably injured would, in some instances and some days after the event, fail to excrete urine. Many injured in this fashion died after a short period of apparent recovery, not from their primary injuries but from kidney failure. This condition, termed *crush syndrome,* inspired Trueta, a surgeon, and his associates to make investigations which have thrown great light upon how the route taken by blood through the kidney may be altered in what is generally termed *shock.*

To understand this matter the student should refer back to Figure 470. This shows that the efferent vessels of the glomeruli in the outer part of the cortex (labeled 1 and 2) empty into the capillary bed of the cortical labyrinth, while those of the glomeruli near the border of the medulla, which Trueta terms

the *juxtamedullary glomeruli* (labeled 3 and 4), empty almost entirely into the arteriolae rectae spuriae which supply the capillary beds of the medulla (the capillary beds of both the cortex and the medulla are, of course, continuous (Fig. 470). Furthermore, it is to be observed that the juxtamedullary glomeruli are larger than those nearer the surface of the kidney, and, as has been noted, the lumens of their efferent vessels may be larger than the lumens of their afferent vessels.

Trueta and his associates found that injuries, such as those occasioned when limbs are crushed, can reflexly cause spasm of certain blood vessels in the kidney. In general, the chief effect is on the peripheral two-thirds of the interlobular arteries, which become constricted. Another factor that can have much the same effect as spasm of these vessels is a plasma loss from the circulatory system, for the amount of fluid in the circulatory system is an important factor in keeping blood vessels open. Accordingly, it is easy to visualize that spasm in the smaller arterial vessels in the kidney and a lack of fluid in the circulatory system (as can occur in untreated shock) could result in the smaller arterioles becoming pinched off and this could lead to impaired function in, or even in the death of, kidney tissue. Since the greatest effect would be exerted on the smaller arterial vessels, the impairment of circulation would be greatest toward the periphery of the kidney. Conditions can arise, therefore, when it is possible for blood to continue to circulate through the juxtamedullary glomeruli while ceasing to circulate through the glomeruli in the outer part of the kidney. Under these conditions, the whole outer part of the cortex becomes relatively pale and bloodless. Thus, all the blood that circulates through the kidney passes through the more deeply disposed glomeruli (the juxtamedullary ones), and since the efferent vessels of these empty almost entirely into the arteriolae rectae spriae, the blood from them is conducted to the capillary beds of the medulla rather than to those of the cortex.

LYMPHATICS OF THE KIDNEY

As was explained in Chapter 6, lymphatic capillaries, in most parts of the body, serve the purpose of draining away and returning to the blood stream that portion of tissue fluid that is not absorbed by the venous ends of capillaries. Moreover, when blood capillaries are injured, so that they exude substantial quantities of colloid into the tissues (Fig. 95), the presence of lymphatic capillaries is particularly advantageous because they are permeable to the colloid and so help return it to the blood stream.

The problem relating to the production and the absorption of tissue fluid, and hence to the role of lymphatic capillaries, in the kidney is considerably different from that in most parts of the body. Such tissue fluid is produced in the kidney by glomerular capillaries and passes into the lumens of nephrons as glomerular filtrate. Practically all of the other capillaries in the kidney are comparable with the venous ends of ordinary capillaries in that they are concerned with absorption and not with the production of fluid. Therefore, it is obvious that, except in glomeruli, tissue fluid is not produced in the parenchyma of the kidney; it is merely resorbed through the walls of nephrons back into capillaries. Furthermore, as has been pointed out, the blood that supplies the capillary beds of the tubular portions of nephrons has a relatively increased content of colloid and is admirably suited to draw fluid back into the capillaries.

Lymphatic capillaries, if they were present in glomeruli, would provide an alternative route of escape for tissue fluid; hence, if they were present, they would interfere with glomerular capillaries delivering tissue fluid into the lumens of nephrons. Therefore, it is not surprising that lymphatic capillaries have not been found in glomeruli. Since tissue fluid is not produced by capillaries elsewhere in the kidney parenchyma, but only absorbed, and since the blood in these beds has passed through glomeruli and so has an increased colloid content which makes it admirably suited to absorbing fluid, there does not seem to be much need for lymphatic capillaries here either, so it is not surprising that, with the possible exception of some in the medulla, lymphatic capillaries do not appear to be present in kidney parenchyma but only where there are substantial amounts of connective tissue, in particular that associated with the blood vessels.

The distribution of the lymphatics of the kidney has been investigated in recent years by Peirce and by Rawson. Peirce, using stab injections and other methods, could not satisfy himself that there were any lymphatics in the kidney other than those that accompany the blood vessels. He found that the periarterial plexuses were richer in lymphatics than the perivenous plexuses and that the lymphatics of the plexuses could be traced from the renal artery and vein along the interlobar, arcuate and interlobular vessels to the capsule of the kidney where they communicated with capsular lymphatics. However, they were not found to extend into the actual parenchyma of the cortex or the medulla from these vessels. He found valves in the larger lymphatics in the hilus of the kidney. Rawson, somewhat later, studied the lymphatics of a kidney which had been invaded by cancer cells, and he used their presence for mapping out the lymphatics. In general, Rawson found lymphatics in the same sites as those described by Peirce but he also found evidence of some lymphatic capillaries which began beneath the epithelium of the tip of the medullary pyramid and extended toward the base of the medullary pyramid where they emptied into the lymphatics associated with the arcuate vessels. However, none were found in the actual parenchyma of the cortex.

POSTNATAL GROWTH OF THE KIDNEY

The growth of the kidney, in early postnatal life, has been investigated more extensively in the rat than in any other species; hence, most of the information given here relates to the studies made on this animal.

It has been shown both by Kittelson and Arataki that only about one third of the number of glomeruli that are to be found in the adult are present at birth. Glomeruli continue to be formed for about 100 days after birth, but the majority are formed in the first 3 to 4 weeks.

The first-formed glomeruli are in the region close to the medulla, and many of these undergo a physiologic atrophy (Hartroft) and disappear. However, in some instances their afferent and efferent vessels may remain and

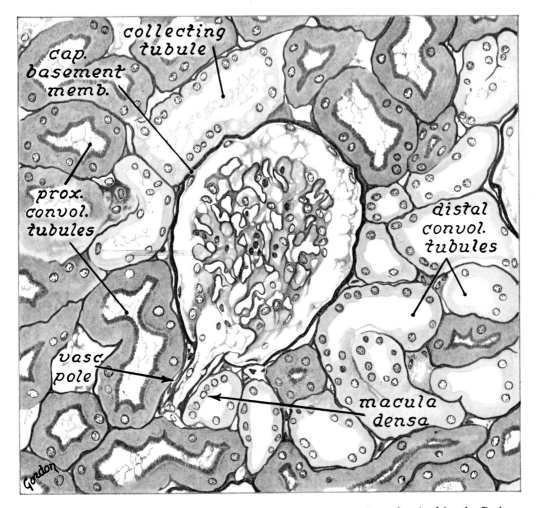

FIG. 464. Drawing of a section of human kidney fixed in formalin and stained by the P. A. Schiff technic followed by hematoxylin. Note the P. A. S. positive brush borders of the proximal convoluted tubules and that the cytoplasm of the cells of these tubules stains more deeply than that of the cells of the distal convoluted or collecting tubules. Note the P. A. S. positive basement membranes that surround the tubules. Basement membrane is also present under both the visceral and the parietal layers of Bowman's capsule. The numerous capillaries that lie between adjacent tubules are collapsed and hence not seen in this preparation. The vascular pole of the glomerulus has been cut obliquely and is not as prominent as it otherwise would be.

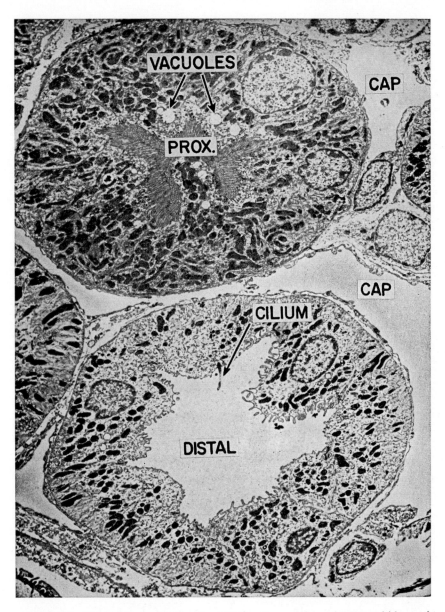

Fig. 465. Electron micrograph (× 3,000) of a section of mouse kidney. A proximal convoluted tubule (*top*) and a distal convoluted tubule (*bottom*) are cut in cross section. Their surrounding capillaries appear as empty spaces. Nuclei and mitochondria are obvious in the cells of both tubules. The lumen of the proximal tubule is filled with microvilli, while that of the distal tubule is open. Microvilli are sparse and short in the distal tubule cells, and occasionally a cilium can be seen. (One is visible here in the cell nearest to the proximal tubule.) (Rhodin, J.: *in* Clark, G. L. (ed.): Encyclopedia of Microscopy, New York, Rheinhold)

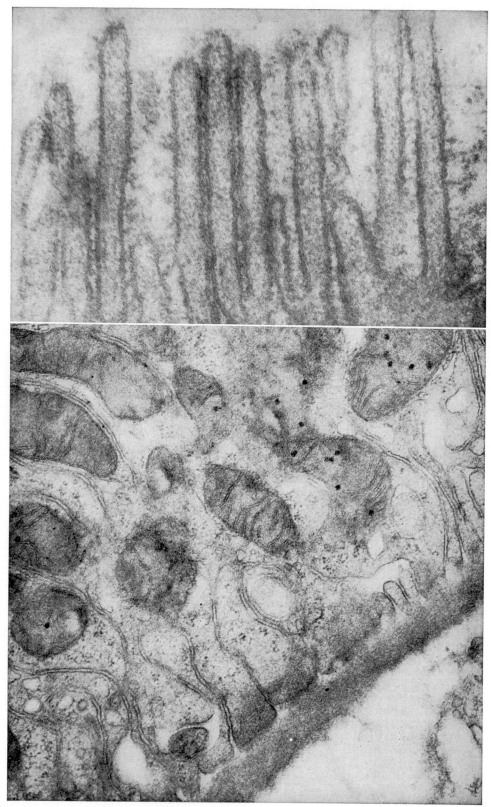

FIGURE 466. (*Caption on facing page*)

injected capillaries

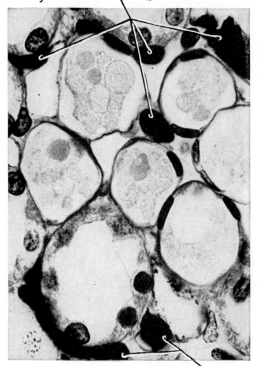

injected capillaries

FIG. 467. High-power photomicrograph of a section of the medulla of a rat's kidney, showing thin loops of Henle cut in cross section. The capillaries are injected with India ink and hence are black. (Preparation and photomicrograph of Dr. W. S. Hartroft)

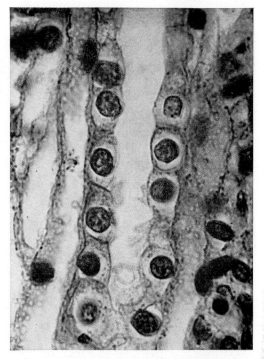

FIG. 468. Medium-power photomicrograph of a section of the medulla of a rat's kidney, showing a collecting tubule cut in longitudinal section. Notice that the adjacent borders of its cells are distinct. (Preparation and photomicrograph of Dr. W. S. Hartroft)

fuse to constitute a few arteriolae rectae verae. The oldest glomeruli, which are also the largest, are to be found near the arcuate vessels. At birth, the outer part of the cortex of the kidney is undifferentiated, and it is here that new nephrons are formed. After birth, renal corpuscles develop in the outer cortex of the kidney (the nephrogenic zone). The tubule of each new nephron then becomes connected to the duct system. The youngest nephrons are those situated in the outer cortex immediately beneath the capsule, and these are not fully differentiated for about 3 months after birth. The glomeruli of these nephrons are the smallest in the kidney. Figure 452 illustrates the classic theory of the development of the renal corpuscle. This theory has the advantage of being easily understandable, but recent work indicates that the renal corpuscle develops *in situ* and not by invagination

FIG. 466. Electron micrographs of a section of parts of a proximal convoluted tubule from a rat kidney. The upper one ($\times$ 120,000) is of microvilli of the brush border, and each is seen to be covered by an extension of the cell membrane which shows two thin dark lines separated by a light interval. The lower micrograph ($\times$ 47,500) is of part of the base of the proximal tubule cell. The homogeneous basement membrane is seen (*lower right*) and the cell membrane adjacent to it is inflected into the cytoplasm as a series of parallel double membranes. Mitochondria showing cristae and dense mitochondrial bodies lie in the cytoplasm between these membranes. (Preparation by Dr. H. Movat)

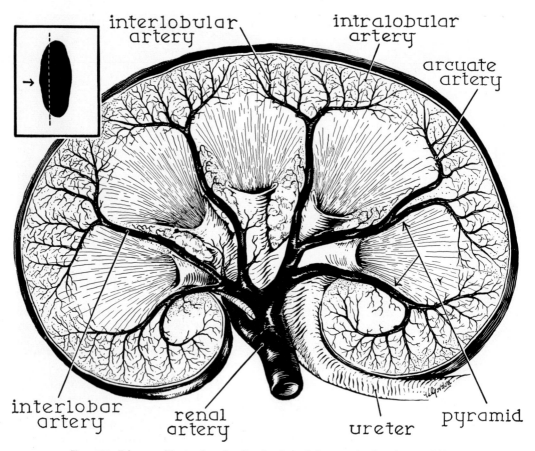

interlobular artery

intralobular artery

arcuate artery

interlobar artery

renal artery

ureter

pyramid

FIG. 469. Diagram illustrating the distribution of the arteries in a human kidney.

by capillaries of the blind end of a previously formed tubule. In the renal cortex, a clump of cells is associated with the end of a developing tubule. Some of these cells become the parietal and visceral epithelial cells of Bowman's capsule, and others become endothelial cells. The capillaries so formed later connect with the vascular system.

The size of the kidneys in postnatal life is affected both by the diet and by hormones. High protein diets make the kidneys become larger. Injections of male sex hormone also make the kidneys of experimental animals become larger. The increase in size that occurs with high protein diets or male hormone treatment is brought about by nephrons increasing in size and not in number.

If one kidney is removed from adult animals the remaining kidney becomes larger. The increase in size is due to the nephrons becoming larger and not more numerous. How-

ever, in individual nephrons there is an increase in the number of cells of which they are composed, and mitotic figures can be seen in the nephrons of the remaining kidney for a period following the removal of the other. The kidneys also become larger during pregnancy; this is termed a physiologic hypertrophy, and mitotic figures have been found in the nephrons as they enlarge in this condition.

THE URETER

The wall of the ureter has 3 coats: (1) a mucous membrane, (2) a muscular coat and (3) a fibro-elastic adventitia.

Mucous Membrane. This consists of only 2 layers, an epithelial lining and a lamina propria. The epithelium is of the transitional type (Fig. 472) and is from 4 to 5 cells in thickness, except in the pelvis, where it is somewhat thinner. Transitional epithelium is described in detail in Chapter 11, and infor-

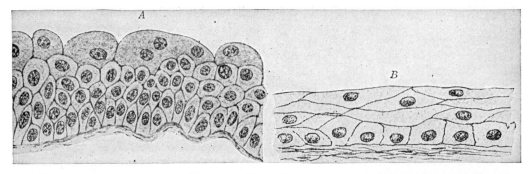

F IG. 472. Drawings of transitional epithelium from the human bladder: (*A*) in collapsed condition; (*B*) in distended condition. (Addison: Piersol's Normal Histology, ed. 15, Philadelphia, Lippincott)

male is a part of both the reproductive and the urinary systems, its description may be postponed until the male reproductive system is considered. However, the urethra of the female serves no genital function but only a urinary one; hence, its structure will be described here.

The female urethra is said to vary in length from 2 to 6 cm. There is some difference of opinion about its average length, different estimates ranging from about 3 cm. to about 4½ cm. It is a fairly straight muscular tube lined by mucous membrane. The musculature of its wall consists of 2 coats of smooth muscle fibers; those of the inner one are disposed longitudinally, and those of the outer coat, circularly. At its external orifice striated muscle fibers reinforce the smooth ones to form an external sphincter.

In cross section the lumen of the urethra is seen to be roughly crescentic. The mucous membrane is thrown into longitudinal folds. The epithelium of most of the urethra is stratified or pseudostratified columnar in type. However, transitional epithelium is present near the bladder and stratified squamous near the external orifice. The relatively thick connective tissue lamina propria, particularly in its deeper part, which is sometimes called the *submucosa,* is rich in elastic fibers and plexuses of veins; the latter are sufficiently extensive to give the deeper portions of the lamina propria a resemblance to erectile tissue.

In many sites the epithelium extends into the lamina propria to form little outpocketings. These little glandlike structures commonly contain mucous cells. In the aged, con-

cretions may form in them. True glands, opening by fine ducts into the lumen of the urethra, have also been described as being present, particularly in its upper part.

INNERVATION OF THE URINARY SYSTEM

Nerve fibers reach the kidney by way of the renal plexus. This is a network of nerve fibers that extends along the renal artery from the aorta to the kidney. The bodies of ganglion cells also may be present in the renal plexus; if so they are to be regarded as outlying cells of diffuse celiac and aortic ganglia. Most of the fibers in the renal plexus are those of the sympathetic division of the autonomic system and are derived from the cells of the celiac and the aortic ganglia. Parasympathetic fibers occur in the renal plexus in smaller numbers. These are derived from the vagus nerve, whose fibers, to reach the renal plexus, course through the celiac plexus without interruption.

The nerve fibers from the renal plexus follow the arteries into the substance of the kidney. Harman and Davies have recently described their distribution within the organ. They penetrate glomeruli to form extensive perivascular networks in these structures. They also supply the epithelium of the convoluted tubules, the transitional epithelium of the pelvis and the walls of the arteries and the veins.

Since transplanted kidneys, which are necessarily removed from a nerve supply, and kidneys left in situ but with the nerves that supply them cut, both function in a fairly normal fashion, it is obvious that the functions of the kidney are not fundamentally dependent on nervous mechanisms. However, nervous mechanisms control kidney function to some extent. It seems likely that most of the control is mediated by way of the sympathetic fibers that terminate in the blood vessels. The way in which this nervous regulation can operate to cause the blood to circulate chiefly through the juxtamedullary glomeruli, as in crush syndrome, has already been described. The part played by the parasympathetic, vagus-derived fibers in the kidney is obscure. One might speculate as to whether they affect the secretory activities of the cells of the proximal convoluted tubules in some way. But it seems clear that the nervous regulation of kidney function is chiefly mediated through sympathetic vasomotor nerves.

Afferent impulses travel over nerves in the renal plexus, for cutting the fibers of the plexus abolishes pain of renal origin.

Both sympathetic and parasympathetic fibers course along the ureter. But they do not seem to be particularly concerned with the normal peristaltic movements that sweep down the musculature of this tube, for the movements continue if these nerves are cut. Some of the nerves here carry afferent impulses.

The bladder is supplied by fibers from both the sympathetic and the parasympathetic divisions of the autonomic system. The parasympathetic fibers are derived from the sacral outflow. The terminal ganglia to which they lead are present in the bladder wall; hence, in sections of bladder the student may occasionally observe ganglion cells. Stimulation of the parasympathetic fibers to the bladder leads to relaxation of the sphincter and contraction of the muscle of the bladder; hence, the act of evacuating the bladder, called micturition, is brought about by impulses traveling along parasympathetic fibers from the sacral outflow. Obviously, impairment of the spinal cord above the level at which these fibers arise interferes with micturition. The sympathetic fibers exert an effect opposite to those of the parasympathetic, hence, their stimulation tends to relax the musculature of the bladder wall and constrict the sphincter.

The desire for micturition is not experienced in the normal individual until the bladder comes to contain a moderate amount of urine. The tonus of the smooth muscle of the bladder wall remains fairly constant as the bladder fills. It is only when the organ becomes well filled that the degree of tonus becomes increased to the point where afferent fibers are stimulated. In very young children micturition occurs reflexly when this point is reached. But as children become older they gain a considerable degree of voluntary control over this reflex. For example, an adult, on feeling the desire to micturate, may voluntarily postpone the act, and in so doing, may lose for a time the desire to micturate. This is probably accomplished by voluntary considerations somehow resulting in sympathetic stimulation which relaxes the tonus of the bladder wall so that the afferent impulses (set up by increased tone and responsible for the desire to micturate) are for a time abolished.

The fact that an individual can refrain from micturating, even though the desire to micturate is experienced, and the fact that an individual can micturate even though the desire for micturition (requiring afferent stimulation) is not present, both suggest the existence of a mechanism by which voluntary control is exerted over autonomic neurons. In considering this it should be kept in mind that the urethra is provided with a sphincter of striated muscle under voluntary control, as well as the internal sphincter of smooth muscle that is innervated by the autonomic system. It would not be surprising if reflexes controlling the smooth muscle sphincters were set up by the tightening or the relaxation of the voluntary sphincters so that both tended to act in harmony. In other words, perhaps what appears to be voluntary control over autonomically innervated smooth muscle sphincters is, at least in part, indirect rather than direct.

REFERENCES

URINARY SYSTEM REFERENCES—GENERAL

Allen, A. C.: The Kidney: Medical and Surgical Diseases, New York, Grune & Stratton, 1951.

Bell, E. T.: Renal Diseases, Philadelphia, Lea & Febiger, 1946.

Goldblatt, H.: Experimental hypertension induced by renal ischemia, Harvey Lect. *33*:237, 1937-38.

Huber, G. C.: Renal tubules *in* Cowrdy's Special Cytology, ed. 2, p. 933, New York, Hoeber, 1932.

McManus, J. F. A.: Medical Diseases of the Kidney, Philadelphia, Lea & Febiger, 1950.

Oliver, J.: New directions in renal morphology: a method, its results and its future, Harvey Lect. *40*:102, 1944-45.

Smith, H. W.: The Kidney—Structure and Function in Health and Disease, ed. 2, New York, Oxford, 1956.

Symposium: Histochemistry and the elucidation of kidney structure and function, J. Histochem. *3*:243, 1955.

References on Glomeruli, Including Their Fine Structure

Bergstrand, A.: Electron microscopic investigations of the renal glomeruli, Lab. Invest. *6*:191, 1957.

Book, M. H.: The secreting area of the glomerulus, J. Anat. *71*:91, 1936.

Boyer, C. C.: The vascular pattern of the renal glomerulus as revealed by plastic reconstruction from serial sections, Anat. Rec. *125*:433, 1956.

Dunihue, F. W.: Cellular components of the renal glomerulus, Anat. Rec. *127*:286, 1957.

Elias, H.: The structure of the renal glomerulus, Anat. Rec. *127*:288, 1957.

Hall, B. V.: Studies of normal glomerular structure by electron microscopy, Proc. Fifth Ann. Conf. Nephrotic Syndrome, p. 1, New York, National Nephrosis Foundation, 1953.

————: Further studies of the normal structure of the renal glomerulus, Proc. Sixth Ann. Conf. Nephrotic Syndrome, p. 1, New York, National Nephrosis Foundation, 1954.

Kirkman, H., and Stowell, R. E.: Renal filtration surface in the albino rat, Anat. Rec. *83*:373, 1942.

Lewis, O. J.: The development of the blood vessels of the metanephros, J. Anat. *92*:84, 1958.

————: The vascular arrangement of the mammalian renal glomerulus as revealed by a study of its development, J. Anat. *92*:433, 1958.

McGregor, L.: The finer histology of the normal glomerulus, Am. J. Path. *5*:545, 1929.

McManus, J. F. A.: Structure of the glomerulus of the human kidney, Am. J. Path. *24*:1259, 1948.

McManus, J. F. A., Lupton, C. H., Jr., and Graham, L. S., Jr.: The demonstration of the intercapillary space of the human renal glomerulus, Anat. Rec. *110*:57, 1951.

Pease, D. C.: Fine structures of the kidney seen by electron miscroscopy, J. Histochem. *3*:295, 1955.

Pease, D. C., and Baker, R. F.: Electron microscopy of the kidney, Am. J. Anat. *87*:249, 1950.

Richards, A. N.: Urine formation in the amphibian kidney, Harvey Lect. *30*:93, 1934-35.

Rytand, D. A.: The number and size of mammalian glomeruli as related to kidney and to body weight, with methods for their enumeration and measurement, Am. J. Anat. *62*:507, 1938.

Smith, J. P.: Anatomical features of the human renal glomerular efferent vessel, J. Anat. *90*:290, 1956.

Vimtrup, B.: On the number, shape, structure and surface area of the glomeruli in the kidneys of man and mammals, Am. J. Anat. *41*:123, 1928.

References on the Vascular Pole and JG Cells

Bing, J., and Kazimierczak, J.: Renin content of different parts of the periglomerular circumference, Acta path. et microbiol. scandinav. *50*:1, 1960.

Dunihue, F. W.: The effect of adrenal insufficiency and desoxycorticosterone acetate on the juxtaglomerular apparatus (abstr.), Anat. Rec. *103*:442, 1949.

Dunihue, F. W., and Robertson, Van B.: The effect of desoxycorticosterone acetate and of sodium on the juxtaglomerular apparatus, Endocrinology *61*:293, 1957.

Garber, B. G., McCoy, F. W., Marks, B. H., and Hayes, E. R.: Factors that affect the granulation of the juxtaglomerular apparatus, Anat. Rec. *130*:303, 1958.

Goormaghtigh, N.: Existence of an endocrine gland in the media of the renal arterioles, Proc. Soc. Exper. Biol. & Med. *42*:688, 1939.

————: Facts in favour of an endocrine function of the renal arterioles, J. Path. & Bact. *57*:392, 1945.

————: La fonction endocrine des arterioles renales, Louvain, Fonteyn, 1944.

————: Histological changes in the ischemic kidney with special reference to the juxtaglomerular apparatus, Am. J. Path. *16*:409, 1940.

Hartroft, P. M., and Hartroft, W. S.: The effects of dietary factors and administration of desoxycorticosterone acetate (DCA) on juxtaglomerular cells of the rat (abstr.), Anat. Rec. *112*:39, 1952.

————: Studies on renal juxtaglomerular cells, J. Exper. Med. *102*:205, 1955.

Hartroft, P. M., and Edelman, R.: Renal juxtaglomerular cells in sodium deficiency *in* Moyer and Fuchs (eds.): Edema, pp. 63-68, Philadelphia, Saunders, 1960.

Hartroft, P. M., Newmark, L. N., and Pitcock, J. A.: Relationship of renal juxtaglomerular cells to sodium intake, adrenal cortex and hypertension *in* J. Moyer (ed.): Hypertension, pp. 24-31, Philadelphia, Saunders, 1959.

Marks, B. H., and Garber, B. G.: The juxtaglomerular apparatus as an extra adrenal site of ACTH action, Anat. Rec. *133*:306, 1959.

McManus, J. F. A.: Further observations on the glomerular root of the vertebrate kidney, Quart. J. Micro. Sc. *88*:39, 1947.

Pitcock, J. A., Hartroft, P. M., and Newmark, L. N.: Increased renal pressor activity (renin) in sodium deficient rats and correlation with juxtaglomerular cell granulation, Proc. Soc. Exper. Biol. & Med. *100*:868, 1959.

Selye, H., and Stone, H.: Pathogenesis of the cardiovascular and renal changes which usually accompany malignant hypertension, J. Urol. *56*:399, 1946.

Tobian, L., Janecek, J., and Tomboulian, A.: Correlation between granulation of juxtaglomerular cells and extractable renin in rats with experimental hypertension, Proc. Soc. Exper. Biol. & Med. *100*:94, 1959.

Wilson, W.: A new staining method for demonstrating the granules of the juxtaglomerular complex, Anat. Rec. *112*:497, 1952.

REFERENCES ON OTHER PARTS OF THE NEPHRON, INCLUDING FINE STRUCTURE

Bensley, R. R., and Steen, W. B.: The functions of the differentiated segments of the uriniferous tubule, Am. J. Anat. *41*:75, 1928.

Dalton, A. J.: Structural details of some of the epithelial cell types in the kidney of the mouse as revealed by the electron microscope, J. Nat. Cancer Inst. *11*:1163, 1951.

Edwards, J. G.: Functional sites and morphological differentiation in the renal tubule, Anat. Rec. *55*:343, 1953.

———: Studies on aglomerular and glomerular kidneys, Am. J. Anat. *42*:75, 1928.

Fawcett, D. W.: Structural specializations of the cell surface *in* Palay, S. L. (ed.): Frontiers in Cytology, pp. 19-41, New Haven, Conn., Yale Univ. Press, 1958.

Holton, S. G., and Bensley, R. R.: The function of the differentiated parts of the uriniferous tubule in the mammal, Am. J. Anat. *47*:241, 1931.

Longley, J. B., and Fisher, E. R.: Alkaline phosphatase and the periodic acid Schiff reaction in the proximal tubule of the vertebrate kidney, Anat. Rec. *120*:1, 1954.

Marshall, E. K., Jr.: A comparison of the function of the glomerular and aglomerular kidney, Am. J. Physiol. *94*:1, 1930.

Pease, D. C.: Electron microscopy of the tubular cells of the kidney cortex, Anat. Rec. *121*:723, 1955.

———: Fine structures of the kidney seen by electron microscopy, J. Histochem. *3*:295, 1955.

Rhodin, J.: Correlation of ultrastructural organization and function in normal and experimentally changed proximal convoluted tubule cells of the mouse kidney, Karolinska Institutet, Stockholm, Aktiebolaget Godvil, 1954.

———: Anatomy of the kidney tubules, Internat. Rev. Cytol. *7*:485, 1958.

Richards, A. N., and Walker, A. M.: Methods of collecting fluid from known regions of the renal tubules of amphibia and perfusing the lumen of a single tubule, Am. J. Physiol. *118*:111, 1937.

Ruska, H., Moore, D. H., and Weinstock, J.: The base of the proximal convoluted tubule cells of rat kidney, J. Biophys. & Biochem. Cytol. *3*:249, 1957.

Sjöstrand, F. S., and Rhodin, J.: The ultrastructure of the proximal convoluted tubules of the mouse kidney as revealed by high resolution electron microscopy, Exper. Cell. Res. *4*:426, 1953.

REFERENCES ON THE RENAL CIRCULATION

Barclay, A. E., Daniel, P., Franklin, J. K., Prichard, M. M. L., and Trueta, J.: Records and findings obtained during studies of the renal circulation in the rabbit, with special reference to vascular short-circuiting and functional cortical ischaemia, J. Physiol. *105*:27, 1946.

Baringer, J. R.: The dynamic anatomy of the microcirculation in the amphibian and mammalian kidney, Anat. Rec. *130*:266, 1958.

Bensley, R. D.: The efferent vessels of the renal glomeruli of mammals as a mechanism for the control of glomerular activity and pressure, Am. J. Anat. *44*:141, 1929.

Bialestock, D.: The extra-glomerular arterial circulation of the renal tubules, Anat. Rec. *129*:53, 1957.

Daniel, P. M., Peabody, C. N., and Prichard, M. M. L.: Cortical ischaemia of the kidney with maintained blood flow through the medulla, Quart. J. Exper. Physiol. *37*:11, 1952.

———: Observations on the circulation through the cortex and the medulla of the kidney, Quart. J. Exper. Physiol. *36*:199, 1951.

Daniel, P. M., Prichard, M. M. L., and Ward-McQuaid, J. N.: The renal circulation in experimental hypertension, Brit. J. Surg. *42*:81, 1954.

Graves, F. T.: The anatomy of the intrarenal arteries and its application to segmental resection of the kidney, Brit. J. Surg. *42*:132, 1954.

———: The anatomy of the intrarenal arteries in health and disease, Brit. J. Surg. *43*:605, 1956.

Grollman, A., Muirhead, E. E., and Vanatta, J.: Role of kidney in pathogenesis of hypertension as determined by study of effects of bilateral nephrectomy and other experimental procedures on blood pressure of dog, Am. J. Physiol. *157*: 21, 1949.

MacCallum, D. B.: The arterial blood supply of the mammalian kidney, Am. J. Anat. *38*:153, 1926.

————: The bearing of degenerating glomeruli on the problem of the vascular supply of the mammalian kidney, Am. J. Anat. *65*:69, 1939.

Machado Simoes de Carvalho, A. A.: Contribuicao para o estudo da circulacao renal, Coimbra, Imprensa de Coimbra, 1954.

More, R. H., and Duff, G. L.: The renal arterial vasculature in man, Am. J. Path. *27*:95, 1950.

Morison, D. M.: A study of the renal circulation, with special reference to its finer distribution, Am. J. Anat. *37*:53, 1926.

Pease, D. C.: Electron microscopy of the vascular bed of the kidney cortex, Anat. Rec. *121*: 701, 1955.

Trueta, J., Barclay, A. E., Daniel, P., Franklin, K. J., and Prichard, M. M. L.: Renal pathology in the light of recent neurovascular studies, Lancet *2*:237, 1946.

————: Studies of the Renal Circulation, Oxford, Blackwell, 1947.

REFERENCES ON THE CONNECTIVE TISSUE, THE LYMPHATICS AND THE NERVES OF THE KIDNEY

Barrington, F. J. F.: The nervous mechanism of micturition, Quart. J. Exper. Physiol. *8*:33, 1914.

DeMuylder, C. G.: The "Neurility" of the Kidney, Oxford, Blackwell, 1952.

Gruber, C. M.: The autonomic innervation of the genito-urinary system, Physiol. Rev. *13*:497, 1933.

Harman, P. J., and Davies, H.: Intrinsic nerves in the kidney of the cat and the rat, Anat. Rec. *100*:671, 1948.

Kirkman, H.: The number and distribution of macrophages and fibroblasts in kidneys of albino rats with emphasis on twenty-five day males, Am. J. Anat. *73*:451, 1943.

————: A comparative morphological and cytochemical study of globule leucocytes (Schollenleukocyten) of the urinary tract and of possibly related cells, Am. J. Anat. *86*:91, 1950.

Leeson, T. S.: An electron microscopic study of the postnatal development of the hamster kidney, with particular reference to intertubular tissue, Lab. Invest. (in press) 1960.

Marshall, E. K., Jr., and Krolls, A. C.: Studies on the nervous control of the kidney in relation to diuresis and urinary secretion: II. The effect of unilateral excision of the adrenal, section of the splanchnic nerve and section of the renal nerves on the secretion of the kidney, Am. J. Physiol. *49*:302, 1919.

Peirce, E. C.: Renal lymphatics, Anat. Rec. *90*: 315, 1944.

Rawson, A. J.: Distribuion of the lymphatics of the human kidney as shown in a case of carcinomatous permeation, Arch. Path. *47*:283, 1949.

REFERENCES ON THE DEVELOPMENT AND THE GROWTH OF THE KIDNEY

Andrew, W., and Pruett, D.: Senile changes in the kidneys of Wistar Institute rats, Am. J. Anat. *100*:51, 1957.

Arataki, M.: On the postnatal growth of the kidney, with special reference to the number and size of the glomeruli, Am. J. Anat. *36*:399, 1926.

Clark, S. L., Jr.: Cellular differentiation in the kidneys of newborn mice studied with the electron microscope, J. Biophys. & Biochem. Cytol. *3*: 349, 1957.

Hartroft, W. S.: The vascular development of the kidney of the pig, Tr. Roy. Soc. Canada, Sec. V (Biol. Sc.) *35*:67, 1949.

Kittelson, J. A.: The postnatal growth of the kidney of the albino rat, with observations on an adult human kidney, Anat. Rec. *17*:385, 1917.

Kurtz, S. M.: The electron microscopy of the developing human renal glomerulus. Exper. Cell Res. *14*:355, 1958.

Leeson, T. S.: Electron microscopy of the developing kidney: an investigation into the fine structure of the mesonephros and metanephros of the rabbit, J. Anat. *94*:100, 1960.

Leeson, T. S., and Baxter, J. S.: The correlation of structure and function in the mesonephros and metanephros of the rabbit, J. Anat. *91*: 383, 1957.

MacDonald, M. S., and Emery, J. L.: The late intrauterine and postnatal development of human renal glomeruli, J. Anat. *93*:331, 1959.

Rawlinson, H. D.: Compensatory hypertrophy of the kidney of the young rat with special emphasis on the role of cellular hypoplasia, Anat. Rec. *104*:263, 1949.

Sulkin, N. N.: Cytologic study of the remaining kidney following unilateral nephrectomy in the rat, Anat. Rec. *105*:95, 1949.

Chapter 26

The Endocrine System

INTRODUCTION

Development and General Structure. As was explained in Chapter 13, some glands lose their connection with the epithelial surface from which they develop and so become islands of epithelium completely surrounded by connective tissue (Fig. 134). Since such glands possess no ducts, they are termed *ductless glands,* and since they must secrete into the substance of the body, rather than through a duct onto a surface, they are called *endocrine glands* or *glands of internal secretion.*

The functioning cells of endocrine glands must deliver their secretion into blood capillaries. For this to occur, the secretory cells must abut directly on blood capillaries. This leads to endocrine glands, in general, having a very simple microscopic structure; they consist of either cords or small clumps of cells, interspersed between capillaries and supported by delicate connective tissue (Fig. 134).

Storage of Secretion. In some endocrine glands secretion accumulates extracellularly in such a way that it is stored in the central part of a clump of secretory cells; this converts a clump of cells into a follicle (Fig. 142). But the clumps of cells in most endocrine glands do not develop into follicles; hence, in most endocrine glands there is no arrangement for the storage of more secretion than can be accommodated in the cytoplasm of secretory cells, where in some instances it may be demonstrated as secretion granules (Fig. 500).

The Nature of Hormones. The secretions of most endocrine glands are chemical substances called *hormones* (from *hormao* = I arouse to activity). The many different hormones made by the various endocrine glands exert numerous different effects. In general, however, these are all of the "arousing to activity" sort. The activity and, to a large extent, the normal microscopic structure of many parts of the body are dependent on these parts of the body being supplied more or less continuously by way of the blood stream with small amounts of hormones made by endocrine glands. Only minute quantities of the various hormones are necessary in the blood stream to keep different parts of the body roused to normal activity.

Although most endocrine glands make hormones, a gland can properly be termed endocrine even if it does not make a hormone provided that it secretes a useful product into the substance of the body. The liver, for example, secretes sugar into the blood stream and for this reason is properly termed an endocrine gland. It is, of course, an exocrine gland as well, because it secretes bile into a duct system.

The Endocrine System. The hormone-producing endocrine glands are said to constitute the endocrine system because the functioning of one affects the functioning of others. The fact that the various endocrine glands interact with one another so extensively suggests that under normal conditions some sort of balance must be struck between their various activities. The particular balance that is struck probably differs in different individuals, and so different individuals are said to have somewhat different endocrine constitutions.

This chapter deals with all of the hormone-producing endocrine glands except the gonads (*gone* = seed) or sex glands of the female and the male; these will be considered in the next two chapters, which deal with the reproductive systems of the female and the male, respectively. With the exception of the gonads and the placenta of pregnancy, the hormone-producing endocrine glands are:

1. The pituitary gland (hypophysis cerebri)
2. The thyroid gland
3. The parathyroid glands
4. The adrenal glands
5. The islets of Langerhans of the pancreas

Little clusters of cells, scattered about in various parts of the body, and said to comprise the paraganglia, will also be considered in this chapter as will the pineal body. Both the paraganglia and the pineal body have been suspected of having an endocrine function.

General Functions. Some endocrine glands are essential to life. Others are responsible for growth and for such differences as exist between the male and the female forms and for most other male and female characteristics. Hormones play a very important role in the intermediate metabolism of carbohydrates, proteins and fats and in the mineral balance of the body. One hormone controls the metabolic rate of cells in general. In addition to affecting the growth and the form of the individual, hormones affect the temperament, the feelings and the emotions. Experimentally, they may be used to convert a fierce male animal into a motherly creature solicitous for the young. Indeed, the former fierce male, given the proper hormones, will feed the young at its breasts, for the development of the breasts and their capacity to produce milk are also due to hormones. It seems probable that a good many of the physical and emotional differences between people have their bases in people inheriting different types of endocrine constitutions.

Diseases are caused by Hypofunction and Hyperfunction. That different normal people have different endocrine balances suggests that what could be considered to be the normal production of most endocrine glands cannot be set very precisely. Obviously, the function of certain endocrine glands must be considered normal if it ranges within certain limits. But, as the physiologic limits of function are exceeded, either by the production of too little or too much hormone, pathologic states ensue. Hence, since there are many hormones, there is a large group of diseases that are caused by different hormone deficiencies and excesses. The study and the treatment of these constitutes much of the subject matter of the branch of medicine termed *endocrinology*.

Summary of How Knowledge Developed About Endocrine Glands and Hormones. The first intimation of the function of the endocrine glands generally came from the observation that some clinical syndrome, observed during life, could be correlated after death with the diseased state of one of the bodies we now know to be endocrine glands. Next, the effects

of too little secretion of each gland generally were determined by the experimental removal of the gland. This step depended on the development of modern surgical technics. The next step was the preparation of active extracts from the glands of animals. This step awaited the development of the proper chemical methods. When active extracts became available, the effects of the hyperfunction of any particular endocrine gland could be determined. By removing different glands from experimental animals it became possible to prove that some of the disease states seen in man were due to the hypofunction of a particular endocrine gland. Further, giving animals large doses of active glandular extracts made it possible to show that certain other disease states of man were due to the hyperfunction of certain endocrine glands. It became established that, in general, there are two different diseases that can result from the misbehavior of any one of the endocrine glands: one from its hypofunction and the other from its hyperfunction. Next, and this was of great importance for the clinical treatment of hypofunction, highly purified extracts were prepared, and in the instance of many hormones, the formula of the hormone was determined. This has permitted some hormones to be synthesized.

THE PITUITARY GLAND OR BODY (HYPOPHYSIS CEREBRI)

Some Gross Features. The pituitary gland is ovoid. It measures about 1.5 cm. in the transverse plane and about 1 in the sagittal plane and is from 0.5 to 0.75 cm. or more thick. It becomes larger during pregnancy. It lies immediately below the base of the brain, to which it is attached by the pituitary stalk (Fig. 473). It rests in a depression in a bony prominence on the upper surface of the sphenoid bone. This bony prominence is shaped something like a Turkish saddle with a high back and a high front, and for this reason it is termed the *sella turcica*. The pituitary gland sits, as it were, in the saddle and so has bony protection in front, below and behind. The dura mater dips down to line the seat of the saddle and so envelop the pituitary gland. Furthermore, a shelf of dura mater, the diaphragma sellae, extends over most of the top

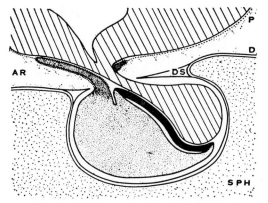

Fig. 473. Diagram of a sagittal section of the hypophysis cerebri, showing relation of the pars tuberalis to the meninges. *Lines,* brain floor and pars nervosa; *fine stipple,* pars anterior; *coarse stipple,* pars tuberalis; *solid black,* pars intermedia; SPH, sphenoid bone; P, pia mater; D, dura mater; DS, diaphragma sellae; AR, arachnoid spaces. (Atwell, W. J.: Am. J. Anat. *37*:174)

of the gland to complete its enclosure (Fig. 473, *DS*). The degree of protection that it is afforded is in relation to its importance.

In a sagittal section the pituitary gland of many animals can be seen to be separated into an anterior and a posterior lobe by a cleft which runs downward and posteriorly from near the attachment of the stalk. Such a cleft may be seen in the pituitary gland of a young child, but in the human adult it is replaced by a row of follicles. The 2 lobes so separated are divided into 4 parts. The main body of the gland anterior to the cleft or row of follicles is termed its *pars anterior* (Fig. 473, *fine stipple*). A projection from this, the *pars tuberalis* (Fig. 473, *coarse stipple*), extends up along the anterior and lateral aspects of the pituitary stalk. A rather narrow band of glandular tissue disposed along the posterior border of the cleft or row of vesicles comprises the *pars intermedia* (Fig. 473, *solid black*). The remainder of the gland (all that is posterior to the narrow cellular band that makes up the parts intermedia) is called its *pars posterior* or *parts nervosa* (Fig. 473, *lined*). The pars nervosa is not so wide as the pars anterior and more or less fits into a concavity on the posterior aspect of the pars anterior but is separated from it, of course, by the pars intermedia.

Development. The pars anterior, the pars tuberalis and the pars intermedia all have a microscopic structure fairly typical of endocrine glands. However, the pars nervosa does not; it resembles nervous rather than glandular tissue (Fig. 479). Its origin provides the reason. It develops as a downgrowth from the base of the brain. The other parts of the gland develop from an epithelial surface as do endocrine glands in general. We shall elaborate:

The anterior part of the mouth results from the inward bulging of ectoderm to form the oral fossa. Very early in development, before the bones of the skull have formed, the ectodermal lining of the roof of the oral fossa is in very close contact with the floor of the developing brain (which at this stage has a tubular form), and indeed it soon becomes adherent to it. This connection does not break as mesenchyme proliferates and gradually separates the developing brain from the developing mouth. As a consequence, the gradual separation of the brain and the mouth causes both the lining of the oral cavity and the floor of the brain to be drawn out into funnel-shaped structures with their tips in contact. The funnel-shaped extension of the roof of the oral fossa that points toward the brain is called *Rathke's pouch*. By the end of the second month of development this pouch breaks away from the oral ectoderm and thereupon becomes a hollow island of epithelium surrounded by mesenchyme except at its uppermost part where a peninsula is attached to the downward extension of the floor of the brain (Fig. 474). The main body of the hollow island of epithelium becomes more or less flattened around the anterior surface of the downgrowth of the brain. The cells of the anterior wall of the hollow epithelial island proliferate so that its anterior wall becomes greatly thickened. This becomes the pars anterior of the pituitary gland, and an upward extension of it becomes the pars tuberalis. The posterior wall of the island becomes the pars intermedia. The central cavity of the epithelial island between the pars anterior and the pars intermedia becomes flattened to form the cleft previously described, and the downward extension from the floor of the brain becomes the pars nervosa of the gland.

A residuum of cells of a character similar to those of the pars anterior may be present in the pharynx at the site from which the anterior lobe develops (Fig. 474). If so, they are said to constitute the *pharyngeal hypophysis*.

The part of the pituitary gland that develops from the epithelium of the oral cavity (pars anterior, intermedia and tuberalis) is often referred to as the *adenohypophysis*, and the part that develops from the brain as the *neurohypophysis*.

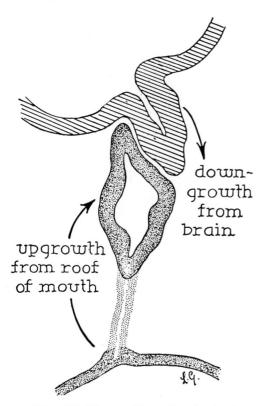

FIG. 474. Diagram illustrating the development of the pituitary gland from its two main sources.

THE PITUITARY GLAND AS A POSSIBLE LINK BETWEEN THE NERVOUS AND THE ENDOCRINE SYSTEMS

The experiencing of sensations, feelings, impulses, drives and emotions is a function of the nervous system. Likewise, the selection of the particular response that is to result from stimuli in the external or the internal environment of an individual is a function of the nervous system. Yet as we study the endocrine glands we shall see that hormones have a great effect on the way people feel and on

the way they react to stimuli. Hormones are responsible for some of the "impulses" or "drives" that operate via the nervous system to motivate human activity. For example, what is generally termed sex "instinct" or "drive" depends fundamentally on certain hormones being, or at least having been, liberated into the blood stream. However, the relation between the nervous and the endocrine systems is reciprocal because the activities of the nervous system affect the functioning of endocrine glands. When we study the adrenal medulla we shall find that under conditions of emotional stress it secretes a hormone into the blood stream that reinforces the functioning of the sympathetic division of the autonomic nervous system. In addition, this hormone may affect directly and/or indirectly the secretory activity of the anterior pituitary gland, and the hormones from this gland affect other glands. All in all, there is a very complicated interrelationship between the nervous and the endocrine systems, and the question arises as to what anatomic means are provided to permit these two systems to affect one another.

Most endocrine glands are not particularly well provided with nerves, and it is doubtful if such nerves as extend into them exert very pronounced effects on their secretory functions. However, there is one great exception to this rule. The medulla of the adrenal gland, as we shall see, has a unique and extensive innervation which permits the sympathetic division of the autonomic nervous system to exert control over its secretory functions. Moreover, the hormone that it produces reinforces the activities of the sympathetic division of the autonomic nervous system so that there is, in the medulla of the adrenal gland, a very important link between the nervous and the endocrine systems.

It might be expected from the fact that the pituitary gland develops from both ordinary epithelial and nervous tissue that it too would provide an important link between the nervous and the endocrine systems. It would be a suitable place for such a link because the pars anterior of the gland controls the secretory activities of most of the other endocrine glands of the body. That close contact between the adenohypophysis and the neurohypophysis is purposeful and does provide the means for a

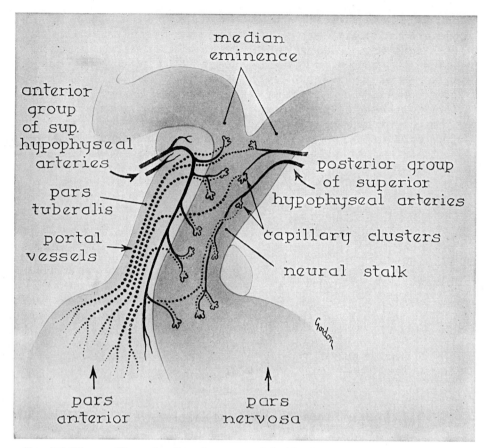

FIG. 475. Diagram illustrating Green's concept of the blood supply of the hypophyseal stalk. The course of arterial blood is indicated by straight lines and that of venous blood by dotted lines. (Redrawn and slightly modified from Green, J. D.: Anat. Rec. *100*:273)

link between the two systems seems to be most probable. But, contrary to what might be expected, the link that is provided is not a nervous one, because the adenohypophysis is not innervated to any extent from the neurohypophysis. Instead, the link appears to be a humoral (fluid) or a hormonal one and depends upon there being a curious arrangement of blood vessels in the region which constitute what is termed the *hypophysioportal circulation* which permits blood from capillaries in the median eminence and the neural stalk (which are nervous tissue) to drain subsequently into the sinusoids that permeate between the secretory cells of the pars anterior. We shall elaborate.

The Blood Supply of the Pituitary Gland. Two main groups of vessels, the *superior* and the *inferior hypophyseal arteries,* supply the gland.

The *superior hypophyseal arteries,* of which there are several, take origin from the circle of Willis. They approach the gland as an anterior group and as a posterior group of vessels (Fig. 475).

The arteries of the *anterior* group penetrate the upper part of the pars tuberalis (Fig. 475) and, in general, turn downward. As they pass downward toward the pars anterior, they give off numerous branches. The uppermost of these pass into the region of the median eminence (Fig. 475), and the ones at lower levels pass into the neural stalk (Fig. 475). All of these vessels end in clusters of tortuous wide capillaries; these have been a subject of study, in particular, by Wislocki and by Green, who should be read for details. Green describes the arterial vessels and the capillary clusters in which they terminate as being enclosed in a curious connective tissue sheath; this has also been described as a glial sheath. The capillary clusters empty into venules which run back in the same sheaths toward the pars tuberalis (Fig. 475, *dotted lines*) where they join with one another to form larger venules (Fig. 475, *dotted lines*), which pass down to empty into the sinusoids of the pars anterior of the gland. Since the system of venules that drains the capillary clusters of the median eminence and the stalk contain venous blood which they empty into a second capillary bed, they constitute a *portal* system of vessels.

The *posterior* group of superior hypophyseal arteries penetrate the posterior aspect of the stalk (Fig. 475). The upper branches from these supply the median eminence, and the lower branches supply lower levels of the stalk. Here again the branches end in clusters of tortuous wide capillaries which, with the vessels that supply and drain them, lie in a connective tissue sheath. The venules from these capillary clusters pass forward to the pars tuberalis (Fig. 475, *dotted lines*) to drain down into the pars anterior; hence, these venules also constitute a part of the hypophysioportal system.

The nerve fibers of the hypothalamohypophyseal tract (which will be described when the pars nervosa of the gland is considered) run in close association with the clusters of capillaries in the stalk but generally remain separated from them by the sheaths that surround the capillaries and the larger vessels. However, these connective tissue or glial sheaths are often thin, and it is possible that although the fibers of the hypothalamohypophyseal tract do not terminate here, some neurosecretory material (to be described later) may pass from fibers to capillaries in this region.

There appears to be no connections other than capillary anastomoses between the median eminence and the remainder of the hypothalamus. Therefore, the hypophysioportal circulation is not concerned with delivering blood from the bulk of the hypothalamus to the pars anterior but with delivering blood from the median eminence and the neural stalk into the pars anterior. According to Green, the portal circulation is not concerned with draining blood from the pars nervosa into the pars anterior. Accordingly, if any hormones or hormonelike substances are delivered into the pars anterior it would seem most probable that they gain entrance to this system from the median eminence and/or the neural stalk.

It is to be noted that not all of the blood that reaches the pars anterior from the superior hypophyseal arteries has passed through capillary clusters in the median eminence and/or stalk because some arterial branches pass directly down the pars tuberalis to the pars anterior (Fig. 475).

The second blood supply of the pituitary gland is obtained from the inferior hypophyseal arteries. There are two of these, one on each side. Each arises from the internal carotid artery (of the same side) as it lies in the posterior part of the cavernous sinus. Each inferior hypophyseal artery passes medially into the floor of the pituitary fossa and reaches the lower part of the gland at its inferolateral aspect. Here each gives off one or two small branches which enter the inferior aspects of the anterior and the posterior lobes. The main vessel on each side passes upwardly in the groove between the anterior and the posterior lobes, giving off numerous branches to the posterior lobe as it does so. At the upper part of each groove each main vessel passes forward between the corresponding lateral lobe and the stalk and then dips down into the lateral connective tissue cores of the anterior lobe. Therefore, the inferior hypophyseal vessels provide the chief blood supply for the pars nervosa of the gland and also the arterial blood for the pars anterior. There does not seem to be any evidence that the blood from this source enters the hypophysioportal system; in other words, the blood supplied to the pars nervosa by these vessels is collected into veins which do not empty into the pars anterior.

We shall discuss further the possible significance of the hypophysioportal system as a link between the nervous and the endocrine systems after the adrenal has been discussed.

THE PARS ANTERIOR

The pars anterior is composed of clumps and cords of cells intermingled with vascular channels. Before describing the different types of

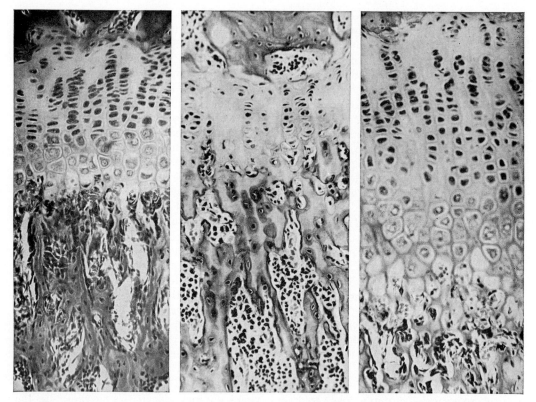

FIG. 476. (*Left*) Low-power photomicrograph of a longitudinal section of a metaphysis of the tibia of a rat nearing full growth. (*Center*) A similar photomicrograph of a metaphysis of a rat of the same age that received large injections of female sex hormone; the sex hormone suppressed the secretion of the growth hormone in the animal concerned. Observe that the epiphyseal disk is thinner and that it lacks a zone of maturing cells. (*Right*) A similar photomicrograph of a metaphysis of the tibia of a rat of the same age as the other two but which received injections of anterior pituitary extract containing growth hormone. Observe that the epiphyseal disk is thicker than at the left. High-power inspection shows many mitotic figures in the disk. (From experiments in collaboration with Dr. W. R. Harris)

cells that are present we shall describe briefly the various hormones made by the gland so that when we describe the cells we shall be able to relate their structures to their functions.

The Hormones of the Pars Anterior

The cells of the pars anterior of the pituitary gland make several (probably 6) different hormones. These will now be described. Four pure hormones have been prepared from extracts of the gland, but these do not account for all the effects that are produced by crude extracts of the gland.

1. **Growth Hormone.** A young animal stops growing after its pituitary gland is removed and thereafter remains a dwarf unless extracts of the pars anterior are given to it. Although the growth of the body as a whole ceases when the pituitary gland is removed, the most striking, and perhaps the most significant, cessation of growth is that of the cartilage cells in the epiphyseal disks of the long bones. When the young cells in the zone of proliferation stop dividing, no new cells are produced to mature and so add to the thickness of the zone of maturation. Since calcification does not cease, the zone of calcification continues to advance into the zone of maturation, and as a result the zone of maturing cells becomes greatly thinned (as in Fig. 476, *center*). Since this zone is an important factor in the thickness of the disk, a reduction in the thickness of this zone makes the disk as a whole thinner. The histologic changes that occur in the epi-

physeal disks after removal of the pituitary gland are described in detail by Evans and Simpson.

If an abnormal growth of the cells that make growth hormone occurs in an individual before full growth is attained and hence before the epiphyseal disks of the long bones have been replaced by bone, the bones grow longer than usual, and so the individual becomes abnormally tall. This condition is termed gigantism. In a normal person, either the secretion of growth hormone ceases or that which is secreted becomes ineffective in the face of other developments at a certain time of life, and at that time the individual stops growing. Certain rare tumors evidently keep on secreting effectively beyond the time when the cells of a normal pars anterior would stop secreting enough hormone to cause more growth. Furthermore, as Evans and Long first showed, if the administration of growth hormone is begun before an animal has stopped growing, the animal will continue to grow; indeed, Evans and Simpson have shown that rats will continue to grow as long as pure growth hormone is administered.

If growth-hormone producing tumors develop after the epiphyseal disks of the long bones have become replaced by bone, that is, after normal growth is over, or if growth hormone is given to a normal animal after its growth is over, no further growth in stature occurs. However, the bones, particularly those of the hands and the feet, tend to become thicker, and there is a great overgrowth of the mandible and a lesser growth of certain other bones in the face. Other tissues (e.g., the skin) are affected as well, but the condition as a whole is termed *acromegaly* (*akron* = extremity; *megas* = large) because the growth of the bones in the head, the hands and the feet makes these extremities large.

It may be of interest to know that the epiphyseal disks of some laboratory animals are unusual in that they do not ordinarily become replaced by bone when their normal growth is over. For example, the epiphyseal disks persist for a long time in the rat; hence, if female rats which have stopped growing (these are called plateaued rats because their growth curve has reached a plateau) are given growth hormone preparations, they will begin to grow again (Fig. 476, *compare left and right*).

Therefore, plateaued rats can be used for determining whether any given preparation contains growth hormone, but they are not as good for this purpose as hypophysectomized rats. They are, of course, much easier to obtain than the latter.

As we shall see, when the islands of Langerhans are considered later in this chapter, the growth hormone of the pars anterior has diabetogenic functions. If enough of it is injected into certain kinds of animals, permanent diabetes results. Growth hormone prepared from the pituitary glands of cattle and pigs produces growth and other metabolic effects in laboratory animals, but it is virtually ineffective in man and monkeys.

Recently, it has been shown that growth hormone prepared from pituitary glands of monkeys and from human pituitary glands obtained at autopsy is effective metabolically in man and monkeys.

2. **Lactogenic Hormone.** During pregnancy, as will be explained in detail when the female reproductive system is considered, certain hormones are produced which make the mammary glands of the female grow and develop greatly. Hence, by the time the offspring is born the mammary glands are large enough to supply the young with an adequate amount of milk. However, a particular stimulus is required for the glands to begin secreting milk and to continue performing this function. This stimulus is provided by a hormone called the *lactogenic hormone* or *prolactin* which is made by the pars anterior of the pituitary gland by cells that are believed to secrete large amounts of it at the termination of pregnancy. Thereafter they continue to secrete this hormone in quantities as long as the offspring is fed at the breast.

The lactogenic hormone has been prepared in crystalline form by White and associates. In addition to stimulating milk secretion, it arouses a maternal attitude in the individual exposed to its action; it will even do this if it is injected into males. It induces broodiness in hens.

In fowl, where the young are fed in part with the epithelial debris that desquamates from the lining of the crop gland of the mother, administration of the lactogenic hormone has been found to increase greatly the rate of epithelial proliferation of the thick lining epithelium of the gland. Indeed, the effect of the lactogenic hormone on the crop gland of the fowl constitutes a biologic method by which this particular hormone may be assayed.

As studies on the lactogenic hormone continued, it became obvious that it was concerned not only in causing fully developed breasts to secrete milk but that it was also concerned in bringing about the growth of the breasts that occurs as a preliminary to milk secretion. This matter will be discussed in more detail in the next chapter.

A third function that has been found for the lactogenic hormone is that of exerting what is termed a luteotrophic effect; that is, it has a function in activating the corpus luteum (to be described in the next chapter) and causing it to secrete the hormone progesterone (to be described in the next chapter). This function of the lactogenic hormone is clearly established in rats but it is not certain whether it has this effect in man.

3. **Trophic Hormones.** In addition to being able to secrete growth hormone and lactogenic hormone, the pars anterior can also secrete certain hormones that, in general, stimulate the growth and the function of many of the other endocrine glands; for this reason they are termed *trophic* (*trophe* = to nourish) hormones. (Some authors substitute *tropic* for *trophic*, and the student who encounters these different spellings of the word may wonder which is correct. We believe that trophic is the correct term. Anyone who wishes to investigate this more deeply should read Parkes, A. S., Nature, *141*:36, 1938.) Four trophic hormones have been identified by their effects, and they are named according to the particular gland that they affect: (1) thyrotrophin (TSH for thyroid stimulating hormone), which affects the thyroid gland; (2) adrenocorticotrophin (ACTH), which affects the cortex of the suprarenal (adrenal) glands; and (3 and 4) two gonadotrophins, the follicle-stimulating hormone (FSH) and the luteinizing hormone (LH). Both of the gonadotrophins are produced in females and also in males, and their actions on the respective gonads of the two sexes will be described in the next two chapters.

The Push-Pull or Feed-Back Theory. The equilibrium that is established between the activities of the different endocrines is achieved chiefly through the agency of the pars anterior. It is, as it were, chairman of the endocrine society. All the different members report to it regularly about their activities, and by secreting trophic hormones it controls the various members' structure and function. Should any particular endocrine gland become lazy, the pars anterior flogs it into activity by secreting the particular trophic hormone that arouses it. For example, should the thyroid gland produce too little thyroid hormone, the pars anterior promptly secretes some extra thyrotrophin, and this makes the thyroid gland work harder. How do the cells of the pars anterior know whether the thyroid gland is working or not? The simplest explanation for this is that they know by the amount of thyroid hormone that is present in the blood that courses through the sinusoids of the pars anterior along which they lie. Indeed, the cells of the pars anterior behave as if they performed regular chemical assays on the blood that passes by them to learn exactly how much of the various hormones the blood contains at these different times.

That the pars anterior is stimulated to secrete more of the specific trophic hormone concerned when the level of any particular hormone falls below its normal concentration in the blood is one of the generalizations of the push-pull or feed-back theory. A second generalization is that the secretion of any particular trophic hormone is suppressed when the concentration of the hormone of the gland it stimulates is raised to a high level in the blood. For example, the presence of a large amount of thyroid hormone in the blood is thought to suppress the secretion of thyrotrophin by the pars anterior.

Microscopic Structure

The glandular cells of the pars anterior are arranged in fairly thick irregular cords that branch with one another (Fig. 477). The cells are supported by delicate reticular fibers. Between the cords are vascular channels considerably wider than capillaries and lined by reticuloendothelium rather than by ordinary endothelium; for these two reasons they are classified as sinusoids rather than capillaries. The sinusoids are surrounded by a more substantial type of connective tissue than that which penetrates the cords to support the glandular cells (Fig. 477).

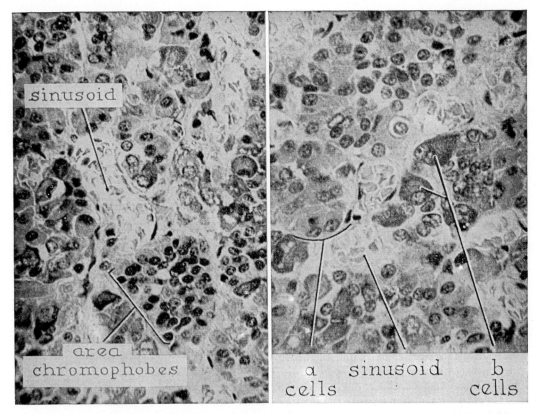

FIG. 477. Two high-power photomicrographs of an H and E section of the anterior lobe of the hypophysis. (*Left*) An area of chromophobes, with their nuclei close together. A sinusoid and some chromophils may be seen also. (*Right*) Acidophils, basophils and sinusoids (a = acidophils, b = basophils).

The glandular cells are of two main types, chromophils and chromophobes; these are present in about equal numbers. This classification is based on whether the *cytoplasm* of the cells likes or dislikes stain. Chromophobes tend to be more or less clumbed together in the central parts of the cords; the chromophils are distributed along the periphery of the cords, so that they abut on the sinusoids (Fig. 477). The cell borders of chromophobes are not so distinct as those of the chromophils. Typical chromophobes are much smaller than typical chromophils; hence, in a nest or a group of chromophobes the nuclei are much closer together than they are in an area or a nest of chromophils (Fig. 477, *left*). This latter fact enables the student to identify clumps of chromophobes very readily. Since the chromophils are much larger than chromophobes, there appear to be more chromophils than chromophobes in the gland, even though they are present in about the same numbers.

With suitable fixation and a Mallory type of stain, the cytoplasm of about 75 per cent of the chromophils is acidophilic. Accordingly, these cells are called *acidophils*. The Gomori staining method demonstrates these clearly (Fig. 478, *bottom, left*). The cytoplasm of the remainder of the chromophils (about 25%) is basophilic; Purves and Griesbach say that this is due to the high content of RNA nucleoprotein in their cytoplasm, and that their basophilia disappears after ribonuclease. In routine sections of the human pituitary gland, stained with H and E, the acidophils can be distinguished from the basophils with some success because, although the granules of the acidophils may not be sharply stained, they impart a pink color to the cytoplasm of the acidophils. The cytoplasm of the basophils, although it may be colored purple-red (instead of blue), is generally of a much deeper hue than that of the acidophils (Fig. 477, *right*). It is a help in identifying these two types of cells to understand that basophils tend to be more numerous toward the periphery of the gland. Therefore, since there are fewer of them than acidophils, they may not be very numerous in the more central parts of the gland.

It is interesting to inquire into which cells make the various hormones of the anterior lobe. This problem has been investigated several ways. One way has been to study those individuals who develop tumors of the pars anterior. Tumors of acidophils cause either gigantism or acromegaly, depending on whether the tumors develop before or after an individual has stopped growing; accordingly, it is concluded that the acidophils make the growth hormone. The origin of the trophic hormones has been investigated in another way. If, for example, the thyroid gland is removed, according to the push-pull theory, the cells that make thyrotrophin should increase their secretion and in order to do so they increase in number. The same reasoning applies if the sex glands are removed, the cells that make gonadotrophin generally increase in number. Experiments of this nature had shown in the past that the number of basophils increased under both conditions. However, in 1950, Halmi showed that two different kinds of basophils could be distinguished by special stains; he termed these *beta* and *delta* cells, respectively. In 1951, Purve and Griesbach used the P.A.S. technic to study the basophils under certain experimental conditions. The basophils are P.A.S. positive most probably because the hormones that they secrete are glycoproteins which have reactive carbohydrate groups and so stain by the P.A.S.

method. They attributed the production of thyrotrophin and gonadotrophin to the basophils, for it was known that these hormones are glycoproteins. Their experiments suggested also that there are two kinds of basophils in the rat, one kind being responsible for producing the gonadotrophin, and the other, thyrotrophin. The basophils of the first type were found to be oval-to-round in shape and generally localized to the lower surface of the anterior lobe and to the upper surface, close to the pars intermedia. The granule content of these cells was found to vary in relation to the gland's content of gonadotrophic hormone, which was varied by experimenal procedures. Therefore, they named these cells *gonadotrophs*. Under most conditions these cells correspond to Halmi's delta cells. The other type of basophils has a polyhedral shape and so is generally more angular than the first type. These are distributed in a more central position in the anterior lobe. The granule content of these cells can be correlated with the gland's content of thyrotrophic hormone; hence, it is concluded that these cells produce the thyrotrophic hormone. Accordingly, Purves and Griesbach termed these cells thyrotrophs; they probably correspond to Halmi's beta cells.

When the sex glands are removed from an animal the gonadotrophs not only proliferate but some of them develop large vacuoles in their cytoplasm so as to attain a signet-ring appearance. These are called *castration* cells. A similar phenomenon may be observed among the thyrotrophs when the thyroid gland is removed.

It is of interest that the push-pull (feedback) arrangement seems to result sometimes

---

FIG. 478. (*Top, left*) Drawing of a nerve cell in the human hypothalamus, showing neurosecretory granules and Nissl bodies in the cytoplasm of the nerve cell. The section was stained with Klüver and Barrera's luxol fast blue-cresyl violet. (Prepared from a section provided by Louis Poirier) (*Center, left*) Drawing of a part of a section of the anterior pituitary of man, stained by the method employed by Ezrin and Wilson (see text). The acidophils are a yellow-orange color. Two types of basophils are to be seen: red and purple. The distinction between chromophobes and chromophils is not so distinct as with most stains. (Preparation supplied by W. Wilson) (*Bottom, left*) A section of the anterior pituitary of man, stained by the Gomori method. The acidophils are red, and the basophils are a light blue-purple. (*Top, right*) Section of the posterior lobe of the pituitary gland of man, stained by the Gomori method. The illustration shows the terminal branchings of a nerve fiber and neurosecretory material around them. A Herring body is also present. (*Bottom, right*) A section of the posterior pituitary of man, stained by the Gomori method. The termination of a nerve fiber, with an accumulation of neurosecretory material around it, is seen beside a capillary into which the neurosecretory material probably passes.

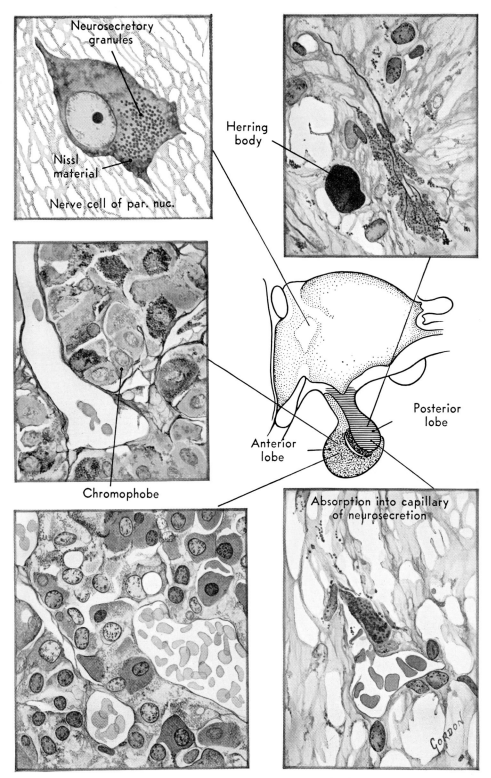

Neurosecretory granules

Nissl material

Nerve cell of par. nuc.

Herring body

Posterior lobe

Anterior lobe

Chromophobe

Absorption into capillary of neurosecretion

FIGURE 478. (*See caption on page 742*)

in broad effects on the pars anterior. For example, the administration of large amounts of female sex hormones will not only suppress the gonadotrophs but also stop growth (Fig. 476) and, under certain circumstances, lactation.

The fact that it is possible to differentiate certain cell types in the anterior lobe by means of special technics, and that there was evidence (from the study of pituitary tumors) to the effect that acidophils make growth hormone, and that in the rat there are special basophils for producing thyrotrophin and gonadotrophin, raised hopes to the effect that by devising still better technics it might be possible to show that there was a special cell type for producing each of the many hormones made by the anterior pituitary gland. The matter has been investigated at length by Catchpole, Halmi, Pearse, Purves and Griesbach, Siperstein et al., Ezrin and Wilson and their associates, Hill, Dawson and Humphrey. Ezrin and Wilson and their group have now studied the pituitary glands of man obtained from nearly 1,800 autopsies. The cases studied included many types of endocrine disorders and the results suggest that the production of hormones by the anterior pituitary gland of man is more complicated than has generally been suspected and that it seems improbable that there is a special cell type for producing each and every anterior pituitary hormone, as will now be described.

Ezrin and Wilson and their associates employ a modified P.A.S. technic, suggested by Ritter and Oleson. In this method the tissue is given a preliminary impregnation with colloidal iron. Some of the P.A.S. positive cells have a strong affinity for the iron. The blue-green color, by which the presence of iron in these cells is revealed, plus the magenta color produced in the same cells by the P.A.S. method, together impart a purple color to these particular basophils (Fig. 478, center, left). The other basophils, which do not take up the colloidal iron, are colored magenta by the P.A.S. method (Fig. 478, center, left). In this staining method orange G is used as an acid stain; hence, the acidophils are colored a yellow-orange (Fig. 478, center, left).

With the method described above, the dividing line between chromophobes and chromophils is not sharp, and, in particular, many transition stages are seen between lightly granulated purple cells and chromophobes (Fig. 478, center, left). Since these are seen more often under conditions when it could be expected that secretion is excessive, it is assumed that the purple cells as they become degranulated turn into chromophobes. In general, lightly granulated "chromophobes" suggest excessive function.

The heavily granulated purple basophils are distributed singly throughout the gland. The red basophils tend to be confined to the anteromedial portion of the gland where they are usually gathered in clumps. The purple basophils are as numerous as red basophils only in the glands of those who have died suddenly. In the glands of those who die after a more or less protracted illness, purple cells are few in number. This suggests that the purple cells are rapidly depleted of their granules under emergency or stress conditions and are the first to respond to the call for more hormone. The hormone that is released most rapidly under these conditions is probably ACTH.

If the "target" glands that are affected by the trophic hormones of the anterior pituitary are either removed or diseased it is conceded that the anterior pituitary produces increased amounts of the hormone that would stimulate the particular target gland that is not functioning. For example, there is a disease known as Addison's disease, in which the cortex of the adrenal gland is destroyed by disease, and it is known that under these conditions the anterior pituitary produces increased amounts of ACTH. Similarly, if the thyroid gland is removed or unable to produce hormones it is known that the anterior pituitary produces increased amounts of thyrotrophin. Under conditions of Addison's disease and cretinism there is a considerable increase of lightly granulated purple cells in the anterior pituitary; these cells are so lightly granulated that they would be termed chromophobes by many staining methods. The red basophils become degranulated only in extremely active glands such as occurs in Addison's disease or cretinism.

Such evidence as Ezrin and Wilson and their associates have obtained from their impressive study suggests that ACTH, TSH, FSH and LH are made by one or both of the two types of basophils, and that in general the blue basophils are the first to respond to increased needs for hormones and that the red basophils probably play the part of housing reserve stores of hormones that are liberated only under extreme conditions.

The evidence linking the acidophils with growth hormone comes chiefly from studying the pituitary glands of acromegalic individuals; these usually reveal some acidophilic overgrowth. However, some hormonally active pituitary tumors removed surgically from acromegalics to save failing vision have been found to be composed chiefly of chromophobes with scanty acidophilic granulation. Therefore, it appears that the cells that produce growth hormone can also release it so rapidly that they have almost none to store.

Acromegaly in women is occasionally associated with persistent lactation; this is termed galactorrhea (*galactos* = milk; *rhoia* = flow), which may or may not be related to a previous pregnancy; this suggests that the cells that produce growth hormone may also produce lactogenic hormone. Furthermore, the pituitary glands of women, during the later stages of pregnancy and in the several weeks following childbirth, contain increased numbers of lightly granulated acidophils. These were originally termed pregnancy cells by Erdheim. It has been suggested that these cells, in addition to producing growth hormone, are responsible for producing the lactogenic hormone that is being secreted by the anterior pituitary gland at this time, as will be described in the next chapter.

Relation between Chromophils and Chromophobes. All transition stages between chromophobes and chromophils (but not between the two types of chromophils) can be seen in a section of the pars anterior. It seems certain that chromophobes can develop into chromophils. Moreover, it seems probable that chromophils can revert into chromophobes. Severinghaus thinks that, in the rat, the Golgi apparatus of the kind of chromophobe that will become an acidophil is different from that of the kind of chromophobe that will become a basophil; hence, he visualizes two types of chromophobes. He traces the various stages by which these accumulate their respective type of cytoplasmic granules to become acidophils or basophils, and those in which they discharge their granules and revert to their particular type of chromophobe again. His papers should be consulted for further details.

The nuclei of the glandular cells of the pars anterior vary greatly in size and in the intensity with which they stain (Fig. 478, *lower left*). Many of the larger ones stain with only moderate intensity, and chromatin granules, lying in nuclear sap, can be seen within them. But in other nuclei, and these are generally smaller, the chromatin appears to be more condensed, and when this condition is accentuated, the nuclei appear pyknotic. It is probable, from the studies of Severinghaus, that the variations in the staining reaction and the size of the nuclei are to be explained by cells being in different stages of their secretory cycle. The nuclei of acidophils probably begin to stain more deeply when the cells that contain them become replete with granules and begin to discharge. As the cell discharges its granules, the chromatin of the nucleus becomes still more condensed and only begins to disperse and reorganize as the cell once more begins to accumulate granules. The darker nuclei, then, are probably those of cells that are beginning to discharge or have discharged their granules, and the lighter, larger nuclei, those of cells accumulating granules.

OTHER PARTS OF THE PITUITARY GLAND

Pars Tuberalis. Although this is an upward extension of the pars anterior, it has a different microscopic structure. The cells it contains are roughly cuboidal in shape and contain no cytoplasmic granules. Their cytoplasm is diffusely and mildly basophilic. The pars tuberalis is fairly vascular. Its function, if any, is unknown.

Pars Intermedia. This is not nearly so well developed in man as in many animals. In man it consists chiefly of (1) an irregular row of follicles which contain pale-staining colloidal materials and are made of pale cells (Fig. 479), and (2) a few rows of moderately sized cells with strongly basophilic granular cytoplasm (Fig. 479, *center*). (The granules disappear very quickly unless fixation is prompt.) These cells may extend into the pars nervosa for considerable distances (Fig. 479, *upper right*).

In certain species the pars intermedia makes a hormone (intermedin) that causes the pigment-containing cells of the animal concerned to expand. This has the effect of altering the color scheme of the organism and permits it to blend better with its surroundings. The func-

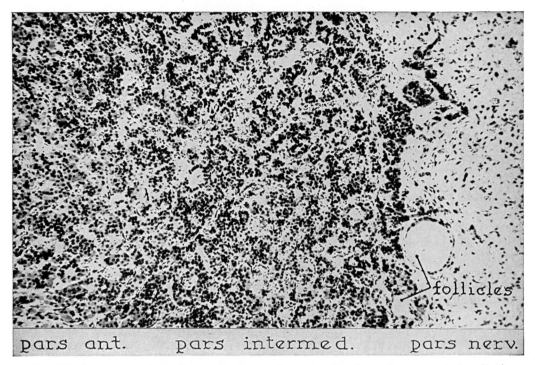

FIG. 479. Low-power photomicrograph of a section extending from the pars anterior (*left*) through the pars intermedia (*center*) into the pars nervosa (*right*) of the hypophysis cerebri.

tion of the pars intermedia in man is not known; whether it is associated in any way with the pigmentation of the body has not been established.

THE PARS NERVOSA

The pars nervosa was investigated over the years in the same way as other endocrine glands. However, the results were not as clear-cut as they were with other glands. Only recently has information become available to explain why this gland has seemed to be so different from the others. But first we shall describe what has been known about the gland for some time.

It was known, for example, that a disease, *diabetes insipidus*, could result from lesions of the pars nervosa. (This is a very different disease from "sugar" diabetes, which will be described later in this chapter.) Diabetes insipidus is characterized by a great production of urine of a low specific gravity. For many years it was believed that this disease is due to the failure of the pars nervosa to make a hormone called the *antidiuretic hormone*. If the antidiuretic hormone is not pres-

ent in the blood stream in sufficient quantities the distal convoluted tubules of the kidney do not absorb their proper share of the glomerular filtrate; hence, the volume of urine is many times greater than normal.

However, there were many puzzling things about the relation of this disease to the pars nervosa. It was known, for example, that the disease could be caused by injuries to the hypothalamus and also by interrupting the nerve tract that leads from hypothalamic nuclei to the pars nervosa (Fig. 480). Nevertheless, the disease could be alleviated by means of extracts prepared from the pars nervosa. Hence, it was assumed that the antidiuretic hormone was made by the pars nervosa but that the pars nervosa required proper innervation from the hypothalamic region if it was to make its hormone.

In addition to containing an antidiuretic hormone, extracts of the pars nervosa, on being injected into animals, were found to cause much of the smooth muscle of the body to contract or develop increased tonus. As chemical extraction methods improved, Kamm and his associates were able to isolate two somewhat different and extremely active fractions from crude extracts. The first of these is termed *oxytocin* (*oxys* = swift; *tosos* = labor) or *pitocin*, and, as its name implies, it acts chiefly on the smooth muscle of the wall of the uterus; so, by stimulating the uterus to contract, it may help in expelling a fetus. The second fraction that may be recovered from crude extracts is called *pitressin*, and it acts on the smooth muscle of the blood vessels (a hypertensive effect) and on that of the intestine. It also has the antidiuretic effect. Recently, the chemical structure of pitocin (oxytocin) and pitressin (vasopressin) has been elucidated by du Vigneaud and his associates, who have also achieved the remarkable feat of synthesizing these complex hormones.

A puzzle was presented by the fact that although hormones could be extracted from the pars nervosa, its microscopic structure was not that of an endocrine gland.

Neurosecretion. Recently, the answer to many of the hitherto puzzling features about the form and the function of the pars nervosa

and its relation to the hypothalamus has been elucidated. It now seems to be established, particularly from Scharrer's work, that the hormones that can be extracted from the pars nervosa are not made in the pars nervosa at all but in the bodies of nerve cells in hypothalamic nuclei, the nerve cells of which produce a *neurosecretion* (Fig. 478, *top, left*). This neurosecretion passes from the cell bodies of the neurons in the supra-optic and the paraventricular nuclei of the hypothalamus down their axons in the hypothalamo-hypophyseal tract, to the pars nervosa (Fig. 480). Here the neurosecretion (which contains the hormone activity) is absorbed into capillaries of the septa of the pars nervosa (Fig. 478, *bottom, right*). If the hypothalamo-hypophyseal tract is interrupted, the neurosecretion cannot reach the pars nervosa to be absorbed, and diabetes insipidus results (unless new absorptive sites are built up).

By means of the chrome alum hematoxylin technic, neurosecretory granules have been ob-

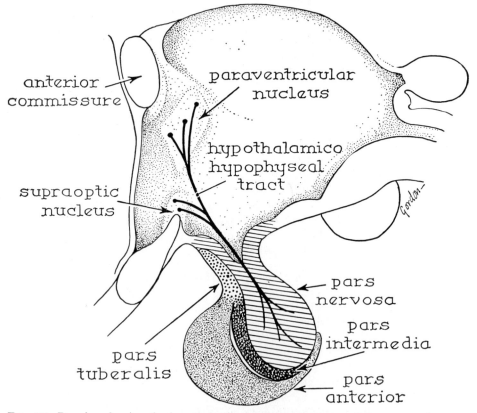

Fig. 480. Drawing showing the hypothalamico-hypophyseal tract and the course of neurosecretion from hypothalamic nuclei into the pars nervosa.

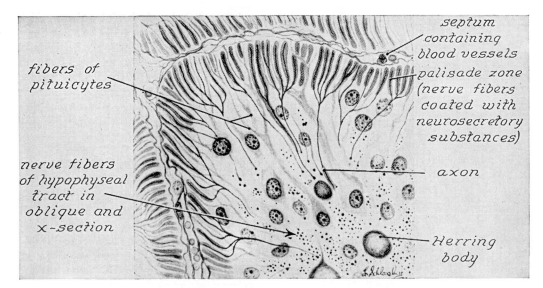

fibers of pituicytes

nerve fibers of hypophyseal tract in oblique and x-section

septum containing blood vessels

palisade zone (nerve fibers coated with neurosecretory substances)

axon

Herring body

FIG. 481. Schematic representation of the histologic organization of a lobule in the pars nervosa of the opossum. (Bodian, D.: Bull. Johns Hopkins Hosp. *89*:354)

served in hypothalamic nuclei in every species studied, including man, where they were first seen by Scharrer and Gaupp. In mammals they are very small granules (see Palay) (Fig. 478, *top, left*). Neurosecretory cells are nerve cells that possess all the ordinary features of nerve cells, including Nissl bodies in their cytoplasm (Fig. 478, *top, left*). In addition, however, they produce secretory material that passes along their axons (Fig. 478, *top, right*) to nerve terminals from which it is discharged into the circulation (Fig. 478, *bottom, right*).

As has been mentioned, the neurosecretory material that accounts for the hormone activity of extracts of the pars nervosa is produced by nerve cells in the supra-optic and the para-ventricular nuclei; it is only stored in, and absorbed from, the pars nervosa. This finding makes the structure of the pars nervosa more intelligible, as we shall see.

Microscopic Structure. In most species the pars nervosa does not exhibit a very well organized structure. However, the microscopic structure of the pars nervosa of the opossum is much more clear-cut, and this has been studied by Bodian in the light of recent knowledge about neurosecretion.

Bodian has shown that the pars nervosa of the opossum is divided into lobules by septa; the latter contain many small blood vessels, and it is into these that most of the neuro-

secretion is delivered (Fig. 481). The more central part of each lobule constitutes a hilus, and this is made up chiefly of bundles of fibers of the hypothalamo-hypophyseal tract. By means of Gomori's staining method, fine granules of neurosecretion can be seen in these nerve fibers. From the region of the hilus the fibers diverge to approach the septum that surrounds the lobule at right angles to it. Near their terminations each one is coated with a wrapping of neurosecretory substance; hence, near their terminations the fibers exist as the central cores of cylinders of neurosecretory material which come into contact with the septa more or less at right angles to them. The neurosecretory material is absorbed from the ends of these cylinders into the blood vessels of the septa. Bodian terms the zone which consists of cylinders that abut on the septa the *palisade zone* of the lobule (Fig. 481).

In the hilus of each lobule the nuclei of pituicytes can be seen (Fig. 481). Pituicytes are a type of neuroglia cell and probably serve a supporting function. However, some still believe that they have a hormone-secreting function. Their cytoplasmic processes (fibers) may extend out between the cylinders of neurosecretory material in the palisade zone (Fig. 481).

Bodies of material that stain with the Gomori technic, which have been known as Herring bodies, are to be seen in the pars

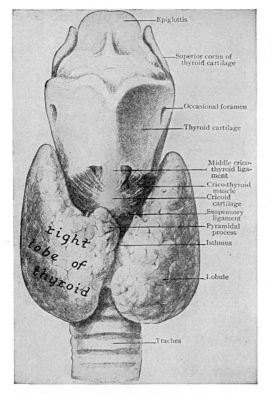

FIG. 482. The thyroid gland in situ. (Huber: Piersol's Human Anatomy, ed. 9, Philadelphia, Lippincott)

nervosa. These are probably terminal bulb formations of fibers of the hypothalamo-hypophyseal tract that end within the substance of the gland, and in which there are accumulations of neurosecretory material (Fig. 478, *top, right*).

It seems probable that the microscopic structure of the pars nervosa of other species is basically similar to that of the opossum but not organized so clearly into lobules by orderly septa; hence, there is probably more absorption of neurosecretory material from the end regions of the fibers into blood vessels that are more irregularly disposed (Fig. 478, *bottom, right*).

THE THYROID GLAND

Introduction. This gland was probably given the name *thyroid* (*thyreos* = an oblong shield; *eidos* = form) because it lies in the neck close to the thyroid cartilage which is shaped like a shield (Fig. 482). It consists of two lobes of dark-red glandular tissue which are joined together by a band of similar tissue called the *isthmus* (Fig. 482). The isthmus lies over the second and the third cartilaginous rings of the trachea, and the 2 lobes, for the most part, fit over the front and around the sides of the trachea just below the larynx, but their upper parts extend for a short distance up its sides (Fig. 482).

The thyroid gland secretes 2 hormones that stimulate the rate at which cells oxidize foodstuffs; hence, the amount of hormone in the blood stream controls the rate of metabolism in the body as a whole. The *metabolic rate* of an individual can be determined clinically to tell how his or her thyroid gland is functioning.

If too little thyroid hormone is produced, the metabolic rate is low. If severe thyroid deficiency occurs during the growing period, a type of dwarfism called *cretinism* (*cretin* = barely human) is produced. If young animals are thyroidectomized, the lack of growth that results is not due entirely to a lack of thyroid hormone in growing tissues because it has been shown that giving such animals growth hormone makes them grow, at least to some extent. Evidently, the changes that occur in the pars anterior as a result of a lack of thyroid hormone in the blood somehow interfere with the production of growth hormone. Cretinism is associated with an impaired mentality. If too little thyroid hormone is produced after full growth is attained, a hard edema of the connective tissues develops in association with a depressed metabolic rate. This condition is termed *myxedema* (*myxa* = mucus) and it too, if severe, may be associated with an impaired mentality. In this form of edema there is an abnormal accumulation of mucopolysaccharide in the intercellular substance.

Thyroid hormones are iodine compounds, and if iodine is not supplied in the diet the gland cannot make its hormones. Marine showed, many years ago, that this leads to the gland overgrowing in an attempt to perform its full function under these conditions. Since iodine is not present in the soil and the water of many parts of the world, there are many regions where enlarged thyroid glands are common. An enlarged thyroid gland is called a *goiter*. Some glands, even though they are enlarged, do not make enough hormone; hence, goiters are sometimes associated with *hypo-*

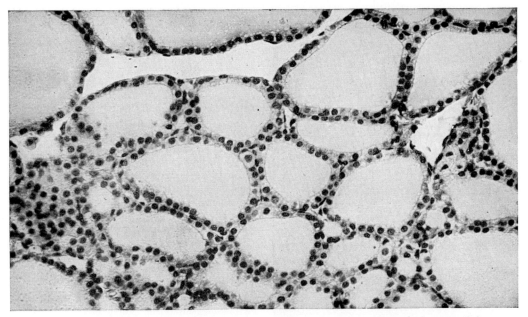

FIG. 483. (A) Low-power photomicrograph of a section of the thyroid gland of a normal dog.

thyroidism. On the other hand, some enlarged glands make far too much hormone; hence, some goiters are associated with *hyperthyroidism.* Too much thyroid hormone in the blood raises the metabolic rate to the point where the individual dislikes heat but can bear cold easily. It also makes the heart go faster and the temperament excitable. Individuals with hyperthyroidism are likely to become thin; they literally metabolize their own tissues.

Microscopic Structure. It is difficult to be precise about the normal microscopic structure of the thyroid gland. Since so many parts of the world are deficient in iodine, and since iodine deficiency leads to compensatory overgrowth of the gland, it is doubtful if strictly normal thyroid glands are ever seen in some regions (the widespread use of iodized salt may eventually remedy this condition). In these regions considerable latitude is allowed in defining the normal; indeed, in most laboratories of pathology, most glands that are not abnormal enough to have caused signs or symptoms during life, even though their microscopic appearance differs from that which is common in regions where iodine is abundant, are called normal. The student, then, should not expect all the thyroid glands that are termed normal to have precisely the same microscopic appearance.

The gland is covered with 2 capsules. The outer one is continuous with, and is part of, the pretracheal fascia which, in turn, is part of the deep cervical fascia. The inner capsule is to be regarded as the true capsule of the gland. It consists of fibro-elastic connective tissue, and it sends septa into the gland to provide internal support and to carry blood vessels, lymphatics and nerves into its substance. The septa divide the gland into lobules, the limits of which may be dimly apparent on the surface of the gland (Fig. 482). However, the lobules are not discrete, because the septa do not join with one another in the substance of the gland in such a way as to enclose completely limited areas of tissue.

Figure 142 illustrates how a clump of cells in an endocrine gland can become a follicle with stored secretion in its central plant. The follicle is the unit of structure of the thyroid gland, and the stored secretion within it is called *colloid.* There are no cords of secretory cells, as there are in so many endocrine glands, in the thyroid.

In the normal gland the follicles vary from being irregularly rounded to tubular in shape (Fig. 483 A). They vary from .05 to 0.5 mm. in diameter (Marine). In a section they appear to vary even more in size. This is due to the fact that in cutting a single section the

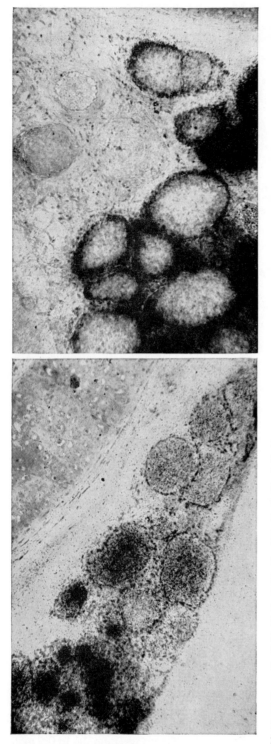

knife passes through the centers of some follicles, the edges of others and through others at various levels between their centers and their edges. Those follicles whose edges are

Fig. 483. (B) Radioautographs of the thyroids of rats sacrificed at 1 hour (*top*) and 24 hours (*bottom*) after administration of a tracer dose of radioiodine. These animals were kept on a diet supplying 20 micrograms of iodine daily. The sections were cut at 5 μ, stained with hematoxylin eosin and coated with photographic emulsion. After developing and mounting of the slides, the accompanying pictures were obtained.

(*Top*) Photomicrograph taken from the thyroid of a rat sacrificed 1 hour following the administration of radioiodine. It shows rings of black granules. The granules are actually located at the junction of the cells forming the walls of each follicle and the colloid in its lumen. It is at this site that iodine appears to become linked to the glycoprotein to form thyroglobulin. Only a very slight reaction is present in the central part of the colloid material. Blood vessels can be seen at the left.

(*Bottom*) Photomicrograph (obtained in the same fashion from a rat sacrificed 24 hours after the administration of radioiodine) showing the black granules indicative of radioiodine deposition throughout the colloid of the thyroid follicles. The newly formed thyroglobulin by this time has filled the follicle lumen, replacing the old nonradioactive thyroglobulin that has been hydrolyzed, releasing the thyroid hormones. (Preparation by C. P. Leblond and J. Gross)

merely shaved by the knife appear in sections as solid clumps of cells (Fig. 483 A, *left*) for the same reason that a thin shaving cut from an orange shows only skin and no pulp. However, some of the solid clumps of cells that are seen in sections are probably not to be explained as shavings from the sides of follicles. The cells in these clumps are larger than the typical follicular cells and have a clear cytoplasm without colloid droplets. They have been called *parafollicular cells* because they are usually seen just beside follicles, occupying the space between the follicle and its basement membrane. They are also found scattered individually among the follicular cells and as buds protruding from the follicles.

Within the substance of lobules, follicles are packed fairly close together. Each follicle is surrounded by a basement membrane which is P.A.S. positive. Between the follicles there is only a delicate reticular network that contains an extensive capillary bed. Marine says that the extensiveness of this is second only to that of the lung. However, for some reason, the capillaries in the reticular stroma do not show to advantage in the sections of thyroid gland prepared by routine methods (Fig. 483 A). Lymphocytes or even lymph nodules may be present in the reticular stroma. A great amount of lymphatic tissue in this site may be the result of an auto-immunity reaction, as will be explained presently.

In a normal gland the epithelium of the follicles is of a low cuboidal type (Fig. 483 A). The colloid contained within the follicles, after fixation, appears in sections as a solid, structureless, acidophilic material (Fig. 483 A). Moreover, in sections of fixed tissue it is often seen to have shrunken away from the follicular epithelium in such a way as to present a serrated rather than a smooth outline. According to De Robertis, colloid, before fixation, is a viscous homogeneous fluid. Colloid consists chiefly of a glycoprotein which becomes combined into a complex with iodine and is called thyroglobulin.

The fine structure of the thyroid will be considered presently.

Use of Radioiodine in Investigating the Histophysiology of the Thyroid. Thyroid hormone, like other secretions, is a product of cellular activity, and in making it, a substantial percentage of iodine is incorporated into its molecular structure. Therefore, the thyroid gland is the seat of a considerable "turnover" of iodine.

To study the uptake of iodine by the thyroid gland, animals are given minimum quantities of radioiodine and then killed at suitable intervals afterward, and radioautographs of the thyroid gland are prepared. Two radioautographs of the thyroid gland prepared by Leblond and Gross are shown in Figure 483 B.

Many findings of Leblond and his associates are incorporated in the following.

STEPS CONCERNED IN THE UPTAKE OF IODINE
BY THE FOLLICLES AND THE PRODUCTION
OF THE THYROID HORMONES

A certain amount of iodine is available in the form of iodide in the normal individual; this constitutes what might be termed the iodide pool of the body. Iodide enters the pool from the diet and from the breakdown of the iodine-containing thyroid hormones in the body. Iodine, which enters the body from the diet, may be in the form of organic or inorganic compounds; the iodine in these compounds is converted to iodide before entering

the pool. The thyroid hormones are metabolized in the tissues where they perform their functions, and the iodide so released also enters the iodide pool.

Some iodine is continuously being lost from the body into the urine, and in animals the ingestion of sodium chloride increases the amount of iodine wasted in this way. Axelrad, Leblond and Isler have shown that if the iodine intake is borderline, the eating of small amounts of salt will precipitate a condition of iodine deficiency resulting in goiter.

Iodide also leaves the pool to enter the thyroid gland where it is synthesized into the thyroid hormones. Some steps in this process take place in the follicular cells of the gland; others, in the lumen of the follicles, as will now be described.

The follicular cells of the gland take up iodide very steadily from the circulating blood in the capillaries that surround each follicle and pass it into the lumens of the follicles where it accumulates to reach concentrations far above that in the circulating blood. At the same time, the follicular cells synthesize an uniodinated glycoprotein, the precursor of thyroglobulin, and secrete it into the lumens of the follicles. Glycoprotein droplets can be demonstrated (with the P.A.S. technic) between the nucleus and the lumen of the follicle. The cells also synthesize oxidizing enzymes which are probably also secreted into the follicle lumen where they convert the iodide to iodine or iodite.

At the borders between cells and lumens the thyroglobulin precursor and iodine (or iodite) react to form *thyroglobulin*, the iodinated glycoprotein which is the "colloid" of the thyroid. This process involves 2 steps: (1) the iodination of tyrosine groups in the glycoprotein and (2) the coupling of the iodotyrosines so formed to each other. This results in the formation of both thyroxine and tri-iodothyronine within the glycoprotein molecules. The glycoprotein, altered in this way, is now called thyroglobulin. After being stored in the lumen of the follicle for a varying length of time, depending on the degree of activity of the follicle, the thyroglobulin is hydrolyzed by a proteolytic enzyme. This enzyme is secreted by the follicular cells into the lumen. It was first discovered by De Robertis who showed that colloid from thyroid follicles contained something that would liquefy gelatin. This proteolytic enzyme hydrolyzes thyroglobulin to its constituent amino acids. Some of these amino acids contain iodine. By the action of an enzyme discovered by Roche and his collaborators, iodine is removed from all of these amino acids except two: thyroxine and tri-

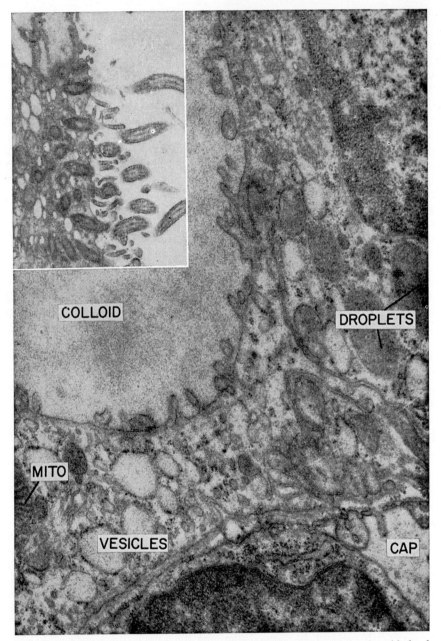

FIG. 484. This electron micrograph ($\times$ 43,000) is of a section of the thyroid gland of a mouse. Part of one follicle is shown, lined by follicular epithelial cells. Microvilli protrude from the apical surfaces of these cells into the colloid. Dilated rough-surfaced vesicles, droplets, mitochondria and part of a nucleus are seen in the cytoplasm. At the base of the follicle (*bottom*) there is a capillary lined by thin, perforate endothelial cytoplasm. Part of the nucleus of an endothelial cell is shown. The inset (*upper left*, $\times$ 30,000) is of the apical part of a follicular cell showing cilia. (Preparation by June D. Almeida)

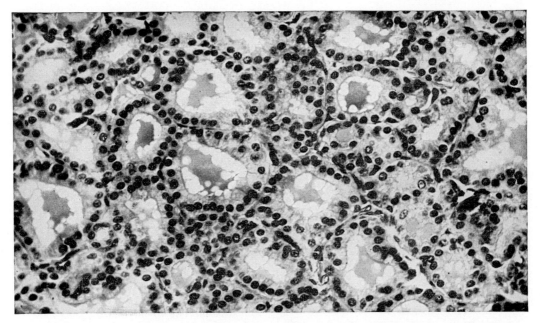

Fig. 485. Low-power photomicrograph of a section of the thyroid gland of a dog that had received 7 daily injections of anterior pituitary extract containing thyrotrophin. This is the type of histologic picture seen in parenchymatous goiter.

iodothyronine. The iodine so released is in the form of iodide; it re-enters the iodide pool. The size of the thyroxine and the tri-iodothyronine molecules is such that they can diffuse back through the cells of the follicles to enter the surrounding capillaries as the thyroid hormones. It should be noted that iodide passes through the follicular cells in a direction opposite to that of the thyroid hormones.

For many years it was generally believed that thyroxine was the only hormone of the thyroid gland. Recently, however, it has been found that while thyroxine is the major hormone made under conditions of iodine sufficiency, a considerable percentage of *tri-iodothyronine* is made under conditions of iodine deficiency. This latter hormone contains less iodine than thyroxine but is more potent in its action; hence, the production of it, rather than of thyroxine, would seem to be a measure designed to conserve iodine when economy is necessary.

Fine Structure. With the E/M, each follicle is seen to be bounded by its own homogeneous basement membrane (Fig. 484). In the cytoplasm of the follicular cells toward their bases, dilated rough-surfaced vesicles are found. Toward the apices are vesicles of the Golgi apparatus, some of which contain homogeneous or finely particulate material, and some darker droplets bounded by a smooth-surfaced membrane. There appears to be a gradation of structures between Golgi vesicles and the droplets. It is possible that these contain the glycoprotein and that enzymes, which are proteins, are formed in association with the rough-surfaced vesicles. From the apices of the follicular cells, short, stubby microvilli protrude into the colloid, and a few ciliated cells also are found in the walls of follicles (Fig. 484, *inset*).

Capillaries that lie between the follicles are lined by an endothelium which is much attenuated or even porous (Fig. 484). Each is covered with its own homogeneous basement membrane.

Action of Thyrotrophin (T.S.H.). Thyroid-stimulating hormone (TSH) from the pituitary increases the production of thyroid hormones by augmenting the iodide-accumulating ability of the follicular cells, by increasing the size and the number of these cells and by increasing the amount or the activity of the proteolytic enzyme which hydrolyzes the colloid so that more hormone becomes available from it for absorption into the blood stream. Colloid in a gland that is being acted upon by more than usual amounts

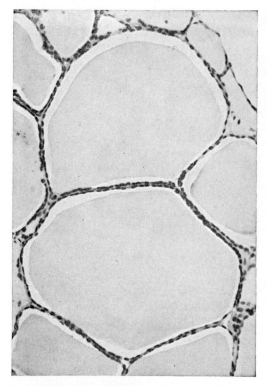

FIG. 486. Medium-power photomicrograph of a small area of a section of a simple colloid goiter.

of thyrotrophin tends to stain pale blue rather than pink in H and E sections and as it is broken down it fills less and less space in the follicles (Fig. 485).

RELATION OF IODINE INTAKE TO GOITER

An enlarged thyroid gland is called a *goiter* (*guttur* = throat). Marine was chiefly responsible for showing that the common types of goiter are the result of the thyroid gland trying to make its iodine-containing hormone without there being enough iodine in the diet. The present generation that has been brought up with iodized salt in its diet probably has difficulty in visualizing the extent of the goiter problem that existed in many parts of the country a few decades ago.

Under conditions of iodine deficiency, the thyroid gland cannot make enough hormone to supply the body, and, as a result, the concentration of thyroid hormone in the blood stream tends to fall. Because of the push-pull mechanism, the pars anterior then secretes

more thyrotrophic hormone than before. This stimulates the thyroid gland both to secrete and to grow. As a result of increased secretory activity the colloid content of the follicle becomes reduced, and the colloid itself becomes thin and pale-staining (Fig. 485). As a result of the stimulation of growth, the epithelial cells of the follicles become taller and increase in number by mitotic division. The follicles thus come to have thicker walls and to be composed of far more cells than before (Fig. 485); this is reflected in an increase in the size of the gland as a whole, although the follicles, as they grow, lose most of their colloid, there being little within them to keep them distended. As a consequence, their walls become collapsed and infolded to a considerable extent. Since the enlargement of the gland is due chiefly to an increase in the number and the size of the epithelial cells of the follicles and not to an increased amount of colloid, the enlarged gland that results from thyrotrophic stimulation is termed a *parenchymatous* goiter.

A parenchymatous change, as described above, is probably the first change that occurs in iodine deficiency. It is to be noted that the need for thyroid hormone is increased at certain times, such as puberty and during pregnancy, and hence that parenchymatous goiters are more likely to develop at those times than others, provided that iodine consumption is kept more or less constant.

Assuming that a parenchymatous goiter has developed in an individual at a time when the supplies of iodine were not adequate for the amount of hormone needed, for example, at puberty, and then that subsequently either the needs for thyroid hormone became less, or a little more iodine was taken in the diet, the microscopic structure of the thyroid would change once more. With a lessened demand for hormone, or with more iodine with which to make hormone, the gland would be able gradually to raise the concentration of hormone in the blood stream. As the concentration of hormone in the blood stream rises, the secretion of thyrotrophic hormone by the pars anterior would gradually be suppressed. With lessened thyrotrophic stimulation, the cells of the follicles of the thyroid gland would then revert to their former state; instead of being high cuboidal or columnar, they would become low cuboidal again (Fig. 486). It has been generally assumed that since the follicles would no longer be stimulated to secrete so much hormone into the blood stream, they would be able to store more within their follicles, and as a result the follicles would increase in size (Fig. 486). It has been generally assumed further that since the follicles, as a result of the preceding proliferation of the cells of their walls, would have more cells in their walls than before, they would be much larger than before when they became distended with colloid. As a result, the gland as a whole would become larger than it was when it was primarily a parenchymatous goiter. Further, since its increase in size would be due primarily to its large content of colloid, it would be termed a colloid rather than a parenchymatous goiter (compare Figs. 483 A, 485 and 486). The concept given above, of how a colloid goiter develops, elaborated by Marine, did not seem to lend itself to experimental verification in rats. However, Fallis has recently produced colloid goiters in hamsters by this means; this substantiates Marine's concept of how colloid goiters develop.

The above-described two types of goiter. (or a combination of the two), which develop as a result of iodine deficiency, are called simple parenchymatous and simple colloid goiter, respectively, to distinguish them from. certain other types of goiter which have a more complex cause. There is one complex type, for example, that is called exophthalmic goiter because it is often associated with a protrusion of the eyes. In this condition the microscopic appearance of the thyroid gland is similar to that of a simple parenchymatous goiter (the histologic picture of thyrotrophic stimulation, as shown in Fig. 485), but, in contrast with a simple parenchymatous goiter, when supplied with adequate iodine, although it may become less active for a time, it tends sooner or later to resume making much too much hormone. Some believe that the primary cause of this condition is in the pars anterior, that for some reason its secretion of thyrotrophic hormone is not suppressed as much as it should be by normal amounts of thyroid hormone in the blood.

A new way of treating certain kinds of hyperthyroidism has been evolved recently. It was discovered that certain drugs, most notably thiouracil, prevent the thyroid gland from properly synthesizing thyroid hormone even if the diet contains adequate amounts of iodine. Therefore, the administration of thiouracil can cut down the production of hormone by the gland and so allay hyperthyroidism. However, in cases of exophthalmic goiter, the use of thiouracil sometimes causes the protrusion of the eyes to become more severe. This and other facts, most notably the demonstration that exophthalmos can be produced by thyrotrophic hormone in animals whose thyroid glands have been removed, suggests that the thyrotrophic hormone, when secreted in large amounts, can cause exophthalmos. The increase in the exophthalmos sometimes observed in the treatment of exophthalmic goiter by thiouracil is probably caused by the lessened amount of thyroid hormone in the blood stimulating the pars anterior to secrete more thyrotrophic hormone. That more thyrotrophic hormone is secreted under these conditions is witnessed by the fact that the microscopic picture in the thyroid gland is one of great activity; even though the thiouracil is preventing thyroid hormone from being synthesized, the gland, flogged by thyrotrophic hormone, presents a picture of great activity similar to that illustrated in Figure 485. It is of interest that thiouracil administered to a normal animal with an adequate iodine intake will soon cause its previously normal thyroid gland to assume the microscopic appearance of a parenchymatous goiter. The explanation for this is obvious.

It is now recognized that some goiters which are associated with hypothyroidism in man result from inherited defects. These defects are manifested by the existence of blocks in any of several of the various steps involved in the production of thyroid hormones for oxidizing iodide to the form in which it can link to the tyrosine groups of the glycoprotein precursor of thyroglobulin. The result is an accumulation of iodide in the thyroid but no synthesis of thyroglobulin, a situation similar to that produced by the administration of thiouracil.

Another similar condition appears to be due to the inherited absence of the system required for coupling iodotyrosines to make thyroxine and tri-iodothyronine in the thyroglobulin molecule. Mono- and di-iodotyrosine then accumulate in the thyroid. A third condition, inherited as an autosomal recessive and resulting in congenital hypothyroidism with goiter, is due to the absence of the enzyme discovered by Roche, which deiodinates the unused portion of iodotyrosines so that the iodide so released may be reutilized in synthesis of thyroglobulin. This causes mono- and di-iodotyrosine to accumulate in the blood and to be lost as such in the urine.

As discussed earlier, one way of determining the extent of the activity of the thyroid is to estimate the effect that thyroid secretion is having on the oxidation processes in body cells by measuring the *basal metabolic rate*. Newer, more direct methods for determining the level of thyroid function are now available.

The thyroid hormones, upon leaving the gland, for the most part become linked to proteins of the globulin type in the blood. The iodine that is in this way attached to protein (*serum protein-bound iodine or PBI*) can be measured, and its level is an accurate indicator of the function of the thyroid gland. Therefore, it is now being widely used in the diagnosis of thyroid disorders.

Another method, that owes its existence to the unique ability of the thyroid to concentrate iodine, is known as the *radioiodine uptake*. Radioiodine in minute quantities is administered to patients, and, at various time intervals thereafter, measurements are made of the rays emanating from their thyroids by means of an externally placed Geiger counter, with no discomfort to the patients. This gives important information concerning the function of the thyroid gland because the rate of upake is high in overactive glands and low in underactive ones.

Radioiodine is used sometimes to treat certain pathologic conditions of the thyroid gland. Since it tends to become concentrated in the colloid of the thyroid follicles, attempts have been made in various centers to treat certain pathologic conditions of the thyroid gland by giving the patients sufficient doses of the material to permit destructive amounts of it to accumulate in the thyroid gland but not elsewhere. Concentration in only one site, with no harmful accumulations elsewhere, is probably a very difficult objective to attain with isotopes, but it is probably more feasible with radioiodine and the thyroid gland than with most isotopes and tissues.

Nerves. The thyroid gland receives post-ganglionic sympathetic fibers from the superior and the middle cervical ganglia. Many of these are vasomotor in type and form plexuses in the adventitia of the blood vessels of the gland. Others end in networks in the reticular stroma between the follicles. Whether these have a secretory function has not been established. Some nerve fibers also reach the gland from the superior and the recurrent laryngeal nerves, but their distribution within the gland and their function are not known. The thyroid gland does not depend on its innervation in order to function, for pieces of the gland, freely transplanted from one part of the body to another, will grow and function.

THE THYROID GLAND AS AN EXAMPLE OF A SECLUDED ANTIGEN

As was mentioned in discussing the formation of antibodies in Chapter 18 (Lymphatic Tissue), it is now known that the mammalian body may sometimes form antibodies against one of its own components; the antibodies so-formed are termed auto-antibodies, and the phenomenon itself, auto-immunity.

Knowledge in this field is as yet in its infancy. There is reason to believe that the further development of knowledge may elucidate the etiology of certain as yet ill-understood diseases of man; indeed, it is not inconceivable that part of what we now regard as the normal process of ageing may eventually be found to be due in part to the immunity-producing mechanisms of individuals, as they grow older, reacting against themselves. In any event, the phenomenon of auto-immunity is of such interest and possible importance that it should be mentioned; and since a good example of it is sometimes provided by the thyroid gland, we shall discuss it here briefly.

As was explained in Chapter 10, immunologic tolerance develops to antigens to which a fetus (or, in many species, a newborn animal) is suitably exposed and as a consequence of this the animal in postnatal life will lack the capacity for reacting against any of these antigens by producing antibodies against them. This is true of heterologous antigens which are injected into the fetus of the newborn animal, and it is reasonable to assume that it is also true of such macromolecules as develop normally in the fetus, which would be antigens if they were injected into other hosts. Therefore, as a general rule, it would seem that an animal does not react against any of its *own* macromolecules in postnatal life, because it has been suitably exposed to them in fetal life and has become immunologically tolerant of them.

However, for a fetus to become tolerant to macromolecules that develop within it during embryonic life requires that these macromolecules either gain entrance to the tissue fluid, or the lymph or the blood of the fetus, so that somehow they can give information to the precursors of antibody-forming cells to the effect that antibodies are not to be made against them. As has already been explained, the period during which immunologic tolerance can be induced terminates around the time of birth. Accordingly, if any antigen forms in the fetus but is kept hidden from the tissue fluid, the lymph or the blood of the body, so that it does not come in contact with the precursor cells of the antibody-forming series, the latter will have no information about it, and so the body will not be immunologically tolerant to it. Hence, if previously *secluded antigens* gain entrance to one of the fluids of the body and so are able to reach antibody-forming cells in postnatal life, the latter will react against them as they would against any foreign antigen.

The thyroid gland provides an example of a secluded antigen. Thyroglobulin or its precursor is a glycoprotein that is secreted by follicular cells into the lumens of follicles, and under normal conditions this glycoprotein does not as such enter any of the fluids of the body. Accordingly, an animal body is not immunologically tolerant to the glycoprotein in the follicles of its thyroid gland. Experimental evidence provided by Witebsky and his associates and by others indicates very strongly that an animal injected with a suitable extract prepared from its own thyroid gland will make antibodies against it.

There is now some reason to believe that the development of auto-immunity against thyroglobulin or its precursor is a contributing factor in the development of a disease of the thyroid gland which is occasionally seen and is called Hashimoto's disease. In this disease the thyroid gland becomes enlarged; this is due primarily to the stroma of the gland becoming increased in amount and heavily infiltrated with lymphocytes and plasma cells and even giving birth to lymphatic nodules. The follicles become atrophic and contain little colloid, and thyroid function is generally impaired. Antibodies to some thyroid protein have been demonstrated in the blood of patients with this disease. Experimentally, it has been shown that if part of the thyroid gland of an animal is excised, disease can be produced in the remaining part by immunizing the animal with extracts prepared from the excised portion. Therefore, Hashimoto's disease would seem to have its origin in thyroglobulin or its precursor somehow gaining access to the stroma of the thyroid gland.

Another example of a secluded antigen is provided by the lens of the eye. Several factors are probably involved in keeping its proteins secluded: (1) its proteins are relatively insoluble; (2) the lens is enclosed by a capsule; and (3) the encapsulated lens lives in a bath of a special fluid, aqueous humor, which provides a more secluded environment than does ordinary tissue fluid. In any event there is evidence that if lens protein escapes, for example, during an eye operation, it can serve as an antigen in the body in which it was formed.

Spermatozoa (male germ cells, to be described in Chap. 28) provide another example of a secluded antigen, for they are formed inside tubules and hence are not in contact with tissue fluid, lymph or blood. It has been shown experimentally that a male can develop antibodies against his own spermatozoa. However, there is an additional reason for a body's not being tolerant to its own spermatozoa; it is that spermatozoa do not develop in the body until postnatal life and then not until the time of puberty. Hence, there is no opportunity for the body to become immunologically tolerant to spermatozoa in fetal life.

Secluded antigens are not the only cause for antibodies sometimes being developed against body components. Interesting as it would be to discuss possible mechanisms which may lead to antibodies being formed against various types of blood cells, and possibly also to some components of intercellular substance in the heart, the kidney and the joint capsules, it would not be proper to do this in connection

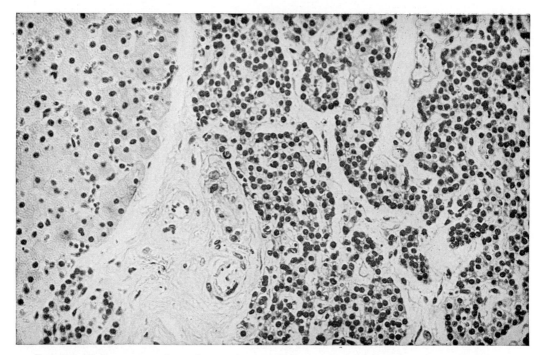

FIG. 487. Medium-power photomicrograph of a small area of a section of the parathyroid gland. An area of oxyphil cells may be seen at the left. The right side shows chief cells.

with the thyroid gland. Some references are given for those interested.

THE PARATHYROID GLANDS

Introduction. There are usually 4 parathyroid glands in each person, but there may be more. They are so named because they are *beside* the thyroid gland. More precisely, they are usually arranged 2 on each side, on the backs of the lobes of the thyroid gland, immediately outside the true capsule of the thyroid gland, but to the inside of its outer capsule of fascia. The upper parathyroids lie about midway between the upper and the lower poles of the lobes, while the lower ones are near the lower poles of the lobes. The upper ones are of a flattened ovoid shape, and the lower ones roughly that of a somewhat flattened sphere. Their length or greatest diameter is slightly more than half a centimeter. They are yellow-brown when seen in the fresh state. Both the upper and the lower parathyroids are supplied by twigs from the inferior thyroid artery, and it is said that these small glands can sometimes be found conveniently by tracing the arterial twigs that arise from the

inferior thyroid artery to their terminations.

The numbers and the sites of parathyroid glands vary in different kinds of experimental animals. In the rat there are only 2 glands, and these lie buried in the substance of the thyroid gland, one in each lobe. In the dog, parathyroid glands may sometimes be found as far down as the bifurcation of the trachea. Even in man, aberrant parathyroid glands are not uncommon, and if a tumor develops in one of these it may be difficult to find.

In the first chapter of this book it was observed that the great disadvantage associated with the specialization of labor in a community, either of cells or people, is the fact that the whole community becomes dependent on each group of essential specialists continuing to live and work. The parathyroid glands illustrate very dramatically the dependence of the whole body on a small number of specialists, for if the parathyroid glands are removed, the whole body, unless special therapy is instituted, perishes.

Microscopic Structure. Each parathyroid gland is covered by a delicate connective tissue capsule. Septa from it penetrate the gland to carry blood vessels and a few vasomotor nerve fibers into its substance. The septa do not divide the gland into distinct lobules. Until a few years before puberty, only one type of secretory cell is found in the gland. This is termed the chief or principal cell. It is smaller than the secretory cells of most endocrine glands; hence, *in the parathyroid gland the nuclei of the parenchymal cells are generally very close together* (Fig. 487). No granules can be seen in the cytoplasm of chief cells. Although their cytoplasm is never very dense or dark-staining, that of some chief cells is darker than that of others. Those with the darker cytoplasm are called *dark chief* cells; and those with very pale cytoplasm, *light chief* cells. Some light chief cells have no stainable substance in their cytoplasm whatsoever; these are called *clear* cells. Chief cells make the only hormone known to be secreted by the gland, and S. H. Bensley has related the different appearances that they present to different stages of a secretory cycle. Her paper should be consulted for details.

Although chief cells are smaller than the cells of most endocrine glands, they are arranged in clumps and irregular cords that are wider than those of most endocrine glands. The cells within the cords and the clumps are supported by reticular fibers. Large capillaries are present between the cords and the clumps.

A few years before puberty, clumps of cells with much larger amounts of cytoplasm than chief cells make their appearance in the gland. In contrast with that of chief cells, the cytoplasm of these contains granules. These are acidophilic; hence, the cells are termed *oxyphil* (*oxys* = acid) cells. The easiest way for the student to detect clumps of these is to look for sites in the gland where nuclei are more widely separated from each other than they are in areas of chief cells (Fig. 487). Such areas are more common in the periphery of the gland. Oxyphil cells are not nearly so numerous as chief cells. Oxyphil cells are not present in the parathyroid glands of most animals. In man, transitions between chief and oxyphil cells are commonly seen; since chief cells appear in the gland first, this suggests that oxyphil cells probably arise from chief cells. The function of oxyphil cells, if any, is unknown.

In the parathyroid glands of older people, occasional clumps of chief cells may form follicles. These probably represent attempts at storing secretion. In addition, the glands of older people often contain considerable amounts of fat.

Function. Although much is known about the effects of the parathyroid hormone, there is much uncertainty about how it produces these effects. We shall first consider some of the effects of too little and too much parathyroid hormone in the circulation, and then we shall speculate on how the hormone could produce these effects.

Effects of Removal. Removal of the parathyroid tissue from an animal causes it to develop a condition called tetany (this is not to be confused with tetanus which is an infection). Tetany is characterized by the development of prolonged or convulsive spasms of certain muscles. When it is very severe, spasms of muscles of the larynx or those responsible for respiratory movements may cause death. The immediate cause of tetany is a lack of a sufficient concentration of calcium ions in the blood; calcium ions routinely act to prevent undue irritability of nervous and neuromuscular mechanisms. Since the level of calcium in the blood falls when the parathyroid glands are removed, it is obvious that the parathyroid hormone in some way helps to maintain a proper level of calcium in the blood. This was not established until 1925 when Collip succeeded in making an extract of parathyroid glands that would raise the level of the blood calcium in dogs from which the parathyroid glands had been removed, and this prevented tetany from developing in them.

Effects of Too Much Parathyroid Hormone. Tumors of the chief cells sometimes occur. Moreover, sometimes parathyroid glands become hyperplastic without actually becoming tumors. In both conditions too much parathyroid hormone may be produced and liberated into the blood stream; this is prone to cause grave effects in the skeleton. The bones become unduly fragile and are easily broken. Roentgenograms show that the amount of bone substance is greatly reduced, and histologic sections reveal a picture which suggests that the bony skeleton is being replaced with ordinary fibrous connective tissue and that bone resorption is greatly stimulated, as is indicated by increased numbers of osteoclasts. The condition is termed generalized osteitis fibrosa. The blood of individuals suffering from this

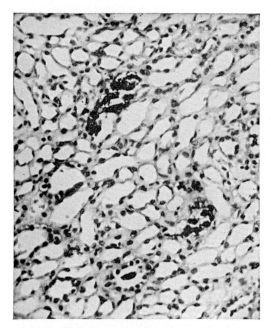

Fig. 488. Medium-power photomicrograph of a section of the medulla of the kidney of a dog that received large amounts of parathyroid hormone. The black material is calcium that has been deposited along the loops of Henle as a result of the kidney's having to excrete excess amounts of this mineral.

disease usually contains increased amounts of calcium, and urine examinations reveal that much calcium is being excreted in urine. The latter effect may lead to the deposition of calcium precipitates in the kidney (Fig. 488), and these in turn may seriously damage the kidneys so that individuals with parathyroid tumors, if left untreated, may die of kidney disease.

Effects of Administering Parathyroid Hormone to Normal Animals. Different kinds of experimental animals vary in their responses to parathyroid hormone, but, in general, if large doses are given to young animals the blood calcium level is increased, and the trabeculae on the diaphyseal sides of epiphyseal plates are soon resorbed. Many osteoclasts are left in the sites previously occupied by trabeculae (Fig. 489). With long-continued administration, osteitis fibrosa develops.

Effects of Parathyroid Hormone in Preventing Osteopetrosis in Certain Strains of Rats and Mice. In Chapter 15 it was pointed out in the section on Bone Resorption that there are certain strains of mice and rats in which bone resorption does not proceed at a normal rate, and, as a consequence, the marrow cavities of long bones come to contain a greatly increased number of trabeculae (this condition is called *osteopetrosis*). The administration of parathyroid hormone to such animals results in the rate of bone resorption becoming more normal.

Direct Effects of Parathyroid Tissue on Bone. Both Barnicott and Chang have shown that transplants of parathyroid gland that are placed directly against bone cause resorption of the surface. Transplants of other glands do not seem to have this effect.

A Primary Action of the Hormone. From the foregoing the conclusion seems to be inescapable that the parathyroid hormone is concerned in controlling bone resorption. Normal growth is associated with bone formation and bone resorption remaining in balance. Much evidence, given above, suggests that the parathyroid hormone controls resorption and that if there is too much hormone in the blood, resorption becomes preponderant over formation.

How Does the Parathyroid Hormone Control Bone Resorption? The question now arises as to whether or not the parathyroid hormone affects the level of the calcium in the blood only because of its effect on controlling bone resorption or whether or not it has other effects that affect the level of calcium in the blood. First, we shall consider how the level of the calcium in the blood affects the parathyroid glands.

Years ago rickets was a common disease, and it was often observed that some rachitic children had enlarged parathyroid glands. However, rickets can be caused by a relative lack of either calcium or phosphorus in the blood; the latter is more common. The author, with Littner, Tisdall, Robertson and Drake, showed, some years ago, that the parathyroid glands become greatly enlarged in rachitic rats when the rickets was caused by a low content of calcium in their blood, but they did not become enlarged in rachitic rats that had a normal calcium, but a depressed phosphorus, level in their blood. Accordingly, it would seem that the secretion and the growth of the parathyroid glands is regulated by the

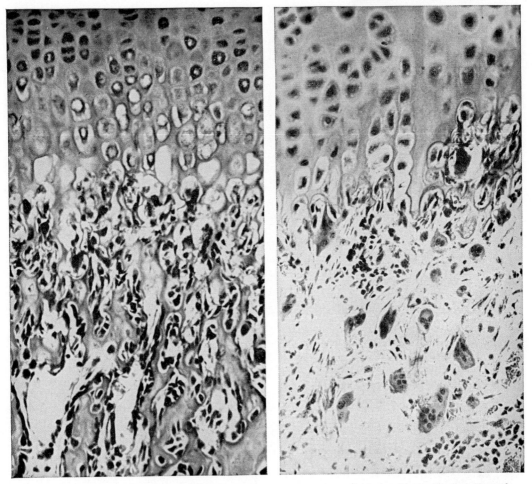

FIG. 489. (*Left*) Low-power photomicrograph of a small portion of a longitudinal section of the metaphysis of a long bone of a young, normal guinea pig. (*Right*) A similar preparation from a litter mate who was given a very large injection of parathyroid hormone 48 hours before. Note that the trabeculae on the diaphyseal side of the epiphyseal disk have melted away and that osteoclasts are left in their place.

amount of calcium that is in the blood; that blood calcium and parathyroid secretion are involved in a simple push-pull arrangement.

It has also been noticed that individuals with certain kinds of kidney disease had hypertrophied parathyroid glands. The kidneys of such individuals cannot excrete phosphorus properly, so the amount of phosphorus in their blood becomes increased. This led to the view that an increased amount of phosphorus in the blood causes the parathyroids to enlarge; this, in turn, suggested that the parathyroid hormone controls phosphorus excretion. However, there is a very curious reciprocal relation between the amounts of calcium and

phosphorus in the blood, so that if the level of one increases, the level of the other falls. So, a high blood phosphorus could cause parathyroid hypertrophy because it depresses the blood calcium level.

It has also been suggested that a primary action of the parathyroid hormone is that of stimulating phosphorus excretion by the kidneys. An argument in favor of this view was the experimental finding that parathyroid hormone does not seem to be effective in raising the blood calcium level in animals from whom the kidneys had been removed. Recently, however, Grollman has shown that if nephrectomized animals are kept alive by means of

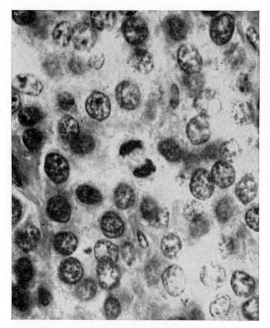

FIG. 490. High-power photomicrograph of a section of the parathyroid gland of a dog that had received several daily injections of anterior pituitary extract. A mitotic figure in a chief cell is to be observed.

peritoneal lavage, parathyroid hormone, administered to them, will increase their blood calcium levels. This would seem to show that the action of parathyroid hormone is not exclusively on the kidneys.

Summary. The evidence outlined above suggests that the parathyroid glands affect, and are directly affected by, calcium rather than phosphate ions. It seems possible that the various effects manifested by parathyroid hormone on the blood calcium level could all be secondary to its primary effect in regulating bone resorption. But there is the further possibility that its effect in regulating bone resorption may be mediated through its affecting some particular enzyme system in the cells that line and cover bone surfaces and that it exerts a similar effect on similar enzyme systems in other organs (for example, the intestine and the kidney) that are concerned with calcium absorption or elimination.

It is difficult to visualize how a hormone, present in only minute amounts in the blood, could have any substantial *direct* effect on calcified intercellular substance. It is much more

reasonable to assume that the effect that parathyroid hormone exerts on bone is mediated through its effects on the cells of bone. The living cells that seem to be chiefly affected by it are the osteogenic cells and the osteoblasts that normally cover and line bone surfaces and perhaps the more superficial osteocytes. Its general effect on the former, as demonstrated in hyperparathyroidism, is to diminish their osteogenic powers, and as a result of this the cells either fuse to become osteoclasts (Fig. 489) or they become fibroblastic in type and make ordinary fibrous connective tissue instead of bone. The changed character of the cells that cover and line bone surface favors resorption and diminishes osteogenesis; this would lead to bone salt being liberated, and this could increase the calcium level of the blood.

It should be pointed out that hyperparathyroidism does not necessarily cause hypercalcemia. For example, it could be expected that a long-continued dietary deficiency of calcium would cause hyperparathyroidism without hypercalcemia, and that such a state of affairs would be reflected in bones by increased resorption and fibrous proliferation. In other words, it is possible that the parathyroid glands, by trying to maintain a normal blood calcium level, could adversely affect the skeleton without ever causing a hypercalcemia.

The Question of Pituitary Control. There is some evidence to show that the parathyroid gland is affected by the anterior pituitary gland. Under ordinary conditions, mitotic figures are rare in the parathyroid gland. After injections with extracts of the pars anterior we observed numerous mitotic figures in the gland (Fig. 490). Other observers have shown that the blood calcium level is raised after injections of anterior pituitary extracts. Certainly, the pars anterior is able to stimulate the parathyroid glands; but whether it does this by means of a special parathyrotrophic hormone is by no means certain.

THE ADRENAL (SUPRARENAL) GLANDS

Some Gross Characteristics

The suprarenal glands are paired, flattened, yellow masses of tissue that lie, as their name implies, in contact with the upper poles of the

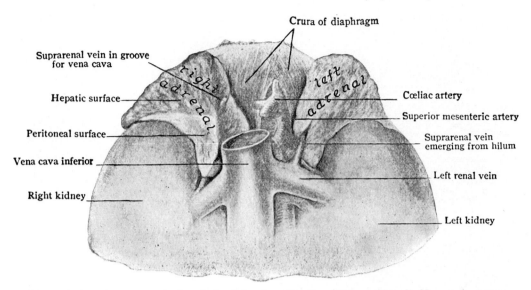

Crura of diaphragm

Suprarenal vein in groove
for vena cava

Hepatic surface

Peritoneal surface

Vena cava inferior

Right kidney

right adrenal

left adrenal

Cœliac artery

Superior mesenteric artery

Suprarenal vein
emerging from hilum

Left renal vein

Left kidney

FIG. 491. Anterior aspect of adrenal glands hardened in situ. (Huber: Piersol's Human Anatomy, ed. 9, Philadelphia, Lippincott)

kidneys (Fig. 491). The right gland—sometimes described as having the shape of a cocked hat—is wedged in the interval between the upper pole of the right kidney and the adjacent inferior vena cava; the left gland—roughly crescentic—occupies the medial border of the left kidney from pole to hilum. Each gland is about 5 cm. long, 3 to 4 cm. wide and somewhat less than 1 cm. in thickness. In many animals the glands, although situated close to the kidneys, do not lie above them; hence, the term *adrenal* (*ad* = to) has a more general application than suprarenal.

Each gland consists of a cortex and a medulla. These two parts have different origins, characters and functions. Therefore, each suprarenal gland is to be thought of as two glands in one. Indeed, in some animals, cortical tissue and medullary tissue form separate bodies no more related to one another anatomically than they are functionally. Many investigators have suspected that there is some reason for the close anatomic association of the two parts of the gland in so many animals, but, although there has been much speculation about this matter, the reason, if any, for the arrangement has not yet been ascertained.

Development

The first intimation of the development of the cortices of the glands is a thickening that

occurs in the mesoderm near the root of the dorsal mesentery. Two substantial masses of cells, one on each side, form in this region and come to lie close to the developing kidney. It seems likely, from the studies of Keene and Hewer, that, as development proceeds, the original mass of cells making up the cortex becomes capped and then surrounded by a second mass of cells derived approximately from the same site as the first. The original or inner mass forms what is called the *provisional* or *fetal cortex of the gland,* and the second or outer mass that subsequently covers it, the *permanent cortex.*

In the meantime, ectodermal cells have migrated from the neural crests (or from the neural tube itself—the source of these cells is somewhat uncertain) to form the celiac ganglia. However, some of these ectodermal-derived cells, instead of developing into ganglion cells, migrate further afield and into the substance of the cortical tissue to take up a position in its central part. A continuous migration of cells from the developing celiac ganglia proceeds almost until the time of birth (and perhaps later), so that by this time a substantial number of cells have taken up a position in the central part of the suprarenal gland to comprise its medulla. The relation of the cells of the medulla to the sympathetic nervous system will be described in detail

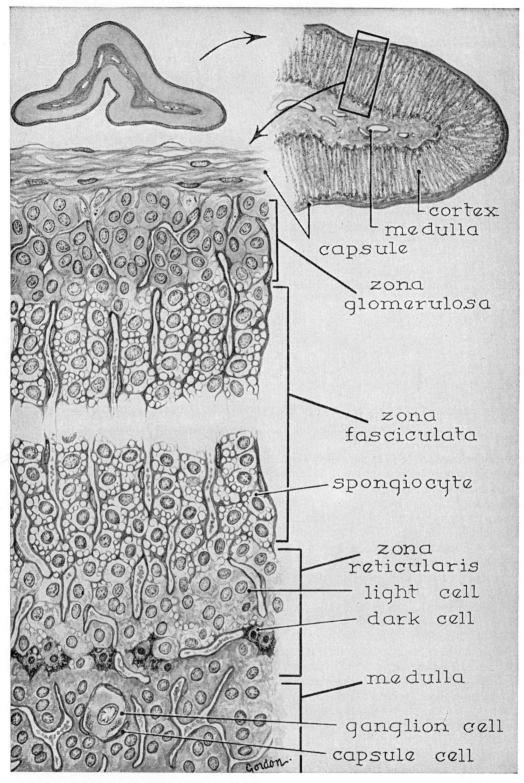

cortex
medulla
capsule
zona
glomerulosa
zona
fasciculata
spongiocyte
zona
reticularis
light cell
dark cell
medulla
ganglion cell
capsule cell

Gordon

Fig. 492. Drawings of various magnifications of an H and E section of an adrenal gland of man.

when we consider the adrenal medulla somewhat later.

The provisional or fetal cortex—derived from the first group of mesodermal cells to separate from the celomic epithelium—becomes arranged into cords of cells separated by blood vessels, and the structure as a whole reaches a high state of development during fetal life. Not only do the cells of the provisional cortex comprise the bulk of the cortical tissue that exists at this time, but also they are so numerous as to make the suprarenal cortex of the fetus an organ of impressive size. The cells of the permanent cortex do not develop to any great extent during this time. However, after birth, the provisional cortex— so highly developed during fetal life—undergoes a rapid involution. As this occurs, the cells of the permanent cortex begin to differentiate, but for a few years they do not become organized into the 3 zones that characterize the adult cortex.

The fact that the provisional cortex has a somewhat different origin from the permanent cortex and is enormously developed in fetal life but involutes after birth suggests strongly that this provisional cortex should be regarded as an endocrine gland in its own right, having a special function in fetal life. Since it involutes after birth, it could be reasoned that the trophic hormones that cause its great development during fetal life are perhaps the gonadotrophiclike hormones (to be described in the next chapter) made by the placenta during pregnancy. One difficulty in determining the function of the adrenal cortex in fetal life is that a comparable development of the gland does not occur in the fetuses of the common experimental animals; hence, the experimental study of the phenomenon is correspondingly restricted.

General Microscopic Appearance of the Gland as a Whole

A general preliminary inspection of a section of the gland should be made with the low-power objective in order to establish certain prominent landmarks. First, the gland will be seen to have a relatively thick capsule of connective tissue (Fig. 492). Next, in the central part of the gland, large veins may be seen (Fig. 492). These are the veins of the medulla, and a moderate amount of connective

tissue is associated with them. Between this connective tissue and that of the capsule is the parenchyma of the gland. Most of this is cortex. Although the medulla occupies the more central part of the gland and so is surrounded by cortex, the gland is so flattened that the medulla generally appears in a section as a rather thin "filling" in a sandwich of cortex (Fig. 492). Moreover, the medulla is not very sharply demarcated from the cortex. However, the cytoplasm of the cells of the medulla is more basophilic than that of the cortical cells; hence, even in a casual low-power inspection of an H and E section, the medulla may generally be identified as a muddy blue layer between two lighter layers of cortex.

With more detailed study it will be observed that the parenchymal cells of both the cortex and the medulla follow the general plan seen in endocrine glands; that is, they are arranged in clumps or cords with vessels between them (Figs. 492 and 495, *right*). The vessels in the cortex have been described by some authorities as capillaries and by others as sinusoids; certainly some of their lining cells are phagocytic and so belong to the reticuloendothelial system. Both narrow capillaries and wider venous channels are found between the clumps and the cords of cells of the medulla; these drain into the large veins mentioned previously.

With this preliminary description of the gland as a whole we are more prepared to consider some details about the structure and the function of its two main parts.

THE ADRENAL CORTEX

Microscopic Structure. The arrangement of the parenchymal cells differs at various levels between the capsule and the medulla. Three different arrangements are seen; hence, the cortex is said to be composed of three different layers or zones. Immediately beneath the capsule the parenchymal cells are grouped into little, irregular clusters (the *zona glomerulosa*) with capillaries between the clusters (Fig. 492). Beneath this is a thick layer (the *zona fasciculata*) in which the cells are arranged in fairly straight cords which run at right angles to the surface and have straight capillaries between them (Fig. 492). Between the zona fasciculata and the medulla is a relatively thin layer (the *zona reticularis*) in which the cells are disposed in cords which run in various directions and anastomose with one another (Fig. 492). Sinusoidal capillaries occupy the interstices between the cords. The student should keep in mind that the three zones described above usually are not sharply defined; hence, such borders as may be set between them are only approximate.

The parenchymal cells of the zona glomerulosa tend to be columnar. Their nuclei are somewhat smaller and darker than those of the next zone; likewise, their cytoplasm is of a more even texture, but it contains some lipid droplets.

The cells of the zona fasciculata are roughly polyhedral. Their nuclei are larger and less dense than those of the zona glomerulosa. Their cytoplasm, in H and E sections, appears to be extensively vacuolated, because in life it contains large numbers of lipid droplets (Fig. 492). Indeed, this feature of the cells of this zone is so pronounced that the cells here are sometimes termed *spongiocytes*. Cholesterol is said to be more concentrated in these cells than in any other part of the body. With appropriate technics these cells can also be shown to contain considerable quantities of ascorbic acid (vitamin C). The adrenocorticotrophic hormone (ACTH), if given in sufficient amounts, rapidly depletes these cells of much of their cholesterol and ascorbic acid. Both tests—the depletion of these cells of either ascorbic acid or cholesterol—have been used in experimental animals to assay the potency of solutions of ACTH. The cells are rich in mitochondria; the E/M has shown these to differ from mitochondria in most cells in the respect that their cristae tend to be tubular villi instead of relatively flat shelves. There has been much discussion as to whether or not histochemical methods identify adrenal cortical hormones in these cells, but it is by no means agreed that this can be done at all accurately.

The cells of the zona reticularis vary in appearance. Some have small dark nuclei and acidophilic cytoplasm and appear to be degenerating. Others have lighter nuclei and cytoplasm. Some cells here contain considerable quantities of pigment (Fig. 492).

Functions. The active crystalline substances that have been recovered from cortical tissue belong to a group of substances called *steroids*. They all have a basic 4-ring structure (the cyclopentenophenanthrene nucleus). The sex hormones, to be described in the next 2 chapters, have the same nucleus. Many other compounds having potent biologic effects, as well as the hormones of the adrenal cortex and the sex hormones, are built around this nucleus. It seems extraordinary that the particular groupings that are attached to certain positions in this nucleus alter so profoundly the type of biologic effect produced by the compound.

The various steroids that have been recovered from the adrenal cortex have been found to have one of three types of effects.

1. Those of the first group are called the mineralocorticoids, and they control the sodium and potassium balance in the body. The most potent is called electrocortin or aldosterone. That it is one function of the adrenal cortex to control sodium and potassium balance is evidenced in Addison's disease, which condition is caused by diseased adrenals, for in this condition, or in adrenalectomized animals, sodium is lost from the body into the urine, and potassium accumulates in the blood. Some amelioration of this state of affairs, which, if prolonged, leads to death, can be accomplished by the administration of extra sodium chloride; for example, adrenalectomized rats can be kept alive for long periods of time by putting sodium chloride in their drinking water. The giving of mineralocorticoids to such animals will, of course, restore their ability to retain salt.

2. Those of the second group are called the glucocorticoids. It seems probable that the chief active one produced in the body is hydrocortisone. Hydrocortisone exerts a great many effects in the body. The precise way it produces these effects is not well understood. To some extent it exerts an effect similar to the hormones of the first group in that it tends to cause sodium retention and potassium excretion. But this is not nearly so pronounced or distinctive an effect as the one it exerts on protein and carbohydrate metabolism. So far as protein is concerned, hydrocortisone is a catabolic hormone which tends to stimulate the conversion of protein and protein precursors into carbohydrate. This effect can be demonstrated very easily by giving hydrocortisone (or cortisone, which probably becomes converted into hydrocortisone in the body) to

suitable experimental animals because it causes increased amounts of glycogen to form in the parenchymal cells of the liver. Insulin also causes liver cells to accumulate glycogen, so it should be explained that the ways in which hydrocortisone and insulin exert this effect are quite different. Insulin acts to cause liver cells to take up glucose from the blood and to store it as glycogen; in other words, the glycogen that appears in liver cells as a result of insulin activity lowers the blood sugar level. On the other hand, hydrocortisone acts to cause the production of carbohydrate in liver cells from protein or protein precursors; hence, hydrocortisone can cause glycogen to be laid down in liver cells without taking glucose from the blood and so lowering the blood sugar level; indeed, its action in causing the formation of carbohydrate from protein provides extra sugar for the blood and tends to raise the level of sugar in it. Hence, insulin has an antidiabetogenic effect in that it tends to lower the blood sugar level, and hydrocortisone has a diabetogenic effect in that it tends to raise the blood sugar level. Normally, of course, these two effects are nicely balanced, but in the absence of either hormone the effects of the other are manifested.

The catabolic effect of hydrocortisone is manifested by its effect on lymphatic tissue also; the administration of the hormone leads to a rapid reduction in the size of the thymus gland, the spleen and other depots of lymphatic tissue, it is believed that in sufficiently large doses it actually causes a breakdown of lymphocytes. Hydrocortisone acts to bring about a reduction in the size of lymphatic organs and tissues in another way also, by causing a reduction in the rate of mitosis in these organs and tissues.

In addition to affecting lymphatic tissue, hydrocortisone affects other connective tissues as well. Its administration, while fractured bones are healing, leads to the formation of less callus tissue than usual. Hydrocortisone also inhibits the proliferation of fibroblasts in the healing of wounds in ordinary fibrous connective tissue. Given in sufficient amounts it slows the growth of the epiphyseal disks of young rats. Hydrocortisone can also inhibit the production of antibodies. All of these effects could be explained at least in part by the fact that amino acids that, under ordinary conditions would be synthesized into proteins, are diverted, under conditions where there is excess hydrocortisone, into the formation of carbohydrate and thereafter metabolized to provide energy. Hence, under conditions of excessive hydrocortisone, protein synthesis is slowed because of there being a deficiency of amino acids for that purpose.

The easiest effect to observe when hydrocortisone is administered is the effect that it has in causing eosinophils to leave the blood vascular system, presumably to enter the substance of the connective tissues; so it produces an *eosinopenia*. In many species it causes lymphocytes also to leave the blood stream in a similar way.

The relation of hydrocortisone to histamine has been considered in Chapter 8.

3. The third group of steroid hormones made by the adrenal cortex are of the sex variety. In some ways and under certain conditions the adrenal glands seem to supplement the gonads with regard to producing hormones of this type. Steroids having sex hormone activity can be recovered from the gland. The administration of certain sex hormones will prolong the life of otherwise untreated adrenalectomized animals. Some tumors that arise in the cortex produce substances having male sex hormone activity. Women developing tumors of this type become masculinized. Although they are fundamentally females, they gradually develop the secondary sex characteristics of the male. Even their genitalia may be profoundly affected. If severe, the condition is termed *pseudohermaphroditism*. It differs from true hermaphroditism in that the individual concerned does not possess gonadal tissue of both sexes; she has only ovaries, and such male hormone as appears in her blood stream is derived from the adrenal gland. Many of the bearded women of circuses are examples of women who have developed masculine traits as a result of tumors or hyperplasias of the adrenal cortex. However, the role of the adrenal cortex in sex is not simply one of manufacturing male hormone; in some instances, adrenal tumors in males are said to exert feminizing effects. Nevertheless, the production of significant amounts of male hormone by the adrenal glands of females would seem to be a more common phenomenon than the production of significant amounts of

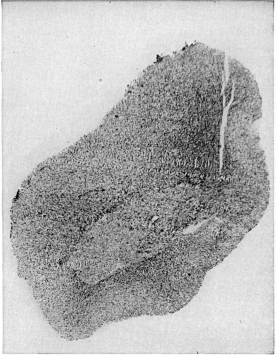

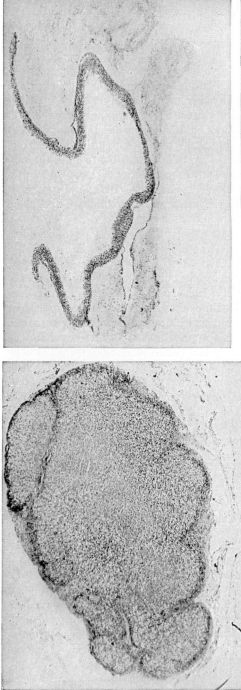

Fig. 493. (*Top left*) Very low-power photomicrograph of a section of the capsule and some of the zona glomerulosa of what is left of an adrenal gland of a rat after the contents of the capsule (*top right*) have been squeezed out from the gland through a hole in the capsule. (*Top right*) Very low-power photomicrograph of a section of the contents of the capsule that may be squeezed out through a hole in the capsule. On transplantation this does not regenerate. (*Bottom left*) Very low-power photomicrograph of the mass of cortical tissue that regenerates in 10 days when the tissue illustrated at the upper left is transplanted either into muscle or into subcutaneous tissue in the rat. (From experiments performed in collaboration with Dr. M. I. Armstrong)

female hormone by the adrenal glands of either sex.

Other effects produced by the cortex have also been described; for example, it is necessary for lactation.

Functions of the Three Zones of the Adrenal Cortex. Two theories have been offered in an attempt to provide an explanation for there being three zones in the adrenal cortex.

First, it has been suggested that the zona glomerulosa is the germinative zone and that nearly all of the new cells that are produced in the adrenal cortex are produced in it by mitosis. Thereafter, the cells so formed are pushed into the zona fasciculata, which, according to this theory, is the hormone-pro-

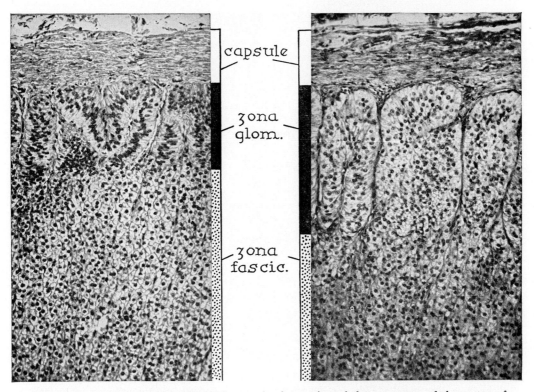

capsule

ʒona glom.

ʒona fascic.

FIG. 494. (*Left*) Low-power photomicrograph of a section of the outer part of the cortex of the adrenal gland of a normal dog. (*Right*) Photomicrograph, at the same magnification, of a similar section of the adrenal cortex of a dog that had received several daily injections of an anterior pituitary extract containing adrenocorticotrophin. Observe the great thickening of the zona glomerulosa. High-power inspection shows many mitotic figures in this zone under these conditions.

ducing zone. Then, after leading a useful life in the zona fasciculata, because of the continued proliferation in the zona glomerulosa, the cells are finally pushed into the zona reticularis, where they degenerate and die. According to this theory the zona reticularis is regarded more or less as the graveyard of the cortex.

A second theory has been suggested, namely, that the three zones represent specializations for the production of the three types of hormones. According to this theory the cells of the zona glomerulosa produce the mineralocorticoids, the cells of the zona fasciculata, the glucocorticoids and the cells of the zona reticularis, the sex hormones.

An important reason for there being conflicting opinions about these matters is that there are considerable differences with regard to the way the adrenals of different species

react to the removal of the pituitary gland and to the administration of ACTH. However, there are certain observations which we think should be emphasized.

First, it has been shown clearly in rats that the transplanted capsule of an adrenal gland to which some of the zona glomerulosa is still attached (Fig. 493) will regenerate a new cortex and also that rats with these transplants will live. Moreover, it has been shown that transplants of the gland minus its capsule and zona glomerulosa do not grow and survive (Fig. 493). Therefore, transplantation experiments in rats suggest that the zona glomerulosa is the regenerative zone of the adrenal cortex.

Secondly, there is evidence indicating that the zona glomerulosa of some animals, particularly rats, is not affected to any great extent by ACTH, and that it makes mineralocorticoids. Hypophysectomized rats show little

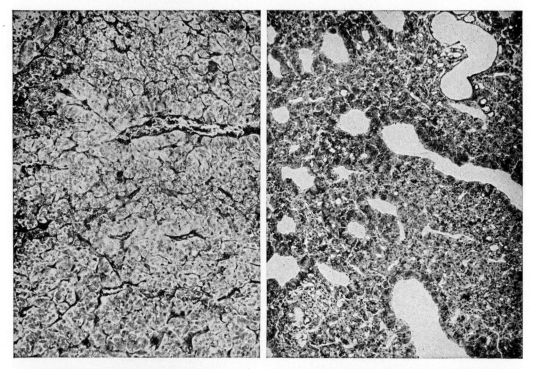

FIG. 495. (*Left*) A section from the medulla of an adrenal gland fixed by immersion in formol-dichromate. The blood vessels, for the most part, are collapsed, and the arrangement of cells as columnar epithelium about the veins is obscured here. The appearance of "cords" and "whorls" of medullary cells is noticeable in some places, but, for the most part, the cells seem arranged irregularly (× 77). (*Right*) A section from the medulla of a gland fixed by perfusion with formol-dichromate, with the blood vessels fixed in a state of distention. The true arrangement of cells as columnar epithelium about the veins is brought out clearly in many parts of the section. Naturally, it will not be apparent unless the vein and its surrounding cells are cut in a favorable plane. A true columnar arrangement about vessels not shown in this section is brought out in serial sections, even in areas which seem irregular between the vessels in this particular picture. Note that the cells are not arranged as columnar epithelium about the small capillaries nor about the tortuous artery seen in the upper right-hand corner (× 77). (Bennett, H. S.: Am. J. Anat. *69*:373)

atrophy of the zona glomerulosa but much atrophy in the zona fasciculata. Moreover, their ability to retain salt is not seriously diminished. However, in our experience in following the day-to-day histologic changes in the adrenal glands of dogs given anterior pituitary extracts, we (Ham and Haist) found literally enormous numbers of mitotic figures in the zona glomerulosa (Fig. 494) but only occasional ones in the zona fasciculata. So, although the zona glomerulosa may be concerned chiefly with secreting mineralocorticoids, we think that it also serves as the chief regenerative zone for cells of the fasciculata that secrete glucocorticoids.

It seems possible that there may be some specialization in the zona reticularis for the production of sex hormones. This interesting zone, at least for the most part, does not appear to be a residuum of the fetal cortex (see Swinyard) which, as has been explained, may very well be concerned with the production of sex hormone in fetal life, but there is some evidence from studies made on pseudohermaphrodites that the cells of this zone are the ones chiefly involved in producing male hormone (see Broster and Vines).

Effects of ACTH on the Adrenal Cortex. Trophic hormones, as has been explained, exert two fundamental effects on the glands they affect: they stimulate both secretion and growth in them. In the thyroid gland the same cells are stimulated both to grow and to secrete. However, in the adrenal cortex the effect of ACTH seems to differ with different species; in some it causes growth primarily in the zona glomerulosa but in others at the site of junction between the two zones, or even some in the zona fasciculata. However, the secretory effect of ACTH is exerted chiefly on the cells of the zona fasciculata; here the effects of a large dose of ACTH are manifested histologically by the cells becoming depleted of much of their cholesterol and ascorbic acid content. Of course, they can adapt themselves to a sustained increase in ACTH by increasing their usual rate of production of cortical hormones. We shall consider the control of the secretion of ACTH itself after we have considered the medulla of the adrenal gland.

The Adrenal Medulla

Microscopic Structure. The cells of the medulla are of a large, ovoid, columnar type and are commonly grouped together in clumps and irregular cords that are arranged around the blood vessels in a special manner (Fig. 495, *right*) that will be described when the relation of their structure to their function is considered. Many of them contain fine granules that are colored brown with chrome salts. This is called the *chromaffin reaction*, and it can be observed in the gross by exposing the freshly cut surface of the gland to a weak solution of chrome salts or chromic acid, whereupon the medulla of the gland becomes brown. The same reaction is given in the test tube by the hormone epinephrine (Adrenalin). That the reaction is given by the cytoplasmic granules of certain cells in the medulla suggests that the granules concerned are either epinephrine or its immediate precursor. The chromaffin reaction does not, as its name implies and as was first believed, depend on the deposition of chromium, but, as Gerard, Cordier and Lison showed, on the oxidation of epinephrine; it can be produced by other oxidizing agents as well as by chromium salts.

Action of Hormone. An active extract of medullary tissue was first prepared by Oliver and Schafer in 1894. It was the first gland from which a pure crystalline hormone was prepared; this was accomplished in 1901. The hormone was named epinephrine. A proprietary name for it is Adrenalin. Recently, it has been shown that what were believed to be pure extracts of the gland actually contain two substances: epinephrine and norepinephrine (noradrenaline). The latter substance may be a precursor of epinephrine. However, the two substances have somewhat different effects.

Because the medulla of the gland is so closely associated with the cortex and because the cortex is essential to life, some time elapsed before it was established that the medulla of the adrenal is not essential to life. Indeed, as experimental work progressed it became obvious that animals deprived of their medullary tissue (provided that their cortical tissue remained intact) suffered little, if any, inconvenience.

Although there has been some controversy about the matter, it now seems to be established that the medulla does not secrete epinephrine rapidly enough to raise the concentration of the hormone in the blood stream to the point where it produces major physiologic effects under ordinary conditions but only under extraordinary conditions. We shall elaborate:

How Secretion by the Medulla Can Affect Secretion by the Cortex—The Effects of Emotional and Physical Stress. As was explained when we dealt with the development of the gland, the parenchymal cells of the adrenal medulla are derived from the same group of cells as those that become the sympathetic ganglion cells of the celiac plexus. However, after migrating into the central part of the adrenal cortex, most of these young developing cells do not differentiate into ganglion cells proper; instead, they differentiate into secretory cells. Nevertheless, they occupy the same position on the two neuron sympathetic chains as do ganglion cells themselves; therefore, they are innervated by preganglionic fibers rather than by postganglionic fibers as are the other types of secretory cells in the body.

From the foregoing it is obvious that the parenchymal cells of the medulla are closely related developmentally to ganglion cells and, therefore, they might be expected to exhibit at least some of the properties of sympathetic ganglion cells. In this connection it will be recalled that, when we discussed the chemical mediation of the nervous impulse, it was explained that sympathetic nerve fibers stimulate the various cells with which they connect by making there a substance that Cannon has termed *sympathin*, which is very similar to, if not identical with, epinephrine.

In discussing the autonomic nervous system we explained also that most smooth muscle, and most glands in the body, are innervated by fibers from both the sympathetic and the parasympathetic systems and that, in general, these two systems more or less oppose one another. Hence, the state of tonus of smooth muscle, or the strength and the rate of its contractions, and the rate and the character of glandular secretion, are determined to an important degree by the relative extents to which the cells of these tissues are stimulated by the two systems. It should now be mentioned that when an individual suffers a severe frustration, for example, if he is kept from obtaining something he wants very badly, or prevented from running away from a situation that he considers very dangerous, he experiences an emotional reaction (rage or fear). The development of rage or fear is generally associated with an increase of sympathetic activity over parasympathetic. The increased sympathetic activity not only results in more sympathin being produced at sympathetic nerve endings, but it also results in the parenchymal cells of the adrenal medulla, with their very direct sympathetic connections, being stimulated to produce epinephrine more rapidly than usual. Enough enters the blood stream to reinforce the sympathin effect at sympathetic nerve endings all over the body.

Therefore, a discharge of epinephrine by the adrenal medulla enhances the effect of the increased sympathetic activity that occurs in association with emotional states. Increased sympathetic activity is fundamentally helpful because it does many things to the body that more or less supercharge it temporarily to help it fight harder or run away faster. The body becomes geared for "fight or flight." The heart beats faster and stronger, the blood pressure becomes increased, and the spleen contracts and adds more blood to the circulatory system. More blood is diverted to striated muscles and less to the viscera. The glycogen of the liver is converted to glucose and liberated into the blood stream. Indeed, a great many more changes occur which temporarily aid the body to greater efforts.

An effective secretion of epinephrine by the cells of the medulla occurs not only as a result of emotional states but also reflexly as a result of the afferent stimulation involved in severe cold, pain and other stress conditions.

All medical students, but particularly those interested in the relation between mental and physical health (psychosomatic medicine), should read the various books written by Cannon. He showed conclusively the profound effects of emotional states on the function of the sympathetic nervous system and the structures innervated by it, and he formulated the "emergency" theory of medullary function. Students will also be interested in reading McDougall, who, in his *Abnormal Psychology*, shows how an emotional state can be produced by a "drive" being frustrated. For example, he explains that one does not experience fear if one can run away from a dangerous situation but only if something, for example, an ideal, prevents and so frustrates one from running away. This helps to explain how emotional states can be prolonged. Furthermore, the psychoanalysts have suggested that one may not be aware of a drive that is being frustrated or of what is frustrating a drive. It is obvious that much skill, insight, knowledge and patience may be necessary to determine why in a patient the mechanism that was designed primarily to operate only occasionally to help overcome obvious frustrations is kept operating over prolonged periods.

Recently, it has become obvious that the autonomic nervous system, probably through the medium of epinephrine secretion and perhaps in other ways also, can affect the secretory activity of the pars anterior of the pituitary gland, causing it, for example, to produce increased amounts of ACTH. This effect is probably mediated through the hypothalamus which makes an ACTH-liberating hormone under stress conditions. The increased secretion of ACTH causes increased amounts of cortical hormones to appear in the body. It has been noted already that Adrenalin exerts many effects which gear the body for flight or fight. Many of these are of such a nature that more fuel would be required for the cellular activity involved for their performance. Extra secretion of the carbohydrate-protein-affecting cortical hormones would supply this extra fuel. But, here again, the long-continued operation of a mechanism designed to operate only temporarily for emergencies could conceivably injure certain parts of the body. Selye has given elaborate consideration to the effects of stress on the organism and the cause of what he terms "diseases of adaptation."

Relation of Microscopic Structure to Function. Bennett and Kilham, and Bennett have shown that the appearance presented by the medulla of an adrenal gland which has not been perfused by way of the veins so as to expand them is misleading (Fig. 495), and that the cells of the medulla, instead of being arranged as is commonly said, in haphazard clumps and cords, are arranged in a very special way in relation to the blood vessels. There are two kinds of the latter: (1) a system of branching veins into which the blood from the cortical sinusoidal capillaries empties and (2) a system of capillaries that are supplied directly by arterioles that penetrate the cortex from the capsule. Bennett has shown that in the distended medulla of the cat the parenchymal cells resemble columnar epithelial cells (Fig. 495, *right*) and are arranged in whorls and cords in such a way that one end of each cell abuts on a vein, and the other on a capillary (Fig. 496). The nuclei of the parenchymal cells are disposed toward the ends of the cells that abut on capillaries, and the secretion granules, which he terms globules, tend to accumulate at the ends of the cells that abut on veins (Fig. 496). This latter fact, together with the position of the Golgi networks in the cells, indicates that the cells discharge epinephrine into the veins rather than into the capillaries. However, the nerve fibers that stimulate the secretory functions of the cells enter them at their capillary ends.

Bennett finds that different cells in the medulla have different contents of secretory globules and postulates that this is due to their being in different phases of a secretory cycle. Moreover, he finds that sympathetic stimulation results in more cells developing secretion droplets and in the droplets becoming larger and more numerous in the cells that contain them.

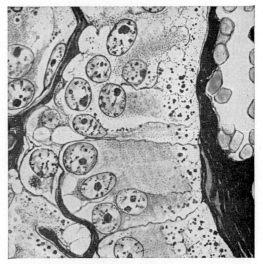

FIG. 496. A group of medullary cells along a vein in an adrenal gland fixed in formol-dichromate and then subjected to silver intensification before counterstaining with hematoxylin and eosin-azure. The vein is to the right and shows plasma containing a reducing substance thought to be epinephrine. The capillaries at the other pole of the cells also contain a similar reducing substance. Note that the nucleus is at the capillary pole of the cell and that the secretion droplets are most abundant at the venous pole of the cell but are also found in smaller numbers at the capillary pole and along the sides of some cells. (Bennett, H. S.: Am. J. Anat. *69*:379)

Paraganglia. The cells of the adrenal medulla, it has been noted, are the result of a migration of developing sympathetic ganglion cells from the site of the developing ganglion to a point some distance from it. This is probably not the only example of the migration of developing sympathetic ganglion cells that occurs, for there are many little clusters of cells that probably originate in the same way to be found behind the peritoneum in various sites. The cells in these little bodies are arranged in clumps and cords and are provided with an extensive blood supply. Since these little bodies are associated with ganglia, they are said to constitute the *paraganglia* of the body. Furthermore, since the cells in these bodies give the chromaffin reaction, the medullary tissue of the adrenal glands and the paraganglia together are often said to constitute the *chromaffin system*. However, it is not clearly established that the cells of the paraganglia function similarly to those of the medulla of the adrenal.

Blood Vessels, Lymphatics and Nerves

Usually each suprarenal gland is supplied by 3 arteries that come from different sources. These break up into many branches as they approach the gland. Some of these supply the capillary beds of the capsule. Others penetrate directly into the medulla to supply the capillary bed of that region with arterial blood. However, the majority empty into the sinusoidal capillaries that run from the zona glomerulosa to the zona reticularis, where they empty into the venous radicles of the medulla. It is said that in the zona fasciculata most cells abut on 2 capillaries, one at each of their ends. However, in ordinary sections, the capillaries of the cortex are often collapsed and hence do not show to advantage. The capillaries of the medulla also empty into the venous radicles of the part. These unite to form a large central vein which emerges from the hilus of the gland. The central vein has numerous longitudinally disposed smooth muscle fibers in its wall. Veins also arise from the capsule. Lymphatics have been described only where substantial amounts of connective tissue are present in the gland; that is, in association with the larger veins and in the capsule.

Fibers from the parasympathetic system reach the suprarenal gland, but their function, if any, is unknown. Little is known about the functions of the sympathetic fibers that are distributed to the capsule and to the cortex. The significant innervation of the gland is that provided by the preganglionic sympathetic fibers that run directly to the parenchymal cells of the medulla. True ganglion cells are also present in the medulla (Fig. 492).

THE ISLETS OF LANGERHANS

Introduction

The general features of the islets of Langerhans of the pancreas have already been described (Chap. 23). Here we shall discuss the cytologic structure of their cells in more detail and in particular how it varies in relation to different functional states.

Diabetes (*diabetes* = a syphon, or running through) was the name used by the Greeks to designate diseases characterized by a great production of urine (polyuria). In the 18th century it was proved that the urine in most cases of diabetes contained sugar; hence, this kind of diabetes was called *diabetes mellitus* (*mellitus* = honeyed) to distinguish it from the other kind in which polyuria was not associated with glycosuria. It was also realized at this time that it was an ill omen for anyone to begin passing large quantities of sugar-containing urine, for, almost invariably, their health would decline steadily from then onward. Many so afflicted literally wasted away, being particularly susceptible while doing so to the development of a great variety of infections and degenerative diseases.

In 1869, Langerhans discovered the islets in the pancreas that now bear his name. However, he did not suspect that they were little organs of internal secretion. Soon afterward, Kuhne and Lea pointed out that the islets contained extensive capillary networks; this was to help later in making other investigators suspect that they had an endocrine function.

Although Cowley, an English physician, had suggested a full century before that there was some relation between diabetes and the pancreas, it was not until 1889 that this was positively established. At this time, von Mering and Minkowski removed the pancreas from each of a group of experimental animals and found subsequently that the animals upon which they had operated were passing increased amounts of urine and that it contained sugar.

Von Mering's and Minkowsky's experiments could be interpreted logically as indicating that a lack of some pancreatic function is responsible for diabetes. But what function? The obvious function of the pancreas known of that time was that of making an external secretion. Nevertheless, the concept of Claude Bernard—that certain bodily functions depend on internal secretions—had by this time made a considerable impression on the scientific world, so further work was done in an attempt to discover whether diabetes results from the pancreas' failing to make a proper external or internal secretion. To determine this point, Hedon performed a very ingenious experiment. He showed that a piece of pancreas grafted back into a depancreatized animal would keep the animal free from diabetes even though the graft had no duct connections. In other words, he showed that the antidiabetic principle made by the panceras was absorbed into the blood—it was an internal secretion.

The foregoing experiments resulted in histologists becoming increasingly interested in the microscopic structure of the pancreas. Laguesse, in particular, studied its development and structure in great detail. He came to the conclusion that the islets were little organs of internal secretion and suggested that they should be investigated in the pancreases of those who died from diabetes. However, he did not believe that islet cells were fundamentally different from acinous cells.

At this time, then, although it was established that diabetes was the result of the lack of an internal secretion, it was not at all clear as to whether acinous cells or islet cells made the secretion; indeed, it was not clear as to whether islet cells were fundamentally differ-

ent from acinous cells. However, this matter was settled soon afterward by Ssobolew and Schultze. They tied off the pancreatic ducts of experimental animals and found that after a time the acinous tissue of the pancreas all became atrophied and that only islet tissue was left. Animals that had this operation performed on them, while they suffered from impaired digestion and certain other complaints, did not develop diabetes.

Only one thing more, it appeared, required to be established to lead to the universal acceptance of the islet theory of diabetes: proof that the islets were diseased in those who die of the disease. This was first provided by Opie. At the turn of the century he found that diabetes in most instances was associated with either a lack of islets or with degenerative changes in such islets as were present. Following the studies of Opie and others on the same matter, all but the very skeptical conceded that diabetes mellitus is due to a deficiency of normal islet cells. The theoretical hormone

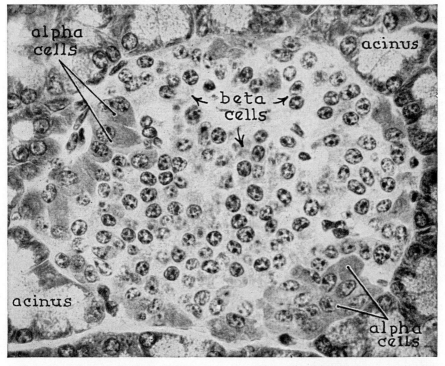

FIG. 497. Oil-immersion photomicrograph of an islet of Langerhans in a section of a guinea pig's pancreas stained by Gomori's method. Alpha cells, with cytoplasm that appears darker than that of the beta cells, may be seen in the periphery of the islet. Most of the interior of the islet is made up of beta cells ranged along capillaries. (Photomicrograph from W. Wilson)

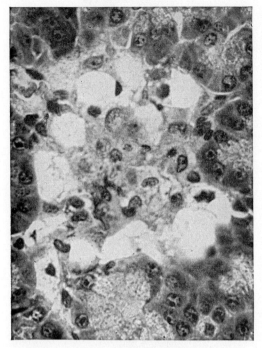

FIG. 498. Oil-immersion photomicrograph of an islet of Langerhans in a section of pancreas of a dog that had been given 11 daily injections of anterior pituitary extract that exerted a diabetogenic effect. The beta cells contain large droplets of fluid. This histologic picture is called hydropic degeneration and is an indication of severe overwork on the part of the beta cells. (Ham, A. W., and Haist, R. E.: Am. J. Path. *17*:812)

made by the cells and deficient in diabetes was even given the name *insulin*.

However, there remained one disturbing fact to be faced: that although the islets in most cases of diabetes were found on histologic examination to be diseased, there were some in which they were not; indeed, in H and E sections, the islets of some of those who died of diabetes appeared normal. Lane's work, which will now be described, was to help provide the explanation for at least some of these apparent discrepancies.

In 1908, Lane, working under the direction of R. R. Bensley, established by means of histochemical methods, not only that the granules of islet cells had different histochemical properties from those of zymogen granules (hence, that islet cells were fundamentally dif-

ferent from acinous cells), but also that two kinds of islet cells could be distinguished by the different chemical properties of their granules. In short, he found that certain alcoholic fixatives dissolved the fine cytoplasmic granules from the majority of the cells of the islets but preserved the granules in a minority of the cells. Conversely, fixatives of the same type made up with water instead of alcohol preserved the granules in the majority of the cells but dissolved those from the minority. The numerous cells with the alcohol-soluble granules he termed *beta cells*, and the scarcer ones with alcohol-resistant, water-soluble granules, *alpha cells*. This led to many different staining technics being devised for coloring alpha and beta cells differently (Fig. 497).

Although not so common as certain other types of degenerative lesions observed in the islets of diabetics, there was one curious type of islet lesion called hydropic degeneration that was sometimes seen. It was given this name because the cytoplasm of islet cells showing this change appeared to be swollen with a watery fluid and contained little stainable substance (Fig. 498). (More recently it has been shown that the clear fluid in hydropic beta cells contains a considerable amount of glycogen.) Between 1912 and 1914, both Homans and Allen showed that if most of the pancreas of an animal was removed and the animal thereafter was fed carbohydrate or protein liberally: (1) hydropic degeneration occurred in the islets of the part of the pancreas that had been left intact and (2) diabetes developed. However, if the animal was given a minimal diet, the islet cells showed no disease, and the animal remained healthy. Using stains based on the findings of Lane and Bensley, both Homans and Allen each showed that hydropic degeneration occurred only in the beta cells of the islets and that this change was preceded by a degranulation of the cells concerned.

These experiments and many others performed by Allen led to the development of what is called the overwork hypothesis. Allen showed that if from four-fifths to nine-tenths of the pancreas were removed from a dog, the remaining portion had enough islets to keep the animal free from diabetes provided that the dog's diet was restricted. However, he found that if such an animal were fed additional carbohydrate or protein, the beta cells in the fragment of pancreas it possessed would become degranulated and hydropic. He assumed that the extra carbohydrate and protein fed the animals placed increased secretory demands on the beta cells and that their consequent degranulation and hydropic degeneration were to be interpreted as evidences of exhaustion through overwork. When the increased food intake was continued, he found that the islet lesions became permanent and that there was no recovery.

The experiments of Allen had, and still have, great implication with regard to the treatment of diabetes. In particular, they have great implication for those who are in danger of developing diabetes, for they show that if any individual overstrains his beta cell capacity by eating too much carbohydrate or protein (fat has a sparing effect on the beta cells), beta cells will be destroyed from overwork and this, of course, will decrease the individual's beta cell capacity and make those that remain more susceptible to overstrain than before.

Since the work of both Homans and Allen showed that only the beta cells became overstrained in diabetes and that alpha cells were not affected in the condition, it became possible to explain why the islets of some people who died of diabetes had seemed to be normal in H and E sections. On investigation with differential staining methods, at least some of these apparently normal islets turned out to be composed mostly of alpha cells. But this is not always true, for at autopsy a certain number of diabetics reveal islets which have reasonably normal beta cells and a moderate content of insulin.

Although the overwork hypothesis led to better treatment, diabetes remained a widespread and usually fatal disease. It could be expected that many investigators would make attempts to recover the islet hormone from the pancreases of animals so that substitution therapy could be employed in man. Some of these earlier attempts to extract the antidiabetic hormone gave some tantalizingly promising results, but this was as far as they went, and the world remained without substitution therapy for diabetes until the time of Banting and Best.

On the afternoon of October 30, 1920, Banting, then a young medical graduate, read in a medical journal an article about the pancreas in which the findings of Ssobolew and others who had tied off the ducts of the pancreas were described. Banting was very much impressed with the fact that the acinous tissue atrophied after duct ligation, and it is generally believed that he began to suspect that previous attempts to obtain an active extract of islet tissue had failed because the enzymes of the acinous tissue destroyed the islet hormone before it could be extracted. In any event, before going to bed that night he had decided to try making extracts from pancreases after their ducts had been tied off for 6 or 8 weeks so that they presumably would contain only islet and not acinous tissue. The events that occurred between the inception of the idea and the accomplishment of insulin, the collaboration of Best and later of Collip, the inevitable succession of encouraging and discouraging results, the lack of funds and above all the dogged persistence of Banting, make an inspiring story. It is well told both by Stephenson and by Harris.

At the conclusion of his Harvey Lecture on the islets of Langerhans in 1915, R. R. Bensley observed: "One of the most inviting fields, apart from the investigation of diabetes, is undoubtedly the investigation of the interrelation of the various internal secreting organs." Fifteen years were to elapse before the wisdom of this prediction was appreciated. In 1930, Houssay and Biasotti showed that diabetes produced in animals by removing the pancreas could be ameliorated by removing the pituitary gland as well, and that such animals, instead of steadily declining in health, as do those from which the pancreas only is removed, would live, free from diabetes, for long periods.

Some intimation that the pars anterior of the pituitary gland can exert a diabetogenic function had, of course, been given previously by the finding that individuals with certain types of anterior lobe tumors tended to develop diabetes. Furthermore, in 1927, Johns, O'Mulvenny, Potts and Laughton had produced signs of diabetes in dogs by giving them injections of anterior pituitary extract. By 1932, several investigators had also observed this phenomenon. However, one group of investigators, Evans and his collaborators, noted

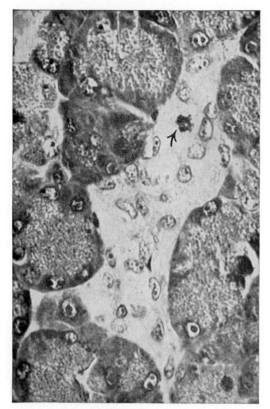

FIG. 499. High-power photomicrograph of an islet of Langerhans in a section of pancreas from a dog which had been given 11 daily injections of a diabetogenic anterior pituitary extract and, in addition, enough insulin to protect the beta cells from becoming hydropic from overwork. Observe the mitotic figure in a beta cell.

degeneration of beta cells and in some mitotic figures. Subsequently, the author (with Haist) showed that anterior pituitary injections given daily to dogs caused a progressive degranulation of beta cells, and that this was followed by hydropic degeneration, usually between the 7th and the 11th days (Fig. 498). Subsequently, further studies, in collaboration with Best, Campbell and Haist, showed that if enough insulin were administered along with anterior pituitary extracts, the degranulation and hydropic degeneration of beta cells was largely prevented (Fig. 499). The similarity between the findings with anterior pituitary extracts and those observed by Allen after partial pancreatectomy and liberal feeding was so obvious it was realized that anterior pituitary extracts injure the beta cells by making them overwork to the point of exhaustion and death.

How crude anterior pituitary extracts accomplish this effect has been the subject of much study. It is obvious that they greatly increase the need of the organism for insulin. This effect is produced in different ways. Anterior pituitary extracts containing adrenocorticotrophic hormone of the anterior pituitary stimulate the adrenal cortex to make more of the cortical hormone that furthers the conversion of protein and protein precursors to sugar in the body. Long and Lukens and their collaborators have shown clearly the effectiveness of the diabetogenic effect of this cortical hormone. In addition, anterior pituitary extracts stimulate the thyroid gland; this also increases the need of the animal for insulin. Furthermore, there is evidence that the anterior pituitary extracts act in some manner to render insulin relatively ineffective.

It is questionable if anterior pituitary extracts contain a pancreatrophic hormone. Certainly, in addition to all the other effects they produce, anterior pituitary extracts stimulate cell division in the acini, the small ducts and the islets (Fig. 499) in the pancreas. It seems most probable that the chief diabetogenic factor made by the anterior pituitary gland is the growth hormone. An argument against there being a pancreatrophic hormone is the fact that islets do not atrophy if the pituitary gland is removed. Yet one gets the impression that anterior pituitary extracts contain something that stimulates beta cells in some direct way so that they become exhausted

something additional. Whereas all the others had noted signs of diabetes only while injections were continued, Evans and his group observed that two animals continued to have diabetes after the course of injections of anterior pituitary extract had been finished. One animal recovered after 2 months, but the second was still diabetic 4 months after the last injection. The importance of this finding was not realized until Young, in 1937, showed that a sufficiently prolonged course of injections of anterior pituitary extract would make dogs permanently diabetic. Richardson and Young made histologic studies of the islets of these dogs. In some islets they found histologic pictures similar to those observed in long-standing cases of diabetes in man; in others they found degranulation and hydropic

more easily under pituitary stimulation than they would in the absence of anterior pituitary stimulation. The matter is too complex to discuss further here.

The foregoing indicates that many diabetogenic influences are normally at work in the body and that they do not produce diabetes because they are opposed successfully by adequate amounts of the antidiabetogenic hormone, insulin, made by the beta cells of the islets. Diabetes develops when the diabetogenic influences are greater than the beta cell potential of the pancreas. In other words, diabetes depends on something positive as well as on something negative. It may now be of interest to comment briefly on the action of the beta cell hormone.

The Action of Insulin

In a normal individual on a normal diet the amount of sugar in the blood remains at a fairly constant level, varying between 0.08 and 0.11 per cent. Since it is dissolved in the blood plasma, sugar, in this concentration, is present in the glomerular filtrate. However, at this concentration, all the sugar in the filtrate can be resorbed as the filtrate passes along the remainder of the nephron. Hence, in a normal individual on a normal diet sugar does not appear in the urine. However, in an untreated diabetic the blood sugar rises above the normal level (*hyperglycemia*) to the point where the increased amounts in the glomerular filtrate cannot all be resorbed as it courses along the remainder of the nephron; hence, sugar appears in the urine (*glycosuria*). The point at which the kidney cannot resorb all the sugar filtered through its glomeruli is said to be its *threshold* for sugar.

The most obvious action of insulin is that it reduces the blood sugar level. It will do this if it is injected either into a diabetic with hyperglycemia or into a normal person. A sufficiently large dose of insulin will reduce the blood sugar level to the point where convulsions and unconsciousness occur. This is called insulin shock. Enough insulin can lower the blood sugar level to the point where death ensues. A certain amount of sugar is required in the blood if life is to be supported. Occasionally islet-cell tumors occur; these may cause hyperinsulinism and hypoglycemia.

Insulin acts to lower the blood sugar level by acting at several sites. In a normal individual the sugar absorbed from a hearty meal would raise the blood sugar level substantially were it not for the fact that some of the sugar taken into the blood is stored as glycogen in the parenchymal cells of the liver and in muscle cells. Insulin facilitates this storage phenomenon. Excess sugar that has been absorbed may also be removed from the blood by being converted into fat and stored in the fat depots. Insulin facilitates this change also. Then, insulin, in addition, facilitates the metabolism of carbohydrate in muscle cells. In this way, it tends to reduce the level of sugar in the blood by speeding up the utilization of carbohydrate. Finally, as has been noted before, insulin opposes the catabolic and antianabolic effects of adrenal cortical hormone.

In view of the foregoing, it is easy to realize that the blood sugar level of an untreated diabetic on an unrestricted diet would exceed the kidney threshold because (1) sugar would not be removed from the blood and stored properly, (2) it would not be metabolized so quickly and (3) extra amounts would be delivered into the blood by virtue of the conversion of protein or protein precursors to sugar by the parenchymal cells of the liver.

Salter and Best have been able to study the effects of giving extra insulin to hypophysectomized animals and have shown that the extra insulin caused the hypophysectomized animals to resume growth; this was manifested by a thickening of their epiphyseal disks and by an increase in the animals' total body protein, fat and water. Hence, the anabolic effect of insulin can account for its exerting a growth hormone effect; however, it is probable that growth hormone and insulin act in different ways on cells to make more energy available in them for protein synthesis.

Cell Characteristics. Under normal conditions, only about 1 to 2 days' supply of insulin is stored in the cytoplasm of the beta cells of the pancreas. However, this is an amount sufficient, or almost sufficient, to cause death if it were all discharged into the blood stream at once. Indeed, a phenomenon much like this actually occurs if an animal is given suitable amounts of alloxan. This chemical exerts a very specific and rapid lethal effect on the beta cells of the islets (Fig. 56, *right*). As soon as they are destroyed, their content of stored insulin is almost immediately washed into the blood stream, and unless sugar is given the animals at this time they may die of hypoglycemia. If the animal survives this preliminary hypoglycemia, it goes on, of course, to develop hyperglycemia.

The fine cytoplasmic granules which are either insulin itself or the immediate precursors of insulin may be demonstrated in fresh pancreas by the supravital methods devised by Bensley for enumerating the islets (Fig. 413). In our experience these granules do not appear to advantage in sections stained by many of the special stains that are used to distinguish alpha from beta cells. But we think that the very fine blue granules that are revealed in beta cells by means of Bowie's neutral ethyl violet-Biebrich scarlet stain are representative of the insulin content of the cell. With Haist, we have observed that the number of beta granules revealed by this method become reduced if animals are starved, given insulin or fed a high proportion of fat. It is obvious that the reduction in the number of granules under these circumstances is not the result of degranulation from overwork but, instead, to a lack of synthesis due to a lack of work stimulus. Therefore, a reduction in the granule content of beta cells can be caused either by overwork or underwork.

The cytoplasmic granules of alpha cells are larger than those of beta cells. A course of injections of a diabetogenic extract of the anterior pituitary gland, which will cause degranulation of the beta cells, does not commonly cause degranulation of the alpha cells.

In some species, for example, in the rat, the alpha cells tend to have a peripheral distribution in islets. In other species, including man and the dog, the alpha cells are scattered throughout the islets but generally show some tendency to form little groups in the more central parts of islets.

The reticular fibers of normal islets are so delicate and sparse that they are scarcely demonstrable. Reticulum that is easily demonstrated is suggestive of pathologic change.

By means of special staining technics, cells which have been termed delta cells and C cells have been demonstrated in the islets of animals of some species. These cells are not numerous, and their functions are unknown.

The nuclei of alpha and beta cells are different in some species, for example, in the guinea pig, but not in most species. Hence, alpha and beta cells cannot generally be distinguished in sections by the morphology of their nuclei.

The mitochondria of islet cells are fine in contrast with the coarser ones of acinar cells. Islet cells have Golgi nets in their cytoplasm; these are present between the nuclei of the cells and the surfaces of the cells through which secretion takes place. Well-defined negative Gogli images can be seen in cells that are actively secreting.

Control of Insulin Secretion. There is much evidence to show that insulin secretion tends to vary in relation to the blood-sugar level and that the blood-sugar level controls insulin secretion.

Alpha Cells and Their Possible Functions. It is difficult to know how alpha cells are related to beta cells. They both arise from the same stem cell in fetal development. In some animals (rats) beta cells develop first, but in others (rabbits) alpha cells develop first. Many cells are seen in islets which cannot be definitely classified as either alpha cells or beta cells, and it would seem that cells having some of the characteristics of both are by no means uncommon. However, it does not seem likely that this finding indicates that either kind can turn into the other kind, for there is little evidence to indicate that this occurs. Alpha cells appear to be unaffected when diabetes is produced either by partial pancreatectomy, anterior pituitary extracts or alloxan. Islets composed only of alpha cells may be encountered in the pancreases of diabetics.

There is reason to believe that the insulin requirements of an animal in which the beta cells have been destroyed are greater than that of an animal from which the entire pancreas has been removed. A possible explanation for this is that the pancreas makes some hormone that has an action opposite to that of insulin and raises the blood-sugar level; indeed, a material called *glucagon*, which raises blood sugar levels, has been found in certain pancreatic extracts. Much evidence has been obtained which indicates that the alpha cells produce glucagon; for example, Bencosme has shown that it is not present in extracts of pancreas that have no alpha cells. Glucagon has many effects similar to hydrocortisone in that if it is administered to an animal in suf-

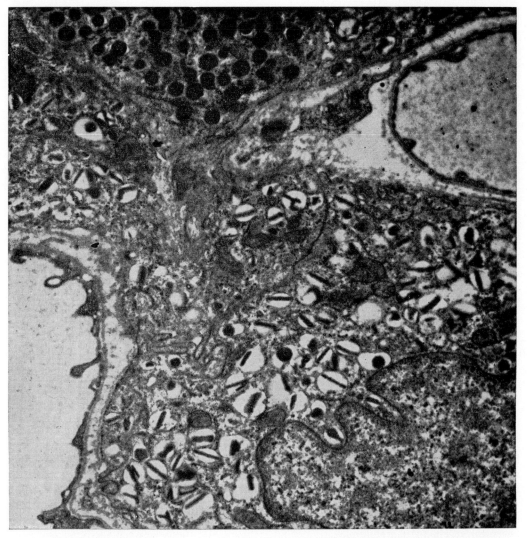

FIG. 500. Electron micrograph (× 12,000) of a section of dog pancreas showing cytoplasm of an alpha cell above and beta cells below. The granules of the alpha cell are round, dark and homogeneous and completely fill the membranous vesicles in which they lie. The granules of the beta cells seen below vary somewhat in appearance but are generally rectangular, and much space can be seen between them and the membranous walls of the vesicles in which they lie. A capillary can be seen at the lower left corner and at the upper right. (Preparation by Dr. Paul Lacy)

ficient quantities it tends to raise the blood sugar and inhibit protein synthesis. However, its physiologic role in the normal individual is not yet clear.

Fine Structure of Granules of Alpha and Beta Cells. The granules of alpha cells are similar in different species, being round, dense and homogeneous, and filling the membranous vesicles in which they lie (Fig. 500, *top.*)

The granules of the beta cells differ in different species.

In the rat and the mouse they are round and homogeneous and enclosed in smooth-surfaced membranous vesicles. However, they can be distinguished from alpha granules because they, in contrast with alpha granules, do not, generally, completely fill the membranous vesicles in which they lie; hence, a space can

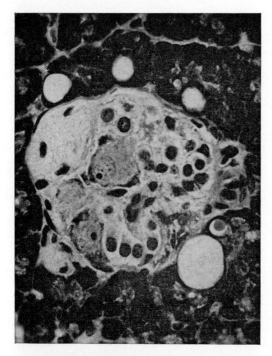

FIG. 501. High-power photomicrograph of a section of a rat's pancreas, showing a neuro-insular complex. Note the large ganglion cells in association with islet cells. (Dr. W. S. Hartroft)

be seen between the edges of beta granules and the membranous vesicles that contain them.

In the dog, beta granules often appear as rectangular crystalloid structures (Fig. 500, *lower part*). The platelike granules do not fill the rounded membranous vesicles which contain them; hence, a comparatively large space can be seen between the long surfaces of the granules and the rounded vesicles in which they lie. In the cat also the beta granules have a crystalloid appearance; but in this species the central part of each granule contains a dense rhomboidal or prismatic structure.

In the guinea pig the beta granules have an irregular shape, with some having a central clear area. Here again the beta granules are withdrawn somewhat from the membranous vesicles in which they lie.

In man the beta granules vary from being round to crystalloid in appearance. Here, again, the beta granules, whatever their shape,

tend to be withdrawn from the membranous vesicles in which they are contained.

Problem of Beta Cell Regeneration. In the light of Allen's overwork experiments, it was anticipated, when insulin was discovered, that the administration of the hormone would lessen the strain on a diabetic's beta cells and so allow them to recover their health and functional capacity. This hope was realized, and there are countless examples of the insulin requirements of diabetics having become reduced as their own beta cells recovered and functioned more normally. But, although there is much evidence to indicate that tired beta cells are often restored, there is not much to indicate that new beta cells are regenerated in any number in the pancreas of the treated diabetic. Hence, most diabetics will remain diabetics until someone discovers some way to make their beta cells regenerate. In this sense, the cause of persisting diabetes is the inability of the beta cells of the pancreas to regenerate. How to induce beta cells to regenerate, or how to induce the ductules of the pancreas to produce beta cells, is a challenging problem for the research worker.

Nervous Control of Islet Cells. The extent to which insulin secretion is affected by the autonomic nervous system, and hence by severe emotional states, has not been worked out as satisfactorily as might be wished, but there is some indication that parasympathetic fibers, traveling by way of the right vagus nerve, stimulate insulin secretion. Furthermore, it has been shown that there are intimate associations between islet cells and ganglion cells in the pancreas. These little aggregates are termed *neuro-insular complexes* (Fig. 501). They have been studied most intensively in recent years by Simard, whose papers should be consulted for further details of their microscopic structure and for a discussion of their significance.

THE PINEAL BODY

The pineal body, also called the epiphysis, is a little cone-shaped body about 1 cm. in length. Although it originates from, and remains connected to, the posterior end of the roof of the third ventricle, it projects backward so that it lies dorsal to the midbrain.

Its development begins early in embryonic life. At this time the roof of the diencephalon,

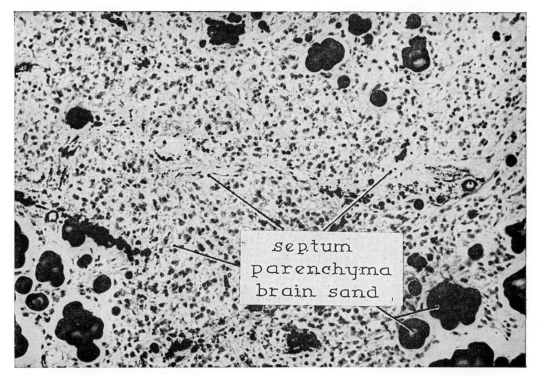

Fig. 502. Medium-power photomicrograph of an H and E section of the pineal body of an adult, showing parenchyma, septa and brain sand.

behind the site of origin of the choroid plexus of the third ventricle, bulges dorsally as a diverticulum. As development proceeds, the walls of the diverticulum thicken so that the lumen of the outgrowth is gradually obliterated. In postnatal life a lumen is to be seen only at the base of the pineal body, where it is called the pineal recess of the third ventricle.

The outgrowth of the roof of the diencephalon that gives rise to the pineal body contains two types of cells. First, the roof itself contains neuro-ectodermal cells; secondly, the pia mater, which covers the outgrowth, contains mesenchymal cells. Both types of cell participate in the formation of the pineal body. The neuro-ectodermal cells give rise to the parenchymal cells of the body and also to neuroglial cells. The mesenchymal cells give rise to the connective tissue of the capsule of the body and to the incomplete partitions of connective tissue that more or less divide the body up into lobules.

On viewing a section of the pineal body, lobules of parenchymal cells may be seen to be incompletely separated from one another by septa of connective tissue that extend into the body from the capsule and carry blood vessels into the substance of the gland (Fig. 502). Delicate support for the parenchymal cells within lobules is provided by neuroglial tissue. The parenchymal cells (Fig. 502) are probably of several types. They are not nerve cells. By special staining methods, del Rio-Hortega has shown that they have complicated arrangements of processes.

The pineal body of mammals is the vestige of the median eye which was probably a functioning organ in certain amphibia and reptiles that are now extinct. Like other vestigial organs in man, it tends to reach its greatest development relatively early in life and thereafter to degenerate. One evidence of the latter process is the formation of calcified bodies of a laminated appearance in the organ. These constitute what is called brain sand (Fig. 502).

The function of the pineal body has been studied by the same means that have been employed for the study of endocrine glands. The effects of the removal of the pineal body from young animals have been investigated, as have the effects of grafting a series of pineal transplants into animals. Various types of extracts made from pineal bodies have been fed or injected into animals. The effects of pineal tumors on men and women have been noted. The net result of all this study is difficult to assess. The experimental results are conflicting. Nevertheless, there is some evidence to suggest that there is some association between the sexual development of the male and the pineal body. However, the nature and significance of this association is still obscure.

REFERENCES

THE ENDOCRINE SYSTEM—GENERAL

Hsia, D.: Inborn Errors of Metabolism, 358 pp., Chicago, Year Book Pub., 1959.

Pincus, G. (ed.): Recent Progress in Hormone Research, vols. 1-15, New York, Acad. Press, 1959.

Pincus, G., and Thimann, K. V. (eds.): The Hormones, vols. 1, 2 and 3, New York, Acad. Press, 1948, 1950 and 1955.

See also textbooks of Endocrinology.

THE PITUITARY GLAND AS A WHOLE AND ITS BLOOD SUPPLY

Atwell, W. J.: The development of the hypophysis cerebri in man, with special reference to the pars tuberalis, Am. J. Anat. 37:159, 1926.

Bailey, P.: The structure of the hypophysis cerebri of man and the common laboratory mammals in Cowdry's Special Cytology, ed. 2, p. 771, New York, Hoeber, 1932.

Geiling, E. M. K., and Lewis, M. R.: Further information concerning the melanophore hormone of the hypophysis cerebri, Am. J. Physiol. 113:534, 1935.

Green, J. D.: The comparative anatomy of the hypophysis, with special reference to its blood supply and innervation, Am. J. Anat. 88:225, 1951.

————: The histology of the hypophyseal stalk and medium eminence in man, with special reference to blood vessels, nerve fibers and a peculiar neurovascular zone in this region, Anat. Rec. 100:273, 1948.

Green, J. D., and Harris, G. W.: Observation of the hypophysio-portal vessels of the living rat, J. Physiol. 108:359, 1949.

Harris, G. W.: The hypothalamus and regulation of ACTH secretion in Ralli, E. P. (ed.): Proc. Third Conf. on the Adrenal Cortex, p. 54, New York, Macy, 1952.

————: Neural control of pituitary gland, I and II, Brit. M. J. 2:559, 627, 1951.

Popa, G. T., and Fielding, U.: A portal circulation from the pituitary to the hypothalamic region, J. Anat. 65:88, 1930.

Rasmussen, A. T.: The morphology of the pars intermedia of the human hypophysis, Endocrinology 2:129, 1928.

Shankland, W. M.: Lymphocytes and lymphoid tissue in the human pituitary, Anat. Rec. 111:177, 1951.

Timme, W., Frantz, A. M., and Hare, C. C. (eds.): The Pituitary Gland, Baltimore, Williams & Wilkins, 1938.

Van Dyke, H. B.: Physiology and Pharmacology of the Pituitary Body, 2 vols., Chicago, Univ. Chicago Press, 1936.

Wislocki, G. B.: The meningeal relations of the hypophysis cerebri: II. An embryological study of the meninges and blood vessels of the human hypophysis, Am. J. Anat. 61:95, 1937.

————: The vascular supply of the hypophysis cerebri of the cat. Anat. Rec. 69:361, 1937.

————: The vascular supply of the hypophysis cerebri of the rhesus monkey and man, Proc. A. Res. Nerv. & Ment. Dis. 17:48, 1938.

THE ANTERIOR PITUITARY GLAND

Astwood, E. B.: Growth hormone and corticotropin in Pincus, G., and Thimann, K. V. (eds.): The Hormones, ed. 3, p. 235, New York, Acad. Press, 1955.

Briseno-Castrejon, B., and Finerty, J. C.: An azocarmine stain for differential cell analysis of the rat anterior hypophysis, Stain Technol. 24:103, 1949.

Catchpole, H. R.: Distribution of glycoprotein hormones in anterior pituitary gland of rat, J. Endocrinology 6:218, 1949.

Halmi, M. S.: The effects of graded doses of thyroxine on the anterior pituitary of hypothyroid male albino rats, Anat. Rec. 112:17, 1952.

————: Two types of basocells in the rat pituitary, thyrotrophs and gonadotrophs vs. beta and delta cells, Endocrinology 50:140, 1952.

————: Two types of basophiles in anterior pituitary of rat and their respective cytophysiological significance, Endocrinology 47:289, 1950.

Koneff, A. A.: Adaptation of the Mallory-azan staining method to the anterior pituitary of the rat, Stain Technol. 13:49, 1938.

Ladman, A. J.: Mitotic activity in the anterior pituitary of the pregnant mouse, Anat. Rec. 120:395, 1954.

Long, C. N. H.: Pituitary-adrenal relationships, Ann. Rev. Physiol. 18:409, 1956.

————: Regulation of ACTH secretion *in* Pincus, G. H. (ed.): Recent Progress in Hormone Research, vol. 7, p. 75, New York, Acad. Press, 1952

Pearse, A. G. E.: The cytochemistry and cytology of the normal anterior hypophysis investigated by the trichrome-periodic acid—Schiff method, J. Path. & Bact. *64*:811, 1952.

————: Histochemistry, Theoretical and Applied, London, Churchill, 1953.

————: Observations on the localisation, nature and chemical constitution of some components of the anterior hypophysis, J. Path. & Bact. *64*:791, 1952.

Purves, H. D., and Griesbach, W. E.: The significance of the Gomori staining of the basophiles of the rat pituitary, Endocrinology *49*:652, 1951.

————: The site of thyrotrophin and gonadotrophin production in the rat pituitary studied by McManus-Hotchkiss staining of glycoprotein, Endocrinology *49*:244, 1951.

————: Specific staining of the thyrotrophic cell of the rat pituitary by the Gomori stains, Endocrinology *49*:427, 1951.

Rasmussen, A. T.: Changes in the proportion of cell types in the anterior lobe of the human hypophysis during the first 19 years of life, Am. J. Anat. *86*:75, 1950.

Rinehart, J. F., and Farquhar, M. G.: The fine vascular organization of the anterior pituitary gland, Anat. Rec. *121*:207, 1955.

Ritter, H. B., and Oleson, J. J.: Combined histochemical staining of acid polysaccharides and 1, 2 glycol groupings in paraffin sections of rat tissues, Am. J. Path. *26*:639, 1950.

Saffran, M., Schally, A. V., and Benfey, B. G.: Stimulation of the release of corticotropin from the adenohypophysis by a neurohypophyseal factor, Endocrinology *57*:439, 1955.

Sayers, G.: Adrenal cortex and homeostasis, Physiol. Rev. *30*:241, 1950.

Selye, H.: Stress, Montreal, Acta, Inc., 1950.

————: Stress and general adaptation syndrome, Brit. M. J. *1*:1383, 1950.

Severinghaus, A. E.: Cellular changes in the anterior hypophysis with special reference to its secretory activities, Physiol. Rev. *17*:556, 1937.

Siperstein, E., Nichols, C. W., Jr., Griesbach, W. E., and Chaikoff, I. L.: Cytological changes in the rat anterior pituitary from birth to maturity, Anat. Rec. *118*:593, 1954.

Spagnoli, H. H., and Charipper, H. A.: The effects of aging on the histology and cytology of the pituitary gland of the golden hamster (Cricetus auratus), with brief reference to simultaneous changes in the thyroid and testis, Anat. Rec. *121*:117, 1955.

Van Dyke, H. B., *et al.*: Protein hormones of the pituitary body, Ann. New York Acad. Sc., Vol. 43, 1943.

White, A.: Preparation and chemistry of anterior pituitary hormones, Physiol. Rev. *26*:575, 1946.

Wilson, W. D., and Ezrin, C.: Three types of chromophil cells of the adenohypophysis, Am. J. Path. *30*:891, 1954.

Wolfe, J. M., and Cleveland, R.: Cyclic histological variations in the anterior hypophysis of the albino rat, Anat. Rec. *55*:233, 1933.

Wolstenholme, G. E. W. (ed.): Ciba Foundation Colloquia on Endocrinology, Anterior Pituitary Secretion, London, Churchill, 1952. (See papers by J. R. Brobeck, J. W. Everett, C. Fortier, J. DeGroot and G. W. Harris, G. W. Harris, G. W. Harris and D. Jacobsohn, D. M. Hume, and V. N. E. Long.)

THE POSTERIOR LOBE OF THE PITUITARY GLAND AND NEUROSECRETION

Bargmann, W., and Scharrer, E.: The site of origin of the hormones of the posterior pituitary, Am. Scientist *39*:255, 1951.

Bodian, D.: Nerve endings, neurosecretory substance and lobular organization of the neurohypophysis, Bull. Johns Hopkins Hosp. *33*:354, 1951.

Duncan, D.: An electron microscope study of the neurohypophysis of a bird, Gallus domesticus, Anat. Rec. *125*:457, 1956.

du Vigneaud, V., Ressler, C., Swan, J. M., Roberts, C. W., Katsoyannis, P. G., and Gordon, S.: The synthesis of an octapeptide amide with the hormonal activity of oxytocin, J. Am. Chem. Soc. *75*:4879, 1953.

Ferguson, J. K. W.: The control of uterine activity in the puerperal rabbit, Am. J. Physiol. *126*:489, 1939.

————: A study of the motility of the intact uterus at term, Surg., Gynec. & Obst. *73*:359, 1941.

Green, J. D., and van Breemen, V. L.: Electron microscopy of the pituitary and observations on neurosecretion, Am. J. Anat. *97*:177, 1955.

Haterius, H. O., and Ferguson, J. K. W.: Evidence for the hormonal nature of the oxytocic principle of the hypophysis, Am. J. Physiol. *124*:314, 1938.

Landgrebe, F. W., Ketterer, B., and Waring, H.: Hormones of the posterior pituitary *in* Pincus, G., and Thimann, K. V. (eds.): The Hormones, ed. 3, p. 389, New York, Acad. Press, 1955.

Palay, S. L.: An electron microscope study of the neurohypophysis in normal, hydrated and dehydrated rats, Anat. Rec. *121*:348, 1955.

———: Neurosecretory phenomena in the hypothalamo-hypophyseal system of man and monkey, Am. J. Anat. *93*:107, 1953.

Rennels, E. G., and Drager, G. A.: The relationship of pituicytes to neurosecretion, Anat. Rec. *122*:193, 1955.

Scharrer, E., and Scharrer, B.: In Handbuch der mikroskopischen Anatomie des Menschen, vol. 6, p. 953, Berlin, Springer, 1954.

———: Neurosecretion, Physiol. Rev. *25*:171, 1945.

———: Neurosecretion *in* Recent Progress in Hormone Research, vol. 10, p. 183, New York, Acad. Press, 1954.

Scharrer, E. A., and Wittenstein, G. J.: The effect of the interruption of the hypothalamo-hypophyseal neurosecretory pathway in the dog, Anat. Rec. *112*:387, 1952.

Various Authors: Pubblicazoni della Stazione Zoologica di Napoli, vol. 24, Supp., 1954.

Welsh, J. H.: Neurohormones *in* Pincus, G., and Thimann, K. V. (eds.): The Hormones, ed. 3, p. 97, New York, Acad. Press, 1955.

THE THYROID GLAND

Axelrad, A. A., Leblond, C. P., and Isler, H.: Role of iodine deficiency in the production of goiter by the Remington diet, Endrocrinology *56*:387, 1955.

Barker, S. B.: Thyroid, Ann. Rev. Physiol. *17*:417, 1955.

———: The Thyroid, Brookhaven National Laboratory, Upton, N. J., Associated Universities Inc., 1955.

Bélanger, L. F., and Leblond, C. P.: A method for locating radioactive elements in tissues by covering histological sections with a photographic emulsion, Endocrinology *39*:8, 1946.

Braunsteiner, H., Fellinger, K., and Pakesch, F.: Electron microscopic observations on the thyroid, Endocrinology *53*:123, 1953.

Dempsey, E. W.: The chemical cytology of the thyroid gland, Ann. New York Acad. Sc. *50*:336, 1949.

De Robertis, E.: Cytological and cytochemical bases of thyroid function, Ann. New York Acad. Sc. *50*:317, 1949.

———: Intracellular colloid in the initial stages of thyroid activation, Anat. Rec. *84*:125, 1942.

———: Proteolytic enzyme activity of colloid extracted from single follicles of the rat thyroid, Anat. Rec. *80*:219, 1941.

De Robertis, E., and Nowinski, W. W.: Mechanism of therapeutic effect of iodine on thyroid gland, Science *103*:421, 1946.

Dziemian, A. J.: Proteolytic activity of the thyroid gland, J. Cell. & Comp. Physiol. *21*:339, 1943.

Follis, R. H., Jr.: Experimental colloid goiter in the hamster, Proc. Soc. Exper. Biol. & Med. *100*:203, 1959.

Gersh, I., and Caspersson, T.: Total protein and organic iodine in the colloid and cells of single follicles of the thyroid gland, Anat. Rec. *78*:303, 1940.

Gorbman, A.: Some aspects of the comparative biochemistry of iodine utilization and the evolution of thyroidal function, Physiol. Rev. *35*:336, 1955.

Gross, J.: Effects of 3:5:3'-L-triiodothyronine in myxoedema, Lancet *262*:1044, 1952.

———: Physiological activity of 3:5:3'-L-triiodothyronine, Brit. M. Bull. *8*:593, 1952.

———: Thyroid hormones, Brit. M. Bull. *10*:218, 1954.

Gross, J., and Leblond, C. P.: The presence of free iodinated compounds in the thyroid and their passage into the circulation, Endocrinology *48*:714, 1951.

Gross, J., and Pitt-Rivers, R.: Experimental study of thyroid metabolism with radioactive iodine, Brit. M. Bull. *8*:136, 1952.

———: Tri-iodothyronine in relation to thyroid physiology *in* Recent Progress in Hormone Research, vol. 10, p. 109, New York, Acad. Press, 1954.

Harington, C. R.: The Thyroid Gland; Its Chemistry and Physiology, London, Oxford Univ. Press, 1933.

Leblond, C. P.: Behavior of radio-iodine in resting and stimulated thyroids, Anat. Rec. *88*:285, 1944.

Leblond, C. P., and Eartly, H.: An attempt to produce complete thyroid deficiency in the rat, Endocrinology *55*:26, 1952.

Leblond, C. P., Fertman, M. B., Puppel, I. D., and Curtis, G. M.: Radio-iodine autography in studies of human goitrous thyroid glands, Arch. Path. *41*:510, 1946.

Leblond, C. P., and Gross, J.: Thyroglobulin formation in the thyroid follicle visualized by the "coated autograph" technique, Endocrinology *43*:306, 1948.

Levitt, T.: The Thyroid: A Physiological, Pathological, Clinical and Surgical Study, Edinburgh, Livingstone, 1954.

Marine, D., *et al.*: The relation of iodine to the structure of the thyroid gland, Ann. Int. Med. *1*:349, 1908.

Means, J. H., *et al.*: Thyroid function as disclosed by newer methods of study, Ann. New York Acad. Sc., vol. 50, 1949.

Michel, R.: Thyroid, Ann. Rev. Physiol. *18*:457, 1956.

Monroe, B. G.: Electron microscopy of the thyroid, Anat. Rec. *116*:345, 1953.

Nadler, N. J., and Leblond, C. P.: The site and rate of formation of thyroid hormones, Brookhaven Sympos. Biol. No. 7, p. 40, 1955.

Nadler, N. J., Leblond, C. P., and Carneiro, J.: Site of formation of thyroglobulin in the mouse thyroid as shown by radioautography with leucine-H^3, Proc. Soc. Exper. Biol. & Med. 1960 (submitted for publication).

Rawson, R. W., Rall, J. E., and Sonenberg, M.: The chemistry and physiology of the thyroid *in* Pincus, G., and Thimann, K. V. (eds.): The Hormones, ed. 3., p. 433, New York, Acad. Press, 1955.

Rienhoff, W. F., Jr.: Gross and microscopic structure of thyroid gland in man, Contrib. Embryol. *123*:99, 1930.

Roche, J., and Michel, R.: Nature, biosynthesis and metabolism of thyroid hormones, Physiol. Rev. *35*:583, 1955.

————: Thyroid hormones and iodine metabolism, Ann. Rev. Biochem. *23*:481, 1954.

Roche, J., Michel, R., Tissitzsky, S., and Michel, Mme.: Sur la formation d'iodures a partir de la diiodotyrosine dans le corps thyroide et sur leur reutilisation, C. R. Acad. Sc. *232*:2148, 1951.

Sugiyama, S.: Studies of the histogenesis of the thyroid gland of the guinea pig: I. The thyroid cells (follicle cells and parafollicular cells), Anat. Rec. *120*:363, 1954.

Sugiyama, S., and Sato, T.: Studies of the histogenesis of the thyroid gland of the guinea pig: II. Quantitative measurements of the follicles and correlation with function, Anat. Rec. *120*: 379, 1954.

Wissig, S. L.: The anatomy of secretion in the follicular cells of the thyroid gland, I. The fine structure of the gland in the normal rat, J. Biophys. & Biochem. Cytol. *7*:419, 1960.

Auto-immunity in the Thyroid Gland

Roitt, I. M., Campbell, P. N., and Doniach, D.: The nature of the thyroid autoantibodies present in patients with Hashimoto's thyroiditis (lymphadenoid goitre), Biochem. J. *69*:248, 1958.

Witebsky, E., and Rose, N. R.: Studies on organ specificity. IV. Production of rabbit thyroid antibodies in the rabbit, J. Immunol. *76*:408, 1956.

Witebsky, E., Rose, N. R., and Shulman, S.: The autoantibody nature of the thyroiditis antibody and the role of thyroglobulin in the reaction, Lancet, *1*:808, 1958.

The Parathyroid Glands

Albright, F., and Reifenstein, E. C.: The Parathyroid Glands and Metabolic Bone Disease, Baltimore, Williams & Wilkins, 1948.

Barnicot, N. A.: The local action of the parathyroid and other tissues on bone in intracerebral grafts, J. Anat. *82*:233, 1948.

Bartter, F. C.: The parathyroids, Ann. Rev. Physiol. *16*:429, 1954.

Bensley, S. H.: The normal mode of secretion in the parathyroid gland of the dog, Anat. Rec. *98*:361, 1947.

Bhaskar, S. N., Schour, I., Greep, R. O., and Weinmann, J. P.: The corrective effect of parathyroid hormone on genetic anomalies in the dentition and the tibia of the *ia* rat, J. Dent. Res. *31*:257, 1952.

Bhaskar, S. N., Weinmann, J. P., Schour, I., and Greep, R. O.: The growth pattern of the tibia in normal and *ia* rats, Am. J. Anat. *86*:439, 1950.

Burroughs, R. B.: Variations produced in bones of growing rats by parathyroid extracts, Am. J. Anat. *62*:237, 1937-38.

Castleman, B., and Mallory, T. B.: The pathology of the parathyroid gland in hyperparathyroidism, Am. J. Path. *11*:1, 1935.

Chang, H.: Grafts of parathyroid and other tissues to bone, Anat. Rec. *111*:23, 1951.

De Robertis, E.: The cytology of the parathyroid gland of rats injected with parathyroid extract, Anat. Rec. *78*:473, 1940.

————: The cytology of the parathyroid and thyroid glands of rats with experimental rickets, Anat. Rec. *79*:417, 1941.

Drake, T. G., Albright, F., and Castleman, B.: Parathyroid hyperplasia in rabbits produced by parenteral phosphate administration, J. Clin. Invest. *16*:203, 1937.

Foster, C. L.: Studies on the parathyroid of the mouse, J. Anat. *80*:171, 1946.

Grafflin, A. L.: Cytological evidence of secretory activity in the mammalian parathyroid gland, Endocrinology *26*:857, 1940.

Greep, R. O., and Kenny, A. D.: Physiology and chemistry of the parathyroids *in* Pincus, G., and Thimann, K. V. (eds.): The Hormones, ed. 3., p. 153, New York, Acad. Press, 1955.

Grollman, A.: The role of the kidney in the parathyroid control of the blood calcium as determined by studies on the nephrectomized dog, Endocrinology *55*:166, 1954.

Ham, A. W., Littner, N., Drake, T. G. H., Robertson, E. C., and Tisdall, F. F.: Physiological hypertrophy of the parathyroids, its cause and its relation to rickets, Am. J. Path. *16*:277, 1940.

Howard, J. E.: Present knowledge of parathyroid function, with especial emphasis upon its limitations *in* Wolstenholme, G. E. W., and O'Connor, C. M. (eds.): Ciba Foundation Symposium on Bone Structure and Metabolism, p. 206, London, Churchill, 1956.

McLean, F. C.: The parathyroid glands and bone *in* Bourne, G. H. (ed.): The Biochemistry and Physiology of Bone, p. 705, New York, Acad. Press, 1956.

Pappenheimer, A. M., and Wilens, S. L.: Enlargement of the parathyroid glands in renal disease, Am. J. Path. *11*:73, 1935.

Patt, H. M., and Luckhardt, A. B.: Relationship of a low blood calcium to parathyroid secretion, Endocrinology *31*:384, 1942.

Raybuck, H. E.: The innervation of the parathyroid glands, Anat. Rec. *112*:117, 1952.

Schelling, D. H., and Remsen, D.: Renal rickets; report of a case showing four enlarged parathyroids and evidence of parathyroid hypersecretion, Bull. Johns Hopkins Hosp. *57*:158, 1935.

Schour, I., Bhaskar, S. N., Greep, R. O., and Weinmann, J. P.: Odontome-like formations in a mutant strain of rats, Am. J. Anat. *85*:73, 1949.

Thomson, D. L., and Collip, J. B.: The parathyroid glands, Physiol. Rev. *12*:309, 1932.

(*See also* references on Bone Resorption and Osteoclasts in Chap. 15)

THE ADRENAL GLAND AS A WHOLE

Grollman, A.: The Adrenals, Baltimore, Williams & Wilkins, 1936.

Hartman, F. A., and Brownell, K. A.: The Adrenal Gland, Philadelphia, Lea & Febiger, 1949.

Hewer, E. E., and Keene, M. F. L.: Observations on the development of the human suprarenal gland, J. Anat. *61*:302, 1927.

Jayne, E. P.: Cytology of the adrenal gland of the rat at different ages, Anat. Rec. *115*:459, 1953.

Kitchell, R. L., and Wells, L. J.: Functioning of the hypophysis and adrenals in foetal rats: Effects of hypophysectomy, adrenalectomy, castration, injected ACTH, and implanted sex hormone, Anat. Rec. *112*:561, 1952.

Swinyard, C. A.: Growth of human suprarenal glands, Anat. Rec. *87*:141, 1943.

THE ADRENAL CORTEX—GENERAL

Gaunt, R., *et al.:* The adrenal cortex, Ann. New York Acad. Sc., vol. 50, 1949.

Noble, R. L.: Physiology of the adrenal cortex *in* Pincus, G., and Thimann, K. V. (eds.): The Hormones, ed. 3., p. 685, New York, Acad. Press, 1955.

Yoffey, J. M. (ed.): The suprarenal cortex *in* Proc. of the Fifth Sympos. of the Colston Res. Soc., London, Butterworth, 1953.

THE ADRENAL CORTEX—SPECIAL

Addison, T.: On constitutional and local effects of disease of suprarenal capsule, M. Classics *2*:244, 1937.

Bennett, H. S.: Life history and secretion of cells of the adrenal cortex of the cat, Am. J. Anat. *67*:151, 1940.

Bongiovanni, A. M.: Physiology of adrenal cortex in infancy and childhood, Am. J. M. Sc. *222*:710, 1951.

Broster, L. H., and Vines, H. W. C.: The Adrenal Cortex: A Surgical and Pathological Study, London, Lewis, 1933.

Deane, H. W., and Greep, R. O.: A morphological and histochemical study of the rat's adrenal cortex after hypophysectomy, with comments on the liver, Am. J. Anat. *79*:117, 1946.

Feldman, J. D.: Endocrine control of the adrenal gland, Anat. Rec. *109*:41, 1951.

————: Histochemical reactions of adrenal cortical cells, Anat. Rec. *107*:347, 1950.

Glick, D., and Biskind, G. R.: The histochemistry of the adrenal gland: I. The quantitative distribution of vitamin C, J. Biol. Chem. *110*:1, 1935.

————: Studies in histochemistry: IX. The quantitative distribution of vitamin C in the adrenal gland at various stages of development, J. Biol. Chem. *115*:551, 1936.

Hench, P. S., Kendall, E. C., Slocumb, C. H., and Polley, H. F.: The effect of a hormone of the adrenal cortex (17-hydroxy-11-dehydrocorticosterone: compound E) and of pituitary adrenocorticotrophic hormone on rheumatoid arthritis, Ann. Rheum. Dis. *8*:97, 1949.

Hoerr, N.: The cells of the suprarenal cortex in the guinea pig: their reaction to injury and their replacement, Am. J. Anat. *48*:139, 1931.

————: Histological studies on lipins: II. A cytological analysis of the liposomes in the adrenal cortex of the guinea pig, Anat. Rec. *66*:317, 1936.

Holmes, W. N.: Histological variations in the adrenal cortex of the golden hamster with special reference to the X zone, Anat. Rec. *122*:271, 1955.

Lever, J. D.: Electron microscopic observations on the adrenal cortex, Am. J. Anat. *97*:409, 1955.

Long, C. N. H.: Pituitary-adrenal relationships, Ann. Rev. Physiol. *18*:409, 1956.

Miale, J. B.: Connective tissue reactions—a critical review: I. The effects of ACTH and cortisone on allergic reactions and the collagen diseases, Ann. Allergy 9:530, 1951.

Ralli, E. P. (ed.): Proceedings of Third Conference on the Adrenal Cortex, New York, Macy, 1952.

Schaberg, A.: Regeneration of the adrenal cortex in vitro, Anat. Rec. 122:205, 1955.

Selye, H.: Physiology and Pathology of Exposure to Stress, Montreal, Acta, Inc., 1950.

van Dorp, A. W. V., and Deane H. W.: A morphological and cytochemical study of the postnatal development of the rat's adrenal cortex, Anat. Rec. 107:265, 1950.

Williams, R. G.: Studies of adrenal cortex: Regeneration of the transplanted gland and the vital quality of the autogenous grafts, Am. J. Anat. 81:199, 1947.

THE ADRENAL MEDULLA

Bennett, H. S.: Cytological manifestations of secretion in the adrenal medulla of the cat, Am. J. Anat. 69:333, 1941.

Bennett, H. S., and Kilham, L.: The blood vessels of the adrenal gland of the adult cat, Anat. Rec. 77:447, 1940.

Cannon, W. B.: Bodily Changes in Pain, Hunger, Fear and Rage, New York, Appleton, 1920.

Cannon, W. B., and Rosenblueth, A.: Autonomic Neuroeffector Systems, New York, Macmillan, 1937.

Cori, C. F., and Welch, A.: The adrenal medulla, J.A.M.A. 116:2590, 1941.

Lands, A. M.: The pharmacological activity of epinephrine and related dihydroxyphenylalkylamines, J. Pharmacol. & Exper. Therap. 96:279, 1949.

THE ISLETS OF LANGERHANS

Allen, F. M.: Diabetic experiments, Tr. A. Am. Physicians 53:320, 1938.

————: Studies Concerning Glycosuria and Diabetes, Cambridge, Harvard, 1913.

————: Pathology of diabetes: I. Hydropic degeneration of islands of Langerhans after partial pancreatectomy, J. Metabolic Res. 1:5, 1922.

Banting, F. G., and Best, C. H.: The internal secretion of the pancreas, J. Lab. & Clin. Med. 7:251, 1922.

Bencosme, S. A.: The histogenesis and cytology of the pancreatic islets in the rabbit, Am. J. Anat. 96:103, 1955.

Bencosme, S. A., and Lazarus, S. S.: Glucagon content of pancreatic tissue devoid of alpha cells, Proc. Soc. Exper. Biol. & Med. 90:387, 1955.

Bencosme, S. A., and Liepa, E.: Regional differences of the pancreatic islet, Endocrinology 57:588, 1955.

Bencosme, S. A., Mariz, S., and Frei, J.: Studies on the function of the alpha cells of the pancreas, Am. J. Clin. Path. 28:594, 1957.

Bensley, R. R.: Structure and relationships of the islets of Langerhans, Harvey Lect. 10:250, 1915.

Bensley, S. H.: Solubility studies of the secretion granules of the guinea pig pancreas, Anat. Rec. 72:131, 1938.

Bensley, S. H., and Woerner, C. A.: The effects of continuous intravenous injection of an extract of the alpha cells of the guinea pig pancreas on the intact guinea pig. Anat. Rec. 72:413, 1938.

Best, C. H., Campbell, J., Haist, R. E., and Ham, A. W.: The effect of insulin and anterior pituitary extract on the insulin content of the pancreas and the histology of the islets, J. Physiol. 101:17, 1942.

Bowie, D. J.: Cytological studies of the islets of Langerhans in a teleost, Neomaemis griseus, Anat. Rec. 29:57, 1924.

Bryans, F. F., Kinash, B., Ashworth, M. A., and Haist, R. E.: The effect of hypophysectomy on the growth of the islets of Langerhans, Diabetes 1:358, 1952.

Campbell, J., Davidson, I. W. F., and Lei, H. P.: The production of permanent diabetes by highly purified growth hormone, Endocrinology 46:558, 1950.

Campbell, J., Haist, R. E., Ham, A. W., and Best, C. H.: The insulin content of the pancreas as influenced by anterior pituitary extract and insulin, Am. J. Physiol. 129:328, 1940.

Dohan, F. C., and Lukens, F. D. W.: Persistent diabetes following the injection of anterior pituitary extract, Am. J. Physiol. 125:188, 1939.

Evans, H. M., Meyer, K., Simpson, M. E., and Reichert, F. L.: Disturbance of carbohydrate metabolism in normal dogs injected with hypophyseal growth hormone, Proc. Soc. Exper. Biol. & Med. 29:857, 1931-32.

Gomori, G.: Observations with differential stains on human islets of Langerhans, Am. J. Path. 17:395, 1941.

————: Studies on the cells of the pancreatic islets, Anat. Rec. 74:439, 1939.

Ham, A. W., and Haist, R. E.: Histological effects of anterior pituitary extracts, Nature 144:835, 1939.

————: Histological studies of trophic effects of diabetogenic anterior pituitary extracts and their relation to the pathogenesis of diabetes, Am. J. Path. 17:787, 1941.

Hédon, E.: Physiologie normale et pathologique du pancréas, Paris, Masson, 1901.

Homans, J.: The relation of the islets of Langerhans to the pancreatic acini under various conditions of secretory activity, Proc. Roy. Soc., London, s.B. 86:73, 1912-13.

Houssay, B. A.: Diabetes as a disturbance of endocrine regulation, Am. J. M. Sc. 193:581, 1937.

Houssay, B. A., and Biasotti, A.: Le diabète pancréatique des chiens hypophysectomisés, Compt. rend. Soc. biol. 105:121, 1930.

———: Hypophysectomie et diabète pancréatique chez le crepaud, Compt. rend. Soc. biol. 104:407, 1930.

———: The hypophysis, carbohydrate metabolism and diabetes, Endocrinology 15:511, 1931.

———: Les troubles diabètiques chez les chiens privés d'hypophyse et de pancréas, Compt. rend. Soc. biol. 105:124, 1930.

Johns, W. S., O'Mulvenny, T. O., Potts, E. B., and Laughton, N. B.: Studies on the anterior lobe of the pituitary body, Am. J. Physiol. 80:100, 1927.

Lane, M. A.: The cytological characters of the areas of Langerhans, Am. J. Anat. 7:409, 1907.

Lawrence, R. T. B., Salter, J. M., and Best, C. H.: The effect of insulin on nitrogen retention in the hypophysectomized rat, Brit. M. J. 2:437, 1954.

Long, C. N. H., Katzin, B., and Fry, E. G.: The adrenal cortex and carbohydrate metabolism, Endocrinology 26:309, 1940.

Long, C. N. H., and Lukens, F. D. W.: The effects of adrenalectomy and hypophysectomy upon experimental diabetes in the cat, J. Exper. Med. 63:465, 1936.

Long, C. N. H., Lukens, F. D. W., and Dohan, F. C.: Adrenalectomized depancreatized dogs, Proc. Soc. Exper. Biol. & Med. 36:553, 1937.

Mering, von, J., and Minkowski, O.: Diabetes mellitus nach Pankreasextirpation, Arch. exper. Path. u. Pharmakol. 26:371, 1889.

O'Leary, J. L.: An experimental study on the islet cells of the pancreas in vivo, Anat. Rec. 45:27, 1930.

Opie, E. L.: Histology of the islands of Langerhans of the pancreas, Bull. Johns Hopkins Hosp. 11:205, 1900.

———: Pathological changes affecting the islands of Langerhans of the pancreas, J. Exper. Med. 5:397, 527, 1900-01.

Richardson, K. C.: The influence of diabetogenic anterior pituitary extract on the islets of Langerhans in dogs, Proc. Roy. Soc. London, s.B. 128:153, 1939-40.

Richardson, K. C., and Young, F. G.: Histology of diabetes induced in dogs by injection of anterior-pituitary extracts, Lancet 1:1098, 1938.

———: The "pancreatropic" action of anterior pituitary extracts, J. Physiol. 91:352, 1937.

Salter, J., and Best, C. H.: Insulin as a growth hormone, Brit. M. J. 2:353, 1953.

Schulze, W.: Die Bedeutung der Langerhansschen Inseln in Pankreas, Arch. mikr. Anat. 56:491, 1900.

Sergeyeva, M. A.: Microscopic changes in the islands of Langerhans produced by sympathetic and parasympathetic stimulation in the cat. Anat. Rec. 77:297, 1940.

Simard, L. C.: Le complexe neuro-insulaire du pancréas chez les mammifères adultes, Rev. canad. biol. 1:2, 1942.

Ssobolew, L. W.: Zur normalen und pathologischen Morphologie der inneren Secretion der Bauchspeicheldrüse, Virchow's Arch. path. Anat. 168:91, 1902.

Stetten, DeW., Jr., and Bloom, B.: The hormones of the islets of Langerhans in Pincus, G., and Thimann, K. V. (eds.): The Hormones, ed. 3, p. 175, New York, Acad. Press, 1955.

Thomas, T. B.: Cellular components of the mammalian islets of Langerhans, Am. J. Anat. 62:31, 1937-38.

Woerner, C. A.: Studies of the islands of Langerhans after continuous intravenous injection of dextrose, Anat. Rec. 71:33, 1938.

Young, F. G.: Experimental investigations on the relationship of the anterior hypophysis to diabetes mellitus, Proc. Soc. Exper. Biol. & Med. 31:1305, 1938.

———: Permanent experimental diabetes produced by pituitary (anterior lobe) injections, Lancet 2:372, 1937.

———: The pituitary gland and carbohydrate metabolism, Endocrinology 26:349, 1940.

THE PINEAL BODY

Bailey, P.: The pineal body in Cowdry's Special Cytology, ed. 2, p. 787, New York, Hoeber, 1932.

Gladstone, R. J., and Wakeley, C. P. G.: The Pineal Organ, London, Ballière, Tindall & Cox, 1940.

Chapter 27

The Female Reproductive System

INTRODUCTORY REMARKS ABOUT SEX

Under normal conditions, the embryo that forms when a female germ cell (an ovum) is fertilized by a male germ cell bearing an X chromosome develops the form and the organs of a female. Correspondingly, the embryo that forms when a female germ cell is fertilized by a male germ cell bearing a Y chromosome develops the form and the organs of a male. Hence, under normal conditions, the reproductive system that develops in any given embryo is determined by the chromosome complement of the male germ cell that fertilizes the ovum, as will be explained in the first part of the next chapter.

However, the chromosome complement of the fertilized ovum does not control the formation of the reproductive system of the embryo in the way that at first might be thought; that is, by limiting the embryo's potentiality to form the organs of one specific system. Hence, an embryo that forms from an ovum fertilized by a male germ cell bearing an X chromosome is not limited to forming a female reproductive system, for, as we shall see, such an embryo, under certain abnormal environmental circumstances, may develop male rather than female organs. Indeed, it appears that every young embryo, no matter which chromosome complement is present in the ovum from which it arises, has the *potentiality* to develop either type of reproductive system. Nevertheless, since under normal conditions the one of the two potentialities realized in any given embryo is determined by the chromosome complement of the fertilized ovum, it may be concluded that the chromosome constitution, while it does not limit, exerts a profound *directing* influence on development.

The way that the chromosome complement of a fertilized ovum directs the development of a male or a female reproductive system in an embryo is not understood. As we shall see, sex hormones probably play some part in the matter, but there are other factors involved.

Before discussing the matter further we shall describe something of the development of the sex glands of the embryo and discuss some of the factors that affect their development.

Indifferent Nature of the Early Gonad. The fundamental organ of either reproductive system is the *gonad* (*gone* = seed) or *sex gland*. There are 2 of either sex in each individual. Those of the female are termed *ovaries*; those of the male, *testes*. The gonads have a dual function in each sex. During the period of sexual maturity the ovaries of females regularly produce mature female germ cells that are capable of being fertilized. They also produce female sex hormone. The testes of males produce male germ cells and male sex hormone.

In the early embryonic development the gonads of both sexes are said to be indifferent. A histologic examination of one made at this time gives no indication as to whether it will later become an ovary or a testis. However, as development proceeds, the organization of cells within the previously indifferent glands becomes indicative of whether they will develop into ovaries or testes. Certain features of the indifferent gonad become suppressed, and others accentuated. As a result of these processes, the embryonic gonads of the 2 sexes soon come to have different microscopic appearances.

On rare occasions both male and female gonads, or parts of gonads, develop and remain in a single individual. For example, the left gonad may develop into a testis, and the right one into an ovary, or both testicular and ovarian elements may develop in the same gonad. The development of both male and female gonadal tissue in the same individual is associated with a disturbed development of the other parts of the reproductive system. Instead of developing only male or female organs and structures, such individuals develop various mixtures of both. Such individuals, then, cannot be classified as either males or females, either by their gonads or by the other organs and structures of their reproductive systems. Therefore, such individuals are called *hermaphrodites* (*Hermēs* = Mercury; *Aphroditē* = Venus). By using Barr's technic, hermaphrodites can be shown to be chromosomal males or chromosomal females. If one is the latter, the cells of the male organs that develop in it will reveal the sex chromatin of the female.

Effects of Sex Hormones on the Differentiation of the Indifferent Gonad. That a genetically determined female embryo may be induced by environmental factors to become a hermaphrodite was shown many years ago by Lillie in his classic study of freemartins in cattle. Moreover, Lillie's study gave some intimation of the factors that direct differentiation within the developing reproductive system along one line or another. It had long been known that when cows gave birth to twins of opposite sex, the male calf would grow into a normal male but the female calf often, though not always, would develop a mixture of male and female organs, including male and female gonads. Such an altered female was termed a *freemartin*. Lillie showed that this condition was due to the fusion of the membranes that surround each of the two developing embryos in the uterus of the cow, so that blood could circulate freely between the developing genetically determined male and the genetically determined female. Under these circumstances, the male hormone derived from the developing male embryo circulates through the female, and this stimulates the development of male gonads and other male organs in the female. Such female hormone as is made in the genetically determined female which passes into the circulation of the male does not affect it materially, for the male twin is born normal.

Potentialities for the Development of Characteristics of the Opposite Sex in Adults. In many lower animals, and even in some vertebrates, sex reversal can occur. For example, it has been described in the fowl, and there are reports of hens that, for a time, have laid perfectly good eggs and have then undergone a sex reversal and have become fertile cocks. However, sex reversal is not so complete in these vertebrates in which it has been reported as it may seem, for it does not entail the development of the ability to make sex chromo-

somes other than those provided for by the original genetic constitution of the animal concerned.

In the mammals the potentiality for developing either type of gonad does not seem to persist throughout later development to the same extent as it does in certain lower animals. Hence, if large amounts of male sex hormone are given a mature female mammal, a true sex reversal does not occur, for a testis does not develop. However, a limited potentiality for forming the other organs and structures of the male genital system persists, and this is exercised. Moreover, under these conditions, female organs and structures may regress. The secondary attributes of the male (hair distribution, voice, attitudes, etc.) develop. This condition, to distinguish it from true hermaphroditism, is called *pseudohermaphroditism*. As noted previously, this condition occurs in females who develop adrenal tumors of the kind that secrete masculinizing hormones.

The Two Factors and Their Possible Relationships. From the foregoing it is to be kept in mind that both chromosome constitution and hormones must be considered as factors in the development of the reproductive system. It would be convenient if we could postulate that chromosome constitution determines whether ovaries or testes are to form in any given embryo and that the development of the remainder of the reproductive system depends on the particular hormone that the gonads of the embryo subsequently deliver into the embryonic circulation. But there is no evidence to suggest that any explanation such as this is adequate. This does not mean that hormones play no part in the normal development of the reproductive system; indeed, there is good evidence to indicate that the gonads of the male embryo produce effective amounts of hormone in embryonic life (see Chap. 28). But most authorities consider that there is a good measure of self- as well as hormone-induced, differentiation concerned in the normal development of the two sexes.

To sum up: The somatic cells of any embryo have the same chromosomal constitution as the fertilized ovum from which they develop in so far as they all contain either 44 autosomes plus an XX or an XY combination of sex chromosomes. Nevertheless, either chromosomal male or female embryos have the

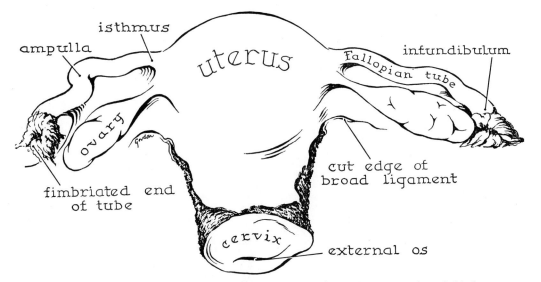

FIG. 503. Drawing of the uterus, the oviducts and the ovaries, as seen from behind.

potentiality to form the reproductive system (including the gonads) of either sex. However, it would seem that any testicular tissue that forms in chromosomal females would not be able to produce germ cells with Y chromosomes.

Sex hormones can influence which kind of reproductive system develops in an embryo but they cannot change the chromosomes. Hence, cells of male organs, if the latter develop in chromosomal females under the influence of male hormones, would have XX combinations of sex chromosomes in them. Both true and pseudohermaphrodites are either chromosomal males or females, and which they are can be determined by the microscopic examination of suitable somatic cells.

The fact that the somatic cells of males and females have different chromosomal constitutions probably explains why there is so much self-differentiation that cannot be explained by hormones in the development of the reproductive systems.

THE PARTS OF THE FEMALE REPRODUCTIVE SYSTEM

The female reproductive system, as may be seen in Figures 503 and 504, consists of 2 ovaries, 2 oviducts (also called uterine tubes or fallopian tubes), a uterus, a vagina, external genitalia and 2 mammary glands (breasts). In the following account the gross

and the microscopic structure of the various parts of the system will be described in a general way. Further details regarding microscopic structure will be presented later.

In the sexually mature woman the ovaries are somewhat flattened, solid, ovoid bodies, roughly of the shape and the size of unshelled almonds (Fig. 503). The anterior wall of each is attached to the back of the broad ligament, close to the lateral wall of the true pelvis, by means of a short fold of peritoneum called the mesovarium (Fig. 503), which conducts vessels and nerves to and from the hilum of the ovary. A rounded ligament, *the ligament of the ovary*, connects the medial end of each ovary with the uterus (Fig. 503). The ovary itself is not covered with typical peritoneum but with germinal epithelium (Fig. 119), an epithelial membrane with special potentialities. The cut surface of the ovary shows a cortex and a medulla; the latter contains many blood vessels and hence sometimes is called the zona vasculosa.

The surface of a mature ovary is scarred and pitted; this is due to its having shed many ova (germ cells). As we shall see, these are contained within the cortex in little epithelial bodies called follicles (to be described later). In a nonpregnant sexually mature woman a follicle of one ovary matures and ruptures through the ovarian surface (and in doing so liberates an ovum) approximately every 28

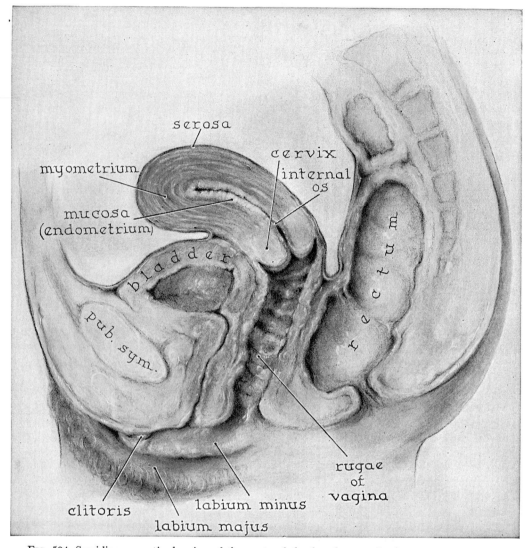

Fig. 504. Semidiagrammatic drawing of the parts of the female reproductive system, as seen in a sagittal section.

days. The phenomenon is known as *ovulation*, and each time it occurs a wound is created on the surface of the ovary. At the site of each wound, immediately after it is created, a little yellow endocrine gland called a *corpus luteum* (to be described later) develops from the remaining parts of the follicle. In the non-pregnant female each little gland grows and functions for somewhat less than 2 weeks; then it regresses. The repair of the ovarian surface, at sites where ovulation has occurred and where corpora lutea have grown and re-gressed, leads to the surface of the ovary's

becoming progressively more scarred. As we shall see, if an ovum becomes fertilized and pregnancy occurs, the corpus luteum that de-velops at the site from which the ovum was extruded grows for several months and be-comes very large. The repair phenomena that take place after the regression of a corpus luteum of pregnancy lead to the formation of a large scar on the surface of the ovary.

When a follicle ruptures through the sur-face of an ovary, an ovum, surrounded by some of the cells of the follicle that still adhere to it, is extruded directly into the peritoneal cavity (Fig. 511). As is illustrated in Figure 503, the open end of each oviduct is funnel-shaped, and the wide end of the funnel is more or less fitted over the aspect of the ovary from which ova are liberated. Figure 503 reveals that the expanded open end of the oviduct is fimbriated (*fimbriae* = fringe), and the fringelike processes that extend from the open end of the tube permit much of the ovarian surface to be encompassed in such a way that a liberated ovum is led into the lumen of the oviduct.

The oviducts (Fig. 503) are the tubes that connect the ovaries to the uterus, whose side walls they pierce; each is covered with peritoneum (the broad ligament is its mesentery). Each oviduct has a muscular wall and is lined with a mucous membrane equipped with ciliated epithelium which will be described later. An ovum cannot move by its own efforts; hence, an ovum, delivered into the open end of the oviduct, must be moved to the cavity of the uterus by actions performed by the walls of the oviduct. It is probable that peristaltic contractions that sweep from the open end of the oviduct toward the uterus are chiefly responsible for moving an ovum to the uterus, although the action of the cilia of the epithelial lining of the tubes may assist.

The mucous membrane of the oviduct is thrown into an extraordinary arrangement of longitudinal folds (Fig. 517, *left*). Each fold has a core of lamina propria. These folds probably ensure that an ovum that enters the open end of the tube is kept in close contact on almost all its sides with living cells and compatible fluids as it passes along the tube. These folds probably also provide a similar protection for male germ cells, should these have been introduced into the vagina (Fig. 504) of the female, for male germ cells make their way up the cervical canal into the cavity of the body of the uterus (Fig. 504), through which they pass to enter the oviducts. It is in the maze created by the folds of mucous membrane in the oviduct that the fertilization of an ovum by a male germ cell occurs (Fig. 513).

The uterus (womb) is a hollow muscular organ with thick walls. It occupies a central position in the pelvis (Fig. 504). In shape it resembles an inverted pear that is somewhat flattened from before backward. Its narrower

part is the body. The uppermost part of the body—that part above the level of the entrance of the oviducts—is the fundus. Since the body of the uterus is somewhat flattened from before backward, its central cavity is slitlike, with its anterior and posterior walls in apposition. In its upper part, this slitlike cavity is continuous at each side with the lumen of an oviduct. The cavity of the body narrows below and is continuous with the cervical canal. This, in turn, opens into the vagina (Fig. 504).

The body of the uterus is lined by a special kind of mucous membrane termed *endometrium* (*metra* = womb) that is pitted with simple tubular glands. It will be described in detail later. In the sexually mature (but not old) nonpregnant woman the innermost (and thicker) part of this layer breaks down and is exfoliated into the cavity of the uterus approximately every 28 days. The process of exfoliation usually takes about 4 days before its course is run, and during these 4 days the raw surface created by the continuing exfoliation bleeds. The mixture of blood, glandular secretion and brokendown endometrium delivered into the cavity of the uterus and passed out through the cervical canal and the vagina constitutes the *menstrual* (*mensis* = monthly) *flow*, and the phenomenon is called *menstruation*. Following menstruation the endometrium regenerates. Ovulation also, it will be recalled, occurs every 28 days. Ovulation, although there is much variation, does not coincide with menstruation but tends rather to occur about halfway between menstrual periods.

The liberation of an ovum from an ovary, its fertilization in the oviduct, the changes that occur in it as it passes along the oviduct to the uterus and its implantation into the endometrium—and this marks the beginning of pregnancy—are all illustrated diagrammatically in Figure 513.

The further development of the fertilized embedded ovum to form an embryo constitutes the separate subject of *embryology* and hence is dealt with in textbooks of embryology. However, the formation of the *placenta*, an organ which permits interchange of dissolved substances between the blood streams of mother and embryo, is described on page 821.

Menstruation does not occur after a fertilized ovum becomes implanted in the endo-

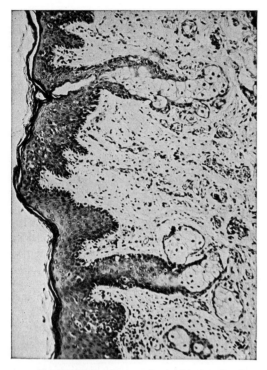

FIG. 505. Low-power photomicrograph of a section cut at right angles to the surface of a labium minus. Observe that there are only rudimentary hair follicles; these produce no hairs but are associated with sebaceous glands.

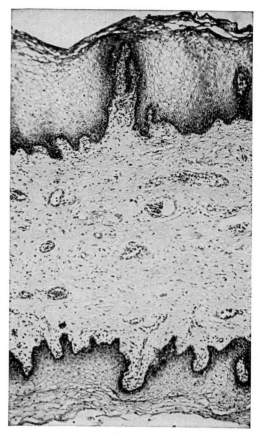

FIG. 506. Low-power photomicrograph of a portion of a section cut through the hymen. Observe that both surfaces are covered with stratified squamous nonkeratinizing epithelium and have high papillae.

metrium; hence, a "missed" menstrual period is a time-honored, though by no means invariable, sign of pregnancy. Menstruation does not occur throughout pregnancy. When the fetus has reached full term, parturition (*parturire* = to be in labor) occurs, and a baby is born. The muscle wall of the uterus, which has become very thick during pregnancy, contracts, and the cervix (Fig. 504)—the outlet of the uterus—dilates, whereupon the fetus, usually head foremost, slips through the dilated cervix and vagina to reach the outside world. The placenta then separates, and the baby begins its independent existence.

The vagina (L. = sheath) is a flattened tube; it serves as a sheath for the male organ in sexual intercourse. Its wall consist chiefly of smooth muscle and of fibro-elastic connective tissue; they are a few millimeters thick. It is lined with a mucous membrane that is thrown into transverse folds known as *rugae* (Fig. 504). The epithelium is of the stratified squamous nonkeratinizing type. This type of epithelium also covers that part of the cervix that projects into the vagina.

The external genitalia consist of several structures (Fig. 504). A collection of fat deep to the skin that covers the symphysis pubis causes the skin to be raised here in the form of a rounded eminence; this is called the *mons pubis* or *mons veneris*. At puberty this eminence becomes covered with hair. Two folds of skin, the *labia majora* (Fig. 504), originate just below the mons pubis. They separate from one another as they pass backward and approach one another again (but do not actually meet) a short distance behind the external opening of the vagina; hence, the vagina opens into the cleft which they enclose. Each of these folds has 2 surfaces covered with skin. The epidermis covering the outer surface of each tends to be pigmented and is equipped

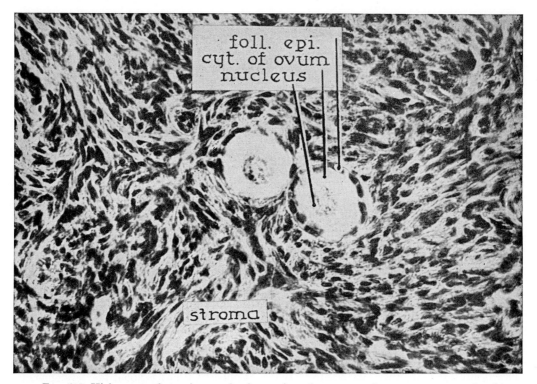

Fig. 507. High-power photomicrograph of a section of an ovary of a mature woman, showing "swirly" stroma at 2 primitive follicles. The germ cell which is labeled ovum is more accurately termed an oogonium at this stage.

with many large hair follicles and sebaceous glands. That of the inner surface also has hair follicles and sebaceous glands, but the hairs are delicate. Sweat glands are also present. The cores of the folds contain fat and some smooth muscle.

Near the anterior end of the cleft between the labia majora is a small body of erectile tissue, the *clitoris* (Fig. 504). This is the homologue of the penis of the male. Two delicate folds of skin, the *labia minora*, arise just anterior to it. After investing part of the clitoris between them they pass backward, following much the same course, as the labia majora to which they lie medial. The labia minora consist of thin folds of skin but possess no hairs (Fig. 505). Sebaceous and sweat glands are found on both their surfaces (Fig. 505). Although the inner surface of each fold consists of skin, it exhibits the pink color of a mucous membrane.

The labia minora enclose the vestibule of the vagina. In the virgin, an incomplete membranous fold, the *hymen* (Fig. 506), projects centrally from the rim of the vestibule and partially occludes the vaginal entrance. Two small glands, the *glands of Bartholin*, which are tubulo-alveolar in type and secrete mucus, are present, one on each side of the vestibule. Each drains into a duct that empties into the groove between the hymen and the labium minus on the side on which the gland is situated. Two elongated masses of erectile tissue, constituting the bulb of the vestibule, are disposed beneath the surface along each side of the vestibule. These two masses approximate each other in front. Many mucous glands are present beneath the surface around the vestibule. The urethral orifice is in the mid-line between the labia minora and between the opening of the vagina and the clitoris (Fig. 504).

The external genitalia are richly provided with sensory nerve endings.

THE OVARY: OVULATION AND HORMONE SECRETION

Basic Microscopic Features. The ovary is covered with a single layer of *germinal epithelium*. In young women this is cuboidal

(Fig. 119) but it becomes flattened later in life.

The connective tissue substance of the ovary is called its *stroma*. It consists of spindle-shaped cells and intercellular substance. Most of the stroma of the cortex contains a high proportion of cells to intercellular substance; hence, in sections it appears heavily nucleated (Fig. 507). Moreover, the bundles of cells and fibers that make up most of it run in various directions; hence, in sections the stroma of the cortex has a characteristic "swirly" appearance (Fig. 507). However, the layer immediately beneath the germinal epithelium differs from the bulk of the stroma in that it has a higher proportion of intercellular substance, and its fiber bundles and cells are both arranged more or less parallel with the surface (Fig. 119). This special layer is called the *tunica albuginea*, and the white appearance that its name suggests is due to its great content of intercellular substance and lack of vascularity.

In contrast with the dense texture of the stroma of the cortex, that of the medulla is loosely arranged. It differs further from that of the cortex in containing more elastic fibers, some smooth muscle cells and, in addition, extensive convolutes of blood vessels, particularly veins. The veins may be so large and contain so many blood cells that in a section the student may mistake one for an area of hemorrhage. Small blood vessels extend from the medulla into the cortex.

The origin of ova has been much disputed. Until recently it was believed that all ova form in prenatal life. Witschi and Chiquoine traced the migration of primitive germ cells in mammals from the endoderm of the yolk sac to the developing gonad, and Chiquoine and Rothenberg believe that the high content of alkaline phosphatase in these cells is in some way related to their migratory behavior. Latta and Pederson have shown that ova continue to form in the ovaries of experimental animals when they are sexually mature. To form ova, cells from the germinal epithelium invade the stroma (Fig. 511, *upper left*) to form little clusters which lose their connection with the surface; each isolated cluster constitutes a primary follicle. The innermost cell of each enlarges to become what is termed an oogonium, and the remaining cells form a single layer of follicular epithelium cells around it

(Fig. 507). Vermandevan Eck, in a study of adult monkeys, recently found that an oogonium has an average life of 6 months, 4 months being required for the growth of a primary follicle into a mature follicle. From 200,000 to 400,000 follicles have been counted in a single ovary.

Changes That Occur at Puberty and Their Cause. In early childhood the pars anterior of the anterior pituitary, while producing growth hormone, produces very little gonadotrophic hormone. As a consequence, the ovary develops only in keeping with the remainder of the body. But as the time of puberty approaches, the pars anterior (one group of basophils) begins to produce gonadotrophic hormone. This causes the ovaries to begin liberating an ovum into an oviduct approximately every 28 days. Moreover, the ovary, under gonadotrophic stimulus, begins to function as an endocrine gland. It makes 2 hormones.

The primary hormone made by the ovary is *estrogen*. This is the basic female sex hormone. On being liberated into the blood stream at puberty, it brings about the development of the secondary sex characteristics of the female. The breasts enlarge and become rounded. Increased amounts of fat appear under the skin of the hips and the buttocks. The growth of hair is stimulated in certain parts of the body, particularly in the pubic region; its distribution here is somewhat different from that of the male in that its upper border forms a straight line rather than running up to a middle point as it does in the male. The larynx does not increase further in size as it does in the male. Libido is aroused; this soon becomes directed toward the opposite sex. Other effects of estrogen will be described presently.

The secondary hormone made by the ovary at puberty is *progesterone* (progestin). This is made by the corpus luteum that develops each time an ovum is liberated (Fig. 511). Since corpora lutea do not persist for more than 2 weeks after ovulation in the nonpregnant female, progesterone is not made continuously except during pregnancy. In the nonpregnant woman the chief function of progesterone is to prepare the uterus for the reception of a fertilized ovum. It does this anew each month even in a virgin. The preparation consists of making the endometrium grow thick and succulent so that a fertilized ovum may easily become embedded in it and be nourished adequately. It has been believed also that it tends to make the uterine muscle quiescent so that it does not contract and expel the developing embryo. However, recent work has cast doubt on this hypothesis. Unless a fertilized ovum becomes implanted in the endometrium (or elsewhere), the corpus luteum of the ovary does not continue making progesterone for more than 2 weeks after ovulation has occurred. If the corpus luteum had a mind, one might visualize its thinking at this time that, "unless fertilization has occurred by now it won't occur this month, for this month's ovum, by this time, will have died; hence, there is no point in maintaining the endometrium in a special state any longer." And, drawing these conclusions, the corpus luteum degenerates and stops making progesterone. As a result, the endometrium, brought to a high state of development by this hormone, disintegrates, desquamates and bleeds; this constitutes menstruation, and, as may be concluded, menstruation is caused primarily by the failure of the corpus luteum to continue making progesterone. After the next ovulation, of course, a new corpus luteum will develop in the ovary and make more progesterone but, unless pregnancy occurs, the same sequence of events will be repeated. If pregnancy occurs, the corpus luteum does not degenerate; hence, menstruation does not occur. The reason for the corpus luteum's persisting when pregnancy occurs will be explained presently. The need for a persisting corpus luteum, and the continued secretion of progesterone, when pregnancy occurs, is obvious.

From the foregoing it may be concluded that the secondary sex characteristics that develop in the female at the time of puberty are due to the ovaries' secreting the primary sex hormone, estrogen, at this time. It may also be concluded that menstruation, which begins at the time of puberty, is due to the ovaries regularly secreting, and as regularly ceasing to secrete, the secondary hormone of the ovary, progesterone. The third conclusion that may be drawn is that the ovary begins to liberate ova and to function as an endocrine gland only because it is stimulated to do so by the gonadotrophic hormone secreted by the pars anterior of the pituitary gland. Hence, puberty is caused primarily by an anterior pituitary

hormone appearing in the circulation. Experimentally, sexual maturity can be induced in very young animals by injecting them with gonadotrophic hormone.

Why the anterior pituitary should begin to secrete gonadotrophic hormone at a certain time of life is not definitely known. Age, temperature, other hormones, physical activity, afferent impulses from the stimulation of light and other types of sensory receptors, and even psychological factors, have all been suspected of stimulating gonadotrophic secretion. The matter is complex; Matthews found that although a virgin pigeon will ovulate in the spring if it is placed in a cage with a male, or, after a slightly longer time, if it is separated from a male by a glass partition, or, after a considerably longer time if it is placed in a cage with another female, it will not ovulate if it is kept in a cage by itself unless it is provided with a mirror.

Before describing the histologic changes that occur in the ovary when it is stimulated by gonadotrophic hormone which result in its liberating an ovum from its surface and variously producing 2 hormones, we should deal briefly with the fact that the gonadotrophic hormone does not appear to be a single substance, but, instead, a complex of 2 fractions. These have different effects and are secreted in different quantities and at different times throughout the menstrual cycle. The first fraction is called the *follicle-stimulating hormone*; and the second, the *luteinizing hormone*. From now on, as is common practice, these 2 hormones will be referred to as F.S.H. and L.H., respectively. We shall now describe the effects that these 2 hormones produce on the ovary, particularly with regard to their respective effects on maturation of follicles, liberation of ova and hormone secretion.

The Development of Follicles. Of the hundreds of thousands of primary follicles present in the 2 ovaries at birth, only from 300 to 400 come to maturity and liberate oocytes from the surfaces of the ovaries after puberty. Most of the primary follicles of the ovary degenerate either as they are or after some degree of spurious development. The spurious development and the death of a follicle is termed *atresia*, and follicles showing the histologic changes of degeneration or death are termed *atretic follicles*. Their microscopic ap-

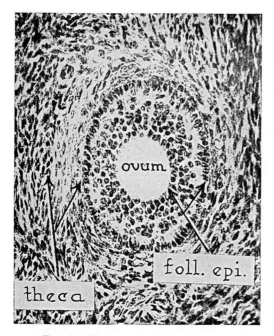

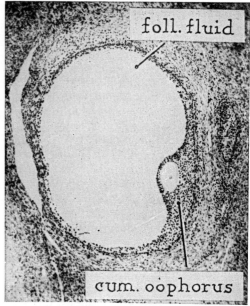

Fig. 508. Low-power photomicrograph of a section of an ovary of a mature woman, showing a follicle surrounded with stratified epithelium which has not yet begun to secrete fluid. The plane of section was such that the knife did not pass through the nucleus of the primary oocyte which is labeled "ovum." The theca may be seen indistinctly separated from the ovarian stroma.

Fig. 509. Very low-power photomicrograph of a section of an ovary of a mature woman, showing a developing follicle distended with follicular fluid and the ovum contained in a cumulus oophorus.

pearance will be described after we have considered those associated with the normal development of follicles.

A primary follicle is from 40 to 50 μ in diameter. It consists chiefly of a relatively large oogonium which is wrapped with a single layer of flattened follicular epithelial cells (Fig. 507). The nucleus of the oogonium is large and centrally disposed. Its membrane stains with moderate intensity. Chromatin granules are not prominent in it, so its interior is pale except for the nucleolus which is well-stained and prominent (see left follicle in Fig. 507). The cytoplasm is pale and contains yolk granules which are spread throughout it evenly.

The earliest sign indicating that a primary follicle is beginning to develop is given by the follicular epithelial cells. At first these become cuboidal, then columnar and then, as a result of their proliferation, stratified (Fig. 508);

the follicle is then known as a secondary follicle. In the meantime, the primary oocyte that it contains increases in size, but its growth is not proportional to that of the follicular epithelium; hence, this latter tissue soon comes to constitute the bulk of the follicle. When the primary oocyte has become somewhat more than twice its original diameter, a thick membrane that stains deeply, the *zona pellucida* (Fig. 510), develops around it. Probably both the oocyte and the innermost follicular epithelial cells contribute to its formation.

After the follicular epithelial cells, by their continued division, have come to constitute a covering for the primary oocyte, many cells thick, fluid begins to accumulate in little pools between them (Fig. 511). These pools of fluid are at first small and are seen roughly halfway between the periphery of the ovum and the border of the follicle. The precise origin of this fluid, which is called *follicular fluid*, is not known; its composition suggests that it is something more than tissue fluid, hence that it must be at least modified by the follicular cells among which it accumulates. The follicle continues to enlarge because the follicular epithelial cells continue to proliferate by mitosis and because fluid continues to accumulate between them. The smaller pools fuse with each other so that larger ones are formed, and the continuance of this process leads eventually to the bulk of the follicle coming to be composed of a large more or less central pool of fluid which is not spherical because the oocyte, which now is termed a secondary oocyte, together with the follicular cells that cover it, projects into the single large pool of fluid, like a little hill, from one side (Fig. 509). The little hill of follicular cells that contains the ovum is known as the *cumulus oophorus* (*cumulus* = a heap; *oon* = egg; *phorus* = bearer).

While the follicle is developing, as described above, the ovarian stroma that immediately surrounds the follicle becomes organized into a membrane called the *theca* (*theke* = a box). This more or less spherical box of stroma ensheathes the epithelial follicle closely. As development proceeds, the cells of the theca become differentiated into 2 layers. The innermost layer, the *theca interna*, is relatively cellular and is provided with many capillaries (Fig. 510). The outer layer, the *theca externa*, is more fibrous and not so vascular (Fig. 510). However, the line of demarcation between the 2 layers is not usually very distinct.

A fully developed follicle is so large in relation to the thickness of the cortex that it causes a bulge on the surface of the ovary (Fig. 511). Moreover, as the follicle develops it tends to move toward the surface of the ovary; hence, the cortex between the outermost part of the follicle and the surface of the ovary becomes very thin.

(*A Note on Terminology.* Gatz has recently criticized the varied and inexact terminology that is used so often in describing the development of eggs and follicles. If we interpret him correctly he suggests the following: The egg contained in a primary follicle should be termed an *oogonium*. When the epithelium of the follicle becomes stratified the follicle is termed a *secondary follicle*, and the egg that it contains, a *primary oocyte*. When the follicle matures the primary oocyte undergoes a miotic division (to be explained in the next chapter); this results in the formation of a *secondary oocyte* and a *polar body* or *polocyte*. The secondary oocyte is discharged at

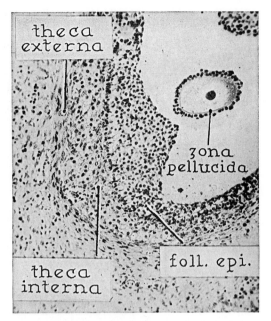

FIG. 510. Low-power photomicrograph of a section of an ovary of a mature woman, showing a developing follicle. The secondary oocyte, with some surrounding follicular epithelial cells, appears to be free in the follicle, but this appearance is probably due to the plane of the section. The oocyte shows a well-developed zona pellucida, and the 2 layers of the theca are apparent.

ovulation, and on fertilization it completes another division giving off another polocyte and becoming an *ovum* which becomes known, as soon as the male and female pronuclei it contains fuse, as a *zygote*.)

All the changes described up to this time, relating to the development of a primary follicle into a mature one that bulges from the surface of the ovary, are brought about by F.S.H. and can be demonstrated easily in young animals by administering F.S.H. to them. If F.S.H. administration is continued after mature follicles reach the surface, ovulation occurs, but this is due to the F.S.H. having stimulated estrogen production in the ovary and the estrogen in turn having stimulated the anterior pituitary to secrete L.H.; this is shown by the fact that the same dose of F.S.H. that will cause ovulation in intact animals will not cause ovulation in hypophysectomized animals (which have no pituitary glands to make L.H.).

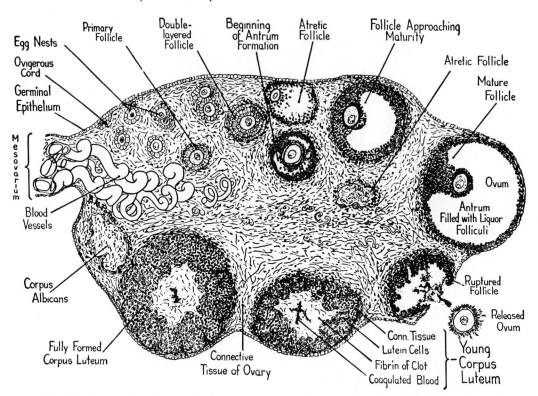

FIG. 511. Schematic diagram of an ovary, showing the sequence of events in the origin, the growth and the rupture of an ovarian (graafian) follicle and the formation and the retrogression of corpus luteum. Follow clockwise around ovary, starting at the mesovarium. (Patten, B. M.: Human Embryology, New York, Blakiston Division of McGraw-Hill)

L.H. has two actions. Its first one is to cause the follicle to burst; how it does this is not known precisely; but its causing increased vascularity in the theca interna with increased tissue fluid production is probably a factor. When the follicle bursts, the secondary oocyte, which is still surrounded by some follicular cells which comprise a *corona radiata* for it, is liberated into, or close to, the open end of the oviduct (Fig. 511).

The second action of L.H. is that of its stimulating the formation of a functional corpus luteum in the follicle from which the ovum is extruded. However, there is another school of thought which subscribes to the idea that after having acted to cause ovulation, L.H. only starts a corpus luteum on its way, and that the further growth of the corpus luteum is caused by a third anterior hormone, *luteotrophin* (which is probably the same thing as lactogenic hormone), being secreted at this time. While the role of luteotrophin is well

established in the rat, it is by no means clear that it is the hormone that makes the corpus luteum grow and secrete progesterone in man. Therefore, we shall assume that L.H. is the hormone that is instrumental in bringing about the formation of a functional corpus luteum in man.

After the ovum and part of the follicular fluid have been extruded at ovulation, the follicle collapses sufficiently to permit the edges of the wound made on the surface of the ovary by the rupture of the follicle to come together (Fig. 511). Moreover, the reduction in size of the follicle causes the remaining follicular cells and those of the theca interna to be thrown into folds (Fig. 511). Only the theca externa retains its original shape. The rupture and subsequent collapse of the follicle usually results in some bleeding (though in man this is not so much as has generally been thought in the past). The escaped plasma and red blood cells become mixed with such follicular

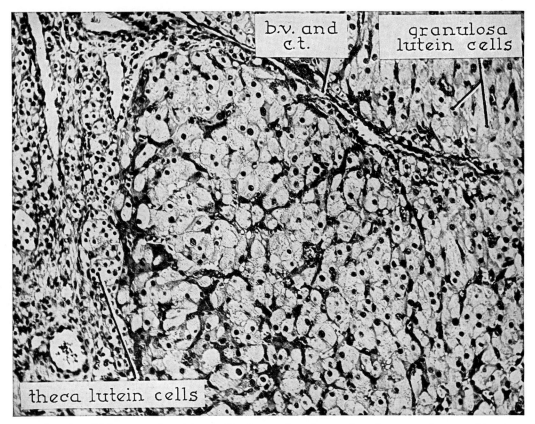

FIG. 512. High-power photomicrograph of a portion of a section of a corpus luteum of pregnancy. Observe the large, pale granulosa luteal cells with vacuoles in their cytoplasm. The theca luteal cells are smaller.

fluid as remains in the central part of the follicle. Strands of fibrin then form from the fibrinogen of the escaped plasma.

Under the continued stimulus of L.H., the follicular epithelial cells that remain in the follicle enlarge greatly (Fig. 512) to become what are called *follicular* or *granulosa lutein* cells. Their cytoplasm becomes vacuolated as a result of its accumulating lipoid. Lutein pigment also forms in their cytoplasm, but somewhat later. When enough of this accumulates it imparts a yellow color to the corpus luteum. The cells of the theca interna, that before ovulation had become enlarged and vacuolated, also become lutein cells and contribute to the size of the corpus luteum. These are called *theca lutein* cells (Fig. 512), but, although they are of a connective tissue origin, they develop many of the characteristics of granulosa lutein cells, which, of course, are of epithelial origin.

Capillaries from the theca interna grow in among the cords and the clumps of lutein cells as the latter develop; hence, the corpus luteum comes to have a fairly typical endocrine gland structure (Fig. 512). Fibroblasts from the theca interna grow into the more central part of the corpus luteum and there form an undifferentiated type of connective tissue which contains a high proportion of amorphous intercellular substance. This connective tissue tends to surround the remains of the follicular fluid and clotted blood that are still present in the central part of the corpus luteum (Fig. 511).

Following ovulation, under the continued stimulus of L.H., the corpus luteum develops for about 14 days, attaining a diameter of from 1.5 to 2 cm. (Fig. 511). Not as many mitotic figures are to be observed in it as might be expected; hence, much of the growth that it manifests over this period is probably due to its cells becoming increasingly hypertrophied. As noted before, unless the ovum, liberated from the follicle before it becomes a corpus luteum, is fertilized, the anterior pituitary gland secretes only enough L.H. to sustain the corpus luteum for about 14 days. After the secretion of L.H. fails, the corpus luteum begins to involute; this is associated with its vessels permitting blood to escape into its substance. Moreover, when L.H. fails, the corpus luteum no longer continues to secrete enough progesterone to maintain the endometrium in a luxuriant condition, so that most of it disintegrates and is cast off.

The failure of the corpus luteum, in addition to precipitating menstruation, has another effect. Previous to its failure, the corpus luteum has secreted enough progesterone into the blood stream to inhibit the anterior pituitary from secreting F.S.H. With little F.S.H. in the blood stream, the development of follicles in the ovary is not encouraged; hence, during the periods in which progesterone is secreted, follicular development comes to a standstill in the ovary. But when the progesterone level falls as a result of the failure of the corpus luteum, the anterior pituitary begins to secrete F.S.H. again; hence, follicles again begin to develop in the ovary, so, in about 2 weeks after the failure of the corpus luteum, another follicle has matured and reached the surface of the ovary. Moreover, under the stimulus of F.S.H., the ovary has also been stimulated to produce estrogen. This encourages the repair of the endometrium following menstruation, but, as its concentration in the blood stream increases, it also stimulates the anterior pituitary to begin again the secretion of L.H. When enough L.H. is secreted, ovulation occurs, and another corpus luteum forms. If pregnancy does not ensue, the whole series of events described above is repeated.

Summary of Hormonal Factors Concerned in the 28-Day Cycle

1. At the time of menstruation the anterior pituitary begins to secrete F.S.H.

2. F.S.H. causes follicles to develop in the ovary and makes the ovary secrete estrogen. After being stimulated by F.S.H. for about 2 weeks, a follicle matures and arrives at the surface of one ovary.

3. The estrogen secreted by the ovary during these 2 weeks keeps the sex organs of the female in a developed state and aids libido. Toward the end of the 2-week period, the concentration of estrogen in the blood stream becomes sufficient to stimulate the anterior pituitary to begin secreting L.H.

4. The anterior pituitary continues to secrete L.H. for about 2 weeks. The first effect of L.H. is to cause the mature follicle at the surface of the ovary to rupture; it then causes a corpus luteum to develop in the remains of the follicle and to secrete progesterone for about 2 weeks.

5. The progesterone, in general, quiets the uterine muscle and builds up the endometrium so that it is suitable for the reception and the nourishment of a fertilized ovum. It also keeps the anterior pituitary from secreting effective amounts of F.S.H., so follicular development in the ovary is stilled, and estrogen production is diminished.

6. The anterior pituitary secretes L.H. for less than 2 weeks. It stops probably because the falling blood estrogen level fails to stimulate it, and the rising progesterone level inhibits it. When it ceases secreting L.H., the corpus luteum stops making progesterone, and menstruation occurs.

7. The decreased amount of progesterone in the blood is not sufficient to inhibit the anterior pituitary, so it begins again to secrete F.S.H. The cycle is then repeated (see 1).

It should be kept in mind that the foregoing is only a working hypothesis that appears reasonable in the light of our present knowledge. Since methods for estimating the blood content of all the various hormones mentioned are not yet available, it is obvious that much in the hypothesis is based on inference from animal experiments. Another point that should be mentioned is that some investigators have questioned if there are actually 2 gonadotrophic hormones. Nevertheless, the hypothesis given above is the one that is generally adopted, and a knowledge of it has proved to be useful in the understanding and the treatment of ovulatory and menstrual disorders. However, the student will find it worth while to investigate this hypothesis a little more deeply by learning something about the sex cycles of the females of other families of the animal kingdom. These are more easily understood than those of the human female, and some knowledge of them facilitates greatly the development of a proper perspective on the cause and the nature of the changes that succeed one another in the human cycle. For this reason, and also to enable the student to keep in mind the bases for the biologic assay of hormones and the bases for pregnancy tests, the sex cycles of certain common laboratory animals will now be described.

Sex Cycles in Lower Animals

The Estrous Cycle. Anyone with a little knowledge of the breeding habits of domestic or wild animals knows that the mating impulse of the female is dormant for most of the year and becomes aroused only at certain seasons. At these times the female is said to have come into *heat* or *estrus* (*oistros* = mad desire), and only at these times will the female mate with a male. There is a wide variation among the females of different kinds of animals with respect to the number of times they come into estrus each year. In some kind, estrus occurs only once a year, in many it occurs 2 or 3 times a year, and in still others it occurs every few days.

The phenomenon of estrus is caused by the ovaries of an animal more or less suddenly secreting a large amount of estrogen. The ovaries are stimulated to do this by the anterior pituitary's secreting F.S.H. The latter hormone, as well as stimulating the ovary to secrete estrogen, also stimulates follicular growth in the ovary and brings a crop of mature follicles to its surface. In other words, F.S.H. not only prepares the stage for ovulation but, at the same time, stimulates the ovary to secrete estrogen and so makes the female eager to mate at the very time when a mating could be expected to be fertile. This is the basic reason for the dual action of F.S.H.

Estrus, as such, does not occur in the human female. However, its counterpart does occur at about the time of ovulation, because, at that time, F.S.H. has acted on the ovary both to make it secrete estrogen and to bring a follicle to its surface. But, although the amount of estrogen made by the ovary of the human female is greater at this time than at other times in the cycle, the proportional increase is not nearly so great as that which occurs in lower animals at the time of estrus. In lower animals, a greatly increased concentration of estrogen in the blood stream is the dominant factor in arousing the mating impulse of the female and in causing it to mate.

That estrogen plays a basic role in arousing the mating impulse in the human female is obvious from the changes that occur in the average girl's interests after puberty. But, although estrogen provides the physiologic basis for the development of a mating impulse in the human female, the strength of that impulse thereafter does not ebb and flow in relation to the amount of estrogen present in the blood stream to anything like the same extent that it does in the lower animals. It is true that some surveys have shown that if all other things remain constant (and they seldom do), the mating impulse of some women is somewhat enhanced at the time of ovulation and, more commonly, a short time before menstruation. The first of these examples is probably to be explained by an increased estrogen content in the blood and the second by an increased progesterone content, which acts to augment the estrogen effect. But the changes in the intensity of the impulse caused by ordinary hormonal variations are not comparable with those that are caused by psychological factors (for example, by falling in love). Indeed, the psychological factors become so much more important than the hormonal that a woman who has been happily married for many years does not necessarily experience any substantial decrease in libido if her ovaries are removed. In other words, estrogen is necessary to establish the basis on which mating reflexes of various types may be built in the human female, and after these are well established they tend to remain.

Pseudopregnancy. The events that follow estrus in the females of various kinds of animals differ considerably (provided that the female does not mate with a male). A comparison of the events that follow estrus in the rabbit, the rat and the dog families is of interest.

When an isolated female rabbit comes into estrus, ovulation does not occur automatically; instead, the female rabbit remains in estrus until it mates. However, on mating, ovulation occurs. Since ovulation depends upon the anterior pituitary's secreting L.H., it is obvious that some factor other than a relatively high blood estrogen level is necessary in some animals to cause the anterior pituitary to secrete enough L.H. to cause ovulation. If a female rabbit is mated with a sterile male, ovulation still occurs; therefore, it is obvious that ovulation does not depend on male germ cells being introduced into the female but upon such nervous stimulation as is involved in the female's mating with the male. That this nervous factor is instrumental in causing ovulation by stimulating the anterior pituitary to secrete L.H. has been shown by the fact that if the anterior pituitary is removed immediately after a female rabbit mates, ovulation does not occur. It is not known to what extent sexual excitement or the nervous stimulation involved in the mating procedure stimulates the secretion of L.H. in the human species, but the fact that it is so fundamental to L.H. secretion in some animals suggests that it could conceivably play some part in modifying the time of ovulation in the human female. However, most authorities are doubtful that it does.

If a female rabbit is mated with a sterile male, not only does ovulation occur, but corpora lutea also develop in the ovary from which the ova are liberated. These, for a time, grow and develop and make progesterone, and, as a result, the animal begins to exhibit all the signs of pregnancy except that its uterus does not contain any embryos. This false pregnancy that develops in the rabbit after it mates with a sterile male, which is due to corpora lutea growing and secreting progesterone, is called *pseudopregnancy*. It continues for a considerable time, though not for so long as a true pregnancy. Its maintenance is due presumably to the anterior pituitary's continuing to secrete L.H. for a considerable time after the act of mating. However, after a time the anterior pituitary "discovers" that true pregnancy has not occurred and it ceases to secrete L.H., and, as a result, the corpora lutea in the ovaries involute and the pseudopregnancy comes to an end. It is to be kept in mind that the termination of a pseudopregnancy in the rabbit has many points in common with menstruation in the human female.

The estrous cycle of the rat is different from that of the rabbit, for the isolated female rat remains in estrus for only a few hours and then begins a new estrous cycle. A new cycle is repeated approximately every 4 days. The rat ovulates spontaneously at the time of estrus. Nevertheless, if it does not mate, functional corpora lutea do not develop in its ovaries; hence, no progesterone is made to inhibit the anterior pituitary from secreting F.S.H., and so, after estrus, the anterior pituitary begins again to secrete F.S.H. This brings a new crop of follicles to the surface of one of the ovaries in 4 days' time and stimulates the production of enough estrogen to put the rat into estrus by the time the follicles mature.

If a female rat mates with a sterile male at the time of estrus, the sexual excitement and the nervous stimulation associated with the mating procedure cause the anterior pituitary to secrete enough L.H. to make functional corpora lutea develop in the ovary. These secrete enough progesterone into the blood stream to cause pseudopregnancy and to prevent the anterior pituitary from secreting F.S.H. and so causing a new estrous cycle to begin. Therefore, the mating of a female rat with a sterile male upsets its estrous cycle. When the pseudopregnancy has run a course of several days it terminates because the anterior pituitary ceases to secrete enough L.H. to maintain the corpora lutea. When these involute and cease making progesterone, the anterior pituitary thereupon is permitted once again to secrete F.S.H., so a new estrous cycle begins.

The estrous cycle of the female of the dog family is different still. An isolated bitch normally comes into estrus twice a year. Ovulation occurs spontaneously at estrus; evidently the high level of estrogen in the blood at the time of estrus is sufficient to cause the anterior pituitary to secrete L.H. and cause ovulation. Moreover, the anterior pituitary, following ovulation, continues to secrete L.H. for a considerable time, and, as a result, pseudopregnancy automatically follows estrus in the isolated bitch. This continues approximately half as long as a real pregnancy. Under the influence of progesterone the uterus enlarges, the belly droops, and the mammary glands begin to enlarge. Observing these phenomena, most owners of bitches who are not familiar with the phenomenon of pseudopregnancy begin to wonder if the isolation they imposed on their pets at the time of estrus was as efficient as they thought. But at about this time the pseudopregnancy terminates. The endometrium, previously built up by the action of progesterone, reverts back to its normal thickness;

this is accomplished usually without any external bleeding, although some slight hemorrhages into the substance of the endometrium have been observed.

However, the bitch does bleed externally at the time of estrus, and for many years this led medical men to assume that menstruation in the human female was comparable with estrus in lower animals. However, from many different kinds of investigation, it has now become obvious that ovulation does not commonly occur at the time of menstruation but, most commonly, a few days before the halfway point between 2 menstrual periods. The time of ovulation seems to be rather inconstant, and the evidence suggests that there are instances of its having occurred very early and very late in the cycle. It is of interest that a slight amount of bleeding occurs from the endometrium of some women at the time of ovulation; it is this rather than the bleeding of menstruation that is comparable with the estrous bleeding observed in some lower animals.

Moreover, it should be clear from the foregoing that menstruation in the human female is the counterpart of the termination of a pseudopregnancy in lower animals. It is of interest that the human female is representative of the type of animal in which ovulation occurs spontaneously; the nervous stimulation involved in mating, though it may conceivably affect the time of ovulation to some extent, is not essential for a functional corpus luteum to develop and institute pseudopregnancy. The reason for the termination of pseudopregnancy in the human female being associated with such a severe and prolonged event as menstruation, when pseudopregnancy terminates in so many lower animals with almost no disturbance, is probably to be explained by the special pattern of the blood vessels that supply the lining of the uterus in human females; these will be described later.

A little reflection on the foregoing facts should emphasize the importance of progesterone to the institution and the continuance of pregnancy. In some animals Nature is so economical that corpora lutea do not form following estrus unless the animal mates. However, in others Nature takes no chances and has arranged for functional corpora lutea to develop following ovulation even if the female does not mate at this precise time. It is of interest that if the human female were not a

representative of this type of animal it would be necessary in those instances when artificial insemination is performed to adopt measures to ensure that functional corpora lutea would develop in the ovaries.

ANOVULATORY CYCLES

In the foregoing, menstruation has been described as the result of the termination of a pseudopregnancy. However, occasionally both women and higher monkeys experience bleeding from the endometrium at the time of menstruation without previous ovulation and thus without the development of a corpus luteum in the ovary. These unusual instances of menstrual bleeding without previous ovulation (anovulatory menstruation) are probably due to preceding variations in the level of blood estrogen. We shall elaborate:

If estrogen is withdrawn, for example by removal of the ovaries from a sexually mature woman, the endometrium may bleed as a consequence. Furthermore, if estrogen is given to a female at a standard rate for a time and then the dosage is considerably reduced, but not entirely stopped, bleeding from the endometrium will occur not immediately but *only* after an interval of some days. Therefore, it is believed that the bleeding that occurs in anovulatory menstruation is to be explained as a delayed response to the reduction in the estrogen output of the ovary that occurs following the maturation of a follicle.

Anovulatory cycles in women are not rare; de Allende has shown that a perfectly healthy woman may have 3 or 4 anovulatory cycles a year with a higher proportion near puberty and the menopause.

THE CORPUS LUTEUM IN PREGNANCY

That progesterone is essential for the continuance of pregnancy already has been explained. We shall now comment briefly on how the production of progesterone is maintained when pregnancy occurs.

If pregnancy does not occur, a corpus luteum grows in the ovary of the human female for only about 14 days and reaches a diameter of from 1.5 to 2 cm. It then begins to involute because its growth and function are no longer stimulated by L.H. Some bleeding occurs into its substance, and its cells accumulate fat. As its characteristic cells degenerate further, it shrinks in size, and it finally becomes a small

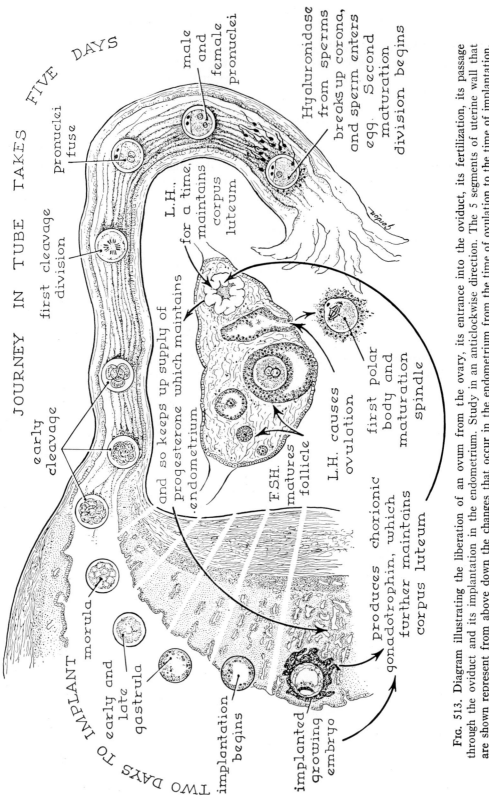

JOURNEY IN TUBE TAKES FIVE DAYS

Pronuclei fuse

first cleavage division

early cleavage

male and female pronuclei

Hyaluronidase from sperms breaks up corona, and sperm enters egg. Second maturation division begins

L.H., for a time, maintains corpus luteum

and so keeps up supply of progesterone which maintains endometrium

F.S.H. matures follicle

L.H. causes ovulation

first polar body and maturation spindle

produces chorionic gonadotrophin, which further maintains corpus luteum

morula

early and late gastrula

implantation begins

implanted growing embryo

TWO DAYS TO IMPLANT

Fig. 513. Diagram illustrating the liberation of an ovum from the ovary, its entrance into the oviduct, its fertilization, its passage through the oviduct and its implantation in the endometrium. Study in an anticlockwise direction. The 5 segments of uterine wall that are shown represent from above down the changes that occur in the endometrium from the time of ovulation to the time of implantation. (Redrawn and modified from Dickenson, R. L.: Human Sex Anatomy, Baltimore, Williams & Wilkins)

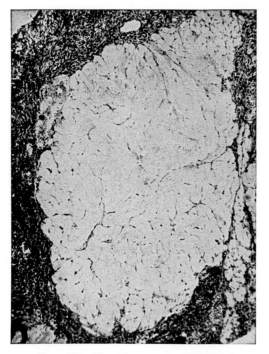

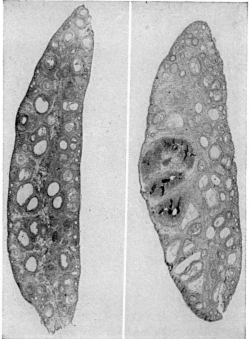

Fig. 514. Very low-power photomicrograph of a section of an ovary of a mature woman, showing a corpus albicans that has formed as a result of the degeneration of a corpus luteum of menstruation.

Fig. 515. (*Left*) Very low-power photomicrograph of a section of an ovary of a virgin rabbit that was injected with urine from a nonpregnant woman. Mature unruptured follicles may be seen close to the surface. This is the picture seen in a negative test. (*Right*) Very low-power photomicrograph of a section of the ovary of a virgin rabbit that was injected with urine from a pregnant woman. Notice that two of the surface follicles at the left side are very large and are filled with blood as a result of the occurrence of ovulation. On high-power examination, each of these may be seen to have a lining of typical granulosa luteal cells. This is the picture seen in a positive test.

white scar called a *corpus albicans* (Figs. 511 and 514).

If pregnancy occurs, the corpus luteum continues to grow and function and attains a diameter of about 5 cm. in the third month of pregnancy. At that time, or somewhat later, it begins to involute. However, the involution of a corpus luteum of pregnancy at this late date does not cause menstruation, because by this time the placenta has begun to manufacture progesterone and hence the involution of the corpus luteum of pregnancy does not cause a progesterone deficiency. Indeed, it appears that the ovary containing the corpus luteum of pregnancy may be removed much earlier than has been generally believed without interrupting the pregnancy because of the placenta's soon becoming competent to make enough progesterone to support pregnancy. The involution of a corpus luteum of pregnancy leaves a substantial scar on the ovary.

Why should pregnancy prevent a corpus luteum in an ovary from involuting 2 weeks after ovulation? A corpus luteum begins to

involute in the nonpregnant female because L.H. fails. It might be assumed, then, that pregnancy somehow prevents an L.H. failure. Actually, this is not quite what happens, but something very similar does occur. A new hormone that acts very much like L.H. is made, probably by the cells of the chorionic vesicle (later, by the placenta), soon after the ovum becomes implanted in the endometrium (Fig. 513, *lower left*). This hormone is usually called *chorionic* or *placental gonadotrophin*. It differs chiefly from L.H. in that it cannot do everything that L.H. can do in an animal from which the anterior pituitary gland has been removed. However, if such an animal is given some anterior pituitary gonadotrophic hormone, chorionic gonadotrophin then exerts an L.H. effect. In other words, given a little collaboration by the anterior pituitary, chorionic gonadotrophin acts similarly to L.H.

Pregnancy Tests. Chorionic gonadotrophin is made in abundance in pregnancy, and it is responsible for making the corpus luteum continue to grow and secrete progesterone (Fig. 513). So much chorionic gonadotrophin is made in pregnancy that it is excreted in the urine. Indeed, so much of this hormone is excreted that the urine of a pregnant woman, injected into an animal, causes profound biologic effects. This is the basis for many of the animal tests for pregnancy. An excellent and commonly employed one is the Friedman modification of the Aschheim-Zondek test. This will now be described.

It will be recalled that the virgin rabbit, on coming into estrus, remains in estrus, with mature follicles present at the surface of an ovary, until it mates with a male (Fig. 515, *left*). In other words, in the rabbit, ovulation awaits the secretion of L.H., which occurs normally only as a result of the sexual excitement and the nervous stimulation associated with the act of mating (sometimes the presence of a male in the vicinity is enough to cause enough L.H. secretion to cause ovulation; hence, males should be excluded from the testing laboratory). It is obvious that if some L.H. were injected into a virgin rabbit in estrus, ovulation would immediately occur, and it would be easy, on inspecting the ovaries of the rabbit soon afterward, to see that it had occurred, from finding hemorrhagic follicles (Fig. 515, *right*) and young corpora lutea. Likewise, if chorionic gonadotrophin were injected into a vein of a rabbit, the same results would be obtained, for this hormone, in an animal with an intact anterior pituitary gland, acts like L.H. There is so much chorionic gonadotrophin in the urine of a pregnant woman that a relatively small amount of urine injected into a vein of a virgin rabbit in estrus will cause ovulation and corpus luteum formation (Fig. 515, *right*). Since there is no chorionic gonadotrophin in the urine of a nonpregnant woman and not enough L.H. to have any

effect on a rabbit, it is obvious that the injection of urine into a virgin rabbit in estrus permits a decision to be made as to whether the urine was obtained from a pregnant or a nonpregnant woman (Fig. 515).

ATRETIC FOLLICLES

It can now be understood that the cortex of the ovary of a sexually mature nonpregnant woman who, however, has borne children, may contain a great variety of structures: primary follicles, normal follicles in various stages of development, follicles in various stages of atresia, perhaps a functioning corpus luteum of menstruation and scars of old corpora lutea of menstruation and of pregnancy. We shall now describe some of the features of some of these structures in more detail so that the student may have some general principles for differentiating among them in sections.

It is to be remembered that, out of many large follicles that are brought close to the surface of the ovary of a woman at the time of ovulation, only one usually appears to survive and liberate an oocyte. It seems probable, according to Allen, Pratt, Newell and Bland, that the other large ones all undergo atresia. They do not, then, remain in a state of suspended animation, waiting for an opportunity to ovulate in a subsequent month, but die. For ovulation to occur in another month requires that a new set of follicles develop and approach the surface.

In a given section of ovary, there may be, then, many large atretic follicles and, if they are just beginning to undergo atresia, it may be difficult to distinguish them from normal follicles. If atresia has proceeded for any length of time, the student's task is easier, for later on, in atresia, fibroblasts grow into the breaking-down follicle and replace it with connective tissue (Fig. 516, *right*). But before this occurs the detection of atresia requires the use of less obvious criteria. Two early signs of the condition are the pulling away of the follicular epithelium from the theca interna (or a break in the follicular epithelium) and pyknotic nuclei in the follicular epithelial cells. Allen *et al.* note that the cumulus oophorus becomes detached in atresia, but this, of course, cannot be established from the study of a single section. The histologic signs of cell death may, of course, be observed in the ovum

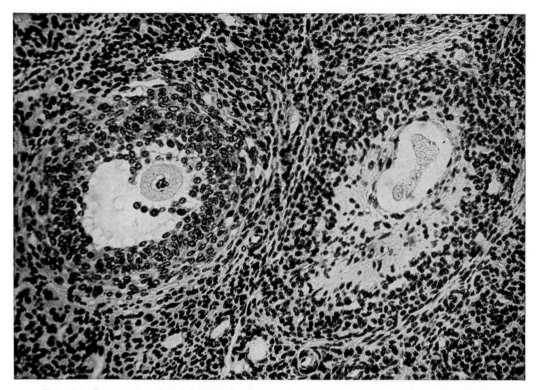

Fig. 516. Low-power photomicrograph of a section of an ovary of a guinea pig, showing a normal, developing follicle at the left and an atretic follicle at the right. Observe that the oocyte has degenerated in the atretic follicle and that fibroblasts have grown into the central part of the follicle.

in atresia, but the ovum may not be seen in the part of the follicle through which the section under view has been cut.

In distinguishing old atretic follicles from degenerate corpora lutea it is helpful to keep in mind that the term atresia is reserved for follicles that degenerate before ovulation occurs, and hence that there has been little reason for bleeding to have occurred in them. On the other hand, old corpora lutea, whether of menstruation or pregnancy, usually contain blood pigment that remains behind in them to indicate that they were once the site of a hemorrhage.

The Ovary After the Menopause

After functioning for 30 odd years, both with respect to liberating ova and secreting hormones, the ovaries appear to become exhausted and, after a short period during which they function sporadically, they finally cease liberating ova and producing hormones. When they fail to liberate oocytes there are, of course, no new corpora lutea formed, and, as a result, the endometrium thereafter neither becomes greatly thickened nor collapses each 28 days. The most obvious sign of ovarian failure, then, is that the menses cease; and, indeed, it is for that reason that this time in a woman's life is described as the *menopause* (*mēn* = month; *pausis* = cessation). The menopause usually occurs somewhere between the ages of 45 and 50, and it marks the end of the reproductive life of a woman. Actually, fertility declines rapidly during the 10 years before menopause. An artificial menopause occurs earlier if the ovaries are removed or if their function is otherwise destroyed as, for example, by irradiation or disease.

The onset of the menopause is usually indicated, though not always, by other signs and symptoms. Commonly, the function of the vasomotor nerves becomes disturbed, and women suffer from what are called "hot flushes."

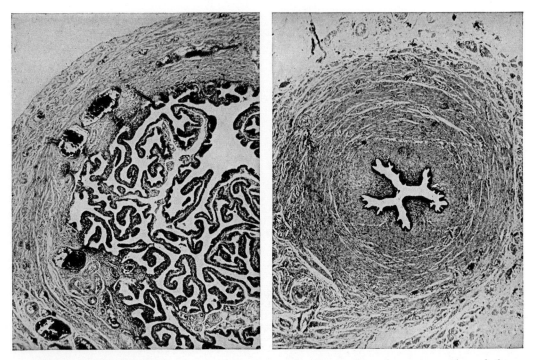

Fig. 517. (*Left*) Very low-power photomicrograph of a portion of a cross section of the ampulla of an oviduct of a mature woman. The dark areas in the muscle coat are congested veins. Observe the complex longitudinal folds that are cut in cross section. (*Right*) Very low-power photomicrograph of a cross section of the isthmus of an oviduct.

Moreover, they may find it more difficult, for a time, both from physiologic and psychological reasons, to maintain their usual adjustment to life; hence, some women exhibit a certain amount of emotional instability at this time. Indeed, in the very badly adjusted, the menopause may precipitate serious mental illness. Other symptoms, such as headache, insomnia and alterations in the rate of the heart beat, are sometimes experienced. Much can now be done to alleviate the more distressing symptoms that occur at this time by the judicious administration of sex hormones.

It should be clearly understood that the hormonal disturbances that occur at the menopause are due to ovarian failure and not to the failure of the anterior pituitary. Indeed, as the estrogen level of the blood falls after the menopause, the push-pull arrangement between estrogen and F.S.H. leads to F.S.H. being secreted in such increased amounts that fairly large quantities of it appear in the urine. Hence, if the urine of a woman who has passed the menopause is injected into a young animal,

it will stimulate follicular development and estrogen production in that young animal and so bring about a precocious puberty in it. There is no point, then, in giving a woman gonadotrophic hormone at this time to stimulate her ovaries. On the other hand, the administration of estrogen to a women at the time of the menopause could be expected to suppress, to some extent, the increased F.S.H. secretion that ordinarily occurs at this time, as well as to produce other beneficial effects.

The ovary of a woman who has recently passed the menopause is to be distinguished by the relative absence of: (1) primary follicles, (2) follicles in various stages of normal development or showing early atresia and (3) recent corpora lutea. As the years pass, the ovary becomes increasingly shrunken, consisting almost altogether of old fibrous tissue.

It seems probable that the falling-off in progesterone production is more abrupt at the menopause than the falling-off in estrogen production. New corpora lutea are necessary if progesterone production is to be carried on for any great length of time. Estrogen production by the ovary, though diminished, may be carried on for some time after the menopause. It is not entirely clear as to which cells in the ovary manufacture estrogen either before or after the menopause; such evidence as is available suggests that both the cells of the follicular epithelium and those of the theca interna of developing and mature follicles participate in the process. So, as long as epithelial and theca elements persist in the ovary, some estrogen might be produced. Moreover, it is probable that there are some, though not very important, extra-ovarian sources of estrogen in the body.

The great decrease in estrogen production that occurs at the menopause may be reflected sooner or later in substantial tissue changes in certain parts of the body. Those parts of the female reproductive tract that are dependent on this hormone for the maintenance of their structure tend to become atrophic. For example, the functional capacity of the glands associated with the external genitalia becomes diminished; the external genitalia themselves tend to atrophy, and the vaginal lining may become very thin and increasingly susceptible to infection. Substitution therapy can do much to relieve these conditions when they occur.

THE OVIDUCTS

Each oviduct (Fig. 503) is about 12 cm. long and consists of 4 parts: (1) an intramural part—that portion of the tube that extends through the wall of the uterus; (2) an isthmus—the short narrow part of the tube next to the uterus; (3) an ampulla—the longest part of the tube, about the diameter of a pencil and extending from the isthmus to, (4) an infundibulum—the flared termination of the tube provided with processes or fimbriae. The wall of the oviduct is made up of 3 layers, a mucous membrane, a muscular coat and an adventitial serous coat (Fig. 517).

Mucous Membrane. The epithelium consists of a single layer of columnar cells. There are 2 types of these, ciliated and secretory, and they alternate irregularly with one another (Fig. 518, *top*). Their relative and absolute heights vary in relation to different times in the menstrual cycle. Beginning shortly after menstruation, according to Snyder, they both increase in height, and at the time of ovula-

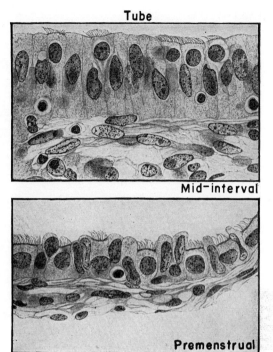

FIG. 518. (*Top*) Human oviduct about midinterval stage (camera lucida drawing; × 700). (*Bottom*) Tube at premenstrual stage (camera lucida drawing; × 700). (Snyder, F. F.: Bull. Johns Hopkins Hosp. *35*:146)

tion they are both about 30 μ high (Fig. 518, *top*). Following this, however, the ciliated cells become much shorter, and the nonciliated secretory cells, though they too become somewhat shorter, come to project between the ciliated cells into the lumen of the tube, thus making the free epithelial surface somewhat irregular (Fig. 518, *bottom*). A few small cells with dark-staining nuclei may be scattered about in the epithelial membrane close to the basement membrane. They are probably young secretory cells, although occasional lymphocytes are to be found in this site. It is not believed that the nonciliated cells become ciliated or vice versa. The cilia beat toward the uterus. Their fine structure is shown in Figure 129. The nature of the secretion of the secretory cells is not known; Novak and Everett found that it did not become colored with stains for mucin or glycogen. However, Siegler indicates that glycogen may form in the lining cells of the oviducts of immature monkeys

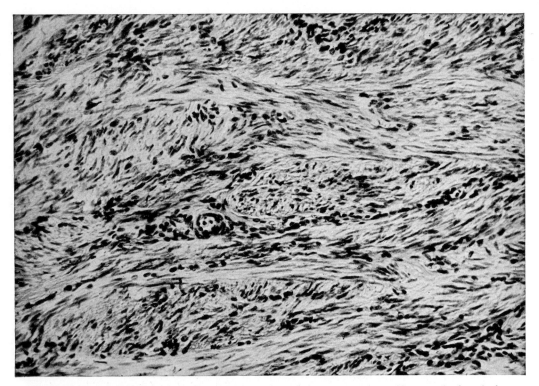

Fig. 519. Low-power photomicrograph of a section of the myometrium. Observe the interlacing bundles of smooth muscle fibers.

if the animals are injected with one of the gonadotrophic hormones. It may be assumed that the secretions in the tube, whatever they may be, are in some way nutritive or otherwise helpful for the ovum and that the hormonal stimulation of the cells concerned in making secretions occurs at a time when an ovum would be likely to be passing along the tube.

The lamina propria of the mucous membrane is of the ordinary connective tissue type except that its cells have potentialities similar to those of the endometrial stroma, for they react similarly if a fertilized ovum inadvertently becomes implanted in the mucosa of the oviduct.

As described in the general account of the parts of the reproductive system, the mucous membrane of the oviduct is thrown into extensive longitudinal folds (Fig. 517, *left*). These become reduced in size and extent in the isthmus (Fig. 517, *right*) and amount to little more than ridges in the intramural portion of the tube.

Muscle Coat. This consists of 2 layers: an inner one of circularly or somewhat spirally disposed smooth muscle fibers and an outer

one of longitudinally disposed fibers. However, the line of demarcation between the 2 layers of muscle is by no means clear-cut, and since some connective tissue extends between the bundles of muscle fibers, the muscle coats may be difficult to identify in anything more than a general way. The inner coat of circular fibers is thickest in the intramural portion of the tube and least prominent in the infundibulum. Peristalticlike movements of the muscle are believed to be accentuated around the time of ovulation. The tonus, as well as contractions of the muscle, has been shown to be affected by hormones.

The histologic structure of the serosa is typical.

THE BODY AND THE FUNDUS OF THE UTERUS

The wall of a uterus (Fig. 504) varies in thickness from 1.5 cm. to slightly less than 1 cm. It consists of 3 coats, which from without in, are (1) a thin serous coat or *serosa,* (2) a thick muscle coat or *myometrium,* (3) a mucous membrane or *endometrium.*

The serosa—in reality the peritoneal invest-

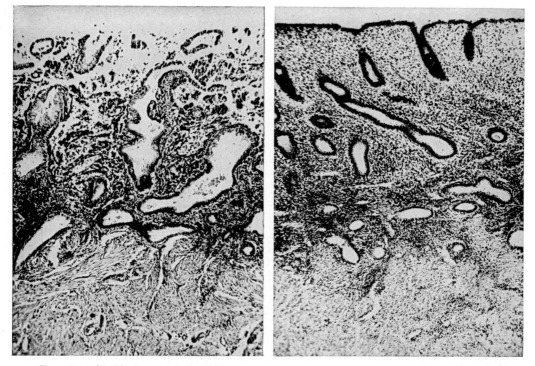

FIG. 520. (*Left*) Low-power photomicrograph of a section of the endometrium and the adjacent myometrium near the end of menstruation. Observe the raw inner surface and notice that all but the most deeply situated parts of the glands and the stroma associated with them are degenerating and being cast away. (*Right*) Low-power photomicrograph of the same region in a section taken from a uterus in which the endometrium was in an early proliferative phase. Observe that the previously raw surface has become epithelized and that the glands are straight.

ment of the organ—consists of a single layer of mesothelial cells supported by a thin connective tissue membrane; it is continuous at each side of the organ with the peritoneum of the broad ligament and is deficient in the lower half of the anterior surface (Fig. 504).

The myometrium consists of bundles of smooth muscle fibers separated from one another by connective tissue (Fig. 519). The bundles are arranged so as to form 3 rather ill-defined layers. The outermost and innermost layers are thin and consist chiefly of longitudinally and obliquely disposed fibers. The middle layer is much thicker, and in it the smooth muscle fibers tend to be disposed circularly. The larger blood vessels of the wall of the uterus are mostly contained in this middle layer; hence, it is sometimes called the *stratum vasculare*. The smooth muscle fibers in this layer, in the uterus of the nonpregnant woman, are about 0.25 mm. in length. They become 10 times as long and many times as thick during pregnancy. The great increase

in the thickness of the myometrium in pregnancy is brought about not only by a hypertrophy of previously existing fibers but also by an increase in the number of fibers; the new ones being derived, in all probability, both from the division of pre-existing fibers and from the transformation of undifferentiated cells in the connective tissue between the bundles into smooth muscle cells.

THE ENDOMETRIUM

This, the mucous membrane that lines the body and the fundus of the uterus, consists of an epithelial lining and a connective tissue lamina propria which is continuous with the myometrium. Customarily, the lamina propria is referred to as the *endometrial stroma*, and hereafter we shall use this term. The stroma is beset by simple tubular glands whose mouths open through the epithelial surface into the lumen of the uterus and whose deepest parts almost reach the myometrium (Fig. 520, *right*). The glands are composed of columnar

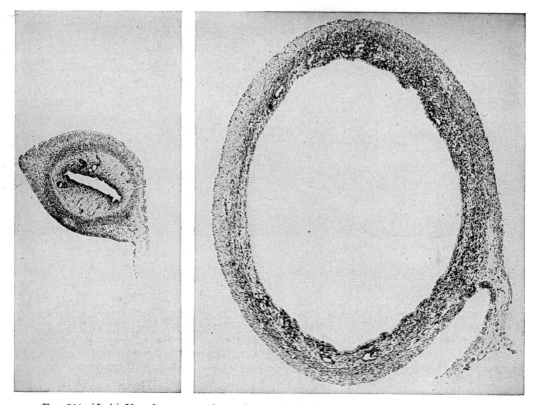

Fig. 521. (*Left*) Very low-power photomicrograph of a cross section of one horn of the uterus of a rat a month after its ovaries were removed. The uterus has atrophied as a result of estrogen deficiency. (*Right*) Photomicrograph, at the same magnification, of the same type of preparation made from a rat treated identically, except that the rat from which this specimen was obtained was given large doses of estrogen for a few days before the specimen was recovered. This illustration shows not only that estrogen makes the cells of an atrophied uterus grow but also that estrogen makes its epithelial cells secrete, for this uterus is enormously distended with secretion.

epithelium similar to that which lines the cavity of the uterus. Some of the glands branch in their deeper parts.

It is helpful to describe the endometrium as consisting of 2 chief layers: a thick superficial one, called the *functional* layer, and a thin deep one, called the *basilar* layer. The functional layer is so-called because is character changes greatly during the menstrual cycle; indeed, at menstruation it is mostly shed (Fig. 520, *left*). The character of the basilar layer does not change to any great extent during the menstrual cycle, and it remains through menstruation to regenerate another functional layer after the menstrual flow ceases.

Endometrium During the Menstrual Cycle. In the first part of this chapter, the menstrual cycle was stated to be a 28-day one. As might

be supposed, it is by no means constant; it may be a few days shorter or several days longer. Furthermore, the length of the cycle may vary in the same individual from time to time. It is usual to number the days in the cycle from the first day of menstruation; this is a concession to medical practice because the first day of menstruation is a date which a patient can set with exactitude. Most commonly, menstruation lasts for 4 days, but periods a day shorter or a day longer are common.

It is usual to describe the endometrium as passing through several different phases in each menstrual cycle. For example, the endometrium from days 1 to 4 is said to be in its *menstrual phase* (Fig. 520, *left*). From day 4 until a day or two after ovulation the endometrium is said to be in its *estrogenic, pro-*

liferative, reparative or *follicular phase* (Fig. 520, *right*). During this time it grows from something less than 1 mm. to 2 or 3 mm. in thickness. Its growth during this period is encouraged by the estrogen that is being secreted by the ovary as a follicle matures and approaches the surface (hence the terms estrogenic and follicular). Figure 521 illustrates how potently estrogen can affect the growth of the uterus. After ovulation occurs it probably takes the corpus luteum that develops a day or two to secrete enough progesterone to affect the endometrium, and since the estrogenic phase lasts until the progestational phase begins, the estrogenic phase can be considered to last a day or two past the time of ovulation. The last day of the estrogenic phase cannot be set with any exactitude because of the variability of the time of ovulation. Such evidence as exists is somewhat conflicting, but ovulation probably occurs somewhere between days 8 and 20 and rarely before or after this period (see Siegler: *Fertility in Women*). With the understanding that the time of ovulation varies considerably, for convenience we shall say that it occurs at day 14 and, therefore, that the endometrium is in its estrogenic phase from days 4 to 16. In some part of the endometrium this phase probably begins even before day 4. The latter part of the estrogenic phase is often termed the *interval phase*. This term is used to depict that period that ensues after the endometrium has become thoroughly repaired but has not yet begun to be affected by progesterone. The last phase of the menstrual cycle is called either: (1) the *progestational phase,* because the changes that occur in the endometrium during this phase are due to the action of progesterone, or (2) the *progravid* (*gravid* = heavy, pregnant) *phase,* because pregnancy, when it occurs, begins in this phase, or (3) the *secretory phase,* because the epithelial cells of the glands actively secrete at this time. This phase begins about 2 days after ovulation and lasts normally for 12 to 14 days. That the corpus luteum grows and functions for about 14 to 16 days seems to be a much more constant phenomenon in the menstrual cycle than the time of ovulation. The last day or two of the progestational phase is sometimes called the *ischemic* (*ischo* = I keep back; *haima* = blood) *phase* because the vessels that supply the more super-

ficial parts of the functional layer of the endometrium become shut off for variable periods during this time, and the endometrium suffers from a lack of blood supply, as will be described in more detail later.

Relation of the Progestational Phase to Fertility. As has been noted, the purpose of the endometrial changes that occur during the menstrual cycle is to ensure that the endometrium is freshly and suitably prepared each lunar month for the reception of a fertilized ovum. The special preparation required for this purpose is brought about by progesterone (however, estrogen provides the basis on which the progesterone effect is exerted). Since an ovum cannot be fertilized before it is liberated from the ovary, there is no point in progesterone's being secreted, and the endometrium's being prepared for the ovum's reception, before the time of ovulation. However, it might be thought that since it takes the corpus luteum that develops after ovulation a day or two to secrete enough progesterone to begin to affect the endometrium, a promptly fertilized ovum might conceivably seek implantation before the endometrium was in a well-developed progestational phase. However, it seems probable that a fertilized ovum usually seeks implantation in the endometrium when the endometrium is in almost exactly the right condition for its reception. We shall elaborate:

Such evidence as is available suggests that an ovum is capable of being fertilized for only a day or two after ovulation. Although estimates vary about the possible life of male germ cells in the female genital tract, it does not seem probable that they remain capable of fertilizing an ovum for more than a very few days after they are introduced into the female genital tract. Therefore, if sexual intercourse is to be fertile, it is important that it should be performed as close as possible to the time of ovulation. Since the time of ovulation varies, those doctors interested in the treatment of sterility are exploring ways and means for determining the time of ovulation fairly precisely by various tests (see Farris: *Human Ovulation and Fertility*). It seems probable that an ovum, fertilized promptly after ovulation, takes 5 days to traverse the oviduct and then probably a few more days to become implanted in the endometrium (Fig.

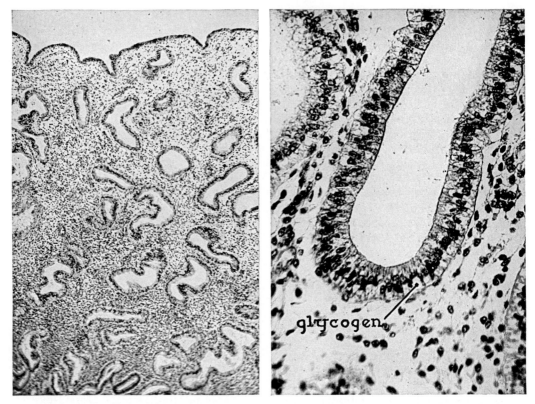

FIG. 522. (*Left*) Low-power photomicrograph of the inner portion of the endometrium in the early progestational phase. (*Right*) High-power photomicrograph of one of the glands. At this stage glycogen is present between the nuclei and the bases of their cells.

513). By this time progesterone has been acting on the endometrium for about a week, and this is time enough for the endometrium to have become properly prepared for the fertilized ovum's reception and future nourishment.

Details of Microscopic Appearance in Different Phases. It is convenient to describe first the structure of the endometrium in the later stages of the estrogenic phase (the interval phase). The endometrium at this time is from 2 to 3 mm. thick. The epithelial cells that line the surface and comprise the glands are low columnar in form. Most of them are secretory, but the mucus they secrete at this time is thin and watery. A little glycogen is present in their cytoplasm. Patches of ciliated columnar cells are scattered about among the secretory cells. The glands in the functional layer of the endometrium tend to be narrow and straight. The stroma consists of star-shaped mesenchymal cells whose cytoplasmic processes connect with each other. The cells are adherent to a network of reticular fibers. Metachromatically staining amorphous intercellular substance is not so abundant at this time as somewhat earlier. Leukocytes are not common in the stroma in this phase.

In the progestational phase the endometrium becomes more than twice as thick as it was in the interval phase. The increase in thickness is partly due to the cells of the gland and the stroma dividing by mitosis, partly due to increased amounts of tissue fluid in the stroma (edema) and partly due to the glands' accumulating increased amounts of secretion. Except in the more superficial part of the functional layer and in the basal layer, the glands become wide, tortuous and sacculated (Figs. 522, *left*, and 523). Their cells come to contain considerable amounts of glycogen. At first this accumulates between the nuclei and the bases of the cells (Fig. 522, *right*), but later it appears between the nuclei and the free borders of the cells; the latter thereupon become ragged in appearance (Fig. 523). The mucous secretion in the glands becomes much thicker and more abundant than formerly. The cells of the stroma begin to enlarge and become very sensitive to physical stimuli and respond quickly to invasion (by a fertilized ovum or even by experimentally introduced objects) by undergoing what is called a *decidual reaction* (the word decidua, *deciduus* = a falling off, refers to the membrane into which the functional zone of the endometrium becomes transformed during pregnancy and is cast off at the time of birth). Stroma cells evidence this reaction by becoming large and pale, and their cytoplasm comes to contain glycogen and lipoid droplets. Some degree of decidual reaction occurs even without an implantation stimulus.

The changes that occur in all but the latter part of the progestational phase are due to the action of progesterone, working in collaboration with such estrogen as is still present in the circulation. It is presumed that, in general, these changes are designed to make the endometrium nutritive for a fertilized ovum; for example, the glycogen that forms may serve as a readily available form of carbohydrate.

The changes that occur toward the end of the progestational phase, provided that pregnancy does not occur, have been described by Markee. This investigator studied them by implanting bits of the endometrium of monkeys into the anterior chambers of their eyes, where they became vascularized and could be observed directly for hours. Markee found that the endometrium, toward the end of what we have termed the progestational phase, begins to regress (shrink). Regression, according to Markee, always precedes menstrual bleeding. In order to explain how the regression of the endometrium, which in all probability occurs because of the decreasing stimulation of both estrogen and progesterone at this time, may act to institute bleeding in, and the breakdown of, the functional layer of the endometrium, we must first describe the special features of the blood supply of the endometrium.

Blood Supply of the Endometrium. Daron has studied the arterial supply of the endometrium of the monkey in the various phases of

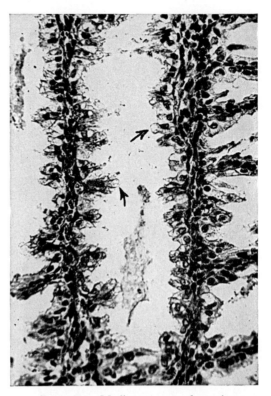

Fig. 523. Medium-power photomicrograph of a section of endometrium in the late progestational phase. Observe the ladderlike appearance of the gland photographed and note that the free borders of the cells of the gland are ragged because there is glycogen at this site.

the menstrual cycle by injecting the blood vessels of the animal and then freezing and fixing the uterus in situ. Both cleared thick sections and ordinary serial sections were used in his study. Essentially, he found that 2 types of arteries lead from the stratum vascularis of the myometrium to the endometrium. Those of the first type, on approaching the endometrium, assume a coiled form and, without branching to any great extent, maintain their coiled form as they extend through the endometrium to its superficial part; there they terminate in a fountainlike arrangement of precapillary arterioles which supply the capillary beds of the inner part of the endometrium. The second type of artery that Daron describes extends from the stratum vascularis of the myometrium to end, after pur-

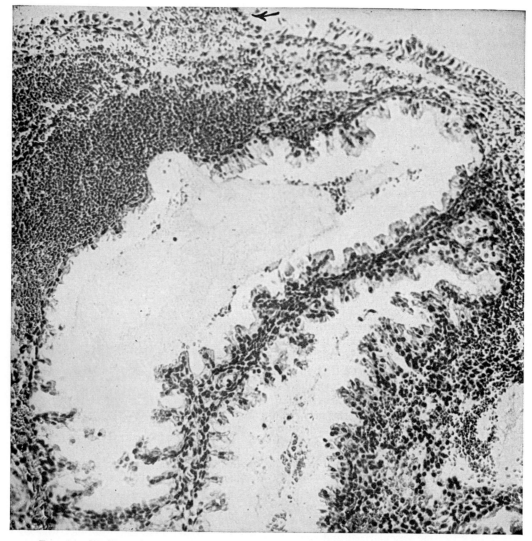

Fig. 524. Medium-power photomicrograph of a section of endometrium at the beginning of menstruation. Observe that a pool of blood has formed in the stroma (*upper left*), that the epithelial lining of the uterus has become discontinuous in the upper middle part of the picture, and that red blood cells are entering the lumen of the uterus at the site indicated by the arrow.

suing a straight course, in the deeper (outer) layer of the endometrium. The blood supply of at least the more superficial (inner) part of the functional layer of the endometrium, then, is derived from the coiled arteries.

Ischemic and Menstrual Phases. The coiled arteries are of the greatest importance in menstruation; indeed, the phenomenon of menstruation occurs only in those few members of the animal kingdom in which the endometrium of the female has this particular type of blood vessel. Markee has paid particular attention

to the changes that occur in these vessels in the latter parts of the progestational phase. He finds that, as the endometrium regresses, the coiled arteries become increasingly coiled to accommodate themselves to the thinning endometrium. As menstruation approaches, the circulation in them slows, and beginning the day before menstruation, the coiled arteries, one by one, become constricted for prolonged periods of time so that the endometrium that lies over them becomes blanched. After a coiled artery has remained constricted for a time, it dilates, and as blood once more reaches the arterioles and capillaries supplied by the artery (these have suffered from a lack of blood supply during the period of vasoconstriction) it escapes through their walls into the stroma. By this means little pools of blood accumulate beneath the endometrial surface (Fig. 524). These soon rupture through the epithelium into the uterine cavity (Fig. 524, *top*). Meanwhile, the coiled artery concerned has become constricted again, and its terminal portions die. The same sequence of events is repeated in other arteries. As small pieces of endometrium become detached, arterioles may bleed directly onto the surface rather than into the stroma. As the deeper parts of the functional layer become involved, veins become opened, and they too slowly bleed. Eventually, over a few days, most of the functional layer of the endometrium is lost.

The cause of the progressive disintegration of the endometrium appears to be a lack of blood supply. That the functional layer of the endometrium is supplied by coiled end-arteries facilitates the effectiveness of vasoconstriction in causing an almost complete ischemia of the inner part of the endometrium. That the endometrium regresses and so causes the coiled arteries to become more or less buckled before menstruation, probably further facilitates the effectiveness of the vasoconstriction process in causing the necrosis of the endometrium. The reason for the basal layer's not being lost during menstruation lies in its different blood supply.

The cause of the regression of the endometrium in the latter stages of the progestational phase, and the vasoconstriction of the coiled arteries that follows in its wake, is hormone deficiency. Although both estrogen and progesterone are deficient at this time, progesterone failure is the more important precipitating factor; indeed, menstruation can be delayed by the administration of extra progesterone. The student, then, may find it helpful to think of menstruation as the result of the termination of a pseudopregnancy in the uterus of an animal in which the more superficial part of the endometrium is supplied by coiled arteries. Nevertheless, it is to be kept in mind that a reduction in the blood estrogen from the level attained in the midpart of the cycle plays some part in the process, for in anovulatory cycles (which are less common in women but occur commonly in some seasons in monkeys), bleeding occurs at the regular time for menstruation without ovulation's having occurred, without a corpus luteum's having formed, without progesterone's having been secreted and without the endometrium's having passed through a proper progestational phase. Hence, estrogen withdrawal, as it is often termed, can, by itself, cause retraction of the endometrium and bleeding from coiled arteries. Nevertheless, in women it is commonly progesterone failure that precipitates the endometrial breakdown.

Early Part of Estrogenic Phase. The basal layer of the endometrium, with its separate arterial supply, is left intact throughout the cycle (Fig. 520, *left*). When the menstrual phase has run its course, the epithelium from the glands grows out over the denuded surface and rapidly covers it again (Fig. 520, *right*). Mitotic figures become numerous both in the gland and in the stroma cells. Amorphous intercellular substance is formed in noticeable amounts in the stroma; according to both S. H. Bensley and Sylvén, this precedes the substantial formation of reticular fibers, and the amount of it decreases as the fibers develop. Repair is so rapid that an interval type of endometrium is soon produced.

THE PLACENTA

Some General Considerations. The placenta is an organ that develops during pregnancy in the lining of the uterus. When fully developed it has the shape of a flat cake (*placenta* = cake), approximately 15 cm. in diameter and 3 cm. in thickness. As we shall see, it develops partly from the fetus and partly from the mother. Its primary function is to permit substances dissolved in the blood of the fetus to diffuse into the blood of the mother and vice versa. Its design permits this to occur over a vast area. Under normal conditions the blood of the fetus and the blood of the mother neither mix nor come into direct contact with one another. They are always separated by what is termed the placental barrier; this, as we shall see, is a membrane composed of certain tissues. In the placenta, food and oxygen, dissolved in the mother's blood, diffuse through the placental barrier into the blood stream of the fetus, and by this means life and growth

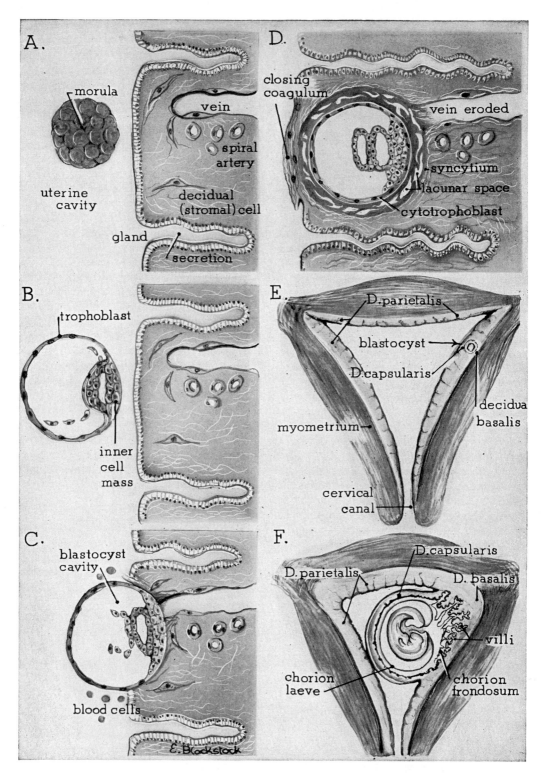

FIG. 525. Diagrams A, B, C and D illustrate the stages in the formation of the blastocyst and the embedding of the blastocyst in the uterine wall. The relationships of the growing embryo to the uterus are shown in diagrams E and F.

are supported in the fetus until it is born. Likewise, waste products dissolve through the barrier from the blood of the fetus to that of the mother and are eliminated by the mother's excretory organs. Blood passes to and fro from the fetus to the placenta by means of blood vessels in the umbilical cord; the latter structure connects the fetus to the placenta during pregnancy. At birth the fetus is expressed from the uterus, still connected by means of the umbilical cord to the placenta. One task of the attending physician is to tie the umbilical cord, for soon after the delivery of the baby the placenta is expressed from the uterus; hence, it can no longer perform its function. Indeed, after it becomes detached from the lining of the uterus its detached surface represents an open wound from which the fetus could bleed if its cord were not tied.

Development. Fertilization of the ovum usually occurs in the uterine tube (Fig. 513). The ovum then passes along the tube, taking about 4 days to reach the uterus. By this time several cell divisions have occurred, and it consists of a clump of cells. Since it now resembles a mulberry (Fig. 325 A) it is called a *morula*. A cavity then appears in this previously solid mass of cells after which it is called a *blastocyst* ("cyst" because it has a cavity and "blasto" because it will form something) (Fig. 525 B). The blastocyst remains free in the uterine cavity for only 2 or 3 days (Fig. 525 B), after which it becomes *implanted* in the wall of the uterus (Figs. 525 C and D). Usually, therefore, implantation begins 6 or 7 days after fertilization. At this time, the endometrium (Fig. 522) has been under the influence of progesterone for several days; hence, it is "receptive" toward the ovum. The site of implantation may be anywhere on the wall of the uterus but usually is high up toward the fundus on the anterior or the posterior wall (Fig. 525 E).

The wall of the blastocyst (Fig. 525 B and C) is, at first, composed of a single layer of cells called the *trophoblast* (*trephein* = to nourish, *blastos* = germ) because the cells of this layer obtain nourishment for the embryo that will develop inside the blastocyst (Fig. 525 C) from a mass of cells called the *inner cell mass* (Fig. 525 B). In describing the formation of the placenta we shall not concern ourselves with the further history of the inner cell mass; this is done in textbooks of embryology.

The trophoblast of the blastocyst becomes fixed to the free surface of the endometrial epithelium. At the point of contact the cells of the trophoblast proliferate to become several cells thick (Fig. 525 C). The uterine epithelium breaks down at this point, probably because of the enzymatic activity of the trophoblast. This leaves a gap in the uterine lining which permits the blastocyst to sink into the endometrial stroma (Fig. 525 C and D). The defect in the endometrium is closed temporarily by a plug of fibrin and cellular debris called the closing coagulum (Fig. 525 D). Later, the endometrial epithelium grows over the embedded blastocyst to restore the uterine lining. The blastocyst then lies surrounded by stromal cells in the superficial layer of the endometrium (Fig. 526).

By the 11th day after fertilization the cells of the trophoblast have divided and formed 2 layers. The cells of the inner layer are well defined; this layer is called the *cytotrophoblast* because it is clearly composed of many individual cells (Fig. 527, *top*). The outer layer is much thicker and does not consist of well-defined cells but of a continuous mass of cytoplasm containing many nuclei (Fig. 527). Since the cells of this layer are joined together, this layer constitutes a syncytium (*syn* = together), and the layer itself is called the *syncytiotrophoblast* (Figs. 525 D, 526 and 527). At this stage there are a few small spaces, called *lacunae* or *lakes* in the syncytium. By the 15th day these have increased in size and often become confluent. Moreover, they are filled with blood from the uterine veins and the venous sinuses which the trophoblast has eroded. Only later does the trophoblast erode maternal (spiral) arteries so that these too deliver blood into these spaces.

As the lacunae enlarge, the strands of trophoblast left between them are called *primary trophoblastic villi* (Fig. 526). Each villus consists of a core of cytotrophoblast covered with an outer irregular layer of syncytiotrophoblast. The villi that extend out from the blastocyst around its whole periphery come into contact with the endometrium in which the blastocyst is buried, and cells from the

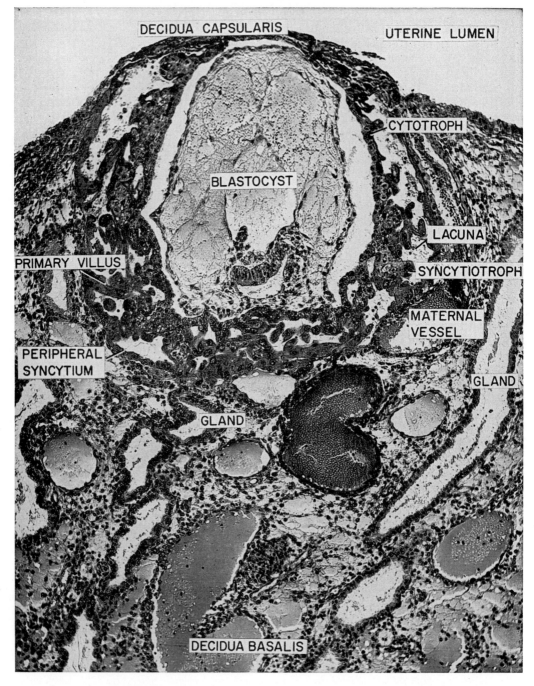

Fig. 526. This photomicrograph is of an embryo 12 days after fertilization (the Barnes embryo) embedded in the uterine wall. Primary villi, lacunae, blastocystic trophoblast and inner cell mass are shown. (There is an artefactual space between the trophoblast and the developing mesoderm.) In the uterine mucosa (decidua), glands and maternal blood vessels are seen with decidual cells in the stroma. (This embryo is approximately at the stage illustrated diagrammatically in Figure 525 D.) (From Prof. W. J. Hamilton)

villi apply themselves to the endometrium to form a lining for the cavity in the endometrium in which the blastocyst lies (Fig. 525 D). This lining of the cavity is peripheral to the blastocyst, and so it is called the peripheral syncytium. Hence, at this time, trophoblast cells form a covering for the blastocyst and a lining for the cavity in which it lies, and between the two are strands of cells, the villi, which partially separate lacunar spaces (Fig. 525 D), which are filled with maternal blood. Soon the peripheral syncytium is replaced by cells of the cytotrophoblast which come from the cores of the villi, and when this has happened the cavity in the endometrium in which the blastocyst lies is lined with cytotrophoblastic cells. When the lining is constituted of these it is referred to as the *trophoblastic shell*.

Up until the 15th day villi consist of cytotrophoblast covered by syncytiotrophoblast. The mechanism of their growth is not absolutely clear. Mitoses are common in cytotrophoblast but not very common in the syncytiotrophoblast. It would seem that the latter grows by cells of the cytotrophoblast fusing to become syncytiotrophoblast and perhaps also as a result of amitosis occurring in syncytiotrophoblast.

The structure of the villi begins to change around the 15th day. By this time the different germ layers are forming in the embryo, and mesoderm has grown out from the developing embryo to form a lining for the trophoblast that surrounds the blastocyst. When the trophoblast has gained a lining of mesoderm it is called the *chorion* (*chorion* = skin). The mesoderm from the chorion then extends into the villi to provide them with mesodermal cores; when this happens the villi are called *secondary* or *definitive villi*. These grow and branch. Fetal blood vessels develop in the mesoderm in their cores, and later these vessels become connected with the fetal circulation.

So far the changes that have been occurring in the trophoblast have taken place all around the periphery of the blastocyst. From here on, developments differ in various sites around the circumference of the blastocyst. To explain these we must introduce some further terms.

The endometrium that lies between the blastocyst and the myometrium is called the *basal plate* (Fig. 525 E, *decidua basalis*), and it is on this side of the blastocyst that the placenta will develop from the chorion. This is accomplished by the villi (with their cores of mesoderm) continuing in this site to grow and branch. In so doing they, of course, continue to destroy and erode more and more endometrium. As they do this, the raw surface of the endometrium, as it becomes exposed, becomes covered with cytotrophoblastic cells from the tips of the villi. Since the lacunae between villi are filled with maternal blood and the capillaries of the villi with fetal blood, diffusion of dissolved substances can occur between the maternal blood in the lacunar spaces and the fetal blood in the capillaries of the villi.

The processes that are described above in the region of the basal plate lead to the formation of the placenta; this will be described in more detail presently.

The Fetal Membranes; the Deciduae. All but the deepest layer of the endometrium of the uterus is shed when a baby is born. Since this portion of the endometrium of the pregnant uterus is destined to be shed, much like the leaves of deciduous trees in the Fall, all but the deepest layer of the endometrium in a pregnant uterus is referred to as the *decidua* (Fig. 525 E). Various areas of the decidua are called by different names which designate their positions relative to the site of the implanted ovum.

The *decidua parietalis* (*parietal* means forming, or situated on, a wall) lines the entire pregnant uterus except that in the area where the placenta is forming (Fig. 525 F).

The *decidua capsularis* is the portion of endometrium that overlies the developing embryo; it forms a *capsule* over it (Fig. 525 E and F). As the embryo becomes larger the decidua capsularis has to cover a larger and larger area, and it becomes very thin and atrophic. After 3 months, the size of the chorionic sac that contains the embryo has become so large that the decidua capsularis comes into contact with the decidua parietalis at the opposite surface of the uterus; hence, the uterine cavity is obliterated. Thereupon, the decidua capsularis blends with the decidua parietalis and as it does so it disappears as a separate layer.

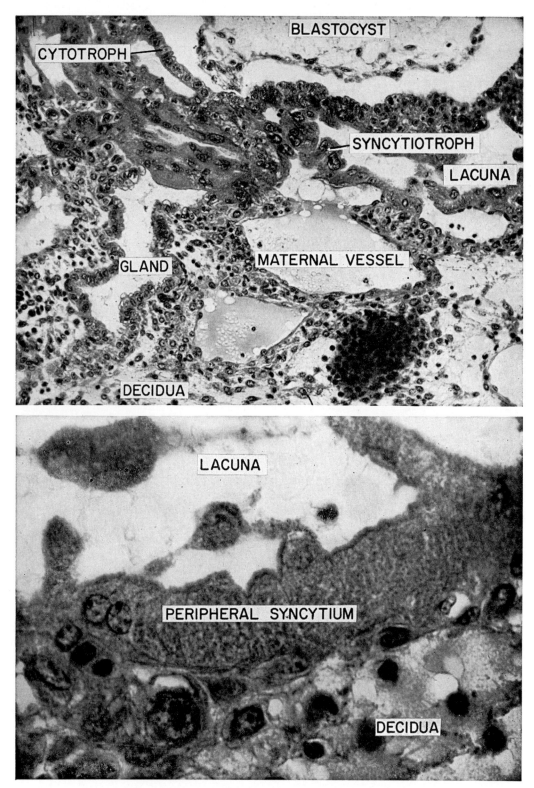

FIG. 527. (*Top*) Part of a 12-day implantation site. Lacunae are lined by syncytium; the latter has eroded a maternal artery and a uterine gland. The space near the top between embryonic membrane and trophoblast is an artefact. (*Bottom*) Site of contact between syncytium and maternal decidua. Note absence of cell boundaries in syncytium. (Both photomicrographs from Professors J. D. Boyd and W. J. Hamilton)

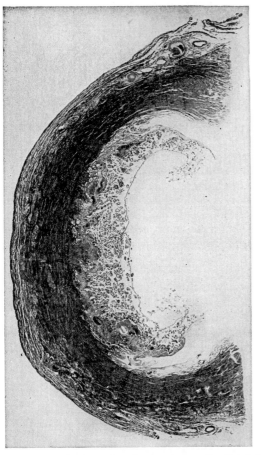

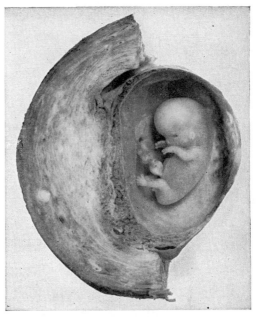

Fig. 528. (A, Left) This low-power photomicrograph is of part of the uterus with the placenta in situ, showing numerous villi cut in cross section lying in the intervillous space. The embryo, which was 15 mm. long, has been removed. (B, *Right*) This photograph is of part of the uterine wall with the placenta, fetus and fetal membranes. On the right, the wall of the chorionic sac (in which the fetus lies) is smooth. This is the chorion laeve. On the left, the fetal part of the placenta is formed by the chorion frondosum. This embryo was 36 mm. long. (From Professors J. D. Boyd and W. J. Hamilton)

The *decidua basalis* consists of the compact zone of the endometrium that lies between the chorionic sac and its contained embryo and the basal layer of the endometrium (Figs. 525 F, 528 A and B). The decidua basalis becomes the maternal part of the placenta.

Until about 12 to 16 weeks, the entire surface of the chorionic sac is covered with chorionic villi. As the sac enlarges those villi associated with the decidua capsularis degenerate and disappear, so that by 16 weeks the greater part of the surface of the sac is smooth. This large area is called the *chorion laeve* (*levis* = smooth) (Figs. 525 F and 528 B). The remainder of the surface of the sac, that is, the part adjacent to the decidua basalis, continues to be covered with villi which keep growing and branching. This part, which constitutes the fetal part of the placenta, is called the *chorion frondosum* (Figs. 525 F, 528 A and B). By 16 weeks, the placenta is discoid in shape, consisting of the chorion frondosum and the associated decidua basalis. At the time of birth, the placenta occupies about 30 per cent of the internal surface of the expanded uterus. The progressive increase in its thickness from around the 3rd to the 7th month is due mainly to the villi becoming elongated. The relative weights of placenta and fetus at various stages of pregnancy are: 1 month, 6:1; 4 months, 1:1; birth, 1:7. At birth the placenta weighs about 450 Gm., is 15 to 20 cm. in diameter and about 3 cm. thick.

HISTOLOGY OF THE PLACENTA

The Villus. The most important structure in

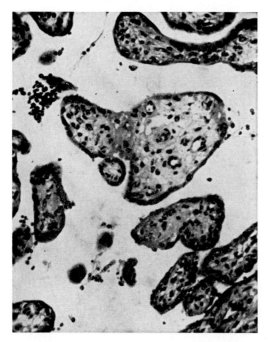

FIG. 529. This photomicrograph is of a section of a mature placenta showing villi lying in the intervillous space. Each villus is covered by a thin layer of syncytiotrophoblast and contains fetal capillaries and mesoderm.

the placenta is the chorionic villus. The early villus is a compact, bushlike tuft with its base attached to, and arising from, the chorion and its tip attached to the decidua (Fig. 526). By the 2nd month, side branches are formed with free tips, many of which later fuse with similar branches of adjacent villi to create a villous spongework. It is doubtful if such fusion permits anastomosis between fetal blood vessels contained in the respective cores of fusing villi. However, the cytotrophoblast at the tips of the main villi fuses to form a continuous placental covering for the eroded surface of the decidua basalis. In the fully formed human placenta, there are usually 8 to 15 large villi, each of which, together with its many branches, forms a *fetal cotyledon*, i.e., a fetal lobule.

Villi are alike histologically. A section of placenta cuts villi in all planes, and between them is maternal blood. From any one section of placenta viewed under the microscope, it is difficult for the student to visualize the

morphology and the physiology of the respective fetal and maternal circulations, which will be described later, but the student can examine the tissue layers that comprise the *placental barrier* that separates fetal from maternal blood.

In each villus there is a fetal capillary blood vessel lined with typical endothelium, with the endothelial nuclei protruding into the lumen (Fig. 529). The capillary is contained in the loose connective tissue core of the villus. In the core there are some scattered smooth muscle fibers; recently these have been described by Arey as spindle-shaped or branching cells containing demonstrable myofibrils. Larger cells with large spherical nuclei (the cells of Hofbauer) also are seen in the cores of villi; possibly these are phagocytic. The trophoblast covering each villus consist of two well-defined layers until approximately the middle of the 3rd month of pregnancy, after which the cytotrophoblast progressively disappears until at term only isolated clumps of its cells are left.

The cytotrophoblast, also called Langhan's layer, consists of large, discrete, pale cells with relatively large nuclei; the cells rest on a well-defined basement membrane. Their cytoplasm contains vacuoles and some glycogen but no lipid. Wislocki and Bennett considered the vacuoles to be an expression of metabolic exchange instead of a sign of degeneration. Under the E/M the cells of the cytotrophoblast, as described by Wislocki and Dempsey, reveal glycogen, mitochondria and ergastoplasm, the last being equivalent to the cytoplasmic basophilia seen with the light microscope. They found also some material of high electron density located interstitially between cells; this they consider to be iron, which is known to be abundant in the tissue.

The syncytiotrophoblast is a dark, variably thick layer in which numerous small nuclei are irregularly dispersed (Fig. 527 B). This layer becomes progressively thinner throughout pregnancy. Its outer surface has an irregular border, which often shows cytoplasmic streamers, an appearance which suggests a considerable plasticity of the cells during life. The E/M shows the outer surface to have many microvilli. The cytoplasm ranges from being delicately vacuolated to foamy. It contains mitochondria, Golgi material and lipid droplets. The lipid droplets may be very large and abundant early in pregnancy, but later they become smaller and less numerous. Glycogen is usually absent, or present in very small amounts. After the cytotrophoblast has disappeared the syncytiotrophoblast rests on a condensed network of reticular fibers.

By the time of birth, the layers of tissue that constitute the placental barrier between maternal and fetal blood become very thin (Fig. 529). The outermost layer consists of only a thin layer of syncytium in which a few mitochondria and fat droplets are visible. The cytotrophoblast has mostly disappeared with only occasional cells persisting beneath the layer of syncytium. The middle layer is delicate connective tissue consisting chiefly of reticular fibers. The innermost layer is the endothelium of the fetal capillaries. Wislocki and Dempsey, with the E/M, describe the placental barrier as consisting of a layer of syncytium bearing microvilli, a stout basement membrane, a connective-tissue space containing collagenic fibrils, a basement membrane around the capillary and finally the endothelium of the fetal capillary.

At intervals along a villus the syncytium is aggregated into protuberances of cytoplasm that contain many nuclei; these protuberances are called *syncytial knots* or *sprouts*. It is known that some of these syncytial sprouts break off to become free in the intervillous space; from here they can pass to the maternal circulation and on to the lungs of the mother.

Present in young placentae and becoming increasingly abundant in older placentae are irregular masses of an eosinophilic, homogeneous substance called *fibrinoid*. Its amount increases progressively during pregnancy; this gives an indication of the age of a placenta. At birth aggregations of it may be visible to the naked eye. Such masses have a white appearance and are called *white infarcts*. In sections, fibrinoid is eosinophilic.

As already noted, the maternal part of the placenta consists of the decidua basalis.

The zone where the trophoblastic shell is in contact with the endometrium is variously called the *junctional, composite,* or *penetration zone*. The last term relates to the fact that during the growth of the placenta the maternal tissue undergoes degeneration and necrosis in this zone as it is penetrated by trophoblastic villi. In this zone, it is possible to distinguish decidual cells (derived from endometrial stroma) from cytotrophoblastic cells because the former are surrounded with collagenic and reticular fibers, but the latter have no fibrillar material between them. The endometrial stromal cells of the decidua basalis almost all take on the appearance of *decidual* cells; they become large, polygonal, and rich in glycogen and lipid droplets. The epithelial cells lining the endometrial glands during pregnancy are rich in mitochondria, glycogen and lipid droplets. By the 3rd month, these glands in the decidua basalis are stretched and appear as horizontal clefts. The decidua basalis as a whole (the basal plate) consists chiefly of a connective tissue stroma, the cells of which are of the decidual type, endometrial glands, fibrinoid, and small clumps of trophoblast cells are also present. As Boyd and Hamilton recently have described, the fetal syncytium may penetrate through all layers of the maternal endometrium and even into the myometrium. Giant cells may be present in the basal plate, and these are believed to be derived from the fetal syncytium. Passing through the basal plate are spiral arteries which open eventually into the intervillous spaces. They are lined with endothelium, but near their openings they are lined with cells of the syncytiotrophoblast type; these do not institute clotting. This growth of these cells into the maternal spiral arteries probably reduces the pressure at which maternal blood is delivered into the intervillous space.

The maternal decidua is eroded more deeply opposite the main villi than elsewhere, and this leaves projections of decidual tissue between the main villi, extending from the basal plate toward the chorion (Fig. 530). Such projections are called *placental septa,* and they divide the placenta into lobules or cotyledons, with each area of placenta between adjacent septa being a *maternal cotyledon* (Fig. 530). That the placental septa are mainly of decidual and not trophoblastic origin has been proved recently by Sohval, Gaines and Strauss, who showed that when the fetus was male the nuclei of the septa are of the female type. Maternal vessels, particularly veins, often make short excursions into the base of a septum; this also suggests that the septa are of decidual and not trophoblastic origin.

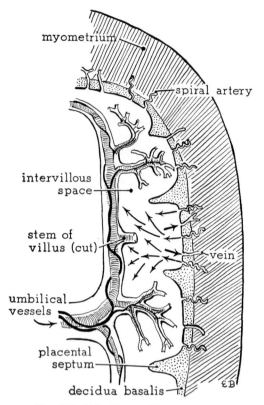

FIG. 530. This diagram illustrates the circulation of fetal and maternal blood in the placenta. Blood from the fetus reaches the placenta by the 2 umbilical arteries (*left, dark*), passes to the villi and is returned to the fetus by the single umbilical vein (*left, cross-hatched*). Maternal blood enters the intervillous space via numerous spiral arteries and returns to the maternal circulation through many veins. There is no mingling of the two bloods. Placental septae, which subdivide the placenta into cotyledons, are also shown.

However, some cells toward the apices of the septa are undoubtedly of fetal origin, being derived from trophoblast and deposited, as it were, on the summits of the septa. From the 4th month, the tissues of the decidua basalis become extraordinarily "loose," being composed chiefly of a very dense venous plexus with dilated and distorted uterine glands. The latter have very thin walls, and secretion persists in them until late in pregnancy. Toward the margins of the placenta, the decidua is more compact.

The Intervillous Space. *Blood Circulation.*

The intervillous space develops very rapidly to become an enormous blood sinus bounded on one side by the chorion (chorionic plate) and on the other by the basal plate (Fig. 530). The space is labyrinthine in development and in form because the villi in it are variously connected to each other. The space is incompletely divided into compartments by the placental septa. The intervillous space is much expanded toward the embryonic side; this expanded part is the *subchorial lake* or *space*. Here there are only the main stems of the villi, and, just as there is more air space in a dense forest between the trunks of the trees than there is further from the ground between the many branches, there is more space here for blood. The *marginal sinus* is the marginal prolongation of the subchorial lake at the periphery of the placenta, and thus is circular in form when viewed from the surface.

Maternal blood enters the intervillous space through several hundred arterioles that traverse the decidua basalis, there being many such arterioles in each cotyledon or lobule (Fig. 530). Blood drains into numerous veins which open over the entire surface of the basal plate. Maternal blood pressure drives the blood entering the intervillous space high up toward the subchorial lake. After bathing the villi, venous blood flows back toward the venous orifices in the basal plate. Contractions of the myometrium and the fetal pulse in the villi possibly assist the circulation.

Attachment of Placenta. One question, not yet definitely answered, is what mechanism holds the placenta in place. The association of degenerating maternal tissue and fetal trophoblast in the junctional zone, together with the presence of fibrinoid (Nitabuch's membrane), has been noted already, but this does not provide a firm attachment because it is here that separation occurs during labor. Probably the chief mechanism for holding the placenta in place is pressure. The chorionic sac is relatively tense throughout pregnancy, and early in development it fully occupies and obliterates the uterine cavity (Fig. 528 B). The growth of the chorionic sac and its contents requires that the uterus must grow to accommodate it; hence, the uterus hypertrophies, and hyperplasia occurs in the myometrium throughout pregnancy. With the pressure so engendered there would be little tendency for the placenta to move in relation to the uterine wall.

Functions of the Placenta. These may be summarized as: (1) Nutrition of the embryo, particularly with respect to carbohydrates, fats, proteins, water and salts which pass by diffusion from maternal to fetal blood. This has been discussed recently at some length by Dancis. (2) Respiration, oxygen passing from maternal to fetal blood and carbon dioxide passing in the reverse direction. (3) Excretion of metabolites and waste products. (4) As a barrier to particulate matter and bacteria, although some antibodies and viruses can pass the placental barrier. (5) Synthesis of estrogen, progesterone and chorionic or placental gonadotrophin. Enzymes with a local action, for example, those associated with digestion of maternal endometrium, also are formed in the placenta.

Age Changes. *Histopathology.* Some of the age changes seen in the placenta already have been described; for example, the thinning of the placental barrier and the virtual disappearance of the cytotrophoblast, and the formation of fibrinoid (Fig. 529). Paine has described the main features of aging in a *normal* placenta as a slow but progressive thinning of the syncytium, a gradual thickening of the walls of the fetal blood vessels in the villi, and a progressive conversion of the gelatinous fetal-type mesoderm of the stroma of the villi into an adult type of areolar fibrous tissue. These changes are accelerated in cases of hypertension and toxemia.

THE CERVIX

The cervix is the lowest and relatively narrow segment of the uterus (Fig. 504). Both the substance of its wall and the mucous membrane that lines its canal are of a different character from those of the body of the uterus.

The recent study of Danforth indicates that the amount of smooth muscle and elastic tissue in the wall of the cervix is not as great as has been generally supposed. He finds that the wall of the cervix is composed chiefly of dense collagenic connective tissue and that smooth muscle fibers, on the average, comprise only about 15 per cent of its substance. Furthermore, he finds that elastic fibers, except in the walls of its blood vessels, are relatively scarce.

The cervix, it should be remembered, must become widely dilated at parturition in order to permit the passage of the fetus. It is important, for many reasons that will become obvious when clinical work is encountered, to know whether the relaxation of the smooth muscle fibers in its wall is an important factor in permitting the cervix to dilate. Danforth's studies do not suggest that the cervix ordinarily contains enough smooth muscle to exert a very strong sphincter effect. Hence, it would seem that the main factor that permits the cervix to dilate at parturition, in response to the mechanical force exerted upon it, is the softening that occurs in its intercellular substance. This is associated with an increased blood supply and an increased tissue fluid content, which are probably due to the hormones of pregnancy.

Danforth has shown that so little elastic tissue is present in the cervix, except in its blood vessels, that it could scarcely be expected that stretched elastic fibers are a very important factor in bringing about the slow contraction of the cervix that occurs after parturition. What then makes the cervix become constricted again? It seems not unlikely that although the cervix does not contain enough smooth muscle to enable it to act as a true sphincter, it does contain enough smooth muscle to help it contract to some extent after birth, particularly since after birth the smooth muscle fibers would be in a stretched state and would have become sensitized to such oxytocin as is secreted by the posterior lobe of the pituitary gland at this time. But its further return probably involves a new organization of its fibrous tissue.

The cervical canal is flattened from before backward. A longitudinal ridge or raphe is present both on the anterior and the posterior surface of the canal, and from these ridges mucosal folds extend at angles toward each side. The ridges do not directly face one another, so that when the lumen is collapsed they fit alongside one another.

The mucous membrane of the cervical canal consists of epithelium and a connective tissue lamina propria. It contains numerous large, branched, tubular glands that, in the vaginal end of the canal, tend to slant from the lumen toward the body of the uterus (Fig. 531, *left*).

The epithelium of the mucous membrane consists of tall mucus-secreting columnar cells.

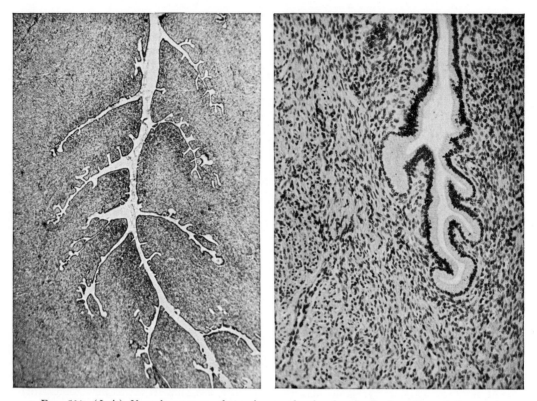

FIG. 531. (*Left*) Very low-power photomicrograph of a longitudinal section of the cervix, showing the cervical canal and the glands which extend out from it. The upper end of the photograph represents the end of the section nearest the vagina. (*Right*) Medium-power photomicrograph of the same section, showing the terminal part of one of the glands. The character of the stroma which immediately surrounds the glands and that of the general stroma of the cervix are also shown.

In H and E sections their cytoplasm is pale, and their deeply stained nuclei are seen to be close to their bases (Fig. 531, *right*). Ciliated cells are sometimes seen. The same type of epithelium is found in the large, wide, branched tubular glands that extend deeply into the lamina propria and even somewhat beyond (Fig. 531, *right*). The lamina propria is a cellular type of fibrous connective tissue. The nuclei are of the fibroblast type and are relatively close together. The cytoplasm of the cells cannot be seen clearly in an H and E section, nor can the character of the not overly abundant intercellular substance between the cells be seen to advantage (Fig. 531, *right*).

On the whole, the mucous membrane of the cervical canal is of a dense structure and is firmly attached to the fibrous connective tissue wall that lies outside it. The lamina propria contains no coiled arteries and does not change much during the menstrual cycle. However, the secretion of mucus by the cervical glands becomes increased at the time of ovulation; the secretion of the cervical glands is evidently stimulated by estrogen. The glands sometimes become closed off, whereupon they may become converted into cysts. These are called *nabothian follicles*. These may cause elevations on the surface of that part of the cervix that projects into the vagina and so be seen or felt on a vaginal examination.

The portion of the cervix that projects into the vagina is covered by stratified squamous nonkeratinizing epithelium similar to that which lines the vagina (which will be described presently) and with which it becomes continuous. This type of epithelium extends usually for a very short distance into the cervical canal, where it undergoes a transition into

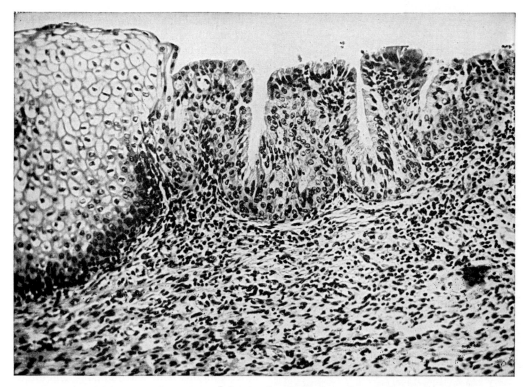

FIG. 532. High-power photomicrograph of a longitudinal section of the cervix near the site where the cervical canal opens into the vagina. The stratified squamous nonkeratinizing epithelium that covers the vaginal portion of the cervix and extends for a very short distance into the canal may be seen at the left, and the columnar epithelium that lines the remainder of the canal, at the right. The zone of transition between the 2 types of epithelium is immediately left of center.

the columnar type that lines most of the canal (Fig. 532). In some instances the zone of transition between the two types of epithelium is farther in; however, in others the columnar epithelium of the canal may continue out from the canal to cover little areas of the vaginal surface of the cervix close to the beginning of the canal; if so, these areas are termed physiologic erosions. (The stratified squamous nonkeratinizing epithelium which normally covers the cervix is pink-gray in color: columnar epithelium appears red. Hence the term "erosion.")

The portion of the uterus with which the cervix connects is sometimes termed the isthmus of the uterus. The isthmus is supposed to be the narrowed segment of the organ that begins, at its cervical end, where the typical mucous membrane of the cervix begins to change into the endometrial variety. The

upper end of the isthmus is supposed to be the site where the lumen becomes constricted (the internal os) before opening out into the wide cavity of the body. However, the landmarks for both the beginning and the end of the isthmus are neither very obvious nor constant in position. The line of transition between the cervical type of mucous membrane and the endometrial type may be gradual and the so-called internal sphincter not at all obvious. Danforth has shown that the wall of the so-called isthmus is composed chiefly of smooth muscle, and so he regards the isthmus as part of the body. It does not become dilated in pregnancy as soon as does the body, but when there is a need for more room to accommodate the fetus and the membranes than can be conveniently provided by the body, the isthmus becomes expanded and elongated to provide extra accommodation. Eventually, the

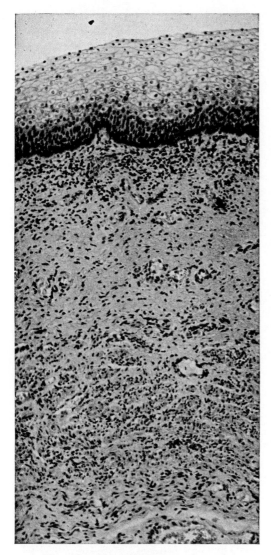

FIG. 533. Very low-power photomicrograph of a section of the wall of the vagina. Note that the more superficial epithelial cells are large and pale because of their glycogen content. The smooth muscle coats of the wall may be seen below the middle of the photograph.

more fibrous cervix itself becomes the only segment of the organ that is not expanded during pregnancy. The isthmus, then, is best considered, not as a separate part of the organ, but as the lower end of the body.

THE VAGINA

The vagina is a musculofibrous tube lined with a mucous membrane (Fig. 533). Under ordinary conditions it is collapsed and the mucous membranes of its anterior and posterior walls are in contact. Except in the upper part of the tube, a longitudinal ridge is present on the mucosal surface of both the anterior and the posterior walls. From these two primary ridges numerous secondary ridges or *rugae* extend toward the sides of the tube (Fig. 504). No glands are present in the mucous membrane. The epithelium is of the stratified squamous type, and the way in which its character alters in relation to the level of sex hormones in the blood stream will be discussed presently. The lamina propria on which the epithelium rests is of a dense connective-tissue type. It may exhibit lymph nodules. Farther out toward the muscle coat, the lamina propria— which in this site is sometimes regarded as a submucosa—becomes loose in texture and contains numerous blood vessels, particularly veins. Elastic fibers are numerous in the lamina propria directly under the epithelial lining, and they extend out through the mucous membrane to the muscular layer. The latter contains both longitudinally and circularly disposed smooth muscle fibers, but these are not gathered into discernible layers (Fig. 533). Longitudinally disposed fibers predominate. A fibrous adventitia lies outside the muscular coat and this connects the vagina with adjacent structures. The upper part of the posterior wall of the vagina is covered with peritoneum (Fig. 504).

Vaginal Smears. In recent years it has become common to study, particularly by means of films or smears, the cells that are found in the vagina. Such cells as are present in vaginal washings may be derived from: (1) the endometrium of the body of the uterus, (2) the cervical canal, (3) the vaginal surface of the cervix or the lining of the vagina. Their study may be informative for two reasons. (1) Since the character of cells in these various sites is affected by the particular hormone concentrations that exist in the blood stream, the cells found in vaginal washings may give some indication about the state of the hormone balance of the individual at the time they are obtained; and (2) cells suggestive of having desquamated from an early cancer, growing in the cervix or the body of the uterus, may sometimes be found on an otherwise routine check of a patient and so indicate the need

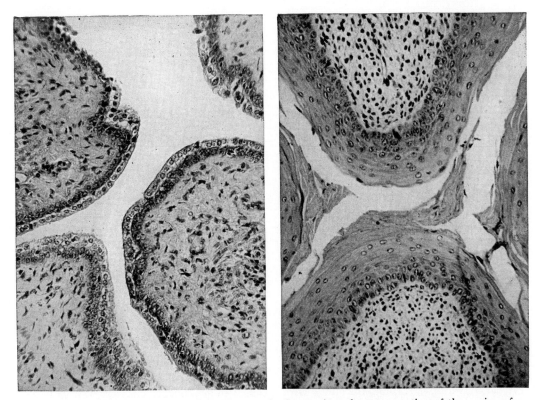

FIG. 534. (*Left*) Low-power photomicrograph of a portion of a cross section of the vagina of a rat from which the ovaries were removed. This shows that, under conditions of estrogen deficiency, the vaginal epithelium becomes thin, and the superficial cells nucleated. (*Right*) A similar preparation from a rat treated identically, except that it was given a large injection of estrogen 2 days before the section, was obtained. Observe that the epithelium has become greatly thickened, and that the surface layers are heavily keratinized. This picture is similar to that seen in a normally occurring estrus.

for more detailed examination for cancer. For both these reasons it has become common practice to study—both by the film method and by concentrating with the centrifuge and sectioning the clumps so obtained—the free cells of vaginal washings, cells obtained by gently wiping the lining of the vagina or the covering of the cervix and the cells aspirated or otherwise obtained from the entrance of the cervical canal.

Cyclic Changes in the Vaginal Epithelium. It is to be kept in mind that the earlier investigators who attempted to prepare ovarian extracts that contained sex hormones had no ready way to find out if their extracts contained the active hormones they sought. In other words, there were no biologic tests by which the hormone content of any given extract could be assayed conveniently and accu-

rately. Therefore, it was of the greatest importance when Stockard and Papanicolaou discovered, in 1917, that the vaginal epithelium of the guinea pig becomes keratinized at the time of estrus. Hence, whether or not any given guinea pig was in estrus could be ascertained by noting the presence or the absence of keratinized cells in a vaginal smear. A little later, Allen worked out the estrous cycle of the mouse and found that its vagina also became keratinized at the time of estrus. Therefore, it became obvious that the keratinization of the vaginal epithelium was one of the effects of the estrus-producing hormone. However, mature mice and rats come into estrus spontaneously every 4 days, so that they are not suitable animals to use to test for the estrus-producing hormone in any given extract. However, the vaginal epithelium of immature animals or of mature animals from which the ovaries have been removed remains nonkeratinized, so these serve as excellent test animals. Actually, mature female rats or mice whose ovaries have been removed are better test animals for several reasons. Using the keratinization of the vaginal epithelium as a criterion of the presence of an estrus-producing hormone in the blood, Allen and Doisy, in 1923, were able to show that an extract made from follicular fluid aspirated from large follicles in hogs' ovaries contained the estrus-producing hormone. From this point on, progress was rapid, and soon estrus-producing hormones were obtained in pure form and their chemical structure elucidated.

The changes that occur in the vaginal epithelium throughout the 28-day cycle of the mature human female are not nearly so pronounced as those that occur in many lower animals. However, such changes as do occur are more easily interpreted in the light of a knowledge of the pronounced ones that occur in the estrous cycle of the rat or the mouse. Therefore, this will be described briefly.

As noted before, the rat and the mouse have a 4-day estrous cycle. This is divided into 4 periods: *proestrus, estrus, metaestrus* and *diestrus*. In proestrus, follicles approach the surface of the ovary, the uterus becomes swollen with secretion, and its blood vessels become engorged. The epithelium of the vagina becomes thick as a result of proliferation in its deeper layers, but its most superficial cells are still nucleated. However, cells with keratohyalin granules appear beneath the superficial nucleated cells. The epithelial membrane thus comes to have a 2-layered appearance. In estrus or thereabouts, ovulation occurs, and throughout this stage the uterus remains swollen and red. The vaginal epithelium has now become thick and heavily keratinized (Fig. 534, *right*), and the mating impulse is aroused. The keratinized epithelium probably plays a protective function in the mating procedure. If mating does not occur, the animal passes into the metaestrus stage. As this progresses the uterus becomes smaller and the vaginal epithelium much thinner (similar to Fig. 534, *left*). The basement membrane disappears, and polymorphonuclear leukocytes invade the epithelium and pass through it to appear in great numbers among the epithelial

cells that are seen in vaginal smears (Fig. 535, *left*). In diestrus, the uterus is small and pale, and the vaginal epithelium is still thin. However, polymorphonuclear leukocytes are confined mostly to the superficial layers of the epithelium. As proestrus develops, great mitotic activity occurs in the deeper layers of the epithelium, and it becomes thick again.

Since only the superficial cells desquamate, they are the only type seen in vaginal smears. Hence, in estrus, the vaginal smears contain only keratinized cells (Fig. 535, *right*). As metaestrus proceeds, vaginal smears contain, first, keratinized cells and then later nucleated cells and large numbers of the polymorphonuclear leukocytes that are making their way through the epithelium at this stage (Fig. 535, *left*). The diestrus stage is characterized by nucleated epithelial cells and leukocytes. In proestrus, the leukocytes have disappeared, so only nucleated epithelial cells are present.

The Epithelium of the Human Vagina. The epithelial lining of the human vagina is stratified and substantial (Fig. 533). Its deepest stratum consists of a single layer of cylindrical cells with oval nuclei. The next stratum is several cell layers in thickness. The cells in this stratum are polyhedral in shape, and it is said that they are joined together with intercellular bridges something like those in the stratum spinosum of the epidermis of thick skin; however, the cells in this stratum of the vaginal epithelium do not have a prickly appearance. The next stratum consists of a few layers of more flattened cells; these contain glycogen. Since this dissolves away in the ordinary preparation of sections, the cells of this and the more superficial strata appear swollen and empty. The most superficial stratum consists of several layers of more flattened but somewhat swollen cells, all of which possess nuclei.

The epithelium lining the vagina of the human female differs in two important respects from that lining the vagina of the mouse or the rat. First, since there is no true period of estrus in the human female, there is no time in the menstrual cycle when the epithelium becomes frankly keratinized. At the time of ovulation, which is the counterpart of estrus, the epithelium may show certain tendencies toward keratinization but, unless the epithelium is unduly exposed to air or some other unusual environmental factor, it does

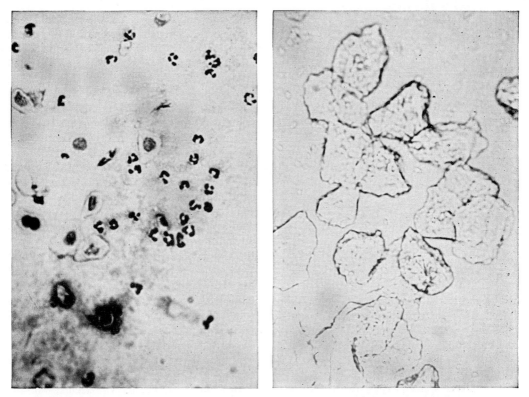

Fig. 535. (*Left*) High-power photomicrograph of a stained vaginal smear obtained from a rat in the later stages of metaestrus. Note the nucleated epithelial cells and the characteristic polymorphic nuclei of many granular leukocytes. (*Right*) High-power photomicrograph of a stained vaginal smear obtained from a rat in estrus. Observe that the smear contains nothing but large, very pale-staining, non-nucleated squames of keratin.

not develop true keratin; hence, the surface cells always contain nuclei. Secondly, the epithelial cells of the more superficial layers of the vaginal epithelium tend to accumulate considerable quantities of glycogen in their cytoplasm, particularly at the time of ovulation. This has two possible functions: (1) it may serve as nutriment for male germ cells during their passage through this organ, and (2) it is fermented by bacteria in the vagina which convert it to lactic acid. This may be an important factor in maintaining a suitable type of bacterial flora in the vagina.

The appearance of the cells that desquamate from the lining of the vagina and from the covering of the vaginal surface of the cervix has been studied at great length by Papanicolaou by the smear method; his publications should be consulted for full information on this matter. Essentially, such progesterone as is secreted during the menstrual cycle appears

to have no effect on the vaginal epithelium. The amount of estrogen secreted at the time of ovulation, while not enough to cause keratinization, does, however, have some effect. Papanicolaou considers that there is a relative increase in acidophilic cells with small dark nuclei in the vaginal smear at this time. The development of acidophilic properties by the surface epithelial cells is evidently preliminary to cells becoming keratinized, but this is as far as the process usually goes. There are also other criteria that may be employed. Evidently, in the hands of an experienced individual, the study of desquamated vaginal cells in smears may be helpful in determining the time of ovulation and the effectiveness of estrogen therapy and in diagnosing atrophic conditions of the vaginal epithelium that are due to estrogen deficiency.

The ability of estrogen to thicken and even keratinize the vaginal epithelium is taken ad-

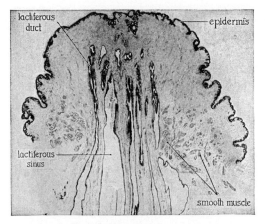

Fig. 536. Very low-power photomicrograph, lightly retouched, of a section of a nipple cut perpendicular to the skin surface.

vantage of in the treatment of certain vaginal infections, particularly those that occur in children, for in them the epithelium is thin and vulnerable.

THE MAMMARY GLANDS (BREASTS OR MAMMAE)

Development. The first step in the development of mammary glands in man occurs near the end of the 6th week of embryonic life. At this time, in embryos of either sex, the ectoderm becomes thickened along two lines, each of which runs from the axilla to the groin of the same side. These are called the "milk lines," and their epithelial cells have the potentiality to grow down into the underlying mesenchyme at any point along either line to form mammary glands. Usually, in man, invasion of the underlying mesenchyme by epithelial cells destined to form mammary glands occurs at only one site along each line. However, in many animals mammary glands develop at many sites along each line so that in later life such animals have two rows of mammary glands with which to feed their large families. Occasionally, extra mammary glands develop along the milk line in man (and sometimes elsewhere); if so, they are called *supernumerary nipples* or *breasts.* Among civilized peoples supernumerary breasts are usually removed surgically for cosmetic and other reasons. Aberrant mammary gland tissue in the axilla may not become obvious until pregnancy or lactation causes it to swell.

As the embryo develops, the epithelial cells at the point along the milk line where a breast is to develop form a little cluster from which up to 20 or more separate cords of epithelial cells push into the underlying mesenchyme in various directions. Each one of these original cords of cells develops into a separate compound exocrine gland; hence, each breast is actually composed of many separate compound glands, each of which empties by a separate duct through the nipple. During fetal life the cords of cells that invade the mesenchyme branch to some extent and tend to become canalized so that at birth a rudimentary duct system has formed. At birth there is no obvious difference between the degree to which the glands of the female and the male infant are developed. During the first few days of life the glands of a baby may become distended for reasons to be described later. The condition soon subsides.

Changes at Puberty. As puberty approaches, the breasts of the female, which up to this time have been flat, become enlarged and more or less hemispheric in shape. The nipple becomes more prominent. The changes in the breasts constitute one of the secondary sex characteristics of the female that appear at this time. Most of the increase in their size is due to fat accumulating in the connective tissue between their lobes and lobules. At puberty the epithelial duct system develops beyond a rudimentary stage, but this change is not so striking as the increased amount of fat in the connective tissue. It is not believed that true secretory units develop at this time; the formation of these awaits pregnancy.

In the male, the mammary glands usually experience no or little change at puberty, remaining flat. Uncommonly some considerable enlargement closely resembling that which occurs in the female may occur: this condition is called *gynecomastia.*

Estrogen, probably in conjunction with some lactogenic hormone (the secretion of which would be dependent on estrogen appearing in the circulation), brings about the changes in the female breast described above. The progesterone that is periodically secreted from the time of puberty onward may play a contributing role. Estrogen given to males tends to make their rudimentary mammary glands develop into the feminine type.

Histologic Structure of a Resting Breast.

The breast of a sexually mature nonpregnant female is termed a *resting breast* to distinguish it from one that is in the process of active growth in pregnancy or one that is functioning in lactation.

The *nipple* is a cylindrico-conical structure of a pink or brownish-pink color. It is covered with stratified squamous keratinized epithelium. Numerous papillae of an irregular shape extend into the epidermis from the dermis to approach the surface closely; hence, over papillae the epidermis may be very thin (Fig. 536). The main ducts from each of the many separate glands that make up the breast are called the *lactiferous ducts,* and they ascend through the nipple (Fig. 536) to open by separate orifices on its summit; the orifices are so minute that they cannot be seen with the naked eye. The epithelium of the lactiferous ducts, close to their orifices, is similar to that which covers the nipple. Deeper in the nipple the lactiferous ducts are lined with 2 layers of columnar epithelial cells that rest on a basement membrane.

The substance of the nipple consists of dense connective tissue and smooth muscle (Fig. 536). The fibers of the latter are arranged both circularly around the lactiferous ducts and parallel with, and close beside, them as they ascend through the nipple. Many blood vessels and encapsulated nerve endings are also present.

The epidermis of the nipple, like that of the vagina, is sensitive to estrogen. In relation to the problem of "sore nipples"—a condition which develops when some women attempt to nurse their babies—it is perhaps of interest to note that estrogen may be lacking in a woman shortly after she has given birth to a baby. The reason for this is that the function of estrogen production is largely taken over by the placenta during pregnancy; hence, when the placenta is delivered after birth, a woman is deprived of what has been her chief source of this hormone. Eventually, of course, her ovaries will produce a sufficiency, but it is possible that there may be a period of time when the epidermis of the nipple suffers from a lack of stimulation by estrogen. Indeed, Gunther ascribes one type of sore nipple to estrogen deficiency, and, in some experiments in collaboration with Gunther, the author found that feeding human placenta tissue to rats greatly thickened the epidermis of their

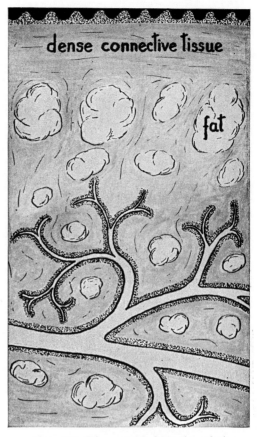

FIG. 537. Diagram to show the relation of the layers of the dermis to the connective tissue of the breast. The papillary layer of the dermis and the intralobular connective tissue of the breast are comparable and are both stippled in the illustration. The dense connective tissue dermis of the skin is seen to be prolonged deeply, in the form of septa or ligaments, which pass between lobules of fat, to become continuous with the interlobular connective tissue of the breast.

nipples. However, there are certain complications, too involved to discuss here, in connection with attempting to use estrogen to thicken the epidermis of the nipples of women who have just begun to nurse their babies.

The skin surrounding the nipple, the areola, is of a rosy hue. It becomes pigmented in pregnancy, and after pregnancy never returns to its original shade; it always retains some pigment. Large modified sweat glands, but not so large or so modified as the mammary glands themselves, lie beneath the areola and open onto its surface; these are called the areolar

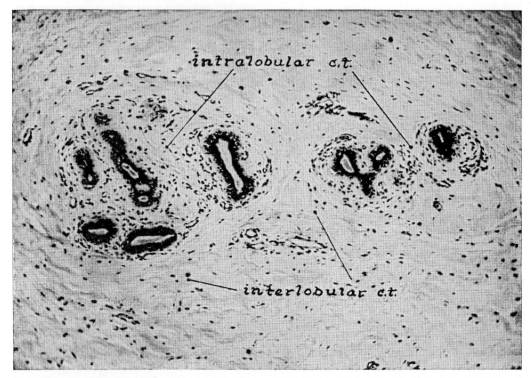

Fig. 538. Low-power photomicrograph of a section of a resting breast. Observe that the ducts are each surrounded by cellular intralobular connective tissue and that the 2 lobules shown are separated and otherwise surrounded by relatively noncellular interlobular connective tissue.

glands (of Montgomery). Sebaceous glands and large sweat glands are present around the periphery of the areola. Smooth muscle fibers are disposed, both circularly and at right angles to the skin surface, beneath the areola.

The lactiferous ducts from the different lobes of the breast converge under the areola to enter the base of the nipple. As they near the point at which they converge, the ducts are believed to become somewhat expanded. These widened segments of the ducts are termed the *lactiferous sinuses* (Fig. 536) and, in the lactating breast, they are believed to act as little reservoirs for milk. Whether these expanded portions of the ducts may be seen in the gross when a resting breast is dissected is questionable.

The many separate glands that are drained by individual ducts through the nipple constitute the lobes of the breast. Each lobe consists of many lobules; hence, each main lactiferous duct gives rise to many branches that, since they run within lobules, are called *intralobular ducts*. The parenchyma of the lobes and the lobules is generally considered to be

disposed in the subcutaneous tissue (the superficial fascia). Nevertheless, the parenchyma of the mammary glands which, it must be remembered, develops from the epidermis of the skin, does not, in a sense, entirely escape the confines of the dermis. It will be recalled that the dermis consists of 2 layers, and that the papillary layer (which abuts directly on the epidermis) is more cellular and of a finer texture than the coarser and noncellular reticular layer that lies deep to it (Fig. 537). When cords of epidermis grow down into the mesenchyme to form the duct system of the breast, it would seem that they carry, as it were, the developing papillary layer of the dermis along with them to form a soft cellular connective tissue wrapping for each duct (Fig. 537) or a common wrapping for small adjacent groups of ducts. Then, between these single, or groups of, epithelial ducts so wrapped, substantial bundles and partitions of coarse noncellular connective tissue extend down from the reticular layer of the dermis that overlies the breast to separate the lobes and the lobules from one another and to hold the whole breast paren-

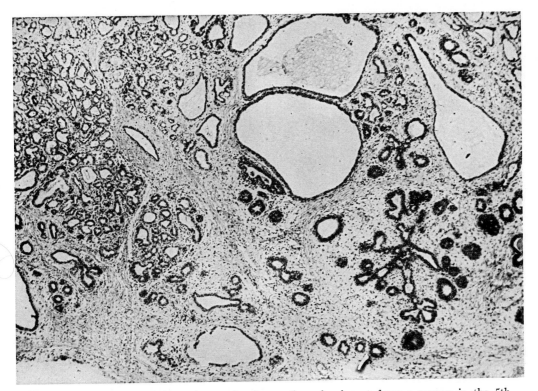

FIG. 539. Low-power photomicrograph of a section of a breast from a woman in the 5th month of pregnancy. The ducts have proliferated and, at the left side, they have given rise to alveoli.

chyma tightly to the skin (Fig. 537). The larger of these bundles and partitions are termed the *suspensory ligaments of Cooper*. Fat accumulates in them (Fig. 537), so that they hold the fat of the breast in place as well as the epithelial parenchyma. Fat also accumulates in the connective tissue between the breast parenchyma and the skin that overlies it and the fascia that lies beneath it.

From the foregoing, the appearance of a section cut from almost any site in a resting breast, and in any plane, may be anticipated. In such a section, epithelial parenchyma will be scanty; indeed, such as is present consists only of single ducts or little clusters of ducts widely separated from one another by connective tissue (Fig. 538). Most of the ducts seen in a section are cut obliquely or in cross section; occasionally, a portion of one may be cut in longitudinal section. Occasionally, a large lactiferous duct may be observed in a section that has been cut more or less haphazardly from the breast, but almost all the ducts that are commonly seen are of the dif-

ferent orders of branches that arise from the lactiferous ducts. Since the branches of the main ducts run out into the lobules that dangle, as it were, from the main ducts, most of the ducts seen in a section are inside lobules and hence are termed intralobular ducts. Their walls are generally composed of 2 layers of epithelial cells that have pale cytoplasm and pale oval nuclei. The long diameters of the nuclei in the inner layer of cells are commonly at right angles to the direction of the duct, and those of the outer layer are parallel with the duct. But the arrangement of epithelial cells in these ducts is variable. The epithelial cells of the ducts rest on a basement membrane.

Each duct is surrounded by a tunic of relatively cellular connective tissue that is about as thick as the duct is wide (Fig. 538). This cellular connective tissue that abuts on the epithelium of the ducts is the counterpart of the papillary layer of the dermis that abuts on the epidermis (Fig. 537). The cellular connective tissue that surrounds the individual

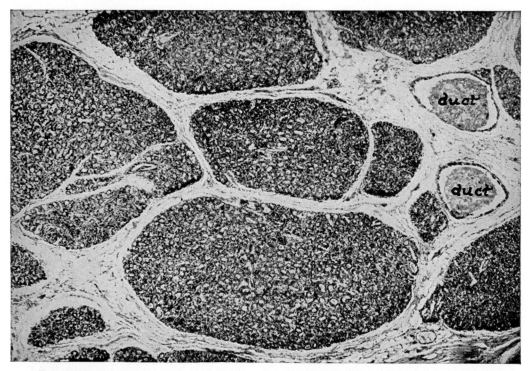

FIG. 540. Low-power photomicrograph of a section of a lactating breast. The lobules illustrated, although greatly expanded by a great content of alveoli, are not, in this section, cut through their widest parts. The interlobular septa are thicker in this photomicrograph than they are in most sites in the section.

ducts in a group of ducts may be confluent. Since this *cellular* connective tissue that invests the ducts is inside lobules, it is termed *intralobular* connective tissue. Fibroblasts are numerous in it and may be easily identified by their large, oval, pale and apparently naked nuclei (Fig. 538). Macrophages, lymphocytes and plasma cells are also normal cellular constituents of the intralobular connective tissue.

Single ducts or groups of ducts, invested with intralobular connective tissue, are separated from one another by thick partitions of coarse and *relatively noncellular* dense *interlobular* connective tissue. The connective tissue of these may be regarded, as is indicated in Figure 537, as a deep extension of the reticular layer of the dermis (the larger partitions seen are the suspensory ligaments of Cooper). The interlobular connective tissue often contains lobules of fat within its substance; the fat of the breast, then, is tied to the skin by the interlobular connective tissue.

Changes That Occur in the Breast at Pregnancy. The resting breast probably contains

no secretory alveoli but consists only of a duct system. As pregnancy proceeds, a great development of the duct system occurs, and, finally, secretory alveoli develop at the ends of the smaller branches of the duct system. By the end of the 5th month of pregnancy the lobules are packed (and greatly expanded) with alveoli (Fig. 539). The intralobular connective tissue becomes broken up as alveoli bud from the ducts within lobules, so that the intralobular connective tissue eventually becomes reduced to a series of filmlike partitions between adjacent alveoli; however, these contain extensive capillary networks. The alveoli themselves are composed of a single layer of columnar cells. Curved myoepithelial cells are sometimes seen to be fitted around their periphery. Because of the great expansion of epithelial elements within the lobules, the partitions of interlobular connective tissue become greatly stretched and thinned (Figs. 539 and 540).

Most of the epithelial growth that occurs in the breast in pregnancy occurs before the end of the 6th month. In the later stages of pregnancy further growth occurs, but very slowly. However, the breasts continue to enlarge; this is due chiefly to the cells of the alveoli beginning to secrete a fluid that expands them (and the breast) from within. This secretion is not milk; milk appears only after parturition, as will be explained presently.

Cause of Growth of Breasts in Pregnancy. Any explanation for human breasts enlarging in pregnancy is based to a great extent on what has been learned from animal experiments. These experiments have yielded many contradictory results. One reason for this is that different workers have worked with different animals, and it seems that the hormone mechanisms that operate in pregnancy vary considerably throughout the animal kingdom. This makes it difficult to interpret such experimental results as have been obtained and to apply them to man with any precision. Nevertheless, certain facts have been established.

1. It has been clearly established that estrogens, suitably administered to intact animals, bring about a great development of their mammary glands. In some animals estrogen alone will prepare the breasts for function. However, in others progesterone also is needed to bring about a proper development of secretory aveoli at the ends of the duct system. Since large amounts of estrogen are made by the placenta during pregnancy, and since large amounts of progesterone are also produced, first by the corpus luteum and later by the placenta, it might seem that the explanation for the growth of the breasts in pregnancy is very simple: that their growth is stimulated directly by these two hormones. But the explanation is not quite so simple, as we shall see.

2. It has been established that a growth of the breasts comparable with that of pregnancy can be brought about by injecting animals with certain types of anterior pituitary extracts. In some instances this might be explained by supposing that the extracts, by containing gonadotrophic hormones, would stimulate the ovaries of the injected animals to make estrogen and progesterone, which hormones, in turn, would cause the breasts to develop. But certain anterior pituitary extracts have been shown to cause the breasts to develop in female animals from which the ovaries have been removed. It is obvious, then, that anterior pituitary gland can itself make a hormone or hormones which can bring about the development of the breasts.

3. It has been shown that, although estrogen and progesterone induce a full growth of the breasts in intact animals, they cannot do so if the pituitary glands of the animals concerned are first removed.

4. It has been shown that in many different animals, including man, estrogen can be applied locally to a mammary gland so as to cause the growth of that particular mammary gland without having any effect on the other mammary gland or glands of the same individual.

5. It has been shown that the pituitary glands of animals can be removed when pregnancy is well advanced and that the mammary glands, under these conditions, continue their development provided that the placenta remains functional.

How are these facts to be reconciled in a working hypothesis? At least 2 theories should be considered in this connection. These differ primarily with regard to the question of whether or not the anterior pituitary makes a special hormone that causes breast growth. For convenience we shall term these theories 1 and 2.

Theory 1. According to this theory, the anterior pituitary gland makes a special hormone called the mammogenic hormone (mammotrophin), and this is the factor that directly stimulates breast growth. It is believed that this hormone is made by the anterior pituitary when this gland is stimulated sufficiently by estrogen. Indeed, it has been suggested that there are 2 mammogenic hormones, one made when the pituitary is stimulated by estrogen— and this brings about duct growth in the breast—and a second one—made when the pituitary is stimulated by progesterone— which brings about alveolar development. This theory has received support from experiments that show that the anterior pituitary glands of animals that have been injected with estrogen, or those of pregnant animals, contain more of the factor that stimulates breast growth than ordinary anterior pituitary glands. However, this theory does not explain why estrogen should have a local effect in causing breast growth.

Theory 2. This theory is opposed to the idea of there being a special anterior pituitary mammogenic hormone. In general, this theory attributes breast growth to the collaborative efforts of known anterior pituitary hormones and estrogen and progesterone. It depicts estrogen as having a local effect on the breast, not so much of a growth-stimulating one as an effect in making the vascular bed of the breast permeable to other hormones in the blood stream which could cause breast growth if they were permitted to seep into breast tissue in sufficient amounts. The growth hormone, the adrenocorticotrophic hormone, the lactogenic hormone, the luteinizing hormone, chorionic gonadotrophin, adrenal cortical hormones and progesterone have all been suspected in this connection. It seems most probable that the lactogenic hormone is the most important, although the others are also necessary. This theory would explain why estrogen, though not capable of stimulating breast growth by itself, would, if it were applied locally, affect the capillary permeability of the part and so permit anterior pituitary and other hormones in the blood stream to enter breast tissues and exert a growth effect. On the other hand, if the concentrations of these hormones in the blood were great enough they would enter breast tissue in sufficient quantities without the help of estrogen; this could explain why anterior pituitary extracts, if given in large enough amounts, can bring about breast development in animals with no ovaries.

From all the foregoing it is obvious that the growth of the breasts in pregnancy involves very complex hormone interactions. The idea that estrogen acts to permit other hormones to enter breast tissue directly is attractive.

The Lactating Breast. As noted before, most of the increase in the size of the breasts from the 6th month on is due to secretion accumulating in the alveoli and the ducts. However, as this secretion is made, some appears at, and escapes from, the nipple (in women who have previously borne children, this may occur relatively early in pregnancy). This secretion is not milk but a somewhat different fluid termed *colostrum*. After parturition, colostrum is secreted more abundantly but only for 2 or 3 days, after which the breasts (in human females) begin to secrete milk.

Colostrum contains a higher concentration of protein than does milk but very little fat. It also contains fragments of cells and even whole cells of a large size. These frequently contain phagocytosed fat and are called *colostrum bodies*. It is probable that these cells are phagocytes that have made their way through the epithelium of the alveoli and so gained entrance to their lumens.

It was once commonly believed that a large proportion of the milk obtained by a baby at a single nursing was secreted during the nursing period. It is now generally accepted that almost no milk is secreted during this time and that milk is secreted and accumulates during the intervals between nursings.

MICROSCOPIC STRUCTURE. In the lactating breast the lobules are packed with secretory alveoli among which some intralobular ducts may be seen (Fig. 540). In general, the interlobular septa are greatly thinned; those illustrated in Figure 540 are wider than most. The appearance of alveoli in different parts of a lactating breast varies in that the alveoli in some parts of the breast have high columnar cells and others low columnar cells. Some are distended with secretion, and some contain only a little. It is probable that the alveoli of different parts of the same breast may, at the same time, be in different stages of a secretory cycle.

Milk contains proteins, lactose, fat and mineral salts. Of these constituents, fat is most easily demonstrated by histologic methods in the alveolar cells. In ordinary paraffin sections the fat droplets in the cytoplasm are dissolved, and the spaces they formerly occupied appear as cytoplasmic vacuoles. These are numerous between the free borders of the alveolar cells and their nuclei (Fig. 541). The free borders of the alveolar cells that are in active secretion appear frayed. It is probable that part of the cytoplasm at the free borders of the cells is lost in the process of secretion; hence, the mammary glands are of the apocrine type.

CAUSE OF LACTATION. Hormones are necessary, not only to make the breast develop during pregnancy, but also to make it function after parturition. Furthermore, the hormones that induce lactation are at least somewhat different from those that induce breast growth.

It is generally conceded that a special anterior pituitary hormone, the lactogenic hormone, plays an important part in causing and maintaining lactation. Other hormones are also essential. Moreover, it seems probable that a pure hormone that has been recovered from the anterior pituitary gland (*prolactin*) does not account for all the effects that are exerted by the lactogenic hormone. There is evidence to show that lactogenic hormone may be present in the anterior pituitary glands at times other than during lactation. However, it is probable that the anterior pituitary gland makes more lactogenic hormone immediately following parturition and during lactation than at other times.

There is a very curious relationship between estrogen and the lactogenic hormone. There is much evidence to indicate that enough estrogen in the blood is a requisite for putting the anterior pituitary gland "into a mood," as it were, to make lactogenic hormone in large amounts. For example, if female animals of certain kinds are injected day by day with estrogen and then the estrogen injections are discontinued, the animals will begin to lactate. Yet, while estrogen seems to arouse the desires of the anterior pituitary with regard to producing lactogenic hormone, and causes it to secrete enough to cause breast development, it also tends to prevent the anterior pituitary from realizing its full secretory capacity in connection with lactogenic hormone, for enough estrogen in the blood seems to suppress lactation. Lactation, it must be remembered, does not begin during pregnancy but only after the placenta has been delivered and the body has been released from the effects of the estrogen and other hormones made by this structure. That estrogen can suppress lactation is further indicated by the fact that if sufficient estrogen is given a woman in the days following parturition, lactation is suppressed.

The foregoing could explain why the breasts of a newborn baby, whether male or female, tend to become distended with secretion shortly after birth, as if they, in their very undeveloped state, were attempting to function. This could be due to the estrogen pro-

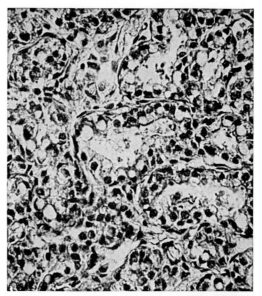

Fig. 541. High-power photomicrograph of a small area of a section of a lactating breast. Notice the vacuoles that represent fat droplets in the secretory cells of the alveoli, particularly at their free borders.

duced by the placenta during pregnancy having stimulated the anterior pituitary gland of the fetus, as well as that of the mother, to try to make lactogenic hormone. Consequently, when the fetus is born and loses its connection with the placenta, its anterior pituitary gland, being now removed from the inhibitory effects of placental estrogen, could secrete enough lactogenic hormone to make the ducts of the mammary glands of the baby secrete a little fluid. This is called *witches' milk*. Since much of this is retained in the ducts, the ducts become temporarily distended.

The maintenance of breast function depends upon the anterior pituitary gland's continuing to secrete lactogenic hormone. This, in turn, depends upon the breasts being emptied regularly. The nervous stimulation from nursing and the psychological factors involved both contribute toward making the anterior pituitary continue the production of this hormone. While the anterior pituitary gland continues to make lactogenic hormone, it seems hesitant to make F.S.H., probably because the lactogenic hormone continues to exert a luteotrophic effect which results in a continued secretion of progesterone, which, in turn, suppresses F.S.H. secretion. Hence, ovulation and menstruation may not occur during the time a mother is nursing her baby. However, this is by no means a universal phenomenon, and women can become pregnant again during the nursing period. It is of interest that while enough estrogen is made during pregnancy to inhibit the anterior pituitary gland from beginning to secrete lactogenic hormone, enough is not made to inhibit an anterior pituitary gland whose lactogenic function is well established from continuing to make the hormone. Consequently, pregnancy does not interfere with a well-established lactation, and a woman may continue nursing one baby after another has been conceived.

A thorough emptying of the breasts at nursing helps maintain and even increases their functional capacities, not only because the nervous stimuli involved somehow stimulate the anterior pituitary to continue to make lactogenic hormone, but also because increased demands for function tend to stimulate the growth of enough further structure to permit the increased functional demands to be met.

Lactation cannot proceed in the absence of the adrenal cortex. The cortical hormone that affects carbohydrate metabolism appears to be the essential factor from this gland. The thyroid hormone also facilitates lactation.

REGRESSION AFTER LACTATION. Since the breasts must be emptied regularly if their structure is to be maintained and if the secretion of lactogenic hormone is to be continued, the discontinuance of breast feeding, provided that the breasts are not regularly emptied by other means, leads to their gradually regaining almost the same type of microscopic structure as they exhibit before pregnancy begins. They do not return to precisely the same state as before because a few alveoli persist in them. But most of the alveoli are resorbed, and the lobules shrink in size. The partitions of interlobular connective tissue again become thick and strong. It is very important that the breasts be properly supported during the time these partitions are thin, but is particularly important during the period while the alveoli are being absorbed, the lobules are shrinking in size and the interlobular partitions are becoming thick again (the 2 to 3 months following the cessation of lactation). If the interlobular septa become

"set" in a stretched state, the breasts will subsequently sag unduly.

The Mammary Glands After the Menopause. The changes that occur in the breast after the menopause are various. The general trend that the breast exhibits is toward atrophy, both of its epithelial and connective tissue components. The intercellular substance of the latter may undergo a hyalin change, but irregular growth and secretory changes may be superimposed upon the general atrophic changes. The epithelium of some ducts may proliferate and that of others secrete and convert the ducts concerned into cysts. Doubtless, estrogen and progesterone deficiency are chiefly responsible for the progressive atrophy that occurs after the menopause. The irregular growth and the secretory changes that are sometimes superimposed on the atrophic changes have been attributed to estrogen, but surely it seems more probable that those that occur around the time of the menopause are caused by anterior pituitary hormones that are secreted more abundantly when the anterior pituitary gland is being released from the restraining influences of estrogen. Certainly much more F.S.H. is secreted by the anterior pituitary after the estrogen level of the blood falls at the time of the menopause, and quite possibly other anterior pituitary hormones, that might act to make the breasts grow and secrete a little, are secreted at the same time. Indeed, it is our opinion that there is some parallelism between the breasts of the newborn and those of a woman who has just experienced the menopause. In both individuals the anterior pituitary has been released from a prolonged period of stimulation by estrogen and, in both, the breasts tend to become cystic. So, whereas the effect of estrogen and progesterone deficiency might, in the end, lead indirectly to breast atrophy, it might be suspected that for a time after the menopause the secretion of some anterior pituitary hormones would complicate the histologic picture seen in the glands.

REFERENCES

GENERAL REFERENCES ON HORMONE CONTROL
OF THE PARTS OF THE FEMALE
REPRODUCTIVE SYSTEM

Allen, E., Danforth, C. H., and Doisy, E. A.

(eds.): Sex and Internal Secretions, ed. 2, Baltimore, Williams & Wilkins, 1939.

Burrows, H.: Biological Actions of Sex Hormones, ed. 2, London, Cambridge, 1949.

Corner, G. W.: The Hormones in Human Reproduction, Princeton, Princeton Univ. Press, 1942.

Hartman, C. G.: The Time of Ovulation in Women, Baltimore, Williams & Wilkins, 1936.

Lillie, F. R.: The free-martin; a study of the action of sex hormones in the foetal life of cattle, J. Exper. Zool. 23:371, 1917.

Novak, E.: Gynecological and Obstetrical Pathology with Clinical and Endocrine Relations, ed. 2, Philadelphia, Saunders, 1947.

———: Textbook of Gynecology, Boston, Little, 1952.

Papanicolaou, G. N., Traut, H. F., and Marchetti, A. A.: The Epithelia of Woman's Reproductive Tract, London, Oxford, 1948.

Parkes, A. S.: The Internal Secretion of the Ovary, London, Longmans, 1929.

Pincus, G., and Thimann, K. V.: The Hormones, vols. 1, 2 and 3, New York, Acad. Press, 1948, 1950 and 1955.

Riddle, O.: Endocrine aspects of the physiology of reproduction, Ann. Rev. Physiol. 3:573, 1941.

Siegler, S. L.: Fertility in Women, Philadelphia, Lippincott, 1944.

SPECIAL REFERENCES ON THE OVARY

Allen, E.: The menstrual cycle of the monkey, *Macacus rhesus,* Contrib. Embryol. 19:1, 1927.

———: The oestrus cycle in the mouse, Am. J. Anat. 30:297, 1922.

Allen, E., Pratt, J. P., Newell, Q. U., and Bland, L. J.: Hormone content of human ovarian tissues, Am. J. Physiol. 92:127, 1930.

———: Human ova from large follicles; including a search for maturation divisions and observations on atresia, Am. J. Anat. 46:1, 1930.

Anderson, E., and Beams, H. W.: Observations on the ultramicroscopic anatomy of a mammalian ovum, Anat. Rec. 134:525, 1959.

Aschheim, S.: Pregnancy tests, J.A.M.A. 104:1324, 1935.

Bacsich, P.: Some observations on near-term human foetal ovaries, J. Endocrinol. 7:14, 1951.

Corner, G. W.: Cytology of the ovum, ovary, and fallopian tube *in* Cowdry's Special Cytology, ed. 2, p. 1565, New York, Hoeber, 1932.

———: Development, organization, and breakdown of the corpus luteum in the rhesus monkey, Contrib. Embryol. 31:117, 1945.

———: Ovulation and menstruation in *Macacus rhesus,* Contrib. Embryol. 15:75, 1923.

———: Relation between menstruation and ovulation in monkeys; its possible significance for man, J.A.M.A. 89:1838, 1927.

Farris, E. J.: Human Ovulation and Fertility, Philadelphia, Lippincott, 1956.

Fevold, H. L., Hisaw, F. L., Hellbaum, A., and Hertz, R.: Sex hormones of the anterior lobe of hypophysis: further purification of a follicular stimulating factor and the physiological effects on immature rats and rabbits, Am. J. Physiol. 104:710, 1933.

Gatz, A. J.: A critique on the discussion of oogenesis in the textbooks of histology, Turtox News 33:106, 1955.

Hartman, C. G.: Physiology of reproduction in the monkey and their bearing on gynecology and anthropology, Endocrinology 25:670, 1939.

Latta, J. S., and Pederson, E. S.: The origin of ova and follicle cells from the germinal epithelium of the ovary of the albino rat as demonstrated by selective intravital staining with India ink, Anat. Rec. 90:23, 1944.

Lever, J. D.: Remarks on the electron microscopy of the rat luteum and comparison with earlier observations on the adrenal cortex, Anat. Rec. 124:111, 1956.

Matthews, L. H.: Visual stimulation and ovulation in pigeons, Proc. Roy. Soc., London, s. B. 126:557, 1939.

Pederson, E. S.: Histogenesis of lutein tissue of the albino rat, Am. J. Anat. 88:397, 1951.

Pincus, G.: The physiology of ovarian and testis hormones *in* Pincus, G., and Thimann, K. V. (eds.): The Hormones, ed. 3, p. 665, New York, Acad. Press, 1955.

Slater, D. W., and Dornfeld, E. J.: Quantitative aspects of growth and oocyte production in the early prepubertal rat ovary, Am. J. Anat. 76:253, 1945.

Yamada, E., Muta, T., Motomura, A., and Koga, H.: The fine structure of the oocyte in the mouse ovary studied with electron microscope, Kurume Med. J. 4:148, 1957.

SPECIAL REFERENCES ON THE OVIDUCTS

Novak, E., and Everett, H. S.: Cyclical and other variations in the tubal epithelium, Am. J. Obst. & Gynec. 16:449, 1928.

Snyder, F. F.: Changes in the human oviduct during the menstrual cycle in pregnancy, Bull. Johns Hopkins Hosp. 35:141, 1924.

Stockard, C. R., and Papanicolaou, G. N.: The existence of a typical oestrus cycle in the guinea pig—with a study of its histological and physiological changes, Am. J. Anat. 22:225, 1917.

SPECIAL REFERENCES ON THE UTERUS

Bartelmez, G. W.: Histological studies of the

menstruating mucous membranes of the human uterus, Contrib. Embryol. *24*:141, 1933.

————: Menstruation, Physiol. Rev. *17*:28, 1937.

Bartelmez, G. W., and Bensley, C. M.: Human uterine gland cells *in* Cowdry's Special Cytology, ed. 2, p. 1523, New York, Hoeber, 1932.

Bensley, S. H.: On the presence, properties and distribution of the intercellular ground-substance of loose connective tissue, Anat. Rec. *60*:93, 1934.

Bo, W. J.: The relationship between vitamin A deficiency and estrogen in producing uterine metaplasia in the rat, Anat. Rec. *124*:619, 1956.

Bo, W. J., and Atkinson, W. B.: Histochemical studies on glycogen deposition in the uterus of the rat, Anat. Rec. *113*:91, 1952.

Corner, G. W.: Influence of the ovarian hormones oestrin and progestin upon the menstrual cycle of the monkey, Am. J. Physiol. *113*:238, 1935.

Daron, G. H.: The arterial pattern of the tunica mucosa of the uterus in *Macacus rhesus,* Am. J. Anat. *58*:349, 1936.

Markee, J. E.: Menstruation in intraocular endometrial transplants in the rhesus monkey, Contrib. Embryol. *28*:219, 1940.

Nicol, T., and Snell, R. S.: The appearances of lipoid in the genital tract of the mature virgin guinea pig during the oestrous cycle, J. Obst. & Gynaec. Brit. Emp. *61*:216, 1954.

Nilsson, O.: Ultrastructure of mouse uterine surface epithelium under different estrogenic influences, Almqvist & Wiksells, pp. 1-387, Uppsala, 1959.

O'Leary, J. L.: Form changes in the human uterine gland during the menstrual cycle and in early pregnancy, Am. J. Anat. *42*:289, 1929.

Sharman, A.: An experimental study of postpartum endometrial repair in the guinea pig and rat, J. Endocrinol. *8*:162, 1951.

————: Post-partum regeneration of the human endometrium, J. Anat. *87*:1, 1953.

Smith, P. E., and Engle, E. T.: Differences in the time of onset of uterine bleeding after cessation of estrin and progestin treatments, Anat. Rec. *71*:73, 1938.

Sylvén, B.: The occurrence of ester sulphuric acids of high molecular weight and of mast cells in the stroma of the normal uterine corpus mucosa, Acta obst. et gynec. scandinav. *25*: 189, 1945.

Wislocki, G. B., and Dempsey, E. W.: Histochemical reactions of the endometrium in pregnancy, Am. J. Anat. *77*:365, 1945.

Young, A.: Vascular architecture of the rat uterus, Proc. Roy. Soc. Edinburgh *64*:292, 1952.

SPECIAL REFERENCES ON THE PLACENTA

Arey, L. B.: The presence and arrangement of smooth muscle in the human placenta, Anat. Rec. *100*:636, 1948.

Barcroft, J., and Barron, D.: Observations upon form and relations of the maternal and fetal vessels in the placenta of the sheep, Anat. Rec. *94*:569, 1946.

Boving, B. G.: Implantation, Ann. New York Acad. Sc. *75*:700, 1959.

Boyd, J. D.: Some aspects of the relationship between mother and child, Ulster M. J. *28*:35, 1959.

Boyd, J. D., and Hamilton, W. J.: The giant cells of the pregnant human uterus, J. Obst. & Gynaec. Brit. Emp. *67*:208, 1960.

————: Development of the human placenta in the first three months of gestation, J. Anat. *94*:297, 1960.

Boyd, J. D., and Hughes, A. F. W.: Observations on human chorionic villi using the E/M, J. Anat. *88*:356, 1954.

Dempsey, E. W., and Wislocki, G. B.: E/M of human placental villi, Anat. Rec. *117*:609, 1953.

Hamilton, W. J., and Boyd, J. D.: Observations on the human placenta, Proc. Roy. Soc. Med. *44*:489, 1951.

————: Development of the human placenta in the first three months of gestation, J. Anat. *94*:297, 1960.

Mossman, H. W.: Comparative morphogenesis of the fetal membranes and accessory uterine structures, Contrib. Embryol. *26*: no. 158, 1937.

Paine, C. G.: Observations on placental histology in normal and abnormal pregnancy, J. Obst. & Gynaec. Brit. Emp. *64*, No. 5, 1957.

Ramsey, E. M.: The vascular pattern of the endometrium of the pregnant Rhesus monkey (Macaca mulatta), Contrib. Embryol. *33*:113, 1949.

————: Vascular adaptations of the uterus to pregnancy, Ann. New York Acad. Sc. *75*:726, 1959.

Sohval, A. R., Gaines, J. A., and Strauss, L.: Chromosomal sex detection in the human newborn and fetus from examination of the umbilical cord, placental tissue and fetal membranes, Ann. New York Acad. Sc. *75*:905, 1959.

Villee, C. A.: The Placenta and Fetal Membranes, Baltimore, Williams & Wilkins, 1960.

Wislocki, G. B., and Bennett, H. S.: Cytology of placental trophoblast, Anat. Rec. *100*:414, 1948.

SPECIAL REFERENCES ON THE CERVIX
AND THE VAGINA

Danforth, D. N.: The fibrous nature of the human cervix, and its relations to the isthmic segment in gravid and non-gravid uteri, Am. J. Obst. & Gynec. *53*:541, 1947.

de Allende, I. L. C., Shorr, E., and Hartman, C. G.: A comparative study of the vaginal smear cycle of the rhesus monkey and the human, Contrib. Embryol. *31*:1, 1945.

Gillman, J.: Cyclical changes in vaginal smear in the baboon and its relationship to perineal swelling, South African J. M. Sc. *2*:44, 1937.

Nicol, T., and Snell, R. S.: The appearances of lipoid in the cells of the vaginal smear of the guinea pig, J. Obst. & Gynaec. Brit. Emp. *61*: 85, 1954.

Papanicolaou, G. N.: The sexual cycle in the human female as revealed by vaginal smears, Am. J. Anat. *52*:519, 1933.

Smith, B. G., and Brunner, E. K.: The structure of the human vaginal mucosa in relation to the menstrual cycle and to pregnancy, Am. J. Anat. *54*:27, 1934.

SPECIAL REFERENCES ON THE MAMMARY GLANDS

Bunting, H.: Cytochemical properties of apocrine sweat gland normally present in the human sweat gland, Anat. Rec. *101*:5, 1948.

Corner, G. W.: The hormonal control of lactation: I. Non-effect of the corpus luteum; II. Positive action of extracts of the hypophysis, Am. J. Physiol. *95*:43, 1930.

Cowie, A. T., and Folley, S. J.: Physiology of the gonadotropins and the lactogenic hormone *in* Pincus, G., and Thimann, K. V. (eds.): The Hormones, ed. 3, p. 309, New York, Acad. Press, 1955.

Dempsey, E. W., Bunting, H., and Wislocki, G. B.: Observations on the chemical cytology of the mammary gland, Am. J. Anat. *81*:309, 1947.

Gardner, W. U.: The effect of ovarian hormones and ovarian grafts upon the mammary glands of male mice, Endocrinology *19*:656, 1935.

————: Growth of the mammary glands in hypophysectomized mice, Proc. Soc. Exper. Biol. & Med. *45*:835, 1940.

————: Inhibition of mammary growth by large amounts of estrogen, Endocrinology *28*:53, 1941.

Gardner, W. U., and Chamberlin, T. L.: Local action of estrone on mammary glands of mice, Yale J. Biol. & Med. *13*:461, 1941.

Gardner, W. U., and White, A.: Mammary growth in hypophysectomized male mice receiving estrogen and prolactin, Proc. Soc. Exper. Biol. & Med. *48*:590, 1941.

Gomez, E. T.: Mammary gland growth in hypophysectomized castrated guinea pigs, Endocrinology *31*:613, 1942.

Gomez, E. T., and Turner, C. W.: Initiation and maintenance of lactation in hypophysectomized guinea pigs, Proc. Soc. Exper. Biol. & Med. *35*:365, 1936.

Gunther, M.: Sore nipples; causes and prevention, Lancet *249*:590, 1945.

Jeffers, K. R.: Cytology of the mammary gland of albino rat, Am. J. Anat. *56*:257, 279, 1935.

Linzell, J. L.: The silver staining of myoepithelial cells, particularly in the mammary gland, and their relation to the ejection of milk, J. Anat. *86*:49, 1952.

Nelson, W. O.: Endocrine control of the mammary gland, Physiol. Rev. *16*:488, 1936.

Petersen, W. E.: Lactation, Physiol. Rev. *24*:340, 1944.

Rawlinson, H. E., and Pierce, G. B.: Visible intraepithelial iron in the mammary glands of various species, Science *117*:33, 1953.

Riddle, O.: Lactogenic and mammogenic hormones, J.A.M.A. *115*:2276, 1940.

Selye, H.: Effect of chronic progesterone overdosage on the female accessory sex organs of normal, ovariectomized and hypophysectomized rats, Anat. Rec. *78*:253, 1940.

Selye, H., Collip, J. B., and Thomson, D. L.: Nervous and hormonal factors in lactation, Endocrinology *18*:237, 1934.

Trentin, J. J., DeVita, J., and Gardner, W. U.: Effect of moderate doses of estrogen and progesterone on mammary growth and hair growth in dogs, Anat. Rec. *113*:163, 1952.

Chapter 28

The Male Reproductive System

THE PARTS OF THE SYSTEM AND THEIR FUNCTIONS

The male reproductive system (Fig. 542) consists of: (1) two gonads, the *testes*, which produce male germ cells and male sex hormone; (2) a copulatory organ, the *penis*, by which male germ cells may be delivered into the vagina of the female; (3) a long, complicated set of tubes and tubules which lead from the testes to the penis and so permit male germ cells made in the testes both to be stored and to be conducted to the male copulatory organ; and (4) certain glands called the male accessory glands, which have much smooth muscle in their walls. These glands not only provide a fluid vehicle for carrying male germ cells through the copulatory organ in the sexual act, but also, by the reflex contraction of the smooth muscle of their walls during the sexual act (certain voluntary muscles also participate), cause a mixture of their secretions and male germ cells (the mixture is called *semen*) to be expressed vigorously from the penis; this phenomenon, of brief duration, is termed *ejaculation*.

From the foregoing it may be realized that the male reproductive system consists of 4 structures or groups of structures that have somewhat different functions. Before considering the details of the microscopic structure of these and the relation of their microscopic structure to their function, it may be helpful to discuss, in a general way, some further features that they possess and their relation to one another.

Some General Features of the Testes. Although the testes develop in the abdomen from the indifferent gonads of the embryo, they migrate, in a way to be described in detail later, so that in postnatal life they are contained in the scrotum. This is a pendulous bag that hangs between the curved anteromedial borders of the proximal parts of the thighs (shown, but not labeled, in Fig. 542). Its wall is thin, being composed of skin, an incomplete layer of smooth muscle (the dartos)

and some subcutaneous tissue. The wall of the scrotum has a considerable surface area, and it is believed that this permits its contents to be maintained at a temperature slightly below that of the body as a whole. This is probably an important requisite in man for the production of male germ cells by the testes. The dartos muscle in the wall of the scrotum contracts in response to cold and certain other types of stimuli; its contraction makes the scrotum smaller and its wall corrugated.

Like the ovaries, the testes perform the two functions of producing germ cells and sex hormone. Male germ cells are called *spermatozoa* (*sperma* = seed; *zōon* = animal). The generic term for substances having male sex hormone activity is *androgen* (*anēr* = man; *gennaō* = I produce).

The structure and the functions of the testes are governed by the gonadotrophic hormone of the anterior pituitary gland. As a boy approaches puberty, the anterior pituitary gland begins to secrete substantial amounts of gonadotrophic hormone. This, in turn, stimulates the testes to begin producing both spermatozoa and androgen. The androgen secreted as a result of the gonadotrophic stimulus brings about the development of the secondary sex characteristics of the male that appear at this time.

The testes have two important functional components. First, tubules, having walls of many cells in thickness and a total length of almost half a mile, are packed into the two testes (Fig. 543). These are the *seminiferous* (*semen* = seed; *ferre* = to carry) tubules. Their walls consist of many layers of cells; those cells of the innermost layers are more or less continuously turning into spermatozoa. These become free in the lumens of the tubules. The second important functional component of the testes consists of clumps of endocrine cells, the *interstitial cells*. These are disposed in the connective tissue stroma between the tubules. It is probable that these produce the androgen that is made by the testes.

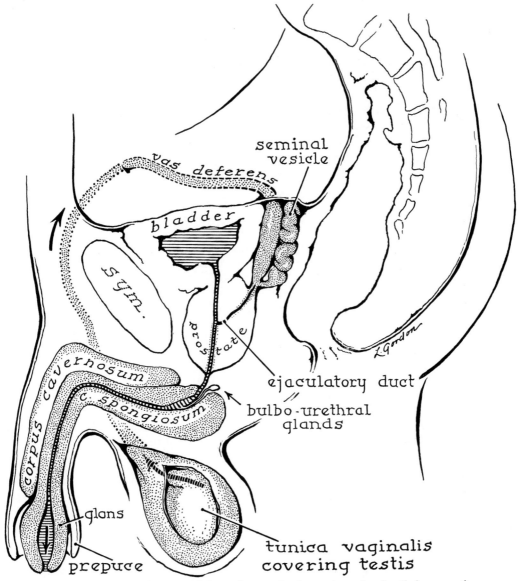

FIG. 542. Diagram of the parts of the male reproductive system, showing their connections with one another.

Each testis is an ovoid body, 4 to 5 cm. long. It is covered with a thick capsule called the *tunica albuginea* because it contains so much white fibrous tissue (Fig. 543). Along the posterior border of each testis, the capsule becomes greatly thickened and extends into the substance of the gland for a short distance to form an incomplete partition. Since it tends to be in the middle of the gland, this abortive partition and the thickened part of the capsule from which it arises are said to consti-

tute the *mediastinum* (*mediastinum* = being in the middle) of the testis (Fig. 543).

The mediastinum of each testis is riddled with a network of passageways that are lined with epithelium. These constitute the *rete* (*rete* = a net) testis (Fig. 543). The seminiferous tubules of the testis all empty into the spaces of the rete.

General Features of the Set of Conducting Tubes and Tubules. The spermatozoa present in the testis or seen in the rete testis are not

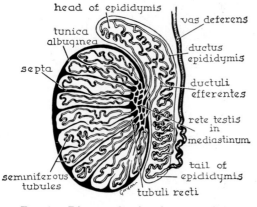

FIG. 543. Diagram showing the parts of the testis and the epididymis.

capable of fertilizing ova. It appears that spermatozoa complete their maturation outside the testis in tubules which are enormously long and convoluted. Some morphologic evidence of this maturation has been observed in the guinea pig in which the spermatozoa were seen to take their definitive shape in the distal part of the tubule only. The names and the general distribution of the tubules through which the spermatozoa must pass to reach the male copulatory organ will now be given.

The spaces of the rete testis, at the upper part of the mediastinum, drain into 15 to 20 tubules called the *ductuli efferentes* (*effere* = to bring out) that arise in this region (Fig. 543). These penetrate the tunica albuginea of the testis and emerge from its upper part. They thereupon pursue an extraordinarily convoluted course as they pass upward. Each tubule is so wound on itself that each forms a little cone-shaped structure. The cones are bound together by loose connective tissue and together they constitute most of the head of a narrow crescentic structure that caps the upper pole of the testis and extends down along one of its sides. Since the testes are alike (twins), this narrow structure that caps each of them is termed an *epididymis* (*epi* = upon; *didymos* = twin).

Each epididymis has a head, a body and a tail. The head fits over part of the upper pole of the testis and consists essentially of the cones of convoluted ductuli efferentes (Fig. 543). The body extends down along the posterolateral border of the testis and consists chiefly of the ductus epididymis. This duct begins in the head where all the ductuli efferentes empty into it. In the body of the epididymis it pursues an extremely convoluted course (Fig. 543). This part of it, if unraveled, would be seen to be several yards long. In the tail of the epididymis, which reaches nearly to the lower pole of the testis, the ductus epididymis gradually assumes a less convoluted course and finally emerges from the tail to become the *ductus,* or *vas, deferens* (*deferre* = to carry away) (Fig. 543).

The ductus deferens ascends from the tail of the epididymis along the posterior border of the testis, medial to the epididymis. It becomes associated with blood vessels and nerves and becomes possessed of coverings derived from the anterior abdominal wall, whose lowest medial part it traverses in a region known as the *inguinal canal.* The ductus deferens, together with the blood vessels and the nerves associated with it and the wrappings it obtains from the tissues of the anterior abdominal wall, constitutes a structure known as the *spermatic cord.* The ductus deferens, in the spermatic cord, traverses the inguinal canal, which leads through the muscles and the fascia of the abdominal wall, to enter the abdominal cavity (however, the ductus remains outside the peritoneum). Here the ductus deferens becomes free of its coverings and, after entering and pursuing a course in the pelvis—a course that need not be described here—reaches the back of the urinary bladder (Fig. 542). An elongated epithelial-lined sac, the *seminal vesicle* (a blind outpouching of the ductus deferens), lies lateral to it on the back of the bladder (Fig. 542). Immediately beyond the point at which the seminal vesicle empties into the ductus deferens, the ductus—which is now the common duct of the testis and the seminal vesicle—is known as the *ejaculatory duct* (Fig. 543). This duct pierces the upper surface of the prostate gland, traverses the substance of this gland and empties into the urethra, which structure, in turn, courses through the prostate gland on its way from the bladder to the penis.

General Features of the Glands That Supply the Fluid Vehicle for Spermatozoa. As noted before, the fluid that is delivered through the penis in ejaculation is called semen, and it is a composite of spermatozoa and a fluid vehicle, most of which is supplied by the seminal vesicles and the prostate gland. Moreover, these two structures, as well as containing epithelial secretory cells which provide the fluid vehicle described above, have a considerable amount of smooth muscle in their walls, and the sudden reflex contraction of these muscles at the time of ejaculation provides part of the force required to eject the semen.

The seminal vesicle has already been described as an outpouching from the ductus deferens near its termination. It does not contain glandular secretory units as such, but instead its lining is composed of secretory cells and is thrown into an enormous number of folds (Fig. 555). The secretion produced by its lining cells accumulates in the cavity of the vesicle, and the engorgement of the vesicle that results from this process, together with the filling of the glands of the prostate gland (to be described later), by stimulating the endings of afferent nerves, is probably a very important factor in arousing sex urge in the male. Moreover, it is probable that a very important reason for the sex urge of males decreasing with age is the fact that the secretory activity of the epithelial cells of these structures is controlled by the amount of male sex hormone in the circulation, and this decreases with age.

The prostate gland—about the size and the shape of a horse chestnut—is essentially a rounded mass of smooth muscle and connective tissue, the substance of which is thoroughly riddled by a great many separate compound tubulo-alveolar glands. The prostate gland surrounds the first part of the urethra as the latter emerges from the neck of the bladder (Fig. 542). The tubulo-alveolar compound glands that extend throughout its substance all drain, by means of about 2 dozen excretory ducts, into the prostatic portion of the urethra.

The Copulatory Organ. The urethra, which courses through the penis to open through its end, serves, in the act of copulation, as a means whereby semen can be delivered from the body. However, the penis, under ordinary conditions, is a flaccid structure and in this state it could not function as a copulatory organ. However, in a male subjected to sufficient erotic influence, the penis becomes greatly increased in size and assumes a more or less erect position. This phenomenon is known as *erection,* and it enables the organ to perform the sexual act. Erection is an involuntary act controlled by the autonomic nervous system. The increased size and the altered position of the organ that occur under these conditions are to be explained by the fact that most of its substance consists of erectile tissue (see p. 666). This is disposed in three long cylindrical bodies arranged, two side by side and known as the *corpora cavernosa,* and one placed medially below the paired ones and known as the *corpus cavernosum urethrae* because it, in its substance, conducts the urethra from one of its ends to the other (Figs. 542 and 559). The corpora cavernosa contain a vast number of little cavities, all connected with the vascular system. When the penis is flaccid the cavities are collapsed and contain only a little blood because the vascular arrangement is such that blood can drain from the cavities more easily than it can enter them. But, under conditions of erotic stimulation, nervous impulses flow to the organ and relax the smooth muscle of the arteries that supply the cavities. This causes greatly increased amounts of blood to enter them, more than can be drained away conveniently. As the cavities of the corpora cavernosa become distended with blood, some of the veins which ordinarily drain blood away from the cavities become compressed. The net result of the great increase of the arterial supply and the impeded venous drainage is that the cavernous bodies become longer, thicker, wider and straighter and, as a consequence, the whole organ becomes enlarged and erect. Subsequently, when the smooth muscle of the arteries that supply the cavities contracts, the rate of drainage of blood from the spaces in the erectile tissue comes to exceed the rate at which it is delivered into the spaces, and, as a result, the organ returns to its flaccid state.

THE TESTES

Development and Descent. Up to the end of the 6th week, the gonads of male and female embryos are indistinguishable. By this time, cells from the germinal epithelium have grown down into the mesenchyme of the gonad, but there is no difference in their arrangement to indicate that the gonad will become an ovary or a testis. However, if the embryo is to become a male, the epithelium in the substance of the gonad, in the 7th week, becomes organized into fairly distinct sex cords, and the mesenchyme immediately beneath the germinal epithelium becomes thickened, indicating that the thick tunica albuginea of the male gonad will form later. As development proceeds, the sex cords become continuous with another group of epithelial cords that become organized somewhat more deeply in the testis and that are the forerunners of the rete. The development of the other ducts of the male genital system, and the manner in which they become connected with each other, involves embryologic considerations too detailed to be dealt with here.

By the 4th month, the elongated mass of tissue comprising the embryonic testis has become sufficiently condensed and rounded to have assumed a form suggestive of its adult shape. The cords of epithelium within it, destined to become the seminiferous tubules, have become more sharply defined from the mesenchyme that occupies the spaces between them which is differentiating into the connective tissue stroma of the gland. Some of the cells of the stroma enlarge and become grouped together to constitute clusters of *interstitial cells*. It appears established that these produce androgen during fetal life and that the testis is a much more active endocrine gland in the fetus than it is after birth until the time of puberty. It seems possible that the development of the interstitial cells of the testis in fetal life may be due to the gonadotrophin made by the placenta.

By the 6th month of fetal life, the cords of epithelial cells develop into seminiferous tubules. These, although called tubules, do not immediately develop lumens. Each seminiferous tubule becomes surrounded by a connective tissue layer which is continuous with the connective tissue of the mediastinum testis. In the testes of many animals the septa that radiate from the mediastinum out through the testis to the tunica albuginea divide the organ into lobules. However, in the testes of man the septa are incomplete.

Within the imperfectly separated lobules of the testes the seminiferous tubules become arranged in the form of long, convoluted, flattened loops (Fig. 543). At the point where each loop closely approaches the mediastinum, the tubule becomes continuous, by means of relatively straight canals (or canaliculi), the *tubuli recti* (*rectus* = straight) (Fig. 543), with the rete testis.

The testis originates in the body cavity behind the peritoneum at the medial side of the developing kidney. As development proceeds and the testis migrates downward, the peritoneum bulges out through the anterior abdominal wall, just above the medial end of the inguinal ligament, into the inguinal canal. The elongated tubular pouch of peritoneum so formed is called the *processus vaginalis* (sheathlike extension). The testis, which by this time lies immediately behind the peritoneum, is pulled down into the inguinal canal behind the processus vaginalis. The processus vaginalis traverses the inguinal canal and descends into the scrotum, arriving there at about the 7th month or somewhat later. The testis, pulling the ductus deferens behind it, follows along behind the posterior wall of the processus vaginalis to reach the scrotum shortly before the time of birth. The posterior wall of the processus vaginalis is invaginated by the testis and so covers its lateral and anterior wall as well as its two poles. In this way the testis comes to be provided with visceral peritoneum (the visceral layer of the tunica vaginalis). The remainder of the processus vaginalis lies in its own half of the inner wall of the scrotum and so constitutes the parietal layer of the tunica vaginalis. The canal by which the processus vaginalis communicates with the peritoneal cavity then becomes obliterated (this may occur before birth but usually occurs after).

Hormonal Control of Descent of the Testes and Maldescent. Occasionally, one or both testes fail to descend into the scrotum during fetal life or immediately after birth. Testes that fail to descend may be held up at almost any point along the course that they normally follow. An individual with undescended testes is termed a *cryptorchid* (*kryptos* = concealed; *orchis* = testis). In some instances, undescended testes descend spontaneously during infancy, but in the majority of instances they do not, and measures must be taken to assist them to gain the scrotum. Unless the testes gain the favorable environment of the scrotum they do not produce

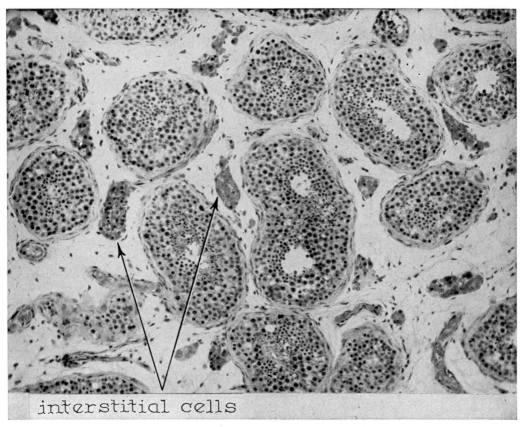

interstitial cells

FIG. 544. Low-power photomicrograph of a portion of a section of a testis of man. Seminiferous tubules, cut in cross and oblique section and separated from one another by a slight amount of interstitial connective tissue, may be seen, as well as some groups of interstitial cells.

spermatozoa; however, the interstitial cells may still produce androgens. As knowledge about sex hormones has increased, it has become apparent that hormones to a considerable degree direct the normal descent of the testes.

As noted before, interstitial cells develop in the testis in significant numbers in the 4th month. This development and the general growth of the organ at this time suggest that it is being stimulated by some trophic hormone. It seems more likely that the trophic hormone concerned would be of placental than of pituitary origin. It is probable that this placental gonadotrophin stimulates the growth of the testis of the male early in fetal life and makes it a functioning endocrine gland.

The androgens thus secreted would bring about the changes in the inguinal canal that permit the testis to descend through it more readily. It would also facilitate the growth of the scrotum and the ductus deferens. So, it seems very probable that the androgen made by the fetal testis is responsible for bringing about these important changes that permit its descent.

Microscopic Appearance from Birth to Puberty. The interstitial cells of the testes are not at all prominent during childhood (from birth to 10 years of age). The seminiferous tubules are small and are composed of two types of cells: the precursors of the definitive germ cells (gonocytes) and the supporting cells. The latter type of cells are numerous and show a small irregular nucleus and a poorly delimited cytoplasm. The gonocytes, fewer in number, have a spherical nucleus and a clearly visible cytoplasmic membrane. During adolescence (10 to 14 years of age), probably under the stimulation of the pituitary

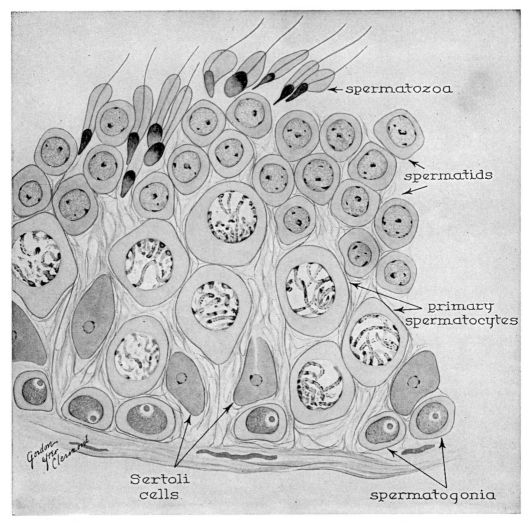

FIG. 545. Drawing of a segment of a human seminiferous tubule, showing the various cell types that form the seminiferous epithelium. (After Clermont)

gonadotrophic hormone, the gonocytes start to proliferate and eventually produce, in large quantity, the spermatozoa. Simultaneously, the supporting cells increase in volume and each comes to have a large, pale-stained polymorphous nucleus and much cytoplasm which extends inwardly from the periphery of the tubule, through the many layers of cells that are concerned with forming spermatozoa, to the lumen of the tubule. These cells are called Sertoli cells (Fig. 545) and are believed to nourish the germ cells. During this period of active growth, the seminiferous tubules develop a lumen while the interstitial cells become distinguishable again in the stroma of the testes.

Spermatogenesis. All the cells of the seminiferous epithelium, except the Sertoli cells, are involved in the production of spermatozoa. The process by which the initial germ cells proliferate and transform into free motile cells, the spermatozoa, is known as spermatogenesis. The initial germ cells, called *spermatogonia* (*gone* = generation), which are generally seen close to the basement membrane of the tubule, are the direct descendants of the gonocytes that are observed in the sex cords of the fetal testis. They have a spherical or ovoid nucleus containing fine chromatin granules and a nucleolus (Fig. 545). These cells proliferate actively, and if the observations made on several mammals can be translated to man, spermatogonia must at the same time renew themselves to maintain their numbers and produce a new generation of germ cells, the *primary spermatocytes* (Fig. 545).

At first the primary spermatocytes are difficult to distinguish from the spermatogonia, but their nuclei soon become intensely stained; this is due to a reorganization of their chromatin into thick prophase chromosomes (Fig. 545). After a peculiar (see below) and long prophase the primary spermatocytes divide, and, as a result of their division, two smaller cells, the secondary spermatocytes, are formed. These secondary spermatocytes have a very short life, and for that reason they are rarely seen in the seminiferous epithelium; they divide, each one giving rise to two smaller cells called *spermatids* (Fig. 545). Spermatids do not divide but instead each undergoes a metamorphosis into a spermatozoon (Fig. 546).

The cell divisions whereby each primary spermatocyte forms two secondary spermatocytes and the divisions whereby each secondary spermatocyte forms two spermatids are of a special character and are called *maturation divisions*. The first of these two divisions (whereby a primary spermatocyte becomes two secondary spermatocytes) is termed a *reduction* or *miotic* (*miosis* = a lessening) division, because in this division the number of chromosomes given each secondary spermatocyte is only half that of the number contained by the primary spermatocyte. Primary spermatocytes have the same number of chromosomes as the somatic cells of the body; in man, this is 46. Since these consist of 23 pairs, somatic cells are said to have a *diploid* (*diplous* = double) number of chromosomes. In the prophase stage of a reduction (miotic) division of a primary spermatocyte, the two members of each pair of chromosomes approach each other so closely that it appears as if each pair were only a single chromosome. The phenomenon of the two members of each pair approaching each other closely is called *synapsis*. In the metaphase of a miotic division the two members of each pair separate from one another, and in the subsequent phases of miosis one member of each pair goes to one daughter cell and one member to the other. As a result, each of the two secondary spermatocytes that form as the result of the miotic division of a primary spermatocyte has only 23 chromosomes—the *haploid* (*haplous* =

single) number, instead of the diploid number. In the next division of maturation, by which each secondary spermatocyte gives rise to two spermatids, the number of chromosomes is not further reduced; thus each spermatid, and hence each spermatozoon, has 23 chromosomes, each of which is a single representative of a former pair.

In the female, the oocyte also undergoes two maturation divisions to form a mature female germ cell or ovum. The first of these occurs immediately before ovulation and the other after ovulation (Fig. 513). However, these divisions do not result in four equally mature germ cells, each with a haploid number of chromosomes, as it does in the male, but only in one mature ovum. Each time the ovum divides its cytoplasm is distributed to the two daughter cells so very unequally that only one of the two cells remains normal and survives; the other, called a *polar body,* eventually degenerates and disappears.

When a mature ovum, with its haploid number of chromosomes, is successfully fertilized by a spermatozoon, with its haploid number of chromosomes, the diploid number of chromosomes is restored in the nucleus of the ovum, with one member of each pair being obtained from the germ plasm of the mother and one from the germ plasm of the father. This provides the basis of inheritance from the two parents.

The two members of one pair of chromosomes—the sex chromosomes—in the primary spermatocyte are not identical, one being an X chromosome and one a Y chromosome. So, when the two chromosomes in a pair separate from one another in miotic division, the X chromosome goes to one secondary spermatocyte and the Y chromosome to the other. As a consequence, half of the spermatozoa that develop in the testes have the X type of sex chromosome and half have the Y type. This is a different arrangement from that which exists in the female, for the sex chromosomes of ova are both of the X type. If a spermatozoon with an X chromosome fertilizes an ovum, the XX combination so formed determines that the embryo that results will be a female. If the spermatozoon concerned has a Y chromosome, the resulting XY combination determines that a male embryo will result.

Transformation of Spermatids into Spermatozoa. The spermatids that result from the

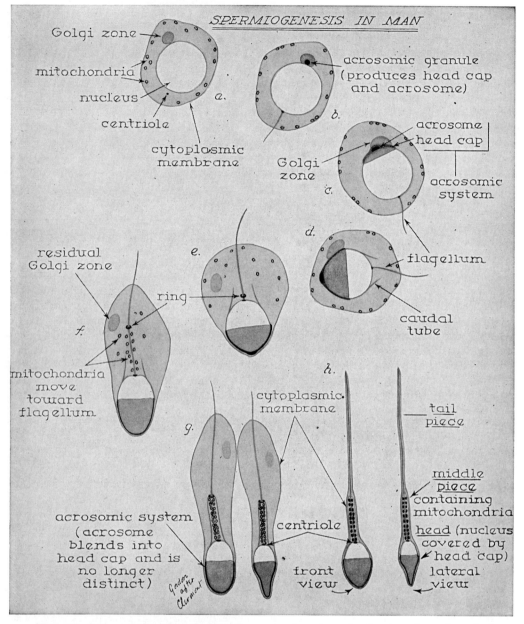

SPERMIOGENESIS IN MAN

Golgi zone

mitochondria

nucleus

centriole

cytoplasmic membrane

a.

acrosomic granule (produces head cap and acrosome)

b.

Golgi zone

c.

acrosome head cap

acrosomic system

d.

flagellum

residual Golgi zone

ring

e.

f.

mitochondria move toward flagellum

caudal tube

h.

cytoplasmic membrane

tail piece

g.

middle piece containing mitochondria

acrosomic system (acrosome blends into head cap and is no longer distinct)

centriole

front view

head (nucleus covered by head cap)

lateral view

Godon after Clermont

FIG. 546. Series of drawings showing the successive stages in the transformation of the spermatid into the spermatozoon. (Modified from Clermont and Leblond: Am. J. Anat. *96*:229)

division of secondary spermatocytes become enveloped by the cytoplasm of Sertoli cells near the lumen of the tubule, and in this environment they undergo a metamorphosis into spermatozoa. This entails a great change in their form. The formation of spermatozoa from spermatids is termed *spermiogenesis*.

The newly formed spermatid (Figs. 545 and 546) shows a centrally located spherical nucleus, a well-delimited Golgi zone close to the nucleus, numerous granular mitochondria lying to the inside of the cytoplasmic membrane and a small centriole (Fig. 546 a). The formation of a spermatozoon involves elabo-

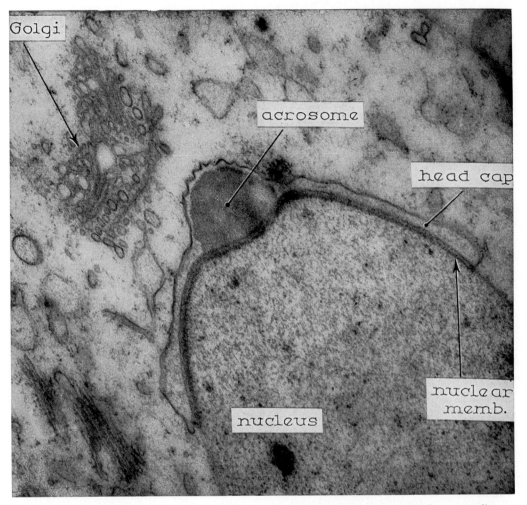

FIG. 547. Electron micrograph ($\times$ 39,000) of a section of a human spermatid (corresponding to Fig. 546 c), showing, in addition to the nucleus and the Golgi zone, the acrosomic system. The acrosome, a hemispherical dense granule, is inside a vesicular structure, the head cap, which also expands on the nuclear membrane. (Fawcett, D. W., and Burgos, M. H.: Ciba Foundation Colloquia on Ageing, vol. 2, p. 86, London, Churchill)

rate changes in all these cellular structures. The first sign of metamorphosis is seen within the Golgi zone; this is indicated by the formation of a dense granule at the surface of the nuclear membrane (Fig. 546 b). This granule, called the *acrosomic granule,* and its derivatives are P.A.S. positive; this indicates the presence of carbohydrates within these structures. The growing acrosomic granule differentiates into two parts: (1) the *acrosome,* which is a small hemisphere on top of the nucleus, and (2) the *head cap,* which is a membranelike structure growing around the acrosome on the surface of the nuclear membrane (Fig. 546, c and d, and Fig. 547). The head cap eventually covers approximately half of the nuclear surface. Once the acrosome and the head cap (the acrosomic system) are well developed, the Golgi zone becomes detached from the head cap and turns into a "residual Golgi zone" (Fig. 546, d and e). As the acrosomic system develops, the centriole becomes attached to the nuclear membrane in an area opposite to the acrosome and gives rise to the vibratile organ of the future spermatozoon, the flagellum. An additional structure appears

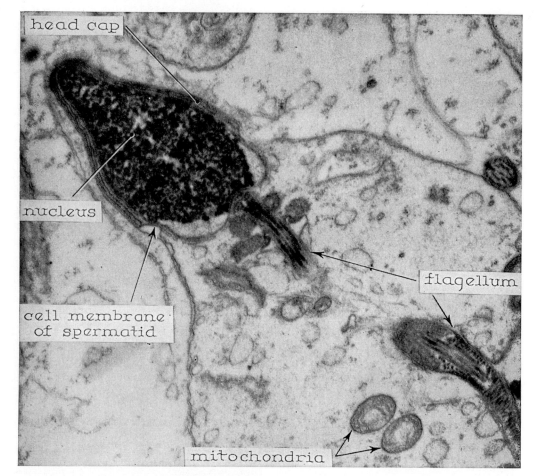

head cap

nucleus

cell membrane of spermatid

flagellum

mitochondria

Fig. 548. Electron micrograph ($\times$ 25,000) of a section of a human spermatid at a more advanced stage of development (corresponding to Fig. 546 g). The nucleus shows a denser osmiophilic material. The head cap is still visible, but the acrosome can no longer be identified. A well-developed flagellum made of numerous filaments is seen extending from the lower end of the nucleus. Mitochondria can also be identified. (Fawcett, D. W., and Burgos, M. H.: Ciba Foundation Colloquia on Ageing, vol. 2, p. 86, London, Churchill)

and surrounds this flagellum; this is the so-called caudal tube, which is made of sub-microscopic filaments attached to the nuclear membrane.

At one stage of spermiogenesis, the acrosome and the head cap orient themselves toward the basement membrane of the seminiferous tubule. This is accompanied by a displacement of the nucleus within the cytoplasm toward the cell membrane (Fig. 546 e). The nucleus then becomes progressively condensed and assumes a slightly flattened and elongated shape. Its anterior end is relatively sharp when it is seen in profile but rounded when it is seen in full face (Fig. 546, g and h). At the

surface of the nucleus, the acrosome blends into the head cap from which it becomes indistinguishable (Fig. 548). Meanwhile, a small ring appears around the flagellum close to the centriole. This ring, once formed, slides along the flagellum for some distance (Fig. 546, e and f). The mitochondria which, up to this stage, have been disposed along the cytoplasmic membrane start to move in the cytoplasm toward the flagellum, more precisely toward the portion of the flagellum between the centriole and the ring (Fig. 546, f, g and h). The mitochondria line up along the flagellum, close to one another, and condense to form a striated collarlike sheath which delimits the middle piece of the future spermatozoon. The fate of the caudal tube is still not well understood, but it probably becomes an additional sheath for the middle piece. As the spermatid completes its development, the cytoplasmic surplus, which is not utilized in the formation of the spermatozoon, is cast off and forms a disintegrating *residual body*. However, a thin layer of cytoplasm, delimited by a cytoplasmic membrane, covers the nucleus, the middle piece and the tail piece (except the extremity) of the spermatozoon.

The structure of the tail piece is similar to that of cilia (Fig. 548), the number and the arrangement of the longitudinal filaments being the same (see p. 225). The net result is that the spermatozoon, though much smaller than the spermatid, retains nuclear elements of the spermatid in its head, some part of its Golgi apparatus in the acrosomic system, most of its mitochondria in the middle piece and its centriole. It is thus able to contribute cytoplasmic as well as nuclear components to the ovum.

When fully formed, spermatozoa leave the Sertoli cells and enter the lumens of the seminiferous tubules. They probably are not motile at this time but are moved along the system of tubules until they reach the upper part of the ductus deferens. When they become mature they become motile and by lashing their tails can move 2 or 3 mm. a minute. This enables them to swim up the female reproductive tract when they are introduced into the vagina.

A cross section of any given seminiferous tubule does not demonstrate cells at all the various stages of development. Commonly, in a cross section, a single tubule reveals groups of cells with those of each group being at the same stage of development. Another tubule will also reveal groups of cells with the cells of each group at the same stage of development, but the stages represented may be different from those represented by the groups of cells in the first tubule. Accordingly, it is necessary to study many cross sections of tubules to see all the stages of development. In the tubules of man the cells of different groups, adjacent to each other along the course of a tubule, may be intermingled in any given cross section, and on superficial examination this may suggest that different stages of de-

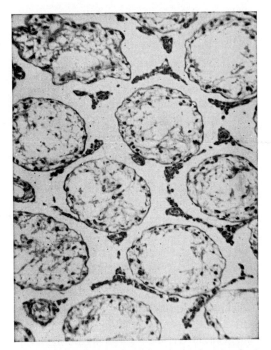

FIG. 549. Low-power photomicrograph of a portion of a section of a testis of a rat that was kept for a considerable period of time on a synthetic diet lacking vitamin E. Observe that the cells concerned in spermatogenesis have disappeared.

velopment are represented by single cells rather than by groups.

Factors Affecting Spermatogenesis. It has already been noted that spermatogenesis does not occur properly unless the testes are maintained at a temperature somewhat lower than that of the body as a whole and unless the cells of the seminiferous tubules are under stimulation by gonadotrophic hormones. A sufficiency of vitamin E in the diet is also essential (Fig. 549). It wiii be recalled that the capacity of the ovary to produce mature germ cells, under the influence of FSH stimulation, ends more or less suddenly, usually when a woman is between the ages of 45 and 50. An event comparable with the menopause of women, a well-defined climacteric, does not occur in the average male. In the male, with increasing age, there is usually no more than a slow decline in the ability of the seminiferous tubules to produce mature germ cells, and there are many authentic cases of men having become fathers at a very advanced age.

Abnormal Spermatozoa. Abnormal spermatozoa are by no means uncommon products of the testes. There are a great variety of these (see Hotchkiss). There is much difference of opinion as to what percentage of spermatozoa may be abnormal without any loss of fertility. The evidence suggests that 10 per cent may be abnormal without any loss, and some investigators have found considerably higher percentages without any loss of fertility. But, although there seems to be a great amount of variation, there seems to be reason to believe that when a quarter, or somewhat fewer, of the spermatozoa are abnormal, fertility is impaired. For example, it has been shown that the semen of bulls with good breeding records average only about 16 per cent of abnormal cells, while those with poor breeding records average about 50 per cent of abnormal spermatozoa.

Concentration in Semen. There are usually more than 100,000,000 spermatozoa in each cubic centimeter of semen in fertile men, and 2 or more cubic centimeters of semen are usually delivered in each ejaculation. So, even if there are a considerable number of abnormal spermatozoa in any given ejaculation, there are a vast number of healthy spermatozoa present in it also. Although there is much variation in individual cases, men whose semen contains only around 50,000,000 spermatozoa per cubic centimeter are not usually so fertile as those whose semen contains considerably more, and those with 20,000,000 or less per cubic centimeter are generally sterile. Although such an enormous number of spermatozoa is produced by the testis, only one spermatozoon actually fertilizes the ovum.

Metabolism of Spermatozoa. In discussing cell respiration (p. 89), a comparison was drawn between fermentative and oxidative types of metabolism. It is of interest to note that spermatozoa obtain their energy requirements chiefly from fermentation; hence, they can live anaerobically. It is probably desirable that they should be able to do so, for in their long journey in the lumens of the various tubes of the male genital system, and in addition, if they are to fertilize an ovum, through the vagina, the cervix, the uterus and the oviduct of the female, they would be most unlikely to receive sufficient oxygen for their maintenance. Carbohydrate, on which they can survive anaerobically by fermentative mechanisms, is present in the secretions of at least several of the tubes through which they pass.

Function of Interstitial Cells. In discussing this matter it is necessary to understand at once that there is a profound difference between fertility and potency in the male. A fertile male may be defined as one who can produce at ejaculation, at least on some occasions, enough semen containing a sufficient number of healthy spermatozoa suspended in a sufficiently normal fluid vehicle to bring about the fertilization of an ovum in a fertile female. A sterile male cannot accomplish this function. Potency refers to another matter— the ability of the male to engage in intercourse. This depends fundamentally on the erection of the penis. A potent but sterile male may be able to ejaculate during intercourse, but the semen expressed will not contain a sufficient number of healthy spermatozoa to cause fertilization of an ovum.

The basis for fertility is spermatogenesis in the seminiferous tubules. The basis for potency is androgen production by the interstitial cells. Therefore, sterility need not cause impotence. Indeed, even eunuchs, though necessarily sterile, are not necessarily impotent unless their testes have been removed before puberty. The reason for this is that if there has been enough time for the androgen produced by the testes after puberty to have thoroughly masculinized the individual, to have established a heterosexual drive and to have permitted reflexes dependent on this drive to be formed, then the individual concerned may have remained potent because of the persistence of the reflexes even though his testes have been removed. Androgen, nevertheless, is concerned with the maintenance of the sex drive in the normal male, but it should be realized that psychological factors are also very important in the maintenance of the drive, once the basis for it has been established by androgen.

A male may be sterilized at operation either by removing the testes or by tying off and cutting the ducti deferentes (vasectomy). The latter operation prevents the egress of spermatozoa from the testes, but the interstitial cells continue to produce androgen, which leaves the testes by way of the blood stream. The testes of the cryptorchid produce androgen but, usually, not spermatozoa. As it is possible for a male to be potent but sterile, it is also possible for an otherwise fertile male to be impotent. In such males, impotency is usually due to emotional factors which interfere with the functioning of the autonomic nervous system in such a way that the blood flow into the cavernous tissue of the penis is not sufficient to cause erection.

It is probable that the secretion of androgen by the interstitial cells is regulated by the anterior pituitary through a push-pull mechanism. When the amount of androgen in the blood stream decreases, the anterior pituitary probably secretes additional gonadotrophic hormone. Then, when this stimulates androgen production and causes increased amounts to be delivered into the blood stream, the secretion of gonadotrophin by the anterior pituitary is temporarily suppressed. It should be anticipated, then, that the administration of androgen to a male will tend to suppress the secretion of gonadotrophic hormone by his anterior pituitary gland and that this in turn will lead to diminished testicular function.

Microscopic Appearance of Interstitial Cells. It has been pointed out that in fetal life interstitial cells develop from the mesenchymal cells of the stroma between the developing seminiferous tubules and that they are much more prominent in the fetal testis from the 4th month on than they are in the postnatal testis between birth and puberty. In the sexually mature male these interstitial cells are distributed either singly or in clumps in the stroma between the tubules, usually in the angular crevices that are created by the round tubules being packed together (Fig. 544). They are large cells, measuring up to 20 or more microns in diameter (Fig. 550). Their spherical to oval nuclei are pale and contain one or more nucleoli. Some interstitial cells are binucleated. In H and E sections the peripheral cytoplasm may be vacuolated because lipoid droplets have been dissolved from it in the preparation of the section. The cytoplasm immediately surrounding the nucleus may appear to be granular; some investigators have described secretion granules in this site. Some interstitial cells contain a brown pigment; this is not melanin, and its precise nature and significance are not known.

The interstitial cells constitute an unusual type of endocrine gland. They do not develop

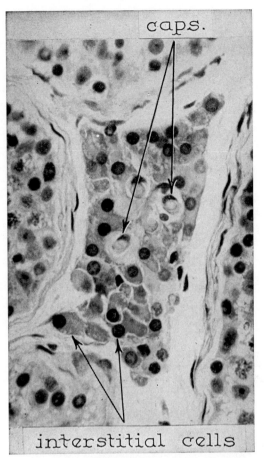

FIG. 550. High-power photomicrograph of a portion of a section of a human testis. Several blood capillaries (*caps.*) cut in cross section may be seen in an island of interstitial cells. This group of cells lies in the connective tissue between the seminiferous tubules. (Section provided by Y. Clermont)

from an epithelial surface, as do most glands, but from a mesenchymal stroma. Since they are scattered about in the stroma, which is abundantly provided with capillaries, they have access to the vascular system (Fig. 550). All in all, they constitute a very diffuse type of endocrine gland.

The cytoplasm of interstitial cells commonly contains lipid droplets and aggregates of a fatty osmiophilic granular material, as well as crystalloids (Fig. 551). Fawcett and Burgos have shown with the E/M that the crystalloids have a complex but orderly internal structure; when they are sectioned they pre-

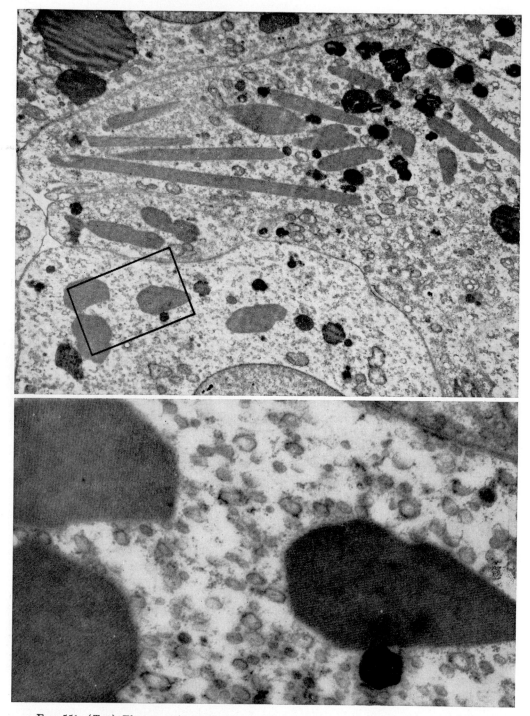

FIG. 551. (*Top*) Electron micrograph (× 8,550) of a section of parts of several interstitial cells. In the cytoplasm, in addition to dark osmiophilic bodies (lipid droplets and pigment granules of a lipoid nature), crystalline structures are visible (the crystalloids of Reinke). (*Bottom*) Electron micrograph (× 51,750) showing a higher magnification of a section of a crystalloid in which a highly ordered internal structure is apparent. (Fawcett, D. W., and Burgos, M. H.: Ciba Foundation Colloquia on Ageing, vol. 2, p. 86, London, Churchill)

sent an appearance not unlike that of a woven fabric (Fig. 551, *bottom*). Christensen and Fawcett have further investigated the interstitial cells and find that the cytoplasm of these cells contains a meshwork of fine, interconnecting tubules (Fig. 552). There are no RNA granules associated with this reticulum. There is some evidence to suggest that this agranular reticulum is the site where male steroid hormones are produced.

Tubuli Recti and Rete Testis. The seminiferous tubules, as they approach the region of the mediastinum testis, become straight and are known as the *tubuli recti*; they empty into the rete testis of the mediastinum (Fig. 543). Spermatogenesis does not occur in the tubuli recti, which are lined by tall Sertolilike cells. The spaces of the rete are lined by cuboidal epithelium, the cells of which are each provided with a single cilium.

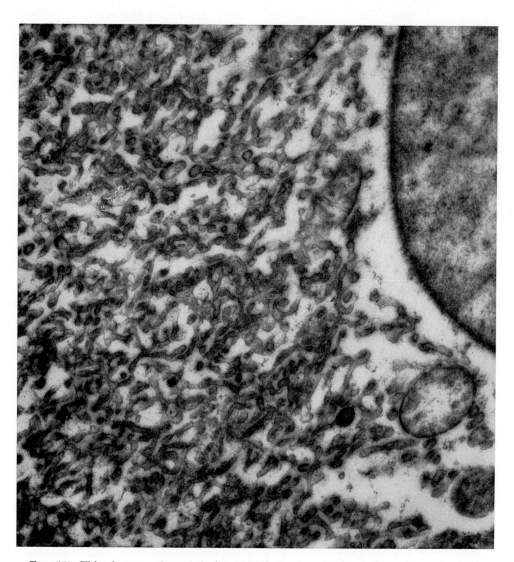

Fig. 552. This electron micrograph ($\times$ 33,000) is of a section of the testis of an opossum and shows part of an interstitial cell. Part of a nucleus is seen at top left, with 4 mitochondria adjacent to it. The remainder of the field is filled with a network of interconnected tubules of agranular endoplasmic reticulum. (From Drs. A. K. Christensen and D. W. Fawcett)

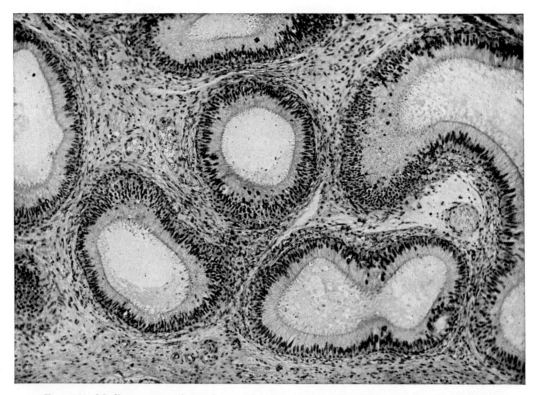

FIG. 553. Medium-power photomicrograph of a section of epididymis, showing the ductus epididymis cut in cross and oblique section. Observe the stereocilia of the tall epithelial lining cells.

THE EPIDIDYMIS

The general structure of the epididymis is described in the first part of this chapter. The further details of its microscopic structure follow.

It is invested in a fibrous covering similar to, but somewhat thinner than, the tunica albuginea of the testis. The ductuli efferentes, in the cone-shaped bodies in which they are arranged, are held together by a delicate vascular connective tissue. The ductules themselves consist of an epithelial lining, a basement membrane and a thin layer of smooth muscle associated with some elastic fibers. The epithelium exhibits alternating groups of high columnar cells which have cilia and low columnar cells which usually do not. The latter cells are probably secretory. From a study of the epididymis of the guinea pig, Mason and Shaver suggested that the combined action of the rete testis, the ductuli efferentes and the proximal portion of the ductus epididymis is

to remove, from the excretory product of the testes, not only excess fluid but also extraneous materials carried with this mass. This reabsorption of fluid at the level of the epididymis would also create a negative pressure which would facilitate the transportation of the spermatozoa from the seminiferous tubule to the epididymis.

The convoluted ductus epididymis, which together with the connective tissue that holds its coils together (Fig. 553) comprises the body and the tail of the epididymis, consists of an epithelial lining, a basement membrane and a thin coat of circularly disposed smooth muscle fibers. The epithelium is tall and regular, and tufts of large nonmotile *stereocilia* (*stereōs* = solid) project toward the lumen from the free margins of the cells (Fig. 553). Cytoplasm extends between the stereocilia, and secretion occurs at this site. Secretion granules and vacuoles may be seen in the cytoplasm between the free margins of the cells and their nuclei.

THE DUCTUS DEFERENS

The ductus or vas deferens is a sufficiently substantial structure to be palpated easily through the skin and the subcutaneous tissue. Its firm consistency is due to its very thick muscular wall and relatively narrow lumen (Fig. 554).

The mucous membrane consists of an epithelial lining and a lamina propria of connective tissue that contains a high content of elastic fibers. It is thrown into longitudinal folds of only moderate height. The epithelium is different in various parts of the ducts. Near the beginning of the duct it resembles that seen in the ductus epididymis. Farther along, the epithelium becomes nonciliated and tends to be pseudostratified.

The muscular coat consists of 3 layers (Fig. 554, *lower*). The inner and the outer layers are each thinner than the middle layer and are composed of longitudinally disposed fibers. The thick middle layer is composed of circularly disposed fibers. The adventitia consists of a loose elastic type of connective tissue and blends with the tissues comprising the spermatic cord which contains arteries, numerous veins, nerves and some longitudinally disposed striated muscle fibers (cremaster muscle). The veins are particularly prominent and form the *pampiniform* (*pampinus* = tendril) plexus; the plexus is so named because the veins wind around the duct similar to the way that tendrils of plants wind around other bodies for support. This is a common site for veins to become varicosed.

A short distance before the ductus deferens is joined by the seminal vesicle, it becomes dilated to form an ampulla. Here the muscular coat, though still thick, is thinner than in the other parts of the duct, and the lumen is considerably larger. The mucous membrane is thrown into very complicated folds similar to those of the seminal vesicle (Fig. 555).

THE SEMINAL VESICLES

The size and the function of the seminal vesicles are controlled to a great degree by hormones; hence, the size and the shape of these structures vary considerably in relation to age. In the sexually mature male they are elongated bodies, 5 to 7 cm. or more long and somewhat less than half as wide at their

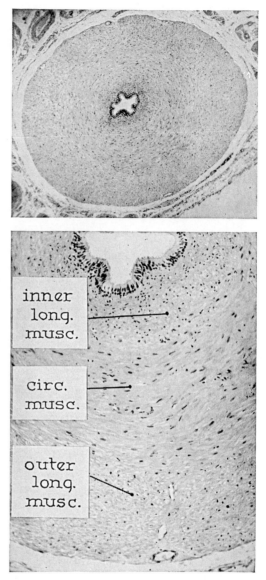

inner long. musc.

circ. musc.

outer long. musc.

Fig. 554. Low-power and high-power photomicrographs of an H and E section of the ductus deferens.

widest point. Their form tapers toward the end at which they join the ductus deferens.

To prevent confusion, it should be explained that the structure seen on gross dissection and called the *seminal vesicle* is essentially a tube that is much longer and much narrower than it appears at first sight. The vesicle is coiled and convoluted. The various coils and convolutions, where they touch one

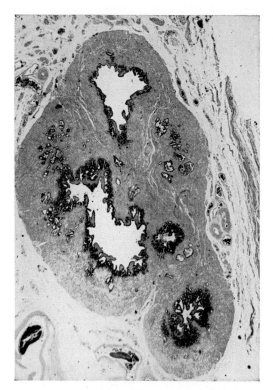

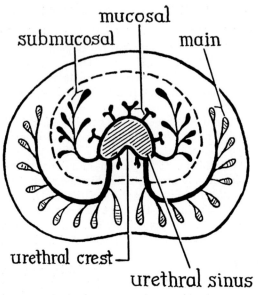

FIG. 555. Very low-power photomicrograph of a cross section of a seminal vesicle.

FIG. 556. Diagram of a cross section of the prostate gland, showing the distribution of the mucous, the submucous and the main glands and where their ducts open. (Redrawn and slightly modified from Grant, J. C. B.: A Method of Anatomy, ed. 4, Baltimore, Williams & Wilkins)

another, are adherent through the medium of connective tissue (Fig. 555); this is the cause of the form and the organization of the body seen on gross inspection. This connective tissue must be dissected if the seminal vesicle is to be unraveled and seen in its true form; if this is done it will be found to consist of a tube about 15 cm. long. The coils and the convolutions are such that if a cross section is cut through the undissected body the seminal vesicle will be cut simultaneously at several points along its length (Fig. 555).

The wall of the tube exhibits 3 coats: an outermost one of fibrous connective tissue which contains a substantial content of elastic fibers, a middle muscular coat and a lining mucous membrane.

The muscular coat is substantial but not so thick as that of the ductus deferens. It consists of 2 layers: an inner one of circular fibers and an outer one of longitudinal fibers.

The mucous membrane of the seminal vesicle is thrown into an extraordinary series of folds (Fig. 555). These permit the vesicle to have an enormous area of secretory epithe-

lium; they also permit the tube to become distended with secretion without the undue stretching of the membrane of secretory cells that line the vesicle. The epithelial lining consists essentially of a layer of tall columnar cells but, between these and the lamina propria, small cells may be irregularly distributed. The small cells in some instances may form a continuous membrane, deep to the tall cells.

Since the folds of mucous membrane are so very numerous and may branch, the lamina propria of the seminal vesicle, as seen in a section, seems to contain glands. However, the glandular appearance, like that presented by the mucous membrane of the gallbladder, is due only to the extensive folding of the mucous membrane.

It was once believed that the seminal vesicle served as a storehouse for spermatozoa. The finding of spermatozoa in the seminal vesicle after death does not necessarily provide support for this theory because spermatozoa may migrate into the vesicles after death. The epithelial cells of the vesicles provide an elaborate, thick, yellow, sticky secre-

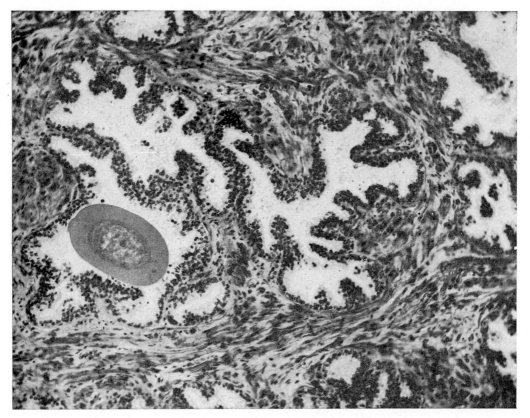

FIG. 557. Medium-power photomicrograph of a small area of a section of the prostate gland. Notice the smooth muscle fibers in the stroma of the gland and the concretion in the lumen of a secretory unit on the left.

tion. This is delivered into the ejaculatory duct during ejaculation and it serves as one of the fluids that constitute a vehicle and also provide nutritive materials for the spermatozoa.

The relation of the structure and the function of the seminal vesicles and the prostate gland to hormones is similar and will be discussed when the microscopic anatomy of the prostate gland has been considered.

THE PROSTATE GLAND

The prostate gland is commonly described as being about the size and the shape of a horse chestnut but it is narrower below than above (Fig. 542). It surrounds the urethra as the latter emerges from the bladder. It is obvious that in this site enlargements of its substance might obstruct the outlet from the bladder. Unfortunately, enlargements of its substance that exert this effect are relatively common in men who have passed middle life.

Their cause is obviously hormonal, for the reverse of enlargement—atrophy—occurs if the testes are removed. The removal of the prostate gland, or some part of it, to free the urethra from obstruction is a relatively common operation in older men.

The prostate gland is of a firm consistency. It is surrounded by a thin capsule that contains both connective tissue and smooth muscle fibers and is to be differentiated from the fascia that lies outside it.

As has already been noted, the substance of the prostate gland is made up of a large number of individual glands; these open by separate ducts into the prostatic urethra and are embedded in a stroma that is a mixture of smooth muscle and fibrous connective tissue.

A cross section of the prostate gland shows that the lumen of the prostatic urethra is V-shaped, with the apex of the V pointing forward (Fig. 556). The part of the posterior wall in the urethra that bulges forward to make the cross-section appearance of its lumen V-shaped is termed the *urethral crest* (Fig. 556). The two arms of the V that pass laterally and backward constitute the *urethral sinuses* (Fig. 556).

The glands that are embedded in the substance of the prostate are of three different orders of size and are distributed in three different areas that are arranged more or less concentrically around the urethra. The mucosal glands are the smallest and are disposed in the periurethral tissue (Fig. 556). They are of the greatest importance in connection with the enlargements of prostatic substance that occur in older men, for it is these glands that commonly overgrow to form *adenomatous* (*aden* = gland; *oma* = tumor) *nodules*. The submucous glands are disposed in the ring of tissue that surrounds the periurethral tissue (Fig. 556). The main, external or proper prostatic glands—and these provide the bulk of the secretion of the gland—are disposed in the outer and largest portion of the gland (Fig. 556). The mucosal glands open at various points around the lumen of the urethra, but the ducts of the submucous and main prostatic glands open into the posterior margins of the urethral sinuses (Fig. 556).

The prostate gland is imperfectly divided into 3 lobes by the passage through it of the ejaculatory ducts. Each lobe is imperfectly subdivided into lobules. The ducts that drain the lobules of the bulk of the organ sweep backward to empty into the urethral sinuses (Fig. 556). In the lobules, the ducts branch into tubulo-alveolar secretory units. These not only produce secretion but also are adapted to storing secretion. As a consequence they may be greatly dilated. To accommodate large amounts of stored secretion, the epithelial lining of the gland is greatly folded, and papillary projections of mucous membrane extend into their lumens at many sites (Fig. 557). This arrangement, together with the fibromuscular stroma that is disposed both between and within the lobules (Fig. 557), gives the gland a distinctive microscopic appearance.

In the healthy, sexually mature male the epithelium of the secretory units and ducts (except immediately before they enter the urethra) is of a tall columnar type. Smaller flattened or rounded cells may be distributed irregularly beneath the tall columnar cells. The tall cells have well-developed Golgi nets between their nuclei and their free borders. Blebs of secretion may sometimes be seen, apparently leaving the free surfaces of the cells. Concretions of secretion, which may be calcified to some extent, are not uncommon in the

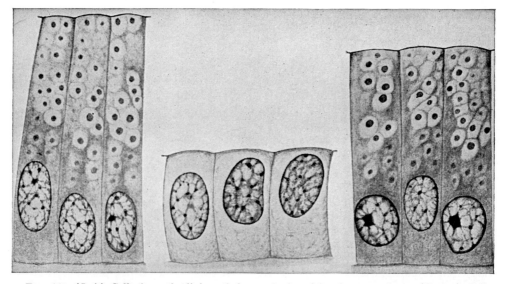

FIG. 558. (*Left*) Cells from the lining of the seminal vesicle of a normal rat. (*Center*) Cells from the same site 20 days after castration. (*Right*) Cells from the same site 20 days after castration; this rat received 29 injections of testis extract, beginning immediately after castration. (Moore, C. R., Hughes, W., and Gallagher, T. F.: Am. J. Anat. *45*:133)

secretory units of the prostate glands of older men (Fig. 557, *left*). The epithelium rests on a fibrous connective tissue lamina propria that contains an abundant supply of capillaries.

The secretion of the prostate gland is a thin, somewhat milky fluid. It contains, among other ingredients, quantities of an enzyme known as acid phosphatase; the function of this is not known, but its detection in the blood stream is of use in the diagnosis of malignant tumors that arise from the secretory cells of the prostate gland.

Effects of Hormones on the Seminal Vesicles and the Prostate Gland. Androgen production by the testes is required to bring about the full development of the seminal vesicles and the prostate gland. Castration, after these structures have fully developed, causes them to atrophy. The most striking microscopic change brought about by castration occurs in the epithelium.

In a sexually mature male the epithelial cells of the seminal vesicles are of the tall columnar type. Their cytoplasm, between their nuclei and free borders, contains abundant secretory granules, each of which tends to be surrounded by a halo (Fig. 558, *left*). If the testes are removed, the epithelial cells shrink, becoming more or less cuboidal (Fig. 558, *middle*). Secretory granules disappear from their cytoplasm. Moore, Hughes and Gallagher have shown that both the height of the epithelial cells of the seminal vesicles and their normal content of secretory granules can be restored by injections of androgen (Fig. 558, *right*).

Moore, Price and Gallagher have shown also that the secretory cells of the prostate shrink in height if the testes are removed and that the prominent Golgi networks of the cells become greatly reduced in size. Both their height and their well-developed Golgi networks can be restored by injections of androgen.

Estrogen injected into male animals causes the epithelium of the seminal vesicles and the prostate gland to change from a tall secretory type into a low nonsecretory type. Moreover, estrogen induces a hypertrophy of the fibromuscular stroma of the prostate and the walls of the seminal vesicles.

The fact that the vigor of the secretory cells of the prostate gland is dependent on androgen is taken advantage of in the treat-

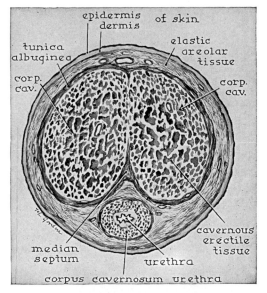

FIG. 559. Diagram of a cross section of the mid-section of the penis.

ment of some malignant tumors that arise from these cells. A certain proportion of cancers of the prostate gland are benefited by castration. Being denied androgen, even malignant epithelial cells of the prostate gland may experience diminished function and growth activity. Likewise, in some instances prostatic cancers respond in a similar fashion to treatment with estrogens.

The hormonal basis for the nonmalignant overgrowths of prostatic tissue that so commonly obstruct the urethrae of older men is not thoroughly understood. Both the glandular tissue and the stroma of the prostate gland participate in these overgrowths. An interesting though unproved theory would relate the overgrowth of the stroma to an increased production of estrogen in the older male. Such a condition could be visualized as arising as a result of the testes' making less androgen as a male ages, and, as a result, the anterior pituitary's making more gonadotrophic hormone which, in turn, might stimulate the latent capacities of the testes for making estrogen.

THE PENIS

Microscopic Structure. The substance of the penis consists essentially of 3 cylindrical bodies of erectile (cavernous) tissue (Fig. 559). Two of these, the corpora cavernosa,

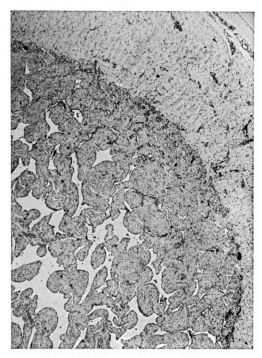

FIG. 560. Low-power photomicrograph of a portion of a cross section of a penis, showing the curved tunica albuginea at the upper right, with erectile tissue at the lower left.

are arranged side by side in the dorsal half of the organ (Fig. 559); this arrangement makes the dorsal surface of the otherwise more or less cylindrical penis somewhat flattened. The third long body of erectile tissue is called the corpus cavernosum urethrae because it conducts the urethra in its substance (Fig. 559) from one of its ends to the other (Fig. 542). It is also termed the corpus spongiosum. This cavernous body lies ventral to the paired corpora cavernosa. Moreover, it extends somewhat beyond the corpora cavernosa and becomes expanded into a more or less blunt cone-shaped body, the *glans*; this constitutes the free end of the penis (Fig. 542).

Each cavernous body is surrounded by a stout sheath of connective tissue called a *tunica albuginea* (Figs. 559 and 560). In the corpora cavernosa, this sheath consists chiefly of collagenic fibers arranged in an inner circular and an outer longitudinal layer, but it also contains elastic fibers. The tunics covering the paired corpora cavernosa come into contact with one another along the mid-line of the penis and fuse to form a median septum (Fig. 559); this is thickest and most complete near the root of the penis. The sheath surrounding the corpus cavernosum urethrae is more elastic than that covering the other 2 bodies. In the glans, a true tunica albuginea is deficient; here the dermis of the skin that covers the glans serves as a tunica albuginea and is continuous with the cavernous tissue that is deep to it.

The 3 cavernous bodies (except where the paired corpora cavernosa are fused) are bound together by elastic areolar tissue called the *fascia penis* (Fig. 559). This also provides a flexible attachment for the skin that covers the penis. The epidermis of the skin of the penis is thin. No coarse hairs are present except near the root of the organ. A circular fold of skin extends forward to cover the glans; this is called the *prepuce* (Fig. 542). It is usually sufficiently elastic to permit its being retracted. However, in some instances it is not, and it may fit too tightly over the glans; this condition is called *phimosis*. Modified sebaceous glands are present on the inner surface of the fold; the secretion from these, in a prepuce that cannot be retracted, may accumulate and serve as an irritant. The common operation by which the prepuce is removed is called *circumcision*.

The substance of the cavernous bodies consists of a 3-dimensional network of trabeculae. These are composed of connective tissue and smooth muscle and are covered with endothelium (Fig. 560). Between the trabeculae are spaces; since the trabeculae are covered with endothelium, the spaces are lined with endothelium. These spaces tend to be larger in the more central parts of the cavernous bodies and smaller near their periphery (Fig. 559). The substance of the glans is made up of convolutes of large veins rather than of spaces separated by trabeculae.

Blood Supply and the Mechanism of Erection. The arterial supply is of two sorts. Branches from the arteria dorsalis end in capillary beds which supply nutriment to the tissues of the organ, including those of the cavernous bodies. From the capillaries of the trabeculae, blood drains into the spaces. The spaces communicate in such a fashion that blood emptied into them can make its way to the more peripheral parts of the bodies, where the spaces communicate with plexuses of veins that are disposed close to the periphery of each cylindrical body. The blood that is instrumental in causing erection is derived chiefly from another and larger set of arteries that enters the substance of the bodies and there gives off branches that are conducted to the spaces by way of the trabeculae. These arteries have thick muscular walls and, in addition, many possess inner thickenings of longitudinal muscle fibers that bulge into their lumens. Many of these arteries that are disposed along the trabeculae are coiled and twisted when the penis is flaccid; this accounts for their being called *helicine* arteries. Many of the terminal branches of these arteries open directly into the spaces of the cavernous tissue.

The smooth muscle of the arteries and the smooth muscle in the trabeculae are supplied both by sympathetic and parasympathetic fibers. Under conditions of erotic stimulation, the smooth muscle of the trabeculae and the helicine arteries relaxes. The arteries tend to straighten, and as a result blood flows freely from them into the spaces. As blood collects in the spaces and dilates them, the venous plexuses in the peripheral parts of the bodies become compressed. With more blood being delivered into the spaces of the cavernous bodies, and with venous drainage from the bodies being impeded, the bodies become enlarged and turgid. The corpus cavernosum urethrae does not become so turgid as its two companions because its sheath is more elastic.

The phenomenon of the penis' returning to its flaccid state after erection is termed *detumescence*. This is brought about by the helicine arteries becoming constricted and by the smooth muscle in the trabeculae contracting; this slowly forces blood from the organ.

The penis is richly provided with a great variety of sensory nerve endings.

THE MALE URETHRA

The male urethra is a tube of mucous membrane. In some sites its lamina propria, which is primarily fibro-elastic tissue, contains smooth muscle fibers and, in many sites, glands. Three facts about the urethra that the student will soon be able to verify when he learns, in his clinical years, to pass a cath-

eter, are that it is about 8 inches long, its course is not straight but instead exhibits a reverse curve (Fig. 542) and (if the catheter employed is of too fine a caliber) that its lining is the seat of many small diverticulae.

The male urethra is commonly described as consisting of 3 parts. On leaving the urinary bladder the urethra enters the base of the prostate gland and courses through it to leave its apex. This portion of the urethra is described as its *prostatic part*. It then pierces the fasciae of the urogenital diaphragm. Accordingly, this portion of it is termed its *membranous part*. It then enters the expanded root (the bulb) of the corpus cavernosum urethrae (Fig. 542) and then extends through the entire length of this cavernous body to the apex of the glans (Fig. 542), where its *external orifice* is situated. The part of the urethra contained in the corpus cavernosum urethrae is called its *cavernous* or *spongy part*.

The prostatic portion of the urethra is more or less V-shaped in cross section. The apex of the V-shaped posterior wall points forward and is called the urethral crest (Fig. 542). A conical elevation on the crest is termed the *colliculus*, and a small diverticulum, the remains of the fetal müllerian ducts, opens through it. The slitlike openings of the ejaculatory ducts may be seen, one on each side of the colliculus, on the urethral crest. The sites of the openings of the prostatic ducts have already been described.

As was noted in Chapter 25, the epithelium of the urinary bladder is of the transitional type (Fig. 561 A). The epithelium that lines the first part of the prostatic urethra is of the same type (Fig. 561 B). However, in the part of the prostatic urethra nearest the membranous urethra the epithelium changes to the pseudostratified or stratified columnar variety (Fig. 561 C).

The lamina propria of the prostatic urethra is composed essentially of fibro-elastic connective tissue. It is very vascular, chiefly because of its great content of venules. Indeed, over the urethral crest the lamina propria contains so many venules and veins that it is sometimes described as erectile tissue. Smooth muscle fibers are also present in the mucous membrane of the prostatic urethra. These are disposed in 2 layers; the innermost one consists of longitudinal, and the outer layer, of

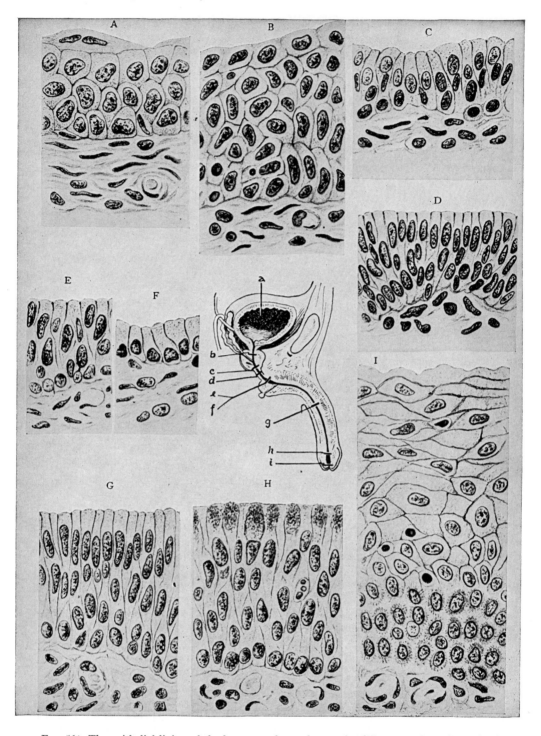

FIG. 561. The epithelial lining of the human male urethra at the different regions shown in the central diagram (× 600). (A) Wall of bladder. (B) Inner portion of prostatic urethra. (C) Outer portion of prostatic urethra. (D) Membranous portion of urethra. (E) Ampulla of urethra on sides and bases of folds. (F) Ampulla of urethra on crest of folds. (G) Middle of cavernous urethra. (H) Inner portion of fossa navicularis. (I) Outer portion of fossa navicularis. (Addison: Piersol's Normal Histology, ed. 15, Philadelphia, Lippincott)

circular, fibers. The latter are highly developed at the internal urethral orifice, where they, reinforced by certain smooth muscle fibers from another source, comprise the *sphincter of the bladder.*

The membranous part of the urethra is the shortest part, being about 1 cm. long. The lining cells here are tall columnar in type and are stratified (Fig. 561 D). Some smooth muscle is present in the lamina propria, but the circular fibers in particular are less numerous than they are in the prostatic portion of the urethra. However, in the membranous urethra, striated muscle fibers of the urogenital diaphragm surround the tube; these comprise the *sphincter muscle of the urethra.* This muscle is sometimes called the *external sphincter of the bladder.* Two small bodies, each about as large as a pea, the *bulbo-urethral* or *Cowper's glands,* are disposed on the under surface of the membranous urethra, close to its mid-line (Fig. 542). Their ducts run forward and medially to open, sometimes by a common opening, on the lower surface of the first part of the cavernous portion of the urethra (Fig. 542), next to be described. The glands themselves are of the tubulo-alveolar type, and their secretory cells are mostly of the mucous type. These glands either secrete more copiously, or their secretion is expressed from them because of the contraction of the smooth muscle fibers in their stroma and the voluntary muscle outside them, under conditions of erotic stimulation. At any rate, their secretion, under these conditions, flows along the urethra to appear at the external orifice of the penis. The function of the secretion of these glands may be that of coating the lining of the urethra with a fluid that will provide a suitable environment for spermatozoa.

The cavernous or spongy part of the urethra is its longest part. As noted before, the urethra becomes expanded in the bulb of the corpus cavernosum urethrae to form the *bulb* of the urethra (Fig. 542). The urethra becomes expanded again in the glans; this expansion of it is termed the *terminal* or *navicular fossa* (Fig. 542).

The epithelium in the cavernous part of the urethra is of the stratified columnar type, although simple columnar epithelium may be present on the crests of folds (Fig. 561 E, F and G). In the inner part of the terminal fossa some goblet cells may be present (Fig. 561 H). In the outer part of the terminal fossa the epithelium becomes stratified squamous in type (Fig. 561 I). This in turn becomes continuous with the stratified squamous keratinizing epithelium that covers the glans.

In the cavernous portion of the urethra the smooth muscle of the urethra proper fades out to be replaced, as it were, by the smooth muscle of the septa of the erectile tissue through which the urethra passes.

Two groups of glands are associated with the urethra. These are often termed the *glands of Littré.* One group, the *intramucosal* glands, consists of small, simple glands disposed in its lamina propria. Although these are present in all parts of the urethra, they are most numerous in its cavernous part. The second group constitutes the *extramucosal* glands. They are somewhat larger than the intramucosal type. Their ducts commonly pass to the urethra at acute angles. The extramucosal glands are not so widely distributed as the intramucosal glands. Both types secrete mucus. In addition to possessing glands, the lining of the urethra is beset by numerous small outpouchings of its mucous membrane; these are called *lacunae.* The glands described above may open into these.

REFERENCES

Male Reproductive System

Allen, E., Danforth, C. H., and Doisy, E. A. (eds.): Sex and Internal Secretions, ed. 2, Baltimore, Williams & Wilkins, 1939.

Burrows, H.: Biological Actions of Sex Hormones, ed. 2, London, Cambridge Univ. Press, 1949.

Clermont, Y., Glegg, R. E., and Leblond, C. P.: Presence of carbohydrates in the acrosome of the guinea pig spermatozoon, Exper. Cell. Res. 8:453, 1955.

Clermont, Y., and Leblond, C. P.: Renewal of spermatogonia in the rat, Am. J. Anat. 93:475, 1953.

———: Spermiogenesis of man, monkey, ram and other mammals as shown by the "periodic acid-Schiff" technique, Am. J. Anat. 96:229, 1955.

Fawcett, D. W., and Burgos, M. H.: Observations on the cytomorphosis of the germinal and interstitial cells of the human testis *in* Ciba Foundation Colloquia on Ageing, vol. 2, p. 86, London, Churchill, 1956.

Ford, C. E., and Hamerton, J. L.: The chromosomes of man, Nature 178:1020, 1956.

Grigg, G. W., and Hodge, A. J.: Electron microscopic studies of spermatozoa, Australian J. Sc. Res. *2*:271, 1949.

Hamilton, J. B.: The role of testicular secretions as indicated by the effects of castration in man and by studies of pathological conditions and the short lifespan associated with maleness, Rec. Prog. Hormone Res. *3*:257, 1948.

Hodge, A. J.: Electron microscopic studies of spermatozoa, Australian J. Sc. Res. *2*:368, 1949.

Hotchkiss, R. S.: Fertility in Men, Philadelphia, Lippincott, 1944.

Huggins, C.: The physiology of the prostate gland, Physiol. Rev. *25*:281, 1945.

Koch, F. C.: The male sex hormones, Physiol. Rev. *17*:153, 1937.

Leblond, C. P., and Clermont, Y.: Spermiogenesis of rat, mouse, hamster and guinea pig as revealed by the "periodic acid-fuchsin sulfurous acid" technique, Am. J. Anat. *90*:167,1952.

Macklin, C. C., and Macklin, M. T.: The seminal vesicles, prostate and bulbo-urethral glands *in* Cowdry's Special Cytology, ed. 2, p. 1771, New York, Hoeber, 1932.

MacLeod, J., and Hotchkiss, R. S.: Effects of hyperpyrexia upon spermatozoa counts in men, Endocrinology *28*:780, 1941.

Mason, K. E.: The specificity of vitamin E for the testes, J. Exper. Zool. *55*:101, 1930.

Mason, K. E., and Shaver, S. L.: Some functions of the caput epididymis, Ann. New York Acad. Sc. *55*:585, 1952.

Metz, C. W.: The male germ cells *in* Cowdry's Special Cytology, ed. 2, p. 1727, New York, Hoeber, 1932.

Meyer, R. K.: Hormones in reproduction, Ann. Rev. Physiol. *7*:567, 1945.

Moore, C. R., Hughes, W., and Gallagher, T. F.: Rat seminal-vesicle cytology as a testis-hormone indicator and the prevention of castration changes by testis-extract injection, Am. J. Anat. *45*:109, 1930.

Moore, C. R., Price, D., and Gallagher, T. F.: Rat-prostate cytology as a testis-hormone indicator and the prevention of castration changes by testis-extract injections, Am. J. Anat. *45*:17, 1930.

Rasmussen, A. T.: Interstitial cells of the testis *in* Cowdry's Special Cytology, ed. 2, p. 1673, New York, Hoeber, 1932.

Roosen-Runge, E. C., and Giesel, L. O., Jr.: Quantitative studies on spermatogenesis in the albino rat, Am. J. Anat. *87*:1, 1950.

Stieve, H.: Entwicklung, Bau and Bedeutung der Keimdrüsenzwischenzellen, Ergebn. Anat. u. Entwcklngsgesch. *23*:1, 1921.

Swyer, G. I. M.: Post-natal growth changes in the human prostate, J. Anat. *78*:130, 1944.

Tjio, J. H., and Levan, A.: The chromosome number of man, Hereditas *42*:1, 1956.

Chapter 29

The System of Sensory Receptors

INTRODUCTION

In Figure 278 a variety of instruments are illustrated, each of which, when wired to a battery, could function to close an electrical circuit. Moreover, each of the instruments is specially designed to close a circuit if it is "stimulated" by a certain kind of stimulus. For example, the telegraph key would complete a circuit if it were touched lightly, another of the instruments would complete a circuit if it were heated, another if it were cooled, another if exposed to light, another if struck by sound waves, and another if its chemical environment were altered.

The same general principles are utilized in the human body. Special instruments, represented by different kinds of nerve endings, respond to different stimuli and convert the energy of the stimulus into the electrical energy of a nerve impulse which is conducted along a nerve fiber to the brain. Moreover, the nerve fibers that lead from these receptors travel to different parts of the brain; this is the anatomic basis for the recognition of different kinds of sensation. However, the allocation of specific sensations (e.g., touch, pain, temperature, etc.) to different receptors is at present undergoing reassessment. Some investigators now believe that some of the specific morphologic receptors may not always subserve the same functions or that any one sensation may not always be appreciated by the same receptor (Oppenheimer, Palmer and Weddell). However, a recent investigation by Duthie and Gairns into sensory nerve endings and sensation in the anal region demonstrated organized receptors of distinctive form in this region. This work tends to support the older idea that different sensations can be attributed to specific types of receptors.

The different sensations which may be perceived by the human body—man's different senses—are: touch, pressure, heat, cold, pain, smell, sight, hearing, taste, position and movement. It is to be realized, moreover, that the appreciation of a sensation is not necessary for reflex actions to occur in the body; for example, most of the afferent impulses that affect the operation of the autonomic nervous system do not appear in consciousness.

The receptors concerned with smell, sight, hearing, taste and perception of movement and position in relation to gravity, are aggregated into what are called *organs of special sense*. These will be described after considering the receptors that give rise to the sensations of touch, pressure, cold, warmth, pain and what may be termed *proprioceptive muscle sense* (a perception of the degree to which different muscles are contracted, and hence of the position of, for example, a leg or an arm in relation to the rest of the body). All the receptors of this latter group are commonly grouped together as those responsible for what is described as *cutaneous* and *deep sensibility*.

The terminations of the afferent nerve fibers concerned in cutaneous and deep sensibility are of 2 general types: *free* and *encapsulated*. The various members of these 2 main types of nerve endings will now be described.

RECEPTORS CONCERNED IN CUTANEOUS AND DEEP SENSIBILITY

Touch. The sensation aroused by light (e.g., "cotton wool") touch is subserved by 3 types of receptors: *Meissner's corpuscles, Merkel's disks* and a basketlike arrangement of *naked nerve endings* disposed around the bases of *hair follicles.*

Meissner's corpuscles are distributed in the connective tissue papillae of the skin just below, and perpendicular to, the epidermis. These corpuscles are not distributed evenly, being most numerous on the palmar surface of the fingers, the lips, the margins of the eyelids, the nipples and the external genital organs. They are somewhat ovoid structures

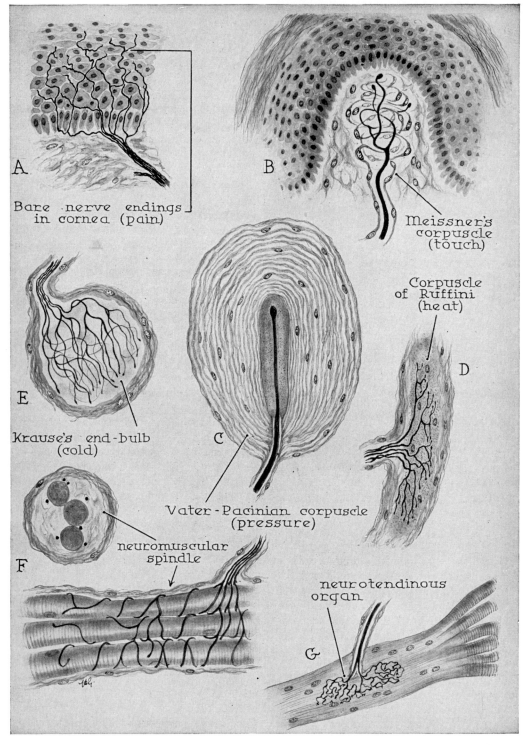

Fig. 562. Diagrams of the various types of nerve endings concerned in cutaneous and deep sensibility.

made up of a central mass of irregular cells penetrated by irregularly curved nerve endings (Fig. 562 B), and they possess a many-layered capsule of connective tissue that is continuous with the endoneurium associated with the afferent nerve fiber.

In the borders of the tongue, and probably in certain other sensitive epithelium, some rudimentary corpuscles of Meissner, called *Merkel's disks*, are found. These consist of expanded disks on the terminal twigs of the branches of nerve fibers that penetrate the stratified squamous epithelium. Each terminal disk is attached to a modified epithelial cell.

Many of the hair follicles are surrounded by a basketlike arrangement of nerve fibers with several types of expanded endings. These are stimulated by the movement of the hairs. Around the hair follicles of rodents this arrangement is still more complicated, and special tactile hairs are present around the nose and the mouth.

Pressure Receptors. Pressure upon the skin of a greater degree than that which elicits the sensation of touch stimulates the more deeply lying receptors known as *Vater-Pacini corpuscles*. These are regarded as the organs of deep pressure, and possibly of vibration sense. They are distributed in the deep regions of the subcutaneous tissue, in the connective tissues near tendons and joints, in the interosseous membranes of the leg and the forearm, in the perimysium of muscles, in the pancreas and its mesentery, in serous membranes, under mucous membranes, in the mammary glands and in the external genitalia of both sexes.

The *pacinian corpuscle*, as it is often called, is made up of a central elongated granular mass covered with many concentric, thin layers of connective tissue (Fig. 562 C). This arrangement of cells results in a structure with an appearance not unlike that of an onion. The connective tissue laminae are separated by lymphatic spaces lined on their inner sides with a layer of endothelial cells whose nuclei bulge into the spaces. The peripheral laminae are thicker than those more centrally located. At one pole the nerve fiber, after losing its myelin, enters and terminates in a small swelling in the region of the central granular material. The neurolemma and the

endoneurium of the nerve fiber become continuous with the capsule of the corpuscle.

Heat Receptors. The receptor of warmth is the *corpuscle of Ruffini*, lying deep in the skin or even in the subcutaneous tissue. These are present generally but are particularly numerous in the subcutaneous connective tissue deep to the plantar surface of the foot. This receptor is composed of a loose arborization of nerve fibers ending in flattened expansions and interspersed with a peculiar granular material dotted with nuclei. Elongated connective tissue bundles and fibroblasts give support to the structure (Fig. 562 D). Ruffini type endings are probably concerned also with proprioceptive sense, as will be described under the latter heading.

Cold Receptors. The *Krause end-bulb* is believed to be the receptor for cold. These end-bulbs are most prevalent in the dermis of the conjunctiva, the mucosa of the tongue and the external genitalia. Two structurally different types have been described. The simpler is composed of a granular mass enclosed in a connective tissue capsule continuous with the endoneurium of the afferent nerve fiber; the nerve itself penetrates the end-bulb and terminates near the superior pole of the granular mass in a light thickening. The more complex variety is found in the conjunctiva. The afferent nerve, instead of ending bluntly, branches repeatedly in the bulb and ends in several free, enlarged terminations (Fig. 562 E).

Pain Receptors. The element or unit of the receptive mechanism for pain is not a small encapsulated structure innervated by a single nerve fiber but rather an appreciable area over which the naked terminal branches of one neuron are distributed. In the cornea, the naked branches of one neuron extend between epithelial cells (Fig. 562 A) over as much as one quarter to one half its surface area. In any area of normally innervated skin the terminals of many such units overlap intricately.

Pain fibers in the skin arise from a nerve plexus deep in the corium by way of a superficial plexus of unmyelinated and thin, myelinated fibers. The fibers leaving this superficial plexus are all unmyelinated, though they may have their origin in myelinated fibers. These naked fibers branch freely and end in fine, beaded terminals beneath and between the cells of the deep layers of the epidermis. Naked endings are also present in many of the connective tissues of the body, but not in all.

The pain endings do not respond selectively to one variety of stimulus but to any type, whether it be mechanical, chemical or thermal, provided that it is sufficiently intense. Therefore, the sensation of pain serves a protective purpose, giving warning of the injurious nature of a stimulus, rather than information as to its specific quality.

Receptors for Proprioceptive Muscle Sense. Certain encapsulated receptors in muscles and tendons are sensitive to the degree to which muscles are contracted and tendons are tensed; the nervous impulses they set up permit an individual to realize, for example, the position of a limb when the eyes are closed, and to adjust automatically a muscular effort to a particular load. There are 3 important types of these receptors.

Neuromuscular spindles are disposed in striated muscles. They consist of small groups of attenuated muscle fibers around which the endings of the sensory nerve fibers are coiled in corkscrew fashion (Fig. 562 F); they are so arranged that changes in the length of the muscle or in the tension exerted by it stretch the terminal parts of the nerve fiber. The muscle spindles are surrounded by a capsule of several layers of connective tissue (Fig. 562 F). After entering the spindle, the muscle fiber may branch and anastomose like a cardiac muscle fiber. Two or more large myelinated nerve fibers enter the spindle along with several unmyelinated fibers.

Neurotendinous organs are found at the junctions of muscles and tendons and in the aponeuroses of muscles. These consist of small bundles of collagenic fibers with numerous nuclei, enclosed within a capsule of connective tissue (Fig. 562 G). A large myelinated nerve fiber enters the spindle, usually at its middle, and there subdivides into smaller unmyelinated branches, terminating in leaflike plates.

Ruffini Endings in Joint Structures. As was noted under Nerve Supply in Chapter 16, which deals with joints, Gardner has pointed out the presence of numerous Ruffini type endings in the capsules of synovial joints. These endings are in sites where they would be compressed by certain types of joint movement, so it seems probable that they also are important in connection with proprioceptive sense.

THE OLFACTORY ORGAN

In the introduction to the chapter on nervous tissue it was explained that, as multicellular organisms were evolved, the first neurons that developed represented specializations of surface ectodermal cells (Fig. 273). Moreover, it was observed that as evolution proceeded, the nerve cell bodies of most afferent neurons came to migrate, as it were, along their axons (Fig. 277), eventually to take up a more central and better-protected position in cerebrospinal ganglia (Fig. 275). In addition, it was noted that there was one exception to this general rule; hence, that there is one site in the body where the cell bodies of afferent neurons remain, as it were, at the surface. This site is the *olfactory area*. Actually, the olfactory area consists of 2 areas, for there is one in each of the 2 nasal cavities. The mucous membrane lining the nasal cavities in the 2 olfactory areas constitutes the *olfactory organ*. The nerve cell bodies present in the epithelium of the mucous membrane at this site are highly sensitive with regard to being selectively stimulated by odors of different kinds. It should be kept in mind that having nerve cell bodies at the surface is a more hazardous arrangement than having them deeply disposed with their fibers running to a surface, for if a mucous membrane containing nerve cell bodies is injured by a disease process or by trauma, the nerve cell bodies that are destroyed cannot be regenerated, whereas a surface innervated by fibers alone can be reinnervated after an injury by the regeneration of fibers from the cell bodies of deeply situated nerve cells. So, as might be expected, the sense of smell is often impaired; indeed, Smith, from his investigations, has estimated that, on the average, about 1 per cent of the fibers of the olfactory nerve (which leads from the receptors to the brain) are lost each year of life. In some individuals, all olfactory fibers are lost at a comparatively early age, usually as a result of the destruction of the olfactory cells in the membrane by the infections to which the nasal mucous membrane is so commonly susceptible.

Gross Characteristics. The mucous membrane of the olfactory areas is of a yellow hue,

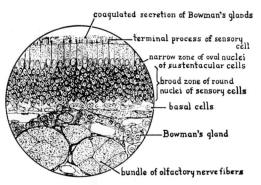

coagulated secretion of Bowman's glands

terminal process of sensory cell

narrow zone of oval nuclei of sustentacular cells

broad zone of round nuclei of sensory cells

basal cells

Bowman's gland

bundle of olfactory nerve fibers

FIG. 563. Drawing of a portion of a section (low-power) of the olfactory area of a rat. (Smith, C. G.: Arch. Otolaryng. *25*:136)

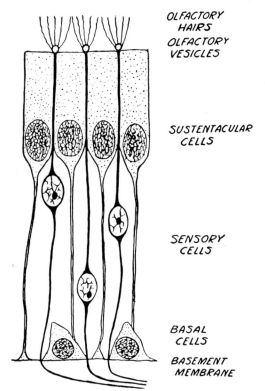

OLFACTORY HAIRS

OLFACTORY VESICLES

SUSTENTACULAR CELLS

SENSORY CELLS

BASAL CELLS

BASEMENT MEMBRANE

FIG. 564. Diagram showing the arrangement of the different types of cells in the olfactory area. (Smith, C. G.: Canad. M. A. J. *39*:139)

in contrast with the pink hue of the mucous membrane lining the respiratory portion of the nose. It is disposed so as to line most of the uppermost part of the roof of each nasal cavity, beginning in front of the anterior termination of the superior concha and extending backward for about 1 cm. From the roof it extends down both sides of each nasal cavity; on the lateral side it extends so as to cover most of the superior concha, and on the medial side, for about 1 cm. down the nasal septum.

Microscopic Structure. The mucous membrane of the olfactory organ consists of a thick pseudostratified epithelium (Fig. 563) and a thick lamina propria.

The *epithelium* consists of 3 kinds of cells; (1) sustentacular, (2) olfactory or sensory and (3) basal.

The *sustentacular* (*sustentaculum* = a prop) cells are tall cylindrical cells disposed perpendicular to the surface (Figs. 563 and 564). In their deeper parts they are much narrower than in their superficial parts. Although, in the more superficial part of the membrane, they are packed closely together, their more or less cylindrical shape precludes their constituting an imperforate layer. The delicate processes (dendrites) of the sensory or olfactory cells, the cell bodies of which lie more deeply, are thus able to reach the surface by way of the crevices left between them (Fig. 564).

The cytoplasm of the sustentacular cells contains a yellow-to-brown pigment; this accounts for the yellow color of the olfactory area in the gross.

The nuclei of the sustentacular cells are disposed just above the middle of the epithelial membrane. They are oval, and since they lie in approximately the same plane, they appear in a section that is cut at right angles to the surface as a row or two of oval nuclei that runs parallel with the surface (Fig. 563). This row or two of oval nuclei is commonly referred to as the *narrow zone of oval nuclei* to contrast it with the more deeply disposed *wide zone of round nuclei* (of the sensory cells) that lies below it (Fig. 563).

Deep to their nuclei the sustentacular cells become much thinner, and in this region their cytoplasm becomes reduced to little more than strands (Fig. 564); these extend to the thin basement membrane. The basal cells, which are more or less triangular, are disposed irregularly along the deepest layer of the epithelium (Figs. 563 and 564).

The *sensory or olfactory* cells are of the nature of bipolar nerve cells; hence, each has a cell body and a nerve fiber extending from each of its ends (Fig. 564): one, a dendrite; and the other, an axon. The sensory cells, like the sustentacular cells, are arranged perpendicular to the surface. Their cell bodies are fitted between the sustentacular cells in the region where these become greatly narrowed (immediately below the narrow zone of oval nuclei). The nuclei of the sensory cells in this region constitute the broad zone of round nuclei (Fig. 563). The dendrites of the bipolar cells ascend toward the surface in the crevices between the sustentacular cells. At the surface, each dendrite becomes expanded to form an *olfactory vesicle* and from this, delicate processes called *olfactory hairs* extend from the surface (Fig. 564). The axon of each sensory cell passes from the epithelial membrane into the lamina propria. The axons are unmyelinated, and in the lamina propria they become aggregated to form bundles of *olfactory nerve fibers* (Fig. 563).

The function of the *basal* cells is unknown; they may be of the nature of reserve cells for forming new sustentacular cells when the need arises.

The *lamina propria* is fibro-elastic connective tissue. In its deeper part it contains many veins, and in some of its deeper areas it is almost of the character of erectile tissue. The secretory portions of tubuloalveolar glands (the glands of Bowman) are disposed in the lamina propria of the olfactory mucous membrane (Fig. 563). Indeed, the glands of Bowman, according to Smith, are *confined* to the olfactory area; hence, if they are seen in what appears to be adjacent respiratory mucous membrane, it may be inferred that the latter was once olfactory mucous membrane but has suffered so much from injury that it has lost its olfactory character. The ducts of the glands lead through the epithelium to the surface. These glands make a thin secretion which presumably constantly freshens the thin layer of fluid which continuously bathes the olfactory hairs on the surface of the organ. The gases responsible for odors are thought to dissolve in this fluid and so affect the olfactory hairs.

Bundles of olfactory nerve fibers are encountered in the lamina propria. As noted before, these are composed of the unmyelinated axons of the sensory cells. Collectively, these constitute the *olfactory nerve*, which pierces the skull by way of the cribiform plate of the ethmoid bone to reach the brain.

Relation of Structure to Function. How an individual is able to distinguish different kinds of odors and their relative weakness or strength is a matter that is not well understood. Moreover, the problem does not lend itself to animal experimentation. Much of the factual basis for speculation on this matter has been obtained from studies made on individuals whose sense of smell has returned, at least in part, after the olfactory organ has been injured by a disease process which was not severe enough to destroy all the sensory cells but only of sufficient severity to render them functionless temporarily, after which most of them recovered. Space does not permit a recital of the important studies made in this connection or an adequate discussion of their interpretation. Therefore, we shall only suggest some possible implications that could be derived from them.

First, as man is provided with certain receptors specialized to be stimulated easily by different kinds of stimuli (touch, pressure, etc.), it might be assumed that the sensory cells of the olfactory area itself are specialized so that different ones are sensitive to different odors. However, there are so many different kinds of odors that it is inconceivable that there could be special receptors for each and every kind; this leads, then, to the concept of the existence of olfactory cells specialized for only certain basic odors. The reason for man's being able to discern such a great variety of odors could be due to various combinations of the receptors for the basic odors being stimulated by these different and complex odors. Support for this idea has been derived from finding that when the sense of smell is being recovered after having been lost, a few odors may smell as before, others are different than they were before, and still others cannot be smelled at all.

Moreover, there is evidence to suggest that the different receptors for the different kinds of basic odors are not spread evenly throughout the olfactory area; hence, damage to one part of the organ may result in certain substances smelling differently from before or not at all, whereas, other substances, under these conditions, smell both quantitatively and qualitatively as before.

It would seem, then, that a reasonable working hypothesis in the light of present knowledge would be: (1) that olfactory cells

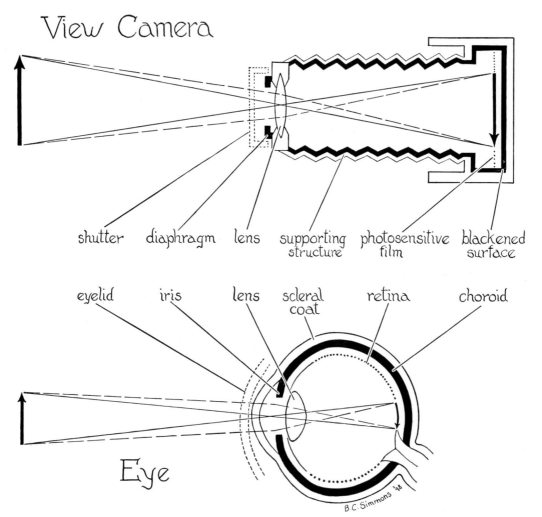

View Camera

shutter   diaphragm   lens   supporting   photosensitive   blackened
                                 structure   film   surface

eyelid   iris   lens   scleral   retina   choroid
                          coat

Eye

B.C. Simmons '48

FIG. 565. Diagram illustrating the similarities between the eye and a camera.

are of different types, specialized to be easily stimulated by certain basic odors: (2) that the receptors for the basic types of odors are not distributed evenly throughout the whole olfactory area but are segregated, to some extent; (3) that man's ability to recognize such a great variety of different odors is due to these different odors stimulating different combinations of the receptors for the basic odors and (4) that the strength of an odor bears some relation to the number of receptors stimulated by it.

THE EYE

INTRODUCTION

The eye, except for being rounded, has most of the structural features of the common and familiar camera. The eyelids comprise its shutter (Fig. 565). The eye has an iris diaphragm (Figs. 565 and 571). This has an advantage over the kind found in cameras, for it contracts and dilates automatically in relation to the amount of light available. The eye has a lens (Fig. 565); this, being composed of altered transparent epithelial cells, is more elastic than the glass lens of a camera. Advantage is taken of its elasticity, for the lens of the eye is suspended in such a way that muscle action can alter its shape and so change its focal length. As a consequence, the eye need not be shortened or elongated when objects at different distances are successively brought into focus as is necessary in a camera with a rigid lens. The plastic or metal sides and back of a camera have their counterpart in the eye

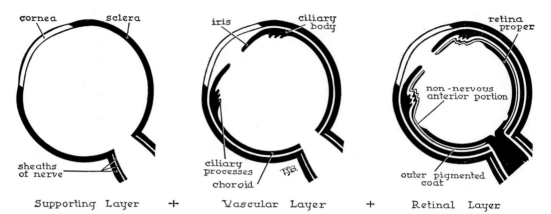

Supporting Layer   +   Vascular Layer   +   Retinal Layer

FIG. 566. (*Left*) Diagram of the supporting coat of the eye. (*Center*) Diagram showing the vascular coat of the eye inserted on the inside of the supporting coat. (*Right*) Diagram showing the retinal coat of the eye on the inside of the outer 2 coats.

in a strong connective tissue membrane, the *sclera* (Fig. 565). The counterpart in the eye of the light-sensitive film used in a camera is a membrane of living cells of nervous origin, the *retina*, which lines, not only the back, but the sides of the eye as well (Fig. 565). Then, finally, just as black paint is used to blacken all the interior surfaces of a camera that might leak or reflect light, black pigment is distributed generously between the retina and the sclera and in other sites where it would be useful.

However, unlike many modern cameras, the lens of the eye is not placed at its very front; in this respect the eye is like an old-fashioned camera which has its external aperture covered with a glass window to keep out the dust, and its lens inside, a short distance behind the glass window. The transparent window in the central part of the front of the eye is of a curved form and is called the *cornea* (Fig. 567). This is composed chiefly of a tough but transparent type of dense connective tissue that is continuous with the opaque connective tissue of the sclera that surrounds and supports the remainder of the eye.

Windows not only permit householders to see out; they also permit the curious to see in. The cornea is like a window in this respect as well, for, with an instrument called an ophthalmoscope, the physician can direct a beam of light into the eye and at the same time look through the instrument and study the appearance of the various structures within the eye as they are successively illuminated. By this means much useful information, not only about the eye, but about the health of the body as a whole, may be obtained.

GENERAL MICROSCOPIC STRUCTURE .

The microscopic structure of many parts of the eye is complex, and an exhaustive treatment of the histology of this organ is not justifiable in a general textbook. Reference books are listed at the end of this chapter for those who require specialized knowledge. Furthermore, even such details of structure as should be given in a textbook of histology are best postponed until the student has read a very general account of the structure of the eye and has learned the names of its various parts and how they co-operate in the functioning of the organ. For this reason, we shall first give a very general account of the structure of the organ and then, later, give some details about the structure of some of its more important parts.

The eye is a nearly spherical structure about an inch in diameter. It is contained in the anterior part of a bony socket, the *orbit*. Between the eye and the bony wall of the orbit in which it lies are fat, connective tissue, muscles and the glandular tissue that provides the tears. The eye is suspended by ligaments in such a fashion that voluntary muscles in the orbit (but outside the eye) can move the eye so that one can look up and down and from side to side.

In describing the microscopic structure of the eye it is convenient to describe first the structure of its *wall*, then its contents (these constitute the *refractive media* of the eye) and finally the *accessory structures* of the eye such as eyelids, tear glands and ducts and so on.

The Wall of the Eye. The wall of the eyeball consists of 3 layers which, from without in, are designated by the general terms of (1) supporting layer, (2) middle layer and (3) retinal layer (Fig. 566). All 3 layers are not present in all parts of the wall of the eye.

The *supporting layer* consists essentially of a dense connective tissue membrane. Around most of the eye this is called the *sclera* (*scleros* = hard) (Fig. 566). The sclera is white in color; the part of the sclera that shows is the "white" of the eye (Fig. 571). The part of the supporting layer covering the central part of the anterior portion of the eye bulges forward slightly and is transparent; this is called the *cornea* (Fig. 566). The supporting layer completely encloses the other layers of the eye except at one site posteriorly where there is an opening to permit the optic nerve to enter the eyeball.

The *middle layer* of the wall of the eye is often called the *uveal* (*uva* = grape) *layer* or *tract* because when the sclera is dissected away the middle layer is exposed and is seen to resemble the skin of a blue grape in that it is pigmented and surrounds the jellylike contents of the eye. The middle layer of the eye is very vascular; hence, it is sometimes called the *vascular layer* of the eye.

The middle illustration in Figure 566 shows the middle layer inserted on the inner surface of the supporting layer. In the posterior two thirds of the eye the middle layer consists of only a thin membrane; this thin posterior segment of the middle layer is called the *choroid*. Moreover, in this illustration it will be seen that toward the anterior part of the eye the middle layer becomes thickened to form what is called the *ciliary body*. This, as a thickened rim of tissue, encircles the anterior part of the eye. From it, what are termed the *ciliary processes* extend inwardly (Fig. 566, *center*). The middle layer of the eye continues anteriorly to constitute the *iris* (diaphragm) of the eye (Fig. 566, *center*). The iris is the pigmented part of the eye that may be seen through the cornea (Fig. 571); depending on the pigment content of the iris, eyes are said to be blue, brown or some other color. Indeed, pigment is abundant in all parts of the middle coat; this helps to lightproof the wall of the eye and to cut down reflection. The middle coat of the eye conducts blood vessels and, in addition, in its anterior part, it contains smooth muscle. The smooth muscle in the iris causes its aperture, the *pupil* of the eye (Fig. 571), to contract or dilate. The smooth muscle of the ciliary body affects the tension of the ligament that suspends the lens, not in the way that might at first be expected, i.e., by its contraction, tensing the ligament that suspends the lens, but instead, by its contraction, easing the tension on the ligament. This is how it permits the eye to accommodate its focus for near objects. The muscle of the ciliary body is, then, an important factor in the mechanism of accommodation.

The position of the *retinal layer* is illustrated on the right side of Figure 566. It consists of 2 layers; the outermost one is pigmented and lines the entire inner surface of the middle layer of the eye. The inner layer of the retina is composed of nervous tissue. The nervous part of the retina, as such, does not extend into the anterior part of the eye (Fig. 566, *right*), for there, light could not be focused on it. The nervous part of the retina contains special nerve cells called *rods* and *cones*; these are the *photoreceptors*. In addition, the retina contains the cell bodies of many conductor neurons and many nerve fibers. Most of the latter stream toward the site at which the optic nerve leaves the eye through the scleral layer.

Refractive Media of the Eye. A beam of light, on striking the surface of the cornea, passes through the following media before it reaches the retina:

1. The substance of the cornea (Fig. 567).

2. A space between the iris and the lens called the *anterior chamber* of the eye (Fig. 567); this is filled with a fluid called *aqueous humor*.

3. The lens (Fig. 567).

4. The transparent jellylike material of the vitreous body which fills the interior of the eye behind the lens (Fig. 567).

A beam of light is bent when it passes obliquely from a substance of one refractive index into that of another. The cornea is

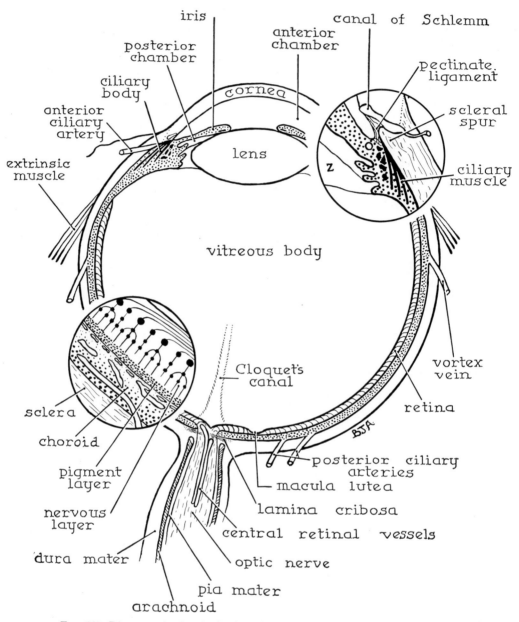

FIG. 567. Diagram of a longitudinal section cut through the middle of the eye.

curved, and the difference between the refractive index of cornea and air is greater than the difference between the refractive indices of any of the media through which light subsequently passes to reach the retina. Hence, with regard to refracting light, the curved anterior surface of the cornea is of the greatest importance. The true lens of the eye has a refractive index which is only slightly greater than that of the aqueous humor in front of it

and that of the vitreous body behind it; its function, then, of bringing light to a focus on the retina, is not of as great a magnitude as that of the cornea. Its unique importance lies in the fact that, being elastic, its focal length can be changed by the pull of muscles on the ligaments which suspend it; hence, it permits light from objects at different distances to be focused sharply.

On passing through the vitreous body and

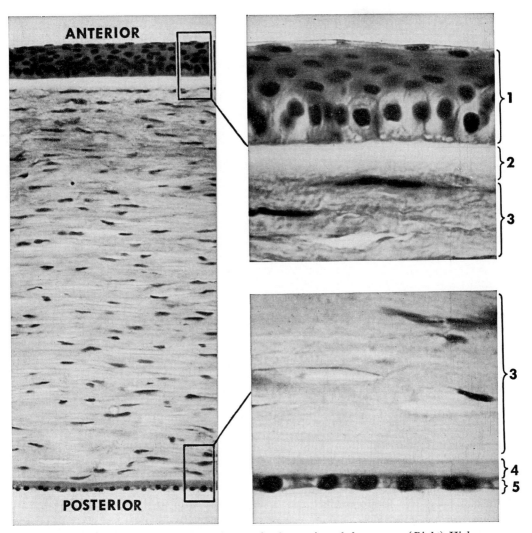

FIG. 569. (*Left*) Low-power photomicrograph of a section of the cornea. (*Right*) High-power photomicrographs of parts of the cornea: (1) stratified squamous epithelium, (2) Bowman's membrane, (3) substantia propria, (4) Descemet's membrane, (5) Descemet's endothelium.

into sclera (and consequently, where Bowman's membrane ends) is called the *limbus* (*limbus* = a border).

The substantia propria comprises about 90 per cent of the thickness of the cornea. It contains flattened connective tissue cells that are disposed between parallel bundles of collagenic fibers called *lamellae* (Fig. 569, *left*). While most of the fibers in a lamella are disposed parallel with the surface, those of one lamella run at an angle to those of the next. The fibers of some lamellae join with those of adjacent lamellae to bind the substantia propria together.

As was pointed out in Chapter 5, collagenic fibers, and perhaps fibrils, are bound together by an amorphous cementing substance. In the substantia propria this material is true hyaluronic acid sulfate. True hyaluronic acid sulfate has not been recovered from connective tissue elsewhere in the body. It is assumed that the binding together of collagenic fibrils and fibers in the substantia propria by this substance (as well as their regular arrangement) is responsible for the unique transparency of this membrane.

Deep to the substantia propria is Descemet's membrane (Fig. 569, 4). This is com-

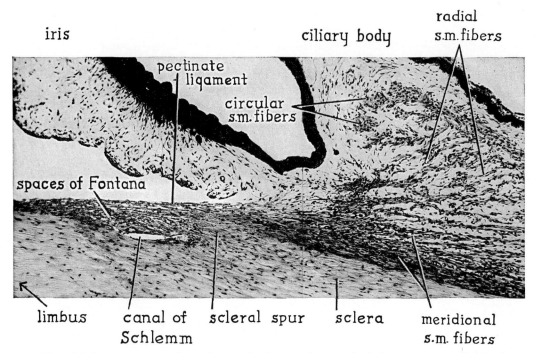

iris   ciliary body   radial
                                                            s.m. fibers

pectinate
ligament

circular
s.m. fibers

spaces of Fontana

limbus   canal of   scleral spur   sclera   meridional
           Schlemm   s.m. fibers

FIG. 570. Two low-power photomicrographs (mounted in continuity) of a portion of a longitudinal section of an eye, showing the region of the angle of the iris. The tissue labeled "spaces of Fontana" is now commonly referred to as the trabecular meshwork.

posed of a special kind of elastic material. In this respect it is different from Bowman's membrane, which does not stain with elastic tissue stains. Applied to the inner side of Descemet's membrane is a single layer of endothelial cells; this layer is called *Descemet's endothelium* (Fig. 569, 5).

FINE STRUCTURE. The fine structure of the cornea has been investigated with the E/M by Sheldon, and that of Descemet's membrane by Jakus. References to their studies are given at the end of this chapter.

TRANSPLANTATION. Homologous transplants of cornea are made with a considerable amount of success. In the past it was believed that cornea was an exception to the general rule about homologous transplants and that the cells of the transplants survived in their new hosts. There were reasons for thinking that cornea might be different from other tissues because the cornea is normally nonvascular, and it does not contain any lymphatics. Furthermore, it has a high proportion of intercellular substance to cells. Maumenee says that it has been shown experimentally that the epithelium and the endothelium of a homolo-

gous transplant of cornea are lost in a few days. The only cells of the transplant that survive for any length of time are some of the connective tissue cells within the substance of the cornea. Recently, it has been shown by Basu and Ormsby, by making corneal grafts from female cats to males, and vice versa, and then determining the chromosomal sex of the cells by the sex chromatin technic, that the connective tissue cells of the graft do live for at least long periods of time. By the same technic it has been shown that the stromal cells of grafts in man live for at least a year, which is as long as they have been followed. The surface epithelium is regenerated from the host, so that it covers the transplant in a few days. The regeneration of the endothelium takes longer. The connective tissue cells within the substance of the cornea are replaced only very slowly from the host.

Sclera. The sclera is a tough, white, connective tissue membrane that consists of bundles of collagenic fibers with flattened fibroblasts between the bundles (Fig. 570). Some elastic fibers are mixed with the collagenic ones. The fibers are not arranged as regularly as those of the substantia propria of the cornea, and the cementing substance with which they are associated is probably of a somewhat different composition, since the sclera is opaque. The sclera is thick enough to permit its being sutured from the outside without the needle penetrating into the middle layer of the wall of the eye. It is not as thick as the cornea, except at its posterior pole; at the midportion of the globe (the *equator*) it is slightly less than 0.5 mm. thick. However, it is strong enough in adults to withstand very high intra-ocular pressures, should this condition occur, without stretching.

The relative opacity of the sclera, as compared with the cornea, is due to a very important degree to its greater water content. This can be shown very dramatically by blowing a jet of air on an exposed portion of sclera, for this makes it completely transparent. The reason the cornea remains transparent is that water is lost from its surfaces, so if either of its surfaces becomes damaged it may become opaque in that area. For example, if some of the vitreous comes and stays in contact with its posterior surface at any point, the cornea becomes opaque at that point.

It is important in connection with testing the intraocular pressure of the eye by means of a tonometer, which is placed on the cornea, to know that the scleras of different eyes are rigid to different degrees; hence, if the rigidity of the sclera is extreme, it may give an erroneous pressure reading.

At the posterior part of the eye the outermost part of the sclera is continuous with the dural sheath and usually with the arachnoid sheath also of the optic nerve (Fig. 567). Its innermost layers are continuous with the pia mater. Moreover, the innermost layer of the sclera, in the form of a perforated disk, bridges what would otherwise be a gap in the sclera, and through this the optic nerve leaves the eye (Fig. 576). The fibers of the optic nerve pass through the perforations of the disk. This part of the sclera is called the *lamina cribrosa* (*cribrum* = a sieve).

The sclera as a whole, being composed of dense connective tissue, is poorly supplied with capillaries. However, many larger vessels pierce it obliquely to gain entrance to the middle layer of the eye. The direction of these vessels, in passing through the sclera, is such that on reaching the inner aspect of the sclera

they attain a point on the circumference of the eye closer to the anterior pole than the point at which they approached the exterior of the sclera (Fig. 567). The anterior ciliary arteries enter beside (or slightly in front of) the ciliary body (Fig. 567), and both short and long posterior ciliary arteries pass through the sclera behind the equator (Fig. 567). The long posterior ciliary arteries, on entering the middle coat of the eye, take a direct course to the ciliary body; the short ones branch. Four large vortex veins which drain most of the blood from the middle coat pass obliquely backward through the sclera near the equator of the eye (Fig. 567). The ciliary arteries have companion veins.

Choroid. The choroid is that part of the middle layer of the eye behind the ciliary body. It is only 0.1 to 0.2 mm. thick. It nourishes the outer layers of the retina. It consists of 3 layers.

1. THE EPICHOROID. This, its outer layer, consists chiefly of elastic fibers that are attached to the sclera. Many nerve fibers that terminate in *chromatophores* are present in it. The chromatophores are large pigmented cells that may be seen, although they are not labeled, in Figure 574. Some have branched irregular cytoplasm like that of an amoeba. Whether this pigment is actually produced by these cells or taken up from pigment produced in the retina has been a point of much controversy. During a short phase of early fetal life, before pigment is present, the future pigment cells of the choroid have been found to be dopa-positive. Moreover, the choroid has been shown at the same time to contain melanogen, the mother substance of melanin. This evidence, along with the fact that fuscin, the pigment of the retina, is slightly different from melanin, suggests that melanin is produced by the pigment cells of the choroid and thereafter stored in situ. It is interesting that melanin pigment, recovered from the uveal tract, has different immunologic properties from that of other parts of the body. Through the epichoroid run the two unbranching posterior long ciliary arteries. A few smooth muscle fibers are present in this layer in its anterior part; these represent the beginning of the ciliary muscle.

2. VESSEL LAYER. The choroidal vessels that are supplied by the short posterior ciliary arteries and drained by the 4 vortex veins lie

in this, the middle layer of the choroid (Fig. 574). The stroma is similar to that of the epichoroid.

3. CHORIOCAPILLARIS. This, the inner layer of the choroid network (Fig. 574), consists of a single layer of capillaries which, however, are among the largest seen in the body. Some of them, especially those outside the macula (to be described presently), are as wide as sinusoids; these permit a rapid transfer of blood from the arterial to the venous side.

BRUCH'S MEMBRANE. Separating the choriocapillaris from the outer coat of the retina lies a glassy membrane (*Bruch's membrane*). This has both elastic and cuticular components, formed by the choroid and the retina, respectively. Bruch's membrane is semipermeable, and through it pass the essential metabolites for the photoreceptors.

Ciliary Body. The 3 strata of the choroid are continuous anteriorly with the ciliary body. This extends forward to a site where a narrow, short flange of sclera, called the *scleral spur,* projects inwardly (Figs. 567 and 570). The ciliary body, as a thickening of the middle coat of the eye, forms a ring on the inner side of the sclera, behind the scleral spur (Figs. 567 and 570). When an eye is cut in longitudinal section the ciliary body is cut in cross section. In cross section it appears as a triangle, with its base facing the anterior chamber and its apex passing into the choroid posteriorly (Fig. 567). The elastic epichoroid, in the ciliary body, is replaced by fibers of ciliary muscle. These are of the smooth variety and they comprise the bulk of the ciliary body (Fig. 570).

Structures Involved in the Mechanism of Accommodation. The smooth muscle fibers of the ciliary body are disposed so as to pull in 3 different directions. Accordingly, 3 groups of fibers are distinguished: (1) the *meridional* (a meridian runs from pole to pole, crossing the equator of a globe at right angles) fibers, which arise in the epichoroid near the ciliary body and pass forward to end in the scleral spur (Fig. 570); (2) the *radial* fibers, which are to the inside of the meridional fibers and fan out posteriorly to make a wide attachment to the connective tissue of the choroid (Fig. 570); and (3) the *circular* fibers, which lie near the inner edge of the ciliary body near its base and are arranged so as to encircle the eye at this site (Fig. 570).

To understand how the contraction of smooth muscle fibers in the ciliary body affects the shape of the lens, certain features of the lens and the mechanism by which it is suspended must be described.

The lens (Fig. 567) is of the biconvex type, with its posterior surface exhibiting a greater convexity than its anterior. It is composed essentially of long prisms, called *lens fibers,* that are cemented together to constitute a transparent medium. The lens fibers evolve from epithelial cells. Most of the first fibers that form in the lens develop from the epithelial cells of the posterior layer of the embryonic lens (Fig. 568) and hence run in an anteroposterior direction. When epithelial cells become lens fibers they lose their nuclei; hence, lens fibers cannot reproduce themselves. But living epithelial cells persist at the equator of the lens and these proliferate and differentiate throughout life to give rise to new lens fibers which are added to the existing ones much as new layers are added to the sides of a tree. This results in the slow growth of the lens throughout life.

The lens is surrounded with a thick, homogeneous, elastic capsule of intercellular substance. The lens capsule is constantly under tension and hence constantly "seeks" to make the elastic lens assume a more globular form.

As the lens ages it loses water and becomes denser and less elastic. Consequently, its range of focus becomes diminished, often sufficiently for individuals to require supplementary lenses (in the form of glasses) for focusing near objectives sharply.

The lens is attached to the ciliary body by means of the *zonule* (Fig. 567, *upper right,* Z). In sections this exhibits a fibrillar form, and for this reason the zonule is sometimes called the *suspensory ligament of the lens.* But it is probable that much of its fibrillar appearance is due to fixation artefact and that in reality the zonule is composed of a gel and represents a specialized portion of the vitreous body, the mass of gel that lies behind it, which will be described presently.

The zonule has a broad zone of attachment both to the capsule of the lens around its equator and to the ciliary body (Fig. 567). Now, it might be thought, as was noted before, that matters would be arranged so that the contraction of the smooth muscle fibers of the ciliary body would pull on the zonule, which would in turn pull on the equator of the lens so that the lens would become flatter and hence accommodated for distant objects. Actually, the contraction of the smooth muscle of the ciliary body produces the opposite effect. Instead of tensing the zonule, the contraction of the smooth muscle of the ciliary body, the fibers of which are firmly attached to the sclera in the region of the scleral spur, pulls the part of the ciliary body to which the zonule is attached, *forward* and *inward*. This effect, since the attachment of the zonule to the ciliary body is posterior to its site of attachment to the lens, relaxes the tension of the zonule and hence permits the lens, which itself is under tension from its capsule, to assume a more globular shape, and hence become accommodated for close objects. It is to be noted, then, that muscular contraction is required for viewing close objects; this is one reason why reading "tires" the eyes more than viewing distant objects does.

Iris. The iris is a colored disk with a central, variable aperture, the pupil (Fig. 571). It is not a flat disk, for the lens pushes against its central part (the *pupillary margin*) from behind so that its more central part is more anterior than its periphery (Fig. 567).

The space behind the iris, and elsewhere limited by the lens, the vitreous body and the ciliary body, is called the *posterior chamber* of the eye (Fig. 567); the space in front of the iris (and at the pupil, in front of the lens), and otherwise limited by the cornea and the most anterior part of the sclera, is called the *anterior chamber* of the eye (Fig. 567). Both the anterior and the posterior chambers are filled with a fluid called *aqueous humor*. A certain amount of circulation takes place in this fluid. In all probability the fluid is formed in the posterior chamber and then passes into the anterior chamber, from which it is resorbed by mechanisms to be described presently. Since the posterior border of the pupillary margin of the iris and the anterior surface of the lens press against each other, the iris acts like a valve in that fluid from the posterior chamber can force the pupillary margin of the iris away from the anterior surface of the lens to enter the anterior chamber, but fluid tending to move in the reverse direction presses the pupillary margin of the iris against the lens and so closes the opening between the 2 chambers. Posteriorly, the iris is lined by

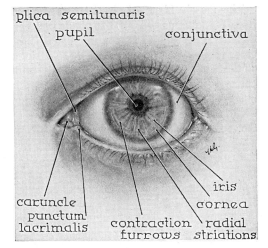

FIG. 571. The eye, as seen from in front.

2 layers of pigmented epithelial cells continuous with the 2 layers of retinal epithelium that line the ciliary body (Fig. 570). Anteriorly, the iris is covered imperfectly with squamous endothelial cells comparable and continuous with those of Descemet's endothelium.

The iris (Fig. 570) is well supplied with vessels and networks of nerve fibers. The arteries, branches of the major arterial circle, course spirally through its stroma like a corkscrew, so that their lumens will not be much affected by changes in the radius of the iris. They have a thick collagenous adventitia which prevents kinking when the spirals are compressed and makes the vessels appear as radiating gray lines in pale or blue irises. Throughout the stroma are scattered *chromatophores* which are concentrated mostly at the anterior border (Fig. 570). The vessels do not extend to this border.

Encircling the pupil, about 1.5 mm. from its margin, is a scalloped line formed, in a manner which need not be described here, by the regression of the membrane that extended across the pupil in embryonic life (Fig. 571). This line divides the iris into a pupillary and a ciliary portion (Fig. 571). Crypts opening anteriorly are found in the pupillary portion; they form as a result of the incomplete atrophy of the pupillary membrane. Shorter crypts are also found in the anterior surface of the ciliary portion. The contraction furrows (Fig. 571) appear as deeper folds encircling the anterior surface of the iris.

The muscle fibers of the iris are derived from the anterior cells of the pigmented epithelial layer; this is a continuation of the outer retinal layer of the eye. The constrictor of the pupil is the sphincterlike muscle composed of circularly arranged smooth muscle fibers near the pupillary margin. How firmly the iris is held against the anterior surface of the lens depends on the tone of these fibers. The dilator of the pupil is less distinct and consists of a thin sheet of radially disposed fibers near the back of the iris. The fibers are not typical smooth muscle fibers and are called *myo-epithelial* cells.

The pupillary size is automatically controlled by a nervous reflex in which the *retina* is the *receptor* organ, and the muscles of the iris the *effectors*. When the eye looks at a bright object the pupil is reflexly constricted, thereby decreasing the amount of light that can enter the eye, and vice versa. To anyone who has studied photography the pupillary size has a still further significance. A dilated pupil, like a dilated aperture in a camera, results in a diminished "depth" of focus. For this reason, glasses prescribed when the pupil is dilated are likely to be more accurate than those prescribed when the pupil is not.

The color of the iris is due to melanin pigment. As was noted in discussing the color of skin, melanin pigment, seen through a substantial thickness of tissue, appears blue. Hence, if the melanin pigment in the iris is limited to the epithelial cells that line its posterior surface, the iris (provided that the stroma ahead of the pigment is of a usual density) appears blue. If the stroma is somewhat denser than usual, the pigment at the back of the iris gives a gray color to the eye. If sufficient pigment is present in chromatophores in the substance of the stroma as well as in the epithelium at the back of the iris, the iris appears brown. In the white race the final color of the iris is not necessarily developed at the time of birth.

Region of the Angle of the Iris. It has already been observed that the site at which the sclera becomes continuous with the cornea is called the *limbus* (Fig. 570) and that immediately behind it the internal surface of the sclera is thrown into a ridge, the *scleral spur*, that extends inward and forward (Fig. 570). The scleral spur, of course, encircles the

eye. Immediately in front of the scleral spur a furrow dips into the inner layer of the sclera; this is called the *scleral furrow* (in Fig. 570 this is not labeled as such but as spaces of Fontana), and it too encircles the eye. At the bottom of the furrow a canal (or a group of anastomosing canals) lined by endothelium is situated. This is called the *canal of Schlemm* (Fig. 570), and it too encircles the eye. In a meridional section, the scleral spur, the scleral furrow and the canal of Schlemm are, of course, all cut in cross section (Fig. 570).

The scleral furrow is filled in (over the canal which lies at its bottom) with a loose meshwork of connective tissue; this extends from the cornea, at the anterior side of the furrow, backward to the anterior border of the scleral spur. The spaces in the meshwork were in the past called the *spaces of Fontana* (Fig. 570) and they communicate with the anterior chamber. The spaces which are now commonly referred to as the trabecular spaces are lined by endothelium; this is continuous with that which lines the cornea and covers the anterior surface of the iris. Hence, aqueous humor is present in the trabecular spaces. The middle (uveal) coat of the eye extends forward to provide a lining for the wall of the eye between the iris and the scleral spur. In the horse this lining is so strong and well developed that it is called the *pecinate ligament*. Sometimes this name is used for its relatively undeveloped counterpart in man (Fig. 570).

Ciliary Processes. About 75 little ridges, each about 2.0 mm. long, 0.5 mm. wide and about 1 mm. high, project inwardly from the ciliary body, immediately behind its point of junction with the iris, into the posterior chamber of the eye. These are termed the *ciliary processes,* and a few are usually to be seen in a single longitudinal section of an eye (Fig. 572, *left*).

As is indicated in Figure 566 (*center*), the cores of the ciliary processes are the counterparts in this particular region of the choriocapillaris since they consist chiefly of capillaries that are supported by a delicate connective tissue (Fig. 572, *right*). The processes are covered with two layers of epithelium; these represent the continuation of the 2 layers of the retina forward (compare the middle and the right drawings in Fig. 566). The cells of the deeper of the 2 layers are

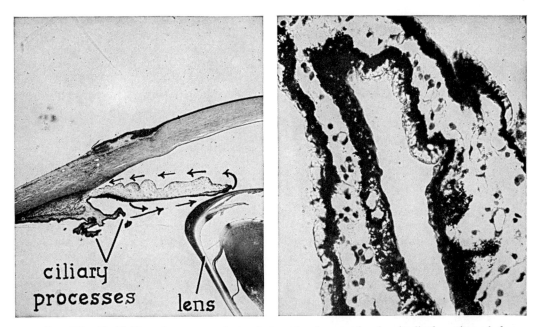

FIG. 572. (*Left*) Very low-power photomicrograph of part of a longitudinal section of the eye, showing the ciliary processes. The arrows indicate the course of the circulation of the aqueous humor. (*Right*) High-power photomicrograph of a section of the ciliary processes of a rabbit. Notice the large capillaries in the loose, delicate connective tissue that makes up the stroma of the processes.

pigmented (Fig. 572, *right*). The superficial layer is called the ciliary epithelium. The epithelial layer, as a whole, rests on a membrane that is continuous with Bruch's membrane and separates the epithelium from the vascular stroma of the processes.

With the E/M, Pease has shown that the ciliary epithelium (the layer that abuts on the aqueous humor) contains many deep folds of the cell membrane. These begin from the free surface and extend almost through to the deeper sides of the cells. Moreover, Pease has shown that the free surfaces of the cells are covered with a basement membrane. The folds and the basement membrane are both concerned, in all probability, with the transport of fluid required in connection with the secretion of aqueous humor.

Aqueous Humor: Formation, Circulation and Absorption. Aqueous humor is a thin watery fluid containing most of the diffusable substance of blood plasma and is very similar to blood serum in composition. For example, the albumin-globulin ratio is the same in both aqueous humor and serum. However, whereas serum has a protein content of 7 per cent, aqueous humor contains only 0.02 per cent. Like serum, the aqueous humor contains no fibrinogen and therefore cannot clot. It has been a matter of some controversy as to whether it should be regarded primarily as a dialysate of blood plasma, comparable with tissue fluid, or as a secretion. For one thing it is hypertonic in relation to blood and in all probability not only the factors concerned in tissue fluid formation and absorption (hydrostatic and osmotic pressure), but specific cellular activities as well, participate in controlling its quality and its rate of formation and absorption. Friendwald describes some of the complex cellular activities concerned in the matter, and his paper should be read for further information about this subject.

Although aqueous humor is thin and watery, it has been shown to contain considerable quantities of hyaluronic acid. However, this material, as was explained in Chapter 5, commonly appears in connective tissue as a soft, jellylike, amorphous type of intercellular substance. Its jellylike form in most connective tissues is due to its being present in a highly polymerized state, for its molecular aggregates are of a very large size. It was also observed in Chapter 5 that the enzyme hyaluronidase has the ability to depolymerize hyaluronic acid. It is of interest that it has been determined from studies made on the eyes of cattle that the hyaluronic acid in the aqueous humor is normally about 95 per cent depolymerized; this, then, is the reason for the aqueous' having such a low viscosity. This suggests that hyaluronidase has a normal function in the eye in keeping the molecular aggregates of hyaluronic acid from becoming of a large size. If they did become of a large size, they probably could not drain away from the eye by the escape mechanism to be described presently; hence, hyaluronic acid would accumulate in the eye and so change both the physical state and the osmotic pressure of the aqueous humor to the detriment of the eye. It would appear, then, that the action of hyaluronidase in keeping the hyaluronic acid of the eye depolymerized represents a normal physiologic function of the enzyme.

Although the general principles with regard to the formation and the absorption of tissue fluid that have been explained in Chapter 6 are fundamental to the understanding of the formation and the absorption of aqueous humor, there are certain differences in the mechanism that operates in the eye from that which operates in most tissues. These differences are due to the fact that tissue fluid in the eye is under considerably greater pressure than it is in most sites in the body. In most sites the tissues surrounding capillaries are not under very great tension; hence, a relatively low hydrostatic pressure in the capillaries is sufficient to drive tissue fluid out through their walls at their arterial ends. Correspondingly, the tissue substance in which blood vessels are embedded is under so little tension that venules are not compressed, even though the hydrostatic pressure within them is extremely low. However, surrounded by a tough, inelastic, fibrous tunic, the contents of the eye are under constant tension; the usual intra-ocular pressure ranges from about 20 to 25 mm. of mercury. This requires, then, that the blood within the capillaries of the eye be under a considerably greater hydrostatic pressure than the general intra-ocular pressure if the osmotic pressure of the colloids of the plasma is to be overcome and tissue fluid (aqueous humor) elaborated. Furthermore, it requires that the blood in intra-ocular veins also be under considerable hydrostatic pressure; otherwise, the veins within the eye would be collapsed by the intra-ocular pressure.

Although it is possible that any capillaries close to the anterior or the posterior chambers could contribute to the formation and the absorption of aqueous humor, it is highly probable that the capillaries of the ciliary processes, and to a much lesser extent those at the back of the iris, elaborate most of it. It is not unlikely that the hyaluronic acid of the aqueous is also formed in the delicate connective tissue that forms the cores of the ciliary processes. The most important mechanism for the absorption of aqueous humor is situated in the angle of the iris and will be described presently.

It is to be noted that, since the fibrous tunic of the eye cannot stretch and since structures within the eye are normally of a constant size and incompressible, a normal intra-ocular pressure depends on a proper balance between the formation and the absorption of aqueous humor. If conditions should develop in the anterior part of the eye which in another part of the body would cause edema, for example, interference with the absorption of tissue fluid, the eye cannot swell; instead, the intra-ocular pressure becomes increased. An increase in intra-ocular pressure, sufficient to be incompatible with the continued health of the eye, constitutes the condition termed *glaucoma,* and it is obvious that the treatment of the condition would be directed toward increasing the absorption of aqueous humor and/or decreasing its production.

Although under certain conditions aqueous humor can be produced very rapidly and removed very rapidly, it appears that under normal conditions it is formed and absorbed very slowly, probably at about the rate of 2 cu. mm. a minute. After aqueous humor is formed it passes from the posterior chamber between the lens and the iris to enter the anterior chamber (Fig. 572). There it moves toward the angle of the iris, where most of it enters the trabecular spaces (Fontana), from which it is absorbed into the canal of Schlemm.

The canal of Schlemm (Fig. 570) probably has no direct communication with the trabecular spaces except perhaps very fine pores that can be seen only with the E/M (see Holmberg, Garron, Speakman); hence, aqueous humor, to enter the canal, probably must pass through a delicate membrane, including the endothelium lining the canal. The canal contains aqueous humor during life; this drains outwardly through *collector trunks* in the sclera. These pass out under the bulbar conjunctiva where they are known as *aqueous veins* because they contain aqueous humor; in this position they may be seen with a slit lamp during life. The aqueous veins connect with blood-containing veins so that eventually aqueous humor is emptied into the venous system. Interference with the flow of aqueous humor in the collector trunks and the aqueous veins may be a factor in glaucoma. After death, blood may back up into the aqueous and the collecting veins and into the canal of Schlemm so that it may be seen in these sites in sections.

The Vitreous Body. The vitreous body is a mass of transparent gelled amorphous intercellular substance; the cells responsible for its formation are not known with certainty. It is bounded by the internal limiting membrane of the retina, the lens and the posterior zonular membrane (Fig. 567). In addition to transmitting rays of light, its bulk helps, anteriorly, to hold the lens in place, and posteriorly, to keep the inner coat of the retina in apposition with the outer pigmented coat. If vitreous is lost, as occurs unavoidably in some surgical procedures, the 2 latter coats of the retina may become separated.

The vitreous, as has been shown by Adler, also plays a part in the metabolism of the retina, allowing the transfer of metabolites through it.

Through the vitreous body runs Cloquet's canal, the remnant of the primitive hyaloid system or primary vitreous (Fig. 568, 4). Cloquet's canal runs from the papilla toward the posterior surface of the lens and is usually inconspicuous in life. In some instances the primitive hyaloid structures persist and may interfere with vision.

The vitreous is denser at its periphery. The dense peripheral vitreous, while it is adherent to the internal limiting membrane of the retina over all its area, is particularly adherent at the papilla. It is also adherent to the posterior surface of the lens near its edge.

COMPOSITION OF THE VITREOUS BODY. The vitreous body is of the nature of a hydrophilic colloidal system. The dispersed phase of the system probably consists both of a complex protein (vitrein) which has pronounced hygroscopic qualities and *hyaluronic acid*. The dispersion medium of the system in a sense may be thought of as aqueous humor; in any event, it contains the crystalloids normally dissolved in aqueous humor. Under normal conditions the vitreous humor is gelled. It is very easily denatured by drying or fixation, and it then exhibits a fibrillar structure that may be seen with the light microscope. However, such fibrillar structure as it possesses during life and imparted to it by its molecular constitution cannot be seen with the ordinary light microscope. It was believed that lost vitreous was not replaced, but Pirie has shown that it re-forms in rabbits.

The Retina. In learning the layers of the retina the student should understand clearly that the terms "inner" and "outer" are used (as they are with regard to the layers of the wall of the eye) not with reference to the body as a whole but with regard to the *center* and the *exterior* of the eye. Hence, the inner of any 2 layers of the wall of the eye or of any 2 layers of the retina itself is the layer closer to the center of the eye. Moreover, the student should realize that from the study of skin and mucous membranes a habit of thinking of the layer next to the free surface of a membrane as its outer layer may have become established. Such a habit leads to difficulty in the study of the eye, for the free surface of the retina (the layer next to the vitreous body) is the *inner* layer of the retina and *not* its outer layer.

It will be recalled that the retina develops from the optic vesicle (an outgrowth from the brain) and that it is at first constituted of 2 main layers because the anterior wall of the optic vesicle (Fig. 568, 1) becomes invaginated backward into its posterior half to make a 2-layered optic cup (Fig. 568, 2, 3 and 4). It is the inner layer of the optic cup that develops into the nervous portion of the retina. The outer wall of the cup does not develop into nervous tissue but instead into a layer of pigmented epithelium. The cells of this layer are of a somewhat flattened cuboidal shape (Fig. 575) when seen in profile and hexagonal

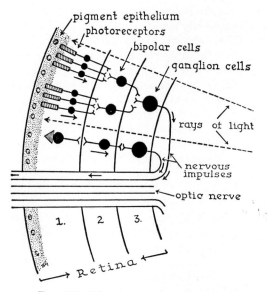

pigment epithelium
photoreceptors
bipolar cells
ganglion cells
rays of light
nervous impulses
optic nerve
1.   2.   3.
Retina

Fig. 573. Diagram showing the arrangement of the 3 layers of neurons in the retina. Observe that the light and the nervous impulses travel in opposite directions.

when seen in full face. They contain a pigment which is probably an unusual type of melanin called *fuscin* (L., dusky) (Figs. 574 and 575). It has been reported that these cells, in embryonic life before they come to contain pigment, are dopa-positive; hence, there is reason for assuming that they make the pigment they contain.

The retina is commonly described as consisting of 10 layers. These are labeled from the outside in (Figs. 574 and 575). Therefore, the first layer of the retina is the layer of pigmented epithelium, the layer that develops from the original outer layer of the optic cup. This layer, it should be noted, becomes more firmly attached to the choroid than to the inner and nervous part of the retina from which, it must be remembered, it was originally separated by a cleft. Consequently, when eyes are removed for histologic study, the nervous portion of the retina commonly becomes detached from the layer of pigment epithelium, which remains adherent to the choroid (Fig. 576). The nervous part of the retina is 0.4 mm. thick posteriorly but thins out anteriorly to half this thickness.

Before considering the microscopic structure of the other 9 layers of the retina, it is helpful to recall that the cell bodies of most afferent neurons in the body are confined to cerebrospinal ganglia which, though close to the C.N.S., are not actually in the C.N.S. However, axons from these ganglion cells enter the C.N.S to synapse there with connector neurons which in turn synapse with still others and so on. The neurons in the afferent chains sooner or later make connections with those of efferent chains, and so reflex phenomena are possible.

The arrangements with regard to the photoreceptor cells are quite different from the usual arrangement described above. The cell bodies of the photoreceptors are not disposed in ganglia but in the substance of the retina. Furthermore, the cell bodies of the first 2 neurons of the afferent chains that lead from the photoreceptors are also disposed in the retina (Fig. 573). If it is remembered that the retina is an outgrowth from the brain this does not seem so remarkable, for since connector neurons are confined to the tissue of the C.N.S. and since tissue of the C.N.S. migrates, as it were, into the retina, during embryonic development, the presence of connector neurons in the retina might be expected.

However, it might be expected that the photoreceptor cells would be present in the innermost layer of the retina because this is the first layer of the membrane that is struck by light after it passes through the vitreous body. Indeed, in some invertebrates this arrangement is to be found. But in vertebrates the photoreceptors are placed in the *outer part* of the retina, at right angles to its surface, so that their free ends abut on the first layer of the retina, the layer of pigmented epithelium.

With these few points in mind, Figure 573 should be consulted. In this diagram the layer of photoreceptors may be seen, apposed to the layer of pigment epithelium. Each cell in the photoreceptor layer has a dendritic process that extends from the region of the nucleus of the cell outwardly to the layer of pigmented epithelium. The dendritic processes of the photoreceptors are of 2 general shapes, resembling either *rods* or *cones*, and accordingly, the photoreceptors are classified as rod or cone cells. The axons of the rod and cone cells pass inwardly and synapse with the dendrites of the nerve cells in the middle part of the retina. These, of course, are to the inside of the rod and cone cells and are called *bipolar cells* because they have only 2 processes: a dendrite and an axon (Fig. 573). The axons

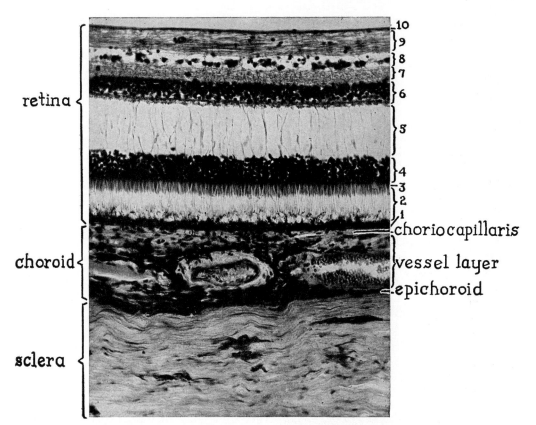

retina

choroid

sclera

10
9
8
7
6
5
4
3
2
1
choriocapillaris
vessel layer
epichoroid

Fig. 574. Low-power photomicrograph of a portion of a section cut through the wall of the eye, showing the retina, the choroid and some of the sclera. The numbers refer to the layers of the retina, which are described in the text and shown in diagrammatic form in Figure 575.

of the bipolar cells pass inwardly and synapse with the dendrites of the third and innermost layer of nerve cells, the *ganglion cells*. (It should be understood that these cells do not constitute a ganglion; they are called ganglion cells because they are large and otherwise resemble the nerve cells of ganglia.) The axons of the ganglion cells pass inwardly to the inner border of the retina, where they turn at right angles toward the site of exit of the optic nerve, running in the innermost part of the retina, parallel with the surface of the eye (Fig. 573).

To affect the rod- and cone-shaped processes of the photoreceptors, light from the vitreous must pass through the inner 2 layers of nerve cells of the retina and through the cell bodies of the photoreceptors themselves. Then, when the light reaches the rod- and cone-shaped dendritic processes of the photoreceptors and nervous impulses are set up, the nervous impulses must pass in the reverse di-

rection, *inwardly*, through the bipolar and ganglion cells to the innermost part of the retina and from here, along the axons of the gangion cells, to the site of exit of the optic nerve. Obviously, for this arrangement to be functional, the nerve cells and their processes that are situated to the inner side of the rod- and cone-shaped dendritic processes of the photoreceptors must be readily permeable to light.

Having gained some knowledge of the arrangement of the nerve cells in the retina, it is easy to learn the 10 classic layers of this structure. These will now be described, and in the following description, the photomicrograph of the retina (Fig. 574) and the diagram of it, in both of which the layers are numbered (Fig. 575), should be consulted with reference to each layer described.

Layer 1, the *layer of pigment epithelium*, consists of the layer of pigmented epithelial cells (already described) that develops from

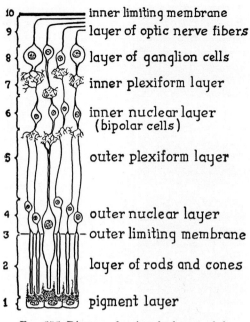

10 — inner limiting membrane
9 — layer of optic nerve fibers
8 — layer of ganglion cells
7 — inner plexiform layer
6 — inner nuclear layer (bipolar cells)
5 — outer plexiform layer
4 — outer nuclear layer
3 — outer limiting membrane
2 — layer of rods and cones
1 — pigment layer

FIG. 575. Diagram showing the layers of the retina.

the outer layer of the optic cup (see also Fig. 568).

Layer 2, the *layer of rods and cones*, consists of the dendritic cytoplasmic processes of the photoreceptors. These are packed closely together, side by side, in this layer, looking like bacilli; hence, this layer is sometimes known as the bacillary layer.

Layer 3, the *external limiting membrane*, is a sievelike membrane composed of the inward extensions of what are termed Muller's fibers. These are neurologic elements in the retina; the cells that are responsible for these fibers are in the same layer as the bipolar cells, as will be described presently. The dendritic processes of the photoreceptors extend through the holes in the sievelike external limiting membrane and are thereby supported.

Layer 4, the *outer nuclear layer*, is the layer formed by the closely packed nuclei of the photoreceptors.

Layer 5, the *outer plexiform layer*, is the layer in which the axons of the rods and the cones synapse with the dendrites of the bipolar cells. Since several rods may synapse with a single bipolar cell and, except at the fovea (to be described later) more than one cone, the dendrites of bipolar cells must branch into

terminal networks; these, suitably stained, give this layer a plexiform appearance.

Layer 6, the *inner nuclear layer*, consists of the nuclei of the bipolar cells and the nuclei of the cells that account for Muller's supporting fibers. The nuclei of the latter have more cytoplasm surrounding them than have the nuclei of the bipolar cells; furthermore, they tend to lie in the outer part of the layer. To the inside of the layer of nuclei of the bipolar cells, the nuclei of some nerve cells of the association type, called *amacrine cells*, are present. Blood vessels, from the inner part of the retina, extend outwardly as far as this layer.

Layer 7, the *inner plexiform layer*, is the layer in which the axons of the bipolar cells synapse with the dendrites of the ganglion cells. The latter have fine networks at their terminations; these give the layer a plexiform appearance when sections are suitably stained.

Layer 8, the *ganglion cell layer*, is the layer in which the large ganglion cells are disposed, together with some neuroglial cells. Retinal blood vessels are also present in this layer.

Layer 9, the *layer of nerve fibers*, consists of the axons of the ganglion cells; these, after having reached the innermost part of the retina, have turned at right angles to pass thereafter parallel with the inner surface of the retina toward the site of exit of the optic nerve. To aid transparency they possess neither myelin sheaths nor sheaths of Schwann. Spiderlike neuroglial cells, the inner branches of Muller's fibers and blood vessels are also present in this layer.

Layer 10, the *inner limiting membrane,* is a delicate homogeneous structure composed of the fused, inwardly directed, terminations of Muller's fibers.

The cytoplasmic dendritic processes of the rod cells as they pass toward the region of the outer limiting membrane are constricted and known as *rod fibers* (Fig. 575). As they extend farther outward toward the layer of pigmented epithelium, they become expanded into rods that are roughly of the shape of pen flashlights, and, like the latter, the rods are used for night vision. The cones are broader than the rods, and their dendritic processes at no point between their nuclei and their free ends become constricted into fibers. Visual acuity in bright light and color vision are both dependent upon the cone cells. In bright light the ends of the rods become invested by the pigment of the cells of layer 1, while in dim light the reverse occurs, and the ends of the cones tend to become invested by pigment (Fig. 575).

The mechanism for light reception is by no means completely established. The tips of the rods contain visual purple or rhodopsin, a red coloring matter derived from vitamin A, which is thought to be involved in the generation of nervous impulses when stimulated by dim light. This theory is supported by the observation that night vision is impaired in vitamin A deficiency. Rhodopsin becomes bleached to an opaque white if it is exposed to light, but it regenerates in the dark. In this regard it is of interest to note that Nature has logically arranged that the pigment of the outer retinal coat invests the ends of the rods when the retina is exposed to bright light, sparing it for use in dim light. Should separation occur between the 2 retinal coats, as in detachment of the retina, the separated portion becomes gray and relatively opaque. The ends of the cones are thought to contain a substance which has an action similar to rhodopsin in the production of nervous impulses.

Since the layer of rods and cones contains no blood vessels whatsoever, all nourishment comes to this layer from diffusion and largely from the choriocapillaris.

FINE STRUCTURE. The morphogenesis and the fine structure of retinal rods has been investigated extensively by DeRobertis, whose contributions to this subject are listed in the references at the end of this chapter.

MACULA LUTEA AND FOVEA CENTRALIS. Very close to the posterior pole of the eye there is a little depression of the retina; here the retina is more yellow than elsewhere (after death); hence, it is called the macula lutea (yellow spot). The cells and the fibers of the inner layers of the retina diverge from the center of this area so that the photoreceptors in the central and most depressed part of this area, which is called the *fovea centralis*, are not covered to the same extent as the photoreceptors in other parts of the eye. No blood vessels are present in the retina over this area. The receptors here are all cones; moreover, these, though longer than usual, are not so thick as usual; hence, more are packed into this small area than elsewhere. Therefore, this area is specialized in several ways for the greatest degree of visual acuity. Only the image formed in this area is interpreted clearly and sharply by the brain. For example, as one reads this page, although he is aware of words arranged in lines from top to bottom, he can see accurately only a very little at a time. In other words, in order that the brain may receive a detailed interpretation of this page, the fovea centralis, like the electron beam originating in the television picture tube, must scan the image of the page, letter by letter, word by word and line by line, from top to bottom. Fortunately, however, most words or groups of words can be recognized from experience merely by their general configuration, thereby saving much time.

Nerve fibers from this specialized area are provided with more room at the papilla (the site of exit of the optic nerve) and consequently are less heaped up and more securely arranged than are the other more converging retinal fibers. Hence, if edema should develop at the papilla, the fibers coming from the macular area are the last to be involved.

SENSITIVITY TO LIGHT. The sensitivity of the retina to stimulation by light is incredibly great. Hecht *et al.* have estimated that only a single quantum is sufficient to stimulate one rod and that 6 rods discharging into a common pathway may result in a nervous impulse along the path. There are practically 7 million cones in the human retina and 10 to 20 times that number of rods. Since the number of nerve fibers in the optic nerve has been estimated at from $\frac{1}{2}$ to 1 million, there is, of course, much overlapping of neurons.

Optic Nerve. Like the nerve fiber layer of the retina, the optic nerve at the papilla is composed of unmedullated nerve fibers, containing glial supporting tissue and some capillaries. At the lamina cribrosa, the nerve fibers, arranged in bundles, are interspersed by a fibrous meshwork extending from the sclera (Fig. 576). After piercing the lamina cribrosa, the nerve fibers become myelinated, thus swelling the size of the optic nerve (Fig. 576). They do not acquire a sheath of Schwann, and, consequently, they resemble the nerve fibers of the white matter of the cord or brain. The sheaths covering the nerve have already been described and are illustrated in Figure 567.

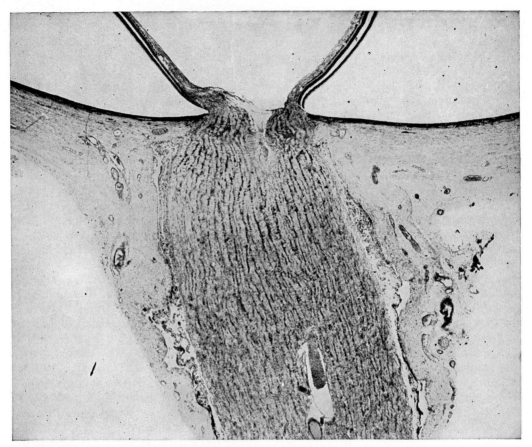

FIG. 576. Low-power photomicrograph of a section through the wall of the eye at the site of exit of the optic nerve. Observe that the inner layer of the retina is detached from the outermost layer of pigmented epithelium. Separation commonly occurs along this line when eyes are fixed and sectioned.

INTERNAL APPEARANCE

It has been mentioned above that the eye is the window of the body, and that structures within the eye may be seen from the outside. Indeed, the eye is the only site where structures lying deep to the ectoderm of the body can be seen without artificial exposure or interruption of the integrity of the body surface. Since many of the functional and disease changes which occur in the body are reflected in changes in the structure of the eye, this fact is of great importance.

To look within the eye an instrument called the *ophthalmoscope* is ordinarily used. This provides a bright source of light, the rays of which are projected through the cornea into the patient's eye, thereby providing sufficient light for the operator of the instrument to see the fine structures in the back or fundus of the eye. With another instrument, the slit lamp microscope, the microscopic details of the conjunctiva, the cornea, the iris, the lens, the ciliary body and even the anterior portion of the vitreous can be studied in the living eye.

Figure 577 is a black-and-white representation of the fundus of a living right eye as viewed with the ophthalmoscope. The cup-shaped surface of the retina, gray in Figure 577, is red (the red reflex) in life because light is reflected back from the red blood cells in the very large capillaries of the choriocapillaris. The whole background has a granular appearance, due in part to the irregular distribution of pigment in the retinal epithelium and in part to the coarse aggregation of pigment cells in the vascular layer of the choroid.

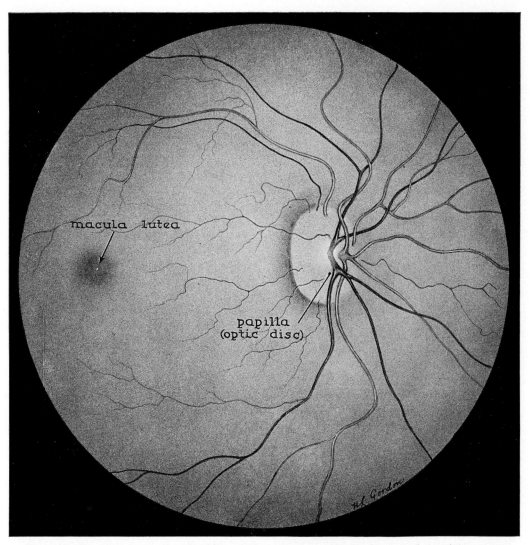

macula lutea

papilla
(optic disc)

FIG. 577. Drawing, in black and white, of the appearance of the fundus of the right eye as seen through the ophthalmoscope.

The unmedullated fibers of the retina (layer 9) converge at the site of exit of the optic nerve. Here, there is much heaping up of the retinal fibers. This constitutes what is known as the *papilla*. In this region the nerve fibers are loosely arranged; consequently, accumulation of tissue fluid in the nervous tissue of the retina results in a obvious swelling of the papilla; this is a valuable early clinical sign of certain pathologic conditions. Since the papilla is of a disklike shape about 1.5 mm. in diameter, it is often called the *optic disk*. It appears much larger when seen through the refracting media of the eye than it does if it is exposed. Because the white lamina cribrosa (white fibrous tissue) is pierced by gray nerve fibers and is supplied by a capillary network, the papilla has a pale pink color in contrast with the redness of the retina elsewhere. Should the capillaries become atrophied, the papilla appears gray, and the little perforations of the lamina cribrosa, now not so obscured, appear more prominent. Should the nerve fibers atrophy, the papilla becomes chalky white; this appearance may be exaggerated later by the proliferation of glial and fibrous tissue.

The central portion of the papilla, called

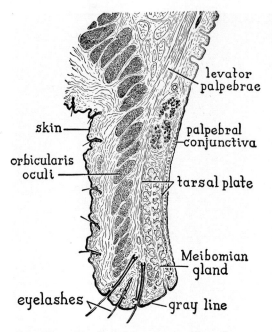

skin —

orbicularis
oculi —

eyelashes

levator
palpebrae

palpebral
conjunctiva

tarsal plate

Meibomian
gland

gray line

Fig. 578. Drawing of a section (low-power) cut perpendicularly through the upper eyelid. (After Duane, A.: Fuch's Textbook of Ophthalmology, ed. 8 revised, Philadelphia, Lippincott)

the *physiologic cup,* is a funnel-like space created by the diverging nerve fibers. An increase in intra-ocular pressure (and other conditions) may displace the lamina cribrosa and its nerve fibers posteriorly. This results in the whole papilla's becoming depressed and cup-shaped, a condition referred to as *cupping of the disk.*

The central retinal artery and vein make their appearance at the center of the physiologic cup, and, hugging its medial side (Fig. 577), they radiate over the inner surface of the retina, branching as they go (Fig. 577).

In placing the papilla inframedially, Nature reserved an area at the posterior pole of the eye, the *macula lutea* (Fig. 577), to subserve the highest efficiency for visual acuity. The depressed central part of this area, the *fovea centralis* (L., central pit), lies about 2.5 papillary diameters laterally from the margin of the papilla and a little below its center. The size of the macula is variable but is usually only slightly larger or smaller than the papilla.

Naturally, large retinal vessels, which would otherwise interfere with vision, do not traverse

the macula (Fig. 577). Instead, they pass well above and below it in wide curves; this aids the student in locating the macula with the ophthalmoscope. Smaller vessels extend from the curving blood vessels and also from the medial side of the papilla itself into the macular area, but they never quite reach its center, which is left completely nonvascular. Because of yellow pigment in its superficial layers, the macular area appears yellow in the living (in red-free light) or on exposure after death. In ordinary white light it appears darker and redder than the remainder of the retina (Fig. 577). Its darker color is due to an increased amount of pigmentation in the outer pigmented retinal coat, and the increased redness is due to blood contained in the especially large choroidal capillaries disposed behind this area. The fovea centralis, viewed through the pupil, appears to be a minute bright point because light is reflected, as by a mirror, from its concave walls.

ACCESSORY STRUCTURES (ADNEXA)

Conjunctiva. The conjunctiva is a thin transparent mucous membrane that covers the "white" of the eye as the bulbar conjunctiva (Fig. 571) and that lines the eyelid (which is not seen unless the lid is everted) as the palpebral conjunctiva (Fig. 578). The space in the angle formed by the reflection of the palpebral conjunctiva from (and against) the bulbar is called the *fornix.*

The epithelium is characteristically stratified columnar in type with 3 layers of cells: a deep layer of columnar cells, a middle layer of polygonal cells and a superficial layer of flat or low cuboidal cells. The middle layer is absent in most of the palpebral conjunctiva. As the epithelium approaches the lid margin it changes to stratified squamous in type; this merges with the epidermis of the skin. Scattered through the conjunctival epithelium are mucus-secreting goblet cells. Near the limbus the epithelium of the bulbar conjunctiva becomes stratified squamous in type and is provided with deep papilla. It is continuous with the epithelium of the cornea.

The substantia (lamina) propria of the conjunctiva consists of delicate fibrous connective tissue; this is particularly loose over the sclera. In it are scattered accumulations of lymphocytes; these form nodules near the fornices. The substantia propria, except in the lid, merges into a more deeply situated and thicker meshwork of collagenous and elastic connective tissue.

The palpebral fissure is the space between the free margins of the 2 lids (Fig. 571). At the medial end of the palpebral fissure is a little lake of tears, the lacus lacrimalis. A free fold of conjunctiva, the concave border of which faces the pupil, is present at the medial end of the palpebral fissure; this is called the *plica semilunaris* (Fig. 571), and it is probably homologous to the nictitating membrane of birds. In the very angle of the palpebral fissure at its medial end, a little fleshy mass, the *caruncle* (Fig. 571), protrudes; developmentally, this is a detached portion of the marginal part of the lower lid; hence, it contains a few striated muscle fibers as well as a few hair follicles and sebaceous glands.

Eyelids. Each eyelid is covered on its anterior surface with delicate skin; this contains the follicles of some very fine hairs and some sebaceous and sweat glands (Fig. 578). The dermis is of an unusually loose texture, and the subcutaneous tissue, deep to it, in members of the white races, contains almost no fat. The keratin of the epidermis gradually thins out as the skin approaches the free margin of the eyelid, and here the epidermis becomes continuous with the epithelium of the palpebral conjunctiva, which has already been described as lining the inner (posterior) side of the lid (Fig. 578).

Each lid is reinforced with a plate of dense connective tissue, the *tarsal plate*. This is placed in the posterior part of the lid so that the palpebral conjunctiva is apposed to its posterior surface (Fig. 578). The secretory portions of long, vertically disposed, complex sebaceous glands, called *meibomian glands*, are embedded in the tarsal plate; these open onto the posterior part of the free margin of the lid (Fig. 578). Should one of these glands become infected, a painful pealike swelling develops in the lid.

Deep to the skin covering the anterior surface of the lid are bundles of striated muscle fibers of the orbicularis oculi muscle (Fig. 578). Some of the collagenic fibers from the aponeurosis of the levator palpebrae muscle pass between these bundes to be inserted into the skin that covers the eyelid. Others con-

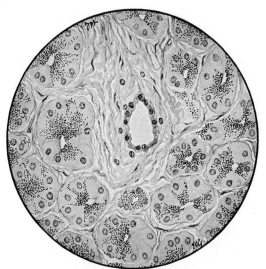

Fig. 579. Drawing of a portion of a section (high-power) of the lacrimal gland, showing secretory units and a duct.

nect with the tarsal plate, and still others continue toward the margin of the lid in front of the plate. This latter sheet of connective tissue becomes more areolar as it approaches the margin of the lid, which it reaches to form the gray line, a surgical landmark of some importance. Along this gray line the lid may be split surgically, opening up the submuscular space known to the ophthalmologist as the *intermarginal space.*

The hair follicles of the eyelashes slant anteriorly as they pass to the surface. They are arranged in 3 or 4 rows, just ahead of the gray line. They are provided with sebaceous glands; these are termed the glands of Zeis. Between the follicles, the sweat glands of Moll are disposed. A sty is the result of the infection of either type of gland.

Tear Glands. Tears are produced by the lacrimal gland and several accessory tear glands. The lacrimal gland lies in the superolateral corner of the bony orbit. It is divided by the lateral edge of the levator palpebrae muscle into 2 lobes: a deep orbital lobe and a superficial palpebral lobe. Something less than a dozen ducts run from the gland to empty along the superior fornix. Most of the ducts from the orbital lobe, to reach their termination, pass through the palpebral lobe. Small accessory tear glands, the glands of

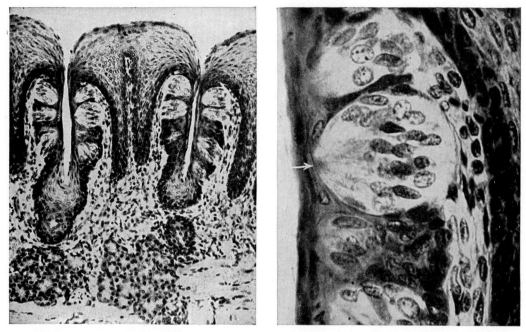

FIG. 580. (*Left*) Low-power photomicrograph of a portion of a section cut at right angles to the upper surface of the tongue of a rabbit in the region of the foliate papillae. These papillae, which are well developed only in certain animals, provide an especially good opportunity for seeing taste buds, which are numerous in this illustration. (*Right*) High-power photomicrograph of a taste bud in the epithelium of the side of a foliate papilla of a rabbit. The arrow occupies the approximate site where a pore (not shown) might be expected and it points to the pit (dark) into which the hairs of the neuro-epithelial cells project.

Krause, are scattered along both fornices, but they are more numerous in the upper one. Still smaller glands are present in the caruncle. It is of interest that the eye may remain healthy in the absence of the lacrimal gland; this suggests that the function of the gland is to some extent that of providing floods of tears on special occasions.

The tear glands develop from the conjunctiva and are of the serous compound tubuloalveolar type. The secretory cells are of a pyramidal columnar form and contain both fat droplets and secretion granules (Fig. 579). The secretory units are surrounded by myoepithelial cells which lie to the inside of the basement membrane.

The secretion of the tear glands is slightly alkaline. In addition to various salts, it contains an enzyme, lyzozyme, which is bacteriocidal. Tears, spread evenly over the cornea and the conjunctiva by the blinking of the lids, keep the surface of the cornea and the conjunctiva moist; this, as noted before, is an essential function. Floods of tears assist in washing foreign particles from the conjunctival sacs and the cornea.

DRAINAGE OF TEARS. On the free margin of each lid, near its medial end, is a little papilla called the *lacrimal papilla*. A small opening, which, however, can be seen with the naked eye, exists near the summit of the papilla; this opening is termed the *punctum* and it leads into the *lacrimal canaliculus*. This is a small tube that runs first in the lid and then medially so as to meet its fellow from the adjacent lid in a little ampulla that extends outwardly from the lateral side of a tubular structure called the *lacrimal sac*. The latter descends as the *nasolacrimal duct*, to open through the lateral surface of the inferior meatus of the nose; by means of this mechanism, tears more or less continually drain into the nose. Should any part of this duct system become blocked, tears, produced at only an ordinary rate, run over onto the side of the face.

The puncta and the canaliculi are lined with stratified squamous nonkeratinized epithelium, and the lacrimal sac and nasolacrimal duct with 2 layers of columnar epithelium which contains goblet cells. The lacrimal papilla is rich in elastic fibers.

TASTE BUDS

The nervous impulses responsible for the sense of taste are set up in little pale-staining bodies which resemble buds or little barrels and are arranged perpendicular to the surface in the epithelium of the mucous membrane of the mouth and the throat (Fig. 580). They are most numerous on the upper surface of the tongue, particularly along the sides of the grooves that surround vallate papillae. However, they are found on fungiform papillae and even in the epithelium between papillae. A few may be present in other parts of the mouth and in the lining of the throat. It is not unusual to see a taste bud in the epithelium on the laryngeal side of the epiglottis. They have been reported in other parts of the larynx.

A taste bud, like an onion, is constricted at both its ends. Moreover, taste buds, when seen in sections, appear to have a layered structure somewhat similar to that of an onion. This is due to the arrangement of their cells, of which there are 2 kinds: *sustentacular* cells and *neuro-epithelial* taste cells. The sustentacular cells are shaped like slices of cantaloupe; they are narrower at each of their ends than in their midsection, and they pursue a curved course from one end of the bud to the other. At the end of the barrel-shaped structure which reaches almost to the surface, they are arranged so as to surround a little central depression or *pit* which communicates with the surface by means of a fine passageway called the *inner taste pore* which extends through such epithelium as covers the end of the taste bud. The site of this is indicated on Figure 580 by an arrow, but the pore itself does not appear in the photomicrograph. (Pores are of such a small caliber that they show only occasionally in sections.) Neuro-epithelial taste cells are intermingled with sustentacular cells in the more central part of the bud. They are long narrow cells. The free end of each extends to the pit at the end of the taste bud, where it gives rise to a short hair that extends into the pit.

The sense of taste from the anterior two thirds of the tongue is mediated by way of the chorda tympani division of the facial nerve and from the posterior third by way of the glossopharyngeal nerve. Terminal fibers enter the deep ends of taste buds and end in intimate contact with the neuro-epithelial taste cells.

Any substance to be tasted must become dissolved in saliva and pass by means of a pore into the pit at the superficial end of a taste bud; here it affects the hairs of the neuro-epithelial cells in some fashion so as to cause a nervous impulse to be set up in the fibers associated with the neuro-epithelial cells. As is true of smell, there are only certain basic tastes: sweet, sour, salty and bitter, and perhaps alkaline and metallic. Doubtless, there are specialized receptors for each. These are not distributed evenly, so that some tastes are detected more easily in some parts of the tongue than in others. It seems incredible that the great variety of flavors of which we are aware are due to various combinations of these few basic tastes. Actually, it is easy to confuse taste and smell to some degree, and many of the more exotic flavors are probably smelled rather than tasted.

THE EAR

INTRODUCTION

In beginning the study of this organ it should be explained that there is a certain amount of ambiguity about the meaning of the term ear. For example, the 2 delicately sculptured flaplike appendages that are attached, one to each side of the head, and termed ears in everyday speech, are, of course, only parts (the auricles) of the 2 organs known as ears by the anatomist. But even the anatomist is not precise about the meaning of the term ear because each ear, as we shall see, consists of 3 main parts (an external, a middle and an inner part), and each of these 3 parts is in itself termed an ear; hence, each (complete) ear is said to consist of an *external ear*, a *middle ear*, and an *inner ear*.

Before attempting to learn the structure of the various parts of the ear the student should understand that the ear is the organ where nervous impulses are set up that are responsible, not only for hearing, but for other senses as well. These include an appreciation of (1) how the head is orientated in space in relation to gravitational forces and (2) whether move-

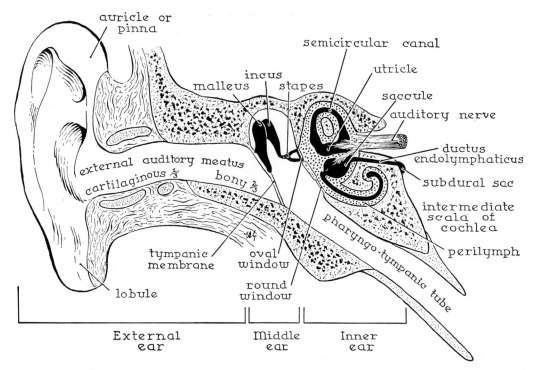

FIG. 581. Diagram of an ear, showing the relations of the external, the middle and the inner ear. (Redrawn and modified from Addison: Piersol's Normal Histology, ed. 15, Philadelphia, Lippincott)

ment of the head takes place (the overcoming of inertia), or, if steady movement of the head is taking place, whether the rate or the direction of the movement is altered. It may seem curious that end-organs concerned in the maintenance of equilibrium are so closely associated with the end-organ for hearing in the body. Actually, however, in the evolutionary scale, the ear was an organ for permitting animals to maintain equilibrium before it was an organ for hearing; the latter function grew, as it were, in some fashion from the former.

It has already been emphasized that a set of mechanical contrivances could be built so that each would respond to a different type of "stimulus" by closing an electrical circuit. A variety of such contrivances is illustrated in Figure 278. Any good student, given the facilities of a physics laboratory, could easily build more. For example, it would be a simple matter to build one that would close a circuit if it were suddenly moved in a certain direction or, if it were in steady movement, if the rate of its movement were suddenly increased or decreased. All that would be needed would be

a trough of water with a float at one end, which, on rising or falling, would close an electrical circuit. A sudden movement of the trough, in the direction of its long axis, would swish the water toward its back end, raise the float (if it were at that end) and so complete a circuit. Or, if the trough were in steady motion, with the water in it quite still, a sudden acceleration would produce the same effect, as everyone knows who has tried to hurry, while carrying a pail, full to the brim with water.

The student, then, may expect to find that a good amount of the structure of the ear is concerned with the "mechanical contrivances" that are present in it to permit sound waves, different positions in space and movement, to affect specific nerve endings (and these alone) in such a way as to set up nervous impulses which are then transmitted to the parts of the brain concerned in the interpretation of these sensations. However, before discussing the structure of these various arrangements in any detail, we shall first give a rough outline of the general structure of the ear and, as best we can, correlate the function of its chief parts with their structure.

GENERAL STRUCTURE

The *external ear* consists of an appendage, the *auricle*, and a tube, the *external auditory meatus* (*meatus* = a passage or canal), which extends from the auricle into the substance of the skull (Fig. 581) to a tiny cavity in the petrous portion of the temporal bone, known as the tympanic cavity or middle ear (Fig. 581). The external auditory meatus, although it extends to the middle ear, does not open into it, because a membrane, called the *tympanic membrane* or *eardrum*, extends across the deep end of the external auditory meatus to form a partition between it and the middle ear (Fig. 581). This membrane, which thus forms a considerable part of the lateral wall of the middle ear, is of a suitable size and thickness and is maintained under a suitable tension to vibrate in accordance with sound waves that reach it by way of the auricle and the external auditory meatus.

Before discussing the general structure of the middle ear further, and explaining how the vibrations set up in the eardrum by sound waves are transmitted across the middle ear to the inner ear which lies still deeper in the petrous portion of the temporal bone, we shall comment briefly on the inner ear, for it is here that the special groups of nerve endings which are selectively stimulated by sound, changes in relation to gravity, and movement are located.

The inner ear consists of a series of membranous tubes that are disposed in various arrangements and planes, together with 2 membranous sacs with which the membranous tubes communicate (Fig. 581). This closed system of membranous tubes and sacs is filled with a fluid termed *endolymph*, and at appropriate sites, to be described later, neuro-epithelial structures, with special types of nerve endings, are arranged in the lining of the system. The whole system of membranous tubes and sacs is so like a maze that it is said to constitute the *membranous labyrinth* (*labyrinthos* = a maze). The membranous labyrinth is loosely fitted into a series of spaces and cavities in the bone; these are of a similar pattern to, though somewhat larger than, the membranous labyrinth. These tubular spaces and cavities, together with the thin layer of compact bone that forms their immediate walls, and in which the membranous labyrinth is loosely fitted, are said to constitute the *bony labyrinth*. Although in some sites the membranous labyrinth is attached to the periosteum that lines the wall of the bony labyrinth, the bulk of the membranous labyrinth is suspended in a fluid termed *perilymph* which fills all the space in the bony labyrinth that is not occupied by the membranous labyrinth.

The most expanded portion of the bony labyrinth lies deep to the bony medial wall of the middle ear; this part of the bony labyrinth is termed its *vestibule* because it is the hallway that would be entered by any microscopic visitor who entered the inner ear from the middle ear. There are no doors opening from the middle ear into the vestibule of the bony labyrinth, so any visitor from the middle ear would have to enter by way of a window. There are two of these in the bony wall that separates the air-filled middle ear from the fluid-filled vestibule of the bony labyrinth; the upper is termed the *oval window,* and the lower one the *round window*. Both windows normally are closed, but in order to describe how they are closed we must digress for a moment.

It has already been explained how sound waves set the eardrum into vibration and that the eardrum constitutes a considerable portion of the lateral wall of the middle ear. A chain of 3 tiny bones, with joints between them, extends across the middle ear from its lateral to its medial wall (Fig. 581). The free end of the first bone of the chain is attached to the eardrum, and the free end of the last bone in the chain fits into, so as to close effectively, the oval window in the medial wall of the middle ear (Figs. 581 and 585). Hence, when sound waves set the eardrum in vibration, the chain of bones transmits these vibrations across the middle ear, and since the free end of the last bone of the chain does not fit rigidly into the window (beyond which is the perilymph of the bony labyrinth) but instead, a little like a piston in a cylinder, the vibrations are transmitted to the perilymph in the vestibule. However, fluid is incompressible; hence, every time fluid is pushed in at the oval window it must push out somewhere else. This occurs at the round window, for this is closed only by a

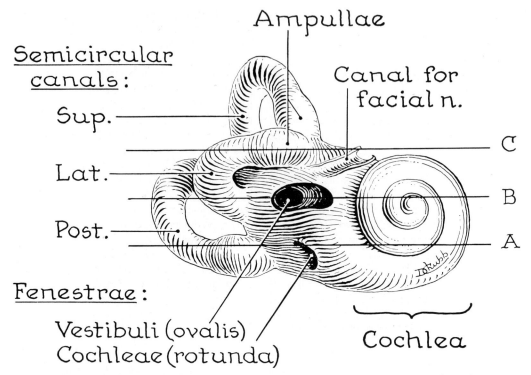

FIG. 582. An anterolateral view of the bony labyrinth. The oval and round windows (labeled fenestrae) may be seen opening into the vestibule; the cochlea extends from the vestibule to the right, and the semicircular canals, to the left. (Grant, J. C. B.: Method of Anatomy, ed. 4, Baltimore, Williams & Wilkins; lines A, B and C have been added)

membrane, and this has sufficient elasticity for this purpose. Having described the mechanical arrangements that exist in the ear to permit sound waves eventually to set up vibrations in the perilymph, we shall leave the matter of how these in turn affect nerve endings until certain other details of the bony and membranous labyrinth are considered.

Although the bony labyrinth (Fig. 582) has a complex form, it may be helpful to think of it as having 3 main parts. The first of these is the vestibule; this has already been described as its most expanded part which is disposed immediately medial to the middle ear. The other 2 main parts of the bony labyrinth may be regarded as 2 extensions of the labyrinth from the vestibule, and in these the bony labyrinth is tubular in form. The more anterior of the 2 tubular extensions of the bony labyrinth becomes wound into a spiral, the successive turns of which are of a decreasing radius (Figs. 581 and 582). Since this coiled part of the bony labyrinth looks something like

a snail's shell it is called the *cochlea* (L., snail shell). The more posterior of the 2 extensions of the bony labyrinth from the vestibule (actually this extension is regarded as a part of the vestibule) takes the form of 3 separate, round, bony tubes, each of which, on leaving the vestibule, follows a semicircular path so that each eventually returns to the vestibule (one may be seen in Fig. 581); hence, each tube communicates at both of its ends with the vestibule (Fig. 582). These bony tubes are referred to as *semicircular canals*, and it is of great significance that they be disposed in different planes, approximately so that the plane of each is at right angles to the planes of the other two (Fig. 582).

As noted before, the membranous labyrinth (Fig. 583) is comprised of a system of membranous tubes and sacs, and it is fitted loosely into the bony labyrinth. Actually, there are 2 sacs in the membranous labyrinth, and these are both present in the vestibule of the bony labyrinth. The more anterior and smaller

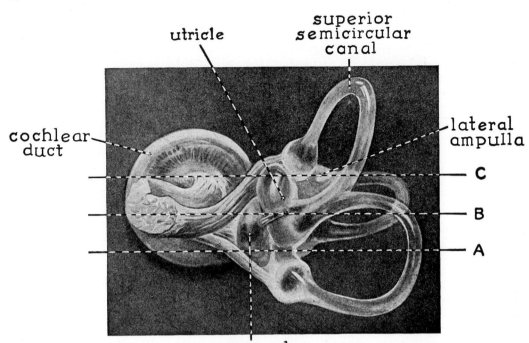

utricle

superior
semicircular
canal

cochlear
duct

lateral
ampulla

C

B

A

saccule

FIG. 583. Drawing of the right membranous labyrinth of a human adult (medial and posterior view). It shows the relation between the cochlear duct, the utricle, the saccule, the semicircular canals and the ampullae. (Spalteholtz, W.: Hand-Atlas of Human Anatomy, ed. 13, Philadelphia, Lippincott; lines A, B and C have been added)

of the two is called the *saccule* (*sacculus* = a small sac) and the larger and more posterior of the two, the *utricle* (*utriculus* = a little skin bag). The 2 sacs are in communication with one another by means of a fine membranous duct (Figs. 581 and 583).

As was explained before, the membranous labyrinth extends into all parts of the bony labyrinth. The membranous tube that extends into the cochlea is given off by the saccule. On entering the basal turn of the cochlea it becomes known as the *cochlear duct*. It is not, as might at first be imagined, a round tube, but instead it has more of the shape of a ribbon, particularly that of a thick wide ribbon that has been "ironed down" along one of its sides so that one side is much thinner than the other. Such a ribbon would be somewhat triangular in shape when seen in cross section. The cochlear duct, of course, is not solid like a ribbon but is hollow and filled with endolymph (Fig. 587).

One side of the ribbonlike cochlear duct is attached to one side of the bony canal of the cochlea and the other side of the duct to the other side of the canal, so that the cochlear duct forms a rough shelf across the bony canal, splitting it into 2 parts along its whole length. In this fashion the cochlear duct ascends up the winding turns of the cochlea always keeping the part of the canal above it—and this is known as the *scala vestibuli* (*scala* = a stairway) (Fig. 587)—separated from the part of the canal that lies below it and which is known as the *scala tympani* (Fig. 587). Both the scala vestibuli and the scala tympani are filled with *perilymph*. (This is identical with cerebrospinal fluid and is in communication, in a way that need not be described here, with cerebrospinal fluid.) However, the cochlear duct keeps the perilymph in the scala vestibuli separated along the whole course of the cochlea from the perilymph of the scala tympani. (Actually, there is a small opening between the scala vestibuli and the scala tympani at the tip of the cochlea, but this may be disregarded for the time being.)

It is obvious, then, that since the perilymph in the scala vestibuli and that in the scala tympani are not in free communication with each other, any vibrations in the perilymph in the scala vestibuli, to reach the scala tympani, would have to be transmitted through the thickness of the ribbonlike endolymph-containing cochlear duct. Now it so happens that the perilymph in the scala vestibuli connects with the perilymph that bathes the inner aspect of the oval window. This perilymph receives vibrations from the eardrum by way of the chain of bones, the last one of which fits into the oval window. Hence, the vibrations of the eardrum are transmitted up into the cochlea by means of the perilymph that extends from the oval window up into the scala vestibuli. However, as was noted before, fluid is incompressible; hence, the bone that fits into the oval window cannot push into the window unless the fluid in the bony labyrinth can push out somewhere else. It is of interest in this connection that the perilymph in the scala tympani is in free communication with that which bathes the inner aspect of the round window. Hence, vibrations transmitted into the oval window and through the perilymph of the scala vestibuli can be transmitted through the thickness of the cochlear duct into the perilymph of the scala tympani and from there to the round window, which "gives" sufficiently to permit the above-described mechanism to operate.

The above-described mechanism allows the vibrations set up by sound waves that strike the eardrum to be transmitted through the thickness of the ribbonlike but hollow cochlear duct along its full length. The end-organ for hearing consists of a narrow ribbon of special neuro-epithelial cells and nerve fibers that is disposed along the floor of the cochlear duct along its whole length. This long ribbonlike end-organ is called the *organ of Corti* (Fig. 587) and it is in it that the nervous impulses responsible for hearing originate when its special cells are stimulated by vibrations transmitted through the cochlear duct from the perilymph of the scale vestibuli into that of the scale tympani. In all probability, vibrations caused by high notes affect the receptors in the more basal part of the cochlea and those from low notes those in the terminal part of the cochlea.

From the foregoing, then, it should be clear that the more anterior tubular extension of the bony labyrinth (from the vestibule) houses the end-organ for hearing, and in a general way it may be understood that the special neuro-epithelial cells in the organ of Corti might be stimulated as a result of vibrations of the perilymph, set up by sound waves, being transmitted through the cochlear duct. We shall consider next the function of the more posterior extension of the bony labyrinth, the semicircular canals.

The semicircular canals (Fig. 582), like the cochlea, are filled with perilymph, but each contains, in addition, a membranous tube (part of the membranous labyrinth) which is filled with endolymph (Fig. 583). In a special expanded part of each membranous tube, called its *ampulla* (Fig. 583), a little mound of neuro-epithelial cells called a *crista* (L., a crest) is present in its wall. The cristae react, in a manner somewhat similar to the float we described at the end of a trough of water, by setting up nervous impulses in response to a sudden movement, or if movement is in progress, to a change in the rate of movement. Since there are 3 of them, and since the membranous tubes that contain them are arranged in 3 different planes, they also react to a change in the direction of a movement. It is probable that, unlike the water in a trough, no current is set up in the membranous tubes in the semicircular canals or in the perilymph outside the membranous tubes when the head is moved, for the caliber of the tubes and of the canals is very small. Nevertheless, sufficient displacement of fluid does occur to affect the cristae when movement begins or ends, increases or decreases or when its direction is changed. The latter, of course, actually represents the beginning of a new movement in a different plane.

The end-organ that sets up the nervous impulses that are responsible for an appreciation of the position of the head in relation to gravitational forces is located in the *utricle*. It consists of a little mass of neuro-epithelial cells and nerve endings, together with some other features to be described presently, and is called a *macula* (L., a spot). A similar macula is also found in the saccule, but it is not thought that this one functions with regard to the sense of equilibrium; if anything, the sense organ in the saccule is probably related in some way to the sense of hearing.

MICROSCOPIC STRUCTURE OF THE PARTS OF THE EAR

Auricle. In lower animals the auricle serves 3 purposes. Since it is movable and shaped like a funnel, it can be pointed at the source of a sound, acting as a natural ear trumpet to collect the sound waves and conduct them to the middle ear. With it the animal can determine the source of the sound by recognizing in what direction the auricle is pointed when the sound is loudest. Burrowing and aquatic animals can close the auricle over the meatus and in this way keep out dirt and water. In man, the auricles is a vestigial structure and can be moved but slightly; it is of little use as a sound-locating or protective structure, and its irregular and flattened shape (Fig. 581) would seem to detract from its function as a collector of sound waves.

The shape of the auricle is maintained by its content of yellow elastic fibrocartilage. It is easy to demonstrate the elastic quality of this cartilage by bending the auricle and then allowing it to snap back into position. The auricle is covered with skin on both sides. The subcutaneous tissue on the posteromedial surface is slightly thicker than that on the anterolateral surface and contains some fat cells. Hair follicles with associated sebaceous glands can be found scattered through the dermis on both sides; these are most prominent near the entrance to the external auditory meatus. At the most dependent part of the auricle lies the *lobule*; this consists of a mass of fat, enclosed in connective tissue septa and covered externally with skin. The relative paucity of nerve endings and the rich capillary bed make the lobule a convenient site for obtaining blood for blood counts.

External Auditory Meatus. Since this canal leading to the drum is an invagination from the surface, it is lined with the stratified squamous epithelium of the skin. To prevent the canal from collapsing, its walls have rigid support. In the outer part this support consists of elastic cartilage continuous with the cartilage of the auricle; in the inner part of the meatus the support is provided by bone. In the outer one third of the canal there are many short hairs, and associated with their follicles are large sebaceous glands. In the submucosa deep to the sebaceous glands there are clusters of tubular *ceruminous* (*cera* = wax) glands; the ducts of these open either directly onto the surface of the canal or into the sebaceous ducts. The ceruminous glands are thought to be modified sweat glands, and their tubules are lined by tall cuboidal or columnar cells. The combined secretion of the sebaceous and the ceruminous glands, called *cerumen*, is supposed to lubricate the surface of the canal and the drum and to keep out insects. Often the cerumen is so efficient in this latter role that it also keeps out sound waves. Syringing the external auditory canal with water may be necessary to remove excesses of wax and to restore hearing. In the inner two thirds of the canal the ceruminous glands are confined to its roof.

Tympanic Membrane. The tympanic membrane is like a sandwich, the filling of which is collagenous connective tissue, and the bread, 2 epithelial coats (Fig. 584). The outer epithelial coat is continuous with the stratified squamous epithelium lining the external auditory meatus; it differs from it in having no papillae except short ones near the margin and also in that over the more central part of the drum it consists of only 2 layers of cells. The epithelium of the mucous membrane of the middle ear flattens out to exist as a single layer of low cuboidal cells; these form the inner covering of the drum. The middle fibrous filling of the drum consists of 2 layers of collagen fibers; the outer ones are dispersed radially and the inner ones circularly. The upper part of the drum is thin and flaccid because of a lack of collagen filling. Therefore, it is known as the *pars flaccida* or *Schrapnell's membrane*.

Middle Ear. The middle ear or tympanic cavity is a tiny epithelial-lined cavity in bone, being roughly the shape of a red blood cell set on edge. The tympanic cavity is described as having 4 walls, a floor and a roof. It is about as high as it is long (about ½ inch), but is very thin; hence, its anterior and posterior walls are narrow. The lateral wall consists largely of the tympanic membrane, and the medial wall is the bone dividing the middle ear from the inner ear. There is a gap between the anterior and the medial walls for a canal, called the *eustachian tube*, which extends for-

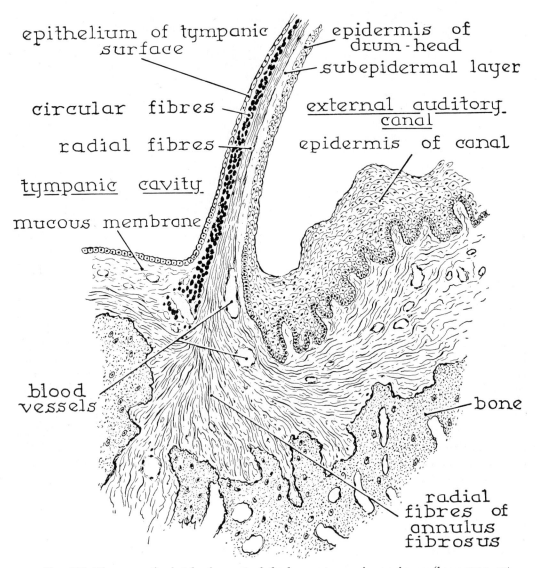

epithelium of tympanic surface

epidermis of drum-head

subepidermal layer

circular fibres

external auditory canal

radial fibres

epidermis of canal

tympanic cavity

mucous membrane

blood vessels

bone

radial fibres of annulus fibrosus

Fig. 584. Diagrammatic sketch of a part of the human tympanic membrane (low-power, cut in cross section). It shows the relation of the drum membrane to the external auditory canal and to the tympanic cavity and the attachment of the membrane.

ward and communicates with the nasopharynx (Fig. 581).

The epithelium lining the cavity consists of simple nonciliated cuboidal cells with no basement membrane. The lamina propria is a thin connective tissue layer, closely adherent to bone. In some areas the cuboidal cells may become several layers thick. When infection occurs, the epithelium may become ciliated or may change to stratified squamous epithelium.

The middle ear houses 3 small bones or ossicles, 2 muscles and a nerve. When followed forward it leads to the pharynx through the *pharyngotympanic* or eustachian tube, and this communication makes it an air-containing cavity and offers a direct route for infection to reach it from the upper respiratory tract (Fig. 581). Indeed, middle ear infections are fairly common complications of head colds, particularly in children. Posteriorly, the tympanic cavity is continuous with a varying number of alveolar spaces in bone, the *mastoid air cells.* These too may become involved in retrograde infections from the nasopharynx.

OSSICLES. The 3 small bones of the middle ear cavity are the *malleus* or *hammer,* the *incus* or *anvil* and the *stapes* or *stirrup.* These bones were doubtless named in the days of the blacksmith's shop and have little connotation for the modern student. The malleus is shaped like a crude hammer with a rounded head, a long handle and a spur in the region of the constricted neck which joins the head to the handle. The incus is shaped like a molar tooth with a body or "crown" and a vertical and a horizontal "root." The stapes, as its name suggests, is shaped like the stirrup of a riding saddle. It consists of a head, a neck, 2 limbs and an oval foot plate. The head of the malleus fits into the "crown" of the incus; the vertical "root" of the incus fits against the head of the stapes (Fig. 581).

The ossicles transmit the vibrations set up in the tympanic membrane by sound waves to one of the two windows present in the medial wall of the middle ear. To do this, the handle of the malleus is firmly attached to the tympanic membrane and carries the vibrations to the incus; the incus transfers the vibrations to the stapes, causing the foot plate of the stapes, accurately fitted in the oval window, to rock to and fro. This carries the vibrations to the perilymph of the vestibule, as has already been explained. During this transfer, the amplitude of the vibration is decreased, but the force is increased because the ossicles are so arranged to exert leverage. The ossicles are atypical long bones, having no epiphyses and reaching approximately their full size during fetal life. The malleus and the incus have small central marrow cavities, while the stapes has none in the adult. The "ends" of these bones are covered with articular cartilage; they are held together by small ligaments, and the malleus and the incus are suspended by ligaments from the roof of the middle ear. The periosteal surfaces of these bones are covered by the mucous membrane of the middle ear cavity.

MUSCLES. The 2 muscles of the tympanic cavity are the *tensor tympani* and the *stapedius.* The tensor tympani muscle is housed in a bony groove (canal) above the cartilaginous roof of the eustachian tube; its tendon crosses

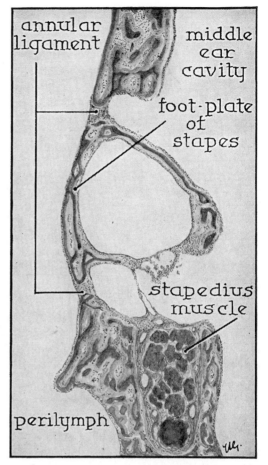

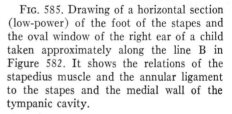

FIG. 585. Drawing of a horizontal section (low-power) of the foot of the stapes and the oval window of the right ear of a child taken approximately along the line B in Figure 582. It shows the relations of the stapedius muscle and the annular ligament to the stapes and the medial wall of the tympanic cavity.

the tympanic cavity mediolaterally to be inserted into the handle of the malleus. The stapedius muscle is housed in the posterior wall of the tympanic cavity (Fig. 585), and its tendon, issuing at the summit of a small projection of bone called the pyramid, is inserted into the neck of the stapes. The way in which these muscles affect the transmission of the sound waves by the ossicles is uncertain. The tensor muscle pulls the malleus inward, thus tensing the tympanic membrane and perhaps accentuating high-pitched sounds. The stapedius pulls the foot plate of the stapes outward, thus reducing the intralabyrinth pressure and perhaps making sounds of low frequency more audible. It has been found that reflex contractions of the stapedius occur during exposure to loud noise. Therefore, it seems that the stapedius plays a protective role, preventing too violent vibrations from injuring the special sense organs in the internal ear.

NERVES. The chorda tympani nerve traverses the middle ear in contact with the inner surface of the drum. It has no functional concern with the ear. In addition, branches of many other nerves can be found in the mucous membrane and the bony walls of the middle ear. The facial nerve runs in a long canal in the medial wall of the middle ear. Its only concern with the ear lies in the fact that it supplies the stapedius muscle. The tympanic branch of the glossopharyngeal (Jacobson's nerve) is the great sensory nerve of the middle ear; the auricular branch of the vagus (Arnold's nerve) supplies the skin of the external auditory meatus. An attack of coughing or vomiting occasionally follows stimulation of the external auditory canal, for example, when a speculum is introduced into it. This is thought to be due to a reflex whose afferent arm is Arnold's nerve.

THE OVAL WINDOW. The foot plate of the stapes sits and is fitted accurately in the oval window. Its periphery is attached to the cartilaginous rim of the oval window by an annular ligament composed of strong collagenous and elastic fibers (Fig. 585). The mucous membrane lining the middle ear cavity is reflected from this onto the stapes. Through the oval window, vibrations are conducted to the perilymph of the vestibule.

THE ROUND WINDOW. Since fluid is in-

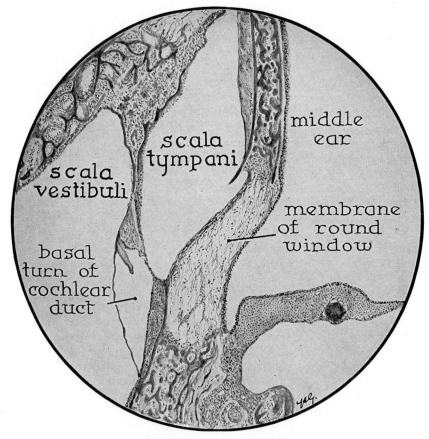

FIG. 586. Drawing of a section (low-power) through the round window of the right ear of a child. It shows the relation of the membrane of the round window to the tympanic cavity and the vestibule.

compressible, there must be some movable object which the perilymph can displace when it is thrust inward at the oval window. This movable object is a moderately elastic membrane which fills in the round window like a flexible windowpane. The membrane has a core of connective tissue and is lined on its middle ear surface by mucous membrane; on its inner side it is lined by the connective tissue of the perilymphatic space of the vestibule (Fig. 586).

The Pharyngotympanic Tube. The simple cuboidal epithelium of the middle ear cavity gives way to respiratory epithelium; i.e., pseudostratified ciliated columnar epithelium, in the pharyngotympanic or eustachian tube. There are rugae in the epithelial coat here, and goblet cells can be found in the lining of the cartilaginous part of the tube. Near the pharyngeal end, a mixed mucous and serous gland is present in the submucosa. Normally, the mucous surfaces of the tube are in contact, and the tube is open only during swallowing. The pressure in the middle ear can be adjusted rapidly to that of the atmosphere only when this tube is open. Thus, when coming down in an airplane, one can prevent discomfort from too high pressure in the middle ear cavity by swallowing; this opens the tube and permits the pressure in the middle ear to become equalized with that of the atmosphere.

The Mastoid Air Cells. In early life the mastoid process and all the petrous bone surrounding the inner ear are normally filled with hemopoietic marrow. In the adult, small air pockets continuous with the middle ear cavity have replaced this marrow in the mastoid region. The process whereby the bone is invaded by these air sacs is known as *pneumatization*; it starts as early as the 3rd fetal month, with the greatest extension occurring between the 3rd year and puberty. However, the degree of pneumatization cannot be used to tell the age of the fetus or of a baby, since some 6-month fetuses show marked pneumatization. The degree of penumatization of the mastoid area varies greatly from person to person, and some investigators believe that minor infections of the middle ear, common in childhood, favor obliteration of the air spaces. From a roentgenographic study on pneumatization in a large series of twins, it was concluded that heredity plays a much more important role than middle-ear infection in determining the extent to which the mastoid and the surrounding petrous temporal bone become pneumatized.

It is often of considerable importance to the surgeon to know the extent of pneumatization of the temporal bone in order that he may drain the pus from infected air cells. To do this he takes roentgenograms of the mastoid area. Unfortunately, however, the roentgenogram does not always distinguish between air pockets filled with pus and marrow spaces filled with fatty marrow, and the disease process can go undetected until the bony trabeculae are eroded.

The lining of the mastoid air cells is a thin mucoperiosteum; the cuboidal cells of the middle ear cavity here become flattened to a simple squamous type and lie adjacent to the periosteum of the mastoid air cells.

The Cochlea. The bony cochlea, as explained before, is part of the bony labyrinth and consists of a bony tube. In describing the cochlea further it is convenient to speak of it as if it were laid flat on its base; then it can be said that the bony tube of which it is composed winds spirally upward around a central pillar of bone called the *modiolus*. Actually, in position in the body, the apex of the cochlea is directed anterolaterally. However, in describing the microscopic anatomy of this structure, we shall assume that it has been laid flat on its base.

In the account of the general structure of the ear it was explained that the portion of the membranous labyrinth that extends into the bony cochlea was of the shape of a hollow ribbon flattened along one of its edges, and that its 2 edges were in apposition with the 2 sides of the bony canal in which it lies so that it separates the bony canal along its whole length into 2 long spiral chambers, the scala vestibuli and the scala tympani. Whereas it is true that the cochlear duct is more or less ribbonlike and that it extends from one side to the other of the bony canal in which it lies, it should be stated now that this explanation is somewhat simplified. The matter will now be elaborated further.

The relations of the cochlear duct, which is part of the membranous labyrinth, to the bony canal in which it lies, which is part of the bony labyrinth, and the position of the organ of Corti in relation to the floor of the cochlear duct, are best learned in a section cut through the center of the cochlea as a whole, but cut through a bony canal at some point along its spiral course at approximately right angles.

A portion of such a section, showing a cross section of the *bony canal*, is illustrated in Figure 587, and this figure should be referred to frequently as the following description is

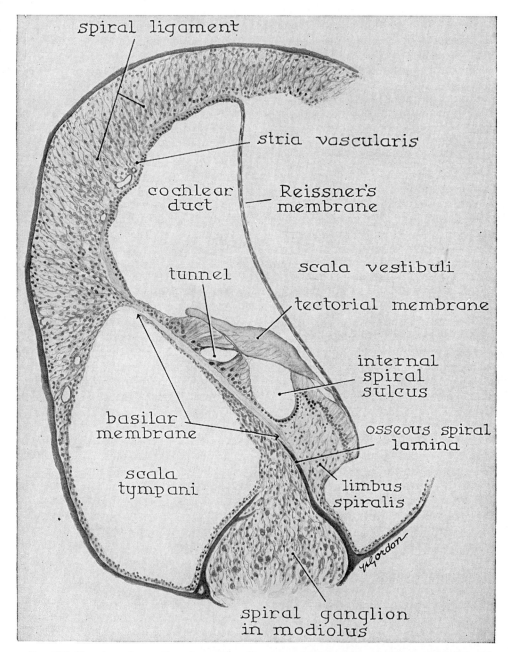

FIG. 587. Drawing of a portion of a section (low-power) of the bony cochlea cut parallel with the modiolus and through it along the line B in Figure 582. A section cut in this plane cuts the bony tube, as it pursues its spiral course, approximately at right angles at several different sites. Only one cross section of the bony tube is illustrated in this figure; it shows the cochlear duct extending across the bony canal, as well as the features described in the text.

read. The term inner, as used in the following description of the cochlea, refers to the central pillar of the cochlea, the modiolus, a portion of which may be seen housing the spiral ganglion (to be described later) at the bottom of the illustration.

The floor of the cochlear duct, in order to extend from the inner to the outer side of the bony canal of the cochlea, is not so wide as might be thought because both the outer and the inner walls of the bony canal of the cochlea bulge toward the center of the canal of the cochlea to support the floor of the cochlear duct and so make the distance it must bridge narrower. The bulge from the inner wall of the bony canal takes the form of a thin shelf of bone called the *osseous spiral lamina* (Fig. 587) because it winds up the modiolus like the thread on a screw. The bulge from the outer surface of the bony canal is not bone but is of the nature of a thickening of the periosteum that lines the canal; this line of thickened and primarily fibrous periosteum that winds up the turns of the cochlea is called the *spiral ligament* (Fig. 587). The floor of the cochlear duct, the *basilar membrane* (Fig. 587), bridges the gap between the osseous spiral lamina and the crest of the spiral ligament. The basilar membrane is made up of a dense mat of collagenic and some elastic fibers. The fibers of this membrane were once called *auditory strings,* and different ones were believed to vibrate selectively with different vibrations. The roof of the cochlear duct, in contrast with its floor, is thin, being composed of only 2 layers of squamous epithelial cells; this is called *Reissner's membrane* (Fig. 587). The outer wall of the cochlear duct is made up of the spiral ligament already described. The upper and larger part (the part nearer Reissner's membrane) is known as the *stria vascularis* (Fig. 589) and is rich in blood vessels which lie directly below a surface layer of deep-staining cuboidal cells. A small part of the outer wall of the cochlear duct, close to the attachment of the basilar membrane to the crest of the spiral ligament, is arranged to form what is known as the *sulcus spiralis externus*. Here, long protoplasmic processes from the surface epithelial cells extend down into the connective tissue of the spiral ligament. Moreover, Shambaugh has found secretory cells, which, though deeply buried

in this area, have access to the surface; he suggests that they constitute a secretory mechanism for replenishing endolymph in the cochlear duct.

The Spiral Organ of Corti. Running along the whole length of the floor of the cochlear duct like a ribbon, and hence resting on the basilar membrane, is the highly specialized end-organ of the nerve of hearing. This is the spiral *organ of Corti* (Fig. 587). When the organ of Corti is sectioned at right angles to its long axis, a triangular central space can be seen. This is known as the *tunnel* (Fig. 587). Situated at the basal angles of this triangle, and forming part of its walls, are, in any given section, 2 darkly staining cells called the *internal* and the *external pillar cells,* respectively. On the outer side of the external pillar cell and on the inside of the inner pillar cells are *hair cells,* usually 3 on the outside and 1 on the inside. These cells are so named because hairs arise from their free surface and give them a ciliated appearance. Underlying and supporting the hair cells are columnar cells, called *Deiter's cells.* Lateral to the outer hair cells is another collection of columnar cells; these are called *Hensen's cells.* Their function is unknown.

Except in the area of the organ of Corti the basilar membrane is lined by low cuboidal cells. To the inside of the organ of Corti the periosteum of the upper surface of the osseus spiral lamina forms a fleshy elevation, the *limbus spiralis* (Fig. 587), which bulges into the duct. The outer margin of this limbus presents a groove known as the *internal spiral sulcus* (Fig. 587); the edge of the limbus spiralis that overhangs this is called the *vestibular lip*. From this lip of the limbus a thin, homogeneous, jellylike membrane extends over, and is in contact with, the cilia of the hair cells of the organ of Corti. This is the *tectorium* or *tectorial membrane* (Fig. 587).

The lining of the scala tympani and of the scala vestibuli (apart from that provided by the basilar membrane, Reissner's membrane and the spiral ligament) is composed of the internal periosteum or endosteum of the bony cochlear canal.

The sound waves, conducted to the organ of Corti by the endolymph of the cochlear duct from the perilymph in the scala vestibuli, affect the hair cells in some way. The stimuli

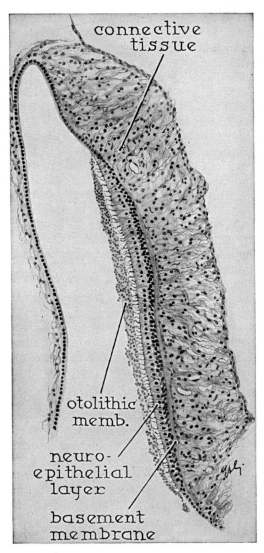

connective
tissue

otolithic
memb.

neuro-
epithelial
layer

basement
membrane

FIG. 588. Drawing of a longitudinal section (low-power) cut through the macula sacculi of a child along the line marked A in Figure 583. It shows the relationship of the macula to the lining of the saccule and the relationship of the otolithic membrane to the neuro-epithelial cells.

so produced are conducted by nerve fibers which begin as telodendria around the bases of the hair cells; these run in the basilar membrane, between the 2 thin plates of bone that constitute the osseous spiral lamina, to their nerve cells in the *spiral ganglion,* which is housed in the modiolus (Fig. 587). These peripheral fibers may be considered dendrites

of the spiral ganglion cells. A single dendrite may have many peripheral branches and so receive stimuli from many hair cells. The bipolar cells of the ganglion send their central processes or axons (as the cochlear division of the acoustic nerve) to end synaptically in the cochlear nuclei of the brain stem.

The Vestibule. In the bony vestibule, filled with perilymph, are suspended the sacs of the membranous labyrinth—the utricle and the saccule. These 2 sacs, filled with endolymph, are joined by the short arms of a Y-shaped tube, the *ductus endolymphaticus.* The long arm of the Y extends through the petrous bone to the posterior cranial fossa, where it ends in a blind subdural swelling, the *subdural endolymphatic sac.* This is a safety valve for endolymph.

Into the utricle open the ends of the 3 membranous semicircular canals. Each has one expanded end or ampulla (Fig. 583). The non-expanded ends of the superior and the posterior ducts have a common opening into the utricle, while the others open independently. Hence, for the 3 canals there are 5 openings.

The utricle and the saccule are lined by flattened epithelial cells, usually called *mesothelium,* resting on a connective tissue membrane. The membranous sacs do not fill the bony vestibular space, nor do they lie free in this space, since fine strands of connective tissue connect them to the endosteum lining the bony vestibule. The saccule and the utricle each contains a flat, plaquelike sensory ending, called a *macula* (Fig. 588).

Maculae. A macula is somewhat similar cytologically to the organ of Corti. It consists of a thickened epithelium, containing 2 types of cells and separated from a connective tissue layer by a basement membrane. One type of cell, the neuro-epithelial cell, is plump, pale-staining and provided at its free end with a tuft of fine hairs. The other type is the supporting cell. These are packed around and between the hair cells. The hairs of the neuro-epithelial cells do not float freely in the endolymph but are embedded in a gelatinous membrane called the *otolithic membrane* (Fig. 588). This membrane contains many fine granules of minute crystalline particles composed of calcium carbonate and protein. Slight changes in pressure or tension on the otolithic membrane, produced by changes in the position of the head, affect the hair cells of the utricle. The stimuli so produced set up nervous impulses which pass into the peripheral terminal branches of the vestibular nerve.

If the otolithic membranes are removed from the maculae of the guinea pig by centrifuging, the animal loses its static sense of position. If both utricles are destroyed, the animal is unable to maintain its balance. It is possible to destroy the saccules in a dog without impairment of balance.

The Semicircular Canals. The membranous semicircular canals are lined with a squamous epithelium similar to that lining the saccule and the utricle. This also rests on a framework of connective tissue. The membranous tubes take up only a small part of the bony canal and are eccentrically placed, being in contact with the concave wall of the bony canal. Filaments of connective tissue join the tubes to the more distant parts of the canal, and perilymph fills the interstices.

The outer wall (most distant from the center of the rough circle made by each tube) of each ampulla presents a transverse ridge in its lining, the *crista*. This is composed of connective tissue, nerve fibers and capillaries. The surface epithelium of the crista is similar to that of the macula, possessing hair cells with large, oval, deep-staining nuclei and supporting cells packed closely, next to the basement membrane (Fig. 589). Resting on the surface of the crista is a membrane which closely resembles the tectorial membrane; this is called the *cupula* (L., a cup) (Fig. 589). It is a gelatinous noncellular membrane which covers the crista and projects up into the endolymph of the ampulla. The cupula differs from the otolithic membrane in that it contains no crystals. The function of the crista has already been explained.

Each crista is supplied by a branch of the vestibular division of the acoustic nerve. These branches of the vestibular nerve to the middle part of the membranous labyrinth are peripheral dendrites of nerve cells which lie in the vestibular (or Scarpa's) ganglion. Their central processes or axons constitute the vestibular division of the 8th nerve and end synaptically in the vesicular nuclei of the brain stem and in the cerebellum, where they initiate postural reflexes to maintain balance.

FINE STRUCTURE. The fine structure of the

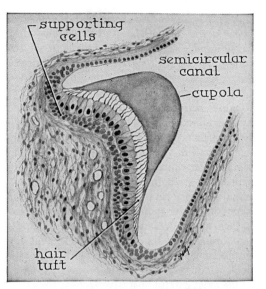

FIG. 589. Drawing of a cross section (low-power) cut through the ampulla (slightly collapsed) of the lateral semicircular canal of the right ear of a child along line C in Figure 583. It shows the crista ampullaris in cross section and the relation of the cupula to the hair cells of the sense organ.

cristae ampulares of the guinea pig has been studied comprehensively with the E/M by Wersall. His study embraces many matters, including the fine structure of the nerves and the nerve endings, and it represents a magnificent contribution.

DEAFNESS

As can be seen from considering the anatomy and the physiology of the ear, anything which interferes with the transmission of the sound waves to the cochlear duct or damages the organ of Corti or the cochlear division of the 8th nerve will interfere with hearing. This may be a thing as easily removed as wax in the external auditory meatus or as permanent as nerve injury. A very serious cause of gradually increasing deafness in the adult is a disease which involves the bony case of the middle and the internal ear. This disease is known as *otosclerosis* and results in the formation of sharply circumscribed bony growths within the otic capsule. The site of predilection of this lesion is near the oval window. Whenever the otosclerotic patches remain within the bony capsule, hearing is not impaired. When they spread beyond the periosteal or endosteal layer in the region of the oval window, they cause immobilization of the foot plate of the stapes. At operation, most of the clinically diagnosed cases show fixation of the stapes.

If this disease progresses to the point where it causes serious deafness, it may be relieved by operation. This operation, called *fenestration,* consists of drilling a hole in the bony medial wall of the middle ear over the lateral semicircular canal. The opening is covered by skin taken from the posterior wall of the external auditory meatus. It is probable that the direction of the sound waves in the inner ear is then reversed, that the waves are transmitted through the round window and that the displacement of fluid is permitted by the artificial window. Occasionally, however, in spite of the most careful operative technic the opening becomes closed by bone; we think that this is a result of regeneration from the osteogenic cells that line the bony canal through which the fenestrum is made.

REFERENCES

DEEP AND CUTANEOUS SENSIBILITY

Adrian, E. D.: The Physiological Background of Perception, Oxford, Clarendon, 1946.

Lewis, T.: Pain, New York, Macmillan, 1942.

Merrillees, N. C. R., Sunderland, S., and Hayhow, W.: Neuromuscular spindles in the extraocular muscles in man, Anat. Rec. *108*:23, 1950.

Nafe, J. P.: The pressure, pain and temperature senses *in* Murchison's Handbook of General Experimenal Psychology, p. 1037, London, Oxford, 1934.

Olmsted, J. M. D.: The special senses, Ann. Rev. Physiol. *7*:509, 1945.

Penfield, W. (ed.): Cytology and Cellular Pathology of the Nervous System, vol. 1, New York, Hoeber, 1932.

Ramón y Cajal, S.: Degeneration and Regeneration of the Nervous System, London, Oxford, 1928.

Sanders, F. K.: Special senses, cutaneous sensation, Ann. Rev. Physiol. *9*:553, 1947.

Takashi, M., Sakai, I., and Usizima, H.: On the terminal neural apparatus detectible in the retroperitoneum of man—a complex pattern of Pacinian corpuscles, Anat. Rec. *122*:17, 1955.

TASTE AND THE OLFACTORY ORGAN

Crozier, W. J.: Chemoreception *in* Murchison's Handbook of General Experimental Psychology, p. 987, London, Oxford, 1934.

Smith, C. G.: Changes in the olfactory mucosa and the olfactory nerves following intranasal treatment with 1 per cent zinc sulphate, Canad. M. A. J. *39*:138, 1938.

————: Incidence of atrophy of the olfactory nerves in man, Arch. Otolaryng. *34*:533, 1941.

————: Pathologic changes in olfactory mucosa of albino rats with "stunted" olfactory bulbs, Arch. Otolaryng. *25*:131, 1937.

————: Regeneration of sensory olfactory epithelium and nerves in adult frogs, Anat. Rec. *109*:661, 1951.

THE EYE

Adler, F. H.: Textbook of Physiology, ed. 3, St. Louis, Mosby, 1959.

Ascher, K. W.: Further observations on aqueous veins, Am. J. Ophth. *29*:1373, 1946.

Ashton, N.: Anatomical study of Schlemm's canal and aqueous veins by means of neoprene casts; aqueous veins, Brit. J. Ophth. *35*:291, 1951.

Aurell, G., and Holmgren, H.: Metachromatic substance in cornea with special reference to question of its transparency, Nord. med. *30*: 1277, 1946.

Basu, P. K., and Ormsby, H. L.: Identification of sex chromatin in corneal stroma cells for the determination of the fate of corneal transplants, Trans. Bull. *23*:435, 1959.

Basu, P. K., Miller, I., and Ormsby, H. L.: Sex chromatin as a biologic cell marker in the study of the fate of corneal transplants, Am. J. Ophth. *49*:513, 1960.

Cook, C., and Macdonald, R. K.: Effect of cortisone on the permeability of the blood-aqueous barrier to fluorescein, Brit. J. Ophth. *35*:730, 1951.

Davson, H.: The Physiology of the Eye, New York, Blakiston Division of McGraw-Hill, 1949.

DeHarven, E., and Coers, C.: Electron microscope study of the human neuromuscular junction, J. Biophys. & Biochem. Cytol. *6*:7, 1959.

DeRobertis, E.: Electron microscope observations on the submicroscopic organization of retinal rods, J. Biophys. & Biochem. Cytol. *2*:319, 1956.

————: Morphogenesis of the retinal rods; an electron microscope study, J. Biophys. & Biochem. Cytol. (Supp.) *2*:209, 1956.

DeRobertis, E., and Franchi, C. M.: Electron microscope observations on synaptic vesicles in synapses of the retinal rods and cones, J. Biophys. & Biochem. Cytol. *2*:307, 1956.

Duke-Elder, W. S.: Text-book of Ophthalmology, ed. 2, St. Louis, Mosby, 1938-1940.

Duke-Elder, W. S., and Davson, H.: The present position of the problem of the intra-ocular fluid and pressure, Brit. J. Ophth. *32*:555, 1948.

Duke-Elder, W. S., Davson, H., and Maurice, D. M.: Studies on the intra-ocular fluids, Brit. J. Ophth. *33*: part 1, Jan., 1949, p. 21; part 2, June, 1949, p. 329; part 3, July, 1949, p. 452; part 4, October, 1949, p. 593.

Duthie, H. L., and Gairns, F. W.: Sensory nerve-endings and sensation in the anal region of man, Brit. J. Surg. *47*:585, 1960.

Friedenwald, J. S.: The formation of the intra-ocular fluid, Am. J. Ophth. *32*:9, 1949.

————: Recent studies on corneal metabolism and growth, Cancer Res. *10*:461, 1950.

Garrow, L. K., and Feeney, M. L.: Electron microscopic studies of the human eye, Part 2, Arch. Ophth. *62*:966, 1959.

Greaves, D. P., and Perkins, E. S.: Influence of the sympathetic nervous system on the intra-ocular pressure and vascular circulation of the eye, Brit. J. Ophth. *36*:258, 1952.

Holmberg, A.: The fine structure of the inner wall of Schlemm's canal, Arch. Ophth. *62*:956, 1959.

Jakus, M. A.: Studies on the cornea: II. The fine structure of Descemet's membrane, J. Biophys. & Biochem. Cytol. (Supp.) *2*:243, 1956.

Krause, A. C., and Sibley, J. A.: Metabolism of the retina, Arch. Ophth. (N.S.) *36*:328, 1946.

Langley, D., and Macdonald, R. K.: Clinical method of observing changes in the rate of flow of aqueous humour in the human eye, Brit. J. Ophth. *36*:432, 1952.

Loewenstein, W. R.: Biological transducers, Scient. Am. *203*:98, 1960.

MacMillan, J. A.: Disease of the lacrimal gland and ocular complications, J.A.M.A. *138*:801, 1948.

Mann, I. C.: The Development of the Human Eye, London, Cambridge Univ. Press, 1928.

Meyer, K.: The biological significance of hyaluronic acid and hyaluronidase, Physiol. Rev. *27*:355, 1947.

Meyer, K., and Chaffee, E.: The mucopolysaccharide acid of the cornea and its enzymatic hydrolysis, Am. J. Ophth. *23*:1320, 1940.

Oppenheimer, D. R., Palmer, E., and Weddell, G.: Nerve endings in the conjunctiva, J. Anat. *92*: 321, 1958.

Pease, D. C.: Infolded basal plasma membranes found in epithelia noted for their water transport, J. Biophys. & Biochem. Cytol. (Supp.) *2*:203, 1956.

Pirie, A.: The effect of hyaluronidase on the vitreous humour of the rabbit, Brit. J. Ophth. *33*:678, 1949.

Polyak, S. L.: The Retina, Chicago, Univ. Chicago Press, 1941.

Reyer, R. W.: Further studies on lens develop-

ment from the dorsal iris of Triturus viridescens in the absence of the embryonic lens, J. Exper. Zool. *125*:1, 1954.

————: Regeneration of the lens in the amphibian eye, Quart. Rev. Biol. *29*:1, 1954.

Sheldon, H.: An electron microscope study of the epithelium in the normal mature and immature mouse cornea, J. Biophys. & Biochem. Cytol. *2*:253, 1956.

Sheldon, H., and Zetterqvist, H.: An electron microscope study of the corneal epithelium in the vitamin A deficient mouse, Bull. Johns Hopkins Hosp. *98*:372, 1956.

Speakman, J.: Aqueous outflow channels in the trabecular meshwork in man, Brit. J. Ophth. *43*:129, 1959.

Tokuyasu, K., and Yamada, E.: The fine structure of the retina studied with the electron microscope, J. Biophys. & Biochem. Cytol. *6*: 225, 1959.

Walsh, F. B.: Clinical Neuro-Ophthalmology, Baltimore, Williams & Wilkins, 1947.

Wanko, T., and Gavin, M. A.: Electron microscope study of lens fibers, J. Biophys. & Biochem. Cytol. *6*:97, 1959.

Wilmer, W. H.: Atlas Fundus Oculi, New York, Macmillan, 1934.

Wislocki, G. B.: The anterior segment of the rhesus monkey investigated by histochemical means, Am. J. Anat. *91*:233, 1952.

Wolff, E.: The Anatomy of the Eye and Orbit, ed. 3, London, Lewis, 1948.

————: The origin of the malignant melanomata, Brit. J. Ophth. *32*:72, 1948.

Woodin, A. M.: Hyaluronidase as a spreading factor in the cornea, Brit. J. Ophth. *34*:375, 1950.

Wyburn, G. M., and Bacsich, P.: Survival of retinal elements in subcutaneous homografts, Brit. J. Ophth. *36*:438, 1952.

Young, M. W.: Photoreception and phonoreception, Neurol., *10*:662, 1960.

THE EAR

Anson, B. J., and Cauldwell, E. W.: The developmental anatomy of the human stapes, Ann. Otol., Rhin. & Laryng. *51*:891, 1942.

Bast, T. H.: A historical survey of the structure and function of the cochlea, Ann. Otol., Rhin. & Laryng. *52*:281, 1943.

Bast, T. H., West, R., Backus, O. L., Krasno, M., and Eyster, J. A. E.: Electrical currents associated with sound reception by the ear, Proc. Soc. Exper. Biol. & Med. *30*:638, 1933.

Davies, D. V.: A note on the articulation of the auditory ossicles and related structures, J. Laryng. & Otol. *62*:533, 1948.

Eggston, A. A., and Wolff, D.: Histopathology

of the Ear, Nose and Throat, Baltimore, Williams & Wilkins, 1947.

Guild, S. R.: Comments on the physiology of hearing and the anatomy of the inner ear, Laryngoscope *47*:365, 1937.

————: Hearing by bone conduction: the pathways of transmission of sound, Ann. Otol., Rhin. & Laryng. *45*:736, 1936.

Hagens, E. W.: Anatomy and pathology of the petrous bone, Arch. Otolaryng. *19*:556, 1934.

————: Pathology of otosclerosis, Arch. Otolaryng. *21*:297, 1935.

Jackson, C., and Jackson, C. L. (eds.): Diseases of the Nose, Throat and Ear, Philadelphia, Saunders, 1945.

Kobrak, H. G.: Animal experiments on the mechanism of the acoustic irritation in the cochlea, Laryngoscope *47*:453, 1937.

Lempert, J.: Lempert fenestra nov-ovalis with mobile stopple, Arch. Otolaryng. *41*:1, 1945.

Lindsay, J. R.: Pneumatization of the petrous pyramid, Ann. Otol., Rhin. & Laryng. *50*:1109, 1941.

Mackenzie, G. W.: The appearance and behavior of the normal tympanic membrane, Laryngoscope *34*:497, 1924.

Montagna, W.: The pigment and fatty substances of the ceruminous glands of man, Anat. Rec. *100*:66, 1948.

Montagna, W., Noback, C. R., and Zak, F. G.: Pigment, lipids and other substances in the glands of the external auditory meatus of man, Am. J. Anat. *83*:409, 1948.

Polyak, S. L., McHugh, G., and Judd, D. K.: The Human Ear, Elmsford, N. Y., Sonotone Corp., 1946.

Potter, A. B.: Function of the stapedius muscle, Ann. Otol., Rhin. & Laryng. *45*:638, 1936.

Shambaugh, G. E.: Cytology of the Internal Ear *in* Cowdry's Special Cytology, ed. 2, p. 1333, New York, Hoeber, 1932.

Wersall, J.: Studies on the structure and innervation of the sensory epithelium of the cristae ampullares in the guinea pig; a light and electron microscopic investigation, Acta otolaryng., Supp. 126, 1956.

Wiggers, H. C.: The functions of the intra-aural muscles, Am. J. Physiol. *120*:771, 1937.

Index